42nd European Photovoltaic Solar Energy Conference and Exhibition (EU PVSEC 2025)

Bilbao, Spain
22-26 September 2025

Volume 6 of 6

ISBN: 979-8-3313-2987-7

42nd European Photovoltaic Solar Energy Conference and Exhibition

Proceedings of the International Conference

22 September – 26 September 2025

Edited by:

C. DEL CAÑIZO
Solar Energy Institute
UPM
Spain

R. KENNY
European Commission
Joint Research Centre
Italy

J. BERGMILLER
WIP Renewable Energies
Germany

J. DE GREGORIO
WIP Renewable Energies
Germany

Edition Team:

B. Yildiz
L. Großhans
A. Michaelsen
U.E. Birgi
WIP Renewable Energies
Germany

Photos at:

Coordination of the Technical Programme:

European Commission Joint Research Centre
Via E. Fermi 1
21020 Ispra (VA)
Italy

Institutional Support:

European Commission

Institutional PV Industry Cooperation:

SolarPower Europe
ESMC – European Solar Manufacturing Council

Supporting Organisations:

AUSTRALIAN PV INSTITUTE
ASOM – Alliance for Solar Mobility
BASQUE ENERGY CLUSTER
BILBAO CONVENTION BUREAU
EASE – European Association for Storage of Energy
ETIP PV – European Technology & Innovation Platform PV
GÜNDER – Turkish Solar Energy Society
IEA PVPS - IEA Photovoltaic Power Systems Programme
INSTITUTO SOLAR DE ENERGÍA SOLAR
LDES – Long Duration Energy Storage Council
NSEFI – National Solar Energy federation of India
NUS /SERIS – National University of Singapore / Solar Energy Research Institute of Singapore
UPM - Polytechnic University of Madrid

Supporting Associations:

EERA – European Energy Research Aliance
EREF – European Renewable Energies Federation
EUREC – The Association of European Renewable Energy Research Centres
VDMA Photovoltaic Equipment

Local Support:
ENTE VASCO DE LA ENERGÍA
EUH – University of the Basque Country

EU PVSEC 2025 realised by:

WIP Renewable Energies
Sylvensteinstr. 2, 81369 Munich, Germany
Tel: +49 89 720 12 735, Fax: +49 89 720 12 791
Email: pv.conference@wip-munich.de
www.eupvsec.org
www.wip-munich.de

Proceedings produced and published by:

WIP Renewable Energies
Sylvensteinstr. 2, 81369 Munich, Germany
Tel: +49 89 720 12 735, Fax: +49 89 720 12 791
Email: pv.conference@wip-munich.de
www.eupvsec.org
www.wip-munich.de

42nd EUROPEAN PHOTOVOLTAIC SOLAR ENERGY CONFERENCE AND EXHIBITION
22 SEPTEMBER – 26 SEPTEMBER 2025

EU PVSEC 2025 COMMITTEES

INTERNATIONAL SCIENTIFIC ADVISORY COMMITTEE (ISAC)

Chair

P. Szymanski, European Commission Joint Research Centre, Director of Energy, Transport and Climate, Petten, The Netherlands

Committee Members

V. Bermúdez Benito, Founder & Principal Consultant, Berbetin, Antibes, France

G.C. Eder, OFI, Vienna, Austria

P. Frankl, Head of the Renewable Energy Division, International Energy Agency, France

M. Getsiou, European Commission, DG RTD, Brussels, Belgium

S.W. Glunz, Head of Division Photovoltaics - Research, Fraunhofer ISE, Freiburg, Germany

N.M. Haegel, Director of the National Center for Photovoltaics, NREL, Golden, USA

R. Kenny, European Commission Joint Research Centre, Directorate for Energy and Transport and Climate, Ispra, Italy

S. Nowak, Managing Director of NET Nowak Energy & Technology, St. Ursen, Switzerland

R. Schlatmann, Chairman of ETIP PV, Head of the Solar Energy Division at Helmholtz-Zentrum Berlin, Germany

W.C. Sinke, TNO Energy Transition, The Netherlands

M. Topič, Head of Laboratory of Photovoltaics and Optoelectronics of the University of Ljubljana, Slovenia

P. Verlinden, Director at Amrock, Visiting Professor at Sun Yat-Sen University, Guangzhou, China

E. Voroshazi, Head of PV module process laboratory, CEA, Le Bourget-du-Lac, France

J. Bergmiller, Managing Director Events & Knowledge Transfer, WIP Renewable Energies, Munich, Germany

J. de Gregorio, Head of Unit, Scientific Services and Cooperation, WIP Renewable Energies, Munich, Germany

CONFERENCE EXECUTIVE COMMITTEE

Conference General Chair

C. del Cañizo, UPM, Madrid, Spain

Technical Programme Chair

R. Kenny, European Commission Joint Research Centre, Directorate for Energy and Transport and Climate, Ispra, Italy

Committee Members

W.C. Sinke, Program Development Manager, TNO Energy Transition, The Netherlands

S. Nowak, Managing Director of NET Nowak Energy & Technology, St. Ursen, Switzerland

M. Topič, Head of Laboratory of Photovoltaics and Optoelectronics of the University of Ljubljana, Slovenia

V. Bermúdez Benito, BERBETIN, France

E. Voroshazi, Head of PV Module Process Laboratory, CEA, Le Bourget-Du-Lac France

H. Ossenbrink, Former European Commission Joint Research Centre, Germany

J. Bergmiller, Managing Director Events & Knowledge Transfer, WIP Renewable Energies, Munich, Germany

J. de Gregorio, Head of Unit, Scientific Services and Cooperation, WIP Renewable Energies, Munich, Germany

2025 SCIENTIFIC COMMITTEE

Programme Technical Chair

R. Kenny, European Commission, Joint Research Centre, Italy

Topic Chairs

Topic 1: Silicon Materials and Cells
F. Schindler, Fraunhofer ISE, Germany

Topic 2: Thin Films and New Concepts
I. Gordon, imec, Belgium

Topic 3: Photovoltaic Modules and BoS Components
T. Barnes, NREL, USA

Topic 4: PV Systems Engineering, Integrated/Applied PV
A.M. Gracia Amillo, FUNDACION CENER, Spain

Topic 5: PV in the Energy Transition
C. Agraffeil, CEA / INES, France

Topic Organisers and Paper Review Experts

Topic 1: Silicon Materials and Cells
F. Schindler, Fraunhofer ISE, Germany
C. Fischer, Wacker Chemie, Germany
G. Hahn, University of Konstanz, Germany
K. Ding, Forschungszentrum Jülich, Germany
P. Roca i Cabarrocas, CNRS-LPICM, France
A. W. Weeber, TNO Energy Transition, The Netherlands
D. Muñoz, CEA / INES, France
S. W. Glunz, Fraunhofer ISE, Germany
K. Bothe, ISFH, Germany
M. Topic, University of Ljubljana, Slovenia
P. Fath, RCT-Solutions, Germany
S. Peters, Hanwha Q CELLS, Germany

M.P. Bellmann, SINTEF, Norway
A. Ciesla, UNSW, Australia
C. Hagendorf, Freiberg Instruments, Germany
X. Yu, Zhejiang University, China
J.S. Lee, KIER, South Korea
R. Brendel, ISFH, Germany
T. Dullweber, ISFH, Germany
J. Horzel, Fraunhofer ISE, Germany
W. Nemeth, NREL, United States of America
R. Turan, METU, Türkiye
F. Menchini, ENEA, Italy
W. Favre, CEA, France

J. Meier, Meier Technologies, Switzerland
J. Schmidt, ISFH, Germany
M. Wright, University of Oxford, United Kingdom
J. Zhao, CSEM, Switzerland
A. Morisset, CSEM, Switzerland
A. Richter, Fraunhofer ISE, Germany
J. Linke, ISC Konstanz, Germany
B. Geerligs, TNO Energy Transition, The Netherlands
S. Dubois, CEA, France
M. Hermle, Fraunhofer ISE, Germany
B. Terheiden, University of Konstanz, Germany
P. Delli Veneri, ENEA, Italy
T. Matsui, AIST, Japan
Y. Ohshita, Toyota Technological Institute, Japan
E. Bruhat, HOLOSOLIS, France
A. Augusto, Dalarna University, Sweden
F. Ferrazza, ENI S.p.A., Italy
A. Otaegi, UPV/EHU, Spain
M.C. Schubert, Fraunhofer ISE, Germany
H. Duman, KalyonPV, Türkiye
N. Usami, Nagoya University, Japan
Y. Zhu, UNSW, Australia
D. Brunner, RENA Technologies, Germany
A. Danel, CEA, France
C. Gerardi, 3Sun, Italy
H.J. Nonnenmacher, Meyer Burger, Germany
P. Verlinden, AMROCK, Australia
Q. Wang, Wang, Qi, China
W. Zhang, Zhang, Weiming, China
Y. Chen, Trina Solar Energy, China
E. Krassowski, CE Cell Engineering, Germany
M. Foti, 3Sun, Italy
D.L. Bätzner, Meyer Burger Research, Switzerland

Topic 2: Thin Films and New Concepts
I. Gordon, imec, Belgium
J.C. Goldschmidt, Marburg University, Germany
F. Schoofs, Oxford PV, United Kingdom
N. Kyranaki, Hasselt University, Belgium
S. Veenstra, TNO Energy Transition, The Netherlands
T. Aernouts, imec, Belgium
A.N. Tiwari, SOLTIWA, Switzerland
G. Siefer, Fraunhofer ISE, Germany
M. Edoff, Uppsala University, Sweden
A. Martí Vega, UPM, Spain
J. Poortmans, imec, Belgium
I. Ramiro, UPM, Spain
T. Magorian Friedlmeier, ZSW, Germany

S. Albrecht, HZB, Germany
S. Berson, CEA, France
P. Carroy, CEA, France
C. Case, Oxford PV, United Kingdom
G. Coletti, FuturaSun, Italy
S. De Wolf, KAUST, Saudi Arabia
U.W. Paetzold, KIT, Germany
H. Sivaramakrishnan Radhakrisnan, imec, Belgium
P. Schulze, Fraunhofer ISE, Germany
L. Wang, Technology Innovation Institute, United Arab
  Emirates
Y. Smirnov, Applied Materials, United States of America
B. Stannowski, HZB, Germany
F. Fertig, Hanwha Q CELLS, Germany
L. Lancellotti, ENEA, Italy
S. Cros, CEA, France
S. Hayase, The University of Electro-Communications, Japan
S. Huang, Macquarie University, Australia
M. Khenkin, HZB, Germany
C. Lin, National Taiwan University, Taiwan

M.S.H. Norton, University of Cyprus, Cyprus
P. Pistor, Pablo de Olavide University, Spain
W. Tress, Zurich University of Applied Sciences,
  Switzerland
A. Aguirre, imec, Belgium
D. Lan, UNSW Sydney, China
M. Saliba, University of Stuttgart, Germany
P. Manshanden, TNO Energy Transition, The Netherlands
L. Vesce, University of Rome II, Italy
I. Dogan, TNO Solliance, The Netherlands
Y. Kuang, imec, Belgium
M. Al Katrib, IPVF, France
M.I. Hossain, QEERI, Qatar
W.H. Chiu, Chang Gung University, Taiwan
C. Chen, Ming Chi University of Technology, Taiwan
C. Fell, CSIRO Energy Technology, Australia
G. Brammertz, imec, Belgium
T. Dalibor, Avancis, Germany
S. Ishizuka, AIST, Japan
A. Redinger, University of Luxembourg, Luxembourg
A. Romeo, University of Verona, Italy
V. Sittinger, Fraunhofer IST, Germany
M. Theelen, TNO/Solliance, The Netherlands
G. Timò, RSE, Italy
A. Kanevce, ZSW, Germany
A. Pérez-Rodríguez, IREC, Spain
R. Gutzler, ZSW, Germany
W. Witte, ZSW, Germany
T. Nishimura, Tokyo Institute of Technology, Japan
C. Qian, University of New South Wales, Australia
J.P. Connolly, CentraleSupelec, France
J.P. Kleider, CNRS/GeePs, France
I. Konovalov, University of Applied Sciences Jena, Germany
Y. Okada, University of Tokyo, Japan
M. Rusu, HZB, Germany
H. Meddeb, DLR, Germany
E. Saucedo, Universitat Politècnica de Catalunya (UPC),
  Spain
P. Vidal-Fuentes, FUNDACIÓ INSTITUT DE RECERCA
  EN ENERGIA DE CATALUNYA, Spain
C. Malerba, ENEA, Italy
C. Becker, HZB, Germany
D. Kuciauskas, NREL, United States of America
M. Ochoa, University of Cantabria, Spain
T. Tayagaki, AIST, Japan
S. Wasmer, WAVELABS Solar Metrology Systems,
  Germany
S. Zandi, UNSW, Australia
C. Messmer, University of Freiburg, Germany
J.B. Puel, Institut Photovoltaïque d'Ile de France (IPVF),
  France
S. Ternes, University of Rome II, Italy

Topic 3: Photovoltaic Modules and BoS Components
V. Bermúdez Benito, BERBETIN, France
R. Preu, Fraunhofer ISE, Germany
R. Gottschalg, Fraunhofer CSP, Germany
T. Barnes, NREL, United States of America
G. Friesen, SUPSI, Switzerland
G. Bardizza, TÜV Rheinland Solar, Italy

V. Barth, CEA, France
A. Faes, CSEM, Switzerland
A. Lennon, Sundrive Solar, Australia
M. Mittag, Fraunhofer ISE, Germany
M.A. Muñoz-Garcia, UPM, Spain
H. Nagel, Fraunhofer ISE, Germany
S. Pietralunga, CNR, Italy
T. Timofte, ISC Konstanz, Germany

S. Feldbacher, PCCL, Austria
A. Halm, ISC Konstanz, Germany
H. Hanifi, AESOLAR, Germany
E. Warren, NREL, United States of America
S. Zhang, Trina Solar Energy, China
X. Zhen, Canadian Solar, China
G. Beaucarne, Dow Silicones Belgium, Belgium
T. Bejat, CEA, France
C. Camus, LayTec, Germany
U. Jahn, Fraunhofer CSP, Germany
G. Oreski, PCCL, Austria
M. Pander, Fraunhofer CSP, Germany
T. Sample, European Commission JRC, Italy
A. Morlier, imo-imomec, Belgium
C. Barretta, PCCL, Austria
P. Gebhardt, Fraunhofer ISE, Germany
C. Sen, UNSW, Australia
O. Arriaga Arruti, CSEM, Switzerland
X. Gu, NIST, United States of America
C. Xiao, Chinese Academy of Sciences, United States of
America
R. Aninat, TNO/Solliance, The Netherlands
S. Mitterhofer, NIST, United States of America
B. Hoex, UNSW, Australia
E. Özkalay, SUPSI, Switzerland
M. Bokalič, University of Ljubljana, Slovenia
S. Bordihn, ISFH, Germany
M. Despeisse, CSEM, Switzerland
J. Govaerts, imec, Belgium
J. Lopez-Garcia, STS-Certified, Spain
M. Pravettoni, Technology Innovation Institute, United Arab
Emirates
T. Stoyanova Lyubenova, Joint Research Centre, Italy
C. Ulbrich, HZB, Germany
J. Moereke, Avancis, Germany
Y.S. Long, ITRI, Taiwan
D. Pavanello, European Commission JRC, Italy
A.K. Vidal de Oliveira, UFSC, Brazil
J. Bengoechea, CENER, Spain
M. Ernst, ANU, Australia
H. Ellis, European Commission JRC, Italy
B. Mihaylov, European Commission JRC, Italy
G. Chowdhury, 3E, Belgium
B. Aissa, QEERI - Qatar Environment and Energy Research
Institute, Qatar

Topic 4: PV Systems Engineering, Integrated/Applied PV
A. Gracia Amillo, CENER, Spain
W.G.J.H.M. van Sark, Utrecht University, The Netherlands
K. Lappalainen, Tampere University, Finland
J.M. Almeida Serra, University of Lisbon, Portugal
I. Tsanakas, CEA, France
C. Buerhop-Lutz, HI ERN, Germany
D. Moser, Becquerel Institute Italia, Italy
F. Frontini, SUPSI, Switzerland
G.C. Eder, OFI, Austria
A. Scognamiglio, ENEA, Italy
A. Chatzipanagi, European Commission JRC, Italy
I. Antón Hernández, UPM, Spain
R.M.E. Valckenborg, TNO, The Netherlands
T. Reindl, SERIS, Singapore
J.R. Gonzalez, European Space Agency, The Netherlands
G. Mütter, Gerhard Mütter e.U., Austria
T. Merdzhanova, Forschungszentrum Jülich, Germany

V. Lara-Fanego, Solargis, Spain
A. Louwen, Eurac Research, Italy
A. Martinez Fernandez, European Commission JRC, Italy
T. Oozeki, AIST, Japan

J. Remund, Meteotest, Switzerland
M. Sengupta, NREL, United States of America
M. Zehner, Rosenheim Technical University of Applied
Sciences, Germany
B. Nouri, German Aerospace Center, Spain
S. Poddar, UNSW, Australia
D. Bachour, HBKU/ Qatar Foundation, Qatar
J. Yang, NREL, United States of America
S. Bouguerra, imo-imomec, Belgium
C. Alonso-Tristán, UBU, Spain
M. Carbone, ENEL Green Power, Italy
M. Dennenmoser, BayWa r.e. Solar Projects GmbH,
Germany
C.W. Hansen, Sandia National Laboratories, United States of
America
A. Neubert, DNV Maritime Software GmbH, Germany
D. Berrian, Belectric, Germany
M. Oliosi, PVsyst, Switzerland
J. Moschner, KU Leuven / EnergyVille, Belgium
C. Bucher, BUAS, Switzerland
B. Wittmer, PVsyst SA, Switzerland
M. Bolen, SB Energy, United States of America
D. Daßler, Fraunhofer CSP, Germany
R. Einhaus, ZSW, Germany
P. Hacke, NREL, United States of America
A. Heimsath, Fraunhofer ISE, Germany
J. Lin, PV Guider, Taiwan
A. Migan-Dubois, GeePs, France
M. Rinio, University of Karlstad, Sweden
J.S. Stein, Sandia National Laboratories, United States of
America
D. Stellbogen, ZSW, Germany
M. Theristis, Sandia National Laboratories, United States of
America
A. Virtuani, CSEM, Switzerland
A. Driesse, PV Performance Labs, Germany
M. Øgaard, IFE, Norway
A. Nobre, SERIS, Singapore
T. Trupke, UNSW, Australia
C. Cornaro, University of Rome II, Italy
G. A. dos Reis Benatto, DTU, Denmark
S. Malik, Fraunhofer CSP, Germany
S. Lindig, Univers SAS, France
M.M. Nygård, Institute for Energy Technology, Norway
P. Alonso Gomez, BayWa r.e., Germany
Y. Assoa, CEA, France
P. Bonomo, SUPSI, Switzerland
V. D'Ambrosio, University of Naples Federico II, Italy
E. Román Medina, Tecnalia, Spain
L.H. Slooff, TNO Energy Transition, The Netherlands
S. Villa, TNO, The Netherlands
M. La Rosa, Glass to Power, Italy
T. Del Caño, Onyx Solar Energy, Spain
X. Zhihao, AIST, Japan
P. Sharif, ODTU-GUNAM, Türkiye
K. Umeda, TAISEI CORPORATION, Japan
S. Boddaert, CSTB, France
N. Lysgaard Andersen, DTU, Denmark
K. Meyer, ISFH, Germany
T. Biel, NET Nowak Energy & Technology, Switzerland
F. Colucci, ENEA, Italy
A. Pascaris, NREL, United States of America
C. Dupraz, INRAE, France
C. Alonso-García, CIEMAT, Spain
A. Lefort, BayWa, Germany
H.N. Riise, IFE, Norway
M.A. Schüler, Next2Sun Technology GmbH, Germany
P.J. Pérez-Higueras, University of Jaén, Spain
K. Oda, Agritree,

M. Berwind, Fraunhofer ISE, Germany
M. Dörenkämper, TNO, The Netherlands
M. Heinrich, Fraunhofer ISE, Germany
B. Newman, Lightyear, The Netherlands
A. Reinders, Eindhoven University of Technology, The Netherlands
T. Tanahashi, AIST, Japan
J. Leloux, LuciSun, Belgium
E. Shirazi, University of Twente, The Netherlands
K. Araki, University of Miyazaki, Japan
K. Nishioka, University of Miyazaki, Japan
R. Campesato, CESI, Italy
V. Khorenko, Azur Space, Germany
G. Kakoulaki, European Commission Joint Research Centre, Italy
H. Toyota, JAXA, Japan
P. Garcia-Linares, UPM, Spain
I. Weiss, Weiss, Ingrid, Germany
A. Hensel, Fraunhofer ISE, Germany
J.S. da Fernandes, Hochschule Offenburg, Germany
Y. Ueda, Tokyo University of Science, Japan
J. Braid, Sandia National Laboratories, United States of America

Topic 5: PV in the Energy Transition
J. Stierstorfer, WIP Renewable Energies, Germany
R. Pestana, R&D Nester, Portugal
P.J. Alet, CSEM, Switzerland
C. Agraffeil, CEA, France
K. WAMBACH, Wambach-Consulting, Germany
C. del Cañizo, UPM, Spain
L. Großhans, WIP Renewable Energies, Germany
M. Getsiou, European Commission DG RTD, Belgium
S. Nowak, NET Nowak Energy & Technology, Switzerland
C. Breyer, LUT University, Finland
I. Kaizuka, RTS Corporation, Japan
G. Masson, Becquerel Institute, Belgium
P. Baliozian, VDMA, Germany
L. Großhans, WIP Renewable Energies, Germany
C. Candelise, Bocconi University, Italy
S. Caneva, WIP Renewable Energies, Germany

G. Barchi, Eurac Research, Italy
R. Bründlinger, AIT, Austria
V. Efthymiou, University of Cyprus, Cyprus
M. Centeno Brito, University of Lisbon, Portugal
F. Carigiet, ZHAW, Switzerland
B. Gaiddon, HESPUL, France
F.Z. Ouchani, Green Energy Park, Morocco
M. Rennhofer, AIT, Austria
G. Adinolfi, ENEA, Italy
W. Schaffer, Salzburg Netz, Austria
A. Haber, e-control, Austria
G. Heilscher, Technische Hochschule Ulm, Germany
A. Anctil, Michigan State University, United States of America
S. Arancón, Plug and Play, Spain
S. Capaccioli, ETA - Florence Renewable Energies, Italy
V. Fthenakis, Columbia University, United States of America
G. Heath, NREL, United States of America
K. Komoto, Mizuho Research & Technologies, Ltd., Japan
W. Palitzsch, LuxChemtech, Germany
S. Ovaitt, NREL, United States of America
M. de Wild-Scholten, SmartGreenScans, The Netherlands
S. Herceg, Fraunhofer ISE, Germany
C. Polacchi, Eurac Research, Italy
N. Espinosa, Universidad de Murcia, Spain
E. Drahi, TotalEnergies OneTech, France
S. Guastella, RSE, Italy

H. Ossenbrink, Band Gap, Germany
D. Polverini, European Commission DG GROW, Belgium
N. Taylor, European Commission JRC, Italy
K.A. Weiß, Fraunhofer ISE, Germany
I. Kafedjiska, Helmholtz Zentrum Berlin, Germany
P. Malbranche, Solar Action, France
S. De Iuliis, ENEA, Italy
T. Haarberg, BNW-Energy, Norway
A. Nayfeh, Khalifa University, United Arab Emirates
E. Vartiainen, Fortum Renewables Oy, Finland
E. Veronese, Eurac Research, Italy
P. Sanchez-Friera, Solkeys, Spain
N. Cherradi, Desert Technologies, Saudi Arabia
S. Nold, Fraunhofer ISE, Germany
H.J.J. Yu, CEA, France
M. Beck, U.S. Department of Energy, United States of America
M. Woodhouse, NREL, United States of America
A.B. Cristóbal, UPM, Spain
G. Ruggieri, Insubria University, Italy
S. Tay, NUS, Singapore

Awards Coordinators

Student Awards Coordinator
A.H.M. Smets, Delft University of Technology, The Netherlands

Student Awards Committee
R. Kenny, EU PVSEC Technical Programme Chair, Italy
C. del Canizo, Conference Chair, UPM, Spain
E. Voroshazi, CEA, France
J. Poortmans, imec, Belgium
P.J. Alet, CSEM, Switzerland
S. Caneva, WIP Renewable Energies, Germany
A. Romeo, University of Verona, Italy
G. Friesen, SUPSI, Switzerland
F. Schindler, Fraunhofer ISE, Germany
J.C. Goldchmidt, Marburg University, Germany
D. Moser, Becquerel Institute, Italy
K. Ding, FZJ, Germany
W.C. Sinke, TNO Energy Transition, The Netherlands
M. Topic, University of Ljubljana, Slovenia
R. Schlatman, HZB, Germany
S. Glunz, Fraunhofer ISE, Germany
A.M. Vega, UPM, Spain
I. Kaizuka, RTS, Japan
P.D. Veneri, ENEA, Italy
J. Bengoechea, CENER, Spain

Poster Awards Coordinator
P. Malbranche, Solar Action, France

Poster Awards Committee
R. Kenny, European Commission JRC, Italy
C. del Canizo, UPM, Spain
W. van Sark, Utrecht University, The Netherlands
I. Tsanakas, CEA INES, France
L. Miranda, Oxford PV, United Kingdom
D. Munoz, CEA INES, France
I. Gordon, imec, Belgium
E. Roman, Tecnalia, Spain
G. Eder, OFI, Austria
I. Antón, UPM, Spain
S. Veenstra, TNO, The Netherlands
J.M. Almeida Serra, University of Lisbon, Portugal
T. Magorian Friedlmeier, ZSW, Germany
J. Stierstorfer, WIP Renewable Energies, Germany

SUBJECT INDEX

Silicon Materials and Cells

Sessions 1CP.1, 1EP.3, 1AO.4, 1AO.5, 1AO.6, 1BO.1, 1BO.2, 1BO.3, 1BO.4, 1DO.9, 1BV.5, 1CV.2

Thin Films and New Concepts

Sessions 2CP.2, 2BO.1, 2CO.1, 2CO.2, 2DO.9, 2DO.6, 2DO.7, 2DO.8, 2AO.2, 2AO.3, 2AO.1, 2BO.8, 2BO.9, 2BO.10, 2BV.1, 2BV.2, 2CV.3

Photovoltaic Modules and BoS Components

Sessions 3CP.1, 3CP.3, 3CO.10, 3CO.11, 3DO.12, 3DO.16, 3DO.19, 3DO.20, 3BO.11, 3BO.12, 3BO.14, 3BO.15, 3AV.1, 3AV.2, 3AV.3

PV Systems Engineering, Integrated/Applied PV

Sessions 4AP.1, 4AO.7, 4AO.8, 4AO.9, 4DO.1, 4DO.3, 4BO.6, 4BO.7, 4CO.8, 4CO.9, 4DO.10, 4DO.17, 4BO.5, 4BO.16, 4BO.17, 4DO.2, 4DO.4, 4DO.5, 4CO.3, 4EO.2, 4BV.3, 4BV.4, 4CV.1, 4DV.1, 4DV.4,

PV in the Energy Transition

Sessions 5CP.1, 5CP.2, 5DO.14, 5DO.15, 5CO.4, 5CO.5, 5CO.6, 5DO.18, 5CO.4, 5CO.5, 5CO.6, 5DO.18, 5EO.3, 5EO.1, 5DV.2, 5DV.3,

FOREWORD

The European Photovoltaic Solar Energy Conference and Exhibition (EU PVSEC) stands as the World's leading and most renowned forum for PV research and development and the biggest conference on PV solar energy. In 2025, celebrating its 42nd edition, the EU PVSEC was the essential meeting and exchanging point for global PV experts from research, development, and industry.

Held from 22–26 September 2025 in Bilbao, Spain, the EU PVSEC 2025 was a resounding success, showcasing a wide range of cutting-edge research results. Bringing together both the Conference and the Exhibition, this edition attracted more than 1600 participants from 61 countries who contributed over 1000 presentations across various fields of science and technology. The event provided an essential platform for the exchange of knowledge and ideas on photovoltaic research, innovations, and applications. In the exhibition area 51 companies from all parts of the world welcomed visitors and presented their products and services.

Conference Highlights

The EU PVSEC covered a broad range of topics with an extensive programme that offers an opportunity for workers from across the entire field of photovoltaics to share their findings, as well as an opportunity for multidisciplinary learning. Rapid advances in materials, designs, and manufacturing processes reflect the accelerating expansion of the global PV market. The programme was arranged into 5 topics as follows:

- Silicon Materials and Cells;
- Thin Films and New Concepts;
- Photovoltaic Modules and Balance of System Components;
- PV Systems Engineering, Integrated/Applied PV;
- PV in the Energy Transition.

Communicating the key messages from the conference, not only to participants, but also to other researchers, key stakeholders, policy makers and the general public was an important added value. We thank the Highlights Committee, composed of selected members of the Scientific Committee, as well as the Session Chairs, for providing a comprehensive summary of the findings and state of the art research that were delivered during this year´s event. Some key highlights are listed below, while further details may be found in the dedicated highlights presentation in the annex of these proceedings.

Cross-cutting themes:

- Demonstrated the versatility of solar technologies, spanning traditional and emerging application areas.
- Sustainability and circularity remain central, with research focused on reducing material use, such as replacing silver with copper, and advancing end-of-life management of modules.
- Ensuring long-term stability and predictable energy yield is equally essential, with many examples of studies on degradation mechanisms and efforts to elucidate their root-causes, such as in the case of UVID.

- The role of artificial intelligence across the PV value chain is rapidly expanding, from design to operations and maintenance, including among many others drone applications.

Latest Solar Innovations in Materials, Cells, Modules and PV Systems:

While silicon solar cells remain the cornerstone of PV technology, perovskite solar cells continue to stand out as the leading complementary technology to silicon, both as standalone devices and in tandem configurations. Research efforts are increasingly focused on enhancing stability, understanding degradation mechanisms, improving durability and scalability, and ensuring full industrial compatibility.

Many companies presented impressive results on industrial-size single-junction perovskite modules as well as perovskite-based tandem modules, and several new efficiency records were announced during the event. The rapid pace of innovation in cell and module architecture underscores the need for accelerated and more robust testing and qualification methodologies. Both the industry and the research community are moving swiftly to assess and improve reliability in this fast-evolving PV landscape.

A major focus in module research remains the optimisation of materials and packaging to ensure long lifetimes and predictable energy yields from high-efficiency cells. In parallel, many innovative advances in the operation and maintenance (O&M) of PV systems were presented and discussed.

Applications, Grid Integration and Storage

"PV can be deployed everywhere": from space applications to agrivoltaics, PV noise barriers, building-integrated photovoltaics (BIPV), floating PV systems, and even vehicles. Among these, agrivoltaics is gaining momentum as a promising dual land use approach, offering economic benefits for farmers while increasing resilience to climate change.

Flexibility solutions, particularly through battery storage, were recognised in many technical presentations as essential to accommodate higher PV penetration levels and to reduce energy curtailment. At the same time, strengthening grid infrastructure and enhancing grid management capabilities remain critical to enable the next phase of large-scale PV integration.

Photovoltaics in the Energy Transition

Options for re-establishing competitive module manufacturing in Europe were extensively analysed, including detailed policy recommendations for industrial support and market growth. Currently, a mismatch persists between global PV module installation rates and production rates, resulting in growing inventories and sharply reduced prices.

Finally, inclusiveness, diversity, citizen participation, awareness, education, and social engagement were underlined as vital dimensions of the sector's long-term sustainability and innovation capacity.

EU PVSEC 2025 Proceedings

Selection for inclusion in the conference was made by the Scientific Committee's paper review experts and topic organisers (see the listing on pages 010002-001-005), to whom we express our sincere gratitude for their comprehensive review work and overall contribution to the success of the conference.

The EU PVSEC 2025 Proceedings contain the full papers covering most of the highlights described above and more. The Proceedings provide a comprehensive overview of the PV solar sector, its current status and future prospects in science, research, innovation, development and deployment extending to 3,750 pages. In addition to the 299 submitted papers, the proceedings include 101 presentations (slides) shown during the plenary and oral presentations as well as 176 poster files of the visual presentations. In total this amounts to 576 publications.

The Conference Proceedings are published as downloadable files and are also fully accessible online. A DOI code (Digital Object Identifier) has been assigned to each paper. This ensures unequivocal and permanent identification and full citability. The EU PVSEC 2025 papers can be viewed and downloaded in a full free open access from the EU PVSEC's Proceedings website https://userarea.eupvsec.org/proceedings.

The proceedings of the EU PVSEC 2025 strengthen the commitment to providing quick and open access to high quality scientific results. This is a powerful source for targeted and quick information search and retrieval, enabling you to search by topic, keywords, paper title, DOI, author, or organization.

We are confident that these Proceedings will play an important role in providing a comprehensive overview of the current actors and activities in the global PV sector and that they will disseminate information on the state-of-the-art of technologies and applications. This can generate further research, add momentum to innovation and promote interest in PV worldwide.

We would like to cordially thank all authors and participants of the EU PVSEC 2025 for their contributions and look forward to welcoming you in Rotterdam, The Netherlands from 14 – 18 September 2026 at the EU PVSEC 2026, the 43rd European Photovoltaic Solar Energy Conference and Exhibition

The Editors

TABLE OF CONTENTS OF EU PVSEC 2025 PROCEEDINGS PAPERS

[1] *Anhalt University of Applied Sciences, Köthen, Germany;* [2] *Fraunhofer CSP, Halle, Germany*

Oral SESSION 2AO.2 Advances in Chalcogenide Devices

Oral SESSION 2AO.3 III-V Based Devices | Tandem and Perovskite Solar Cells

Oral SESSION 2BO.10 Advanced Modelling and Characterisation of Perovskite Solar Cells

Sivaramakrishnan Radhakrishnan[1], Jef Poortmans[1], Johan Lauwaert[3], Bart Vermang[1]
[1] *Hasselt Unversity, Genk, Belgium;* [2] *University of Cyprus, Nicosia, Cyprus;* [3] *Ghent University, Ghent, Belgium*

Oral SESSION 2BO.8 Advanced Conversion Devices

Visual SESSION 2BV.1 New Materials, Devices and Conversion Concepts | New Modelling and Characterisation Techniques

Visual SESSION 3AV.2 PV Module Durability and Reliability

Nathan Roosloot[1], Harsha Walpita[2], Christoph Seiffert[1], Jean Thomas[3], Maarten Dörenkämper[4], Minne M. de Jong[4], Josefine H. Selj[1], Gaute Otnes[1]
[1] *Institute for Energy Technology, Kjeller, Norway;* [2] *University of Oslo, Kjeller, Norway;* [3] *Ciel et Terre, Lille, France;* [4] *TNO, Eindhoven, The Netherlands*

Visual SESSION 3AV.3 PV Modules Characterisation and Performances Assessment

Nikolina Pervan[1], Jutta Geier[1], Christian Veas[1], Gernot Oreski[1]
[1] PCCL, Leoben, Austria

Oral SESSION 4DO.1 PV Tracking and Simulation

4DO.17.2 Model Optimization for Multi-Class Real Time UAV Thermal Anomaly   020374
Detection in Solar PV Systems

*Ghaem Taghipour Kani[1], Seyyed Majid Esmailifar[1], Amirreza Ghahremani[1],
Mohammadreza Aghaei[2]*
[1] Amirkabir University of Technology, Tehran, Iran; [2] NTNU, Ålesund, Norway

4DO.17.3 Optimizing Autonomous Aerial Monitoring of Photovoltaic Power Plants via   020375
an Integrated Software Package and a Digital Twin Based Simulation
Environment

*Mohammad Kolahi[1], Seyyed Majid Esmailifar[2], Amirmohammad Moradi
Sizkouhi[3], Mohammadreza Aghaei[4]*
*[1] University of Isfahan, Isfahan, Iran; [2] Amirkabir University of Technology, Tehran, Iran; [3]
Concordia University, Montreal, Canada; [4] NTNU, Ålesund, Norway*

4DO.17.4 Influence of Irradiance and Drone Altitude in Infrared Thermography   020376
Inspections of Photovoltaic Plants

*Rodrigo del Prado Santamaría[1], Gisele A. dos Reis Benatto[1], Mahmoud
Dhimish[1], Timurhan Koc[1], Rizal Friansyah[1], Thøger Kari[1], Aysha Mahmood[1],
Peter B. Poulsen[1], Sergiu V. Spataru[1]*
[1] DTU, Roskilde, Denmark

4DO.17.6 Strategy for Simple, On-Site Failure Analysis: Investigating Bubbles and   020377
Burn Marks in Backsheets of PV Modules

*Claudia Buerhop[1], Aline Vidal de Oliveira[2], Oleksandr Mashkov[1], Lucas
Nascimento[2], Ricardo Rüther[2], Ian Marius Peters[1]*
[1] Forschungszentrum Jülich, Erlangen, Germany; [2] UFSC, Florianopolis, Brazil

Oral SESSION 4DO.2 Agrivoltaic Technologies

4DO.2.1 Design and Testing of an Innovative Closed Agrivoltaic System: 020378
"Algaevoltaics"

*Alessandra Scognamiglio[1], Aniello Borriello[1], Carmine Cancro[1], Mariam De
Blasi[2], Maria Genovese[2], Marcello Diano[3], Stefano Mazzoleni[4], Fabrizio
Carteni[4], Paola Delli Veneri[1]*
*[1] ENEA, Portici, Italy; [2] Enel Green Power, Pisa, Italy; [3] M2M Engineering, Naples, Italy; [4]
University of Naples Federico II, Naples, Italy*

4DO.2.2 Experimental Investigation of an Agrivoltaic Collector with Planar Spectral   020379
Beam Splitting

*Inga Krasilnikov[1], Abraham Kribus[1], Gur Mittelman[2], Liad Reshef[3], Shay
Ozer[3], Lavi Rosenfeld[3], Helena Vitoshkin[3]*
*[1] Tel Aviv University, Tel Aviv, Israel; [2] Afeka Tel-Aviv Academic College of Engineering, Tel
Aviv, Israel; [3] Agricultural Research Organization, Rishon LeZion, Israel*

4DO.2.3 Agri-PV Potential in Northern Climates An Experimental Study on Panel   020380
Transparency, and Leafy Vegetable Productivity

*Matas Rudzikas[1], Giedrė Samuolienė[2], Justinas Raginskis[3], Piotr Dubravskij[4],
Algirdas Baležentis[1], Skirmantė Baležentienė[1]*
*[1] The Applied Research Institute for Prospective Technologies, Vilnius, Lithuania; [2] The
Lithuanian Research Centre for Agriculture and Forestry, Kaunas, Lithuania; [3] Kaunas
University of Technology, Kaunas, Lithuania; [4] Modern E-Technologies, Vilnius, Lithuania*

Marcus Rennhofer[1], Philipp Mayer-Ullmann[1], Diana Maria Krainer[1],
Gusztav Ujvari[1], Janine Lichtenberger[1], Konrad Kainz[1], Vassilissa Neussl[1],
Bernhard Kubicek[1]
[1] AIT, Vienna, Austria

Visual SESSION 4DV.4 PV System Engineering

5CO.5.6   Environmental Benefits of Silicon Kerf Secondary Products in Pilot Processes 020468
over Conventional Production of Equivalent Products with Primary Raw
Materials in China and Europe

René Peche[1], Matthias Seitz[1], Markus Schönheits[1], Karsten Wambach[1]
[1] bifa Umweltinstitut, Augsburg, Germany

Oral SESSION 5CO.6 PV Recycling and Circularity

5CO.6.4   Quantification of Technical Recyclability of PV Modules for Different   020470
Recycling Scenarios

*Matthias Hämmer[1], Kerstin Baumann[1], Karsten Wambach[1], Markus
Schönheits[1]*
[1] bifa Umweltinstitut, Augsburg, Germany

5CO.6.5   IEC Technical Report 63525 on the Reuse of PV Modules: Final Result   020472

Arvid van der Heide[1], Serge Noels[2], Jan Clyncke[2], Rich Strömberg[3]
*[1] imec, Genk, Belgium; [2] PV CYCLE, Brussels, Belgium; [3] University of Alaska, Fairbanks,
United States of America*

**Plenary SESSION 5CP.1 Si PV Manufacturing: Pushing the Limits of
Performance**

5CP.1.4   Business Model Optimization for European Solar PV: A Study on Costs and   020474
Commercial Strategies

Ian Kenchington[1], Philippe Macé[1], Gaëtan Masson[1], Joris Libal[2]
[1] Becquerel Institute, Brussels, Belgium; [2] ISC Konstanz, Konstanz, Germany

**Plenary SESSION 5CP.2 Perovskite – Silicon Tandems: Towards
Commercialisation | PV Stability in the Field**

5CP.2.3   Total Cost of Ownership, LCA and LCOE Analysis of Perovskite-Silicon   020475
Tandems Compared to Single Junction Crystalline Silicon PV Technologies

*Baljeet Singh Goraya[1], Dilara Maria Subasi[1], Peter Henri Brailovsky[1],
Henning Nagel[1], Patricia S.C. Schulze[1], Martin C. Schubert[1], Jochen
Rentsch[1], Martin Hermle[1], Ralf Preu[1], Sebastian Nold[1]*
[1] Fraunhofer ISE, Freiburg, Germany

Oral SESSION 5DO.11 The Road to Massive PV Deployment

5DO.11.1 Integration of Solar PV in a Norwegian Energy System, Navigating the   020476
Trade-offs between Land Use and Solar Power Production

Petry Kristine Nøttum Haaland[1], Ole-Morten Midtgård[1], Magnus Korpås[1]
[1] NTNU, Trondheim, Norway

Oral SESSION 5EO.1 Citizens Participation and Awareness

Fraunhofer
ISE

Total Cost of Ownership, LCA
and LCOE Analysis of
Perovskite-Silicon Tandems
Compared to Single Junction
Crystalline Silicon PV
Technologies

—

B. Goraya, D. Subasi, P. Brailovsky, H. Nagel, P.S.C.
Schulze, M. C. Schubert, J. Rentsch, M. Hermle, R. Preu,
S. Nold
Fraunhofer ISE, Freiburg, Germany

42nd EU PVSEC, Bilbao, September 24th, 2025

TCO, LCA and LCOE Analysis of Pero-Si Tandems vs. SJ c-Si PV Technologies
Key Questions

1. What are the production costs, carbon footprint and electricity costs of Perovskite-Silicon tandems compared to single junction crystalline-Silicon technologies?

2. What to focus on for making Perovskite-Silicon tandems economically and environmentally competitive?

EU project VIPERLAB:
FULLY CONNECTED VIRTUAL AND PHYSICAL PEROVSKITE PHOTOVOLTAICS LAB

Duration: May 2021 to Nov 2024

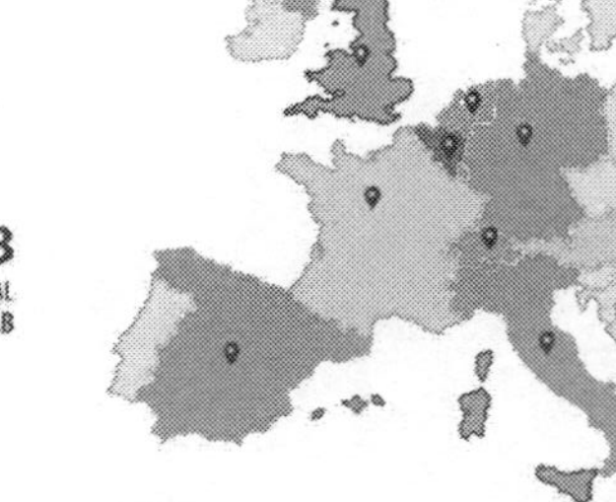

https://www.viperlab.eu/

Fraunhofer ISE

020475-002

Total Cost of Ownership (TCO) of Pero-Si Tandems vs. SJ c-Si PV Technologies

Methodology for Cost Modelling

Production cost assessment for single process steps and TCO for process routes [1].

Equipment and process data for state-of-the-art technology required.

→ Data acquisition for industrial production equipment is crucial for assessment!

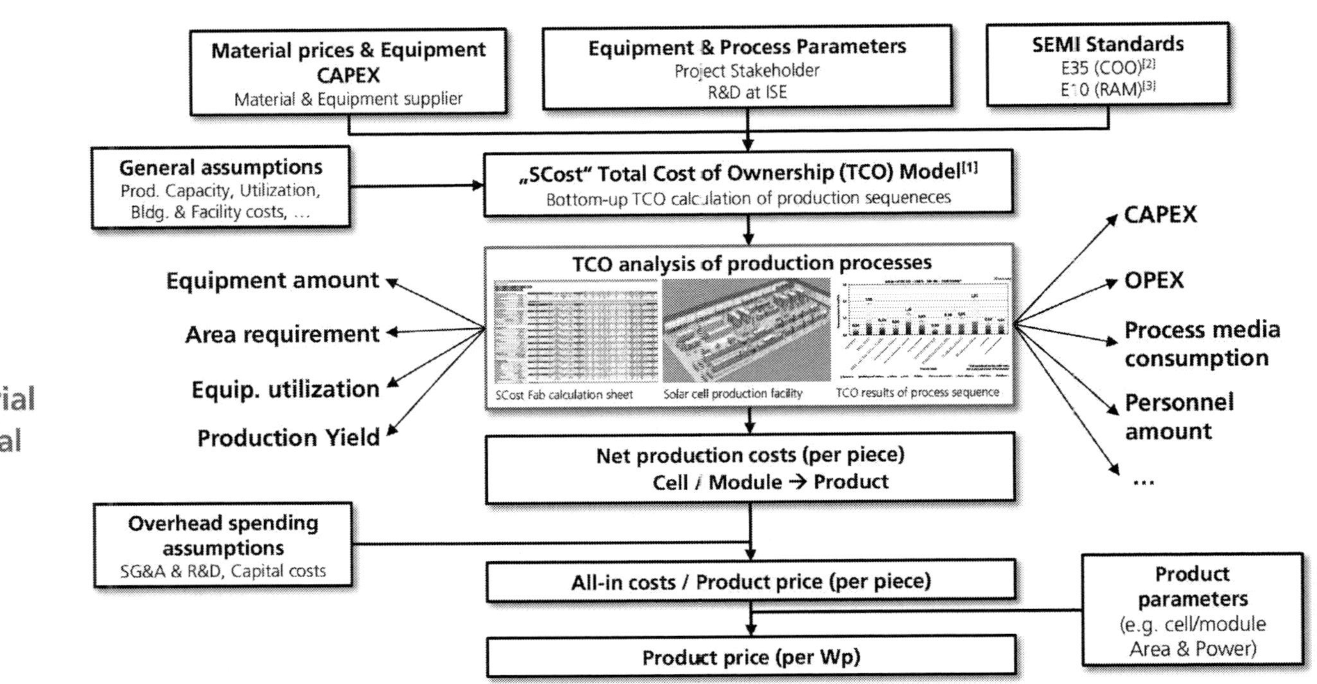

[1] https://www.ise.fraunhofer.de/en/business-areas/photovoltaics-production-technology-and-transfer/technology-assessment-and-transfer.html
[2] Guide to Calculate Cost of Ownership (COO) Metrics for Semiconductor Manufacturing Equipment, SEMI E35-0618.
[3] Specification for Definition and Measurement of Equipment Reliability, Availability, and Maintainability (RAM) and Utilization, SEMI E10-0814E.

Fraunhofer
ISE

020475-003

Total Cost of Ownership (TCO) of Pero-Si Tandems vs. SJ c-Si PV Technologies

Analysed Technologies and Key Inputs for Modelling

4 technologies evaluated for cell (n-Cz 130µm M10 wafer) and module (72 cell glass-glass) production:

- **2 single junction crystalline-Silicon based:**

- **2 fully textured 2-Terminal tandems:**

Location:
Green field production site in Eastern Europe.

Annual output:
Same number of modules produced per year (5.2 to 6.4 GWp/a)

n-Cz 130 µm M10 wafer price:
19 €ct/wafer[1]

1: OPIS avg. wafer price 2024

Fraunhofer
ISE

020475-004

Total Cost of Ownership (TCO) of Pero-Si Tandems vs. SJ c-Si PV Technologies

Analysed Cell Production Sequences

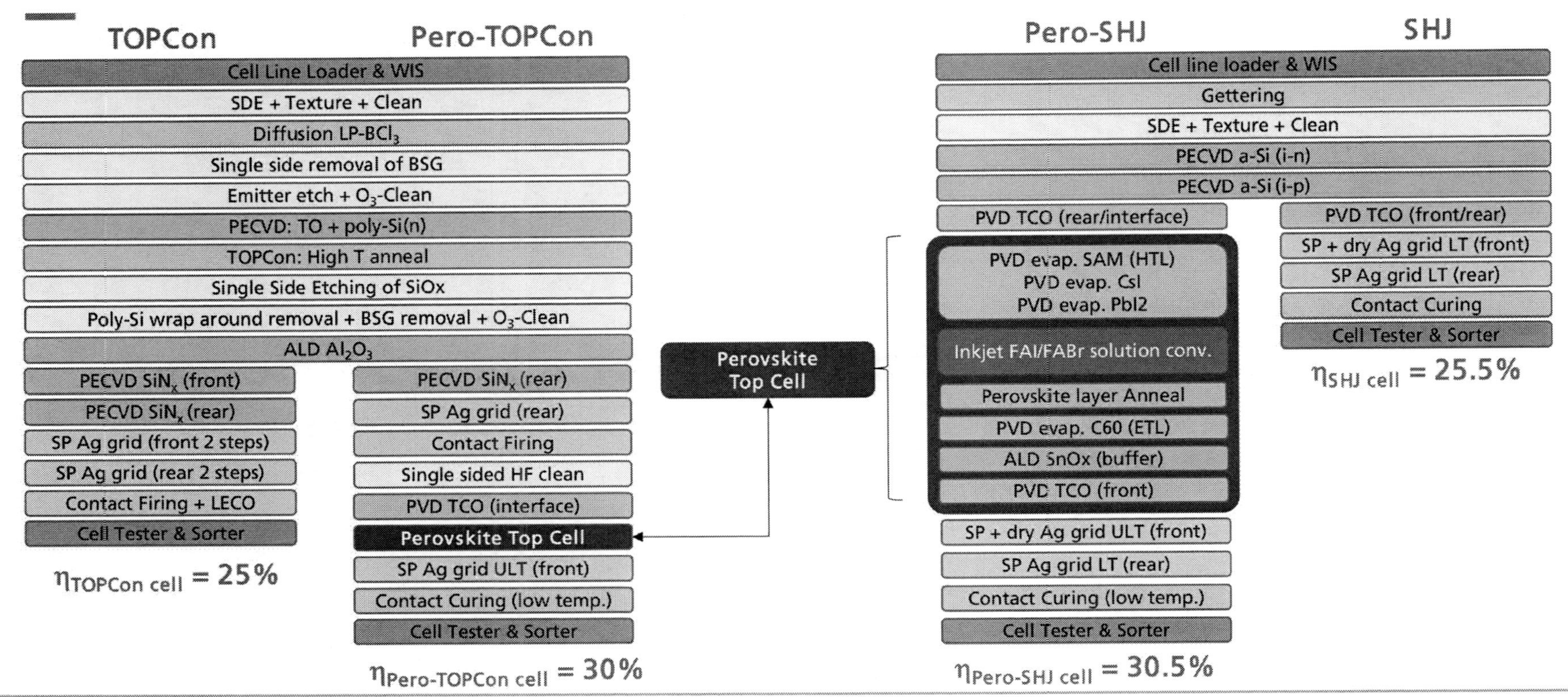

Fraunhofer
ISE

020475-005

Total Cost of Ownership (TCO) of Pero-Si Tandems vs. SJ c-Si PV Technologies

Perovskite Top Cell Material Prices

Very high prices for perovskite materials currently used in research.

Perovskite Materials	Researched price for low volume orders	Price with 50% reduction	Price with 90% reduction	Unit
C60	**41,400**	**20,700**	**4,140**	
FAI	1,167	584	117	
FABr	1,460	730	146	€/kg
SAM 2-PACz	**470,000**	**235,000**	**47,000**	
CsI	**13,600**	**6800**	**1,360**	
PbI2	**3,500**	**1750**	**350**	

PbI_2, CsI, SAM 2-PACz and **C60** have the **largest material cost share**, based on their specific consumptions, of the perovskite top cell.

©Fraunhofer ISE

- Low volume orders based on ISE orders, internet research and from contacting material suppliers.
- Not shown here are the solvents like butanol and ethanol which are bulk materials and will not be impacted by scaling.

020475-006

Total Cost of Ownership (TCO) of Pero-Si Tandems vs. SJ c-Si PV Technologies

Analysed Technologies

4 technologies evaluated for cell (n-Cz 130µm M10 wafer) and module (72 cell glass-glass) production:

- **2 single junction crystalline-Silicon based:**

- **2 fully textured 2-Terminal tandems:**

2 further scenarios for non-optimized tandems with:

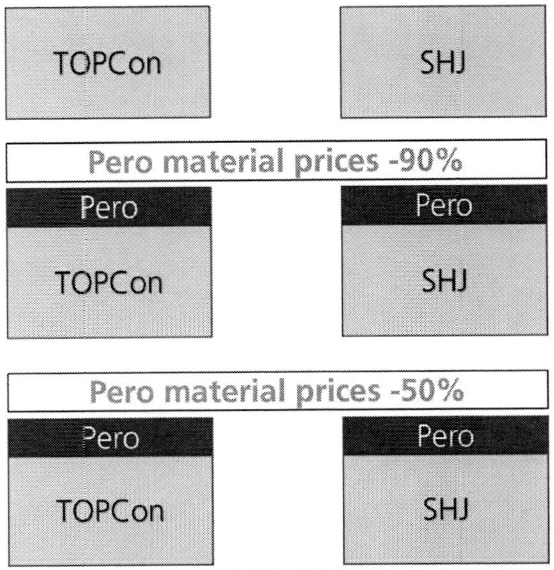

Fraunhofer
ISE

020475-007

Total Cost of Ownership (TCO) of Pero-Si Tandems vs. SJ c-Si PV Technologies
Analysed Module Production Sequence

72 cell Glass-Glass module

2 mm Glass loader1

Lay-up POE1

Combined tabber stringer + Auto bussing

Lay-up Cells / POE2 / 2mm Glass2

Module Lamination

Edge trimming and Framing

Junction box mounting + seal

Curing line

Module Flasher & Sorter

Labelling & Packaging

Butyl edge sealant for Pero-Silicon tandem module instead of silicone for SJs

Materials (e.g. glass, POE, Al-frame, etc.) **account for ~80%** of module production costs for the single junction modules.

Butyl edge sealant for tandems increases module production costs by **~20%** vs. single junction modules.

Cell-type	Eta cell	Eta module / P_{mpp} (72 cells/mod)
TOPCon	25.0 %	23.0 % / 593 Wp
Pero-TOPCon	30.0 %	27.3 % / 705 Wp
SHJ	25.5 %	23.4 % / 605 Wp
Pero-SHJ	30.5 %	27.8 % / 717 Wp

8

©Fraunhofer ISE

- Module dimensions: 2278 x 1134 mm
- CTM (power loss) considered as -0.21% & -1.11% absolute for the SJ and tandems respectively.

Fraunhofer ISE

Total Cost of Ownership (TCO) of Pero-Si Tandems vs. SJ c-Si PV Technologies

All-in Module Cost Comparison for all Technologies

All-in-module costs (Wp) for:

- Pero-TOPCon tandems vs. TOPCon:
  + 5% to + 42%

- Pero-SHJ tandems vs. SHJ:
  -0.1% to +34%

Pero-Si tandems can provide competitive all-in module costs to established & mature SJ technologies.

Focus on reducing perovskite material prices!

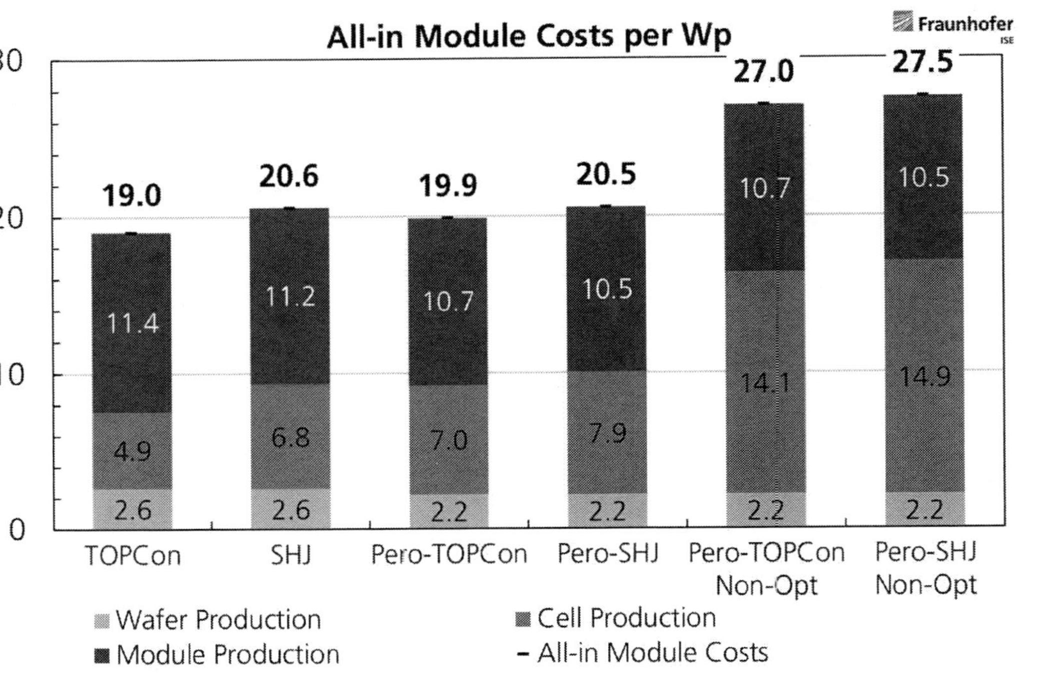

Note: All-in Module costs include SG&A / R&D costs and cost of capital on top of production costs.
Module efficiency: TOPCon - 23%, SHJ - 23.4%, Pero-TOPCon - 27.3%, Pero-SHJ - 27.8%

© Fraunhofer ISE

Fraunhofer ISE

020475-009

LCOE Analysis of Pero-Si Tandems vs. SJ c-Si PV Technologies

General Assumptions and Key Inputs

LCOE evaluation for:
- 10 kWp residential rooftop system
- Location: Southern Germany (GHI: 1300 kWh/m^{2}a)
- Assumed same annual specific PV energy yield for:
  - TOPCon and Pero-TOPCon of 1256 kWh/kWp/a
  - SHJ and Pero-SHJ of 1268 kWh/kWp/a

For TOPCon, SHJ, Pero-TOPCon and Pero-SHJ:
- Degradation rate (1st year/2nd year on): 1 / 0.5 %/year
- System life: 30 years

For non-optimized Pero-Si tandems:
- Degradation rate (1st year/2nd year on): 1 / 1 %/year
- System life: 20 years

Fraunhofer
ISE

020475-010

LCOE Analysis of Pero-Si Tandems vs. SJ c-Si PV Technologies

Nominal LCOE for Residential Rooftop Systems

LCOE Results

- Pero-Si tandems can provide lower LCOE than the SJ counterparts.

- Non-optimized Pero-Si tandems show substantially higher LCOE than SJ counterparts.

Low perovskite material prices, high reliability and stability are key for Pero-Si tandems to provide a competitive LCOE!

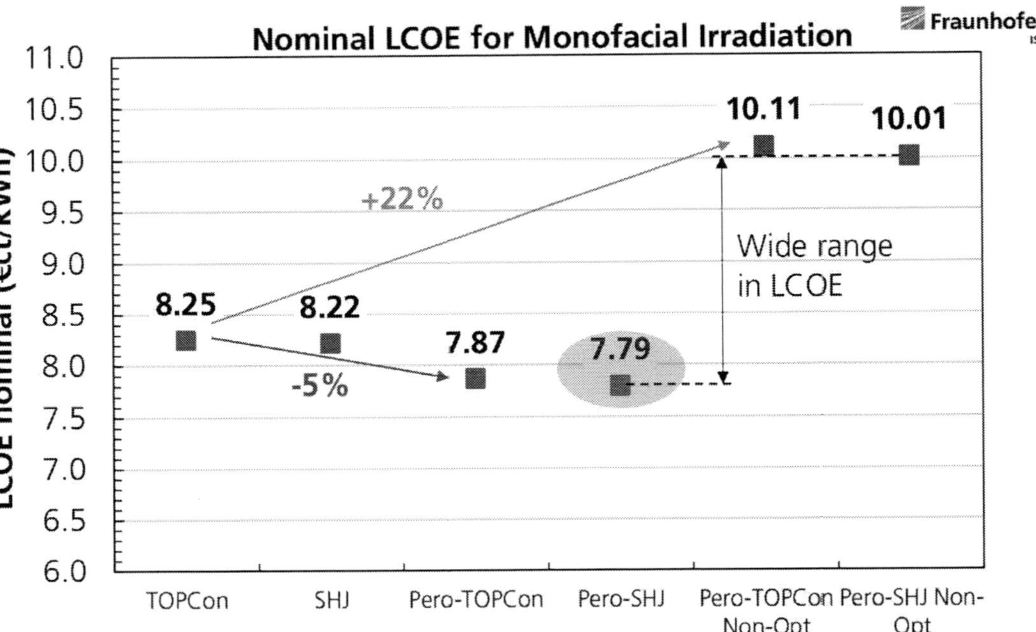

©Fraunhofer ISE

LCOE parameters: System size: 10 kWp (pitched roof); GHI: 1300 kWh/m²a; Degradation (1st year/2nd year on): 1/(0.5/1) %/a; Temp. coeff.: -0.27/-0.32 %/K; System life: 30/20 years; WACC: 5%
BOS costs: Inverter 10 €ct/Wp; Area proportional BOS costs: 103 €/m²; Power proportional BOS costs: 22 €ct/Wp; Soft BOS costs: 23 €ct/Wp; Annual costs: 1 €ct/Wp; Margin: 15% on total PV system costs.

Fraunhofer ISE

LCOE Analysis of Pero-Si Tandems vs. SJ c-Si PV Technologies

LCOE Residential Rooftop – Sensitivity Analysis

Iso-LCOE curves for all assessed technologies.

To achieve the same LCOE:

~2% higher cell efficiency required for Pero-Si tandems compared to SJ technologies.

For the non-optimized Pero-Si tandems, a **cell efficiency gain of >10%** required.

Focus on reducing perovskite material prices, improving reliability and stability of Pero-Si tandems!

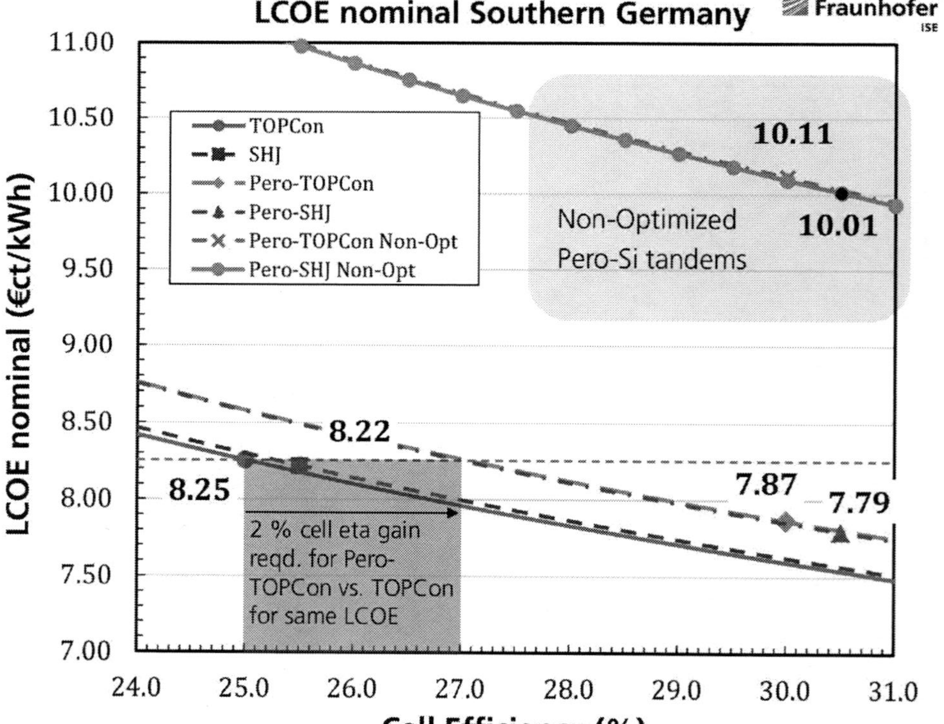

12

©Fraunhofer ISE

LCOE parameters: System size: 10 kWp (pitched roof); GHI: 1300 kWh/m²a; Degradation (1st year/2nd year on): 1/(0.5/1) %/a; Temp. coeff.: -0.27 / -0.32 %/K; System life: 30/20 years; WACC: 5%
BOS costs: Inverter 10 €ct/Wp; Area proportional BOS costs: 103 €/m²; Power proportional BOS costs: 22 €ct/Wp; Soft BOS costs: 23 €ct/Wp; Annual costs: 1 €ct/Wp; Margin: 15% on total PV system costs.

Fraunhofer
ISE

020475-012

Life Cycle Assessment (LCA) of Pero-Si Tandems vs. SJ c-Si PV Technologies

General Assumptions and Key Inputs

Focus on Carbon Footprint in g CO_2-eq/kWh or the Global Warming Potential (GWP)

- Residential rooftop system, functional unit 1 kWh
- Wafers are assumed to be supplied from China.
- Cells and modules are assumed to be produced in Germany.
- Proxy consumables are used for materials not available in the Life Cycle Inventory.

For TOPCon, SHJ, Pero-TOPCon and Pero-SHJ:

- Degradation rate (1st year/2nd year on): 1 / 0.5 %/year
- System life: 30 years

For non-optimized Pero-Si tandems:

- Degradation rate (1st year/2nd year on): 1 / 1 %/year
- System life: 20 years

Climate change within Environmental Footprint 3.0 impact assessment method, the Ecoinvent 3.11 database, allocation cut-off by classification used and the LCA Software SimaPro.

Fraunhofer
ISE

020475-013

Life Cycle Assessment (LCA) of Pero-Si Tandems vs. SJ c-Si PV Technologies

Carbon Footprint or Global Warming Potential (GWP) Assessment

Pero-Si tandems show **lower GWP** than the SJ counterparts.

Non-optimized Pero-Si tandems show **substantially higher GWP** than SJ counterparts.

Perovskite materials and perovskite top cell production only **contributes ~1%** to the GWP of Pero-Si tandems.

Focus on improving reliability and stability of tandems!

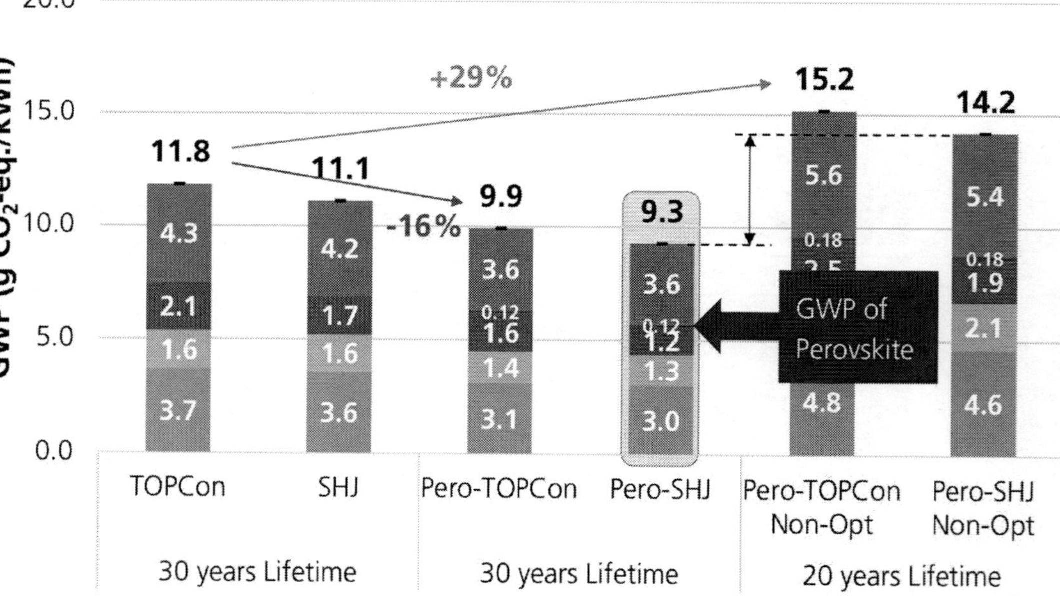

14

©Fraunhofer ISE

Climate change within Environmental Footprint 3.0 impact assessment method, the Ecoinvent 3.11 database, allocation cut-off by classification used and the LCA Software SimaPro.
A.A. Khan et al, Environmental Profile of Scalable Perovskite Silicon Tandem vs. Silicon Heterojunction Technology, tandemPV workshop 2023, Fraunhofer Lighthouse project MaNiTU.

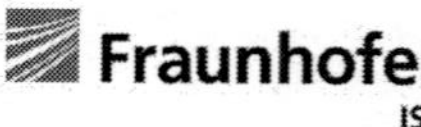

TCO, LCA and LCOE Analysis of Pero-Si Tandems vs. SJ c-Si PV Technologies

Summary & Takeaways

TCO analysis shows that **Pero-Si tandems can provide competitive all-in module costs** to established & mature single junction technologies.

- **Focus on reducing perovskite material prices!**

LCOE analysis shows that **~2% higher cell efficiency required for Pero-Si tandems** (-90% perovskite material price, -0.5%/a degradation rate & 30-year lifetime) compared to single junction technologies to achieve the same LCOE.

- **Focus on reducing perovskite material prices and improving reliability and stability!**

LCA shows **that Pero-Si tandems can provide the lowest carbon footprint / GWP** from all assessed technologies.

- **Focus on improving reliability and stability!**

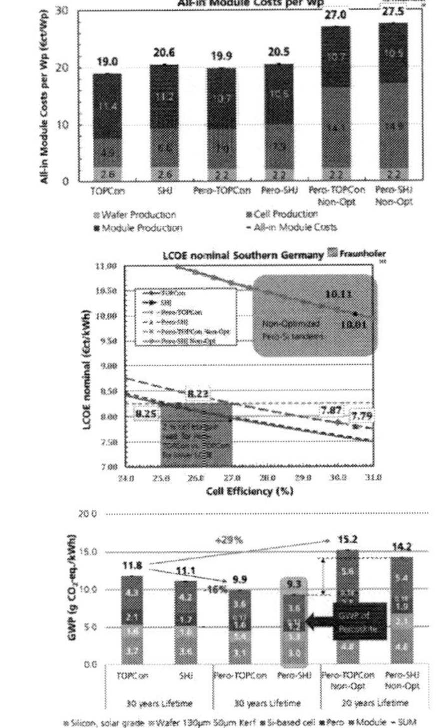

15

Fraunhofer
ISE

Thank You for Your Attention!

—

Contact

Baljeet Singh Goraya
Techno-Economic and Ecological Analyses
baljeet.singh.goraya@ise.fraunhofer.de

Fraunhofer ISE
Heidenhofstrasse 2
79110 Freiburg, Germany
www.ise.fraunhofer.de

This project has received funding from the European Union's Horizon 2020 research and innovation programme under grant agreement N°101006715.

Link to Fraunhofer ISE
contributions of the
42nd EU PVSEC:
https://ise.link/eupvsec2025
available as of 26.09.2025

This presentation was selected by the Sc. Committee of the EU PVSEC 2025 for submission of a full paper to one of the EU PVSEC's collaborating peer-reviewed journals.

INTEGRATION OF SOLAR PV IN A NORWEGIAN ENERGY SYSTEM, NAVIGATING THE TRADE-OFFS BETWEEN LAND USE AND SOLAR POWER PRODUCTION

Petry Kristine Nøttum Haaland, Ole-Morten Midtgård, Magnus Korpås
Department of Electric Energy, Norwegian University of Science and Technology (NTNU),
O. S. Bragstads Plass 2E, 7034 Trondheim
petry.k.n.haaland@ntnu.no

ABSTRACT: In recent years, the expansion of renewable energy sources (RES) has accelerated, with solar photovoltaic (PV) poised to play a central role in future energy systems. However, this growth has led to rising tensions over land use conflicts, along with growing concerns about biodiversity loss and environmental degradation. This study assesses land use requirements across various renewable energy scenarios for Norway, highlighting trade-offs between spatial demands and system configurations. Results show a wide range of land use needs, from 18.43 to 5149 km^2, depending on the scenario and metric applied. Our findings emphasize the importance of consistent land use metrics and the integration of socio-economic factors in energy planning. As RES deployment intensifies, strategic planning is essential to protect ecosystems and maintain public support, both critical for achieving climate targets.
Keywords: Land use requirements, RES, Solar PV, Socio-economics

1 INTRODUCTION

Achieving a climate-neutral economy increasingly depends on the large-scale deployment of renewable energy sources (RES) [1]. Currently, the electricity and heating sectors account for roughly 30% of global greenhouse gas (GHG) emissions. This share is expected to rise due to ongoing electrification across sectors [2], making the integration of RES a critical strategy for emission reduction [3]. Among the available technologies, solar power has seen particularly rapid growth, with forecasts indicating continued strong expansion in the coming years [4].

Several studies have explored long-term planning for power systems [5]–[8]. Yet most optimization models tend to prioritize techno-economic parameters. This narrow focus overlooks key practical constraints, such as land availability, which becomes increasingly relevant as RES deployment scales up [5]. While solar and wind energy are renewable and abundant, the land required for their infrastructure is limited. Consequently, solutions derived from energy system models may not always be viable when spatial limitations are taken into account. As the energy transition will require greater capacity, land-use constraints may challenge the feasibility of proposed configurations [9]–[11].

The rapid expansion of RES has also led to growing concerns about land use, particularly regarding the development of previously undisturbed natural areas. These concerns include potential impacts on biodiversity and ecosystem integrity [12], [13]. To ensure that ecological, recreational, and societal interests are respected, land use must be carefully considered in the planning and implementation of RES infrastructure.

This paper investigates the potential role of solar photovoltaic (PV) in Norway's future energy system, with a particular focus on the trade-offs between land use and increased RES integration. Norway is currently in the early stages of deploying utility-scale PV systems [14]. With a projected power deficit by 2027 and rising electricity demand driven by widespread electrification, expanding generation capacity is becoming increasingly urgent [15]. Solar energy could play a key role in meeting this demand, but its spatial implications must be thoroughly assessed to ensure sustainable integration into the national energy system.

The primary contributions of this paper are as follows: A detailed evaluation of Norway's future power system and potential decarbonization pathways, emphasizing land use considerations and the integration of solar PV technologies. It further explores the trade-offs between land use and RES deployment by analyzing multiple scenarios with varying restrictions for RES integration. Although the analysis is focused on Norway, the insights are relevant to broader contexts facing similar challenges.

The remainder of the paper is structured as follows: Section 2 describes the methodology, including key inputs and assumptions. Section 3 presents the results and discusses the findings, while Section 4 offers concluding remarks.

2 METHODOLOGY

2.1 Model design

A detailed case study of the North European power system is carried out to analyze the trade-offs between land use and the integration of RES. The modeled system consists of six interconnected regions. Regions 1 through 5 represent Norway's electricity system, divided according to its different price zones (NO1–NO5). Region 6, referred to as the Continent, is a simplified representation of the broader North European grid. It aggregates data from Denmark, the United Kingdom, Germany, Belgium, the Netherlands, and Sweden to account for cross-border electricity exchanges between Norway and its neighboring countries. The energy system model is adapted from the framework presented in [16], with modifications made to suit the specific scope and objectives of this analysis.

The analysis is conducted using the GenX modeling framework, an open-source tool designed for optimizing long-term investments in electricity generation, storage, transmission infrastructure, and demand-side technologies to meet a projected electricity demand [17]. GenX formulates the problem as a constrained linear or mixed-integer linear optimization, enabling the identification of cost-effective investment portfolios and operational strategies. The framework operates deterministically and is typically used for capacity expansion planning for a specified future year, based on the optimization formulation in Equation 1.

The GenX model's objective function integrates multiple cost components to reflect the economic considera-

10.4229/EUPVSEC2025/5DO.11.1
020476-001

tions involved in power system planning. The first term captures fixed annual expenditures, encompassing both capital investments and fixed operation and maintenance (O&M) costs. The second and third terms represent variable costs linked to electricity generation and fuel usage. The fourth component introduces penalties for unmet demand and reserve shortages, ensuring system reliability is prioritized. The fifth term accounts for startup costs associated with technologies requiring unit commitment modeling, calculated by multiplying the startup cost by the number of startup events for each generator cluster at each time step. Finally, the model includes costs associated with transmission infrastructure expansion.

In addition to these cost terms, GenX enforces a set of constraints to ensure realistic system behavior. These include technology-specific constraints such as capacity limits, operational bounds, and resource availability, as well as system-wide constraints like reserve requirements, hourly energy balance, and compliance with CO_2 emissions caps. The model also incorporates unit commitment constraints, startup and shutdown dynamics, and storage cycling behavior.

$$
\begin{aligned}
\min \sum_{z \in Z} \sum_{g \in G} & \left(C_{g,z}^{\text{Inv}} \cdot A_{g,z} \cdot \delta_{g,z}^{\text{Inv}} + C_{g,z}^{\text{FixOM}} \cdot \Delta_{g,z} \right) \\
&+ \sum_{z \in Z} \sum_{t \in T} \sum_{g \in G} \left(G_{g,z}^{\text{VarOM}} + G_{g,z}^{\text{Fuel}} \right) \cdot \phi_{g,t,z} \\
&+ \sum_{z \in Z} \sum_{t \in T} \left(C_s^{\text{VarOM}} \cdot \phi_{g,t,z} + C_s^{\text{VarOM}} \cdot \phi_{s,t,z} \right) \\
&+ \sum_{z \in Z} \sum_{t \in T} \left(C^{\text{curt}} \cdot \gamma_{t,z}^e + C^R \cdot \gamma_{t,z}^r \right) \\
&+ \sum_{z \in Z} \sum_{t \in T} \sum_{g \in G} \left(\Pi_{g,z}^{\text{START}} + \epsilon_{g,t,} \right) \\
&+ \sum_{l \in L} \pi_l^{\text{TCAP}} \cdot \Delta \phi_l^{\max}
\end{aligned} \tag{1}
$$

To solve the optimization problem, a detailed configuration of the North European power system is required, including assumptions about generation technologies, demand profiles, and energy storage options. The following section outlines the data inputs and modeling assumptions used in setting up the system.

2.2 Input data and assumptions

The simulations are grounded in projected costs and assumptions for the year 2040. A brownfield optimization strategy is employed, utilizing existing generation assets as documented in [18]. No additional capacity is permitted for hydropower or run-of-river technologies. Furthermore, consistent with the expected coal phaseout, new coal-fired power investments are excluded from the model [19].

Hydropower scheduling is optimized over a one-year horizon, incorporating historical inflow patterns, power-to-energy conversion ratios, reservoir limitations, and minimum storage thresholds. Norwegian inflow data are sourced from [20], while continental data are derived from [21]. Due to the absence of detailed hourly inflow data for run-of-river systems, their inflows are assumed to mirror those of reservoir-based hydropower. Given the relatively minor contribution of run-of-river generation to total output, this simplification is not expected to significantly influence the results. Investment cost estimates for hydropower are taken from [22].

To reflect the variability of RES, hourly capacity factors are extracted from [23]. After analyzing weather data spanning 2007–2019, the year 2013 is selected as representative and used as the benchmark. Nuclear power maintenance is modeled as a flexible resource, with hourly availability data sourced from [21]. Other generation technologies are modeled with fixed capacity factors.

Fuel prices and corresponding CO_2 emissions are based on data from [24] and [25]. Bioenergy is treated as carbon-neutral, following the assumptions outlined in [26]. Technical specifications for all generation technologies are drawn from [27]. Investment, fixed, and O&M costs are aligned with the EU Reference Scenario 2020 [27], and annuity calculations assume a 5% discount rate. To streamline computation, power plants are grouped into clusters with similar characteristics.

Transmission capacities between regions are compiled from ENTSOG and ENTSO-E Ten-Year Network Development Plans (TYNDPs). Hourly electricity demand profiles are derived from historical data [18], scaled using projections from [28] and [29]. Norway's annual demand is set at 199 TWh, while the total demand for Northern Europe is 1708 TWh. Inter-annual demand fluctuations are captured using average variations from 2015 to 2021. The value of lost load is assumed to be 10,000$/MWh.

The model further incorporates two energy storage technologies, lithium-ion batteries with a 4-hour discharge duration and pumped hydro storage (PHS) for seasonal balancing. This enables an evaluation of how different storage solutions affect land use. Battery cost assumptions are based on [30], while PHS costs are sourced from [31]. Details on the model setup, along with comprehensive input data, are available in [32].

2.3 Description of cases

To quantify the role of solar power in Norway's future energy system and examine the trade-offs between land use and increased RES development, four different cases are investigated. The cases are categorized as the following. Case 1: No additional investments allowed in emitting thermal power generation, case 2: No additional investments allowed in emitting thermal and onshore wind power generation, case 3: No additional investments allowed in emitting thermal, onshore, and offshore wind power generation, and case 4: No additional investments allowed in emitting thermal, onshore, and ground-mounted PV power generation. The different cases are displayed in Table I.

Investments are allowed in both the Norwegian and Northern European energy systems, subject to the same investment constraints in each region.

Table I: RES investment options for the different cases.

Case	Onshore wind	Offshore wind	Solar PV Utility	Solar PV Roof
1	X	X	X	X
2		X	X	X
3			X	X
4		X		X

No cases allow for investments in emitting
thermal power capacity.
Abbreviations:
Solar PV Utility: Utility-scale ground-mounted PV,
Solar PV Roof.: Roof-mounted PV.

10.4229/EUPVSEC2025/5DO.11.1

Each case is initially run with a CO_2 cap at 90% of 1990 emission levels, in alignment with the objectives of the European Union [33].

2.4 Land use requirements in energy system modeling

Landscape assessment traditionally lacks standardized units and remains partly subjective. As highlighted in [12], perceptions of landscape impact are inherently personal, shaped by individual experiences and biases. In literature there is currently a large range of estimates and boundary levels for calculation of land use requirements, with land-use information collected either from official documentation, calculated using geometrical rules, or manual drawings [34]. Given the critical role of land use in planning low-carbon energy systems, there is a growing need for methodological consistency [34].

Although exact quantification of land use impacts is complex, researchers have approached the issue using both quantitative and qualitative indicators. Quantitative metrics typically measure the physical area affected, which may include the directly occupied space, required spacing, buffer zones, and areas influenced by noise or visual intrusion [12]. Qualitative metrics, on the other hand, capture public attitudes and aesthetic responses to landscape changes, offering insights into the social dimensions of energy infrastructure [12]. This duality emphasizes the importance of a holistic framework that integrates physical land use assessments with public perception studies [12]. A widely adopted quantitative classification distinguishes between direct and total land use requirements [12].

Direct land use refers to the actual footprint of energy infrastructure, encompassing elements such as access roads, spacing between panels or turbines, and other installations designed to mitigate operational effects. Total land use, by contrast, includes broader considerations such as visual and acoustic impacts, as well as the overall environmental footprint. These additional factors contribute to significant variability in land use estimates across studies and regions, largely due to differing interpretations of indirect impacts [12].

In this study, land use requirements are estimated by calculating the mean values derived from an extensive review of existing literature. The analysis focuses on onshore wind and solar PV technologies, given their anticipated prominence in future energy systems [35]. Although bioenergy could entail substantial land demands due to the large areas required for cultivation and infrastructure [36], our model excludes new bioenergy investments due to their high capital costs. Consequently, bioenergy-related land use is not considered in this assessment.

Offshore wind is assigned a land use value of zero, as it does not occupy terrestrial space. However, it is acknowledged that offshore installations can affect surrounding marine ecosystems and coastal areas [36]. Similarly, rooftop PV systems are assumed to have zero land use requirements, as they utilize pre-existing built environments. The specific land use values applied in this study are summarized in Table II.

3 RESULTS AND DISCUSSION

In the following section, we examine the trade-offs associated with land use requirements under varying restrictions on the deployment of RES, with a particular

Table II: Direct and total land use requirements for different RES ([12], [34], [37]–[49]).

RES	Direct (m^2/MW)	Total (m^2/MW)
Onshore wind	3570	212 778
Utility-scale PV	11 045	30 682

emphasis on the role of solar PV in shaping Norway's future energy system. We analyze land use implications across the different cases, highlighting the balance between minimizing land footprint and enabling RES expansion.

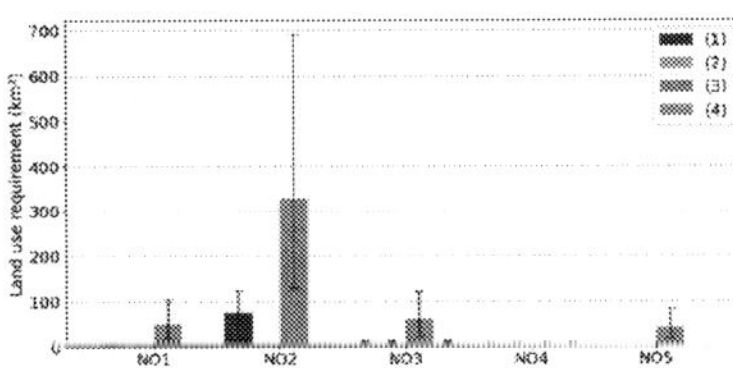

(a) Direct land use requirements.

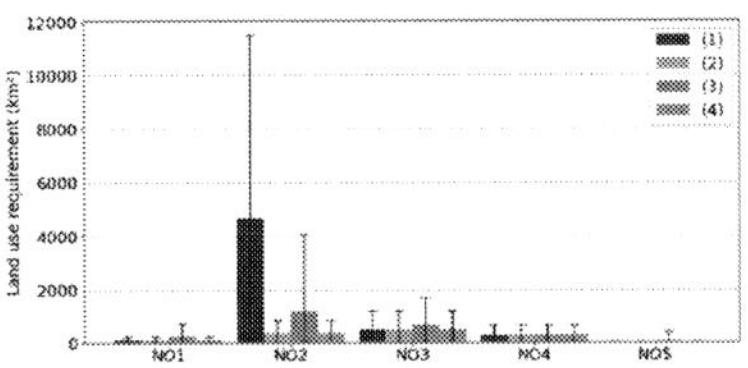

(b) Total land use requirements.

Figure 1: Land use requirements for the different cases in Norway, divided into each price zone. In the figure, (1) - (4) corresponds to case 1 - 4.

Fig. 1 highlights the substantial differences in both direct and total land use requirements across the various modeled scenarios. Case 3 emerges as the most land-intensive in terms of direct land use, primarily due to extensive deployment of ground-mounted PV systems, which dominate the energy mix in the absence of wind capacity. The PV investments are mostly concentrated in NO2, where solar irradiance is comparatively higher. Conversely, NO4 does not feature any PV installations, as prolonged periods of low solar availability during winter make solar energy less viable. Although NO4 experiences extended daylight in summer (the midnight sun), this seasonal peak in solar generation does not align with Norway's electricity demand, which is highest in winter [50]. This misalignment underscores a temporal disconnect between solar energy production and consumption patterns.

In contrast, scenarios that incorporate wind energy generally exhibit lower direct land use. This is largely attributed to wind power's higher capacity factor and the relatively small physical footprint of individual turbines. However, assessing land use based solely on turbine foundations can underestimate the broader spatial impact of wind energy. Adequate spacing between turbines and the associated grid infrastructure contribute to a larger total land footprint and can influence surrounding ecosystems [12]. These broader impacts are evident in Fig. 1b, where total land use requirements increase significantly, especially in onshore wind scenarios.

As illustrated in Fig. 1b, case 1 now shows the highest total land use. Despite lower installed capacities in case 1, the need for greater spacing and supporting infrastructure substantially raises the overall land demand.

Error bars in Fig. 1 reflect the significant uncertainty in land use requirement literature, discussed in Section 2.4.

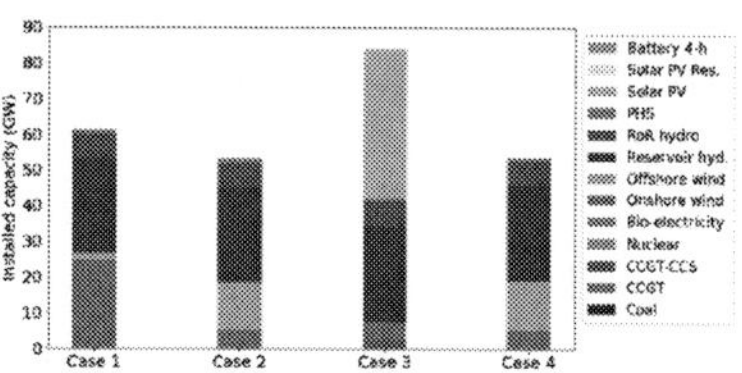

Figure 2: Total installed capacity in Norway for the different cases (in GW). 'Solar PV' refers to ground-mounted photovoltaic systems, while 'Solar PV Res.' denotes residential roof-mounted photovoltaic systems.

Fig. 2 displays the total installed capacity across the different scenarios analyzed. Each case involves a significant expansion of RES, largely driven by anticipated reductions in technology costs by 2040. Case 3, which excludes wind power investments, shows the highest installed capacity overall, with ground-mounted PV systems comprising 89% of the total. This heavy reliance on solar PV is primarily due to its low capital cost, but also reflects the need to offset its lower capacity factor and seasonal generation variability compared to wind. As a result, despite its large installed capacity, case 3 delivers the lowest renewable electricity output due to less efficient capacity utilization. Across all scenarios, no new nuclear capacity is added, reflecting the assumption of prohibitively high capital costs for nuclear projects.

Initially, the model favors onshore wind due to its cost-effectiveness and favorable wind conditions. In scenarios where onshore wind is excluded (cases 2–4), the system compensates by shifting toward more expensive offshore wind or by increasing PV deployment. As shown in Fig. 3, these adjustments lead to higher total system costs and increased average energy prices.

In cases 2 and 4, the absence of onshore wind leads to a greater reliance on offshore wind, which carries higher investment costs. In case 3, the system compensates for limited solar availability by installing additional PV capacity. However, due to the daily fluctuations in solar output, this scenario also requires supplementary investments in carbon capture and storage (CCS) and increased use of natural gas to maintain system reliability and flexibility. These factors contribute to higher overall costs, in addition to increased emissions.

Based on our results, direct land use requirements across the modeled cases range from 0.006% to 0.16% of Norway's total land area [51]. When total land use is considered, these estimates increase markedly, reaching between 0.4% and 1.69%. It is important to note that these calculations do not exclude areas unsuitable for development, such as mountainous regions or ice-covered terrain, implying that the actual land footprint could be even greater. Additionally, the projected rise in electrification across all energy sectors is expected to further amplify land use demands [2].

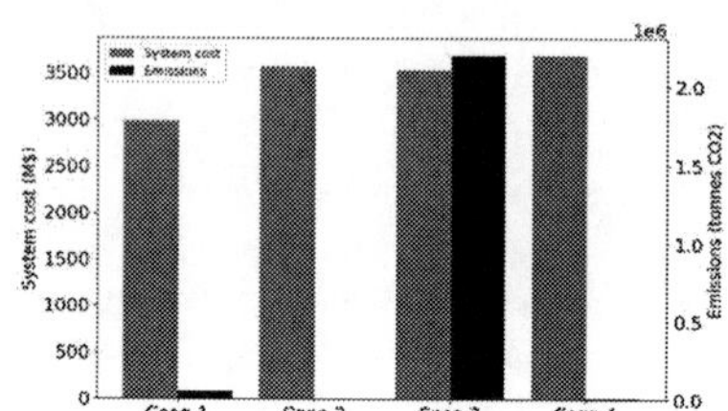

(a) Total system costs (left axis, in M$) and total emissions (right axis, in tonnes CO_2), for Norway.

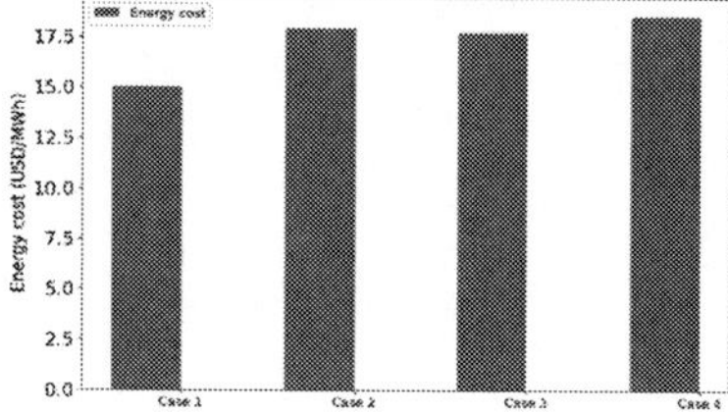

(b) Average energy cost per MWh, for Norway.

Figure 3: Total system costs, energy costs and total emissions for Norway.

These results underscore the significant variability in land use outcomes depending on the selected renewable energy deployment strategy and highlight the spatial implications of transitioning to a power system with 90% renewable energy. However, due to the considerable uncertainty and variation in current land use methodologies these percentages could vary, depending on the specific assumptions and calculation methods applied.

4 CONCLUSION

This study explores how solar power could shape Norway's future energy system, focusing on the balance between land use and renewable energy deployment. Depending on the scenario, meeting climate goals may require between 18.43 and 5149 km^2 of land, up to 1.69% of Norway's total area.

Transitioning to a low-emission system will inevitably impact land use. While different renewable energy strategies can reduce spatial demands, they often involve trade-offs. However, all RES development carry some degree of environmental consequences. To protect ecosystems, and minimize environmental degradation, this must be carefully evaluated and assessed.

Future research should examine land use impacts at the local level and include offshore wind in comparative analyses. Integrating socio-economic factors into energy models will also be essential to fully understand the societal effects of the energy transition.

AI DECLARATION

In preparing this work, we used Copilot to assist with language refinement and to generate initial code for figure plotting. All content produced with the help of this tool was carefully reviewed and revised by us, and we take full responsibility for the final version of the publication.

REFERENCES

[1] K. Calvin et al., "IPCC, 2023: Climate change 2023: Synthesis report. contribution of working groups I, II and III to the sixth assessment report of the intergovernmental panel on climate change [core writing team, h. lee and j. romero (eds.)]. IPCC, geneva, switzerland." edition: First. [Online]. Available: https://www.ipcc.ch/report/ar6/syr/

[2] I. B. Boa Morte, O. d. Q. F. Araújo, C. R. V. Morgado, and J. L. de Medeiros, "Electrification and decarbonization: a critical review of interconnected sectors, policies, and sustainable development goals," *Energy Storage and Saving*, vol. 2, no. 4, pp. 615–630, Dec. 2023. [Online]. Available: https://www.sciencedirect.com/science/article/pii/S2772683523000456

[3] M. Ge, J. Friedrich, and L. Vigna, "4 charts explain greenhouse gas emissions by countries and sectors." [Online]. Available: https://www.wri.org/insights/4-charts-explain-greenhouse-gas-emissions-countries-and-sectors

[4] International Energy agency, "Solar PV – Analysis." [Online]. Available: https://www.iea.org/reports/solar-pv

[5] Y.-k. Chen, J. G. Kirkerud, and T. F. Bolkesjø, "Balancing GHG mitigation and land-use conflicts: Alternative northern european energy system scenarios," *Applied Energy*, vol. 310, p. 118557. [Online]. Available: https://www.sciencedirect.com/science/article/pii/S0306261922000435

[6] M. Victoria, E. Zeyen, and T. Brown, "Speed of technological transformations required in europe to achieve different climate goals," *Joule*, vol. 6, no. 5, pp. 1066–1086. [Online]. Available: https://www.sciencedirect.com/science/article/pii/S2542435122001830

[7] A. Grubler, C. Wilson, N. Bento, B. Boza-Kiss, V. Krey, D. L. McCollum, N. D. Rao, K. Riahi, J. Rogelj, S. De Stercke, J. Cullen, S. Frank, O. Fricko, F. Guo, M. Gidden, P. Havlík, D. Huppmann, G. Kiesewetter, P. Rafaj, W. Schoepp, and H. Valin, "A low energy demand scenario for meeting the 1.5 °c target and sustainable development goals without negative emission technologies," *Nature Energy*, vol. 3, no. 6, pp. 515–527, number: 6 Publisher: Nature Publishing Group. [Online]. Available: https://www.nature.com/articles/s41560-018-0172-6

[8] G. Luderer, Z. Vrontisi, C. Bertram, O. Y. Edelenbosch, R. C. Pietzcker, J. Rogelj, H. S. De Boer, L. Drouet, J. Emmerling, O. Fricko, S. Fujimori, P. Havlík, G. Iyer, K. Keramidas, A. Kitous, M. Pehl, V. Krey, K. Riahi, B. Saveyn, M. Tavoni, D. P. Van Vuuren, and E. Kriegler, "Residual fossil CO2 emissions in 1.5–2 °c pathways," *Nature Climate Change*, vol. 8, no. 7, pp. 626–633, number: 7 Publisher: Nature Publishing Group. [Online]. Available: https://www.nature.com/articles/s41558-018-0198-6

[9] L. Späth, "Large-scale photovoltaics? yes please, but not like this! insights on different perspectives underlying the trade-off between land use and renewable electricity development," *Energy Policy*, vol. 122, pp. 429–437. [Online]. Available: https://www.sciencedirect.com/science/article/pii/S0301421518304762

[10] M. Koelman, T. Hartmann, and T. Spit, "Land use conflicts in the energy transition: Dutch dilemmas," *TeMA - Journal of Land Use, Mobility and Environment*, vol. 11, no. 3, pp. 273–284. [Online]. Available: http://www.serena.unina.it/index.php/tema/article/view/5830

[11] P. Scherhaufer, S. Höltinger, B. Salak, T. Schauppenlehner, and J. Schmidt, "Patterns of acceptance and non-acceptance within energy landscapes: A case study on wind energy expansion in austria," *Energy Policy*, vol. 109, pp. 863–870. [Online]. Available: https://www.sciencedirect.com/science/article/pii/S0301421517303488

[12] R. Ioannidis and D. Koutsoyiannis, "A review of land use, visibility and public perception of renewable energy in the context of landscape impact," *Applied Energy*, vol. 276, p. 115367. [Online]. Available: https://www.sciencedirect.com/science/article/pii/S0306261920308795

[13] V. Kati, C. Kassara, Z. Vrontisi, and A. Moustakas, "The biodiversity-wind energy-land use nexus in a global biodiversity hotspot," *Science of The Total Environment*, vol. 768, p. 144471, May 2021. [Online]. Available: https://www.sciencedirect.com/science/article/pii/S0048969720380025

[14] Energeia, "Solkraftverk i norge." [Online]. Available: https://www.energeia.no/solkraft-i-norge-perspektivnotat

[15] Statnett. Statnetts kortsiktige markedsanalyse. [Online]. Available: https://www.statnett.no/om-statnett/nyheter-og-pressemeldinger/nyhetsarkiv-2022/kortsiktig-markedsanalyse-okende-forbruk-gir-kraftunderskudd-fra-2027/

[16] P. K. N. Haaland, V. Aubin, and M. Korpås, "Quantifying energy-related carbon emissions of low-emission neighborhoods: A comparison of different approaches [unpublished manuscript]," 2025.

[17] J. D. Jenkins and N. A. Sepulveda, "Enhanced decision support for a changing electricity landscape: The GenX configurable electricity resource capacity expansion model."

[18] Power Statistics. Power statistics. [Online]. Available: https://www.entsoe.eu/data/power-stats/

[19] World Economic Forum. G7 countries agree phaseout for unabated coal power, and other top energy stories. [Online]. Available: https://www.weforum.org/agenda/2024/05/energy-news-g7-coal-phaseout-renewables-batteries/

[20] Hydrologiske data - NVE. [Online]. Available: https://www.nve.no/vann-og-vassdrag/hydrologiske-data/

[21] M. Korpås, L. Warland, J. Tande, and K. Uhlen, "Tradewind D3.2 Grid modelling and power system data," 2007.

[22] M. Jafari, M. Korpås, and A. Botterud, "Power system decarbonization: Impacts of energy storage duration and interannual renewables variability," *Renewable Energy*, vol. 156, pp. 1171–1185. [Online]. Available: https://www.sciencedirect.com/science/article/pii/S0960148120306820

[23] Renewables.ninja. Renewables.ninja. [Online]. Available: https://www.renewables.ninja/

[24] ENTSO-E and ENTSOG. ENTSO-e and ENTSOG TYNDP 2024 draft scenarios report. [Online]. Available: https://2024.entsos-tyndp-scenarios.eu/

[25] Our World in Data. Carbon dioxide emissions factors. [Online]. Available: https://ourworldindata.org/grapher/carbon-dioxide-emissions-factor

[26] M. Karmellos, D. Kopidou, and D. Diakoulaki, "A decomposition analysis of the driving factors of CO2 (carbon dioxide) emissions from the power sector in the european union countries," *Energy*, vol. 94, pp. 680–692. [Online]. Available: https://www.sciencedirect.com/science/article/pii/S0360544215015406

[27] European Commision. EU reference scenario 2020 - european commission. [Online]. Available: https://energy.ec.europa.eu/data-and-analysis/energy-modelling/eu-reference-scenario-2020_en

[28] ENTSO-E. Major trends reshaping the power sector — ENTSO-e vision on market design and system operation towards 2030. [Online]. Available: https://vision2030.entsoe.eu/major-trends-reshaping-the-power-sector/

[29] Entso-e and entsog tyndp 2024 draft scenarios report. Accessed: 2024-10-09. [Online]. Available: https://2024.entsos-tyndp-scenarios.eu/

[30] W. Cole and A. Karmakar, "Cost projections for utility-scale battery storage: 2023 update," *Renewable Energy*.

[31] J. P. Deane, B. P. Ó Gallachóir, and E. J. McKeogh, "Techno-economic review of existing and new pumped hydro energy storage plant," *Renewable and Sustainable Energy Reviews*, vol. 14, no. 4, pp. 1293–1302, May 2010. [Online]. Available: https://www.sciencedirect.com/science/article/pii/S1364032109002779

[32] P. Haaland, "Integration-of-solar-PV-in-a-Norwegian-energy-system," Jun. 2025, original-date: 2025-06-06T08:53:00Z. [Online]. Available: https://github.com/pkhaaland/Integration-of-solar-PV-in-a-Norwegian-energy-system

[33] European Commision, "Climate strategies & targets - European Commission." [Online]. Available: https://climate.ec.europa.eu/eu-action/climate-strategies-targets_en

[34] O. Turkovska, K. Gruber, M. Klingler, C. Klöckl, L. Ramirez Camargo, P. Regner, S. Wehrle, and J. Schmidt, "Methodological and reporting inconsistencies in land-use requirements misguide future renewable energy planning," *One Earth*, vol. 7, no. 10, pp. 1741–

1759. [Online]. Available: https://www.sciencedirect.com/science/article/pii/S2590332224004755

[35] International Energy Agency, "World Energy Outlook – Topics." [Online]. Available: https://www.iea.org/topics/world-energy-outlook

[36] J. K. Nøland, J. Auxepaules, A. Rousset, B. Perney, and G. Falletti, "Spatial energy density of large-scale electricity generation from power sources worldwide," *Scientific Reports*, vol. 12, no. 1, p. 21280, Dec. 2022, publisher: Nature Publishing Group. [Online]. Available: https://www.nature.com/articles/s41598-022-25341-9

[37] P. Denholm, P. Brown, W. Cole, T. Mai, B. Sergi, M. Brown, P. Jadun, J. Ho, J. Mayernik, C. McMillan, and R. Sreenath, "Examining supply-side options to achieve 100% clean electricity by 2035." [Online]. Available: https://www.osti.gov/biblio/1885591

[38] J. E. Diffendorfer, B. Sergi, A. Lopez, T. Williams, M. Gleason, Z. Ancona, and W. Cole, "The interplay of future solar energy, land cover change, and their projected impacts on natural lands and croplands in the US," *Science of The Total Environment*, vol. 947, p. 173872. [Online]. Available: https://www.sciencedirect.com/science/article/pii/S0048969724040208

[39] M. Bolinger and G. Bolinger, "Land requirements for utility-scale PV: An empirical update on power and energy density," *IEEE Journal of Photovoltaics*, vol. 12, no. 2, pp. 589–594. [Online]. Available: https://ieeexplore.ieee.org/document/9676427/

[40] C. de Castro, M. Mediavilla, L. J. Miguel, and F. Frechoso, "Global solar electric potential: A review of their technical and sustainable limits," *Renewable and Sustainable Energy Reviews*, vol. 28, pp. 824–835, Dec. 2013. [Online]. Available: https://www.sciencedirect.com/science/article/pii/S1364032113005807

[41] N. Martín-Chivelet, "Photovoltaic potential and land-use estimation methodology," *Energy*, vol. 94, pp. 233–242, Jan. 2016. [Online]. Available: https://www.sciencedirect.com/science/article/pii/S0360544215014863

[42] S. Ong, C. Campbell, P. Denholm, R. Margolis, and G. Heath, "Land-use requirements for solar power plants in the united states," pp. NREL/TP–6A20–56 290, 1 086 349. [Online]. Available: http://www.osti.gov/servlets/purl/1086349/

[43] P. Denholm, M. Hand, M. Jackson, and S. Ong, "Land use requirements of modern wind power plants in the united states." [Online]. Available: https://www.osti.gov/biblio/964608

[44] J. van Zalk and P. Behrens, "The spatial extent of renewable and non-renewable power generation: A review and meta-analysis of power densities and their application in the u.s," *Energy Policy*, vol. 123, pp. 83–91. [Online]. Available: https://www.sciencedirect.com/science/article/pii/S0301421518305512

[45] P. Saunders, *Land Use Requirements of Solar and Wind Power Generation: Understanding a Decade of Academic Research.*

[46] M. S. Kenawi, R. D. Hedger, K. T. Alfredsen, B. K. Sandercock, M. Korpås, and T. H. Bakken, "Land efficiency of renewable energy in Norway: A synthesis of footprint and production density," *Renewable Energy*, vol. 252, p. 123514, 2025. [Online]. Available: https://www.sciencedirect.com/science/article/pii/S0960148125011760

[47] NVE, "Direkte påvirket areal - NVE." [Online]. Available: https://www.nve.no/energi/energisystem/vindkraft-paa-land/arealbruk-for-vindkraftverk/direkte-paavirket-areal/

[48] U. R. Fritsche, G. Berndes, A. L. Cowie, V. H. Dale, K. L. Kline, F. X. Johnson, H. Langeveld, N. Sharma, H. Watson, and J. Woods, "Energy and land use," *Work. Pap. Glob. L. Outlook*, pp. 14–15, 2017.

[49] A. M. Trainor, R. I. McDonald, and J. Fargione, "Energy sprawl is the largest driver of land use change in united states," *PLOS ONE*, vol. 11, no. 9, p. e0162269, publisher: Public Library of Science. [Online]. Available: https://journals.plos.org/plosone/article?id=10.1371/journal.pone.0162269

[50] J. O. G. Tande and K. Vogstad, "(PDF) OPERATIONAL IMPLICATIONS OF WIND POWER IN A HYDRO BASED POWER SYSTEM." [Online]. Available: https://www.researchgate.net/publication/234165681_OPERATIONAL_IMPLICATIONS_OF_WIND_POWER_IN_A_HYDRO_BASED_POWER_SYSTEM

[51] Country Reports, "Norway geography, maps, climate, environment and terrain from Norway | - CountryReports." [Online]. Available: https://www.countryreports.org/country/Norway/geography.htm

Evaluating the impact of photovoltaics for lifecycle global warming potential of buildings according to EN 15978 - a Danish Case Study

Sune Thorsteinsson, Markus Babin, Nanna Lysgaard Andersen, Gisele A. dos Reis Benatto
Technical University of Denmark, Institute of Electrical and Photonics Engineering, 4000 Roskilde, Denmark

ABSTRACT: The EU energy performance of buildings directive (EPBD) has recently been updated to tighten energy performance regulations and is demanding solar solutions on all buildings, to be fully implemented by 2030 through national building codes. However, article 7 also states that life cycle global warming potential (GWP) must be calculated (according to EN 15978) with a reference study period of 50 years, and that national limit values on life cycle GWP must be introduced by 2030. Denmark has since 2023 enforced this methodology with national adaptions and parameters.
This work evaluates the impact of PV on the GWP of buildings following Danish rules, using collected environmental product declarations of PV system components. The results show, that for almost all cases the addition of a PV system increases the GWP of buildings, owing to a combination of a high GWP load of PV materials compared to standard roofing materials, decreasing emission factors (based on political ambitions of climate neutrality), and high impact of component replacement.
Tying the GWP benefits of PV to political ambitions of renewable energy generation decreases the value of PV in countries with high political ambitions and does not appropriately consider buildings as an active part of the energy system. Therefore article 7 in part counteracts the stated intentions of the EPBD and the authors recommend that PV should be excluded from the GWP assessment of buildings.

Keywords: Global warming assessments, Building-integrated photovoltaics, Building attached photovoltaics, sustainability of construction works, Energy performance directive.

1 INTRODUCTION

The European Union has strong aims of energy independence and high ambitions to reach climate goals. Different directives have been agreed on as a means to reach this goal, including several solar strategies. These directives provide an overall framework that is implemented via national legislation in the member states. In particular, the energy performance of buildings directive (EPBD) [1] has recently been updated, tightening energy regulations and in essence making buildings a significant part of the energy system, and demanding solar solutions on all buildings, fully implemented by 2030. However, one aspect not yet analyzed in detail by the PV community is article 7 (and Annex III), demanding that life cycle global warming potential (GWP) must be calculated (according to EN 15978) for all buildings with a reference study period of 50 years. In conjunction, national limit values on life cycle GWP must be introduced in member states and enforced from 2028 onwards. Tracking of the GWP of buildings is an important means to lower the CO_2 emissions from the construction sector, where the emissions are significant [1].

While life cycle assessment (LCA) of PV products and electricity production is well established – including recently updated data [2-5] – few scientific works have addressed the impact of building added (BA) and building integrated (BI) -PV on the life cycle GWP of buildings.
The LCA analysis of PV commonly provides emissions in the range of approximately 16-38 g/kWh for a central European location (GTI of 1331 kWh/m²) and concludes that the highest contributor to the global warming potential is associated cell production and underlying upstream processes [5] and the associated emissions are strongly dependent on the electricity mix at the place of production. Grinham et al [6] have conducted building LCA analysis according to EN 15978 and concluded that the carbon balance for PV is strongly dependent on future scenarios assumed for the carbon load of the grid.
EN 15978:2011 [7] challenges BAPV and in particular BIPV as the GWP load of PV materials per m² is a factor

of 5-15 times higher than that of e.g. common roofing materials. This is in combination with the so-called emission factors used to convert produced energy into global warming potential – typically based on expected future grid emissions.

This work collects environmental product declarations (EPDs) for BAPV and BIPV elements as well as inverters and mounting systems, and uses this data to calculate their impact on the GWP of buildings. It further analyzes how the Danish emission factors are derived, and the potential implications for the BAPV and BIPV market.

2 METHODOLOGY

2.1 The EN 15978 and derived Danish implementation.

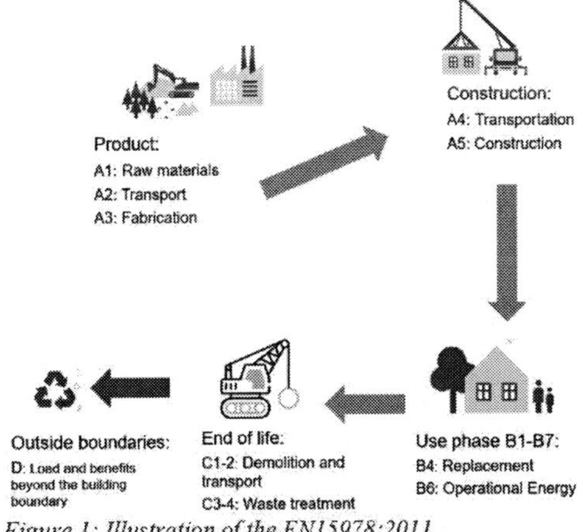

Figure 1: Illustration of the EN15978:2011

EN 15978:2011 divides the buildings life cycle into modules A1-3 (raw material extraction and fabrication), modules A4-5 (construction and transportation), modules

B1-7, covering the "Use" stage, modules C1-4, containing end of life, and module D, gathering all benefits and loads beyond the system boundaries. For compliance with the GWP limit values, only modules A to C can be used. These principles are illustrated in Figure 1.

For the Danish 2025 regulation [8], modules A1-3 (raw material extraction and fabrication), B4 (replacement), B6 (operational energy), C3 (waste processing), and C4 (disposal) are to be included in the assessment – considering a reference study period of 50 years. After summation and normalization by the floor area and consideration period, the total GWP must be below the limit values of 4-8 kg CO_2 eq/(m^2 (floor area)*year), depending on building type, with exceptions for special and agricultural buildings. Separate limits are enforced on modules A4-5 (construction and transportation), based on construction product specific Danish parameters, and any contributions to module D must be declared.

B4 (replacement) is calculated as the sum of modules A1-3 and C3-4, multiplied by the number of replacements needed, rounded up to the nearest integer. Based on the product lifetime stated in a national table – 30 years for PV – one full replacement is needed to reach the reference study period.

The GWP for B6 (only operational energy used for heating and ventilation) is the on-site consumed (or produced electricity), multiplied by an emission factor for a given year, which is published in the Danish building code, shown in Figure 2 [9].

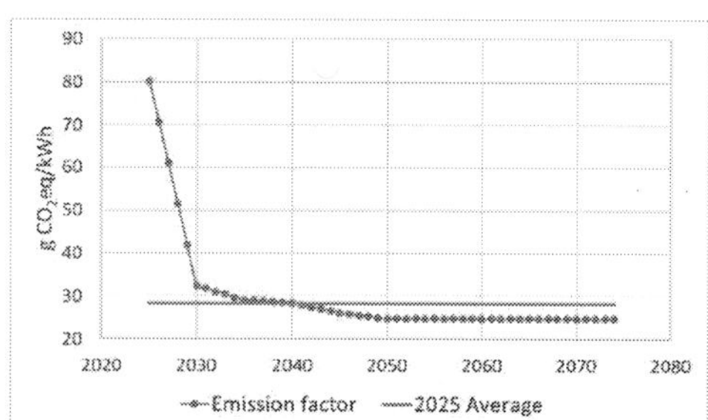

Figure 2: Danish emission factors for 2025

According to the Danish rules [8], only the part of the PV system that contributes to the energy performance compliance of a building up of max 13.2 kWh/(m^2*year) is included in the calculation (with no distinction of ground mounted, BA- or BIPV). Within the energy performance compliance, all PV energy can be assigned to module B6, lowering the GWP of the building. Any energy exceeding this limit, however, cannot be included, and can be considered "outside the energy frame". For BIPV solutions, PV surfaces not part of the energy frame can be counted as cover glass (not specified in further detail), and inverters and stands[1] are to be included for the energy frame part.

In the original Danish implementation, the full GWP of a BIPV system had to be included, but only up to 13.2 kWh/(m^2*year) could be used for CO_2 displacement in B6. This meant that only 5-15 % of the PV energy could be used to reduce GWP – in practice excluding any BIPV

cladding solution. Therefore, this deviation from the EN 15978 standard was introduced, which is also suggested in the updated proposal for the standard.

The data for the GWP assessment can be obtained either from valid EPDs, which is a third party authorized LCA analysis of construction products, or (in the Danish case) from so-called generic data [10]. This generic data is provided for construction products, determined if there is more than 5 EPDs available as the 75 % quartile + 10 % (accounting for modules A-C). For product categories without EPDs it can be derived from the German ÖKOBAUDAT database [11] with an added 10 % margin to promote use of product-specific EPDs [12].

2.2 EPD collection and comparison

EPDs are collected for PV panels, inverters and mounting systems. In the EPDs no differentiation between BIPV and BIPV are made.

The functional unit for inverters is 1 kWh interpreted as the load pr kWh allocated to the inverting functionality of a model plant. With the power rating of the inverter, the converted energy (and lifetime), the load of the inverter can be converted to pr W_{ac}.

For the GWP load calculations a plant DC to AC ratio of 1.3 is assumed. To enable comparison of the GWP loads, inverters loads are converted to pr square meter, using a specific area yield of 200 W/m^2 corresponding to a nominal rated AC power of 154 W_{ac}/m^2.

The PV energy per m^2 is calculated using the performance ratio method, assuming an annual insolation (H) of 1000 kWh/m^2, a performance ratio (PR) of 80% and a degradation rate (d) of 0.5% p.a., these numbers correspond to typical parameters for horizontally mounted PV installations in Denmark. With the product-dependent specific area yield (Y) [Wp/m^2] and assuming system replacement after 25 years, the average annual energy (E_{avg}) are calculated as:

$$E_{avg} = \frac{H}{G_{stc}} * Pr * Y * \frac{1}{25} \sum_{1}^{25} (1-d)^i$$

The degradation-averaged emission factor is calculated as follows:

$$\epsilon_{avg} = \frac{1}{50}\left(\sum_{1}^{25} \epsilon_i (1-d)^i + \sum_{26}^{50} \epsilon_i (1-d)^{i-25} \right)$$

Here, ϵ_i is the emission factor for year i in g(CO_2eq)/kWh. Consequently, the GWP reduction from PV produced electricity is:

$$B6_{GWP,PV} = 50 * \epsilon_{avg} * E_{avg}$$

Based on ϵ_{avg}, the GWP per m2 PV area ($GWP_{PV_{area}}$) for where the PV is providing a neutral GWP contribution, can be calculated as:

$$\epsilon_{avg} = GWP_{system,pr\ KWh} = \frac{2 * GWP_{system,area}}{E_{avg} * 50}$$

$$GWP_{PV_{area}} = \epsilon_{avg} * E_{avg} * 25 - GWP_{inv} - GWP_{mounting}$$

For calculating the PV system GWP load, data from the panel specific EPDs is combined with the average load of the inverters and mounting systems corresponding to 1 m^2 PV. For the BIPV systems the mounting system is omitted as at least 3 of the BIPV systems are roof systems where the panels are directly mounted on the roof battens.

The lifetime of all the inverters is stated in the EPDs

---

[1] In the legislative text "stands" (and not mounting systems) are used not further detailed providing a minor for cut-off limits (e.g. module clamps).

to be 25 years and the lifetime of the mounting systems is assumed to be at least 50 years, therefore a total of 2 inverters and 1 mounting system is used to reach the 50 years.

3 RESULTS

3.1 EPD results

The load for the Danish included phases (A1-3 and C3-4) for the four categories are shown in Figure 3 and the corresponding numbers displayed in Table 1. EPDs for PV panels included both US, European and Asian manufactures and EPDs for inverters were found in the power range from 6-330 kW with 8/9 in the 50-330 kW range.

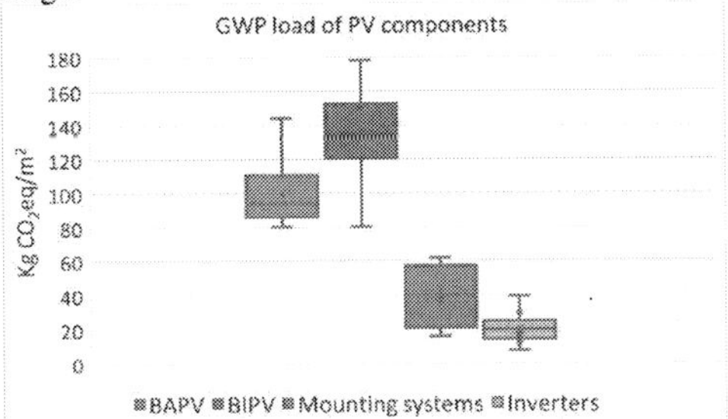

Figure 3: Statistics on collected EPDs

Table 1: EPD statistics (for the BIPV system sum and share the mounting system is excluded).

	BAPV	BIPV	Mounting	Inverter
Average (kg CO_2eq/m^2)	100,0	139,0	39,0	20,0
Samples	10	7	4	9
Min (kg CO_2eq/m^2)	80,5	80,5	16,0	7,6
Max (kg CO_2eq/m^2)	144,0	178,2	61,0	39,3
Average system sum (kg CO_2eq/m^2)	159,0	159,0		
Relative Share	63%	87%	25%	13%

Further a comparison of loads of commonly used building materials (data sourced from Ökobaudat [11]) to PV materials are made in Figure 4.

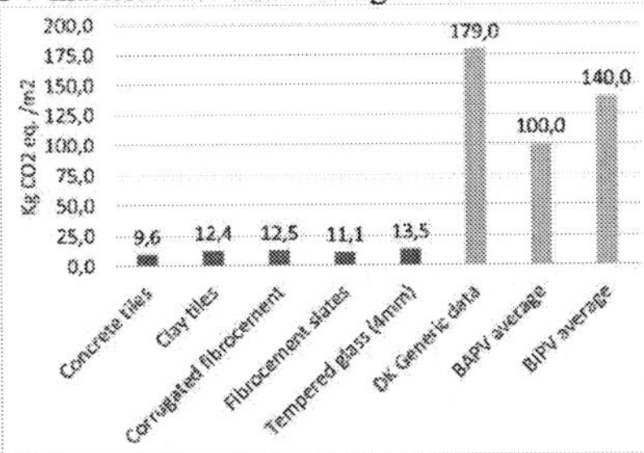

Figure 4: Comparison of GWP for common roof materials.

In summary, the following observations can be made:
- PV materials have a 5-15 times high GWP load compared to commonly used roofing materials.
- No significant dependency of place of production was identified for the PV modules.
- The PV panels are the main contributor to the GWP load, however the inverter and mounting system have non-negligible shares.
- Within each category there is some variability which is subject to further investigation. For the inverters no correlation with nameplate rating were found, however this is to be revisited when more inverter EPDs in a more widespread power range are available. One EPD for a power optimizer was found with a GWP load of 30 g/W corresponding to a load of 5.6 kg/m² using 200 Wp/m² and a sizing factor of 1.

3.2 GWP impact on the building of the PV system

In Figure 5 the CO2 balance for 1 m² is seen over the consideration period together with the expected annual energy production for the average BAPV solution. As expected, the PV deployment has a high carbon intensity and the energy production is used to displace CO_2 during its operation. In year 26 the entire PV plant is replaced, except for the mounting structure. The CO_2 reduction is steep in the beginning and flattens towards the end of the consideration period due to the decreasing emission factors. While the first plant almost entirely displaces its embedded CO_2, the second plant only displaces approximately 80% of its embedded CO_2.

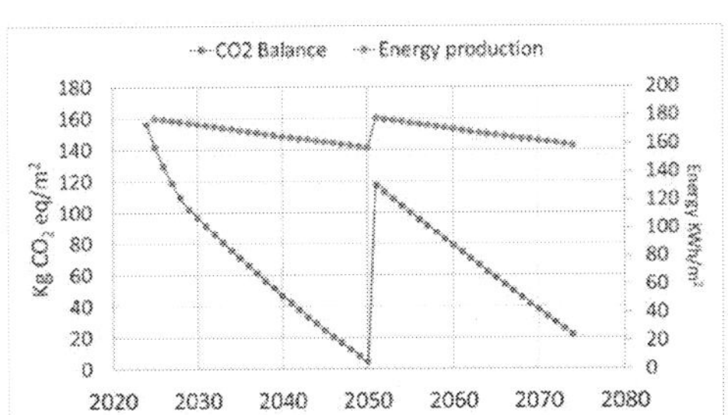

Figure 5: CO2 balance over time.

In Figure 6 the imbedded CO_2 together with the displaced CO_2 is shown for the average and extremes of the BAPV and BIPV systems using the average values of inverters and mounting systems (latter only for BAPV). Values are GWP/(m²PV*year), which are the Danish units used. As can be seen almost all PV systems increase the GWP of the building. Only the lowest GWP BAPV system is lowering the GWP with negligible amounts. What can also be observed is that the materials savings (here clay tiles) from the displaced roof material for BIPV systems are not significant.

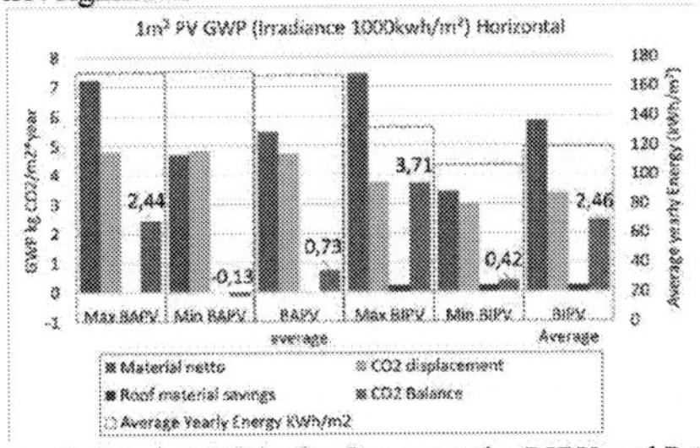

Figure 6: Load and CO₂ displacement for BIPV and BAPV systems

The CO₂ balance final impact on the building GWP calculation depends on the building design, but assuming flat roof with a roof area equal to the useful floor area up to 13.2 kWh/m2 can be included, depending on the building energy performance calculation. For this case, the shown balance will enter the final contribution with approximately 8 % weight for BAPV systems and 11 % for the BIPV systems. Despite the small final impact, a contribution of up to ~0,25 kg CO2 pr m2 pr year corresponds to 6-7% of the lowest GWP limit for buildings, this impact is with some significance, requiring GWP savings on other building parts.

In Figure 7 the lines represent the limits where the PV systems have a neutral influence on the GWP calculation of the buildings where sensitivity analysis is performed for various insolation values using average values for mounting systems and inverters. Dotted lines represent the extrema for mounting and inverters for the 1000 kWh/m2 base case.

As can be seen, neutral GWP contributions are reached at around 80 kg CO_2/m^2 for efficiencies above 22,5 % for the 1000 kWh/year base case, with most of the products being far from these limits. What can also be seen is careful choice of inverter and mounting system can facilitate a positive contribution.

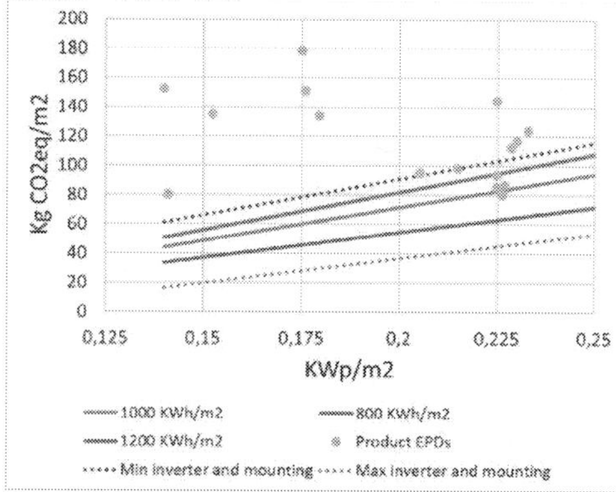

Figure 7: Sensitivity analysis for CO2 contribution

3.3 Emission factors

Prior to discussing the findings it is required to investigate the assumptions behind the emission factors for the Danish case which are shown in Figure 2. Inspecting the emission factors, it can be seen that the 2025 value is around 80 g CO_2/kWh and during the 5 first years fairly rapidly decreases to 30 g CO_2/kWh and from there on over 20 years is reduced to approximately 25 g CO_2/kWh. Based on [9] these numbers are derived from the expected electricity mix needed in the Danish grid to comply with the political aim of 70 % reduction in 2030 and carbon neutrality in 2050 using the national energy agency's forecast from 2022. This forecast (Figure 8) predicts an almost 4-fold increase in electricity production (whereof around 2/3 is expected to be used for P2X). This need is roughly covered by 75 % wind energy and 20 % solar energy and the remaining 5 % covering biomass-based generation and import of electricity.

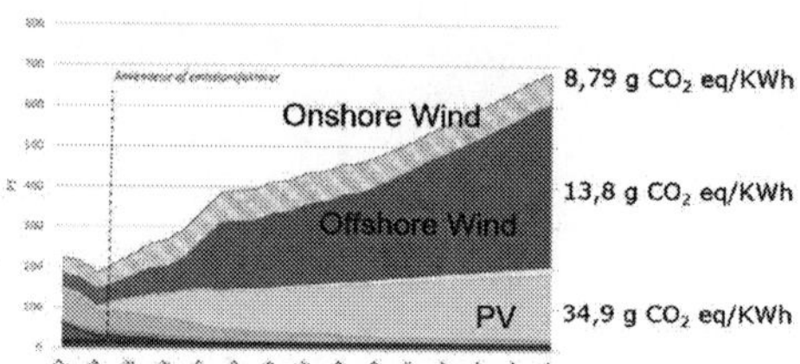

Figure 8: Energy forecast for emission factors adapted from [7].

PV on roof tops are excluded in these calculations, however only as a marginal share in Figure 10 (yellow patterned area). For biomass, only emissions related to processing and transportation are included as biomass is per EU definition sustainable.

In essence, the expected deployment of renewable energy is used to lower the value of the CO₂ displacement on buildings, and at the same time PV on buildings is contributing to lowering the grid emissions. This results in a circular relationship, negatively affecting the CO₂ displacement potential for buildings with marginalization to what exceeds the expected annual additions in renewable energy generation.

4 DISCUSSION

Overall these findings show that the addition of PV generally increases the building GWP according to Danish rules and insolation conditions - for certain products to an extend where compliance to the national GWP limits will require GWP savings elsewhere in the building design. The presented data assumes 2025 deployment, and with the decreasing emission factors later deployment will make the GWP increase even higher.

Denmark already has fairly low emissions from the grid and is especially via the rules in force expected to have so in the future. This results in a disincentive for PV on buildings, as CO₂ displacement is insufficient to compensate for the embedded GWP. In countries with higher emission factors the opposite may be true, with high CO₂ displacement by PV installations allowing the use more carbon-heavy construction products, while still staying within the limits.

Both cases are contradictory to the intentions of the EPBD, where solar PV on buildings is advocated, with buildings being expected to be a significant part of the energy system. The authors acknowledge the importance of a less carbon intensive construction sector, however the way PV is expected to be accounted for in the calculations is not desirable.

Furthermore, calculating the emission factors based on the expected deployment of renewable energy, including solar PV, is not desirable, as solar PV on buildings in most countries also contributes to lowering the emission factors. This results in a circular relationship, which can lead to undesirable effects. Further high political ambitions for carbon neutrality will decrease the GWP benefits, if all EU countries follow the Danish methods.

As has been the case for the past and will be the case in the future, the embodied emissions from the PV and other renewable sources will decrease. Therefore, the emission factors are expected to be updated based on more recent energy projections and LCA data and as the GWP benefit of PV scales with the difference between the embodied CO_2 emissions from the PV plant and the expected grid emissions, the time differences between the EPD and the emission factors publication dates becomes one of the most deciding factors. EPDs have in general a validity of 5 years.

All in all, with a fairly rapidly changing energy system developing towards electrification, the Danish implementation of EN 15978 seems to be an uncertain and volatile method for including PV in the GWP assessment of buildings, and therefore the method is not suitable and counteracts the intentions in the EPBD and associated policies. The challenges described for PV calls for a holistic assessment where PV on buildings are also regarded as a part of the energy system and not marginalized and compared to expected expansion of renewable energy as in the Danish case.

Based on the above, the authors do not see a feasible long-term solution for incorporating PV in a non-circular desirable manner via the EN 15978 standard. While the authors acknowledge that PV has to account for its embedded carbon, including them via the GWP of buildings as per the current methodology does not result in the desirable outcome.

A consensus should be found between the PV community and the construction sector to find a more appropriate method for assessing the GWP impact of PV on buildings. As such, IEA PVPS Task 15 activity A2 is working on expanding this analysis to other countries.

5 CONCLUSION

This study used valid environmental product declarations to assess the global warming potential of PV in buildings following Danish rules derived from EN 15978. The analysis shows that when both inverters and mounting systems are included, the addition of a BA- and BIPV system increases the global warming potential of a building. The increase is caused by a combination of approximately 10 times high load compared to commonly used roofing materials, the need for replacement of the PV system and especially the rapid decreasing emission factors calculated based on expected renewable energy deployment to reach political goals.

The method marginalizes PV, is volatile and uncertain, and therefore is not suitable for this assessment in the authors' opinion. It is debatable whether PV should be excluded from this assessment and assessed via other better suited methods, such as the upcoming Ecodesign rules.

6 ACKNOWLEDGEMENTS

This work was funded by EUDP as part of the "IEA PVPS Task 15 Phase 3" project under grant 134243-534202.

7 REFERENCES

[1] European Union **Directive (EU) 2024/1275 of the European Parliament and of the Council of 24 April 2024 on the energy performance of buildings 2024,** https://eur-lex.europa.eu/legal-content/EN/TXT/?uri=OJ:L_202401275&pk_keywor d=Energy&pk_content=Directive Last visited 1601-2025

[2] Müller, A., Friedrich, L., Reichel, C., Herceg, S., Mittag, M., & Neuhaus, D. H. (2021). A comparative life cycle assessment of silicon PV modules: Impact of module design, manufacturing location and inventory. Solar Energy Materials and Solar Cells, 230, 111277. https://doi.org/10.1016/j.solmat.2021.111277

[3] Stucki, M., Götz, M., de Wild-Scholten, M., Frischknecht, R. IEA PVPS Task 12 2023. Fact sheet: Environmental Life Cycle Assessment of Electricity from PV Systems 2023 update. https://iea-pvps.org/wp-content/uploads/2024/05/Task-12-Fact-Sheet-v2-1.pdf

[4] Fares, Hafsa & Lobaccaro, Gabriele & Nouha, Gazbour & Nygaard Rasmussen, Freja & Chèze, David & Pierrès, Nolwenn & Wurtz, Etienne. (2025). A methodology for assessing environmental impact of building integrated PV in low carbon footprint electricity generation context. Energy and Buildings. 329. 115219. 10.1016/j.enbuild.2024.115219.

[5] Khan, A.A., Reichel, C., Molina, P., Friedrich, L., Subasi, D.M., Neuhaus, H., et al. (2024) Global Warming Potential of Photovoltaics with State-of-the Art Silicon Solar Cells: Influence of Electricity Mix, Installation Location and Lifetime. Solar Energy Materials and Solar Cells, 269, Article 112724. https://doi.org/10.1016/j.solmat.2024.112724

[6] Jonathan Grinham, Henning Fjeldheim, Bin Yan, Tor Dokka Helge, Kristian Edwards, Tine Hegli, Ali Malkawi, Zero-carbon balance: The case of HouseZero, Building and Environment, Volume 207, Part B, 2022, 108511, https://doi.org/10.1016/j.buildenv.2021.108511.

[7] Sustainability of construction works – Assessment of environmental performance of buildings – Calculation method : DS/EN 15978:2011

[8] https://www.bygningsreglementet.dk/tekniske-bestemmelser/11/krav/

[9] Mathilde Sørensen Nilsson, Linda Høibye og Steffen Enersen Maagaard, Emissionsfaktorer El, fjernvarme og ledningsgas 2025-2075, Artelia 2023 https://www.sbst.dk/Media/638282171394687135/Emissi onsfaktorer%20for%20el%20fjernvarme%20og%20ledni ngsgas%20for%202025-2075.pdf (visited Jan 17th 2025)

[10] Social og Bolig styrelsen 2025, Danish Generic data, https://www.bygningsreglementet.dk/media/1o1nnozd/ta bel-7-2025.xlsx (visited August 14th 2025)

[11] https://www.oekobaudat.de/en.html (visited August 14th 2025)

[12] Kragh, J., & Birgisdottir, H. (2023). Udvikling af dansk generisk LCA-data. (1 udg.) Institut for Byggeri, By og Miljø (BUILD), Aalborg Universitet. BUILD Rapport Bind 2023 Nr. 16

DTU

Evaluating the impact of photovoltaics for lifecycle global warming potential of buildings according to EN 15978 - a Danish Case Study

Sune Thorsteinsson, Nanna L. Andersen, Markus Babin, Gisele A. dos Reis Benatto
Technical University of Denmark, Department of Electrical and Photonics Engineering, 4000 Roskilde, Denmark
sunth@dtu.dk

020478-001

DTU

Content

1. Motivation
2. Introduction to EN15978(:2011)
3. Collected EPD data
4. Danish Case study
5. Immediate conclusions
6. Discussion

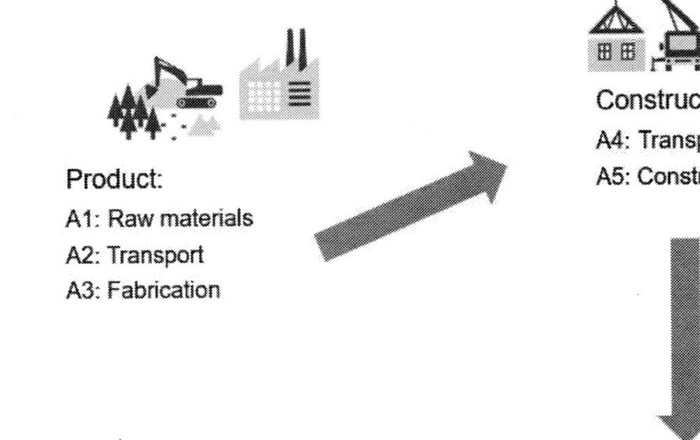

020478-002

Motivation

The newly agreed Energy performance directive for Buildings in EU (EPDB), demands:

- All (new) buildings to be solar ready
- Implemented in National buildings codes

However, what is overlooked in the PV-industry:

- EPD article 7.2 and Annex III:
  - Whole life Carbon via EN15978
  - Consideration period 50 years

- Whole life carbon (WLC) of buildings provides significant CO_2 emissions

Overview of **whole life carbon** regulations and initiatives across Europe

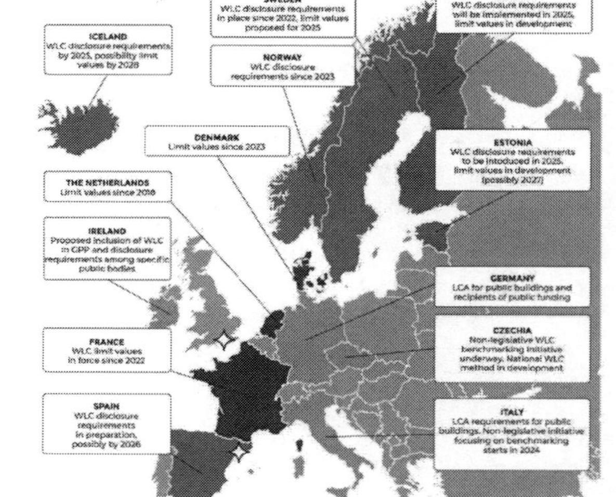

- ● WLC regulation with limit values in force
- ● WLC disclosure requirements in force
- ● WLC legislation (disclosure/limit values) proposed
- ● Other non-legislative requirements in place or preparing for WLC measurement and benchmarking

Timeline for the EPDB

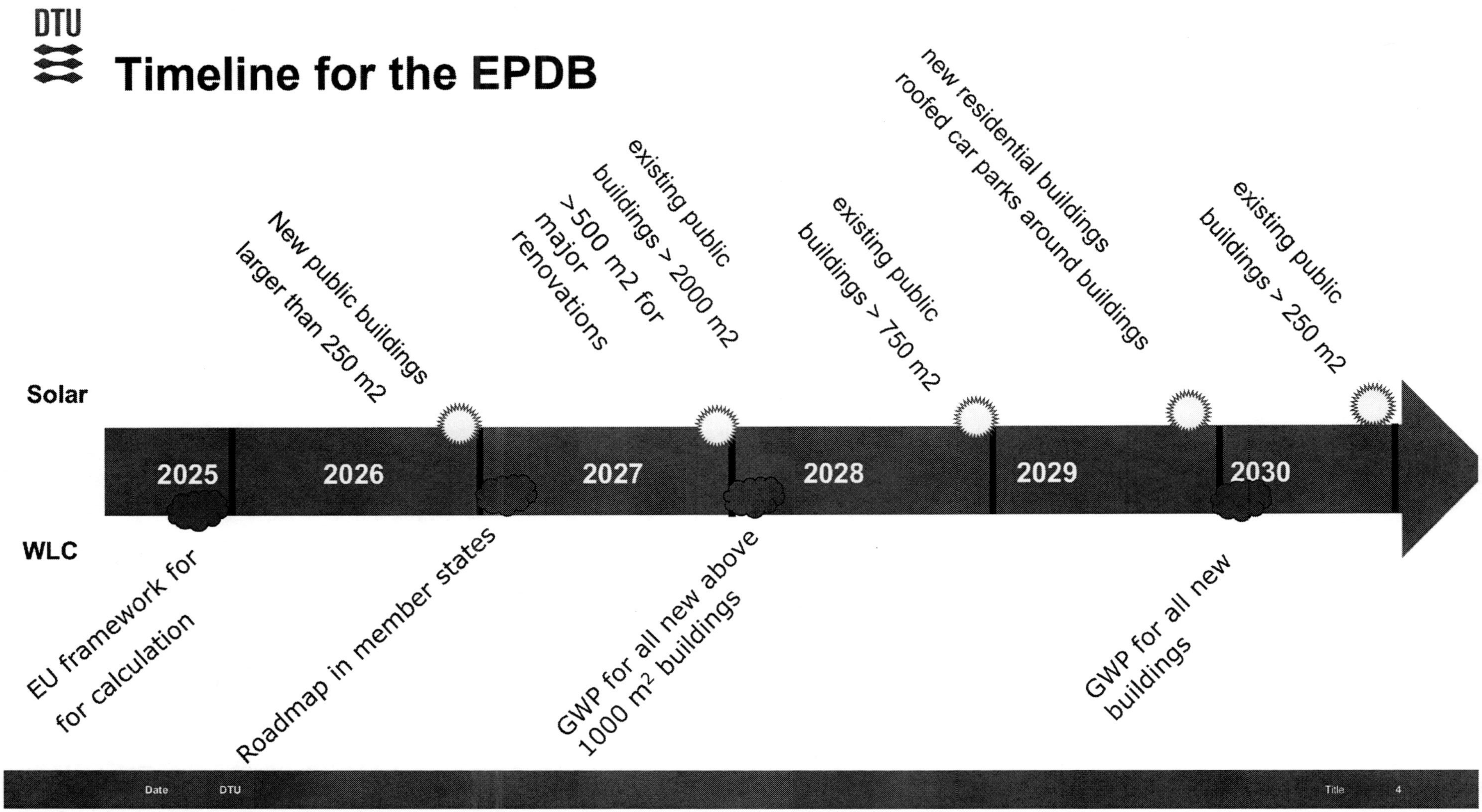

DTU

Few facts on PV and GWP

- **PVs have 10-15 times higher CO_2 load than most roofs**
  - Important to use the PV energy for CO_2 displacement
    - Data collected from:
      - Environmental product declarations (EPDs)
      - Ökobaudat
- **Around ~2/3 of the GWP load is from cell production (C-Si)**
  - Similar load for buildings and other applications

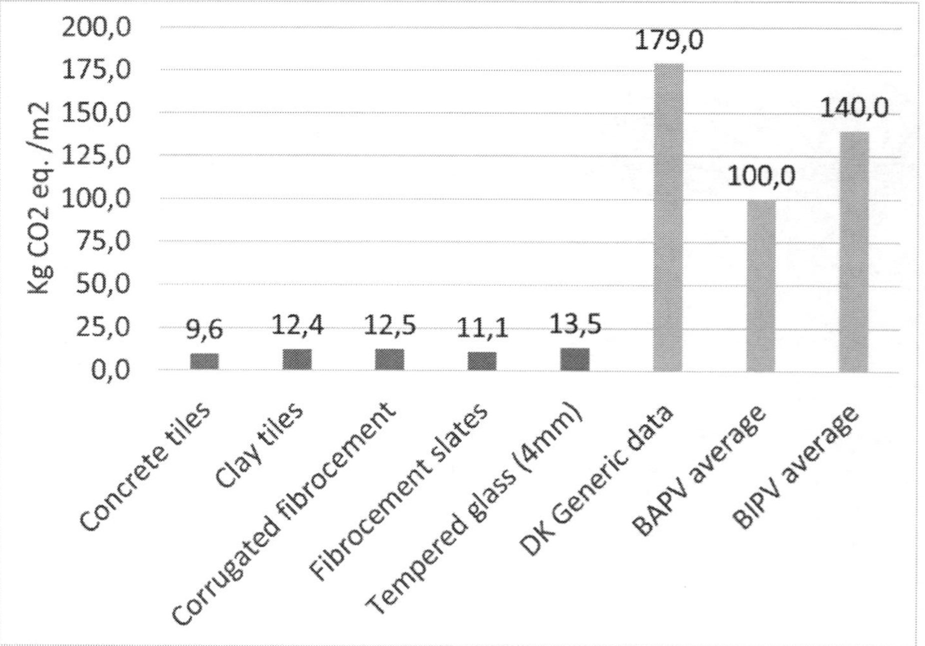

DTU

EN 15978(:2011) Sustainability of construction works

- **Calculate the Whole life LCA of Buildings**
  - Cradle to Grave approach
  - Sums **all** the loads and benefits of all modules

NB direct implementation of EN 15978:2011

➢ BIPV -full load of PV system

➢ Only displace CO_2 from operational energy (smaller fraction)

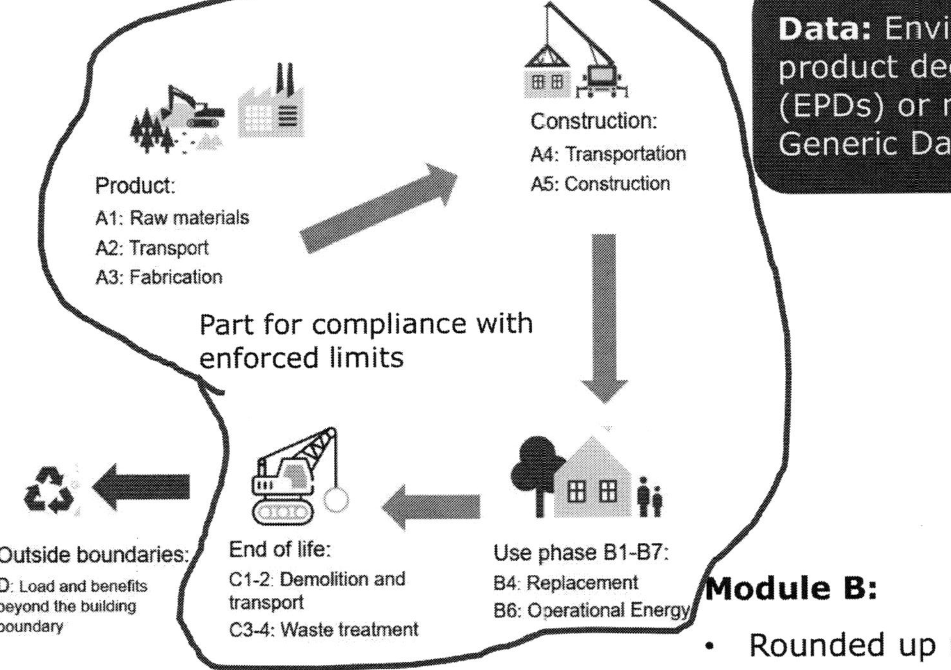

Data: Environmental product declarations (EPDs) or national Generic Data

Module B:

- Rounded up replacements
- Loads from only operational energy substitute with "Most likely impacts"

020478-006

Danish Implementation

- Implementation
  - Follows EN15978, include
    - Significant impact phases included
    - Reference study period 50 years
  - **Danish Limits 4-8 kg CO_2 eq/(m² (floor area)*year)**

  - **Include PV if part of energy performance compliance (up to 13.2) kWh/(m²*year)**
    - Include inverters and "stands"
    - **BIPV roofing:**
    - PV exceeding energy performance compliance, use "cover glass"
  - GWP load of operational energy - use published emission factors

Danish Emission factors

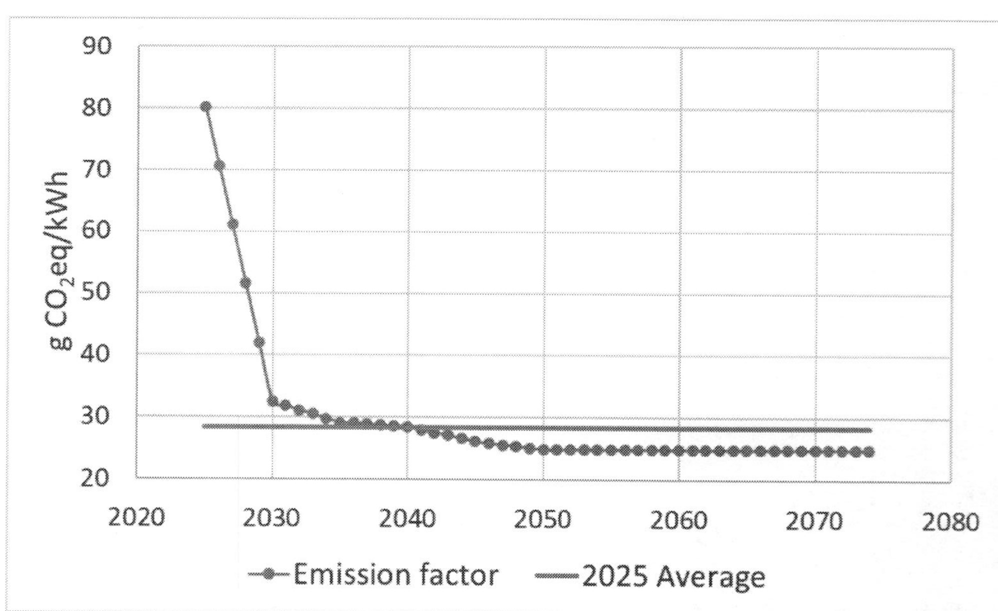

020478-007

DTU

Collected EPDs

Methods:

1. Collected Environmental product declarations (EPDs) for:

- BAPV panels (10)
- BIPV panels (7)
- Inverters (9) (6kW-300 kW)
- Mounting systems for roofs (4)

2. Summed for the included Danish phases

➢ Panels largest contributors
➢ Inverters and mounting structures contributes

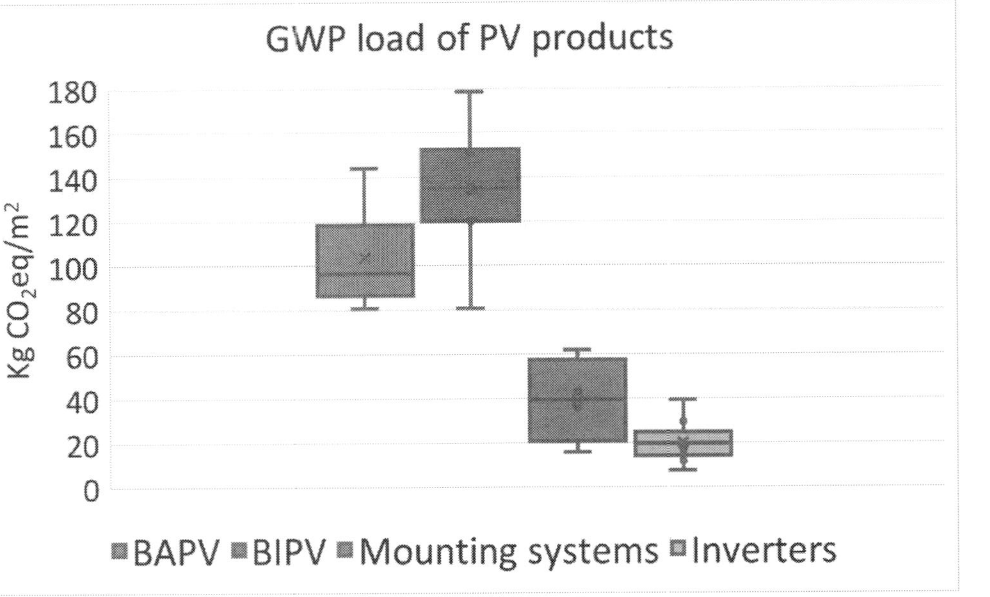

	BAPV	BIPV	Mounting	Inverter
Average system (kg CO_2eq/m^2)	159,0	159,0		
Relative Share	63%	87%	25%	13%

Inverters converted from WP to m^2 assuming 20% module efficiency

And DC AC ratio of 1.3

Mounting systems excluded from BIPV

020478-008

DTU

Danish Case study

Example calculation:

- Calculated the impact of $1m^2$ PV (Danish rules, 2025 deployment)
- CO_2 balance vs time (Average BAPV)
- Replacement after 25 years
  - First plant almost neutral
  - Second plant adds CO2 to the building
    - Energy estimations based on PR method

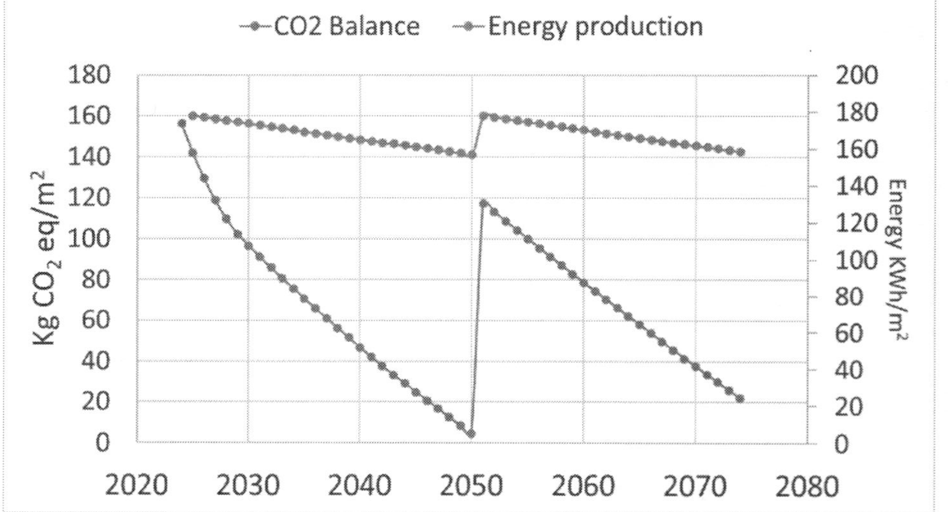

Assumptions (Typical Danish conditions)	
GHI	1000 kWh/m2
Pr	0,8
Degradation	0,5 % P.a
DC to AC Ratio	1,3
Lifetime panels and inverters	25 years
Lifetime Mounting	50 years

Performance ratio based method

$$E_{year,n} = \frac{H}{G_{stc}} * Pr * Y * (1-d)^i$$

CO_2 displacement

$$GWP(t)_{year,n} = \sum GWP_{EPD} - \sum_0^n E_{year,i}\epsilon_i$$

Danish Case study

Methods:

1. Collected Environmental product declarations (EPDs) for:

2. Calculated the GWP impact acc to Danish law:

Findings:

- Almost all PV products increases the GWP of the building!!

- For BIPV, Material savings not significant

- Contribution to final building GWP (depends on building)

  – But can be significant

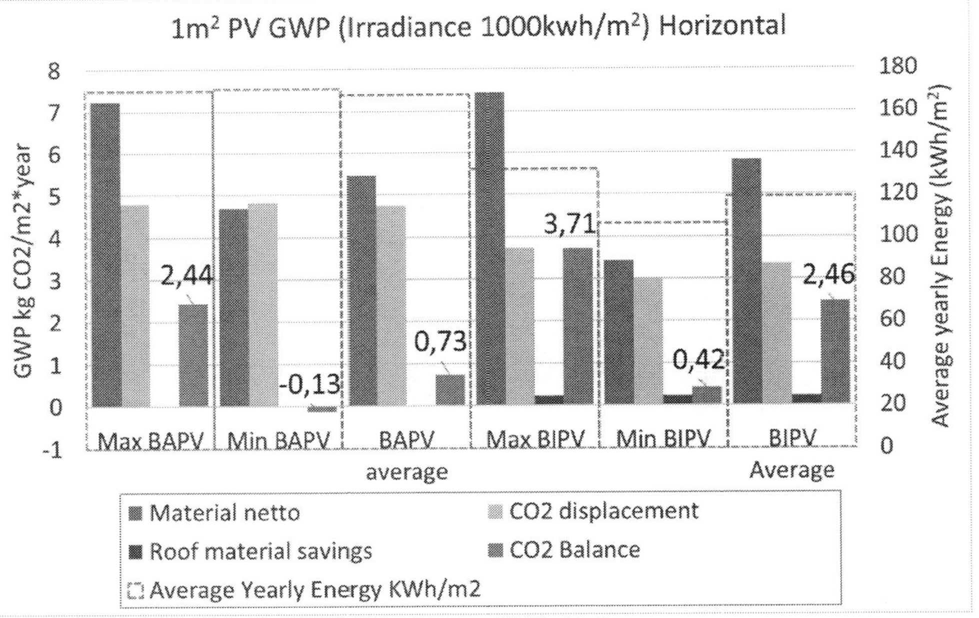

Danish Limits 4-8 kg CO$_2$ eq/(m² (floorarea)*year)

020478-010

DTU

Danish Case study – Emission factors

- Based on the national energy agency's forecast on national electricity mix from 2022

- **Forecast made to achieve political ambitions**
  - Carbon neutrality in 2050
  - 70% reduction in 2030
  - 4 fold increase in electricity production towards 2050
  - Biomass combustion excluded
  - …

  Most~ covered by Wind and (Land based) PV

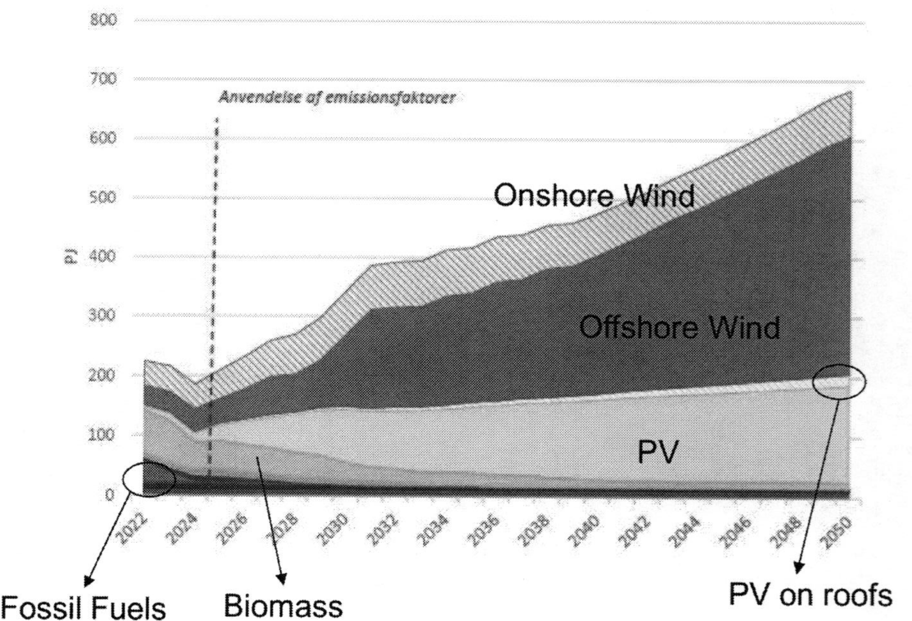

020478-011

Danish Case study – Emission factors

- Derived based on the national energy agencies forecast on national electricity mix in 2022

Findings

- Emission factors reduced with expected deployment of Renewable Energy (RE) incl PV
- CO_2 displacement for PV on buildings is **Circular** and **Marginal**:
  - PV on buildings contributes to lower grid emissions
  - Displacement for PV
    - What exceeds expected deployment of RE
- High political RE ambitions – low benefits of PV on buildings

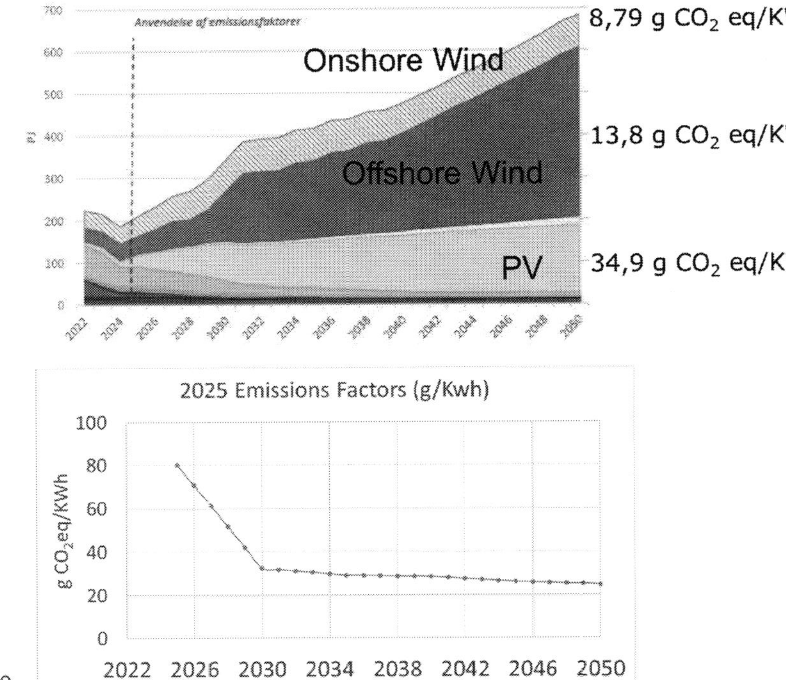

https://www.sbst.dk/Media/638282171394687135/Emissionsfaktorer%20for%20el%20fjernvarme%20og%20ledningsgas%20for%202025-2075.pdf

Conclusions

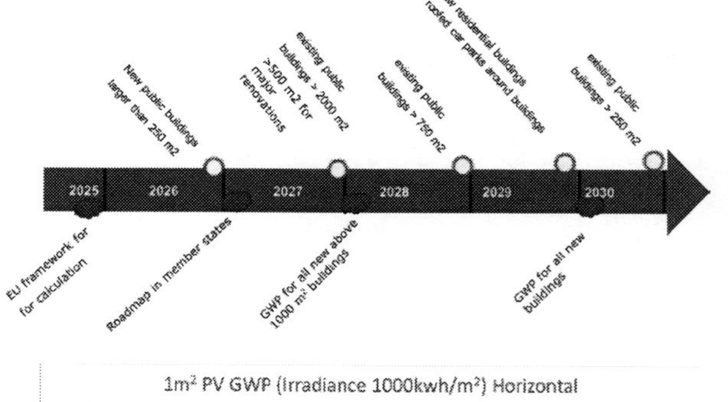

- GWP calculations required for all buildings in whole EU

- PV on buildings increases GWP in Danish implementation

- Benefits of PV **inversely** linked to political ambitions

- High emission factors (in other countries) facilitates use of carbon heavy materials

- BIPV challenge: Only a minor fraction of a BIPV installation can displace CO_2 despite full GWP load acc. To EN15978:2011

- **Overall Danish implementation not desirable for PV on buildings and against the intentions of the EPBD.**

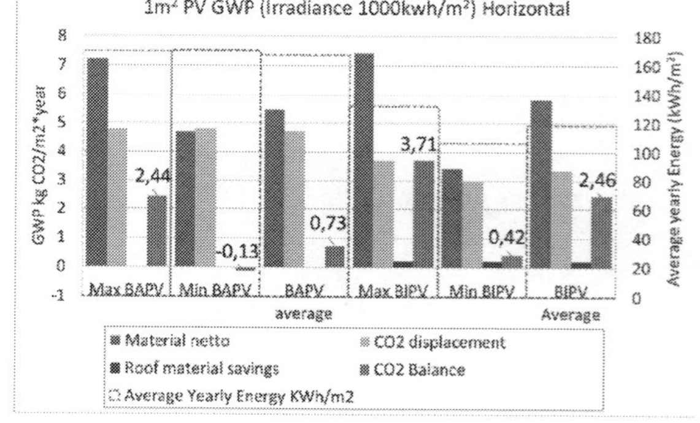

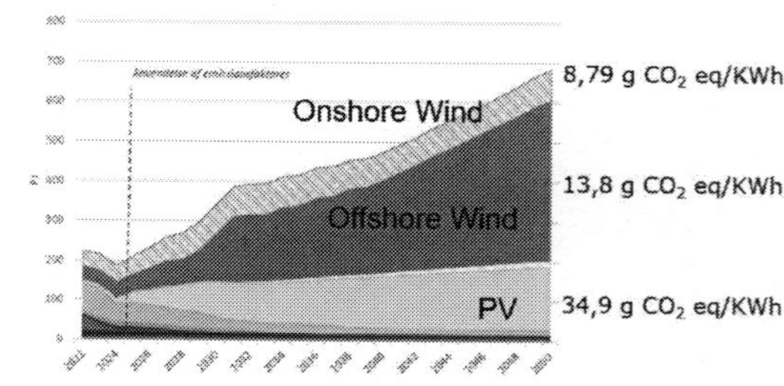

DTU

Maybe time for Reflection

- The Authors personally don't find this method long term sustainable!
- Time to step back and go beyond various standards with sector focus
  - evaluate these methods for PV in a holistic setting

https://nbi.ku.dk/english/www/niels/bohr/koebenhavnerfortolkningen/

.... Similar to Bohr, Heisenberg and Pauli
100 years ago Discussed Quantum Mechanics

020478-014

DTU

Discussion

Is there here a flaw in the EPDB directive?

Should PV be excluded in the GWP assessment of buildings?

Is it better ECO-design framework for the environmental footprint of PV?

Is it at all desirable that Building LCA benefits for PV is tied to the national grid emissions (and ambitions for RE deployment)

IEA PVPS TASK 15 A2, is working on this:
"BIPV in the environmental labelling"
Join if you can contribute
Visit 5DV.2.1 today @ 10:30.

"Expected deployment of renewable energy among PV is used to decrease the benefit of PV on buildings"

020478-015

DTU

sunth@dtu.dk

Thank you

020478-016

Module B

Relevant for PV:

- **B4: Replacement**
  - Rounded up number of replacements to reach consideration period 50 Years:
    - EG: PV lifetime of 30 years
      - » Full load of one replacement (not 2/3 replacement)
- **B6: Energy**
  - Only include operational energy (both on side produced and imported)
    - Operational energy for building operation (heat, ventilation etc.)
    - **Not energy from occupants** (Cooking, washing etc.)
  - … and to CO2 equivalents

"The net environmental benefits and/or loads of energy…. By calculating the substituted impacts … from the most likely corresponding energy supply based on current average technology and practice" (EN15978:2011)

Use phase B1-B7:

B1: Use

B2: Maintenance

B3: Reparation

B4: Replacement

B5: Renovation

B6: Operational Energy

B7: Operational water use

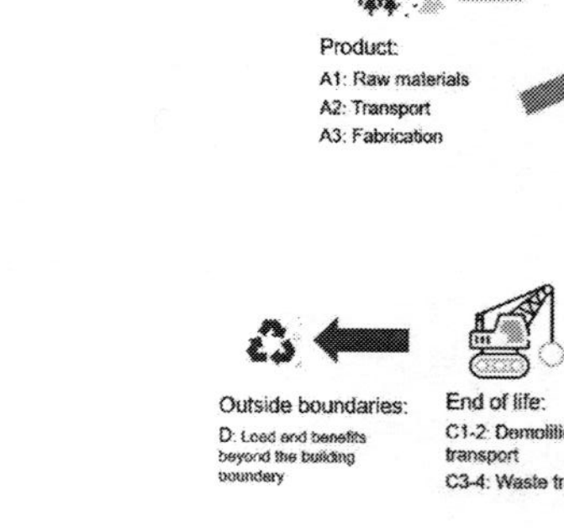

LCA requirements for PV in a danish context

"Sensitivity analysis"

- "Required" GWP/m^2 as a function of efficiency.
  - PV to have zero GWP influence
  - Product EPDs as Datapoints.

Results

- Requirements ~80 kg CO2/m2 for the base case if installed efficiency is 22.5%
- Only one product fulfills that
- Choice of inverter and mounting system is important
- For 2026 deployment its "worse"

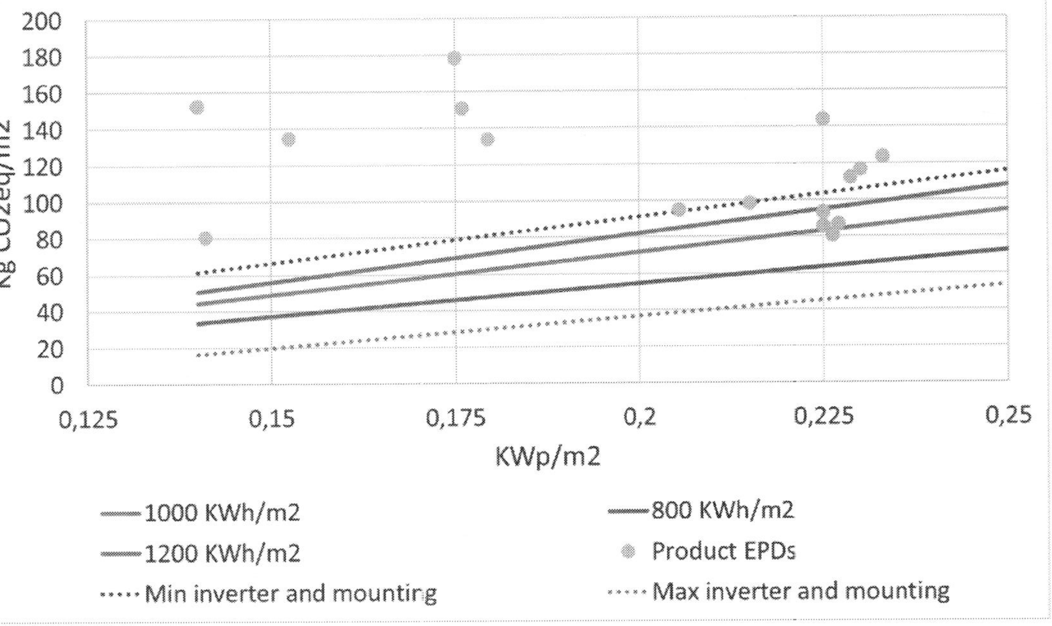

020478-018

EN 15978(:2011) Sustainability of construction works

- **Get rid of text, center figure and add text on the phases where relevant**
- **Calculate the Whole life LCA of Buildings**
  - Cradle to Grave approach
  - Sums **all** the loads and benefits of all materials, processes and utilities used for the building construction and operation
  - **Data:** Environmental product declarations or national Generic Data In a cloud
  - **Operational phase (Module B) Higlightthe NB statement**
    - Rounded up replacements
    - Loads from only operational energy substitute with "Most likely impacts"
- Only Phases A-C to be used for compliance with limits

NB direct implementation of 15978:2011

➢ BIPV -full load of PV system

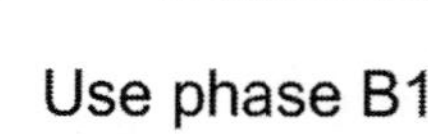

ENERGY RETURN ON INVESTMENT TRENDS OF SOLAR PV IN THE ENERGY TRANSITION

Hasret Sahin[1], A.A. Solomon[1,2], Christian Breyer[1]
[1] School of Energy Systems, LUT University, Lappeenranta, Finland
[2] School of Technology and Innovations, University of Vaasa, Finland
Corresponding author: Hasret Sahin, hasret.sahin@lut.fi

ABSTRACT: Solar photovoltaics (PV) is expected to play a central role in the global energy transition, yet its long-term energy requirements for its installations and operations are often underestimated. This study examines the evolution of energy return on investment (EROI) for solar PV systems between 2015 and 2050 across nine world regions. The analysis uses a dynamic modelling framework that combines life cycle assessment with cost-optimised system modelling, considering both utility-scale and prosumer-scale systems under five transition pathways. These include three rapid transition scenarios aiming for 100% renewable energy by 2035, 2040, and 2050, and two International Energy Agency scenarios that reflect more conservative policy projections. The findings show that under accelerated transitions, utility-scale PV achieves consistent improvements, with most regions converging to EROI values between 30 and 45 by mid-century. The highest outcomes are recorded in the Middle East and Africa, supported by large-scale adoption of single-axis tracking technologies. Prosumer-scale PV systems improve more gradually but still approach an EROI of 30 in most regions. By contrast, conservative scenarios deliver more uneven results, with strong performance in high-resource regions such as the Middle East but much weaker progress elsewhere. These findings highlight that the scale and configuration of solar PV deployment are decisive in shaping long-term energy returns.
Keywords: Solar photovoltaics; EROI; life cycle impact assessment; energy transition.

1 INTRODUCTION

The accelerated deployment of renewable energy (RE) technologies entails considerable embedded energy requirements, which are frequently underrepresented in feasibility assessments [1] [2] [3] [4]. This issue is particularly salient for solar photovoltaics (PV), given their anticipated central role in future electricity generation [5]. As a widely applied metric, physical energy return on investment (EROI), defined as the ratio of usable energy output to the cumulative energy inputs across the entire lifecycle, enables a detailed evaluation of the performance of RE systems [6] [7] [8]. However, reported physical EROI values for solar PV systems vary considerably, influenced by differences in technology type, methodological choices, geographic conditions, and reliance on outdated data [4] [9] [10]. In addition, most existing studies do not account for energy learning rates (ELRs), standardise energy quality across primary sources, and incorporate dynamic systemwide interactions [4] [11] [12].

To address this gap, the present study investigates the dynamic evolution of solar PV EROI trends by using the LUT Energy System Transition Model (LUT-ESTM) [13] [14] with LUT standing for Lappeenranta-Lahti University of Technology. This study briefly introduces the LUT-EROI model for application at technology level. The analysis applies five energy transition (ET) pathways, three LUT-Best Policy Scenarios (LUT-BPS) and two International Energy Agency (IEA) scenarios [15], across nine regions. By integrating life cycle assessment (LCA) with cost-optimised energy system modelling and employing cumulative energy demand (CED) as a key impact indicator, the study provides a comprehensive evaluation of how the EROI of only solar PV systems develops between 2015 and 2050 under contrasting the ET conditions.

2 MATERIALS AND METHOD

This study evaluates the energy requirements of solar PV systems and the evolution of their EROI across nine regions within a systemwide, full sector energy modelling framework. Notably, most technology-level analyses of solar PV EROI are conducted in isolation from the broader power system, which limits the ability to capture the effects of capacity expansion, solar PV deployment dynamics, and system-level interactions with sufficient accuracy [16] [17]. Accordingly, this study analyses systemwide EROI trends for solar PV systems under five transition scenarios introduced by Aghahosseini et al. [15]. These include three LUT-BPS, which examine the effects of accelerated transition timelines (2035, 2040, and 2050), and two IEA scenarios re-simulated within the LUT-ESTM for consistency [14] [15]. The assessment spans nine global regions to capture geographical heterogeneity, with full scenario descriptions and results available in Aghahosseini et al. [15].

2.1 Summary of the energy transition scenarios

The LUT-ESTM is a cost-optimisation model that resolves hourly energy flows across a full year [13] [14]. It is designed to capture near- and medium-term transition pathways towards 100% RE systems, while incorporating external constraints for long-term objectives. The model is applicable at national, regional, and global scales, with an emphasis on RE integration and sector coupling [13] [15].

Within this framework, five scenarios are assessed. The three LUT-BPS scenarios aim to achieve a 100% RE system by 2035, 2040, and 2050, minimising the role of fossil fuels and nuclear power while maintaining cost-effectiveness [15]. For comparison, two IEA scenarios are included: the IEA Sustainable Development Scenario (IEA-SDS), which reflects a Paris Agreement–aligned pathway with expanded roles for nuclear power and carbon capture and sequestration, and the IEA Stated Policy Scenario (IEA-STEPS), which represents a business-as-usual scenario based on current policy commitments [15] [18] [19].

The reason for selecting five different scenarios is the clear treatment of technology switching and replacement, which is a decisive factor in shaping the pace of solar PV systems expansion [4].

2.2 Quantification of energy use for solar PV systems

Energy use is quantified through CED, a standard LCA indicator that captures both direct and indirect inputs [20]. However, differences in system boundaries, data quality, and regional specificity often limit comparability [8] [21] [22]. An additional challenge is the lack of harmonised methods for accounting for qualitative differences among primary energy sources [12], which reduces the robustness of CED-based assessments. Addressing these issues requires a transparent, systemwide framework capable of tracing cascading energy flows. Such an approach involves the development of consistent life cycle inventories, rigorous system-level analysis, and the integration of technical and financial assumptions into energy modelling tools in line with their operational principles.

In this study, CED values are derived from the ecoinvent v3.7.1 database and converted from primary energy equivalent (MJ_{pe-eq}) to an electricity-equivalent basis (MJ_{el}) using standardised conversion factors, following the approaches of Solomon et al. [12] and Sahin et al. [4] [9]. To provide a more detailed representation, structural energy use (construction and decommissioning) is expressed per unit of capacity (MJ_{el}/kW), while operational energy use is expressed per unit of electricity generated (MJ_{el}/kWh), with full load hours treated as part of the operational phase. All PV-related CED values are reorganised by lifecycle stage and adjusted for technological improvements and ELRs at five-year intervals [4] [11] as well as considering technology shifts in the current and future markets. The reference CED value is estimated which decline by 52% in 2050 compared to 2015 level [4] as illustrated in Figure 1.

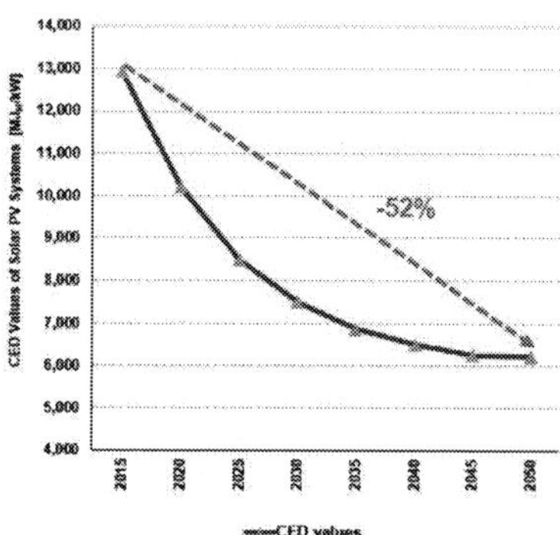

Figure 1: Changes in the CED values of solar PV systems over the years, considering ELRs values [4] [11]. The red line represents the CED values of solar PV systems (MJ_{el}/kW).

Transmission and distribution are excluded, as their contribution to CED is negligible and does not affect EROI estimates. The comprehensive CED database employed in this study is documented in Sahin et al. [17], while the

systemwide EROI methodology is detailed in the studies of Solomon et al. [5] and Sahin et al. [4].

2.3 Technology level LUT-EROI model

The physical EROI is defined as the ratio of usable energy output to the total energy invested across a technology's lifecycle. The LUT-EROI framework extends this concept to a systemwide perspective, allowing the integration of power-to-X technologies and establishing a link between technology-specific and system-level results. In this study, the LUT-EROI methodology of Sahin et al. [4] is followed, but the calculation scope is adjusted from systemwide to technology level.

After conversion of CED values from MJ_{pe-eq} to MJ_{el}, structural CED values are expressed as $E_{capacity}$ (MJ_{el}/kW), representing construction and decommissioning phases, while operational CED values are denoted as $E_{operation}$ (MJ_{el}/kWh) (see Equation 1). Note that $E_{operation}$ only contains yearly upstream fuel supply chain energy requirements for producing the necessary fuels (excluding their intrinsic energy content) and consumables used in operation. For natural gas and oil, dynamic decline functions from Delannoy et al. [23] are applied, expressed in MJ_{el}/kWh, whereas coal is modelled with a fixed exponential decay rate following Sgouridis et al. [24]. For other fuels, upstream energy requirements are taken directly from the ecoinvent database and adjusted to align with this study's modelling assumptions. In the next step, $E_{operation}$ is adjusted to a lifetime perspective by accounting for variations in full load hours. Within a systemwide energy framework, technologies do not operate at their maximum rated load but instead function alongside other technologies, reflecting the integrated operating conditions of the system. Accordingly, for each solar PV system type (fixed-tilted, single-axis, and prosumer-based), the respective full load hours (FLH) and lifetimes are applied to determine the final operational values. These are then combined with $E_{capacity}$ to estimate the total lifecycle energy investment for each solar PV system type. In Equation 1, $E_{inv_{t,n}}$ represents the total lifecycle energy investment for technology, t, where n is the capacity unit (expressed in kW). LT_t states the lifetime of the technology.

$$E_{inv_{t,n}} = E_{capacity} + \left(E_{operation} \cdot FLH \cdot LT_t\right) \qquad (Eq.1)$$

Once $E_{inv_{t,n}}$ is calculated for all solar PV system types, it is normalised by the respective technology lifetime to obtain annual energy investments. This step is necessary because (i) CED values vary over time with ELRs, which is assumed to 14% [11] and (ii) the energy requirements for new solar PV system installations and decommissioning activities also change over time. In Equation 2, the annual electricity generation term ($ES_{t,year}$) is represented as gross generation, since estimating net output for solar PV systems would require location-specific grid loss data, which differs widely across regions. Technology-specific EROI ($EROI_{t,year}$) is calculated using $Capacity_t$, which represents the cumulative installed capacity of each solar PV systems. This is derived by combining the energy investments of newly installed and decommissioned units with the previous year's capacity. In doing so, the method generates dynamic CED values over time and provides more reliable estimates than approaches that assume constant values, particularly for solar PV systems.

$$EROI_{t,year} = \frac{ES_{t,year}}{\sum_{n=1}^{N_t} \frac{E_{inv_{t,n}}}{LT_t} \cdot Capacity_t} \qquad (Eq.2)$$

Technology-specific solar PV systems' EROI values are assessed at five-year intervals for the period 2015–2050. Further methodological details regarding the systemwide EROI are available in Sahin et al. [4].

3 RESULTS AND DISCUSSION

This section begins with a concise overview of solar PV growth across nine regions under five scenarios, drawing on the study of Aghahosseini et al. [15]. It then provides analysis about the EROI trends of solar PV systems per regions. The analysis considers only grid-connected PV capacities and does not include storage options or off-grid systems.

3.1 Regional perspectives on Solar PV expansion during the energy transition

Solar PV deployment rises steeply across all regions under the LUT-BPS scenarios, in sharp contrast to the modest growth projected by the IEA pathways. By 2050, total installed capacity reaches 52.9 TW in LUT-BPS2035 and 58 TW in both LUT-BPS2040 and LUT-BPS2050, while the IEA-SDS and IEA-STEPS cases reach only 10.9 TW and 7.7 TW, respectively. Utility-scale PV systems dominate in every scenario, though their technological composition differs. In the LUT-BPS scenarios, single-axis tracking systems provide around 61% of the total capacity by 2050, with fixed-tilted systems contributing 20–22%. In the IEA scenarios, the balance shifts, with fixed-tilted systems accounting for 94% in the IEA-SDS and 67% in IEA-STEPS. Trackers play a secondary role, appearing only in the IEA-SDS where they reach 20% of the capacity mix. Prosumers-scale solar PV are most prominent in the LUT-BPS2035, reaching 19% due to the shorter ET period favouring distributed uptake, while their shares fall to 17% in other LUT-BPSs and drop further under the IEA scenarios, to 6% in the IEA-SDS and 13% in the IEA-STEPS.

Europe and Eurasia show a distinct pattern, relying heavily on fixed-tilted and prosumer systems. By 2050, fixed-tilted systems represent 7–10% of regional capacity under the LUT-BPS scenarios, with prosumers contributing about 2%. Single-axis trackers remain absent altogether. Under the IEA scenarios, fixed-tilted deployment falls to 6% in Europe and is negligible in Eurasia, while prosumers stagnate at very low levels. In Middle East and North Africa (MENA), Sub-Saharan Africa (SSA), Southeast Asia (SE-Asia), and the South Asian Association for Regional Cooperation (SAARC), the dominant role of utility-scale PV capacity is reinforced. LUT-BPS results show single-axis tracking system rising to 4–9% of capacity by 2050, though fixed-tilted systems remain relevant only in SAARC (8%). In the IEA scenarios, the only significant uptake of tracking system appears in MENA under the IEA-STEPS, reaching 20%. Instead, SAARC records higher fixed-tilted shares, with both IEA-SDS and IEA-STEPS reaching 15%. Prosumer-scale implementation remains minor across all

four regions, never exceeding 1–2%. South America (S-Am) represents a clear outlier: by 2050, single-axis tracking PV accounts for just 2-3% in the LUT-BPS, and a comparable share of fixed-tilted systems in the IEA scenarios. The growth in the prosumers remain limited to about 1% in the LUT-BPS and negligible under the IEA scenarios.

The most dynamic growth is concentrated in Northeast Asia (NE-Asia) and North America (N-Am), which stands out as the most single-axis tracking-intensive regions under the LUT-BPS scenarios. By 2050, single-axis tracking PV system accounts for more than 20% of global PV capacity in N-Am and 22% in NE-Asia. Prosumer-scale system is also more important in these regions, contributing 3-8%, while fixed-tilted systems decline to residual levels (2% or less). In the IEA scenarios, the pattern reverses: fixed-tilted systems account for 15-35% of total capacity, while single-axis tracking systems fall to negligible levels. Prosumer-scale deployment is only visible in NE-Asia, where it stabilises at a modest 7-8%.

3.2 Technology-specific EROI trends of solar PV across regions

The assessment of EROI for utility-scale PV systems provides critical insights into how technology deployment patterns shape long-term energy returns. Since utility-scale installations dominate solar PV capacity across all scenarios, their performance strongly influences regional and global outcomes. The following results examine EROI developments across nine regions under both LUT-BPS and IEA scenarios, highlighting the role of technology composition, particularly the balance between single-axis tracking and fixed-tilted systems in driving efficiency gains and regional disparities.

3.2.1 EROI trends of utility-scale PV system across nine major regions

The evolution of EROI in utility-scale PV systems mirrors the dynamics of large-scale solar expansion during the ET. Under the LUT-BPS scenarios, most regions show steady improvements, with values clustering in the 30-45 range by 2050, though Europe and Eurasia advance more slowly. By contrast, the IEA scenarios reveal a more uneven picture: MENA and SSA retain comparatively high returns above 40 and 34, while Europe, Eurasia, and NE-Asia remain below 30, underscoring the regional disparities that emerge under more conservative ET pathways.

The EROI trends of utility-scale PV systems is strongly shaped by the balance between single-axis tracking and fixed-tilted capacity expansion. Under the LUT-BPSs, the rapid growth of single-axis tracking, accounting for more than 60% of total capacity by 2050, drives significant efficiency gains and higher EROI outcomes across most regions. Table I provides the technology-level EROI estimates of utility-scale PV systems for each region under the LUT-BPSs. By mid-century, MENA and SSA record the highest values at 46 and 43, respectively, supported by large-scale deployment of tracking systems in high-resource areas. S-Am and N-Am also benefit from substantial single-axis tracking adoption, reaching values around 40, while SE-Asia and SAARC exceed 37 and NE-Asia approaches 35. Europe and Eurasia, where fixed-tilted systems remain more dominant and tracking penetration is limited, achieve lower results, stabilising around 31. Across the LUT-BPS2035, LUT-BPS2040, and LUT-BPS2050, the differences lie mainly in the timing of solar PV deployment directly associated with ET time horizon, but all converge toward similar levels by 2050, illustrating how single-axis tracking-led expansion underpins higher energy returns.

Table I: Utility-scale PV system EROI values in 2050 across nine regions for LUT-BPS scenarios.

Regions / EROI value	BPS2035	BPS2040	BPS2050
Europe	25.2	28.4	30.7
Eurasia	25.8	28.9	30.6
MENA	38.6	44.3	45.7
SSA	39.2	41.8	43.4
SAARC	33.3	35.6	37.2
NE-Asia	29.1	32.3	34.8
SE-Asia	33.3	35.9	37.2
N-Am	33.4	37.3	39.8
S-Am	33.8	38.9	40.4

Table II reports the EROI estimates for utility-scale PV systems across all regions under the IEA-SDS and IEA-STEPS scenarios. The technology mix shifts toward fixed-tilted systems, constraining overall EROI growth. Despite maintaining high values in MENA (41) and SSA (34) due to enormous harvestable solar energy resource, other regions record weaker performances compared to the LUT-BPS scenarios. Europe is most affected, falling below 20 by 2050, while Eurasia remains only slightly above 21. NE-Asia also declines relative to the LUT-BPS scenarios, with values of 28 in the IEA-SDS and 25 in the IEA-STEPS. S-Am and N-Am achieve more modest improvements, stabilising around 33, reflecting their limited reliance on tracking systems under these pathways.

Table II: Utility-scale PV system EROI values in 2050 across nine regions for IEA scenarios.

Regions / EROI value	SDS	STEPS
Europe	19.2	17.5
Eurasia	22.0	21.3
MENA	41.1	41.4
SSA	34.7	34.3
SAARC	31.9	33.3
NE-Asia	27.9	24.6
SE-Asia	25.5	25.3
N-Am	32.3	32.6
S-Am	33.5	32.5

In summary, the LUT-BPSs highlight how large-scale adoption of single-axis tracking systems enables most regions to converge between 30 and 45 by 2050, reinforcing the role of technology choice in shaping long-term EROI trends. In contrast, the IEA scenarios, dominated by fixed-tilted deployment, produce uneven results, with only MENA and SSA achieving high returns, while Europe, Eurasia, and NE-Asia lag behind.

3.2.2 EROI trends of prosumer-scale PV system across nine major regions

The EROI trends of prosumer-scale PV systems is closely linked to the growth of utility-scale PV installations. In the LUT-BPSs, values rise steadily and largely converge, with most regions approaching or surpassing 30 by 2050, independent of whether the ET is fast-tracked or gradual. The IEA scenarios, however, display more uneven developments: Europe and SE-Asia achieve the highest improvements, reaching above 40 and 30 respectively, whereas Eurasia and S-Am remain constrained in the 20-25 range, reflecting wider disparities.

In the LUT-BPS2035, rapid early improvements are most evident in resource-rich regions. By 2050, MENA, SSA, and SAARC exceed an EROI of 30, while SE-Asia, NE-Asia, N-Am, and S-Am converge near this benchmark. Eurasia reaches 28, whereas Europe lags behind, remaining at 25. The other LUT-BPS scenarios yield broadly similar outcomes, as the relatively modest expansion of prosumer-scale capacity has only a minor effect on technology-level EROI results. LUT-BPS2040 follows the same trend but with slower progress, illustrating that the difference lies primarily in timing of ET. LUT-BPS2050 represents the most gradual pathway, yet by mid-century the regional pattern remains consistent, with SSA and MENA leading, most other regions clustering around 30, and Europe stabilising at the lower bound of 25. Table III summarises the technology-level EROI estimates of prosumer-scale PV systems for each region under the LUT-BPSs, while the corresponding results for the IEA scenarios are presented in Table IV.

Table III: Prosumer-scale PV systems EROI values in 2050 across nine major regions for LUT-BPSs.

Regions / EROI value	BPS2035	BPS2040	BPS2050
Europe	25.0	25.0	25.0
Eurasia	28.0	28.1	29.2
MENA	34.7	34.7	36.3
SSA	33.6	33.6	35.4
SAARC	33.8	33.8	35.5
NE-Asia	27.0	27.0	28.1
SE-Asia	29.2	29.2	30.3
N-Am	28.6	25.3	27.1
S-Am	25.3	28.6	30.5

Table IV: Prosumer-scale PV systems EROI values in 2050 across nine major regions for IEA scenarios.

Regions / EROI value	SDS	STEPS
Europe	44.0	44.0
Eurasia	25.7	25.7
MENA	32.6	32.6
SSA	33.2	33.2
SAARC	32.1	32.1
NE-Asia	29.5	29.5
SE-Asia	34.6	34.6
N-Am	32.6	32.6
S-Am	26.1	26.1

The IEA-SDS case reveals sharper contrasts across regions. Europe performs exceptionally well, reaching an EROI of 44 by 2050 and surpassing all LUT-BPS outcomes. SE-Asia also exceeds 30, while NE-Asia remains close to this level. N-Am crosses 30, S-Am stabilises between 25 and 30, and Eurasia shows only limited progress. The IEA-STEPS scenario reinforces this divergence: Europe again records values above 40, SE-Asia remains strong, SSA and MENA approach 30, and Eurasia stays below 25. The relatively high EROI results in the IEA scenarios are linked to the decommissioning of prosumer-scale PV systems, which lowers the overall energy requirements of this technology compared with the LUT-BPS cases. At the same time, capacity expansion and improvements in system efficiency emerge as the main drivers of prosumer-scale EROI across all scenarios.

Taken together, the LUT-BPS scenarios indicate a steady convergence of regional EROI values towards 30 by 2050, while the IEA scenarios highlight a more uneven pattern, with Europe and SE-Asia achieving rapid advances and Eurasia and South America lagging behind.

4 CONCLUSIONS

This study examines the long-term evolution of the energy return on investment (EROI) of solar photovoltaics (PV) across nine global regions by applying the LUT-EROI framework in conjunction with the LUT Energy System Transition Model. Through the integration of life cycle assessment, dynamic cumulative energy demand data, and cost-optimised transition pathways, the analysis provides a novel systemwide perspective that captures the effects of technology composition, energy learning rates, and scenario design on technology-level EROI trends. Furthermore, the consistent assessment of both utility- and prosumer-scale PV within accelerated LUT Best Policy Scenarios (LUT-BPS) and International Energy Agency (IEA) scenarios represents a significant methodological advancement over previous static or technology-isolated investigations.

Key findings highlight that:

- Utility-scale PV systems achieve the highest EROI improvements in regions with large-scale adoption of single-axis tracking, converging between 30 and 45 by 2050 under the LUT-BPSs.
- Prosumer-scale PV systems show slower but steady improvements, with most regions approaching an EROI of 30 by 2050, though Europe achieves exceptionally high values above 40 in the IEA pathways. This is mainly due to the reducing overall energy needs compared with the LUT-BPS cases.
- Scenario design shapes the technology-level EROI outcomes. The accelerated ETs favour convergence and higher long-term returns, while conservative pathways produce uneven patterns, with weaker results in Eurasia and South America.
- Solar PV technology mix is the decisive factor. The dominance of fixed-tilted systems in IEA scenarios constrains EROI growth, whereas widespread adoption of single-axis tracking systems in LUT-BPS pathways underpins stronger performance.

Overall, the results demonstrate that ambitious and technology-optimised transition strategies not only enable rapid defossilisation but also improve the energy efficiency of the transition itself, strengthening the case for accelerated deployment of different solar PV system technologies.

In terms of limitations, the spatial aggregation may obscure regional variations in resource availability and system performance, potentially affecting EROI outcomes of solar PV systems. The life cycle inventories from the ecoinvent may not fully capture the solar PV supply chain, and reliance on a single database for cumulative energy demand (CED) values could lead to overestimation. Systemwide EROI results are further shaped by global supply chain dependencies, such as intercontinental transport of PV components, and by the exclusion of emerging solar PV technologies. Recycling processes, as well as transmission and distribution networks, are also omitted due to limited data or their marginal contribution to overall CED.

5 ACKNOWLEDGEMENTS

The authors gratefully acknowledge the public financing of the Academy of Finland for the biophysical limits of the energy transition project (317681).

6 REFERENCES

[1] M. M. Vanegas Cantarero, "Of renewable energy, energy democracy, and sustainable development: A roadmap to accelerate the energy transition in developing countries," 2020, *Elsevier Ltd.* doi: 10.1016/j.erss.2020.101716.

[2] I. Gunnarsdottir, B. Davidsdottir, E. Worrell, and S. Sigurgeirsdottir, "Review of indicators for sustainable energy development," 2020, *Elsevier Ltd.* doi: 10.1016/j.rser.2020.110294.

[3] H. Neofytou, A. Nikas, and H. Doukas, "Sustainable energy transition readiness: A multicriteria assessment index," *Renewable and Sustainable Energy Reviews*, vol. 131, 2020, doi: 10.1016/j.rser.2020.109988.

[4] H. Sahin, A. A. Solomon, A. Aghahosseini, and C. Breyer, "Systemwide energy return on investment in a sustainable transition towards net zero power systems," *Nat Commun*, vol. 15, no. 1, p. 208, 2024, doi: 10.1038/s41467-023-44232-9.

[5] A. A. Solomon, H. Sahin, and C. Breyer, "The pitfall in designing future electrical power systems without considering energy return on investment in planning," *Appl Energy*, vol. 369, p. 123570, 2024, doi: 10.1016/j.apenergy.2024.123570.

[6] D. J. Murphy and C. A. S. Hall, "Year in review—EROI or energy return on (energy) invested," *Ann N Y Acad Sci*, vol. 1185, no. 1, pp. 102–118, 2010, doi: 10.1111/j.1749-6632.2009.05282.x.

[7] C. A. S. Hall, J. G. Lambert, and S. B. Balogh, "EROI of different fuels and the implications for society," *Energy Policy*, vol. 64, pp. 141–152, 2014, doi: 10.1016/j.enpol.2013.05.049.

[8] D. J. Murphy, M. Raugei, M. Carbajales-Dale, and B. Rubio Estrada, "Energy Return on Investment of Major Energy Carriers: Review and Harmonization," *Sustainability*, vol. 14, no. 12, p. 7098, 2022, doi: 10.3390/su14127098.

[9] H. Sahin, A. A. Solomon, A. Aghahosseini, and C. Breyer, "The impact of spatial representation in energy transition modelling on systemwide energy return on investment," *IET Renewable Power Generation*, vol. 18, no. 14, pp. 2706–2722, 2024, doi: 10.1049/rpg2.13117.

[10] H. Sahin, A. A. Solomon, A. Aghahosseini, and C. Breyer, "Uneven Distribution of Natural Resources Impacts on Systemwide Energy Return on Investment ," *(submitted)*, 2025.

[11] M. Görig and C. Breyer, "Energy Learning Curves of PV Systems," *Environ Prog Sustain Energy*, vol. 35, no. 3, pp. 914–923, 2016, doi: 10.1002/ep.12340.

[12] A. A. Solomon, N. B. Manjong, and C. Breyer, "The necessity to standardise primary energy quality in achieving a meaningful quantification of related indicators," *Smart Energy*, vol. 12, p. 100115, 2023, doi: 10.1016/j.segy.2023.100115.

[13] D. Bogdanov *et al.*, "Costs and benefits of highly ambitious energy transition pathways for Europe," *Energy*, vol. 336, p. 138477, 2025, doi: 10.1016/j.energy.2025.138477.

[14] D. Bogdanov *et al.*, "Low-cost renewable electricity as the key driver of the global energy transition towards sustainability," *Energy*, vol. 227, p. 120467, 2021, doi: 10.1016/j.energy.2021.120467.

[15] A. Aghahosseini *et al.*, "More renewable energy leads to a faster transition at lower cost as revealed by comparative analysis of global energy transition scenarios," *(submitted)*, 2025.

[16] Z. Zhou and M. Carbajales-Dale, "Assessing the photovoltaic technology landscape: Efficiency and energy return on investment (EROI)," *Energy Environ Sci*, vol. 11, no. 3, pp. 603–608, 2018, doi: 10.1039/c7ee01806a.

[17] H. Sahin, A. A. Solomon, A. Aghahosseini, and C. Breyer, "Systemwide energy return on investment in a sustainable transition towards net zero power systems (Supplementary Dataset - CED Database.xlsx).," 2024, *Figshare*. doi: 10.6084/m9.figshare.24602349.

[18] IEA, "World Energy Outlook 2021," Paris, 2021. https://www.iea.org/reports/world-energy-outlook-2021

[19] A. Aghahosseini *et al.*, "Energy system transition pathways to meet the global electricity demand for ambitious climate targets and cost competitiveness," *Appl Energy*, vol. 331, p. 120401, 2023, doi: 10.1016/j.apenergy.2022.120401.

[20] M. A. J. Huijbregts *et al.*, "Is Cumulative Fossil Energy Demand a Useful Indicator for the Environmental Performance of Products?," *Environ Sci Technol*, vol. 40, no. 3, pp. 641–648, 2006, doi: 10.1021/es051689g.

[21] R. Frischknecht, F. Wyss, S. Büsser Knöpfel, T. Lützkendorf, and M. Balouktsi, "Cumulative energy demand in LCA: the energy harvested approach," *Int J Life Cycle Assess*, vol. 20, no. 7, pp. 957–969, 2015, doi: 10.1007/s11367-015-0897-4.

[22] D. J. Murphy, M. Carbajales-Dale, and D. Moeller, "Comparing apples to apples: Why the net energy analysis community needs to adopt the life-cycle analysis framework," *Energies*, vol. 9, no. 11, pp. 1–16, 2016, doi: 10.3390/en9110917.

[23] L. Delannoy, P. Y. Longaretti, D. J. Murphy, and E. Prados, "Peak oil and the low-carbon energy transition: A net-energy perspective," *Appl Energy*, vol. 304, p. 117843, 2021, doi: 10.1016/j.apenergy.2021.117843.

[24] S. Sgouridis, D. Csala, and U. Bardi, "The sower's way: quantifying the narrowing net-energy pathways to a global energy transition," *Environmental Research Letters*, vol. 11, no. 9, p. 094009, 2016, doi: 10.1088/1748-9326/11/9/094009.

42nd EU PVSEC, 2025, Bilbao, Spain

Unveiling the evolutionary energy performance of solar PV systems through systemwide EROI perspective

Hasret Sahin, A.A. Solomon, Christian Breyer

LUT University, Lappeenranta, Finland

Table of Contents

Overview and Motivation

Materials and Methods

>> **LUT Energy System Transition Model (LUT-ESTM)**

>> **Energy Transition Scenarios**

>> **Systemwide LUT-EROI model**

Results

>> **Synopsis of Energy Modelling Results**

>> **Regional EROI Patterns of Solar PV Systems**

>> **The Storage Trade-off: Batteries and Solar PV EROI**

Conclusions

Limitations

Unveiling the evolutionary energy performance of solar PV systems through systemwide EROI perspective
More information ▶ hasret.sahin@lut.fi

020480-002

Overview and Motivation

Regional energy system transitions

» Showing regional asymmetries as shaped by strategies and regulations.

» Massive energy requirements are necessary and changing depending on the region.

» Solar PV systems and batteries are central to future power systems, yet their EROI interactions remain underexplored.

Existing energy return on investment (EROI) studies

» Focus mainly on static, technology-level analyses.

» Show wide divergence in solar PV systems EROI values due to location, technology, and boundary definitions.

» Rarely capture dynamic, systemwide effects such as energy learning rates and storage integration.

This research aims to:

» Develop a dynamic framework for assessing solar PV systems and with/without battery options EROI at both technology and system level.

» Analyse five transition scenarios across nine global regions using the LUT Energy System Transition Model (LUT-ESTM).

» Provide insights into systemwide EROI trends at the technology level (2015–2050) under varying pathways, enhancing the robustness of energy transition planning.

Unveiling the evolutionary energy performance of solar PV systems through systemwide EROI perspective
More information ► hasret.sahin@lut.fi

020480-003

Table of Contents

Overview and Motivation

Materials and Methods

>> **LUT Energy System Transition Model (LUT-ESTM)**

>> **Energy Transition Scenarios**

>> **Systemwide LUT-EROI model**

Results

>> **Synopsis of Energy Modelling Results**

>> **Regional EROI Patterns of Solar PV Systems**

>> **The Storage Trade-off: Batteries and Solar PV EROI**

Conclusions

Limitations

Unveiling the evolutionary energy performance of solar PV systems through systemwide EROI perspective
More information ▶ hasret.sahin@lut.fi

LUT Energy System Transition Model (LUT-ESTM)

» Technology-oriented, bottom-up cost-optimisation model.

» Covers ~170 energy technologies.

» Operates with full hourly resolution over an entire year.

» Structured at country, regional, and global levels.

» Uses 5-year time steps to capture transition dynamics and their changes.

» Identifies short- and medium-term pathways guided by long-term targets.

» Minimises system costs while ensuring technology feasibility (Bogdanov et al., 2025; 2021).

References:

Bogdanov, D., Ram, M., Satymov, R., Lopez, G., Mensah, T., Sadovskaia, K., & Breyer, C. (2025). Costs and benefits of highly ambitious energy transition pathways for Europe. Energy, 138477.

Bogdanov, D., Ram, M., Aghahosseini, A., Gulagi, A., Oyewo, A. S., Child, M., ... & Breyer, C. (2021). Low-cost renewable electricity as the key driver of the global energy transition towards sustainability. Energy, 227, 120467.

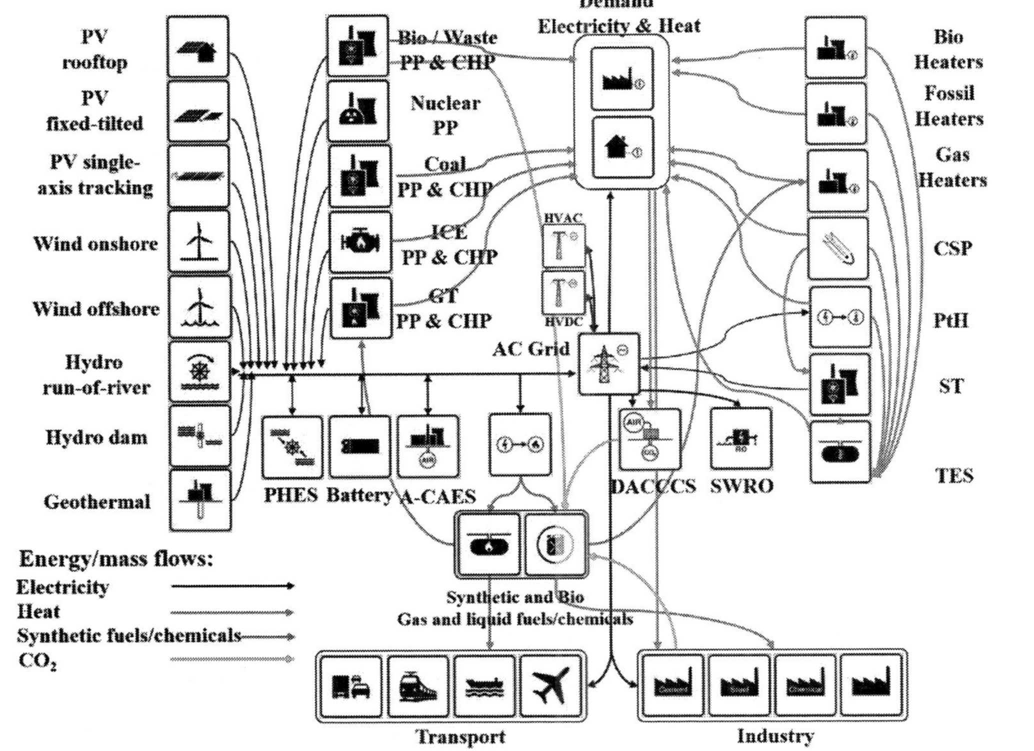

Figure 1. Mapping of technologies and connections within LUT-ESTM.

Unveiling the evolutionary energy performance of solar PV systems through systemwide EROI perspective

More information ► hasret.sahin@lut.fi

020480-005

Energy Transition Scenarios

» **Energy transition scenarios are divided into two groups (Aghahosseini et al., 2025) .**

Group 1: LUT – Best Policy Scenarios (BPS) (optimisation-based).

LUT-BPS2035: **Achieving a 100% renewable energy (RE) system by the year 2035.**

LUT-BPS2040: **Achieving a 100% RE system by the year 2040.**

LUT-BPS2050: **Achieving a 100% RE system by the year 2050.**

» **Fossil & nuclear phased out at end-of-life, no new build.**

» **Cost-optimal RE, wind repowering, full storage mix.**

» **Integration of power-to-X (PtX) systems.**

Group 2: IEA Reference (re-simulated in LUT-ESTM).

Stated Policies Scenario (IEA-STEPS): **benchmark, business-as-usual; fossil & nuclear retained.**

Sustainable Development Scenario (IEA-SDS): **Paris-aligned; coal & oil decline, nuclear & carbon capture and storage (CCS) expand, RE ~60% capacity by 2050.**

» **IEA outputs (capacity, demand, CO_2 costs) retained; LUT-ESTM supplies load/resource profiles.**

» **IEA-NZE (Net-Zero by 2050) could not be used due to intransparency and lack of accessible data.**

Reference: Aghahosseini A, Solomon AA, Bardi U, Creutzig F, Hoekstra A, Jacobson MZ, et al. (2025). More renewable energy leads to a faster transition at lower cost as revealed by comparative analysis of global energy transition scenarios (under review).

Unveiling the evolutionary energy performance of solar PV systems through systemwide EROI perspective
More information ▶ hasret.sahin@lut.fi

Systemwide LUT-EROI model

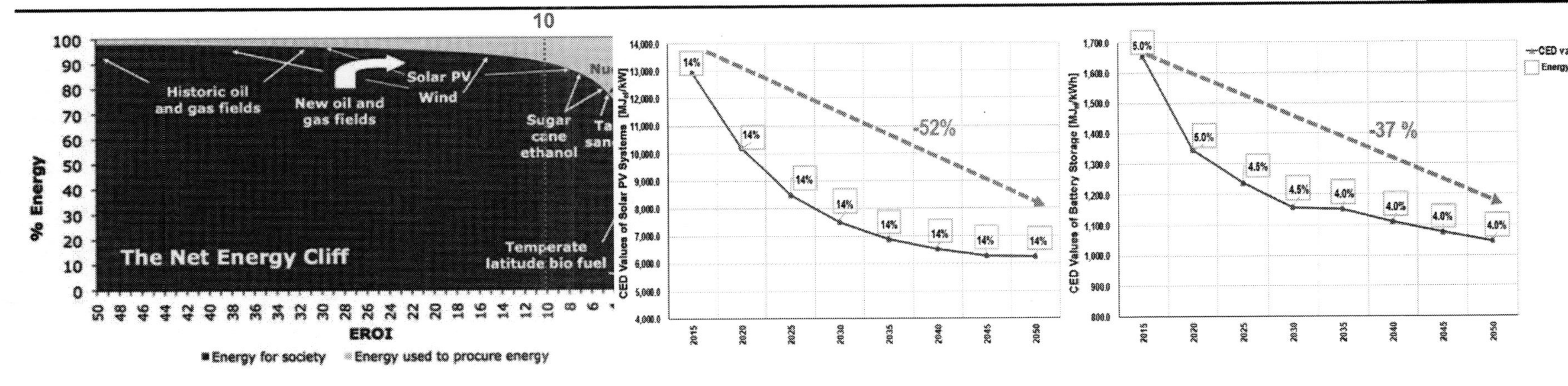

Figure 2. Net Energy Cliff in EROI (Murphy et al., 2010) .

Figure 3. Changes in the CED values of solar PV systems (left) and of battery storage (right) over the years, considering ELR values (Sahin et al., 2024).

» **EROI measures the ratio of usable energy gained vs. energy invested.**

» **The minimum EROI threshold for the society (Critical minimum: ~10)**

  » **Below this, too much energy is reinvested into the system itself.**

  » **Leaves insufficient surplus energy for essential societal functions.**

» **EROI ≈ 10–20: sustainable but limited societal growth.**

» **EROI > 20: enabled industrial growth and high living standards.**

References:

Murphy, D. J., & Hall, C. A. (2010). Year in review—EROI or energy return on (energy) invested. Annals of the new york academy of sciences, 1185(1), 102-118.

Sahin, H., Solomon, A. A., Aghahosseini, A., & Breyer, C. (2024). Systemwide energy return on investment in a sustainable transition towards net zero power systems. Nature Communications, 15(1), 208.

Systemwide LUT-EROI model

EROI

$$EROI = \frac{E_{out}}{E_{inv}} = \frac{E_{an} \cdot LT}{E_{inv}} = \frac{E_{an}}{(E_{inv}/LT)}$$

Eq. 1

Systemwide EROI

$$EROI_{syst,year} = \frac{ES_{year}}{\Sigma_t \frac{(\Sigma_{n=1}^{N_t} E_{inv_{t,n}} \cdot Capacity_t)}{LT_t}}$$

Eq. 2

Invested energy through

$$E_{inv_{t,n}} = E_{capacity} + (E_{operation} \cdot FLH \cdot LT_t)$$

Eq. 3

E_{inv}: Total energy required to deliver that energy of a system and/or an energy source through a lifetime.

E_{out}: Total usable energy (final electricity generation).

E_{an}: Annual electricity generation.

$EROI_{syst,year}$: Annual systemwide approach of EROI.

ES_{year}: Annual net energy generation feeding to the transmission network

$E_{inv_{t,n}}$: The invested energy per unit of kW capacity for a specific technology.

$E_{capacity}$: The adapted CED value per kW

$E_{operation}$: The adapted operation CED value per kWh

N_t: The maximum capacity of the technology.

t : time
n : is the capacity unit (kW or kWh)
LT : lifetime of a technology
FLH : full load hour of a technology
LT_t : the lifetime of a technology

>> **Systemwide EROI based on a unified system-level analysis.**

>> **Assesses system changes over defined time periods.**

>> **Treats the entire energy system as one entity.**

>> **Avoids reliance on individual technology-level EROI values (Sahin et al, 2024; Solomon et al., 2024).**

References:

Sahin, H., Solomon, A. A., Aghahosseini, A., & Breyer, C. (2024). Systemwide energy return on investment in a sustainable transition towards net zero power systems. Nature Communications, 15(1), 208.

Solomon, A. A., Sahin, H., & Breyer, C. (2024). The pitfall in designing future electrical power systems without considering energy return on investment in planning. Applied Energy, 369, 123570.

Unveiling the evolutionary energy performance of solar PV systems through systemwide EROI perspective
More information ▶ hasret.sahin@lut.fi

Systemwide LUT-EROI Model

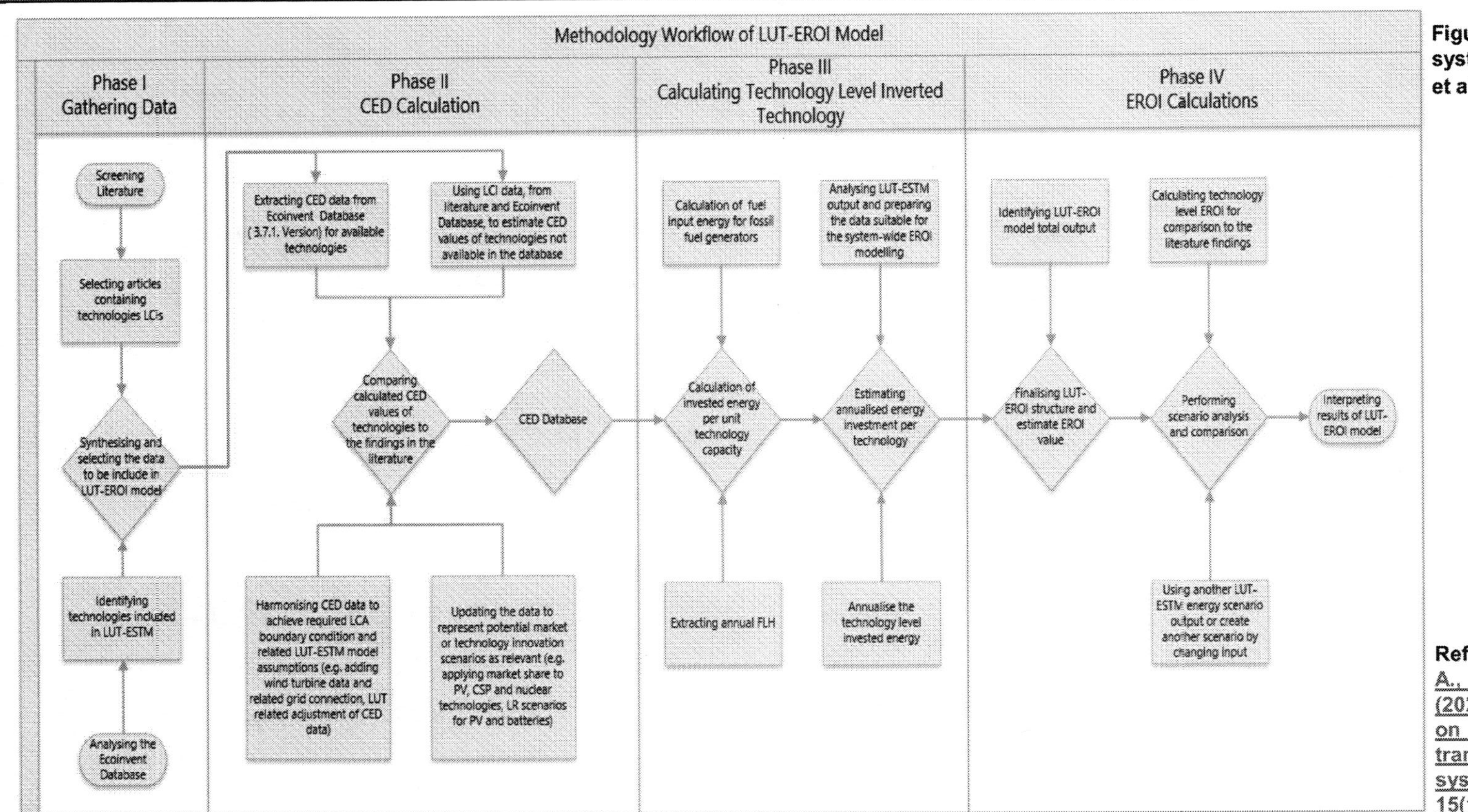

Figure 4. The methodology of systemwide LUT-EROI model (Sahin et al., 2024).

Reference: Sahin, H., Solomon, A. A., Aghahosseini, A., & Breyer, C. (2024). Systemwide energy return on investment in a sustainable transition towards net zero power systems. Nature Communications, 15(1), 208.

Unveiling the evolutionary energy performance of solar PV systems through systemwide EROI perspective
More information ▶ hasret.sahin@lut.fi

Table of Contents

Overview and Motivation

Materials and Methods

» LUT Energy System Transition Model (LUT-ESTM)

» Energy Transition Scenarios

» Systemwide LUT-EROI model

Results

» Synopsis of Energy Modelling Results

» Regional EROI Patterns of Solar PV Systems

» The Storage Trade-off: Batteries and Solar PV EROI

Conclusions

Limitations

Unveiling the evolutionary energy performance of solar PV systems through systemwide EROI perspective
More information ▶ hasret.sahin@lut.fi

020480-010

Synopsis of Energy Modelling Results

Solar PV systems

Figure 5. Installed capacity of solar PV systems of Northeast Asia.

Single-axis solar PV (1-axis):

» **Largest capacity expansion. Strongest growth in Northeast Asia (NE-Asia), Southeast Asia (SE-Asia) and North America (N-Am).**

Fixed-tilted solar PV (0-axis) :

» **Moderate expansion. Notable growth in South Asia and Europe.**

Prosumer-scale solar PV:

» **Plays only a minor role in most regions. Clear increase in NE-Asia and Europe.**

The LUT-BPS scenarios promote prosumer PV more strongly **than the IEA scenarios (Aghahosseini et al., 2025).**

Battery storage growth closely parallels solar PV **capacity expansion.**

Reference: Aghahosseini A, Solomon AA, Bardi U, Creutzig F, Hoekstra A, Jacobson MZ, et al. (2025). More renewable energy leads to a faster transition at lower cost as revealed by comparative analysis of global energy transition scenarios (under review).

11

Unveiling the evolutionary energy performance of solar PV systems through systemwide EROI perspective

More information ▶ hasret.sahin@lut.fi

Regional EROI Patterns of Solar PV Systems
Utility-scale Solar PV System

LUT
University

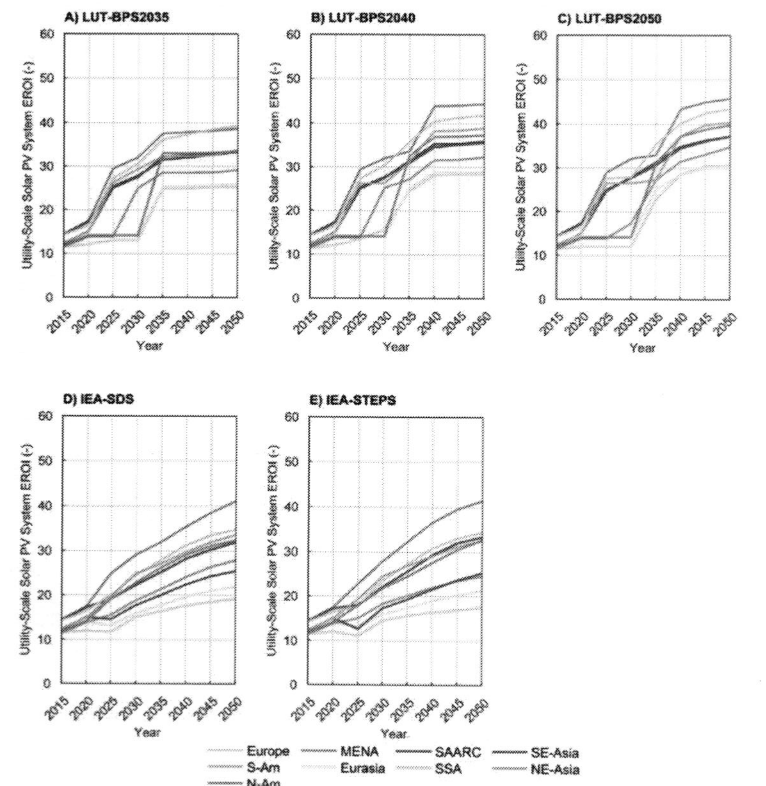

Figure 6. The regional EROI trends for solar PV utility system for nine regions.

Sub-Saharan Africa (SSA) and Middle East and North Africa (MENA):

» LUT-BPS: strongest global performers, exceeding 40 by 2050 (except LUT-BPS2035).

» IEA: MENA remains strong above 40, SSA stabilises around 35.

South America (S-Am), N-Am and SAARC:

» LUT-BPS: values in the range of 30–40 by 2050.

» IEA: more moderate, between 25 and 35.

» SAARC: 30–35 under the LUT-BPS, slightly above 30 under the IEA.

NE-Asia and SE-Asia:

» LUT-BPS: both exceed 30, with SE-Asia higher than NE-Asia (25–35 range).

» IEA: both converge, stabilising between 20 and 25.

Europe and Eurasia:

» IEA: slow progress, EROI at 15–20 by 2050.

» LUT-BPS: faster increase, reaching 25–30.

Reference: Sahin, H., Solomon, A.A., Aghahosseini, A., Breyer, C., (2026) Unveiling the evolutionary energy performance of solar photovoltaic systems through systemwide EROI perspective.

12 Unveiling the evolutionary energy performance of solar PV systems through systemwide EROI perspective
More information ▶ hasret.sahin@lut.fi

Regional EROI Patterns of Solar PV Systems
Prosumer-scale Solar PV Systems

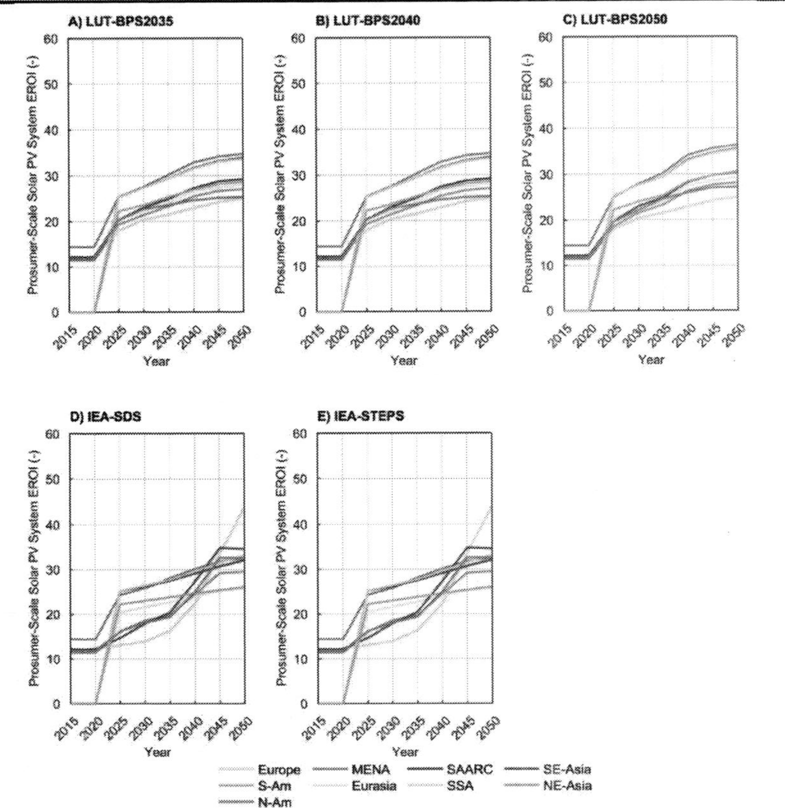

Figure 7. The regional EROI trends for solar PV prosumer system for nine regions.

SSA and MENA:

» LUT-BPS: strongest performers, exceeding 30 by 2050.

» IEA: values remain close to 30.

NE-Asia and SE-Asia:

» LUT-BPS: reach around 30 by 2050.

» IEA: SE-Asia exceeds 30, NE-Asia Asia stays near 30.

Europe:

» LUT-BPS: moderate growth to 20–25 by 2050.

» IEA: strong improvement, reaching 44 by 2050.

Eurasia:

» LUT-BPS: rises close to 30 by 2050.

» IEA: limited progress, staying between 20–25.

S-Am and N-Am:

» LUT-BPS: both reach around 30 by 2050.

» IEA: S-Am stabilises at 25–30, N-Am rises above 30.

Reference: Sahin, H., Solomon, A.A., Aghahosseini, A., Breyer, C., (2026) Unveiling the evolutionary energy performance of solar photovoltaic systems through systemwide EROI perspective.

13 Unveiling the evolutionary energy performance of solar PV systems through systemwide EROI perspective
More information ▶ hasret.sahin@lut.fi

Regional EROI Patterns of Solar PV Systems
Utility-scale Solar PV System with Grid-scale Battery Storage

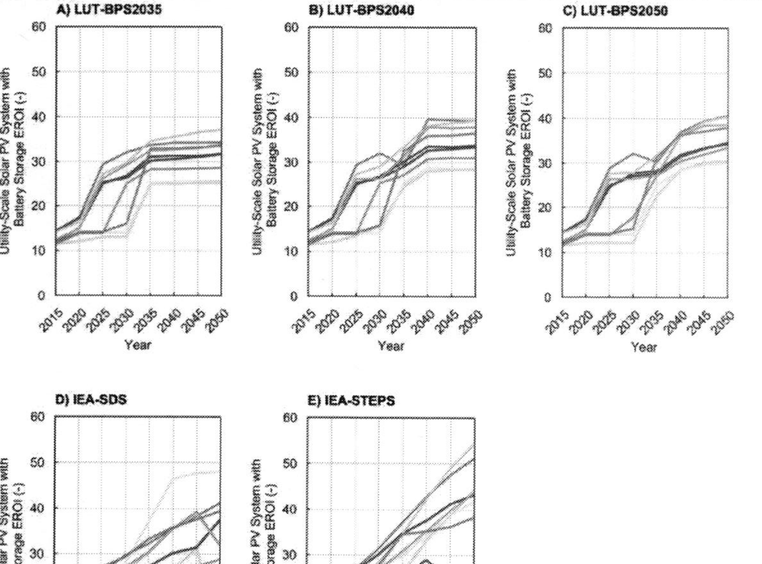

Figure 8. The regional EROI trends for solar PV utility system with complementary battery storage for nine regions.

MENA,SSA and SAARC:

» LUT-BPS: SSA and MENA above 40, SAARC around 35 by 2050.

» IEA: SSA peaks at 54 (IEA-STEPS), all three converge near 40 (IEA-SDS).

S-Am and N-Am:

» LUT-BPS: steady growth, reaching mid-30s to 40 by 2050.

» IEA: stabilise around 30.

NE-Asia and Southeast Asia:

» LUT-BPS: strong rise to 40–45 by 2050.

» IEA: remain moderate, 20–30.

Europe:

» LUT-BPS: lowest values, ~25 (LUT-BPS2030), modest rise to 30 (BPS2040).

» IEA: declines further, dropping to 14 by 2050.

Eurasia:

» LUT-BPS: slow progress, ~30 by 2050.

» IEA: stronger in SDS, reaching 48 by 2050.

Reference: Sahin, H., Solomon, A.A., Aghahosseini, A., Breyer, C., (2026) Unveiling the evolutionary energy performance of solar photovoltaic systems through systemwide EROI perspective.

Unveiling the evolutionary energy performance of solar PV systems through systemwide EROI perspective

More information ► hasret.sahin@lut.fi

Regional EROI Patterns of Solar PV Systems
Prosumer-scale Solar PV System with Prosumer-scale Battery Storage

Figure 9. The regional EROI trends for solar PV prosumer system with complementary battery storage for nine regions.

Europe, MENA, SSA and SAARC:

>> LUT-BPS: reach 30–35 by 2050, among the highest globally.

>> IEA: MENA, SSA, SAARC stay near 30; Europe rises sharply after 2035 to ~45 by 2050.

S-Am and N-Am:

>> Both grow steadily under all scenarios.

>> By 2050: North America >30 in IEA, ~25 in LUT-BPS

NE-Asia and Southeast Asia:

>> LUT-BPS: converge at ~30 by 2050.

>> IEA: SE Asia rises to nearly 35, NE Asia remains closer to 30

Eurasia:

>> Stable across scenarios.

>> Slightly below 30 by 2050.

Reference: Sahin, H., Solomon, A.A., Aghahosseini, A., Breyer, C., (2026) Unveiling the evolutionary energy performance of solar photovoltaic systems through systemwide EROI perspective.

Unveiling the evolutionary energy performance of solar PV systems through systemwide EROI perspective
More information ▶ hasret.sahin@lut.fi

Table of Contents

Overview and Motivation

Materials and Methods

>> **LUT Energy System Transition Model (LUT-ESTM)**

>> **Energy Transition Scenarios**

>> **Systemwide LUT-EROI model**

Results

>> **Synopsis of Energy Modelling Results**

>> **Regional EROI Patterns of Solar PV Systems**

>> **The Storage Trade-off: Batteries and Solar PV EROI**

Conclusions

Limitations

Unveiling the evolutionary energy performance of solar PV systems through systemwide EROI perspective
More information ▶ hasret.sahin@lut.fi

020480-016

Conclusions

>> **Systemwide EROI is shaped** more by system design than technology performance, **this highlights the** need for system-level assessment.

>> **Solar PV is the cornerstone of future energy systems, with** utility-scale PV achieving the highest returns, **while prosumer PV supports decentralisation.**

>> **Battery integration** lowers EROI **but is essential for flexibility and stability.**

>> **Limiting the energy transition period has** little effect on technology-level EROI **but leads to a significant** decrease at the system level.

>> **LUT-BPS** scenarios: **faster short-term gains, more diversification, but** lower overall EROI **due to high prosumer battery use.**

>> **IEA** scenarios: **slower early growth, but** higher long-term EROIs **from utility-scale focus and lower battery demand.**

Unveiling the evolutionary energy performance of solar PV systems through systemwide EROI perspective
More information ▶ hasret.sahin@lut.fi

020480-017

Table of Contents

Overview and Motivation

Materials and Methods

» LUT Energy System Transition Model (LUT-ESTM)

» Energy Transition Scenarios

» Systemwide LUT-EROI model

Results

» Synopsis of energy modelling results

» Regional EROI Patterns of Solar PV Systems

» The Storage Trade-off: Batteries and Solar PV EROI

Conclusions

Limitations

Unveiling the evolutionary energy performance of solar PV systems through systemwide EROI perspective
More information ► hasret.sahin@lut.fi

Limitations

>> Aggregation in spatial representation may obscure regional differences in resource availability and system performance, potentially influencing EROI outcomes.

>> The life cycle inventories for solar PV systems in ecoinvent may not fully capture the entire supply chain.

>> Extracted CED values from only one database might result in overestimation of CED values compared to reality.

>> Systemwide EROI results are further affected by complex international supply chain dependencies, such as the transport of PV components across continents, and by the absence of advanced technologies such as tunnel oxide passivated contact or perovskite PV panels, which are not yet included.

>> Recycling of materials and waste is excluded from CED estimates due to the absence of detailed process data.

>> Transmission and distribution networks are also omitted, as their contribution to overall CED is considered marginal.

Unveiling the evolutionary energy performance of solar PV systems through systemwide EROI perspective
More information ▶ hasret.sahin@lut.fi

Thank you for your attention!

& LUT University

Hasret Sahin, M.Sc., PhD.
Project Researcher
LUT University, Solar Economy Lab Research Group

✉ hasret.sahin@lut.fi

References

» Aghahosseini A, Solomon AA, Bardi U, Creutzig F, Hoekstra A, Jacobson MZ, et al. (2025). More renewable energy leads to a faster transition at lower cost as revealed by comparative analysis of global energy transition scenarios (under review).

» Bogdanov, D., Ram, M., Aghahosseini, A., Gulagi, A., Oyewo, A. S., Child, M., ... & Breyer, C. (2021). Low-cost renewable electricity as the key driver of the global energy transition towards sustainability. Energy, 227, 120467. https://doi.org/10.1016/j.energy.2021.120467

» Bogdanov, Breyer et al., 2021. Full energy sector transition towards 100% renewable energy supply: integrating power, heat, transport and industry sectors including desalination. Applied Energy, 283, 116273. https://doi.org/10.1016/j.apenergy.2020.116273

» Murphy, D. J., & Hall, C. A. (2010). Year in review—EROI or energy return on (energy) invested. Annals of the new york academy of sciences, 1185(1), 102-118. https://doi.org/10.1111/j.1749-6632.2009.05282.x

» Sahin, H., Solomon, A. A., Aghahosseini, A., & Breyer, C. (2024). Systemwide energy return on investment in a sustainable transition towards net zero power systems. Nature Communications, 15(1), 208. https://doi.org/10.1038/s41467-023-44232-9

» Sahin, H., Solomon, A.A., Aghahosseini, A., Breyer, C., (2026) Unveiling the evolutionary energy performance of solar photovoltaic systems through systemwide EROI perspective.

» Solomon, A. A., Sahin, H., & Breyer, C. (2024). The pitfall in designing future electrical power systems without considering energy return on investment in planning. Applied Energy, 369, 123570. https://doi.org/10.1016/j.apenergy.2024.123570

Unveiling the evolutionary energy performance of solar PV systems through systemwide EROI perspective
More information ▶ hasret.sahin@lut.fi

LUT
University
BACKUP SLIDES

CED Value Modifications

Solar PV technologies

- PV module performance has continuously increased; at the same time, the solar PV industry has improved material requirements for the balance of the systems. These combined enhancements have resulted in decreases in cumulative energy demand (CED).

- CED values were recalculated using an average energy learning rate (ELR) of 14% until 2030, following the estimate of Görig and Breyer (2016).

- Note that the CED values in the ecoinvent database report CED values in conventional primary energy units without accounting for energy quality differences of natural energy resources, so standardisation to "joules" with appropriate "conversion factors" is needed to harmonise all energy inputs to the quality level of electricity (Solomon et al., 2024).

- The modified CED values are reorganised considering the global annual production of solar PV technologies, and reference CED values are founded for solar PV systems.

- All CED values are presented as MJ_{el}/kW.

Table 1. Reference CED values for solar PV system from 2015 to 2050.

Reference CED values for solar PV systems (MJ_{el}/kW) (Sahin et al., 2024)	
2015	12,939
2020	10,204
2025	8478
2030	7504
2035	6865
2040	6505
2045	6265
2050	6229

References:

Görig, M., & Breyer, C. (2016). Energy Learning Curves of PV Systems. Environmental Progress & Sustainable Energy, 35(3), 914–923. https://doi.org/10.1002/ep.12340.

Sahin, H., Solomon, A. A., Aghahosseini, A., & Breyer, C. (2024). Systemwide energy return on investment in a sustainable transition towards net zero power systems. Nature Communications, 15(1), 208.

Solomon, A. A., Sahin, H., & Breyer, C. (2024). The pitfall in designing future electrical power systems without considering energy return on investment in planning. Applied Energy, 369, 123570.

Unveiling the evolutionary energy performance of solar PV systems through systemwide EROI perspective
More information ▶ hasret.sahin@lut.fi

CED Value Modifications

Battery storage technologies

» Utility-scale battery and prosumer-scale battery LCIs are derived and adjusted based on the future capacities reported by Xu et al. (2020), while ELR values are taken from Hsieh et al. (2019). In the ecoinvent v3.7.1 LCA database, no data exists for specific battery systems.

» Based on literature reviews and capacity considerations, the CED values for utility-scale and prosumer-scale battery storage are assumed to be the same.

Table 2. ELR implementation on battery storage CED value.

Implementation of ELR on CED values of battery storage (Sahin et al., 2024)		
	Reference CED values for battery systems (MJ_{el}/kWh)	ELR (%) (Hsieh et al., 2019)
CED values obtained from the literature	1654	N/A
2015	1654	5.0%
2020	1346	5.0%
2025	1237	4.5%
2030	1157	4.5%
2035	1152	4.0%
2040	1110	4.0%
2045	1075	4.0%
2050	1046	4.0%

References:

Hsieh, I. Y. L., Pan, M. S., Chiang, Y. M., & Green, W. H. (2019). Learning only buys you so much: Practical limits on battery price reduction. Applied Energy, 239(January), 218–224. https://doi.org/10.1016/j.apenergy.2019.01.138.

Sahin, H., Solomon, A. A., Aghahosseini, A., & Breyer, C. (2024). Systemwide energy return on investment in a sustainable transition towards net zero power systems. Nature Communications, 15(1), 208.

Xu, C., Dai, Q., Gaines, L. et al. Future material demand for automotive lithium-based batteries. Commun Mater 1, 99 (2020). doi.org/10.1038/s43246-020-0009.

Unveiling the evolutionary energy performance of solar PV systems through systemwide EROI perspective
More information ▶ hasret.sahin@lut.fi

References

» Görig, M., & Breyer, C. (2016). Energy Learning Curves of PV Systems. Environmental Progress & Sustainable Energy, 35(3), 914–923. https://doi.org/10.1002/ep.12340

» Hsieh, I. Y. L., Pan, M. S., Chiang, Y. M., & Green, W. H. (2019). Learning only buys you so much: Practical limits on battery price reduction. Applied Energy, 239(January), 218–224. https://doi.org/10.1016/j.apenergy.2019.01.138 .

» Sahin, H., Solomon, A. A., Aghahosseini, A., & Breyer, C. (2024). Systemwide energy return on investment in a sustainable transition towards net zero power systems. Nature Communications, 15(1), 208. https://doi.org/10.1038/s41467-023-44232-9

» Solomon, A. A., Sahin, H., & Breyer, C. (2024). The pitfall in designing future electrical power systems without considering energy return on investment in planning. Applied Energy, 369, 123570. https://doi.org/10.1016/j.apenergy.2024.123570

» Xu, C., Dai, Q., Gaines, L. et al. Future material demand for automotive lithium-based batteries. Commun Mater 1, 99 (2020). https://doi.org/10.1038/s43246-020-00095-x

Unveiling the evolutionary energy performance of solar PV systems through systemwide EROI perspective
More information ▶ hasret.sahin@lut.fi

Projections of PV Power Potential Worldwide: an Update Using CMIP6 Global Climate Models

Pau Mercade Ruiz[1], Gerardo Guerra[1], Gaetana Anamiati[1], Lars Landberg[2]
[1]GreenPowerMonitor a DNV Company
[2]DNV Denmark

25 September 2025

020481-001

Contents

- Objective

- PV power model

- Modelling challenges

- Data specifications

- Results

- Conclusions

DNV

020481-002

Objective

Project PV power production into the future and assess the impact of climate change on future PV power production

Motivation

- World share of electricity production from solar is increasing.

- Electricity production from solar is susceptible to changing climate conditions.

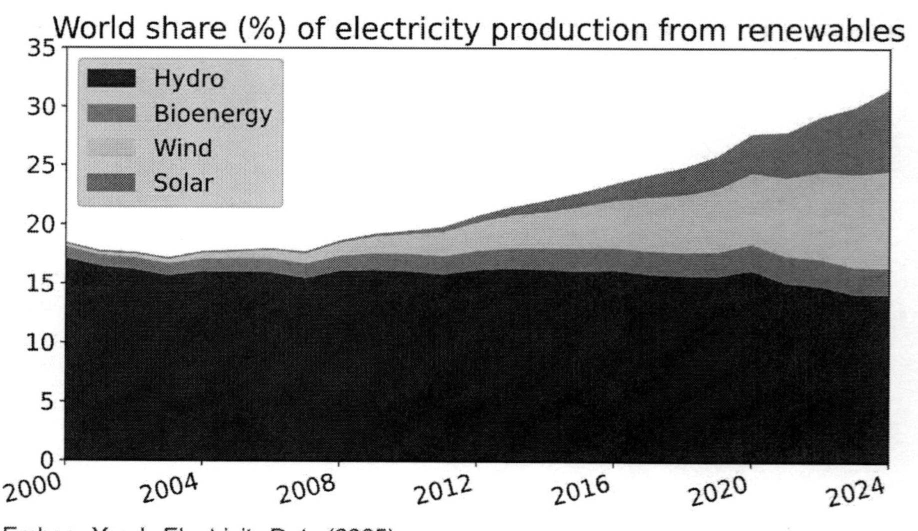

Ember - Yearly Electricity Data (2025).
Data retrieved from:
https://ember-energy.org/data/yearly-electricity-data/

DNV

PV power model

1. PV Power Potential (PVP) is defined as the ratio of PV power produced by the PV system to its nominal power.

2. PVP can be modelled as a linear combination of solar irradiance, the product (*) irradiance * irradiance, irradiance * air temperature, and irradiance * wind speed.

3. Future irradiance, air temperature and wind speed can be modelled using Global Climate Models (GCMs).

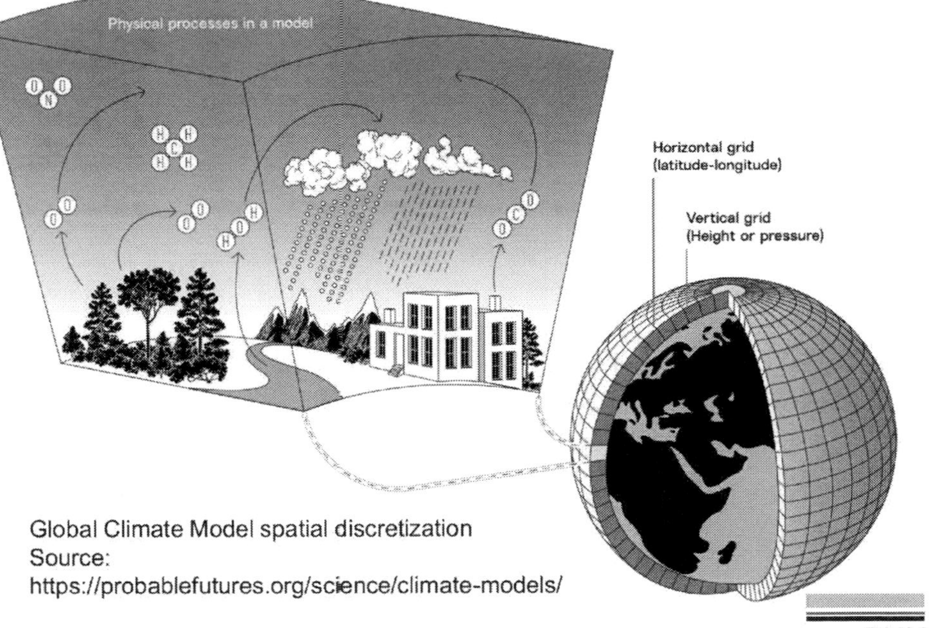

Global Climate Model spatial discretization
Source:
https://probablefutures.org/science/climate-models/

DNV

020481-004

Climate modelling challenges

- Global Climate Models (GCMs) are computationally expensive to run.

- The Coupled Model Intercomparison Project Phase 6 (CMIP6) is a global climate modelling project coordinated by the World Climate Research Programme (WRCP).

- It involves numerous international modelling groups who run simulations of past, present, and future climates using different GCMs to better understand climate change and improve GCMs.

- Large amounts of data have been generated from these climate modelling endeavors, which are then archived and made available to researchers worldwide through the Earth System Grid Federation (ESGF).

DNV

020481-005

PV power potential modelling challenges

- PV Power Potential (PVP) model is nonlinear and meant for instantaneous evaluation.

- PVP model is nonlinear and thus it may render inaccurate results when using daily and monthly Global Climate Model (GCM) data.

- However, daily and monthly GCM data are readily available and computationally inexpensive to handle.

- A method to generate hourly data is developed based on modulating historical hourly data to prescribed monthly GCM data.

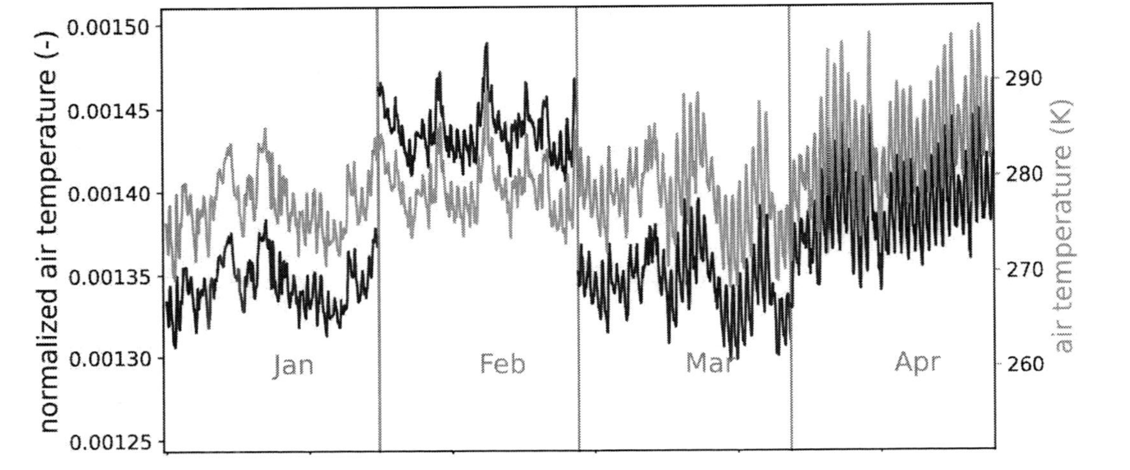

DNV

Data specifications

- Monthly Global Climate Model (GCM)-simulated solar irradiance, air temperature and wind speed.
  - Data retrieved from the Coupled Model Intercomparison Project Phase 6 (CMIP6) database for the historical and SSP5-8.5 experiments.
  - Ensemble consisting of 10 different GCMs.
- Hourly reanalysis solar irradiance, air temperature and wind speed.
  - Data retrieved from the European Centre for Medium-Range Weather Forecasts (ECMRWF) Reanalysis v5 (ERA5) dataset.
- Quantile Delta Mapping (QDM) performed on CMIP6 projections based on historical ERA5 data.

DNV

020481-007

Results period 2061-2090 vs historical 1991-2020

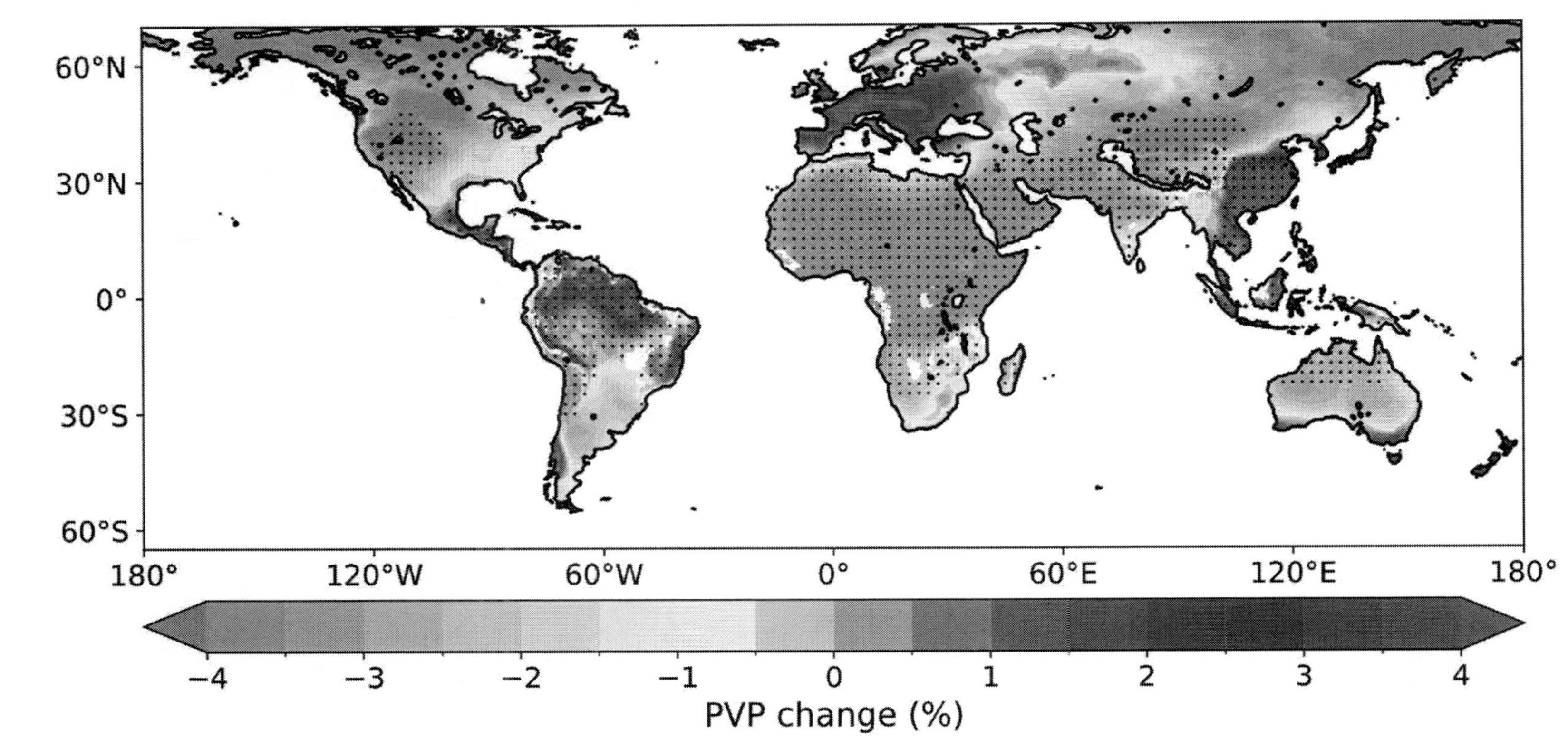

DNV

020481-008

Results period 2061-2090 vs historical 1991-2020

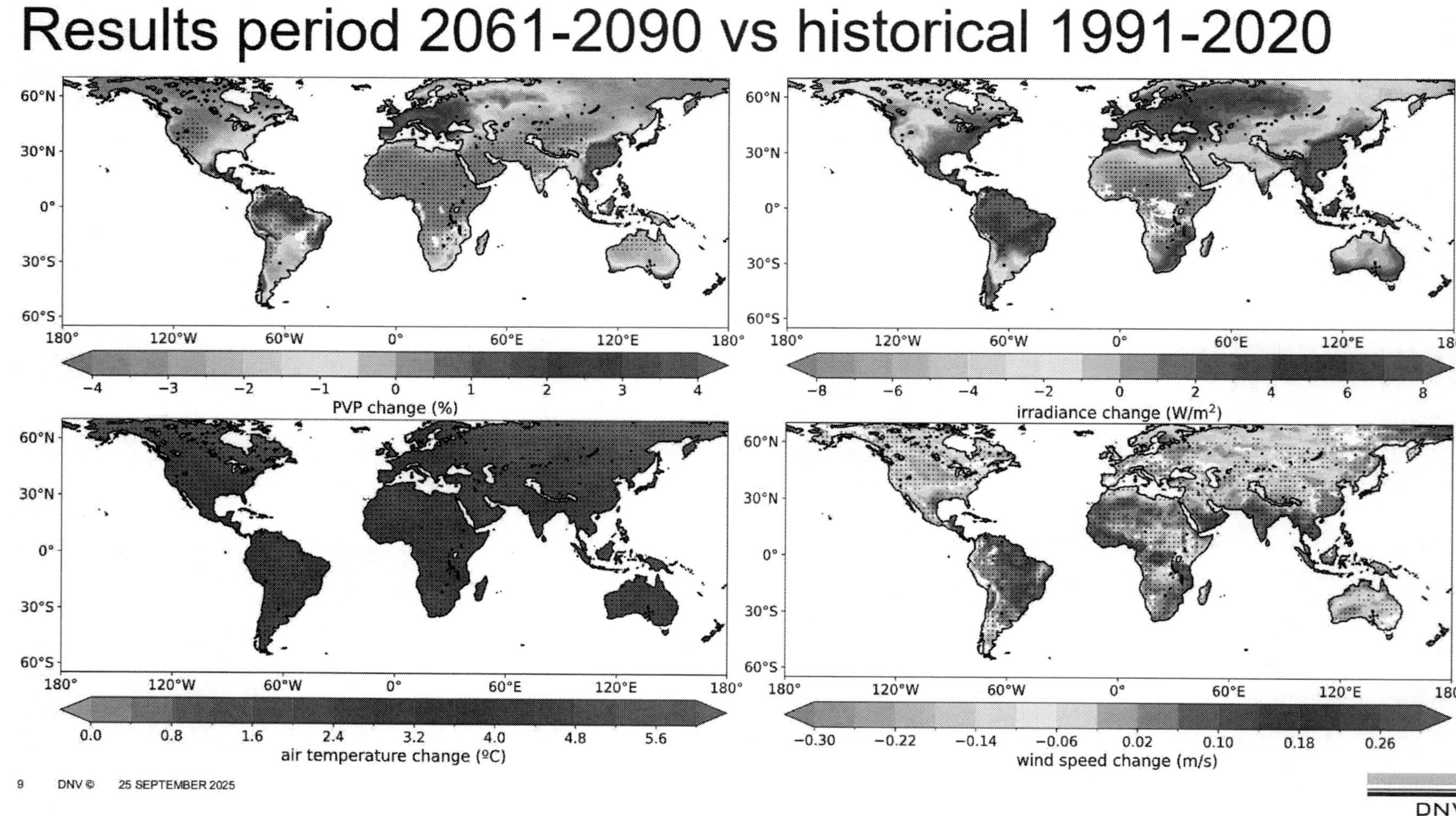

DNV

Results period 2061-2090 vs historical 1991-2020

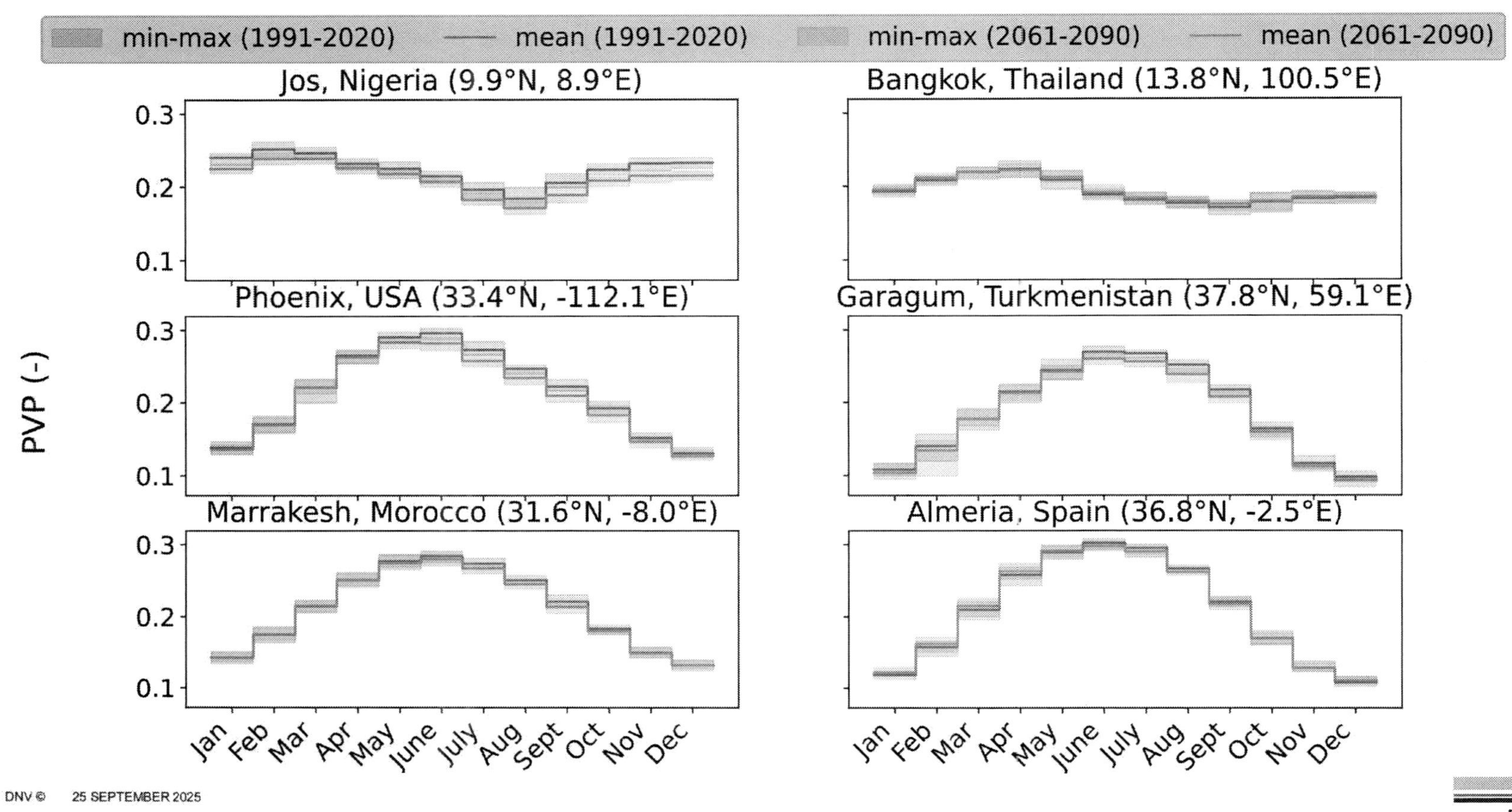

020481-010

DNV

Results period 2061-2090 vs historical 1991-2020

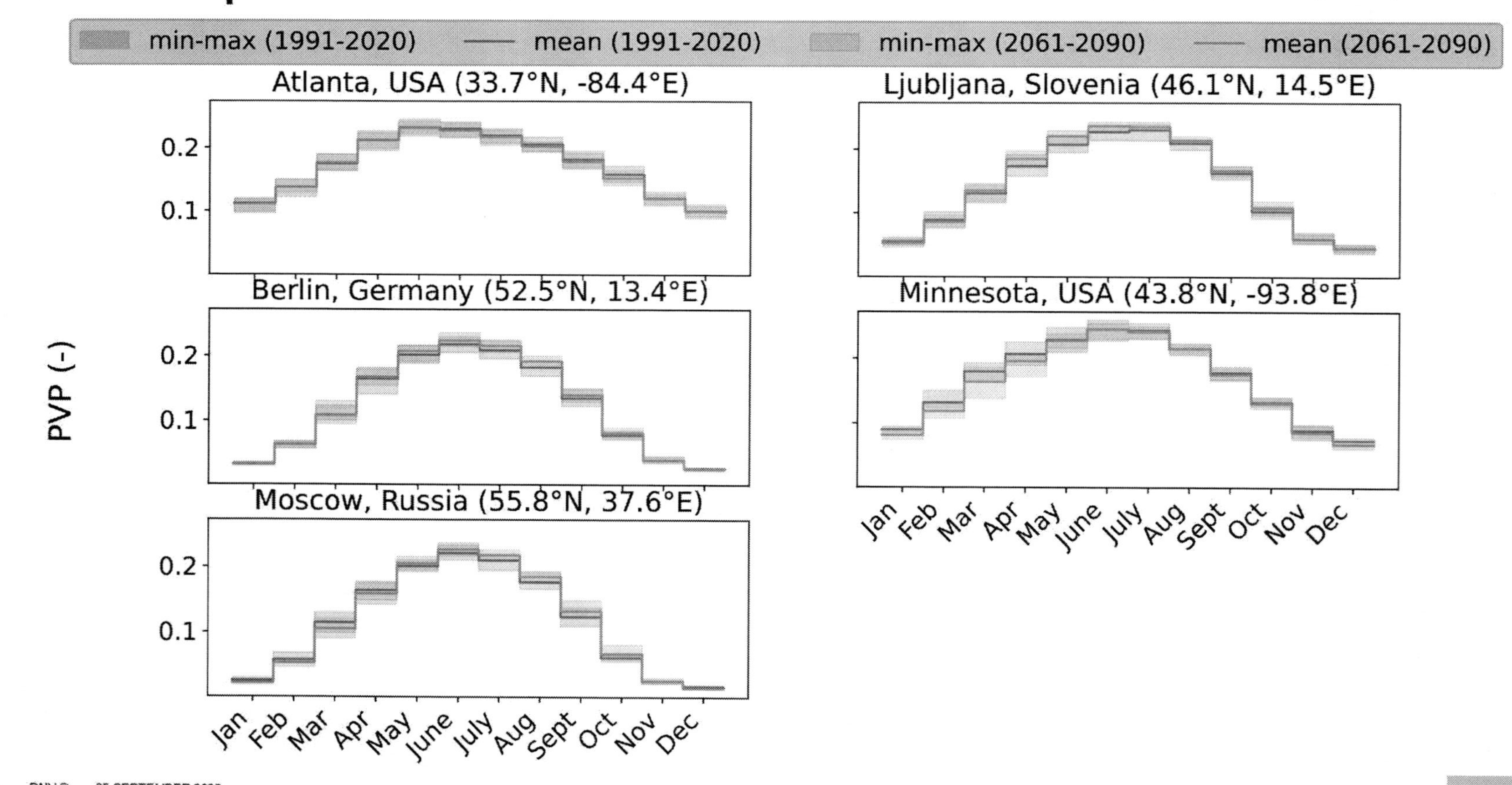

020481-011

DNV

Conclusions

- A method has been developed to enable hourly-resolution climate-dependent nonlinear models be evaluated using monthly Global Climate Model (GCM) data.

- The method has been used to project PVP into the future to study the impact of climate change on the future PVP.

- The results show no major changes in future PVP assuming the worst-case high-emissions scenario.

- Climate modelling has its limitations and should be considered when interpreting these results.

- There are other aspects of PV systems not considered in this study, such as PV efficiency and reliability, that might be more greatly impacted by climate change.

DNV

020481-012

WHEN TRUST MATTERS

www.dnv.com

13   DNV ©   25 SEPTEMBER 2025

DNV

This presentation was selected by the Sc. Committee of the EU PVSEC 2025 for submission of a full paper to one of the EU PVSEC's collaborating peer-reviewed journals.

THE COST OF OWNERSHIP AND MINIMUM SUSTAINABLE PRICE OF POLO BJ CELLS PRODUCED IN GERMANY

Gomez Trillos, Juan Camilo [1]; Buddana, Viswa Harinath [1]; Papantoni, Veatriki [1]; Min, Byungsul [2]; Junge, Sebastian [2]; Kähler, Jan-Dirk [3]; Schneider, Friedrich [4]; Brendel, Rolf [2]; Vogt, Thomas [1]

1 DLR Institute of Networked Energy Systems, Carl-von-Ossietzky-Straße 15, 26129 Oldenburg, Germany
2 Institute for Solar Energy Research Hamelin (ISFH), Am Ohrberg 1, 31860 Emmerthal, Germany
3 Centrotherm International AG, Württemberger Str. 31, 89143 Blaubeuren, Germany
4 LPKF SolarQuipment GmbH

ABSTRACT: This study analyses the Cost of Ownership (CoO) and the Minimum Sustainable Price (MSP) of producing POLO BJ solar cells in a 5 GWp/a production facility in Germany compared to a facility with equal output but producing cells of the PERC concept. Assuming that the POLO BJ concept can achieve a cell efficiency of 24.2% in industrial production, the estimated CoO is 5.79 ¢/Wp, whereas the MSP is 7.16 ¢/Wp. These were found lower than for PERC, assumed with an efficiency of 23.1%, which resulted in a CoO of 6.31¢/Wp and a MSP of 7.75 ¢/Wp, respectively. The higher superior efficiency of POLO BJ also results in lower Levelized Cost of Electricity (LCOE) of between 3.02 and 3.32 ¢/kWh, depending on the module type, which is 0.14 ¢/kWh less than for systems fitted with PERC cells. Overall, this study suggests that POLO BJ solar cells are a cost-effective alternative to PERC cells.

Keywords: Cost of Ownership, Minimum Sustainable Price, Levelized Cost of Electricity, POLO BJ, PERC

1 INTRODUCTION

The global photovoltaic (PV) industry is currently experiencing a rapid growth. Annual installations reached 447 GWp in 2023 and global cumulative installed capacity of approximately 1.6 TWp by the same year [1].

China is currently dominating the PV supply chain, accounting for 92% of polysilicon production, 98% of wafer production and 84.6% of module production [2, 3]. Despite significant growth in PV deployment, Europe's PV manufacturing sector only represents 4% of polysilicon production and an estimate of 2.3 GWp*a-1 cell production capacity [4]. In addition, Germany has the largest share of the EU market, but domestic manufacturing remains modest, with an estimated 1.8 GWP*a^{-1} module manufacturing capacity [4, 5].

Besides the market situation, new technological developments in the field are emerging. The Aluminium Back Surface Field (Al-BSF), standard of the industry until 2013, was succeeded by the Passivated Emitter and Rear Cell (PERC) concept. Predicted physical limitations of the PERC concept at an efficiency of around 24% urged the industry to find new alternatives [6]. Recently, the Tunnel Oxide Passivated Contact (TOPCon) concept has become the incumbent cell type in the market, making use - in contrast to Al-BSF and PERC - of n-type silicon. However, other possibilities are the subject of research, which might have potential towards commercialization.

As a possible alternative, we investigate the p-type back junction (BJ) solar cell featuring n+-type passivating poly-Si on oxide (POLO) rear contacts. With a similar process flow as the well-known PERC concept, the POLO BJ concept could be produced by PERC production lines with minor modifications. POLO BJ has a leaner process flow compared to the current mainstream TOPCon concept, because it has fewer processing steps, including the absence of the boron diffusion. In addition, the POLO BJ cell concept allows up to 50 % less Ag consumption compared to TOPCon, as it uses Al metallization on the front side instead. Finally, further innovations are possible, such as an upgrade to the POLO IBC (interdigitated back contact) concept with only one additional laser process step or an Ag-free metallization by replacing the Ag rear contact with Al. Although the POLO BJ concept has demonstrated high efficiencies of up to 24.2% in practice, it has not undergone commercial production so far [7].

Some previous publications have addressed the manufacturing costs of photovoltaic cells; however, they focus on heterojunction solar cells [8], PERC cells [9, 10] or TOPCon cells [11, 12]. As the manufacturing costs of POLO BJ in Europe have not yet been assessed, this publication fills this research gap by performing a bottom-up cost analysis of the production of POLO BJ cells considering a production capacity of 5 GWp*a-1 in Germany.

2 METHODOLOGY

The main metrics assessed in this analysis were the Cost of Ownership (CoO), and the Minimum Sustainable Price (MSP) of POLO BJ cells. Two alternative manufacturing sequences using either a wet chemical etching process (POLO BJ-W) or laser ablation (POLO BJ-L) for single-side SiO_2 removal were assessed for POLO BJ, as shown in Figure 1. All these calculations were contrasted against the production of PERC cells under similar assumptions.

Figure 1. Comparison of the assumed production sequence for POLO BJ using wet-chemistry (POLO BJ-W), POLO BJ using laser-ablation (POLO BJ-L) and PERC. Source:

10.4229/EUPVSEC2025/5DO.11.6
020482-001

Own figure.

Additionally, assuming that these cells are integrated into modules and PV systems, the Levelized Cost of Electricity (LCOE) of electricity produced with POLO BJ cells was also estimated.

A production capacity of 5 GWp*a^{-1} of POLO BJ PV cells was assumed as the basis for the following calculations. For the calculation, a power conversion efficiency of 24.2% was assumed as the baseline for POLO BJ cells [7]. The wafer format assumed for the production of POLO was M12/G12.

For a fair comparison of the production of POLO BJ cells against PERC cells, the production of the latter concept was assumed with the same output (5 GWp*a^{-1}) and wafer format (M12/G12). For PERC, a maximum efficiency of 23.1% was assumed, in line with the maximum efficiency reported for spot prices in the market [13]. The same geographical scope for the production (Germany), same base prices of chemicals and tool costs were assumed for PERC, with differences only in the process steps required for cell production and the resulting power conversion efficiency.

2.1 Cost of Ownership

The Cost of Ownership (CoO) methodology was used to estimate the cost of producing POLO BJ cells. A Microsoft Excel® template, adapted from a SEMI and VDMA template, was used to calculate the costs step-by-step for the entire production sequence [14, 15]. Factors like capital costs of tools, throughput, footprint, chemical and gas consumption, electricity consumption and labour costs were considered in the analysis for each of the analysed alternatives.

2.2 Minimum Sustainable Price

To obtain comparable results against market prices, the Minimum Sustainable Price (MSP) was also calculated, considering capital costs, operational expenditures and taxes. The approach followed in this study was previously described by Powell et al. 2015 [16]. The calculations assumed 12.5% of operative expenditures including sales, administration, research and development, 3 months of net working capital, 7-year depreciation time for tools and 20-year depreciation time for facilities, and 8% nominal weighted average cost of capital (WACC)

2.3 Levelized Cost of Electricity

The Levelized Cost of Electricity (LCOE) was calculated for utility-scale PV plants using POLO BJ and PERC cells, considering monofacial (glass-backsheet) and bifacial modules (glass-glass). The module production costs and final prices were not accounted in a bottom-up way, but considered by applying a mark-up factor to the total material cost of the modules. Additional cost items for system integration, such as inverters, racking, and installation costs were also considered. Installation locations in Germany and Spain, with different irradiance conditions were considered in the analysis. Temperature corrections, cell-to-module (CTM) losses, and geometrical losses in modules were also assumed. Moreover, a performance ratio of 0.86 and a system lifetime of 25 years for modules and 15 years for inverters was also considered. Finally, a nominal Weighted Average Cost of Capital (WACC) of 5% and an operational expenditure

(OPEX) of 1% CAPEX*a^{-1} were also assumed in the LCOE calculation.

3 RESULTS

The following section summarizes the main results of the analyses carried out in this study, starting by the CoO and MSP, which reflect the cell producer perspective, and moving on to the LCOE, reflecting the final electricity consumer perspective.

3.1. CoO and MSP of POLO BJ and PERC cells

The results summarized in Figure 2 reveal that the CoO of POLO BJ cells are lower compared to PERC cells. The CoO value obtained for PERC cells considering local cell production were 6.31 ¢*Wp^{-1}. Furthermore, the CoO obtained for POLO BJ-W and POLO BJ-L were 5.98 and 5.79 ¢*Wp^{-1}, respectively. Therefore, this translates to a reduction of 5.3% in the CoO of POLO BJ-W compared to PERC and a higher reduction of 8.3% when the POLO BJ-L sequence is considered. The lower costs associated with POLO BJ-L compared to POLO BJ-W can be attributed to the use of a laser process for a one-side SiO2 removal, which reduces chemical and electricity consumption, in addition to the capital costs due to slightly higher throughput of the laser tools.

A similar trend can be found for the MSP, also shown in Figure 2, revealing that POLO BJ-L cells can achieve the lowest value among the considered alternatives, at 7.16 ¢*Wp^{-1}, followed closely by POLO BJ-W cells with an MSP of 7.38 ¢*Wp^{-1} and finally by PERC cells with an MSP of 7.75 ¢*Wp^{-1}. Therefore, the POLO BJ allows a reduction of between 4.7% and 7.6% compared to the PERC alternative. In contrast to the CoO calculations, the MSP calculation considers operating expenses, income tax and capital costs not included in the CoO but also necessary for a financially sustainable operation of a company, which add between 1.37 and 1.44 ¢*Wp^{-1} to the overall CoO, representing a significant 18.6-19.2% of the total MSP in each of the cases considered.

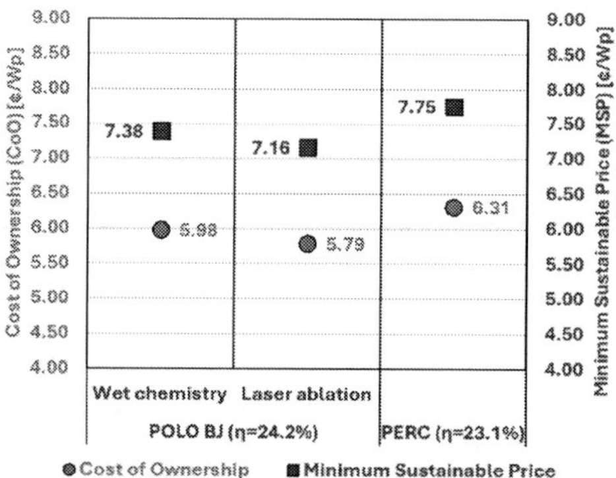

Figure 2. Cost of Ownership (CoO) and Minimum Sustainable Price (MSP) for the POLO BJ-W (Wet chemistry), POLO BJ-L (Laser ablation) and PERC cells. Source: Own figure.

3.2 LCOE of Systems with POLO BJ and PERC cells

Figure 3 presents the results of the LCOE for 5 MWp

utility scale PV systems using modules fitted with POLO BJ-W, POLO BJ-L, and PERC cells in both monofacial and bifacial configurations. According to the results, bifacial glass-glass modules generally result in a lower LCOE compared to monofacial glass-backsheet modules, despite being more expensive to produce. In short, the higher cost incurred to be assumed in the production of these modules types is offset by the additional electricity output due to rear capture of reflected solar irradiance.

The comparison of LCOE results for two selected locations - Germany and Spain - reveals a lower LCOE in Spain due to the higher irradiance, which is representative of Southern European Conditions. In

Germany, the LCOE for systems using monofacial glass-backsheet modules with PERC cells was calculated at 5.19 $¢*kWh^{-1}$. If higher-efficiency POLO BJ-W cells are considered instead, this value decreases to 5.00 $¢*kWh^{-1}$, and further drops to 4.98 $¢*kWh^{-1}$ when using POLO BJ-L cells. As for the results in Spain, the LCOE values for systems with monofacial modules containing PERC, POLO BJ-W, and POLO BJ-L cells are 3.46, 3.34, and 3.32 $¢*kWh^{-1}$, respectively.

The use of bifacial modules decreases further the costs, achieving LCOE values of 4.78, 4.60, and 4.58 $¢*kWh^{-1}$ for PERC-based, POLO BJ-W-based, and POLO BJ-L-based modules, respectively. When the conditions in Spain are considered, the LCOE values decrease further to 3.16, 3.04, and 3.02 $¢*kWh^{-1}$ for systems making use of PERC-based modules, POLO BJ-W cells, and POLO BJ-L cells. Overall, the use of POLO BJ cells instead of PERC cells can lead to a reduction in LCOE of up to 0.20 in Germany or up to 0.14 $¢*kWh^{-1}$ in Spain. These findings suggest that POLO BJ cells offer a more economically viable option for PV systems, particularly when used in bifacial configurations.

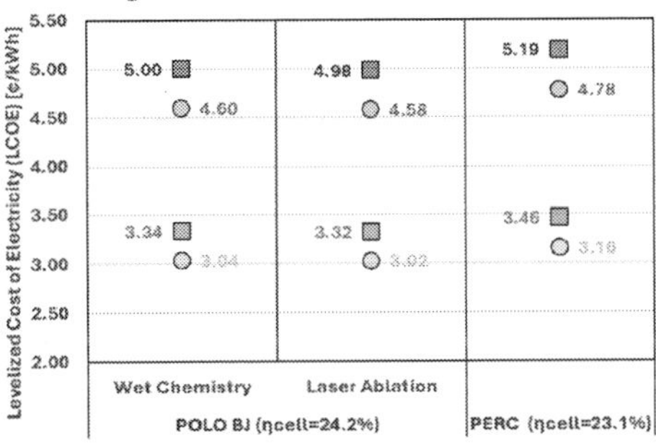

Figure 3. Comparison of the levelized cost of electricity (LCOE) for systems using monofacial glass -backsheet modules and bifacial glass-glass modules built with POLO BJ-W (η_{cell}=24.2%), POLO BJ-L (η_{cell}=24.2%) and PERC cells (η_{cell}=23.1%). Values for Germany and Spain are presented for comparison.

4 DISCUSSION

4.1 Comparison against other studies

Although comparing the results of this study to other publications' results is challenging due to variations in assumptions, production sequences, and calculation methods, some comparisons against other studies were made. To start with this, a study by Kafle et al. 2021 reported "all-in cell" production costs of 11.9 cents per watt-peak ($¢*Wp^{-1}$) for bi-PERC cells and between 12.9-13.2 $¢*Wp^{-1}$ for TOPCon cells [12]. In contrast, this study found minimum selling price (MSP) values of 7.75 $¢*Wp^{-1}$ for PERC and 7.16-7.38 $¢*Wp^{-1}$ for POLO BJ cells. These differences can be attributed to various factors, including production capacity, labour costs, CAPEX, and wafer prices.

Another study by Chang et al. 2022 predicted production costs ranging from 10 to 18 $¢*Wp^{-1}$ by 2025 for PERC cells with a module efficiency of 22.9-25% [10]. The median cost distribution for PERC modules produced in Italy was estimated at 15 $¢*Wp^{-1}$, which is higher than the costs found in this study for monofacial and bifacial glass-backsheet PERC modules (12.66 $¢*Wp^{-1}$ and 15.29 $¢*Wp^{-1}$, respectively) [10]. The results for POLO BJ-W and POLO BJ-L cells fell within a range of 11.84-14.57 $¢*Wp^{-1}$.

A recent study by Nold et al. (2024) reported an average MSP of 12.8 ¢Wp-1 for fully locally produced TOPCon cell manufacturing in Europe [11]. When considering only wafer-to-cell conversion, an MSP of 5.2 $¢*Wp^{-1}$ was found, which is comparable to the MSP of 5.43 $¢*Wp^{-1}$ calculated for POLO BJ-L cells after subtracting wafer costs in our study. Therefore, our results are approximately 4.4% higher than those reported by Nold et al. 2024. This difference can be attributed to variations in overhead, financing, and profit values, as well as equipment and factory depreciation costs.

4.2. Comparison against market prices

The LCOE for PV electricity at utility-scale was reported by IRENA to be 4.4 $¢*kWh^{-1}$ in 2023, with a range of 3.1-11.0 $¢*kWh^{-1}$. Specifically, in Germany, the LCOE was estimated at 6.3 $¢*kWh^{-1}$, being higher than the results obtained in this study, ranging from 4.58 to 5.19 $¢*kWh^{-1}$ [17].

Regarding prices of cells and modules, PV Infolink's latest data shows that 23.1% PERC cells in M12 format are priced at 3.7 $¢*Wp^{-1}$, while high, low, and average prices for PERC cells in M10 format are reported at 8.5, 3.5, and 3.6 $¢*Wp^{-1}$, respectively, mainly based on Chinese production [13]. The estimated Minimum Selling Price (MSP) results in this study are therefore on the upper side of this range when considering local production, which in turn is affected by higher electricity prices and labour costs.

4.3. Limitations

Main limitations of this study include the sole focus on cell production and a simplified approach for module production rather than a bottom-up method. In addition, silicon wafer was considered as market-supplied, but integrated production of poly-silicon, wafers and modules can also have synergies not accounted here. To provide a more comprehensive understanding, future studies should consider the production of polysilicon, wafers, cells, and modules within an integrated supply chain framework.

In addition, other advanced concepts like POLO Interdigitated Back Contact (IBC) with a higher efficiency potential were not considered within this study. Finally, with the growing market share of the n-type silicon based technology TOPCon, a comparative analysis between POLO-based technologies and TOPCon is necessary to provide a fair assessment of their relative merits. This comparison should be based on common assumptions to ensure comparability and provide a clearer understanding of the strengths and weaknesses of each technology.

5 CONCLUSIONS

This study examined the Cost of Ownership and Minimum Sustainable Price of POLO BJ cells assumed with an efficiency of 24.2% and produced using a wet-chemistry and laser-ablation processes in comparison with PERC cells assumed with an efficiency of 23.1%.

The Cost of Ownership (CoO) for POLO BJ cells produced using the wet-chemistry and laser-ablation processes were estimated at 5.98 and 5.79 ¢*Wp^{-1}, respectively, which is lower than the CoO for PERC cells at 6.31 ¢*Wp^{-1}. In the same line, the Minimum Sustainable Price (MSP) for POLO BJ cells was calculated to be lower than that of PERC cells, at 7.38 ¢*Wp^{-1} and 7.16 ¢*Wp^{-1}, respectively, compared to 7.75 ¢*Wp^{-1} for PERC cells.

The impact on the final electricity cost of systems using POLO BJ and PERC was also assessed by means of the levelized cost of electricity (LCOE) cells. The LCOE for monofacial glass-backsheet modules built with POLO BJ cells via laser ablation was calculated to be 3.32 ¢*kWh^{-1} in southern European conditions, while bifacial glass-glass modules had an LCOE of 3.02 ¢*kWh^{-1}. Overall, results CoO, MSP and LCOE show cost advantages of the POLO BJ concept compared to the established PERC concept.

6 ACKNOWLEDGEMENTS

This work was financially supported by the German Federal Ministry for Economic Affairs and Energy (BMWE) under funding code number 03EE1150B (APOLON).

7 REFERENCES

[1] SolarPower Europe, *Global Market Outlook for Solar Power 2024-2028.* [Online]. Available: https://api.solarpowereurope.org/uploads/Global_ Market_Outlook_for_Solar_Power_2024_ a083b6dcd5.pdf (accessed: Jul. 9 2025).

[2] G. Masson, M. de l'Epine, and I. Kaizuka, *Trends in Photovoltaic Applications 2024.* [Online]. Available: https://iea-pvps.org/wp-content/uploads/ 2024/10/IEA-PVPS-Task-1-Trends-Report-2024.pdf (accessed: Jul. 11 2025).

[3] International Energy Agency, *Special Report on Solar PV Gloval Supply Chains.* [Online]. Available: https://iea.blob.core.windows.net/assets/ d2ee601d-6b1a-4cd2-a0e8-db02dc64332c/ SpecialReportonSolarPVGlobalSupplyChains.pdf (accessed: Jul. 9 2025).

[4] Sinovoltaics Group Limited, *Europe Solar Supply Chain Map - Edition 1 - 2025.* [Online]. Available: https://sinovoltaics.com/ (accessed: Jul. 11 2025).

[5] EnergyTrend, *European Solar Industry: Capacity, Challenges, and Future Prospects.* [Online]. Available: https://www.energytrend.com/news/ 20240510-46909.html

[6] B. Min *et al.*, "A Roadmap Toward 24% Efficient PERC Solar Cells in Industrial Mass Production," *IEEE J. Photovoltaics*, vol. 7, no. 6, pp. 1541–1550, 2017, doi:10.1109/JPHOTOV.2017.2749007.

[7] B. Min *et al.*, "24.2% efficient POLO back junction solar cell with an AlO x /SiN y dielectric stack from an industrial-scale direct plasma-enhanced chemical vapor deposition system," *Progress in Photovoltaics*, vol. 33, no. 1, pp. 236–244, 2025, doi: 10.1002/pip.3828.

[8] A. Louwen, W. van Sark, R. Schropp, and A. Faaij, "A cost roadmap for silicon heterojunction solar cells," *Solar Energy Materials and Solar Cells*, vol. 147, pp. 295–314, 2016, doi: 10.1016/j.solmat.2015.12.026.

[9] N. L. Chang *et al.*, "A techno-economic analysis method for guiding research and investment directions for c-Si photovoltaics and its application to Al-BSF, PERC, LDSE and advanced hydrogenation," *Sustainable Energy Fuels*, vol. 2, no. 5, pp. 1007–1019, 2018, doi: 10.1039/C8SE00047F.

[10] N. L. Chang, M. Dehghanimadvar, and R. Egan, "The cost of risk mitigation—Diversifying the global solar PV supply chain," *Joule*, vol. 6, no. 12, pp. 2686–2688, 2022, doi: 10.1016/j.joule.2022.12.003.

[11] S. Nold *et al.*, "Comparative Global PV Manufacturing Cost and Sustainable Pricing Assessment: China, Southeast Asia, India, USA, and Europe," EU-PVSEC2024 - Vienna. Accessed: Jul. 14 2025. [Online]. Available: https:// userarea.eupvsec.org/proceedings/EU-PVSEC-2024/5EO.3.2/

[12] B. Kafle, B. S. Goraya, S. Mack, F. Feldmann, S. Nold, and J. Rentsch, "TOPCon – Technology options for cost efficient industrial manufacturing," *Solar Energy Materials and Solar Cells*, vol. 227, p. 111100, 2021, doi: 10.1016/j.solmat.2021.111100.

[13] InfoLink, *Spot Price.* [Online]. Available: https:// www.infolink-group.com/spot-price/ (accessed: Jul. 11 2025).

[14] VDMA, *Total Cost of Ownership (TCO).* [Online]. Available: https://www.vdma.eu/viewer/-/ v2article/render/46841813 (accessed: Jul. 9 2025).

[15] S. Raithel, J. Amano, D. Bouldin, F. Wessendorf, and F. Buenting, *Total Cost of Ownership in PV Manufacturing Guide.* [Online]. Available: https:// www.vdma.eu/documents/34570/16191053/PV_ CoO-Guide.pdf/5fd20ced-7e43-2405-1192-1fea710bc7c9?t=1644490641814?filename= PV_CoO-Guide.pdf (accessed: 08.082025).

[16] D. M. Powell, R. Fu, K. Horowitz, P. A. Basore, M. Woodhouse, and T. Buonassisi, "The capital intensity of photovoltaics manufacturing: barrier to scale and opportunity for innovation," *Energy Environ. Sci.*, vol. 8, no. 12, pp. 3395–3408, 2015, doi: 10.1039/C5EE01509J.

[17] International Renewable Energy Agency, *Renewable Power Generation Costs in 2023.* [Online]. Available: https://www.irena.org/-/ media/Files/IRENA/Agency/Publication/2024/Sep/ IRENA_Renewable_power_generation_costs_in_ 2023.pdf (accessed: Jul. 11 2025).

THE COST OF OWNERSHIP AND MINIMUM SUSTAINABLE PRICE OF POLO BJ CELLS PRODUCED IN GERMANY

Gomez Trillos, Juan Camilo[1]; Buddana, Viswa Harinath[1]; Papantoni,Veatriki[1]; Min, Byungsul[2]; Junge, Sebastian[2]; Kähler, Jan-Dirk[3]; Schneider, Friedrich[4]; Brendel, Rolf[2]; Vogt, Thomas[1]

[1] DLR, Oldenburg, Germany; [2] ISFH, Hamelin, Germany; [3] Centrotherm International, Hannover, Germany; [4] LPKF SolarQuipment, Suhl, Germany

DLR

Introduction

APOLON – Investor-oriented development of POLO technology for a PV production in Germany and Europe

- Goal: Strengthen European PV manufacturing competitiveness
- Focus : <u>Po</u>lysilicon on <u>o</u>xide (POLO BJ & IBC) technologies
- Key assessments: Cost of Ownership (CoO), Minimum Sustainable Price (MSP), Levelized Cost of Electricity (LCOE)
- Benchmark (POLO) vs. PERC technology

Funded by : BMWE

Project Partners: **ISFH, DLR, Centrotherm, LPKF**

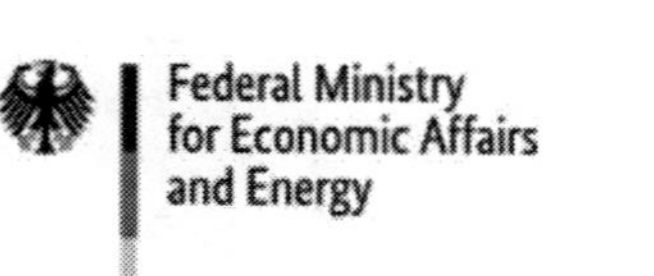

020483-002

China's Dominance in Global PV Supply Chains

- **Why China so dominant?**
  - Cheaper electricity and labour costs
  - Large-scale factories → lower production costs
  - Heavy investment in new technologies (n-type TOPCon, HJT)

- **What this means for Europe?**
  - Global prices are set from China → increased entry barriers and difficulties for new EU manufacturers
  - Strong reliance on China → supply and competitiveness risks, similar to Europe's past challenges with fossil fuel dependence.

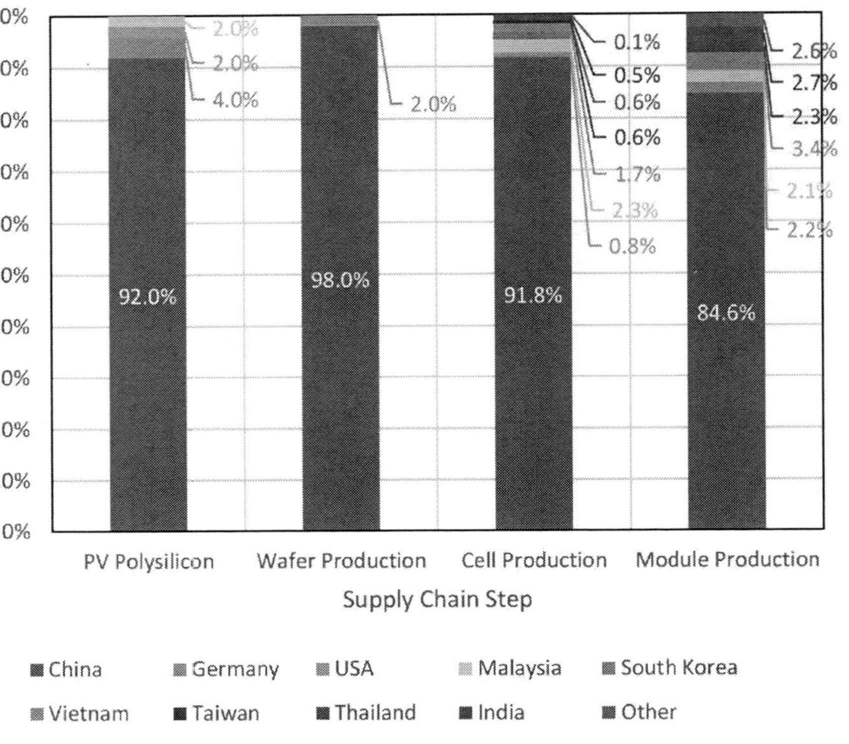

Source: Masson, G.; l'Epine, M.; Kaizuka, I.; Trends in Photovoltaic Applications 2024

PV Cell Price Trend (2023-2025)

- **Drivers of decline:**
  - Large-scale **overcapacity in China** (>500 GW cell capacity)
  - Rapid **Shift to n-type** technologies (TOPCon, HJT) improving efficiency
  - **Economies of scale** in production and supply chains
- **Implications for Europe:**
  - Local production costs: ~$0.20 - 0.25/W → nearly double import prices
  - Policy measures are necessary to compensate the price gap and support European PV competitiveness

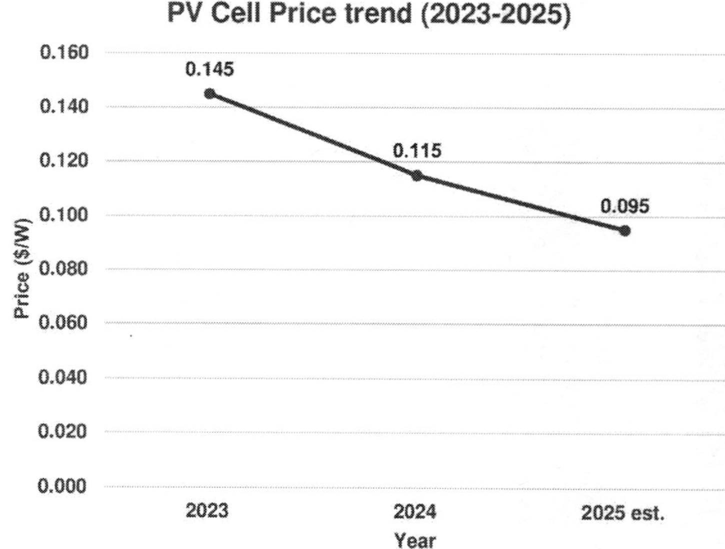

Source: Fall 2024 Solar Industry Update; Winter 2025 Solar Industry Update; PV spot price

Key Cost Metrics

 Cost of Ownership (CoO)

- **Definition:** Manufacturing cost per watt (¢/Wp)
- **Covers:** Materials, energy, labor, consumables, depreciation, yield losses, overheads
- **Tells us:** How much it costs the factory to produce 1 W of cell capacity?

Minimum Sustainable Price (MSP)

- **Definition:** Lowest selling price per watt (¢/Wp) that ensures financial sustainability
- **Covers:** CoO + financing (WACC), SG&A, taxes, profit margin
- **Tells us:** The price floor at which the factory can stay profitable long term

Levelized Cost of Electricity (LCOE)

- **Definition:** Average lifetime cost of electricity per kWh produced
- **Covers:** System CAPEX (modules + BOS), O&M, discount rate, lifetime generation
- **Tells us:** How much one kilowatt-hour of electricity costs over the system's lifetime?

020483-005

Considered Cell Concepts and Production Sequences

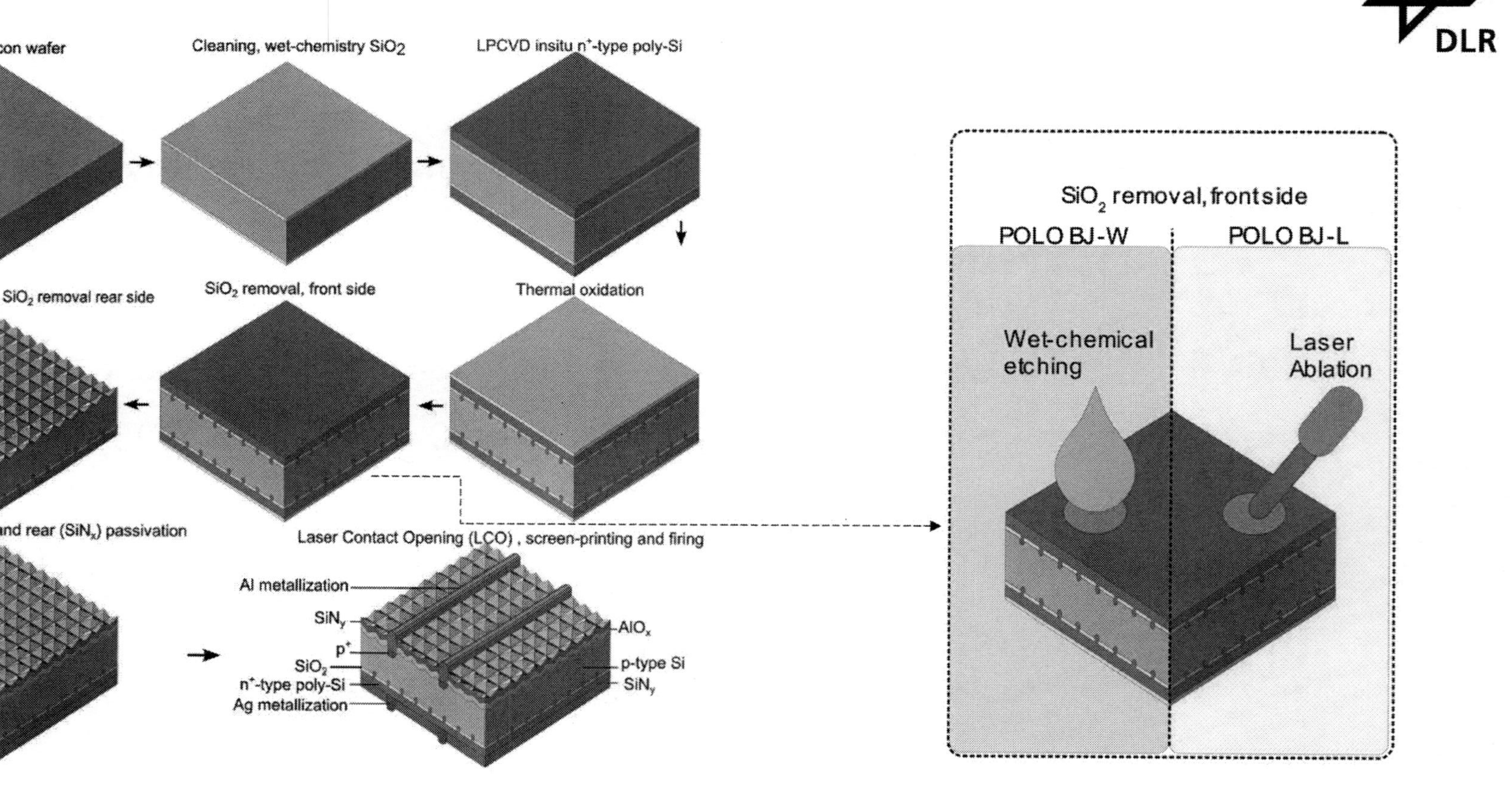

Source: Gomez Trillos, J.C. et al; 2025; The Cost of Ownership and Minimum Sustainable Price of POLO BJ Cells produced in Germany. [Manuscript submitted for publication]

020483-006

Cost of Ownership (CoO)

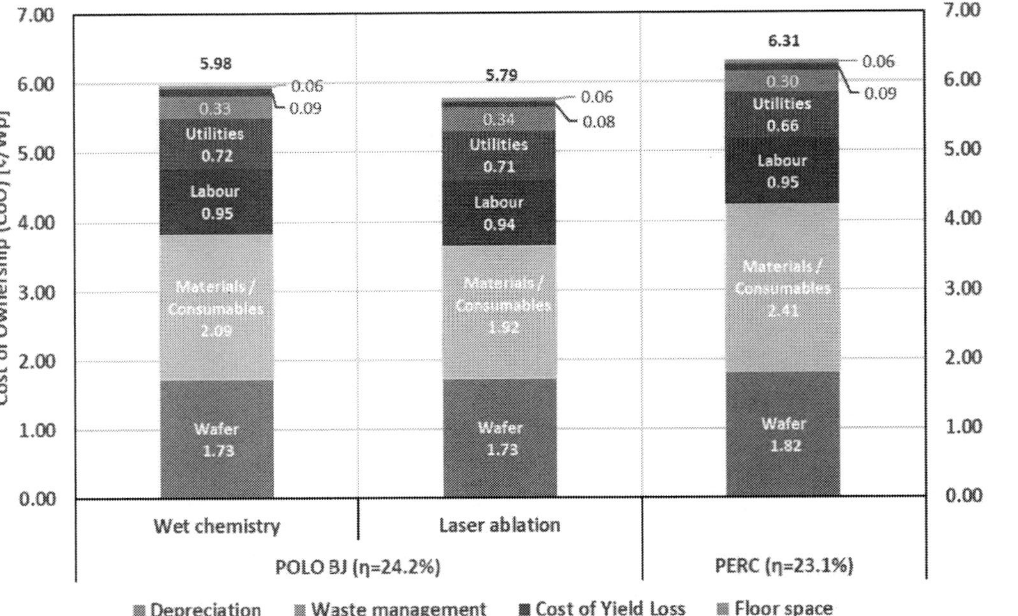

- 'POLO BJ-Laser' achieves lower CoO than 'POLO BJ-Wet' chemistry, mainly due to reduced chemical usage.

- CoO for POLO BJ (η_{cell}=24.2%) is 8.2% lower than that of PERC (η_{cell}=23.1%), therefore highlighting the economic benefits of POLO BJ.

- Dominant cost factors:
    1. Materials & consumables
    2. Wafers
    3. Labour
    4. Utilities

Source: Gomez Trillos, J.C. et al; 2025; The Cost of Ownership and Minimum Sustainable Price of POLO BJ Cells produced in Germany. [Manuscript submitted for publication]

020483-007

Minimum Sustainable Price (MSP)

- MSP of POLO BJ is up to 7.6% lower than PERC (24.2% vs 23.1% effeiciency)

- MSP per Wp driven by higher material costs for PERC and subsequently by the lower efficiency assumption made for this type of cell.

- MSP for POLO BJ is within the range of spot market price range for TOPCon (3.8-11.0 USD ct/Wp, August 2025)

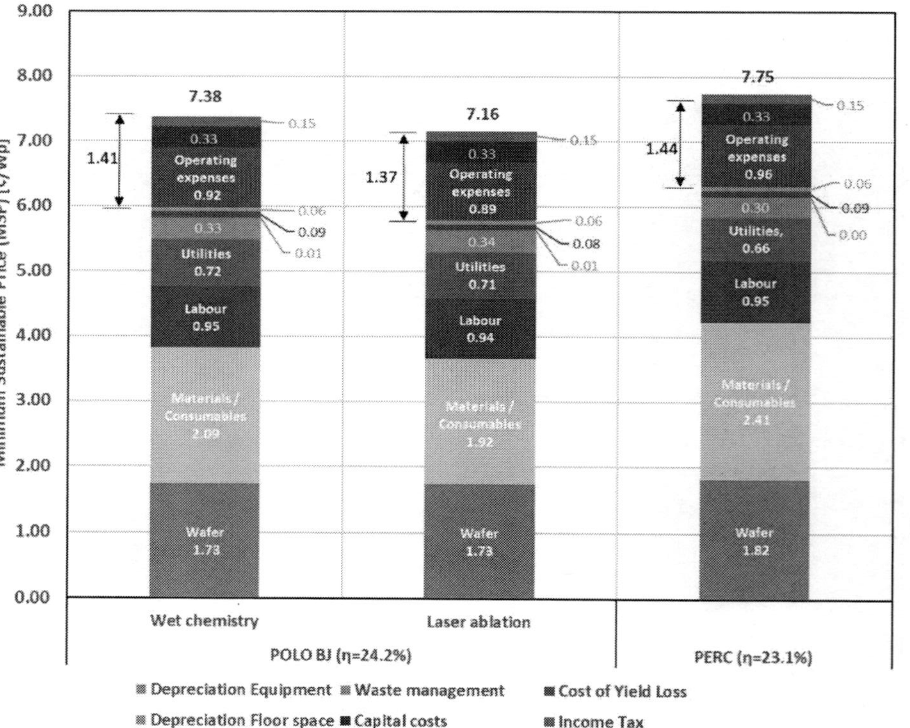

Source: Gomez Trillos, J.C. et al; 2025; The Cost of Ownership and Minimum Sustainable Price of POLO BJ Cells produced in Germany. [Manuscript submitted for publication]

020483-008

Levelized Cost of Electricity (LCOE)

- LCOE(bifacial) < LCOE (monofacial) due to higher electricity yield and despite higher module costs.

- LCOE (Germany) > LCOE (Spain) due to the higher solar resources in Spain.

- LCOE of POLO BJ is up to 0.14 ¢/kWh lower than PERC (Southern Europe, bifacial systems).

- LCOE of POLO BJ is competitive in both Germany and Southern Europe, aligning with reported global values

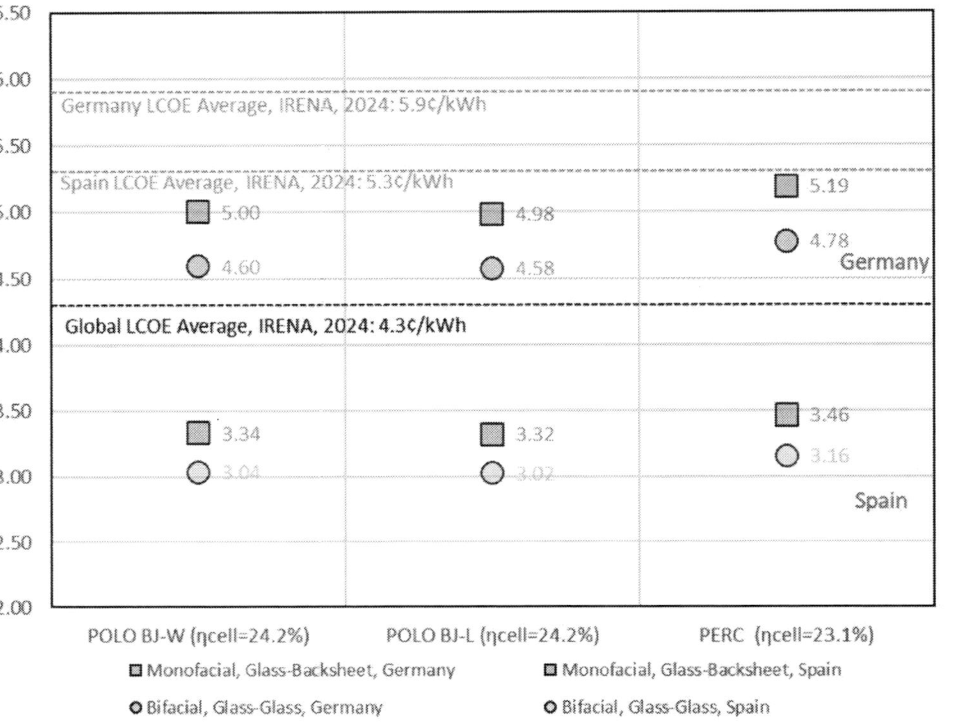

Source: Gomez Trillos, J.C. et al; 2025; The Cost of Ownership and Minimum Sustainable Price of POLO BJ Cells produced in Germany. [Manuscript submitted for publication]

For Global and Germany'y LCOE average: IRENA; 2025; Renewable Power Generation Costs 2024. International Renewable Energy Agency, Abu Dhabi.

020483-009

Pathways for the Reduction of the MSP

Considering a base MSP for POLO BJ – laser cells

- 0.24 ¢/Wp less MSP if efficiency = 25%.

- 0.76 ¢/Wp less MSP for upscaling the plant to 30GWp

- 0.32 ¢/Wp reduction in MSP by lowering Ag from 9 mg/Wp to 6 mg/Wp

- 0.20 c/Wp reduction in MSP through lower WACC (Weighted Average Cost of Capital) and income tax

- All these possibilities combined lead to a reduction of 1.52 ¢/Wp (21.2%$_{rel}$)

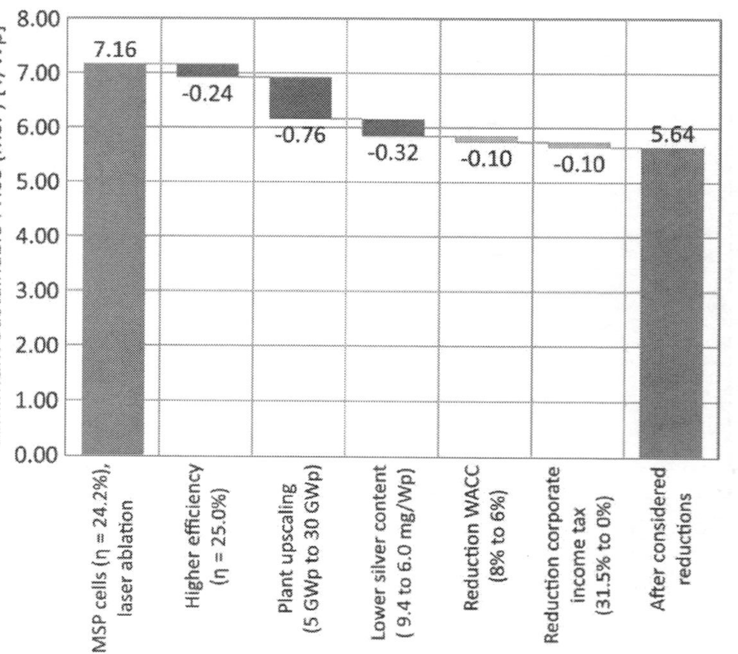

Source: Gomez Trillos, J.C. et al; 2025; The Cost of Ownership and Minimum Sustainable Price of POLO BJ Cells produced in Germany. [Manuscript submitted for publication]

Conclusion

🔑 Key Takeaways

- 💰 **Cost Advantage**
  → **POLO BJ** shows clear economic gains over PERC:
  - Up to 8% lower **CoO**
  - Up to 7–8% lower **MSP**
  - Competitive with **current TOPCon market prices**

- ⚡ **Efficiency and LCOE**
  → 24.2% efficiency assumed (vs 23.1% for PERC)
  → LCOE analysis: POLO BJ delivers **lower electricity costs**, especially in high-irradiance regions

- 🏭 **Upscaling Potential**
  → Combined improvements (efficiency, scaling, silver reduction, financing) can reduce
  - MSP ↓ >20% → ~5.6 ¢/Wp
  - 30 GW scaling + silver savings + 25% eff. + financing

-  **European Relevance**
  → Local production still >30% costlier than China
  → Needs policy support & innovation to close gap

Impressum

Topic:	**The Cost of Ownership and Minimum Sustainable Price of POLO BJ Cells produced in Germany**
Date:	2025-09-22
Author:	Gomez Trillos, Juan Camilo; Buddana, Viswa Harinath; Papantoni,Veatriki; Min, Byungsul; Junge, Sebastian; Kähler, Jan-Dirk; Schneider, Friedrich; Brendel, Rolf; Vogt, Thomas
Institute:	DLR Institute of Networked Energy Systems (Oldenburg)
Credits:	All figures „DLR (CC BY-NC-ND 3.0)", unless otherwise stated

020483-012

Annex

Methodology to Calculate CoO

Plant output	GWp/a

General inputs

Prices	Unit
Cell Efficiency	%
Cell area/format	cm^2
Wafers price	$/piece
Material	$/kg
Utilities	$/kWh
Consumables	$/piece
Labour	$/a*FTE
Floor space	$/a*m^2
Waste disposal	$/m^3
Depreciation time	a

Inputs step i

Item	Unit
Throughput tool	piece/h
Tool number	-
Productive time	h/a
Material	kg/wafer
Tool price	$
Tool footprint	m^2
Utilities	kW
Consumables	piece/a
Waste volume	m^3/h
Labour	FTE/shift
Yield loss	%

Results step i

CoO process i	USD
CoO per cell i	USD/piece
CoO per power unit i	USD/Wp
CoO per area unit i	USD/m^2

Aggregated results sequence

CoO	USD
CoO	USD/piece
CoO	USD/Wp
CoO	USD/m^2

Iterative process to calculate MSP

020483-014

Methodology to Calculate MSP

$$B_{Gross\ income,t} = B_t - C_{var,t} - D_{facility,t} + D_{tools,t}$$

$$C_{var,t} = C_{mat,t} + C_{utilities,t} + C_{waste,t} + C_{labour,t} + C_{yield\ loss,t}$$

$$B_{Operating\ income,t} = B_{Gross\ income,t} - C_{OPEX,t}$$

$$C_{OPEX} = f_{OPEX} * B_t$$

$$C_{tax,t} = B_{Operating\ income,t} * f_{income\ tax,t}$$

$$R_{cash\ flow,0} = C_{Investment,t} + \Delta NWC$$

$$R_{cash\ flow,t} = B_{Operating\ income,t} - C_{tax,t} + D_{facility,t} + D_{tools,t} + \Delta NWC + C_{Investment,t} + B_{salvage,t}$$

$$R_{NPV} = R_{cash\ flow,0} + \sum_{t=1}^{T} \frac{IR_{cash\ flow,t}}{(1+i)^t}$$

$$R_{NPV} = 0$$

$$B_t = B_1 \quad \forall\, t > 0$$
$$C_{var,t} = C_{var,1} \quad \forall\, t > 0$$
$$C_{OPEX,t} = C_{OPEX,1} \quad \forall\, t > 0$$
$$C_{tax,t} = C_{tax,1} \quad \forall\, t > 0$$

September 25, 2025
EUPVSEC 2025, 5DO.14.3

HITACHI

Empirical Analysis of Zero-Shot Cross-Frequency Forecasting for Missing Data Prediction in Real-time PV Management

Issei Suemitsu*, Toru Kono, Ryo Wakabayashi, Jun Tsunoda, Yosuke Yamaguchi, Wenpeng Wei

Research & Development Group, Hitachi, Ltd.

020484-001

Background

Rapid expansion of renewable energy has made energy systems more diverse and complex.

- EMS must control heterogeneous devices with different sampling cycles in real-time.
- Data must be observed at higher frequencies.
- Packet loss or sensor errors leads to frequent missing data.

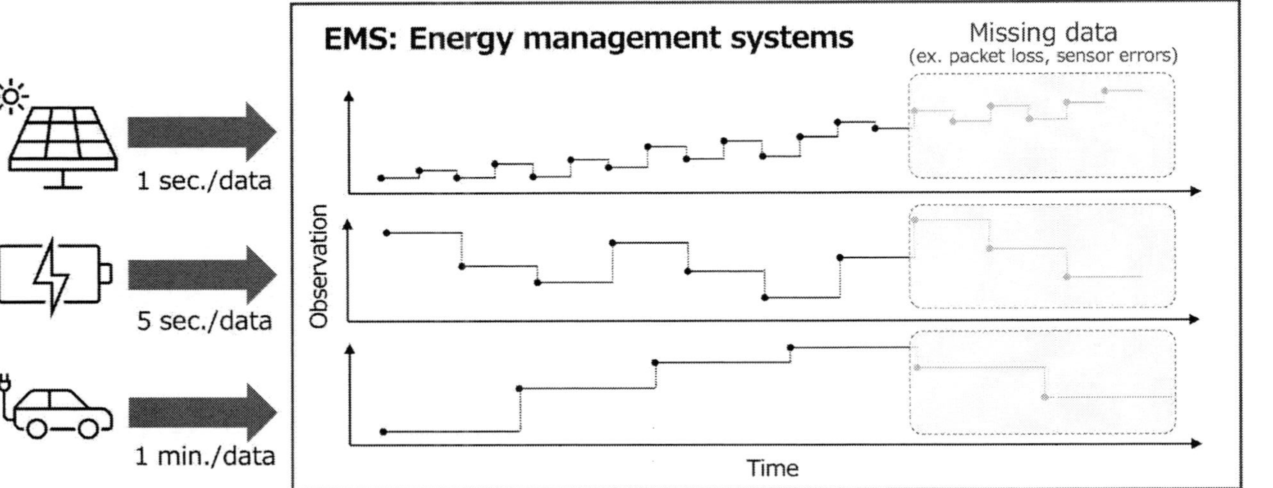

Conventional methods: Rule-based

Rule-based method, like Last-Observation-Carried-Forward (LOCF) rule, is popular to handle missing data in existing EMS.

- LOCF simply copies the last observed value for each missing point.
- Fast and easy to implement, but often fails to capture sudden fluctuations.
- Leads to inaccurate forecasting and potential grid instability.

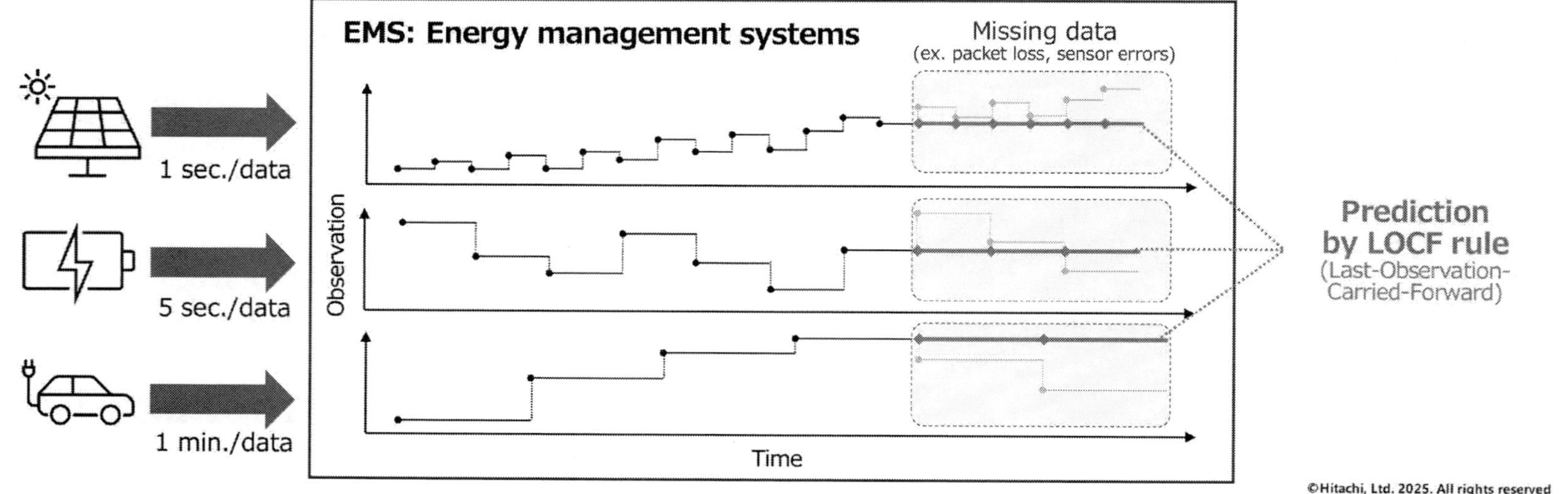

3

020484-003

Conventional methods: Machine learning

HITACHI

ML methods can predict missing values with much higher accuracy, but requires separate models for each device and resolution.

- Leading High data collection and model maintenance costs
- Difficult to scale for large and diverse EMS environments

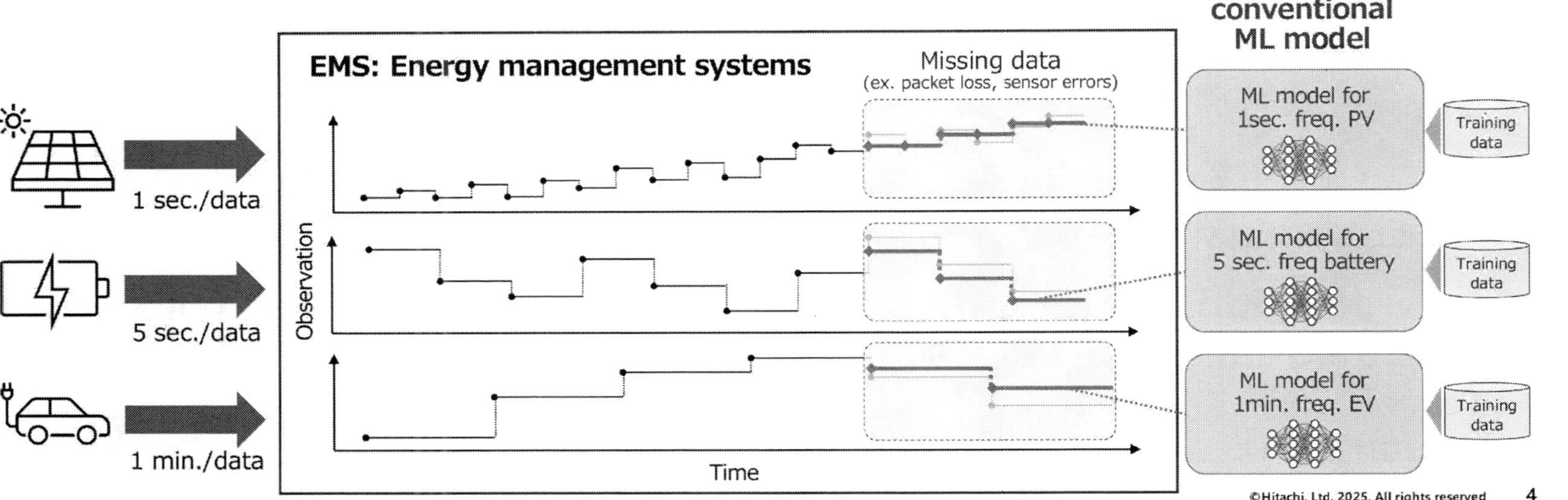

Motivation

Time Series Foundation Models (TSFM) show the significant potential for prediction against unseen targets (zero-shot forecasting).

- Trained on a large dataset with various series to predict unseen ones without retraining.
- But generalization ability to unseen <u>time resolutions</u> is not well validated.
- Our study addresses this gap with empirical analysis.

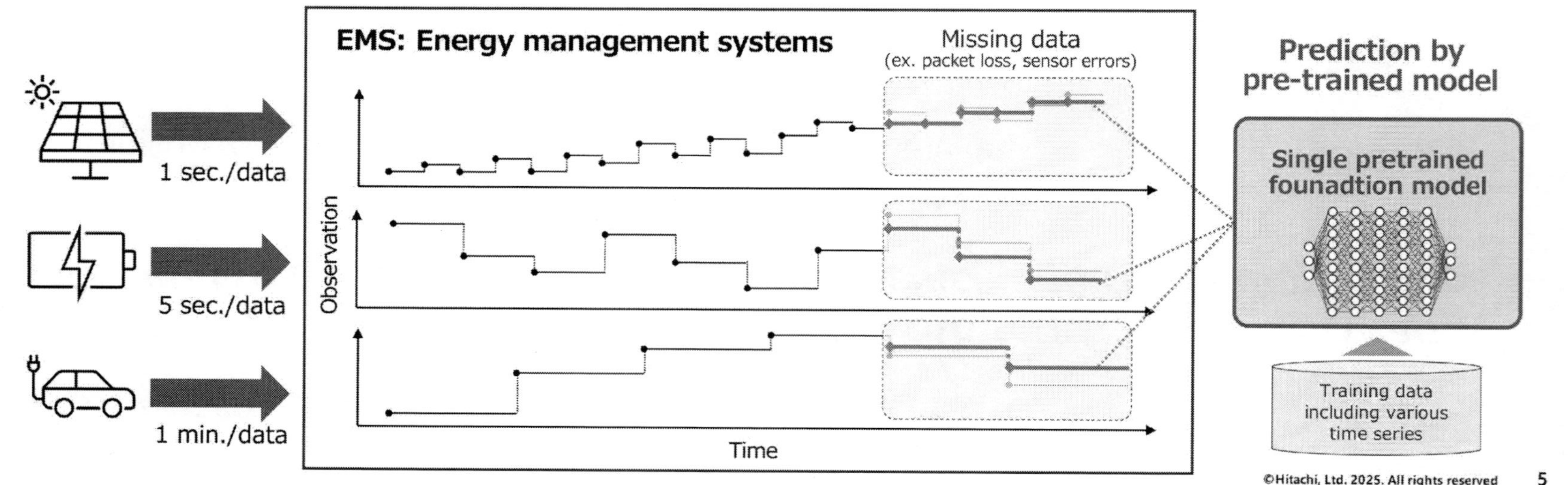

Problem Definition

HITACHI

Zero-Shot Cross-Frequency Forecasting

- Train on time-series dataset including diverse devices and time resolutions
- Evaluate forecasting accuracies at unseen devices and resolutions without retraining
- Research question: which model architectures can generalize across frequencies?

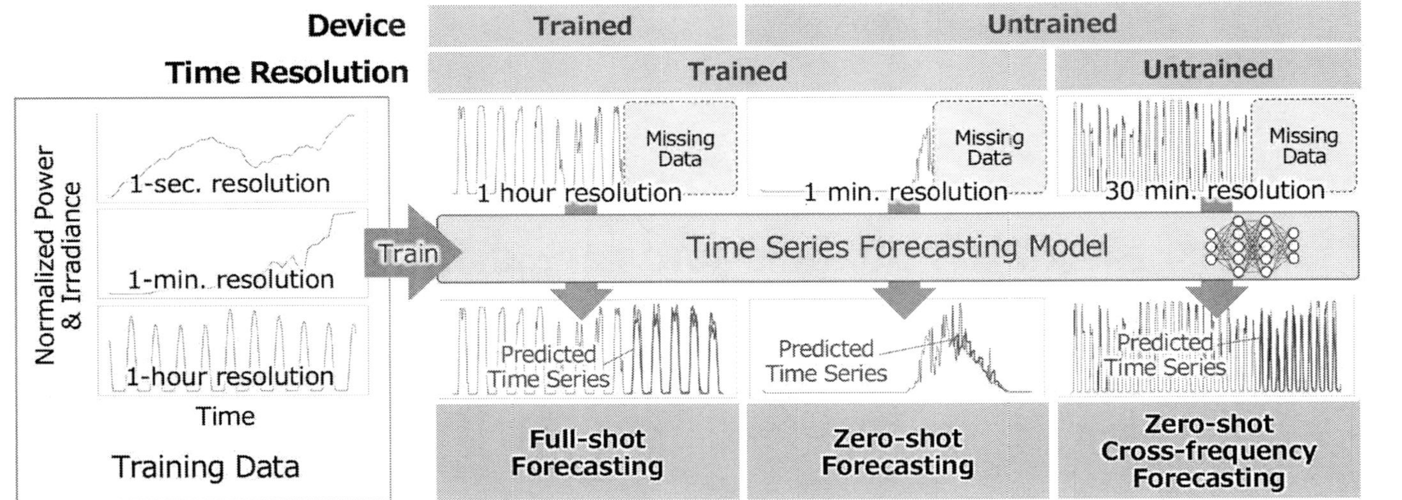

6

020484-006

Research Objectives

① **Construct a large multi-resolution PV & irradiance dataset**

② **Benchmark SoTA forecasting models in zero-shot cross-frequency**

③ **Propose a resolution-aware model using Mixture-of-Experts (MoE)**

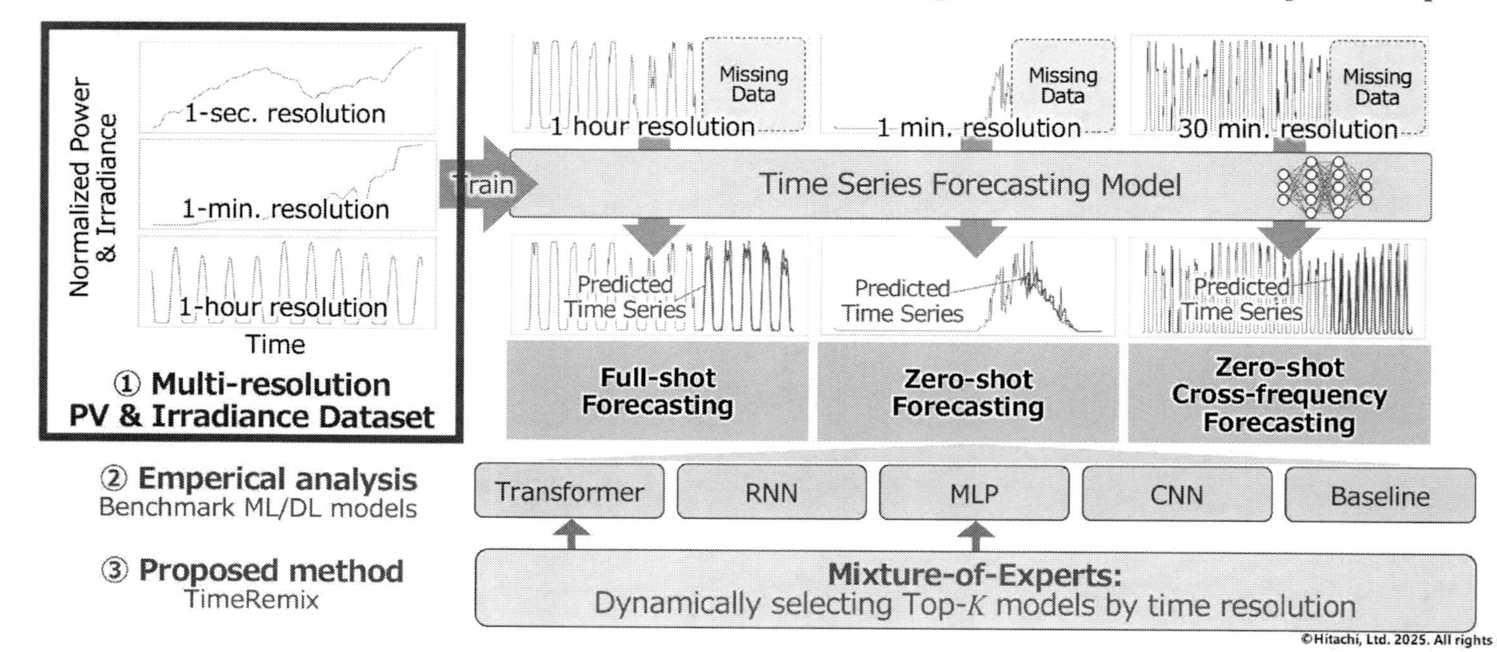

② **Emperical analysis**
Benchmark ML/DL models

③ **Proposed method**
TimeRemix

① Multi-resolution PV and irradiance data

100+ million data points with multiple time-resolutions, integrating 4 public PV & irradiance datasets

- Train: 1 sec, 1 min, 1 hour resolution times series from 3 datasets.
- Zero-shot test: 5 sec – 1 hour resolution (Resampled from Monash dataset)

Table 1: PV and irradiance dataset. Total observations: 174,661,306. * indicates resampled data.

Dataset	Resolution	Series	Length	Observation	Usage
Oahu Solar Measurement Grid [21]	1 second	6	10,321,203	61,927,218	Train/Test
PSML [22]	1 minute	66	1,573,565	103,855,290	Train/Test
DKASC, Alice Springs [23]	1 hour*	21	69,386	1,457,106	Train/Test
Monash Solar Power Dataset [24]	5 second*	1	5,840,017	5,840,017	Test
	30 second*	1	973,337	973,337	Test
	1 minute*	1	486,669	486,669	Test
	5 minute*	1	97,334	97,334	Test
	30 minute*	1	16,223	16,223	Test
	1 hour*	1	8,112	8,112	Test

② Benchmark Setting

Autoregression forecasting task

- **Input:**
  recent $T=120$ observations of the targets & covariates
- **Output:** next $S=24$ step forecast
- Models trained to minimize
  Mean Squared Error (MSE) loss

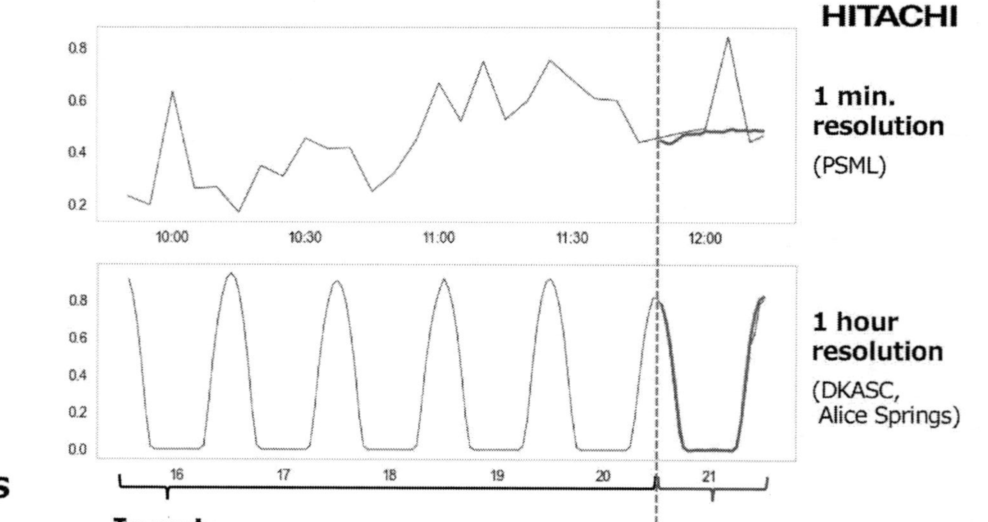

Input:
recent $T=120$ observed targets & covariates

$$X^i_{1:T} = \begin{bmatrix} Y^i_t: \text{Normalized target timeseries} \\ ([0.416, 0.415, 0.413, \ldots]) \\[6pt] Z^i_t: \text{11 past covariates} \\ \textbf{10 time-stamp features} \\ (\text{month, day, hour, min., sec.} \\ \text{converted with sin \& cos}) \\ + \textbf{time resolution } \tau^i \ (1 \sim 3600 \text{ sec.}) \end{bmatrix}$$

y^i_1	$\cdots$	$y^i_T)$
$\sin(month^i_1)$	$\cdots$	$\sin(month^i_T)$
$\cos(month^i_1)$	$\cdots$	$\cos(month^i_T)$
$\vdots$	$\cdots$	$\vdots$
$\cos(second^i_1)$	$\cdots$	$\cos(second^i_T)$
$\tau^i/3600$	$\cdots$	$\tau^i/3600$

Output:
$\widehat{Y}^i_{T+1:T+S}$

y^i_{T+1}	$\cdots$	y^i_{T+S}

② Benchmarked Models

Transformer:

1. **iTransformer**: Encoder-only Series-wise token
2. **PatchTST**: Encoder-only, Patch-wise token
3. **Timer**: Decoder-only, Patch-wise token

Recurrent Neural Network (RNN):

4. **LSTM**: An RNN with gating mechanisms
5. **S-Mamba**: Selective state-space mechanism

Multi-Layer Perceptron (MLP):

6. **TSMixer**: Mixing across multiple channels
7. **TimeMixer**: Multiscale mixing architecture

Convolutional Neural Network (CNN):

8. **TCN**: Causal convolution and skip connections

Baselines:

9. **LOCF**: A simple rule-based method.
10. **Moirai-MoE**: A SoTA pretrained TSFM using MoE (without retraining)

Models #1~9 are trained under same conditions
(3 layers with 512 hidden units, 20% dropout,
100,000 training steps, AdamW with 0.0001 learning rate.)

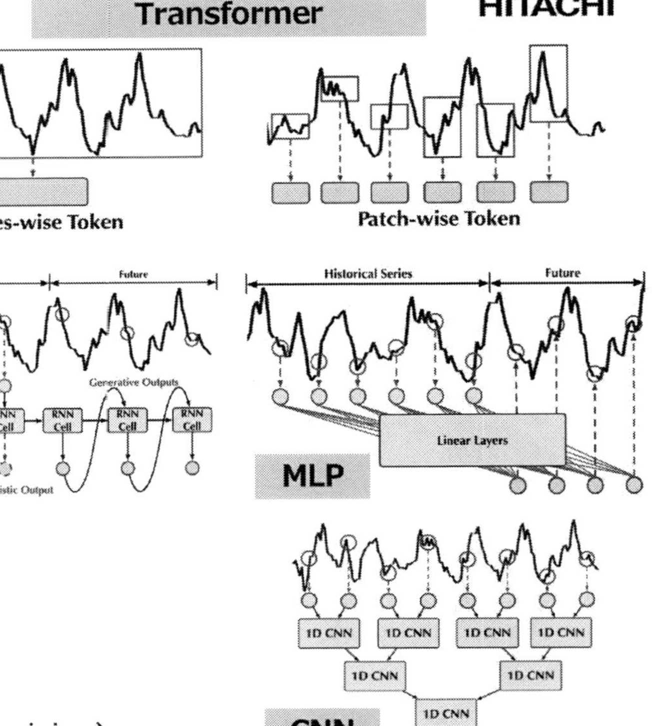

Figures: Wang, Y., Wu, H., Dong, J., Liu, Y., Long, M., & Wang, J. (2024). Deep Time Series Models: A Comprehensive Survey and Benchmark. http://arxiv.org/abs/2407.13278

② Benchmark Results: Zero-Shot Forecasting

Prediction accuracies were influenced by model architectures and time resolutions.

- Transformers show high accuracies at high-frequencies (5–30 sec)
- RNNs & MLPs performed better at lower frequencies (1 min–1 hour)

Zero-shot cross-frequency forecasting performance
(RMSE: Smaller is better)

Legend: 1st | 2nd | 3rd | Untrained

Algorithm	Monash, Solar Power Dataset [24]					
	5 sec.	30 sec.	1 min.	5 min.	30 min.	1 hour
iTransformer	0.0175	0.0635	0.0855	0.1683	0.4268	0.1260
PatchTST	0.0178	0.0631	0.0849	0.1529	0.3882	0.1359
Timer	0.0204	0.0685	0.0899	0.1497	0.4335	0.1291
LSTM	0.0479	0.2855	0.0887	0.1238	0.2349	0.1585
S-Mamba	0.0255	0.0639	0.0836	0.1940	0.4298	0.1388
TSMixer	0.1328	0.1035	0.0830	0.1196	0.3423	0.1353
TimeMixer	0.0334	0.0713	0.0845	0.1535	0.4320	0.1291
TCN	0.0535	0.0998	0.1127	0.1780	0.6076	0.1308
LOCF (Naïve seasonal)	0.0229	0.0652	0.0995	0.1121	0.4576	0.5017
Moirai-MoE	0.1029	0.1436	0.1759	0.2127	0.3684	0.1918

③ Proposed method: TimeRemix

Time Resolution-aware Mixture-of-Experts Forecaster

Adaptively combining multiple expert models specialized for a particular resolution.

- ### Sparse MoE architecture:
  - **Experts** (iTransformer, PatchTST, LSTM, TSMixer, TimeMixer) selected for performances at specific time resolutions.

  - **Gating network** dynamically activates only the top $K=2$ experts for each input series.

  - Final prediction is the weighted-average of selected experts' outputs.

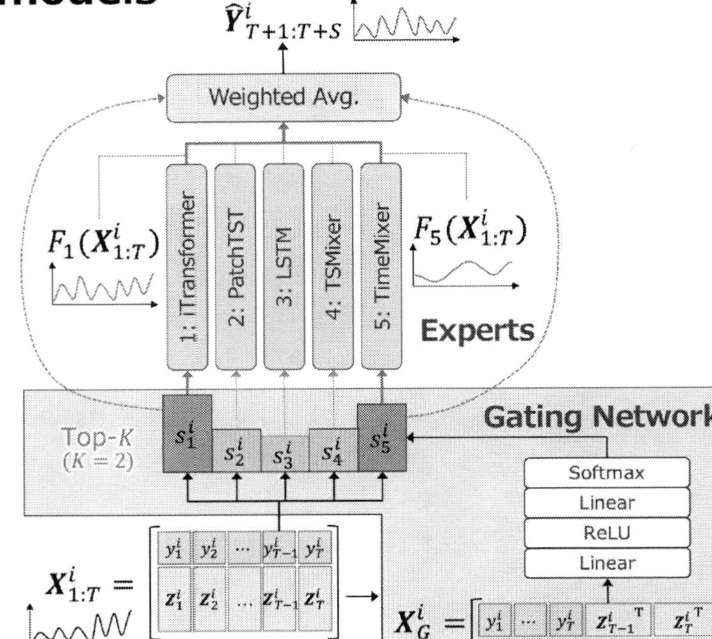

③ Effectiveness of TimeRemix: Accuracy

Robust zero-shot cross-frequency forecasting ability across all resolutions

Zero-shot cross-frequency forecasting performance (RMSE: Smaller is better)

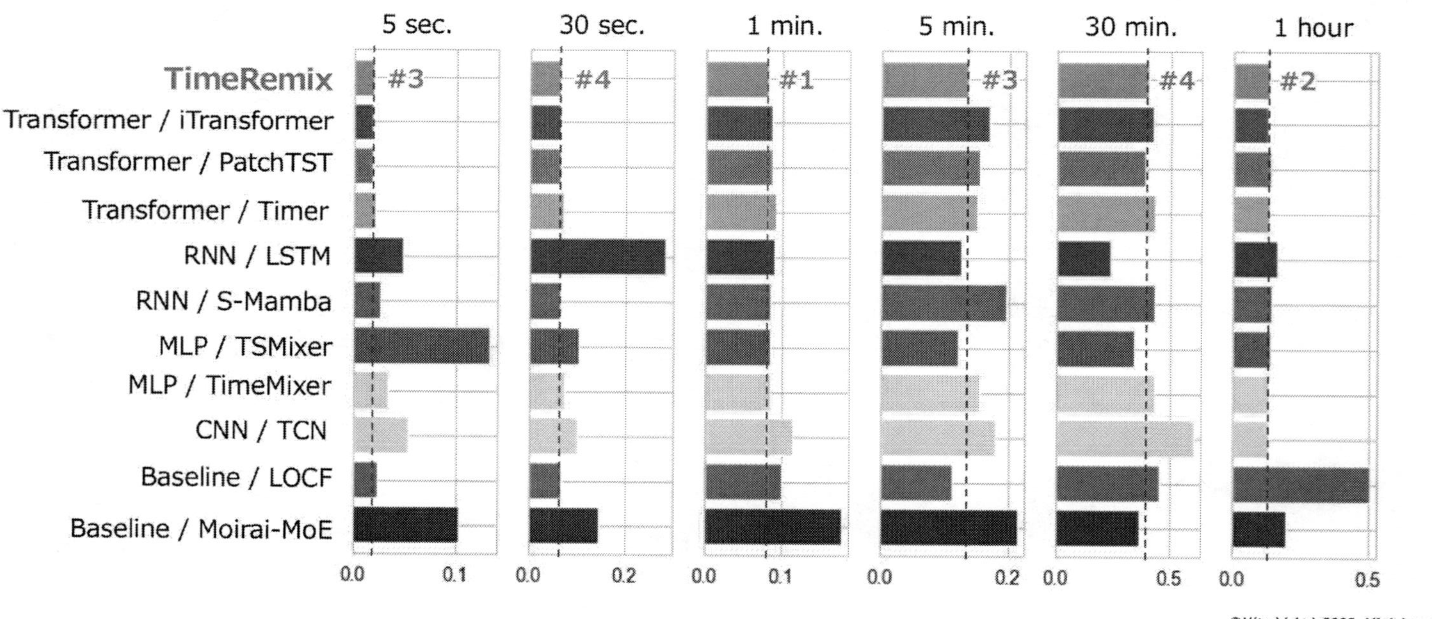

③ Effectiveness of TimeRemix: Efficiency

Balances predictive accuracy with computational efficiency, since only a few experts are activated at once.

- Demonstrates superior generalization capability obtained by sparse MoE.

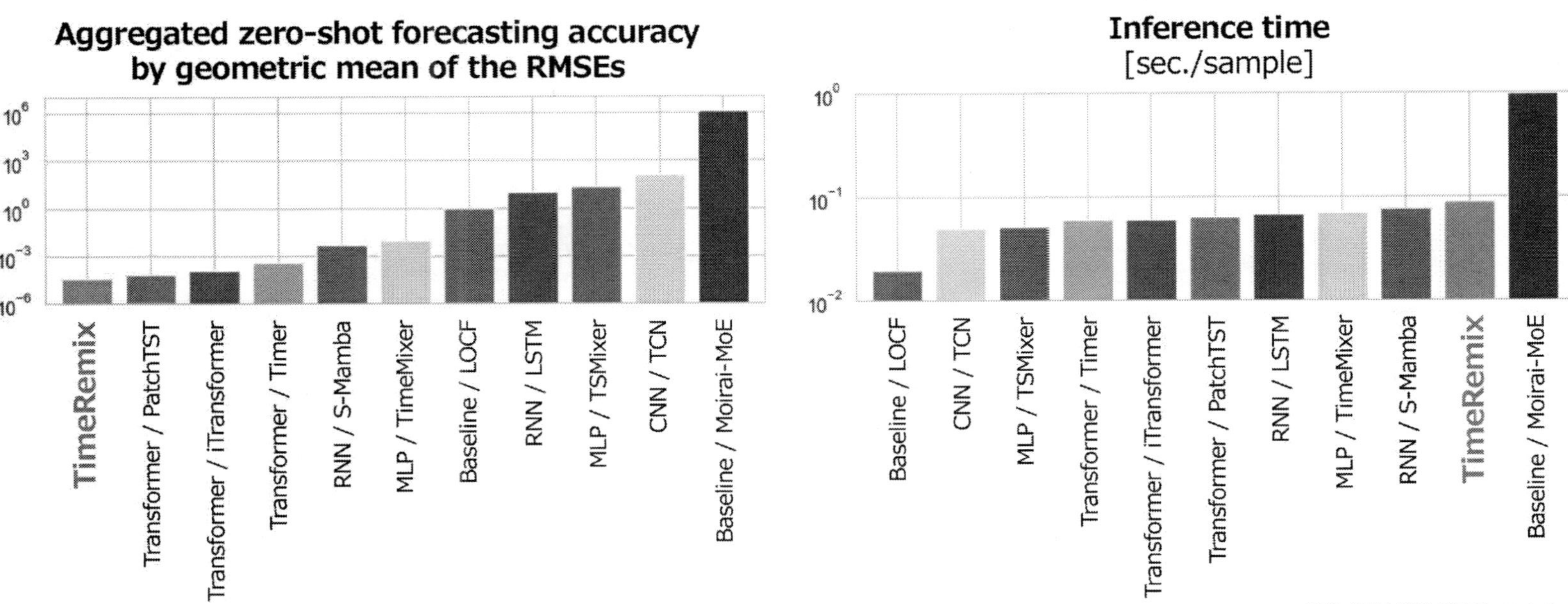

③ Expert selection results

Gating network changes expert selection by time resolution.

- At second-level resolutions, Transformers were selected more often.
- At minute-to-hour resolutions, LSTM and MLPs became dominant.

Average gating weights of experts in zero-shot forecasting
(Higher weight means more frequent expert selection)

	5 sec.	30 sec.	1min.	5 min.	30 min.	1hour
iTransformer	0.709	0.680	0.632	0.554	0.653	0.565
PatchTST	0.170	0.159	0.107	0.021	0.004	0.081
LSTM	0.068	0.104	0.186	0.288	0.125	0.004
TSMixer	0.003	0.000	0.006	0.000	0.051	0.065
TimeMixer	0.050	0.057	0.069	0.137	0.167	0.285

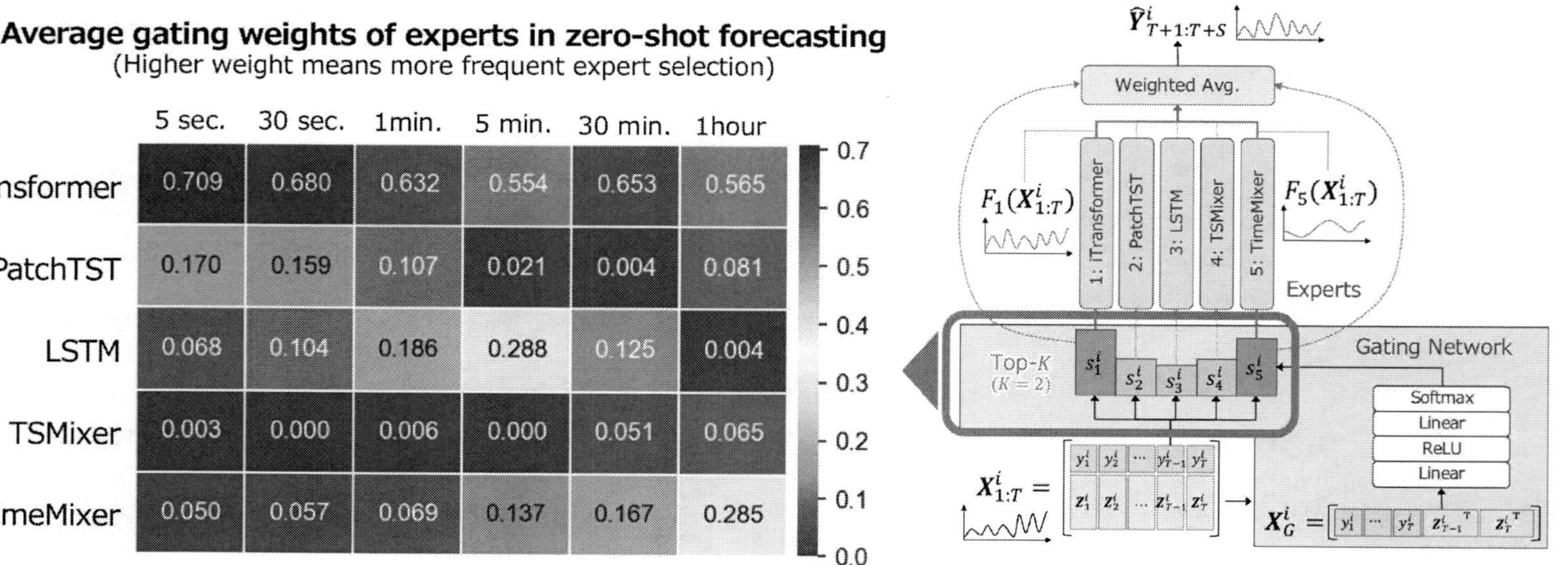

③ Expert selection results

Trend of expert selection matches the benchmark results.

TimeRemix learned to assign appropriate experts according to time resolution.

Average gating weights of experts in zero-shot forecasting

	5 sec.	30 sec.	1min.	5 min.	30 min.	1hour
iTransformer	0.709	0.680	0.632	0.554	0.653	0.565
PatchTST	0.170	0.159	0.107	0.021	0.004	0.081
LSTM	0.068	0.104	0.186	0.288	0.125	0.004
TSMixer	0.003	0.000	0.006	0.000	0.051	0.065
TimeMixer	0.050	0.057	0.069	0.137	0.167	0.285

Zero-shot prediction results of single models (RMSE)

Algorithm	Monash, Solar Power Dataset					
	5 sec.	30 sec.	1 min.	5min.	30 min.	1 hour
iTransformer	**0.0175**	**0.0635**	0.0855	0.1683	0.4268	**0.1260**
PatchTST	**0.0178**	**0.0631**	0.0849	0.1529	0.3882	0.1359
LSTM	0.0479	0.2855	0.0887	**0.1238**	**0.2349**	0.1585
TSMixer	0.1328	0.1035	**0.0830**	**0.1196**	**0.3423**	0.1353
TimeMixer	0.0334	0.0713	**0.0845**	0.1535	0.4320	**0.1291**

③ Visualization of Forecasted Time Series

TimeRemix aligns with the best-performing model at each resolution

- Behaves like Transformer at high frequency, like MLP at low frequency

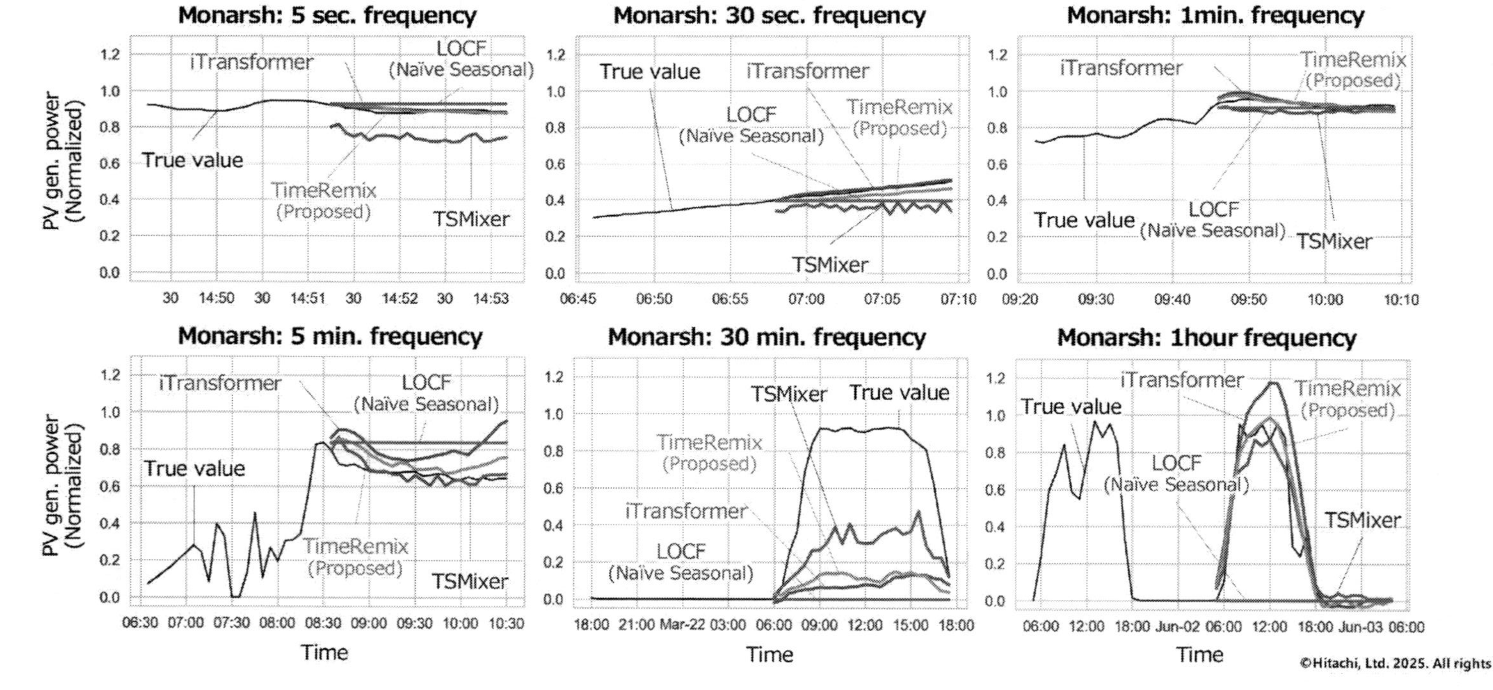

Conclusion

- Built a large multi-resolution dataset (>100M points)
- Benchmarked 10 forecasting methods
- Proposed TimeRemix, achieved robust zero-shot cross-frequency forecasting
- But challenges remain. (e.f. 30 mins forecast is much worse than 1hour)
- Future work: fully resolution-invariant forecasting architectures

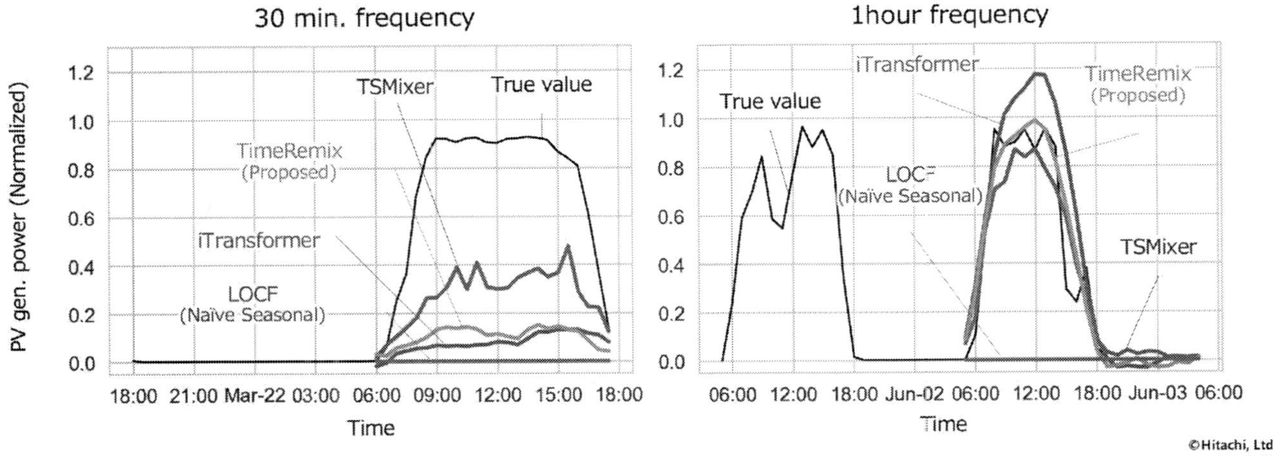

Monash Solar Power Dataset (Zero-shot prediction)

18

020484-018

Acknowledgments

HITACHI

Thanks public dataset providers:

- "Oahu Solar Measurement Grid (1-Year Archive): 1-Second Solar Irradiance; Oahu, Hawaii (Data)" at http://dx.doi.org/10.5439/1052451, reference number NREL Report No. DA-5500-56506,

- "PSML: A Multi-scale Time-series Dataset for Machine Learning in Decarbonized Energy Grids (Dataset)" at https://doi.org/10.5281/zenodo.5130611, reference number Version 0.2,

- "Desert Knowledge Australia Centre. 19/06/2024. Download Data. Alice Springs" at https://dkasolarcentre.com.au/download, reference number 19/06/2024,

- "Solar Power Dataset (4 Seconds Observations)" in Monash Time Series Forecasting Repository at https://doi.org/10.5281/zenodo.3992664, reference number Version 2.

Thank you for your attention.

HITACHI

Cotact: Issei Suemitsu,
Research & Development Group, Hitachi, Ltd.,
1-280 Higashi-Koigakubo, Kokubunji, Tokyo 185-8601, Japan,
Email Address: issei.suemitsu.rj@hitachi.com

① Details of dataset

Dataset	Training period	Validation period	Test period
Oahu Solar Measurement Grid (1 sec. resolution)	**3 months** 2011-07-01 06:00:00 - 2011-10-01-05:59:59	**24 days** 2011-10-01 06:00:00 - 2011-10-25 05:59:59	**7 days** 2011-10-25 06:00:00 - 2011-10-31 20:00:00
PSML (1 min. resolution)	**2 years** 2018-01-01 06:00:00 - 2020-01-01 05:59:00	**10 months** 2020-01-01 06:00:00 - 2020-10-01 05:59:00	**2 months** 2020-10-01 06:00:00 - 2020-12-31 23:59:00
DKACS, Alice Spring* (1 hour resolution)	**6 years** 2016-10-01 00:00:00 - 2022-09-30 23:00:00	**1 year** 2022-10-01 00:00:00 - 2023-09-30 23:00:00	**11 months** 2023-10-01 00:00:00 - 2024-01-31 23:00:00
Monarsh, Solar Power Dataset*	-	-	**11 months** 2019-11-01 00:00:00 - 2020-10-03 23:00:00

* Data from the southern hemisphere has been adjusted by adding 180 days to align with northern hemisphere seasons.

② Benchmarked Models: #1-3

Transformer:

1. **iTransformer**: An encoder-only Transformer, tokenizes the entire time series
2. **PatchTST**: An encoder-only Transformer-based model using patch-wise tokens
3. **Timer**: A decoder-only Transformer-based model using patch-wise tokens

Tokenization

Encoder and Decoder

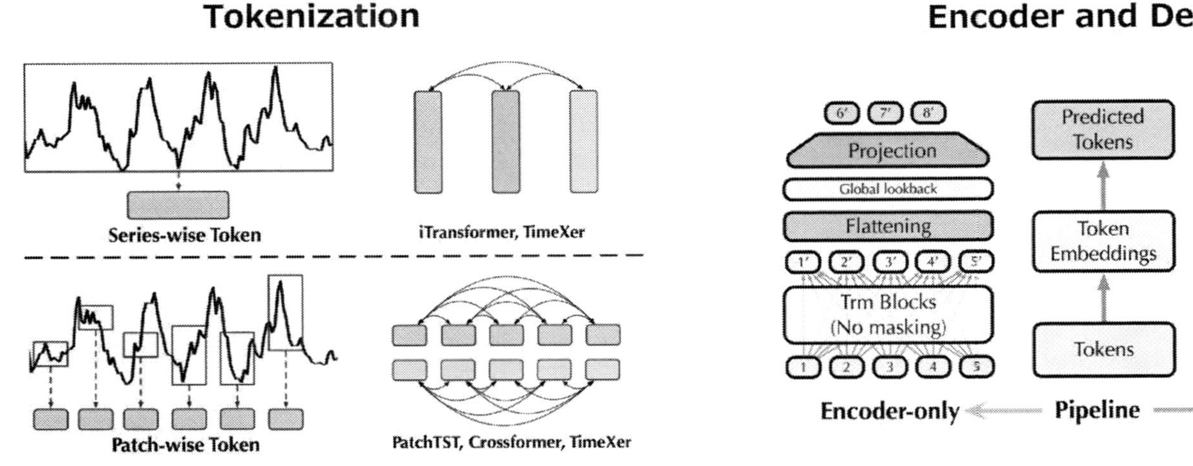

Wang, Y., Wu, H., Dong, J., Liu, Y., Long, M., & Wang, J. (2024).
Deep Time Series Models: A Comprehensive Survey and Benchmark.
http://arxiv.org/abs/2407.13278

Liu, Y., Zhang, H., Li, C., Huang, X., Wang, J., & Long, M. (2024).
Timer: Transformers for Time Series Analysis at Scale.
http://arxiv.org/abs/2402.02368

② Benchmarked Models: #4-7

Recurrent Neural Network (RNN):

4. **LSTM (Long short-term memory)**: An RNN with gating mechanisms

5. **S-Mamba**: A Mabma-based method using a selective state-space mechanism

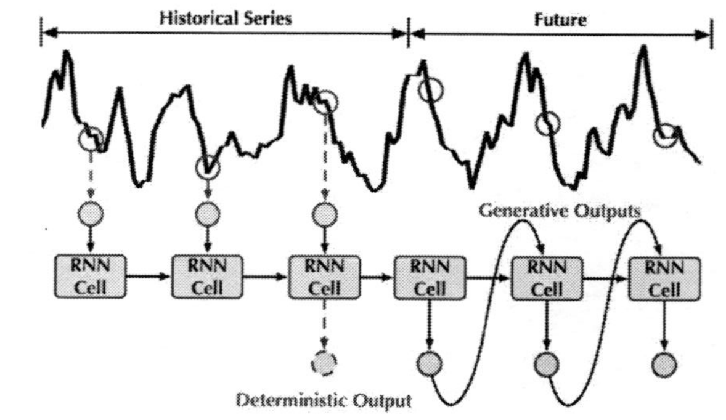

Multi-Layer Perceptron (MLP):

6. **TSMixer**: A MLP-based method mixing time series across multiple channels.

7. **TimeMixer**: A MLP-based method with multiscale mixing architecture

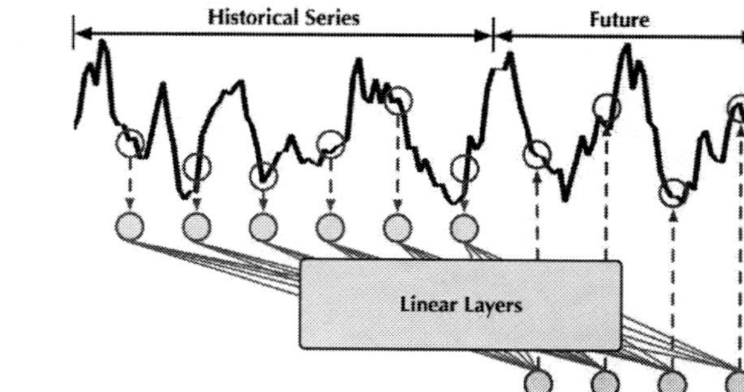

Wang, Y., Wu, H., Dong, J., Liu, Y., Long, M., & Wang, J. (2024).
Deep Time Series Models: A Comprehensive Survey and Benchmark, http://arxiv.org/abs/2407.13278

② Benchmarked Models: #8-10

Convolutional Neural Network (CNN):

8. **TCN**: A DNN model using causal convolution and skip connections

Baselines:

9. **LOCF**: A naive baseline substituting the most recent received value for every future point.

10. **Moirai-MoE**: A SoTA pretrained TSFM with a sparse MoE within the Transformer architecture.

CNN

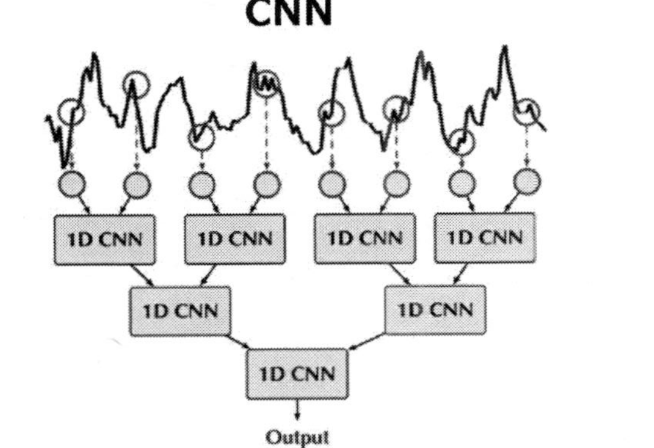

Wang, Y., Wu, H., Dong, J., Liu, Y., Long, M., & Wang, J. (2024). Deep Time Series Models: A Comprehensive Survey and Benchmark, http://arxiv.org/abs/2407.13278

Moirai-MoE

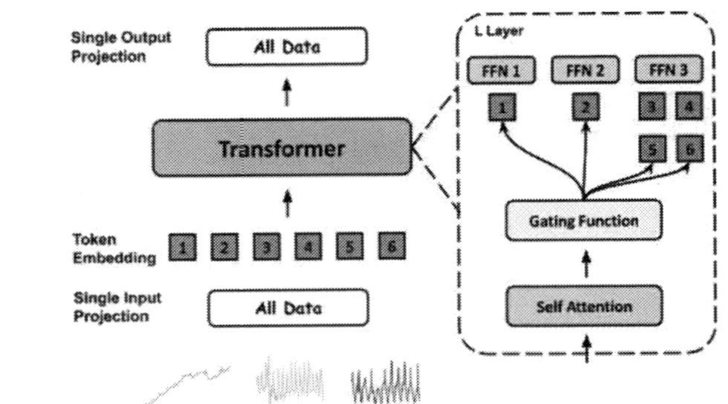

Liu, X., Liu, J., Woo, G., Aksu, T., Liang, Y., Zimmermann, R., Liu, C., Savarese, S., Xiong, C., & Sahoo, D. (2024). Moirai-MoE: Empowering Time Series Foundation Models with Sparse Mixture of Experts. http://arxiv.org/abs/2410.10469

② Benchmark Results: Full-Shot Forecasting

Forecasting at trained datasets and resolutions

- Transformers performed best at high-frequency (1 sec.)
- MLPs were better at low-frequency (1 hour)
- LOCF worked for 1 sec, but failed otherwise.

Full-shot forecasting performance
RMSE (Smaller is better)

1st 2nd 3rd

Algorithm	Oahu Solar Measurement Grid [21] (1 sec.)	PSML [22] (1 min.)	DKASC, Alice Springs [23] (1 hour)	Inference time [sec./sample]
iTransformer	0.0124	0.0458	0.0733	0.0600
PatchTST	0.0123	0.0476	0.0895	0.0638
Timer	0.0151	0.0499	0.0788	0.0593
LSTM	0.0319	0.0475	0.0725	0.0676
S-Mamba	0.0136	0.0460	0.0792	0.0767
TSMixer	0.0183	0.0411	0.0752	0.0520
TimeMixer	0.0179	0.0459	0.0788	0.0686
TCN	0.0294	0.0648	0.0834	0.0494
LOCF (Naïve seasonal)	0.0083	0.0508	0.3977	0.0197
Moirai-MoE	0.2419	0.0583	0.1225	0.9768
TimeRemix (Ours)	0.0146 (#4)	0.0412 (#2)	0.0749 (#3)	0.0892 (#10)

② Full-Shot Results: Visualization

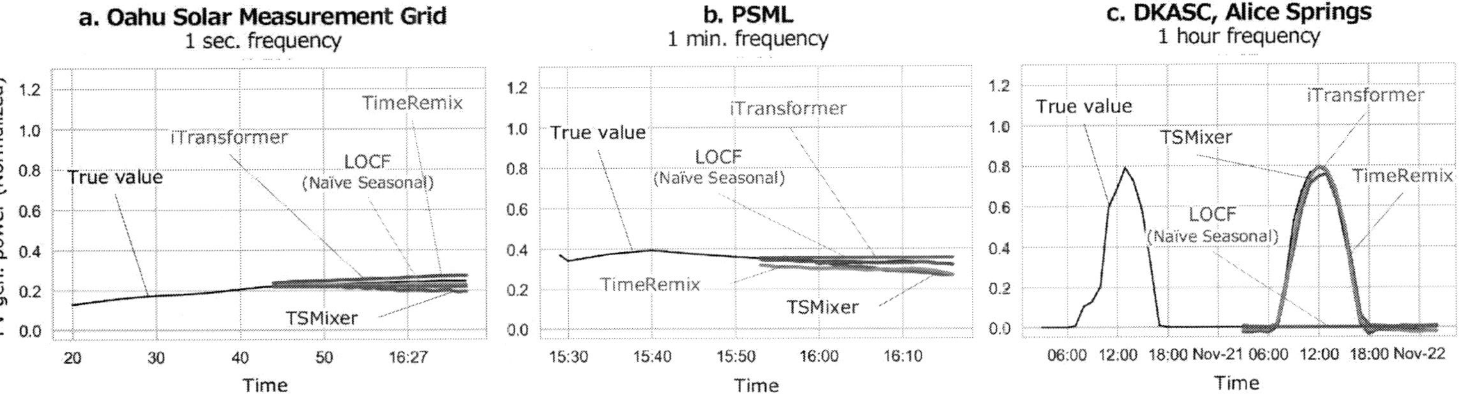

③ Load Balancing Loss

- Sparse gating can cause An **auxiliary load balancing loss** is introduced to mitigate the load imbalance, where some experts are overused while others are underutilized.
- Minimizing the load balancing loss **encourages the gating network to select a diverse set of experts** and provide training opportunities to all experts.

$$\mathcal{L}_{\text{Load}} = M \sum_{m=1}^{M} D_m P_m,$$

$$D_m = \frac{1}{N_{\mathcal{B}}} \sum_{\mathbf{X} \in \mathcal{B}} \mathbb{1} \left\{ \operatorname*{argmax}_{m' \in \mathcal{M}} G(\mathbf{X})_{m'} = m \right\},$$

$$P_m = \frac{1}{N_{\mathcal{B}}} \sum_{\mathbf{X} \in \mathcal{B}} G(\mathbf{X})_m,$$

$$\mathcal{L}_{\text{MoE}} = \mathcal{L}_{\text{MSE}} + \lambda \mathcal{L}_{\text{Load}},$$

$G(\boldsymbol{X})_m$: the gate value of m-th expert

D_m: the fraction to activate expert m

P_m: the proportion of the gating probability allocated to expert m

$\mathbb{1}$: the indicator function that returns 1 if the condition is true and 0 otherwise.

Total loss function: $\lambda = 10^{-5}$

③ Effectiveness of TimeRemix

Robust zero-shot forecasting across all resolutions

- TimeRemix is competitive with each single model by adapting to each time resolution.

Zero-shot cross-frequency forecasting performance
(RMSE: Smaller is better)

1st 2nd 3rd Untrained

Algorithm	Monash, Solar Power Dataset [24]					
	5 sec.	30 sec.	1 min.	5 min.	30 min.	1 hour
iTransformer	0.0175	0.0635	0.0855	0.1683	0.4268	0.1260
PatchTST	0.0178	0.0631	0.0849	0.1529	0.3882	0.1359
Timer	0.0204	0.0685	0.0899	0.1497	0.4335	0.1291
LSTM	0.0479	0.2855	0.0887	0.1238	0.2349	0.1585
S-Mamba	0.0255	0.0639	0.0836	0.1940	0.4298	0.1388
TSMixer	0.1328	0.1035	0.0830	0.1196	0.3423	0.1353
TimeMixer	0.0334	0.0713	0.0845	0.1535	0.4320	0.1291
TCN	0.0535	0.0998	0.1127	0.1780	0.6076	0.1308
LOCF (Naïve seasonal)	0.0229	0.0652	0.0995	0.1121	0.4576	0.5017
Moirai-MoE	0.1029	0.1436	0.1759	0.2127	0.3684	0.1918
TimeRemix (Ours)	0.0194 (#3)	0.0647 (#4)	0.0800 (#1)	0.1345 (#3)	0.4030 (#4)	0.1291 (#2)

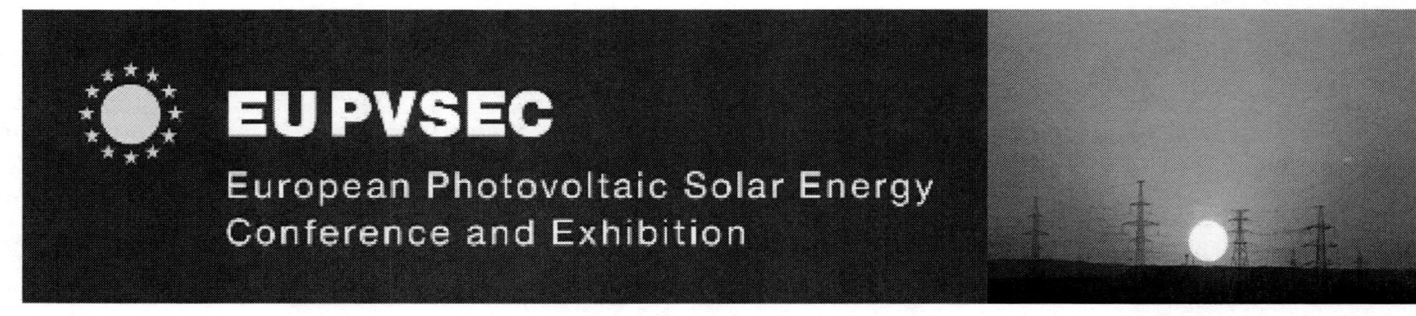

From PV potential to Grid Impact:
An Estimation of the Future PV Penetration in South-Tyrolean Electricity Grid

eurac research Azim Heydari, Enrico Dalla Maria, David Moser, **Grazia Barchi**

edyna Davide Prando, Alessandro Donadello

020485-001

Outline

- Motivation
- Objectives
- PV potential assessment
- Grid impact assessment
- Conclusion & reflection

Context and Motivation

☐ Achieve the energy and climate targets at regional, national and European level

☐ Significant increase of PV installations in 2022

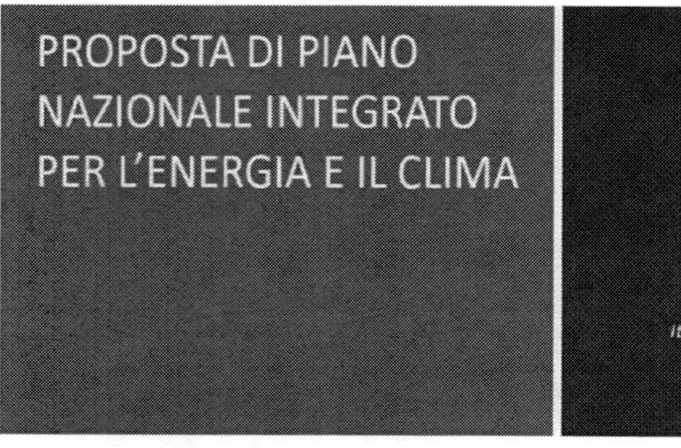

P.A. Bolzano

- PV plant installed in 2022 → 1597 (+209%)
- PV power installed in 2022 → 30.2 MW (+209%)
- PV production in 2022 → 304 GWh

Source: INFotovoltaico – statistiche trimestrali GSE dati al 31/12/2022

Objectives

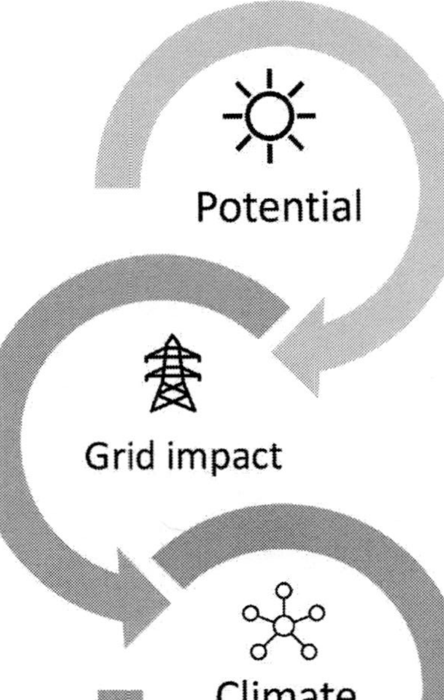

Identify the PV potential aggregated at primary substation level

Evaluate the capacity of the electricity grid to host the identified PV penetration

Comparison of the PV potential, grid hosting capacity and regional climate targets in 2030 and 2040

PV potential assessment – methodology I

Step 1: Identify Primary Substations

- Voronoi Polygons to limit area of the primary substations

Step 2: Detect rooftop

- Identify rooftop within each primary substation area

Step 3: Optimize selection Criteria

- Exclude buildings with insufficient rooftop space

Step 4: Estimate PV potential

- Calculate the rooftop solar PV potential for each primary substation

QGIS

PV potential assessment – results I

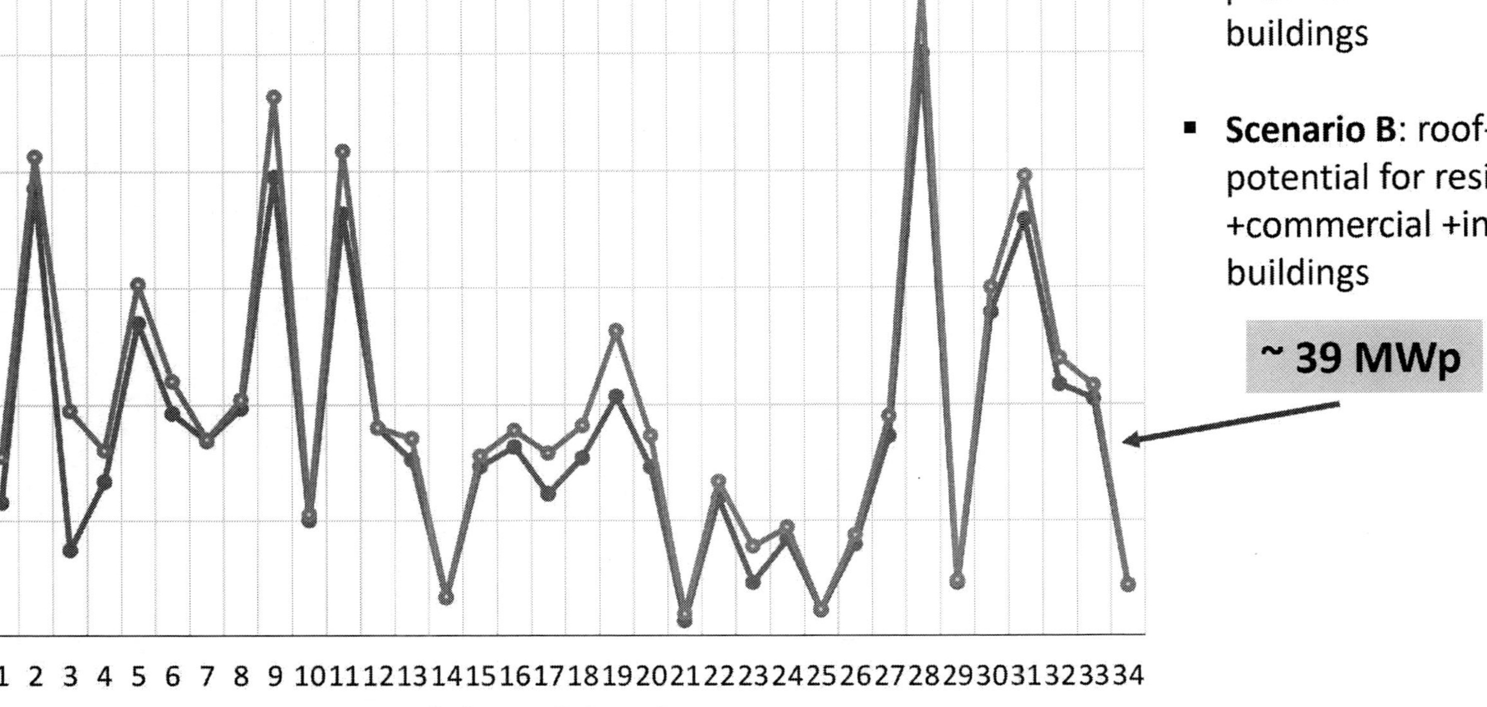

- **Scenario A**: roof-top PV potential for residential buildings

- **Scenario B**: roof-top PV potential for residential +commercial +industrial buildings

...but what about the grid?

Hosting capacity definition

The *amount of PV that can be integrated into a given distribution network keeping its performance within an acceptable range and without modification of the existing power grid infrastructure*

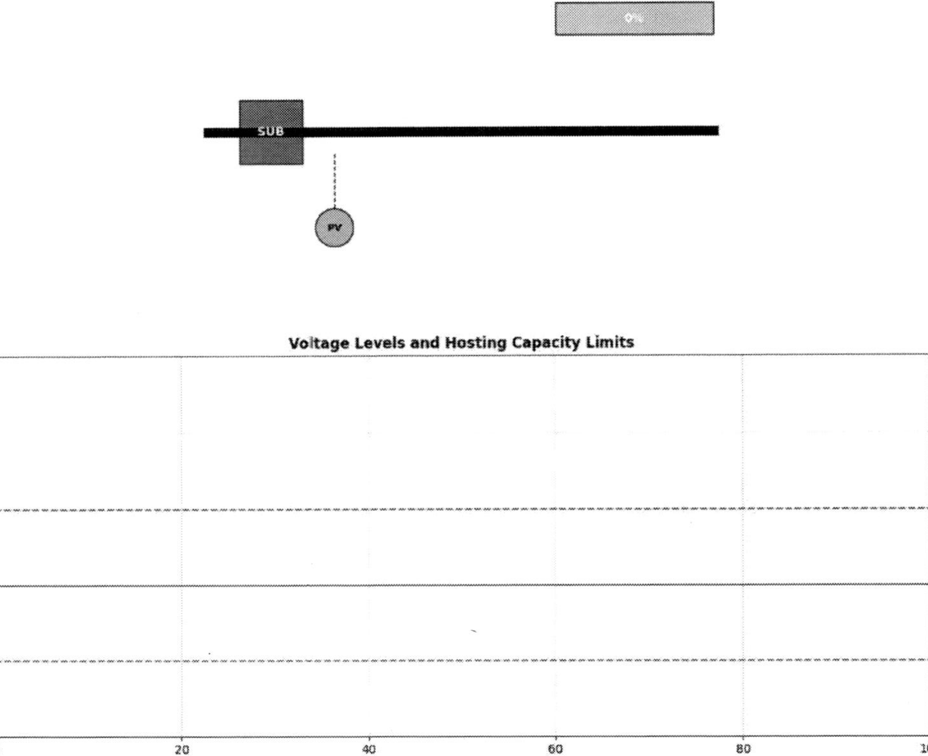

Hosting capacity methodology

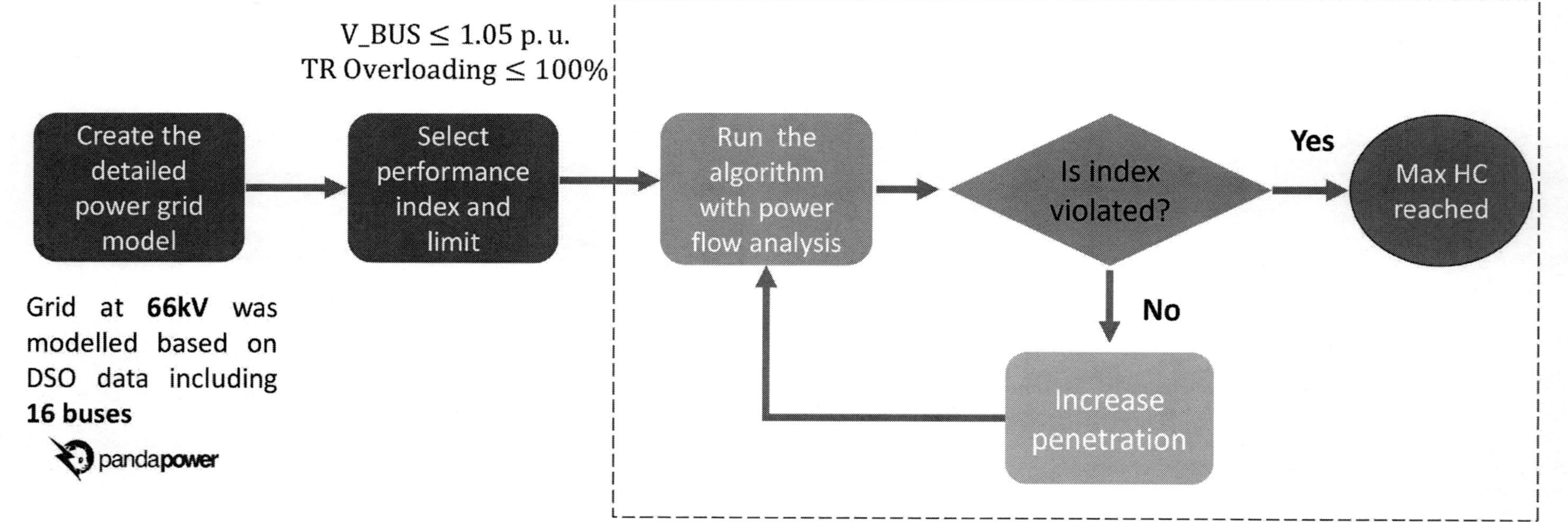

Monte-Carlo Iteration

PV power normally distributed $\rightarrow$ $\mathcal{N}\left(\mu_{PV}, \sigma_{PV}\right)$

PV placement uniformly distributed $\rightarrow$ $\mathcal{U}\left(b1, b_{N}\right)$

PV HC results: PV maximum capacity @ 66kV

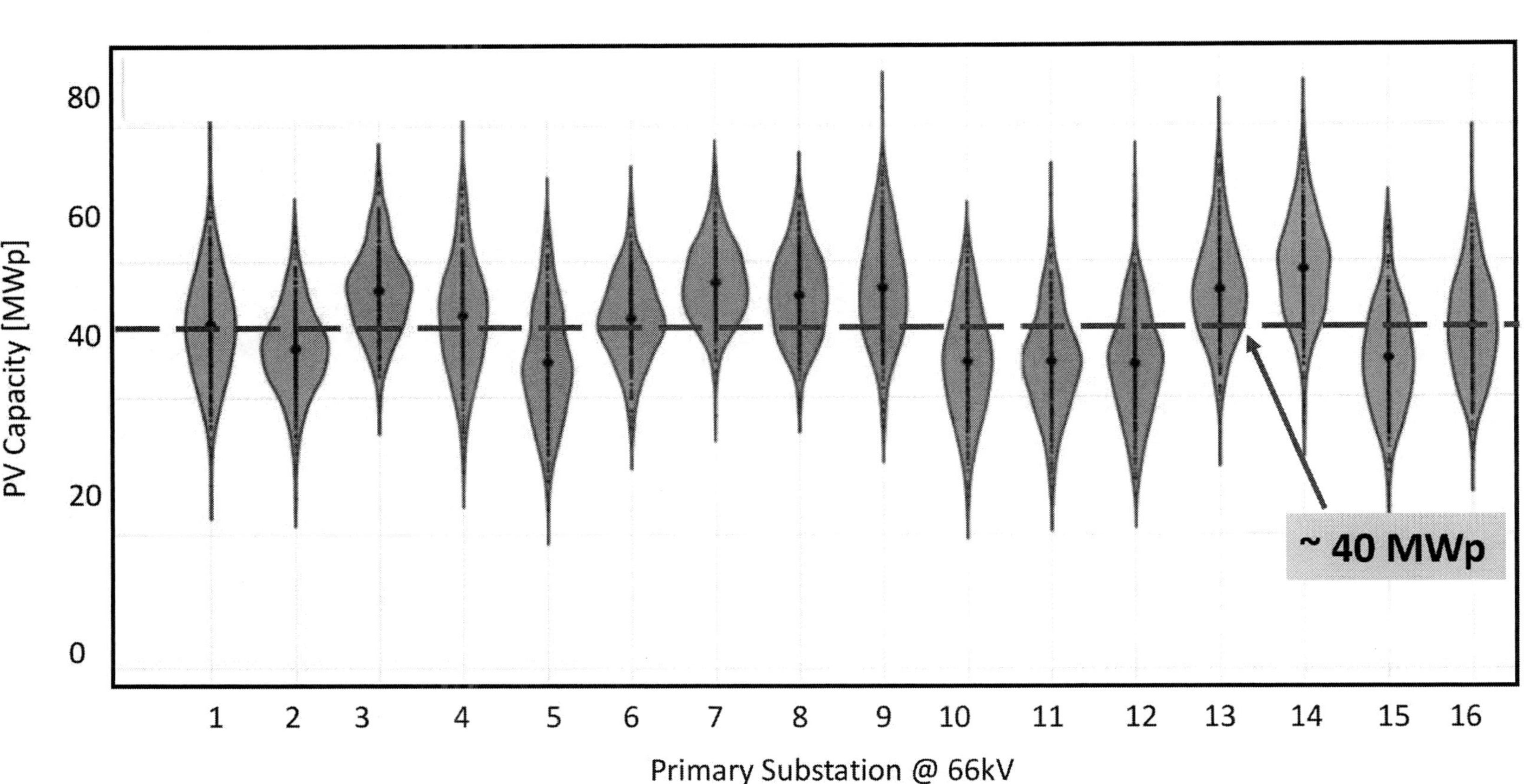

PV HC with respect to the Klimaplan targets

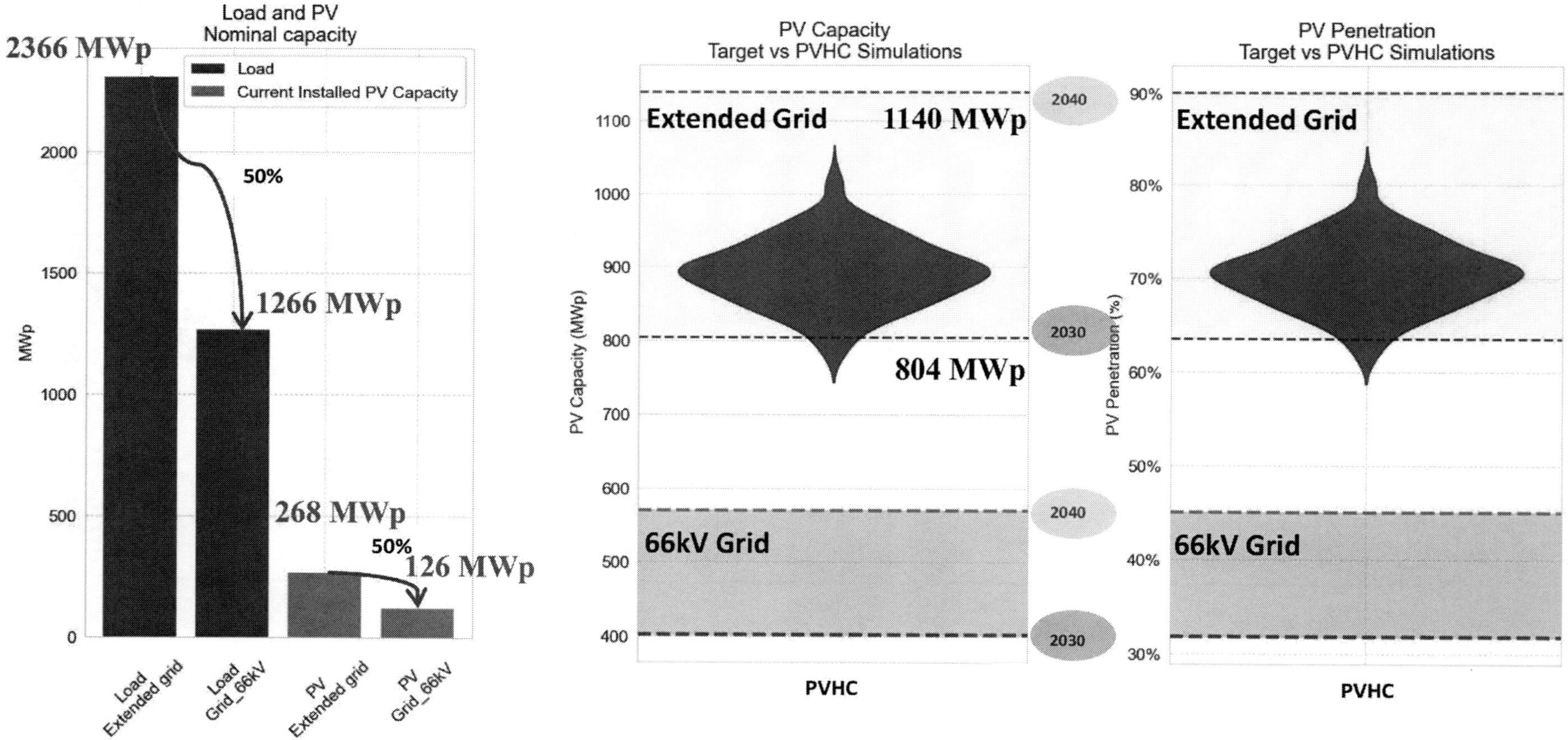

What about considering time-variability?

We used real 15 min load data measured at a primary cabin level provided by an Italian DSO

Actually, in the control zone there is 10 MW of distributed PV capacity, we studied the case in which the **2030 target of 25 MW** will be reached compared with no PV case

TO BE MITIGATED!

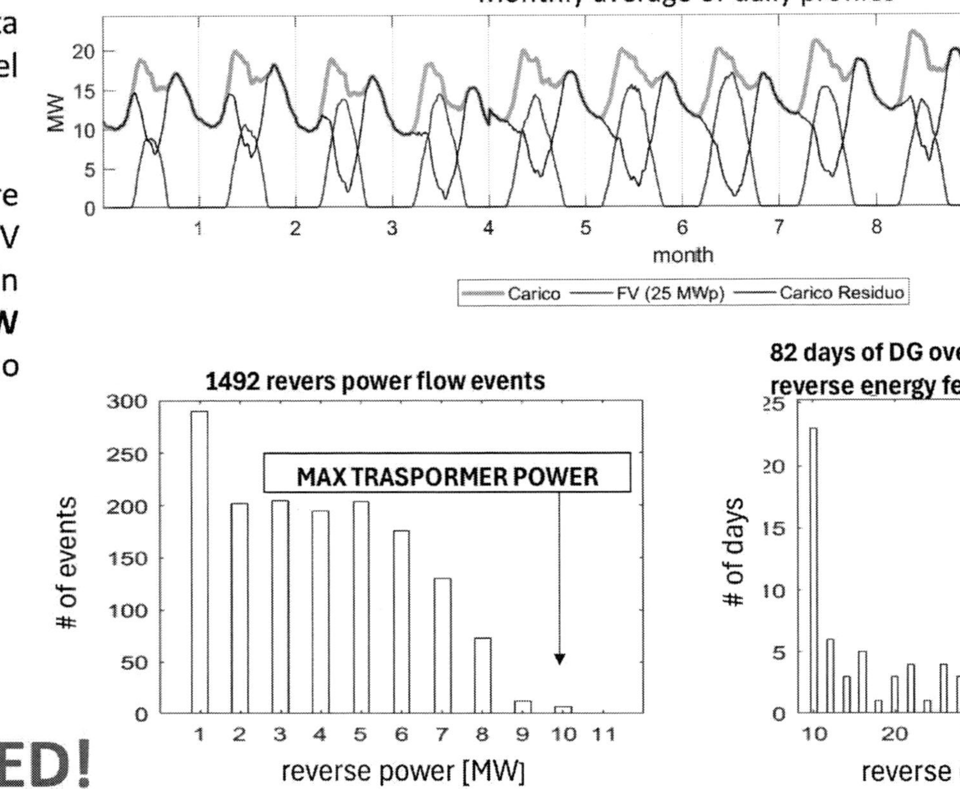

Conclusion & reflection

- An estimation of PV potential of the South-Tyrol region on rooftop and a possible local grid impact has been presented

- The mean PV HC is around 900 MWp, close to the 2030 klimaplan installation targets (804 MWp).

- However, the current HC analysis is limited by neglecting the time-variable nature of PV and load → time-series 2030 simulations reveal reverse power flow

- Limitation in the steady-state assessment of potential and HC and mitigation solution required!

Thank you!

e-mail: grazia.barchi@eurac.edu

ASSESSING THE ECONOMIC VALUE FOR GRID OPERATORS OF QUANTIFIED SMOOTHING EFFECTS FROM PV SYSTEMS WITH VARYING ORIENTATIONS

Johan Lindahl
Becquerel Sweden AB
Staffansvägen 14, 74142 Knivsta, Sweden, johan@becquerelsweden.se

ABSTRACT: As the number of solar photovoltaic (PV) installations grows rapidly, accurate registry data and efficient use of existing grid capacity are increasingly critical for stable and cost-effective distribution grid operation, as well as for enabling further PV deployment without unnecessary physical grid reinforcement. This study employs an innovative remote sensing method that combines aerial imagery, machine learning, and Light Detection and Ranging (LiDAR) data to identify, validate, and simulate PV power generation. The method can detect discrepancies between grid operator registries and actual PV installations and quantify the orientation-based smoothing effects that arise when distributed PV systems have varying azimuths and tilt angles. By accounting for these effects, it can free up significant existing capacity in low-voltage distribution grids, reducing the need for costly reinforcements. Application of the method in three Swedish low-voltage grids demonstrated tangible economic benefits, with planned investments of 400,000 (~€36k) and 1.5 million SEK (~€136k) avoided. The study evaluates the value creation of inventory-based PV mapping and PV orientation smoothing effect analysis from the perspective of grid operators, highlighting the method's potential as a cost-effective, data-driven tool for grid planning, investment prioritization, and integration of distributed PV power generation.
Keywords: Photovoltaics, Grid capacity, Economic value assessment, Remote sensing, Orientation smoothing effect

1 INTRODUCTION

Solar power is expanding at a rapid pace both globally and in Sweden. In 2024, photovoltaics (PV) accounted for 75% of all newly installed power generation capacity worldwide, with a preliminary addition of 600 GW [1]. In the European Union, solar now represents 14% of electricity generation [1], of which about half is distributed PV systems connected to a grid connection point where also consumption takes place. This fast and decentralized growth is fundamentally challenging electricity distribution grids [2] which in northern Europe have traditionally been designed to handle peak demand occurring during cold winter days. In areas with high PV penetration, the most critical loading hours for distribution grids now occur during sunny summer days rather than during winter peaks, marking a paradigm shift in grid planning.

A key challenge for grid operators lies in the lack of detailed information about the grid connected PV systems. Typically, Distributed System Operators (DSOs) only have access to basic data such as the property address and the installed capacity of modules and/or inverters. Missing information includes the azimuth and tilt of the PV systems [3], whether installations consist of multiple orientations, and the total actual PV generation profiles as DSOs only measure the power injected to the grid. In the absence of more detailed information, DSOs face challenges in accurately estimating PV power injected into the grid [4], [5], and it is therefore praxis among DSOs in Sweden (and many more European countries) to assume that all PV systems can produce their maximum power — usually the rated power of the inverters — simultaneously and that no electricity is self-consumed. These assumptions tend to overestimate grid stress, leading to unnecessary and costly reinforcements.

In practice, this scenario cannot occur, since distributed PV systems are typically rooftop-mounted and therefore follow the underlying roof geometry [3]. As a result, their orientations and tilt angles vary considerably [6], producing asynchronous generation patterns and giving rise to a natural 'smoothing effect,' here defined as the PV Orientation Smoothing Effect (POSE).

To address this information gap, an AI-based remote sensing and PV power simulation model package, called *Alfrödull*, has been developed. By combining aerial imagery with Light Detection and Ranging (LiDAR) data, this method can identify more than 95% of all PV systems in a given area [7], [8] and estimate their azimuth and tilt with an accuracy of ±3° in 95% of cases [6]. These parameters are then used to simulate the hourly electricity generation of individual PV systems with high spatial and temporal resolution. Validation against measured data from 40 reference systems shows strong agreement, with coefficients of determination (R^2) in the range 0.83–0.96 [9].

A crucial outcome of this approach is the ability to quantify the POSE, i.e., the reduction in aggregated PV power peaks due to differences in PV system orientations. By simulating the generated power from all PV systems connected to a distribution grid over several years of historical weather data (2017–2024), this smoothing effect has been systematically quantified and analyzed in three Swedish grids, down at the level of individual substations, in a parallel technical study [10].

Building on these results, the present study investigates the value creation of the remote sensing generated data and the economic implications of the quantified POSE analysis from a DSO perspective.

Traditionally, increasing the acceptance limit [11] for PV systems in distribution grids requires physical grid reinforcement, with associated costs determined by the scope and capacity of the grid. If the power lines cannot handle the increased load, they may need to be replaced or upgraded, costing between €10k and €100k per kilometer (in Sweden), depending on whether they are overhead lines or underground cables. Additionally, transformers may require upgrades, which can range from €10k to €500k.

2 DATA

Alfrödull scans were applied to the most recent aerial imagery of three Swedish low voltage grids — June 2024 for Falun (FLN), and May 2024 for Karlshamn (KHN) and

Fagersta (FGA) — covering their respective grid areas. The scans identified 2015 PV systems within FLN, 327 within KHN and 256 within FGA. Of those it turned out that 80, 1 and 28, respectively, were off-grid systems not connected to the distribution grid.

For all grid-connected PV systems in these grids, PV power generation was simulated at 30-minute resolution and subsequently aggregated at the substation level. The POSE was then calculated for each substation as the difference between the maximum aggregated PV output observed over the 2017–2024 period and the sum of the rated AC capacities of the connected inverters, following the methodology described in detail in [10].

3   METHODOLOGY

To assess the perceived value of the *Alfrödull* method from a DSO perspective, two semi-structured interviews were conducted. The first took place with the Head of Grid Market, Oscar Willén, at the Swedish DSO Falu Elnät, and the second with the Head of the Grid Business Area, Benjamin Gacanin, together with the Business Developer, Felix Kjellvåg, at Karlshamn Energi. Full interview transcripts (in Swedish) are available in this research project report [12].

The objective of the interviews was to collect qualitative insights regarding the benefits of improved knowledge about existing solar PV capacity, the potential to avoid or postpone costly grid reinforcements, and the requirements and expectations for a method such as *Alfrödull* to be applicable in routine grid planning.

3   RESULTS AND DISCUSSION

3.1 Detection of Discrepancies in PV Registries

An unexpected value of the *Alfrödull* method, first identified in [7] and confirmed in this study, is its ability to detect discrepancies between PV systems identified through remote sensing and those registered by DSOs.

Once applied to a grid area, *Alfrödull* generates a dataset of PV system polygons that can be compared with the DSO's administrative registry, which is based on notifications submitted by installers or property owners. Both PV databases contain errors, but by aligning them — using property identifiers as a linking key — missing or incorrect entries can be identified, thereby improving overall data quality. Figure 1 illustrates this overlap using a Venn diagram of actual PV installations within the scanned grid areas. Such reconciliation is a necessary first step toward constructing a complete and connected database that can be used to simulate PV generation and quantify the PV orientation smoothing effects.

Because *Alfrödull* relies exclusively on remote sensing data sources, such as aerial orthophotos, LiDAR data and geospatial data from the Swedish Land Survey, it can detect PV modules that are absent from the DSO's registry. Discrepancies may occur when systems are installed without formal notification, when registration processes are incomplete, or when installations are off-grid applications. Conversely, *Alfrödull* may also identify systems inconsistencies in reported system size, for example when the observed module area does not match the registered capacity.

Although effective, *Alfrödull* does not capture every system. Certain types, such as vertically mounted PV

arrays or building-integrated PV (BIPV) systems, remain undetectable in aerial imagery. Even conventional rooftop installations can be overlooked if, for instance, they are heavily shaded at the time of imaging [7]. Nonetheless, the machine-learning-based recognition method achieves an identification accuracy of about 95% [7]. This is supported by the results shown in Figure 1, where 96.7% of all 2,489 grid-connected PV systems in the three scanned grids were correctly identified.

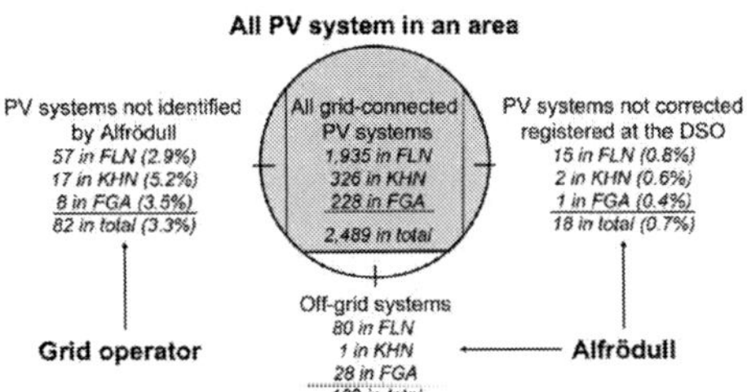

Figure 1. Venn diagram over the results of the inventory scans of three distribution grids.

Cross-checks against DSO registries showed that 79 systems in FLN, one in KHN and 28 in FGA were mounted on buildings without grid connection and were therefore correctly absent from the registries, as Figure 1 shows. The registries, in turn, listed 82 grid-connected systems commissioned before the aerial surveys that *Alfrödull* failed to detect. Conversely, *Alfrödull* identified 18 PV systems across the three grids on grid-connected buildings without corresponding completion reports in the DSO registries, despite the installations being visible in imagery for at least nine months.

In addition, 51 systems in FLN, 35 in KHN and 7 in FGA showed significant discrepancies between observed module area, adjusted using tilt derived from LiDAR data [6], and the registered capacity. Karlshamn Energi followed up on these 35 cases in KHN and confirmed after contact with the system owners that 27 systems indeed had an incorrectly registered size. The causes varied and in some cases included: (1) incorrect information provided at the time of registration by the installer, (2) main fuse capacity had mistakenly been recorded as PV capacity, (3) systems that had been expanded after the initial registration without this being reported, since no change in subscription or fuse rating was required, and (4) in a few instances battery capacity had erroneously been added to PV capacity in the registry.

Both DSOs highlighted in the interviews that the independent inventory added clear value, primarily by identifying missing or incorrectly registered systems. Karlshamn Energi emphasized the benefit of verifying suspected anomalies and proactively contacting customers to correct errors, while Falu Elnät valued the improved overview of actual installed capacity and the reduced uncertainty in grid planning. Although, according to the interviews, the discrepancies in their registry had limited direct economic impact for the DSOs, they noted that errors could lead to missed compensation for customers and pose safety risks for maintenance personnel, as unregistered systems may cause unanticipated reverse power flow.

The findings indicate that remote sensing can serve as a useful tool for improving PV registry quality, which is important for grid planning, load calculations, and future investments. The analysis also highlighted deficiencies in existing routines, which the two DSOs reported intending to address.

3.2 Value of Freed Grid Capacity through POSE

The interviews with two Swedish DSOs highlighted how detailed analyses of orientation-based smoothing effects can inform grid planning and investment decisions in areas with high PV penetration. Both Karlshamn Energi and Falu Elnät confirmed that the rapid increase in PV installations has created local capacity challenges, leading in some cases to concrete investments in grid lines or new substations. For example, Karlshamn Energi had planned a new substation at an estimated cost of approximately 1.5 million SEK (~€136k), while Falu Elnät had implemented minor reinforcements but emphasized that most investments are primarily guided by the age of certain parts of their grid and technical condition rather than PV-induced capacity limits.

Across the three studied grids in [13], POSE, i.e., the overestimation of injected PV power relative to rated AC capacity, ranged from 8.7% in KHN to 11.5–11.8% in FLN and FGA. Maximum POSE at individual substations reached up to 20–24% of rated AC power, highlighting that local effects can substantially exceed grid-average values [13].

Representatives from both DSOs acknowledged the value of the remote-sensing-generated data and the POSE analyses, where Figure 2 illustrates the quantified orientation-based smoothing effects in the FGA grid, serving as an example of the analysis conducted and the type of data delivered to the three DSOs.

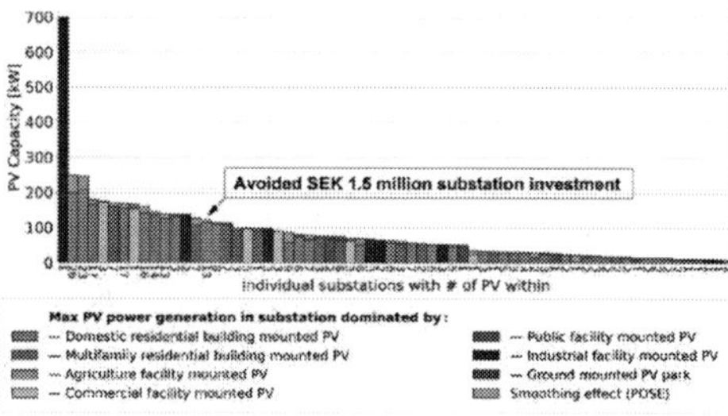

Figure 2. Registered PV capacity at all 91 transformer substations in the FGA grid with at least one PV installation as of May 2024. Each bar represents one substation, with the bar height showing the total rated AC capacity of all connected PV systems—corresponding to the capacity the grid operator assumes could be fed into the grid simultaneously. Bar colors indicate the market segment contributing the largest share of capacity at each substation, while the orange segment denotes the POSE in each substation. Numbers below the bars show the number of PV installations per substation. The arrow points to the substation where Karlshamn Energi had planned a new transformer investment.

The detailed capacity assessments generated by *Alfrödull* were in the interviews described as an important, evidence-based complement to previous methods. Karlshamn Energi reported that the POSE analysis allowed several pending PV customers to be connected without constructing the planned substation, yielding a savings of 1.5 million SEK (~€136k). Similarly, Falu Elnät postponed a planned cable reinforcement costing 400,000

SEK (~€36k) after the POSE analyses indicated more available capacity than previously assumed [10]. Beyond these specific cases, the analyses provide a valuable tool for evaluating other substations as additional PV installations will be installed.

The remote-sensing generated PV power generation data and POSE analysis were particularly appreciated by the two DSOs in early stages of the connection process, enabling faster and more accurate responses to customers while improving the prioritization of grid interventions. For example, Karlshamn Energi used the detailed analyses of interconnected substations to adjust low-voltage grid breakpoints, optimizing capacity utilization without new investments. Falu Elnät emphasized the importance of considering alternative costs, including preserving residual value in existing components, avoiding displacement effects, and limiting increased grid losses.

3.3 Knowledge Gain among the DSOs

Both DSOs also reported a knowledge gain from the analyses. Karlshamn Energi highlighted that some planned investments could have been avoided and that certain customer connections had previously been rejected unnecessarily. This prompted follow-up with customers and internal process improvements, particularly regarding their pre-notifications and post-connection verification. Both interviewees concluded that existing calculation models did not always reflect actual PV power generation, emphasizing the need for data-driven, installation-specific approaches.

3.4 Regulation, Incentives and Governance

The interviewees further noted that current Swedish and EU regulation and incentive structures largely favor traditional physical grid expansion rather than digitalization or innovative, flexible solutions, which complicates the adoption of methods that could optimize existing infrastructure and delay or avoid costly investments. Karlshamn Energi emphasized that economic incentives for data-driven decision-making, increased digitalization, and smarter grid use are currently limited, although these solutions are crucial for handling electrification and future capacity needs cost-effectively. Falu Elnät shared similar views, noting that their historical financial margins allowed testing new technologies despite regulatory uncertainties and unclear guidance on evaluating alternative technologies.

Both DSOs agreed that upcoming EU requirements for greater flexibility and efficient use of existing infrastructure will drive future development. Strategic use of already collected data, particularly at the substation level, was identified as critical. Forecasts for local power generation, such as PV, were highlighted as an important tool for integrating flexibility solutions in operational management, with remote sensing data generated by *Alfrödull* serving as a concrete example of how such data can be leveraged effectively.

Municipal ownership was described as a strength in promoting innovation, sustainability, and long-term capacity planning. Karlshamn Energi noted that their municipal board provides clear strategic goals related to sustainable development and proactive capacity planning, supporting initiatives such as digitalization and flexible grid agreements. Falu Elnät similarly reported that municipal ownership encourages innovation and a broader, long-term perspective, fostering investments that benefit the municipality. Even when objectives such as capacity utilization or innovation are not formally stated in ownership directives, they are actively discussed and prioritized in strategic planning.

4 CONCLUSIONS

This study demonstrates the potential of combining remote sensing and high-resolution PV simulation to optimize grid capacity, guide investment decisions, and facilitate the integration of distributed PV generation, offering a cost-effective and scalable tool for modern distribution grid management.

The *Alfrödull* method enables accurate identification of installed PV systems, detection of discrepancies in DSO registries, and quantification of orientation-based smoothing effects. By accounting for smoothing effects, substantial existing grid capacity can be unlocked, reducing the need for costly physical grid reinforcements, as evidenced by avoided investments of 400,000 SEK (~€36k) and 1.5 million SEK (~€136k) in the participating grids.

Interviews with two Swedish DSOs revealed that the method provides both tangible economic benefits and valuable operational insights, supporting data-driven grid planning, prioritization of grid interventions, and faster customer connections. Moreover, the analyses contribute to improved registry accuracy, reducing risks associated with unregistered or incorrectly registered PV systems.

The study also highlights institutional and regulatory factors affecting the adoption of data-driven solutions. While current incentives and frameworks often favor traditional physical grid expansions, municipal ownership and emerging EU requirements for greater flexibility present opportunities for innovative approaches.

5 ACKNOWLEDGEMENTS

The author gratefully acknowledges financial support from the Swedish Energy Agency (Project number P2024-02998). The Agency had no role in the study's design, execution, or interpretation.

The author also sincerely thanks Oscar Willén at Falu Elnät, and Benjamin Gacanin and Felix Kjellvåg at Karlshamn Energi, for their support in scanning their respective grids, granting permission to publish the general results, and participating in the interviews.

4 REFERENCES

[1] IEA PVPS task 1 *et al.*, "Trends in Photovoltaic Applications — 2024," 2024.

[2] R. Gupta *et al.*, "Spatial analysis of distribution grid capacity and costs to enable massive deployment of PV, electric mobility and electric heating," *Appl Energy*, vol. 287, no. October 2020, p. 116504, 2021, doi: 10.1016/j.apenergy.2021.116504.

[3] S. Killinger *et al.*, "On the search for representative characteristics of PV systems: Data collection and analysis of PV system azimuth, tilt, capacity, yield and shading," *Solar Energy*, vol. 173, no. August, pp. 1087–1106, 2018, doi: 10.1016/j.solener.2018.08.051.

[4] Å. L. Sørensen, J. Hole, D. Bjerkehagen, and H. T. Walnum, "From customers to prosumers: PV systems impact on residential load profiles , peak power , and coincidence," in *CIRED 2025 Conference*, 2025, pp. 1–5.

[5] T. Landelius, S. Andersson, and R. Abrahamsson, "System Imbalance from Solar Energy Trading," in *Proceedings ot the 8th Solar Integration Workshop*, 2018, pp. 1–18.

[6] D. Lingfors, R. Johansson, and J. Lindahl, "Deriving the orientation of existing solar energy systems from LiDAR data at scale," *Solar Energy*, vol. 291, no. 113344, 2025, doi: 10.1016/j.solener.2025.113344.

[7] J. Lindahl, R. Johansson, and D. Lingfors, "Mapping of decentralised photovoltaic and solar thermal systems by remote sensing aerial imagery and deep machine learning for statistic generation," *Energy and AI*, vol. 14, p. 100300, 2023, doi: 10.1016/j.egyai.2023.100300.

[8] Â. Frimane, R. Johansson, J. Munkhammar, D. Lingfors, and J. Lindahl, "Identifying small decentralized solar systems in aerial images using deep learning," *Solar Energy*, vol. 262, 2023, doi: 10.1016/j.solener.2023.111822.

[9] G. Öhgren, L. Molin, M. Lindh, D. Lingfors, and J. Lindahl, "Remote sensing compatible snow loss modelling for PV power simulations," *Solar Energy*, vol. Unpublishe, 2025.

[10] J. Widén, G. Öhgren, E. Lindvall, D. Lingfors, and J. Lindahl, "Quantifying distributed PV orientation smoothing effects and their impact on electricity grid performance," *Manuscript*.

[11] M. H. J. Bollen and S. K. Rönnberg, "Hosting capacity of the power grid for renewable electricity production and new large consumption equipment," *Energies (Basel)*, vol. 10, no. 9, 2017, doi: 10.3390/en10091325.

[12] J. Lindahl, "Alfrödull — Frigörande av nätkapacitet för solceller genom fjärranalys — Slutrapport P2024-02998," 2025.

[13] J. Widén, G. Öhgren, E. Lindvall, D. Lingfors, and J. Lindahl, "Quantifying distributed PV orientation smoothing effects and their impact on electricity grid performance," *Manuscript*.

COST AND RELIABILITY OF 24/7 CARBON FREE ELECTRICITY FROM PV – EVALUATION OF OVERNIGHT SOLAR-PLUS-STORAGE IN ABU DHABI

Harry Apostoleris[1], Kareem Younes[2], Matteo Chiesa[2,3]

[1] EPRI
[2] Khalifa University, Abu Dhabi, UAE
[3] UiT The Arctic University of Norway, Tromso, NO
HApostoleris@EPRI.com

ABSTRACT: This manuscript considers the deployment of PV with battery energy storage systems (PV+BESS) as a resource for 24/7 carbon-free energy (24/7 CFE). Its analysis is based on a real upcoming project in Abu Dhabi that was announced earlier this year to combine 5.2GW of PV with 19GWh of lithium iron phosphate (LFP) batteries to create a "round the clock" solar power station that functions as a 1GW baseload generator suitable for supplying data centers or other large continuous loads that require on-demand power [1]. Using this project as a guide, we study the potential of PV+BESS 24/7 CFE resources from both a cost and reliability perspective, including an estimated cost breakdown and LCOE assessment of the announced plant design based on recent market developments and survey of global PV and BESS projects; availability analysis of 24/7 solar based on a simple dispatch algorithm to assess its suitability as a true baseload generator; and discussion of the implications of real-world 24/7 solar for energy system planning and energy storage requirements to support deep decarbonization. The technoeconomic study finds that a total project cost of 6bnUSD, as reported for the facility planned in Abu Dhabi, can be explained by recent changes in the LFP battery and stationary storage market, leading to total levelized cost of electricity in the range of 60-80USD/MWh, with 97% availability as a baseload resource, with exact cost depending on specific assumptions about systems configuration, load and performance. We consider the cost impact of incorporating peaking gas-fired capacity to back up PV+BESS, as is planned at the Abu Dhabi facility [2]. Through this study we demonstrate how changing battery economics are rapidly shifting Li-ion technology towards longer-duration storage applications, enabling higher cost-effective penetration of PV in national energy systems.

Keywords: energy storage, clean firm power, hybrid power plants, data center energy supply

1 BACKGROUND

1.1 Solar Energy in the UAE

Despite its status a major oil-exporting country, the United Arab Emirates (UAE) has become a global leader in utility-scale solar energy deployment, consistently setting records for scale and low cost in utility-scale PV systems. As analyzed in previous work [3-5], PV projects in the UAE have pushed the limits of economic feasibility based on a combination of low hardware cost, with bulk imports from leading equipment manufacturers (increasing dominated by Chinese vendors); low labor costs strongly tied to the South Asian labor market; and a favorable financing environment with low-rate financing available to projects backed by large state-connected entities. Prices achieved under aggressive PPA auctions (e.g. the first solar PPA at less than <3c/kWh achieved in Dubai in 2017) have often been "ahead of their time," raising questions as to their viability before seeing these prices replicated across the world as global markets "catch up" to the trends being anticipated by aggressive local bids. Recent announcements in the hybrid solar+storage space continue this trend of leading on renewable energy costs, and are illustrative to understand shape of global energy storage market, strategic approaches to energy storage deployment & prospects for further solar energy deployment around the world.

1.2 Energy for AI growth

The UAE has ambitious goals for artificial intelligence, aiming to become a global leader in hosting AI data centers. Global challenges in energy sector resulting from the emergence of new electrical demand from AI (recently on display in the US and elsewhere) have included stress on the energy hardware supply chain – e.g. spiking prices and extended wait times for gas turbines; costs of grid and generation capacity upgrades which have led to rising consumer prices as the cost of building new capacity to serve AI are passed on to ratepayers; and grid stability challenges due to unique and highly variable load profile of AI data centers. In response to this, solutions have been proposed including increasing the flexibility of AI data center loads, as is being explored in EPRI's "DCFlex" initiative [6], or simply to partly or fully insulate data center from the grid through the use of on-site storage for demand smoothing, or generating the needed energy fully on site. On-site or dedicated data center power supply presents a natural use case for "clean firm" power, or 24/7 CFE, where a combination of renewables and energy storage replaces conventional power station. The most recently launched renewable energy project in Abu Dhabi offers an example of how carbon-free or newly carbon-free energy can be supplied to data centers or other large loads from dedicated renewable+storage hybrid facilities.

2 ABU DHABI'S "ROUND THE CLOCK" SOLAR ENERGY PROJECT – COST ANALYSIS

2.1 Description of the plant

The planned "round the clock" solar power plant has been described as part of the country's AI strategy, indicating its intent to be used to power AI data centers. The facility will consist of 5.2GW PV and 19GWh BESS supplying 1GW baseload power to the grid [7]. The plant is part of a total investment of 10bnUSD package for PV+BESS, and open-cycle gas turbine plant providing backup power, and grid connection and upgrades; 6bnUSD of this has been allocated to the PV+BESS component as shown in Table 1 [8]

While the price tag for this project seems low relative to global expectations, recent developments in global markets for PV and particularly batteries offer justification for what, for some, are surprising numbers.

Table I: Total investment in clean firm power supply for AI in Abu Dhabi

	Capacity	Cost ($)
PV +BESS	5.2GW/19GWh	5.2bn
OCGT	1GW	1.35bn
Transmission upgrades		2.5bn

2.2 Market developments: PV

Utility-scale PV in the Gulf region saw falling capex pre-2020, followed by a plateau post-covid at ~600USD/kW. Pure PV PPA prices around 1.5c/kWh have been the norm and are now the expectation for new-build solar in much of the region (Figure 1). Some savings in opex have reported, largely due to the emergence of robotic cleaning as a means to reduce the labor intensiveness of combatting the rapid soiling of modules that occurs in the dusty desert climate of the Gulf.

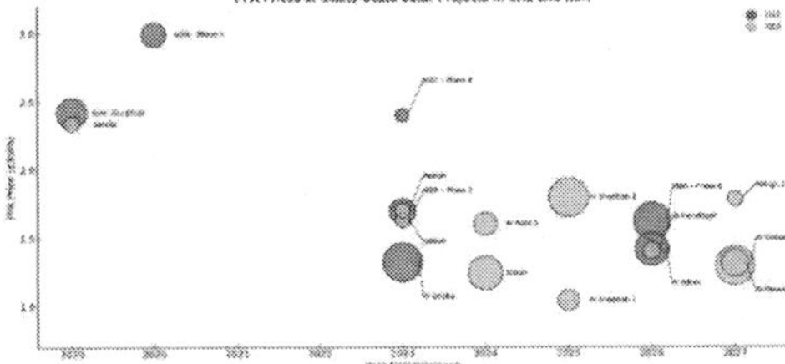

Figure 1: PPA Prices for utility-scale solar in the UAE and Saudi Arabia

Table II: Current costs in Gulf region for utility-scale PV & battery systems

	Cost	Cost ($)
PV	600USD/kW	5.2bn
BESS [9]	90USD/kWh	1.35bn
BESS Construction	240USD/kW	

2.3 Market developments: Batteries

More significant changes have occurred in this decade in the Li-ion battery market, comparable to what occurred in the PV module market in the previous decade, where a combination of industrial scaling and extreme price pressure brought both market prices and production costs dramatically lower. In the case of batteries, much of the growth driving industrial learning has been in the EV industry, where lithium-iron-phosphate (LFP) technology has become dominant. In addition, a mandate in China that utility-scale PV installations include energy storage drove stationary storage product development by Chinese firms. Battery cell prices of 60USD/kWh reported in 2024 [10], with further price drops are expected over next 1-2 years, with. These falling costs have been reflected in recent BESS projects in region, particularly in Saudi Arabia where BESS costs of just over 90USD/kWh usable have been confirmed.

2.4 Overnight and levelized cost assessment

Overall, the past several years have seen core technology cost decreases, particularly in energy storage, coupled with overall inflation & high financing costs. Taking this into consideration, the reported capex for the PV+BESS project is consistent with the current global market and local factors. In Figure 2 we show a modeled cost and LCOE breakdown, based on the values first used in [3] with adjustments to technology costs that have changed in the intervening years.

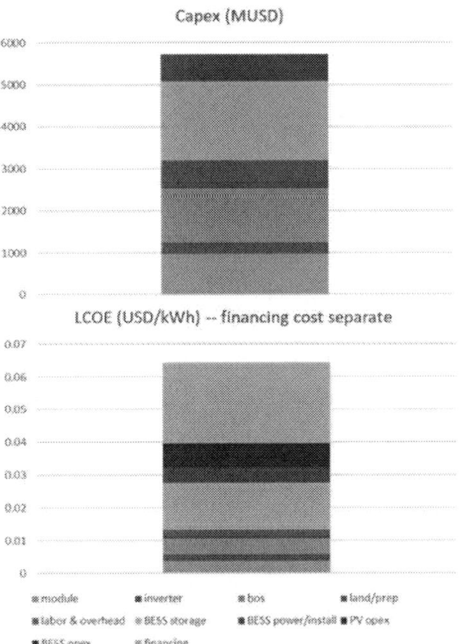

Figure 2: Capex and LCOE estimated breakdown for 24-7 PV+BESS providing 1GW baseload power

3 PERFORMANCE AS A BASELOAD RESOURCE

To assess the performance of the proposed plant as a baseload power resource, we implemented a simple dispatch algorithm where energy generated from solar

1. is dispatched to meet demand
2. After meeting demand, is fed to battery
3. if battery is full, curtailed
4. If demand exceeds solar generation, energy is dispatched from storage
5. if net demand exceeds dispatchable energy from storage, energy shortage is recorded

In Figure 3 we compare the summer day performance of the plant to a rainy or cloudy period with lower solar generation in the winter. Periods of low energy production are seen to challenge system availability as a baseload resource, as the battery is not charged sufficiently during the day to supply a full 1GW at night. These periods reduce the total annual availability to ~97%, which necessitates the inclusion of the gas turbine backup system in order to serve as a true "firm" resource.

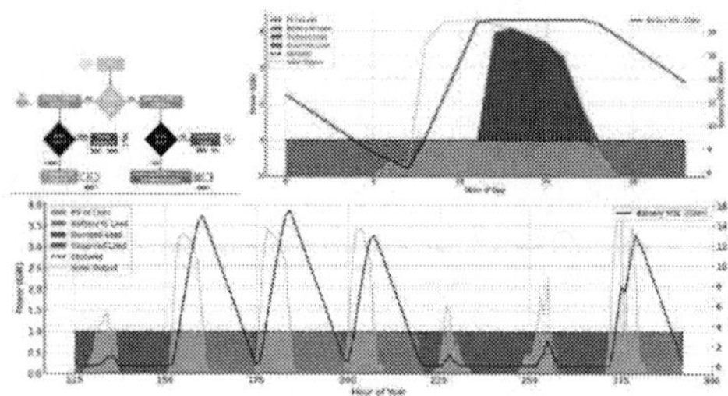

Figure 3: Simple dispatch algorithm (top left) applied on a summer day (top right) and a cloudy winter week (bottom)

4 STRATEGIC ENERGY PLANNING – CLIMBING THE ENRGY STORAGE LADDER

The previous section illustrated how 24-hour energy can be provided from a hybrid PV+BESS system with a fossil fuel backup. However, baseload availability is not necessary for an energy system in transition. Rather, storage can be deployed progressively to address the challenges that arise from higher and higher renewable penetrations in the energy system. In Figure 4 we visualize energy storage requirements as a "ladder" of different storage durations addressing different challenges that arise at different levels of solar adoption [Table 3], highlighting a strategic approach of building storage to meet immediate needs. The falling cost of storage offers an argument in favor of this approach, whereby additional storage hours can be added at lower cost in future years as the need arises. The calculated LCOE for different storage durations at current costs is plotted in Figure 5.

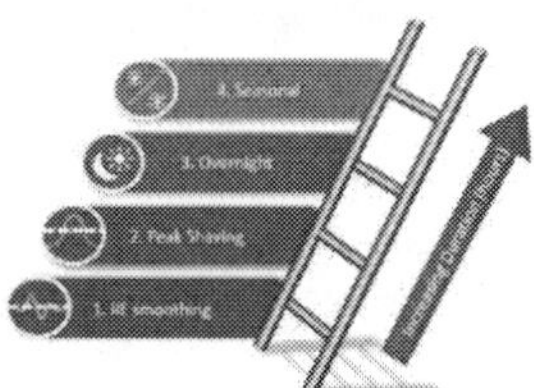

Figure 4: Strategic energy storage deployment, "climbing the ladder" of different use cases as renewable penetration increases

Table III: Use cases for different storage durations in energy systems

Function	Duration
RE smoothing	~1hr
Ramp rate management, peak shaving	~4hr
Overnight storage, island operation	~24hr
Multiday-seasonal storage	days-months

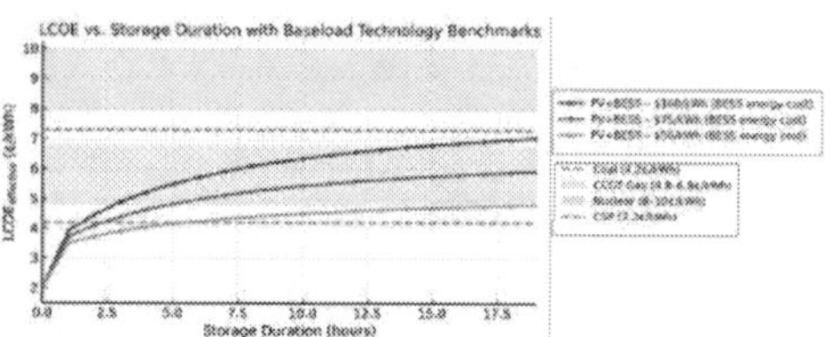

Figure 5: calculated LCOE for PV+BESS at varying storage durations

6 CONCLUSIONS

In this study we have looked at the economics and performance of PV+BESS systems as baseload generation resource. These economics are rapidly evolving due to major changes occurring in battery market, driven by EV adoption, internal policies in China and industrial learning curve previously observed for PV modules. Nominal clean-firm PV+BESS (clean firm) systems appear to be approaching viability in the most favorable markets; however, true firm power requires conventional (e.g. gas turbine) backup for resilience through low-sun periods. More generally we note that "clean-firm" may not always be the most useful concept to guide near-term energy system planning under highly dynamic market conditions; expected future price reductions favor strategic approach to energy storage deployment to maximize the rate of PV adoption, where storage systems are built with the duration necessary to integrate existing PV generation, and longer duration systems are added in the future at lower cost to integrate future PV. Finally we note that, while the energy storage cost revolution that will drive next wave of PV adoption appears to be underway, reliability remains an open question, on which long-term success of PV will depend.

REFERENCES

[1] Masdar, "UAE President witnesses launch of world's first 24/7 Solar PV, Battery Storage gigascale project to be built in Abu Dhabi," 14 Jan 2025. [Online]. Available: https://masdar.ae/en/news/newsroom/uae-president-witnesses-launch-of-worlds-first-24-7-solar-pv-battery-storage.

[2] J. Benny, "Taqa and Ewec to develop 1GW gas turbine plant in Abu Dhabi to support tech push," *The National*, pp. https://www.thenationalnews.com/business/energy/2025/04/03/taqa-and-ewec-to-develop-1gw-gas-turbine-plant-in-abu-dhabi-to-support-tech-push/, 3 April 2025.

[3] Apostoleris, H., Sgouridis, S., Stefancich, M., & Chiesa, M. (2018). Evaluating the factors that led to low-priced solar electricity projects in the Middle East. Nature Energy, 3(12), 1109-1114.

[4] H. Apostoleris and M. Chiesa, "The role of financing in realizing ultra-low solar electricity prices in the Middle East," 2019 IEEE 46th Photovoltaic Specialists Conference (PVSC), Chicago, IL, USA, 2019, pp. 0595-0600, doi: 10.1109/PVSC40753.2019.8980633.

[5] Apostoleris, H., Al Ghaferi, A., & Chiesa, M. (2021). What is going on with Middle Eastern solar prices, and what does it mean for the rest of us?. *Progress in Photovoltaics: Research and Applications*, 29(6), 638-648.

[6] EPRI -- Homepage | DCFlex [https://dcflex.epri.com/]

[7] MEED | Abu Dhabi moves ahead with AI power plants (2024) https://www.meed.com/abu-dhabi-moves-ahead-with-ai-power-plants

[8] Gulf Construction Online: Taqa, Ewec, Masdar in deal to develop $9.8bn energy projects https://gulfconstructiononline.com/ArticleTA/432157

[9] SEC receives Bids for 1,000 MW Battery Energy Storage System Projects - SaudiGulf Projects https://www.saudigulfprojects.com/2025/04/sec-receives-bids-for-1000-mw-battery-energy-storage-system-projects/

[10] Where are EV battery prices headed in 2025 and beyond? | S&P Global https://www.spglobal.com/automotive-insights/en/blogs/2025/01/where-are-ev-battery-prices-headed-in-2025-and-beyond

Cost and reliability of 24/7 Carbon Free Electricity from PV

Evaluation of overnight solar-plus-storage in Abu Dhabi

Harry Apostoleris, EPRI Gulf
Kareem Younes, Khalifa University
Matteo Chiesa, Khalifa University

in X f
www.epri.com

020488-001

Introduction to the authors and the UAE

- **Harry Apostoleris** – EPRI Gulf
  - Gulf region office of EPRI focusing on utility-sector research for GCC countries (Saudia Arabia, UAE, Qatar, Bahrain, Kuwait, Oman)
  - 13 years in UAE -- CPV → PV module & system economics → energy system planning
  - Previously Dubai Electricity & Water Authority (DEWA) R&D Center, Masdar Institute
- UAE has consistently set records for scale and low cost in international utility-scale PV, pushes limits of economic feasibility with combination of
  - Low hardware cost
  - Low labor cost
  - Favorable financing environment
  - Involvement of major state-backed entities
  - E.g. first <3c/kWh PPA for solar (2017), now ~1.5c/kWh typical

EPRI

020488-002

Introduction to the authors and the UAE

- **Harry Apostoleris** – EPRI Gulf
  - Gulf region office of EPRI focusing on utility-sector research for GCC countries (Saudia Arabia, UAE, Qatar, Bahrain, Kuwait, Oman)
  - 13 years in UAE -- CPV → PV module & system economics → energy system planning
  - Previously Dubai Electricity & Water Authority (DEWA) R&D Center, Masdar Institute
- UAE has consistently set records for scale and low cost in internation utility-scale PV, pushes limits of economic feasibility with combination of
  - Low hardware cost
  - Low labor cost
  - Favorable financing environment
  - Involvement of major state-backed entities
  - E.g. first <3c/kWh PPA for solar (2017), now ~1.5c/kWh typical

Apostoleris et al., *Nature Energy* 2018

Kareem Younes
(Khalifa University)

Matteo Chiesa
(Khalifa University)

- Recent announcements in solar + storage are illustrative to understand shape of global energy storage market, strategic approaches to energy storage deployment & prospects for further solar energy deployment around the world

EPRI

020488-003

Background – AI boom and grid impacts

- UAE has ambitious goals for AI/data centers
- Global challenges in energy sector (e.g. in US)
  - Supply/demand impacts
  - Equipment supply chain – e.g. gas turbines
  - costs of grid/capacity upgrades – rising consumer prices
  - Grid stability challenges due to unique load of AI data centers
- Approaches
  - Grid upgrades to manage new load types
  - Data centers as a source of flexibility? [EPRI DC flex]
  - Partly or fully insulate data center from grid (on site storage for smoothing, or fully on site energy production
    - "Clean firm" power where solar+storage replaces conventional power station
  - Abu Dhabi project is on grid, but lessons are applicable to on-site power generation as well

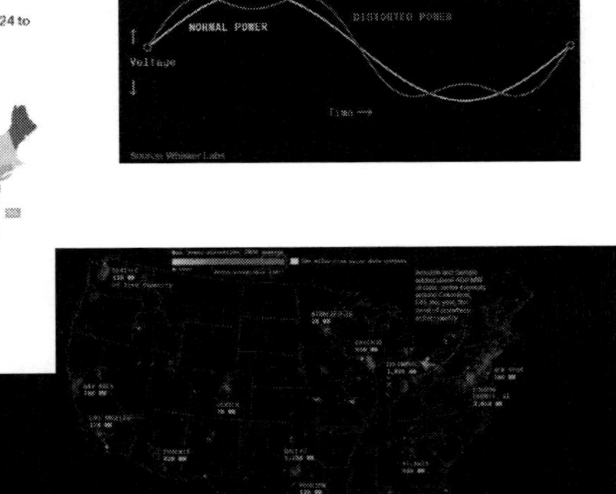

EPRI

020488-004

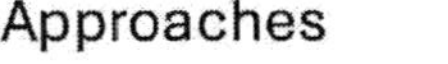

Description of the project

- 5.2GW PV, 19GWh BESS, 1GW baseload supply to grid
- Described as part of AI strategy [MEED | Abu Dhabi moves ahead with AI power plants]
- 6bnUSD investment in plant, total 10bnUSD package for PV+BESS, OCGT backup plant, grid connection/enhancements
- Very low price tag – but so was 2017 PV…..

Component	Capacity	Cost
PV+BESS	5.2GW/19GWh	$6bn
OCGT	1GW	$1.35bn
Grid enhancement		$2.5bn

https://gulfconstructiononline.com/ArticleTA/432157

Masdar, EWEC launch world-biggest 24/7 solar PV and battery project in Abu Dhabi

By Andy Colthorpe
January 15, 2025

Masdar, EWEC world-biggest solar-battery project in Abu Dhabi- Energy-Storage.News

EPRI

020488-005

Market developments – PV systems

- Falling Capex throughout region pre-2020, plateau post-covid ~600USD/kW
  - "Pure" PV PPA prices around 1.5c/kWh – aggressive pricing but consistent with regional expectations
- Some savings in opex reported due to robotic cleaning

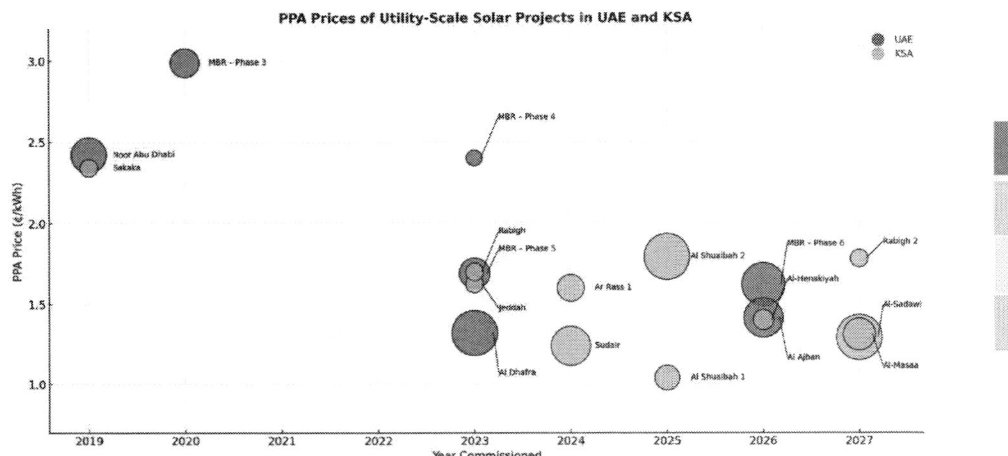

Component	Capacity	Unit cost	Source
PV	5.2GW	$600/kW	UAE/KSA

020488-006

Market developments – BESS

- Major changes in this decade –comparable to module market changes in previous decade

- EV industry drives Li-ion (specifically LFP) manufacturing

- Storage mandate for PV installations drove stationary storage product development by Chinese firms

- Further price drop expected over next 1-2 years

- 2024 – 60USD/kWh battery cell costs [Where are EV battery prices headed in 2025 and beyond? | S&P Global]

- Reflected in recent BESS projects in region (Saudi Arabia)

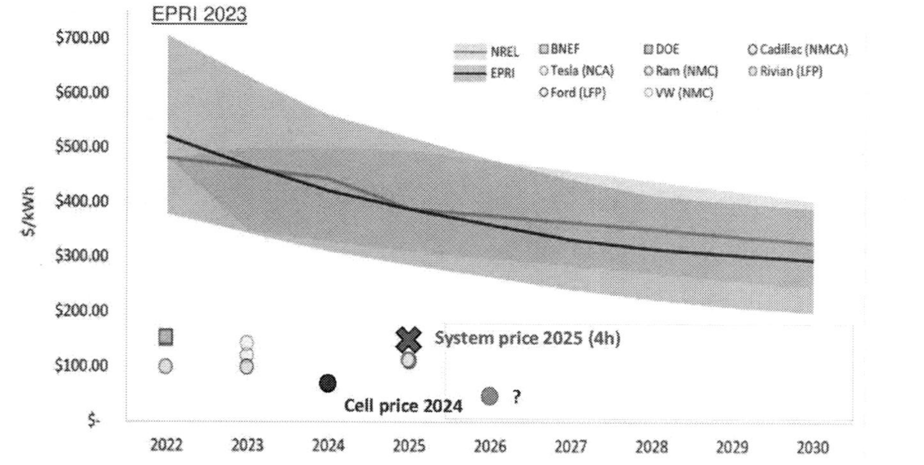

Component	Capacity	Unit cost	Source
PV	5.2GW	$600/kW	UAE/KSA
BESS energy	19GWh	$90/kWh	KSA
BESS power	2.5GW	$240/kW	KSA

SEC receives Bids for 1,000 MW Battery Energy Storage System Projects - SaudiGulf Projects

020488-007

System & levelized electricity cost assessment

- Core technology cost decreases coupled w/ overall inflation & high financing costs
- Reported capex reflects current global market & local factors

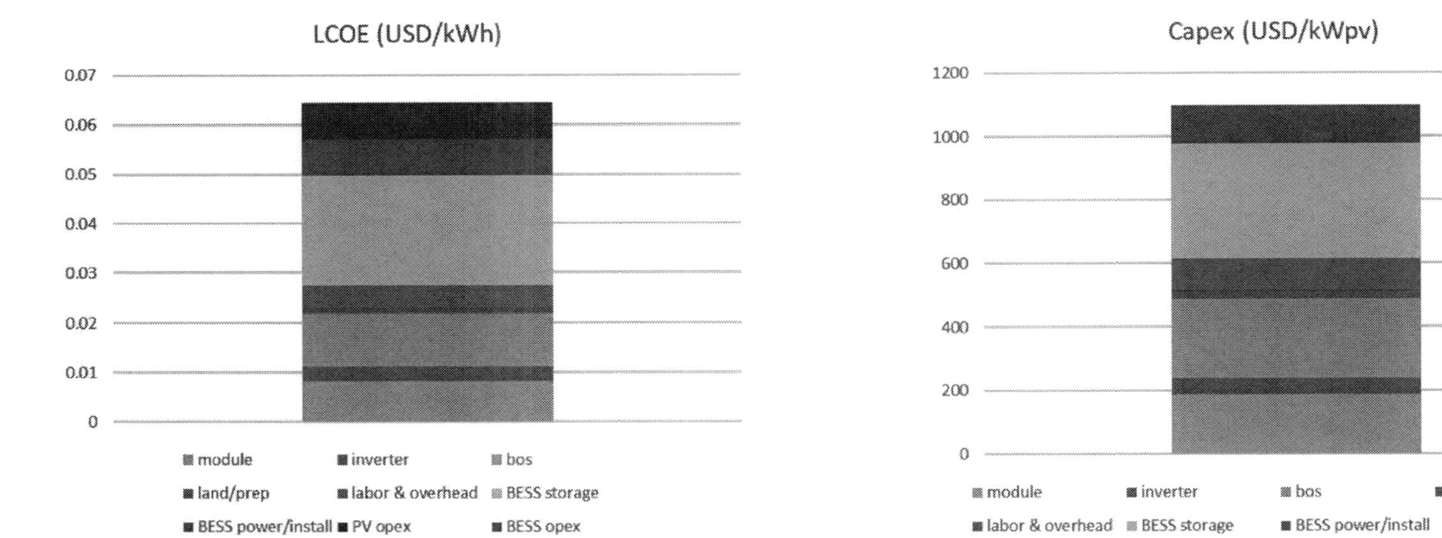

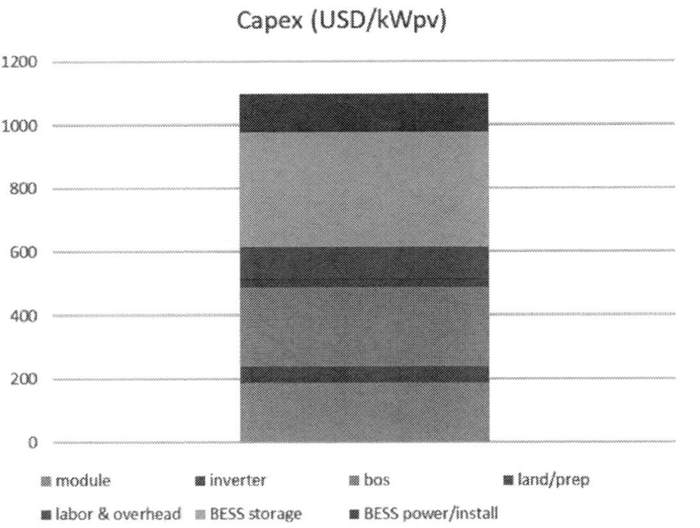

EPRI

020488-008

System & levelized electricity cost assessment

- Core technology cost decreases coupled w/ overall inflation & high financing costs
- Reported capex reflects current global market & local factors

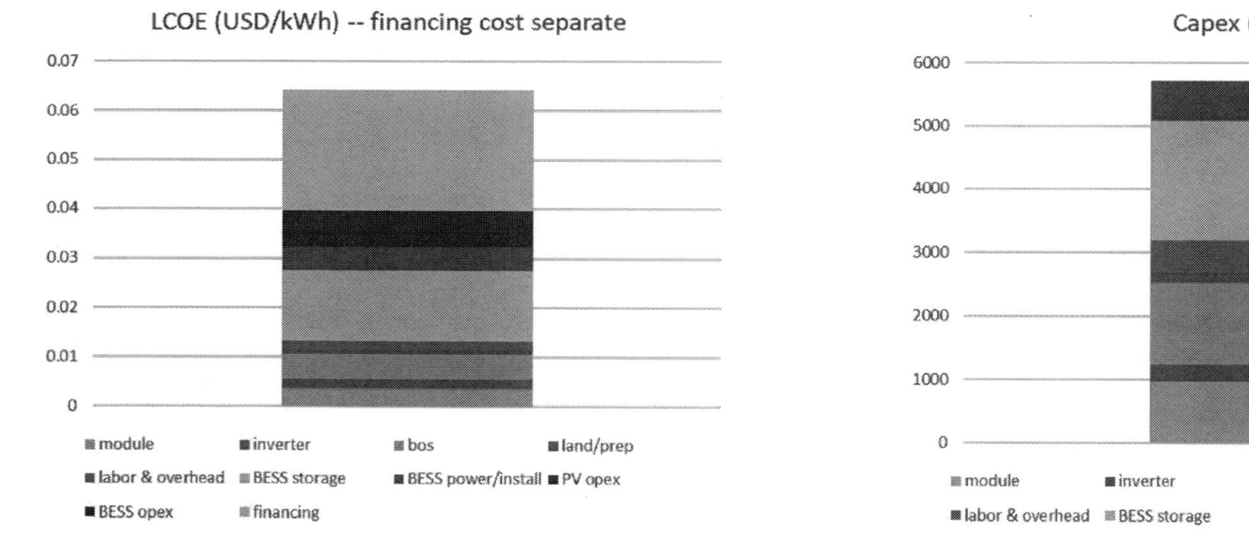

LCOE (USD/kWh) -- financing cost separate

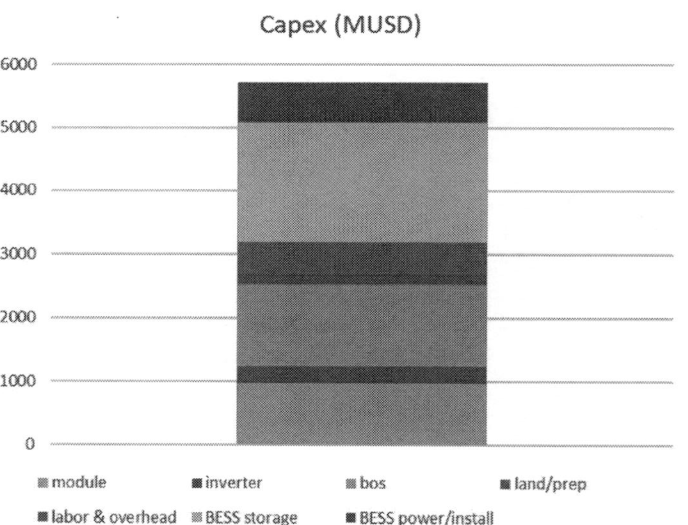

Capex (MUSD)

EPRI

020488-009

Availability as a baseload energy resource – model

- Simple dispatch algorithm implemented where energy generated from solar

  - 1. is dispatched to meet demand

  - 2. After meeting demand, is fed to battery

  - 3. if battery is full, curtailed

  - 4. If demand exceeds solar generation, energy is dispatched from storage

  - 5. if net demand exceed dispatchable energy from storage, energy shortage is recorded

- Summer day performance:

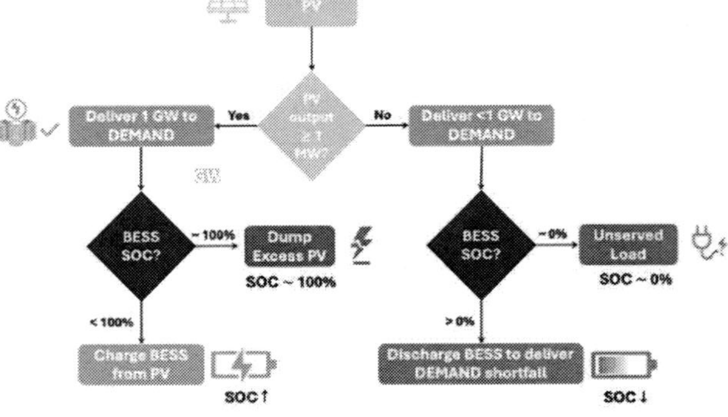

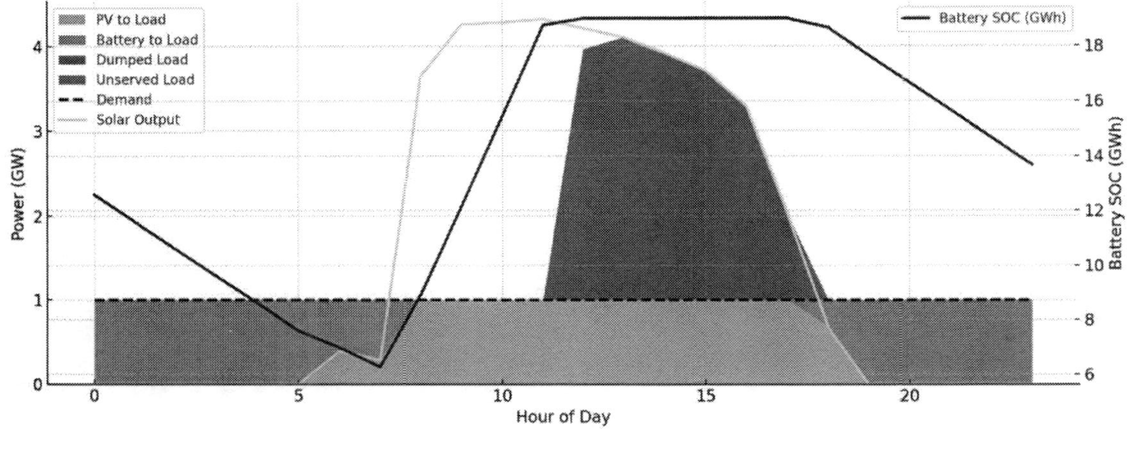

EPRI

020488-010

Availability as a baseload energy resource – results

- Rainy/cloudy periods (or in general periods of lower solar generation) challenge system availability as a baseload resource
- Red areas indicate periods of unserved load (where battery is not charged sufficiently to supply full 1GW at night)
  - Total annual availability ~97%
- This is what necessitates the inclusion of the gas turbine backup system in order to serve as a baseload resources
  - At current pricing, increases LCOE by ~1.5c/kWh

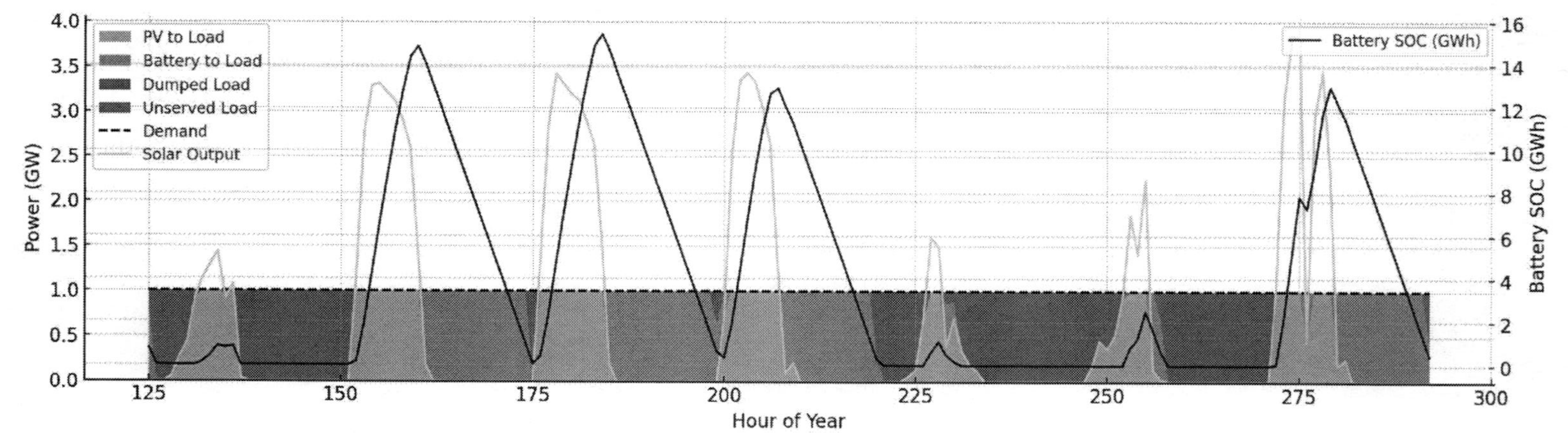

020488-011

EPRI

Strategic energy storage planning – climbing the "ladder"

- However, baseload availability is not necessary for an energy system in transition

- Visualizing energy storage requirements as a "ladder" of different storage durations addressing different challenges that arise at different levels of solar adoption highlights strategic approach of building storage to meet immediate needs

- Falling cost of storage argues in favor of this approach (add needed storage capacity in future when it is cheaper)

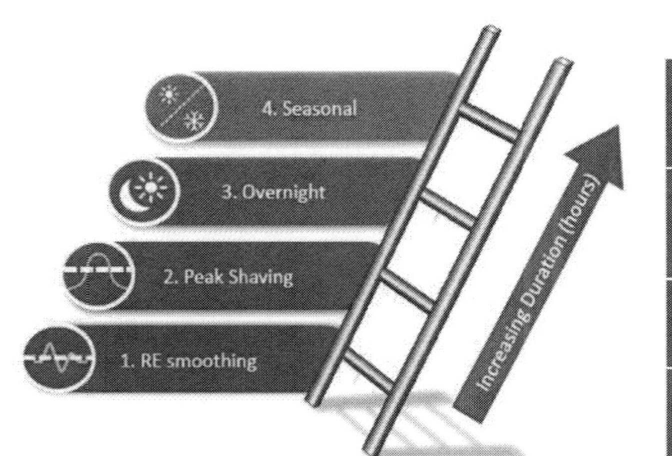

	Function	Duration	Description	Impact on energy system
1	RE & Transient smoothing/Black start/ Primary reserve	<1h	Energy storage under 1-hour duration for smoothing of solar output, frequency regulation & black start	Reduce spinning reserve requirement/ peaker use to balance RE & transient fluctuations
2	Ramp rate management/peak shaving/energy trading	1-4h	1-to-4-hour energy storage for peak shaving and ramp rate management for solar	Avoid peaker operation in normal conditions
3	Overnight storage/Island operation	4-16h	Medium duration or overnight energy storage in non-solar hours	Avoid Combined Cycle plant operation for normal overnight generation
4	Multi-day/seasonal energy shifting	Days-Months	Large-scale seasonal energy storage for balancing seasonal variation in solar output (summer vs winter production)	Avoid nearly all combined cycle plant use; stored energy can provide emergency backup

EPRI

020488-012

Strategic energy storage planning – climbing the "ladder"

- However, baseload availability is not necessary for an energy system in transition

- Visualizing energy storage requirements as a "ladder" of different storage durations addressing different challenges that arise at different levels of solar adoption highlights strategic approach of building storage to meet immediate needs

- Falling cost of storage argues in favor of this approach (add needed storage capacity in future when it is cheaper)

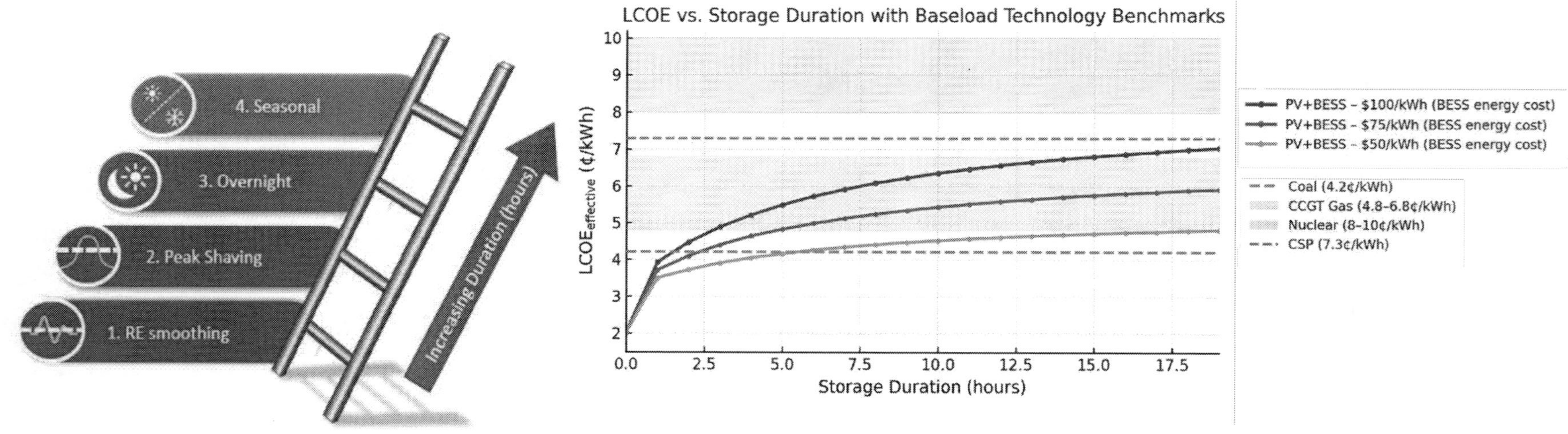

EPRI

020488-013

Conclusions

- Major changes occurring in battery market, driven by EV adoption, internal policies in China and industrial learning curve previously observed for PV modules

- Nominal clean-firm PV+BESS (clean firm) systems are already achievable at viable cost in most favorable markets; true firm power requires conventional e.g. gas turbine backup for resilience through low-sun periods

- Clean-firm may not be the most useful concept to guide near-term energy system planning under highly dynamic market conditions

- Expected future price reductions favor strategic approach to energy storage deployment to maximize the rate of PV adoption, where storage systems are built with the duration necessary to integrate existing PV generation, and longer duration systems are added in the future at lower cost to integrate future PV

- **Storage cost revolution that will drive next wave of PV adoption appears to be underway – but reliability remains an open question, on which long-term success of PV will depend**

EPRI

020488-014

Energy Systems Research @EPRI: More Information

Sign up for the ESCA Newsletter
bit.ly/escanewsletter

See all public research on our website: esca.epri.com

EPRI's Energy Systems and Climate Analysis Group regularly posts public research, news, and events on our website, and newsletter.

Link Tree: bit.ly/m/epriesca

For questions or more information, please contact eea@epri.com

EPRI

020488-015

eurac research

Mitigating the grid impact of solar DG by a VPP firm generation strategy

Marco Pierro & Grazia Barchi(EURAC)

Alessandro Donadello & Davide Prando (Edyna)

Motivations

Distributed PV generation has a number of impacts on the distribution/transmission grid, including:

1. **Faster provision in unit commitment** due to increased load ramps (increasing the "duck curve")
2. **Congestions on transformers** on secondary/primary substations and **cables overload** due to overproduction and thus saturation of hosting capacity at distribution level;
3. **Needs to limit solar generation**, **zero (or negative) energy prices**; **increase of stop/restart** dispatchable generation units, due to overproduction at the transmission grid level;
4. **Needs of additional reserves** due to the increased variability in residual load.

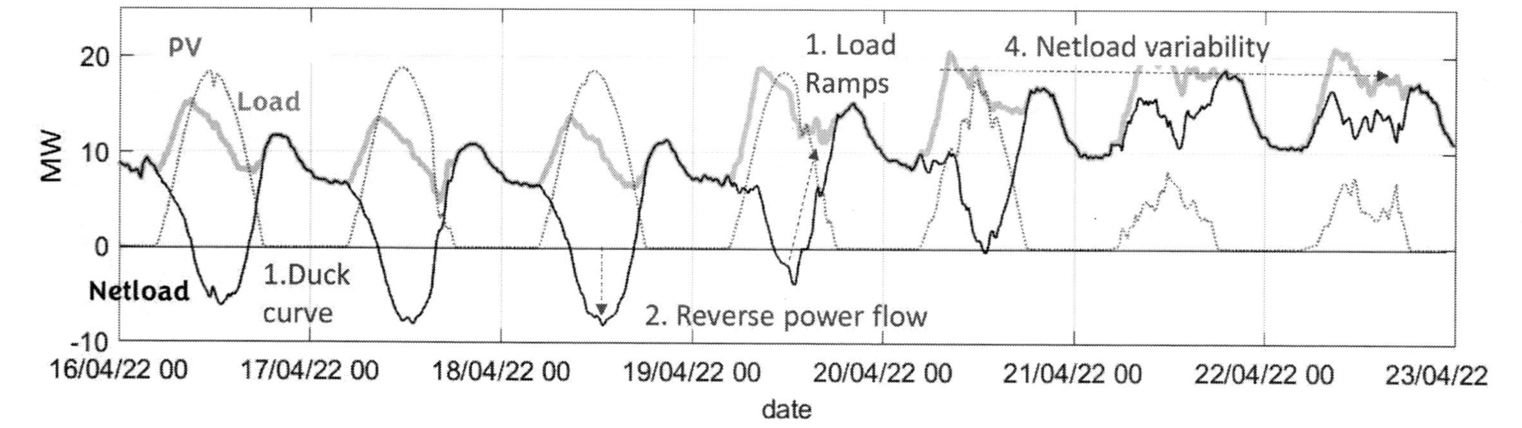

020489-002

Motivations

Available space in the Dutch grid for large-scale commercial users.

High PV installation rate and uncontrolled feed-in, leading to significant congestions and rising costs to balance the grid.

Feed-in capacity

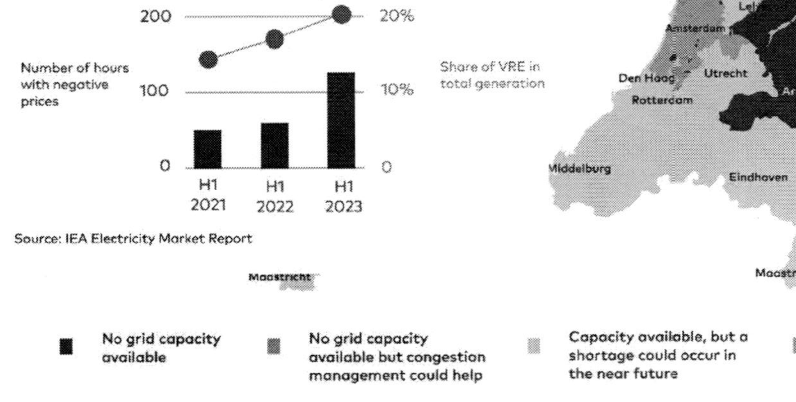

Maastricht

No grid capacity available

No grid capacity available but congestion management could help

Capacity available, but a shortage could occur in the near future

Capacity available

Source: IEA, Fitch Solutions

Actually, these issues start to appear on macro scale

Dutch power grid has **already reached its hosting capacity** for commercial users in many areas

Inequitable access to distributed energy resources due to grid infrastructure limits in California

Anna M. Brockway, Jennifer Conde & Duncan Callaway ✉

Nature Energy **6**, 892–903 (2021) | Cite this article

https://www.gridx.ai/blog/the-netherlands-conundrum-low-grid-capacity-high-feed-in

Aim

The aim of this work is to propose a firm PV strategy to mitigate reverse power flows and netload ramps due to high solar DG and thus increase hosting capacity at primary/secondary station levels

DSOs consider solar DG in the control zone (pertaining to a secondary/primary substation) as produced by a Virtual Power Plant and place batteries (BESS) near the substation

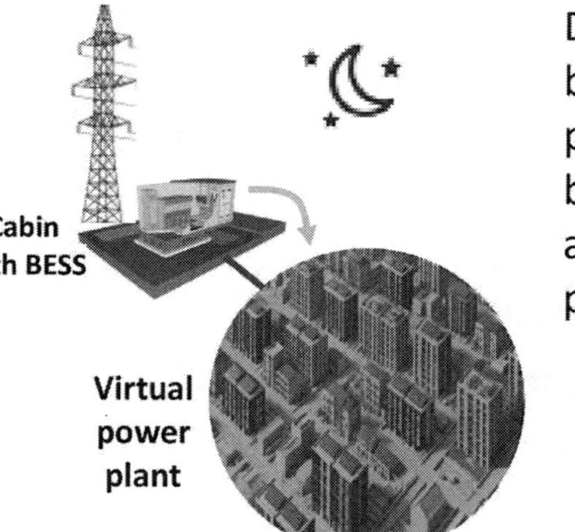

During the daylight batteries absorb from the grid the fraction of the solar DG exceeding a predefined baseload target

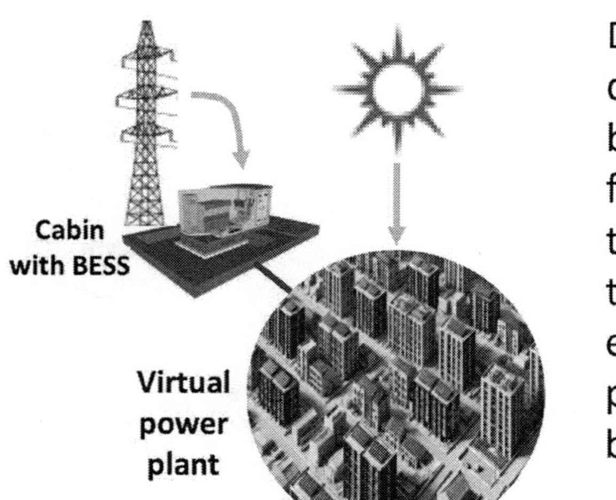

During the night batteries provides the baseload target as much is possible

020489-004

Firm PV-based strategy

With this strategy

1) It would be possible to **redistribute some of the PV DG** (self-consumed or in excess) during the hours of less or no solar generation.

2) Distributed PV & Grid batteries **ensures a baseload round the clock** decreasing the consumption of the control zone without altering its profile

thus

it reduces load ramps, revers power flow and possible congestions at transformer level.

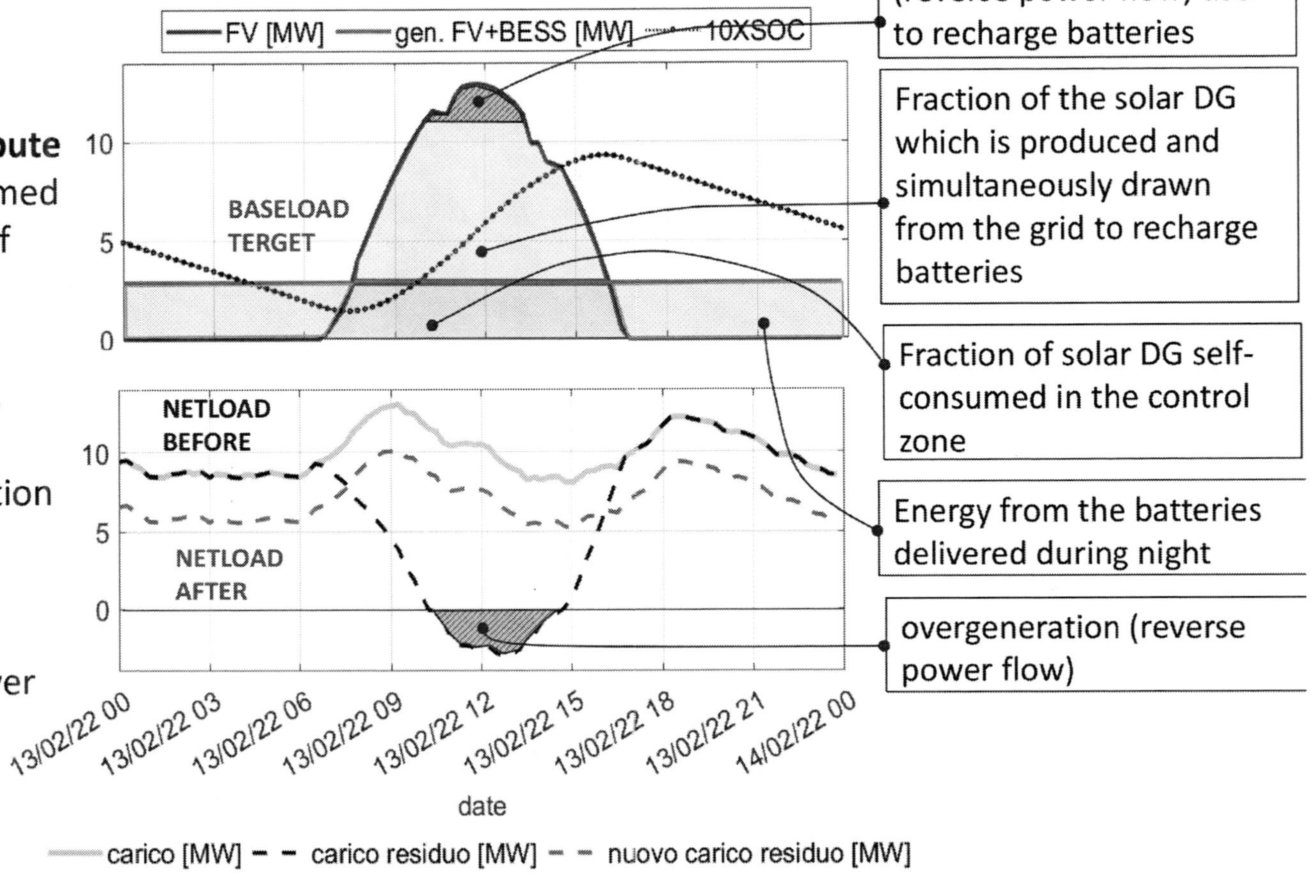

020489-005

Distribute PV generation impact on distribution grid

We used real 15 min load data measured at a primary cabin level provided by an Italian DSO

Actually, in the control zone there is 10 MW of distributed PV capacity, we studied the case in which the **2030 target of 25 MW** will be reached compared with no PV case

In the control zone will be:

- About **1500 revers power flow events** with a max power of **10 MW** from MV/HV

- About **80 days of revers flow** with a max revers energy of **60 MWh per day**

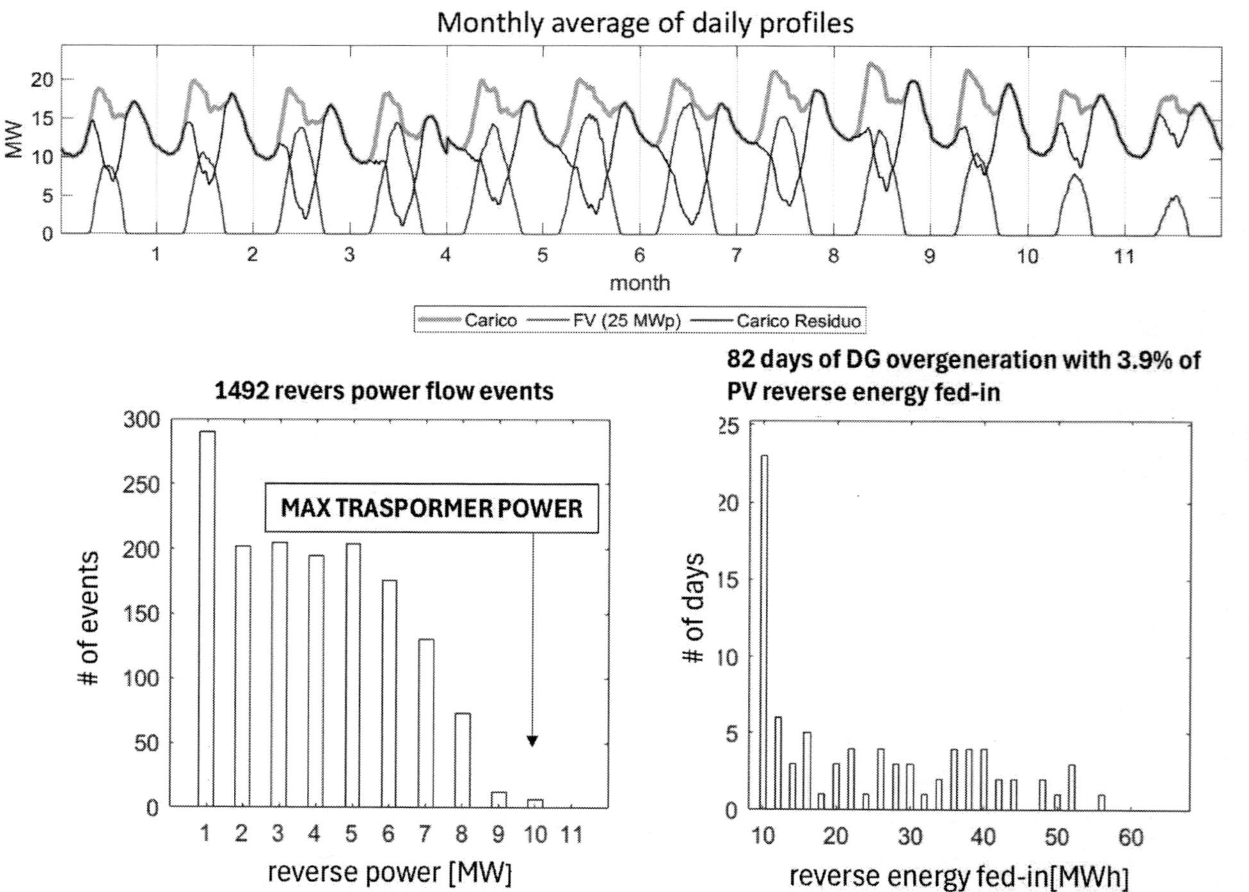

020489-006

Distribute PV generation impact on distribution grid

Ramps on different time scales involve different types of reserves.

Compared to the scenario without PV generation the one with 25 MWp installed **increases ramps on all time scales** especially on the 4-hour one since on clear days less power commitment is required in the middle hours of the day

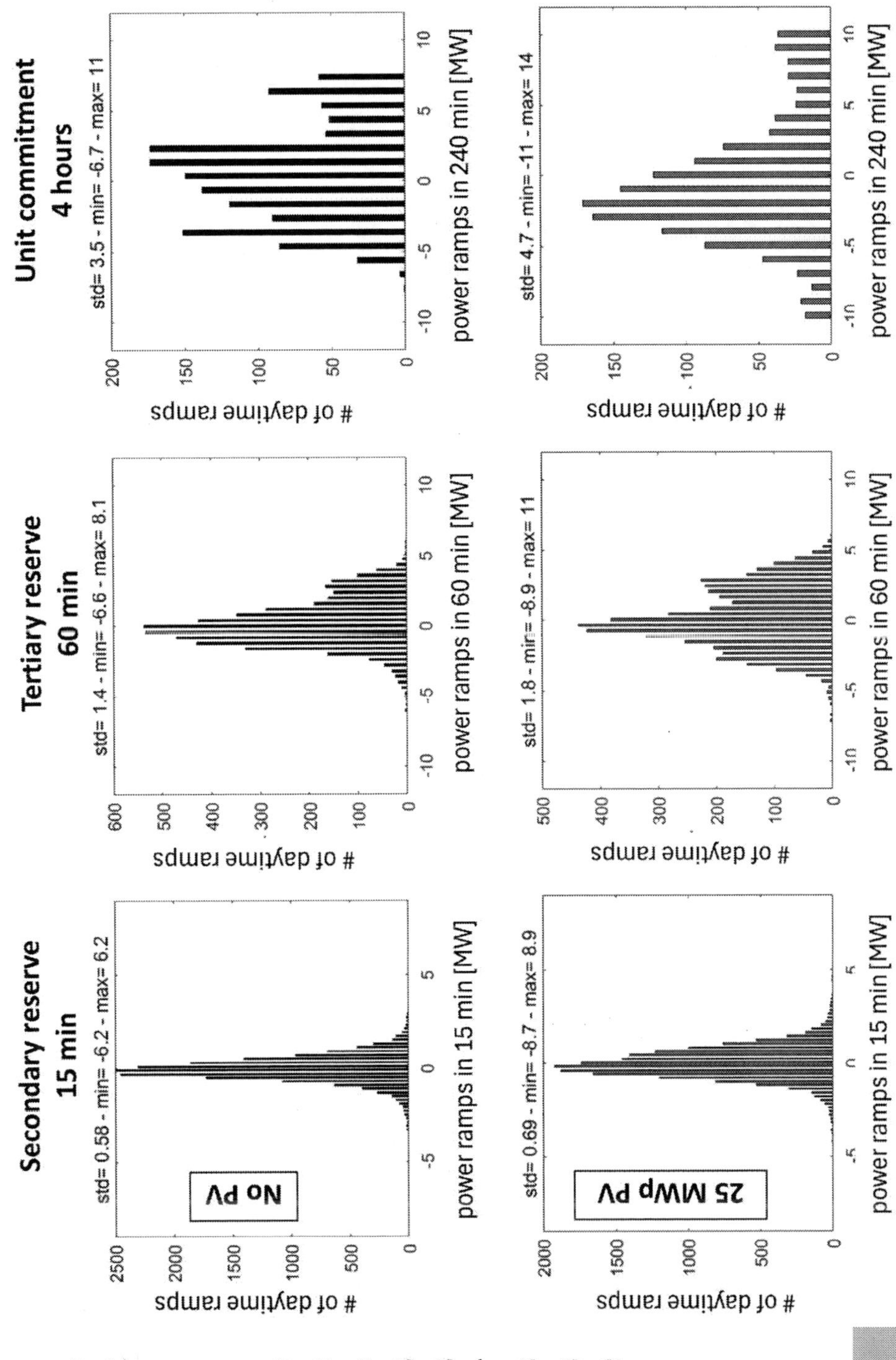

System size

Battery should be able:

- To store the max daily revers energy (60 kWh in this case)

- To fully discarge during nigh and to be recharged with the energy exceeding the baseload target during the next day

- To be not fully regarged during the day otherwise overgeneration power not stored could give rise to reverse power flows

The **baseload level** (set monthly) must:

- be high enough to minimize the energy that needs to be stored

- be not too high to ensure baseload solar production for a large number of hours (76% of the annual hours in this case)

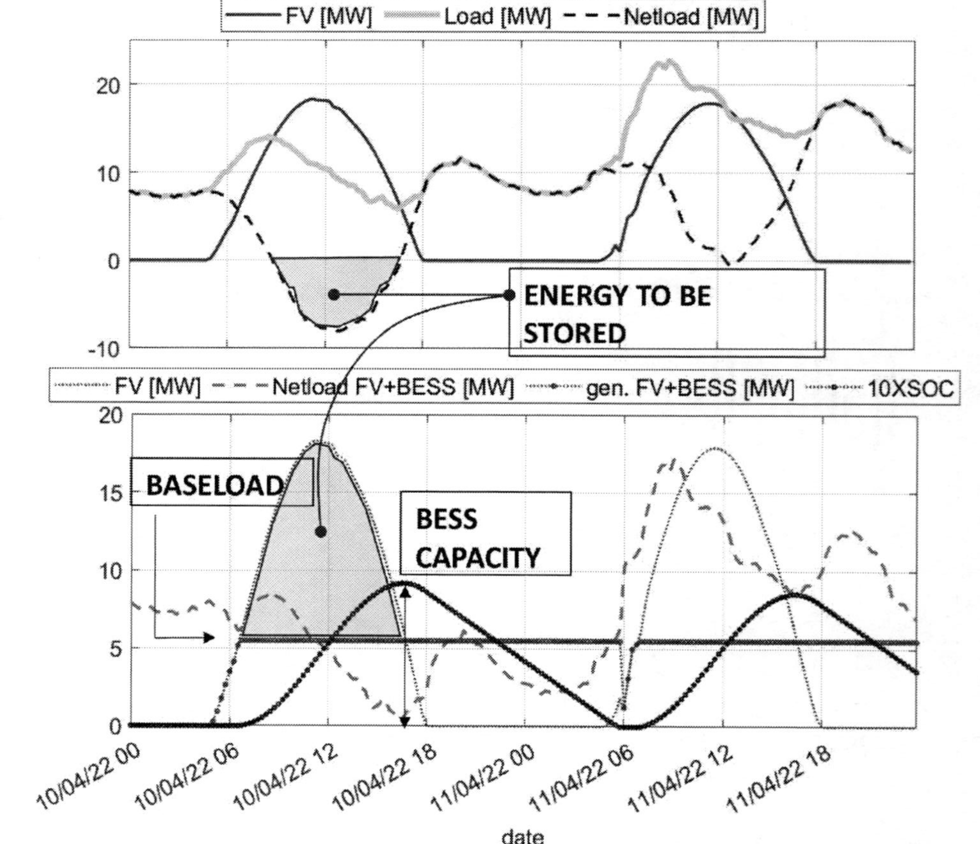

020489-008

Results

Through a not trivial optimization process, monthly baseload levels and battery capacity were assessed.

- The load levels range from a minimum of **1.2 MW** in **December** to a **maximum of 7.6 MW in July**.

- The minimum battery capacity is **82 MWh (3.3 MWh/MWp)** with 20.5 MW of power.

Monthly average of daily profiles

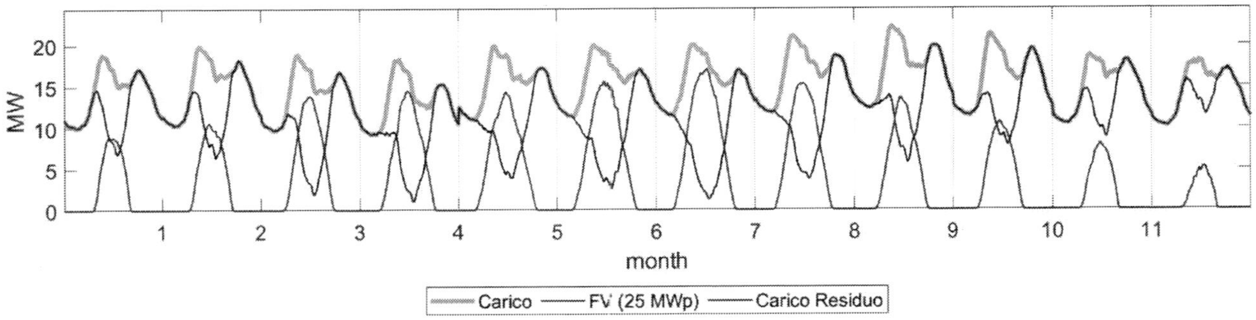

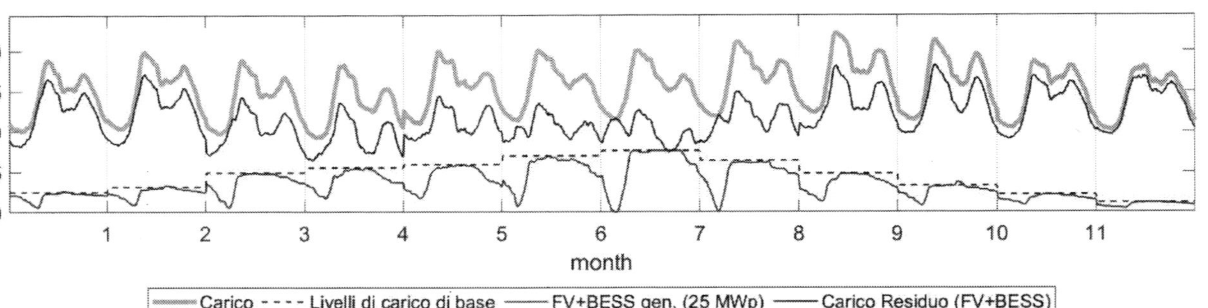

PV DG is transformed in a much more smoothed generation round the clock

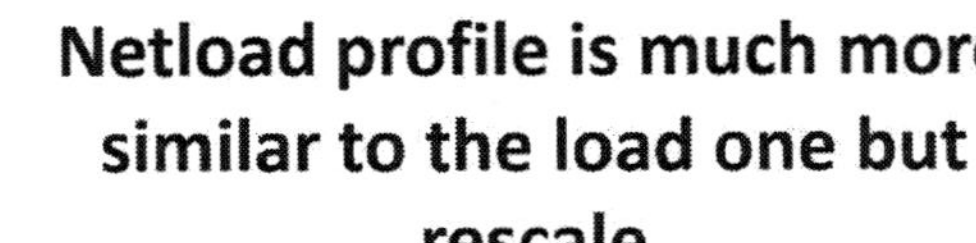

Netload profile is much more similar to the load one but rescale

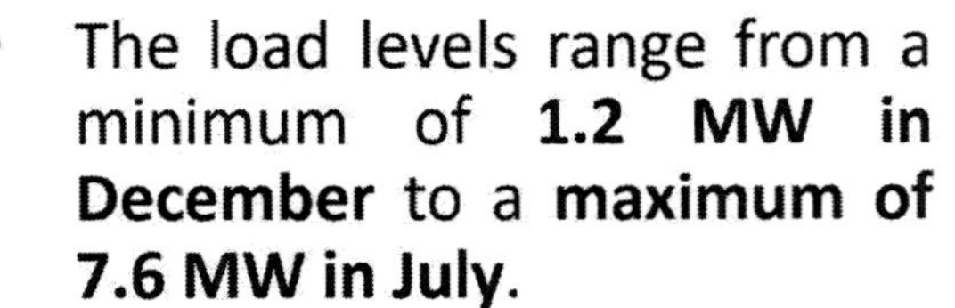

Results

The **number of reverse power flows** is reduced by **96%** and the **maximum reverse power by 33%** from 10 MW to 3 MW

The **generated solar energy fed into the transmission grid** is reduced **from about 4% to less than 0.05%.** Thus, all PV energy generated remains in the control zone

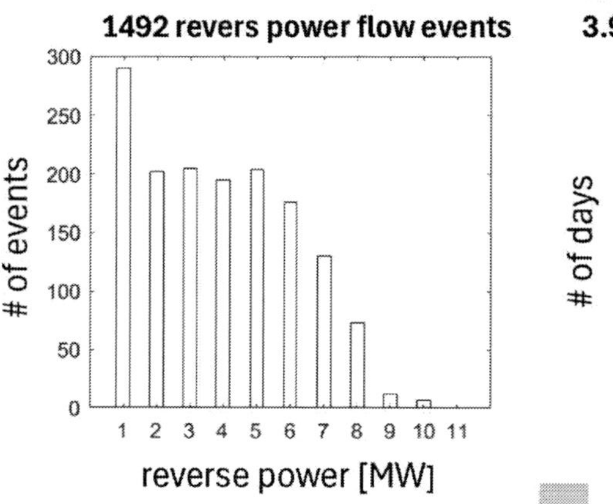

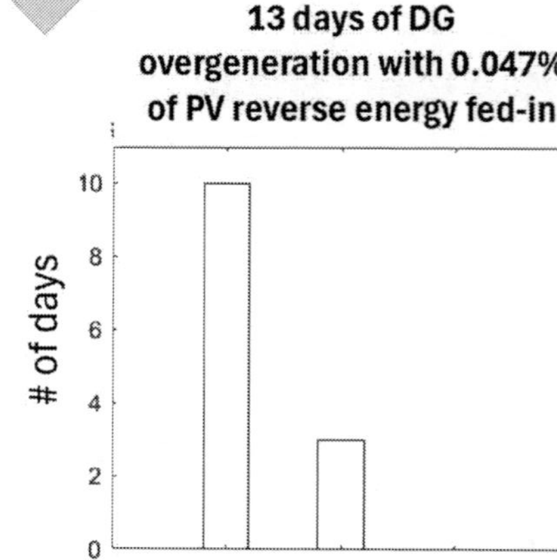

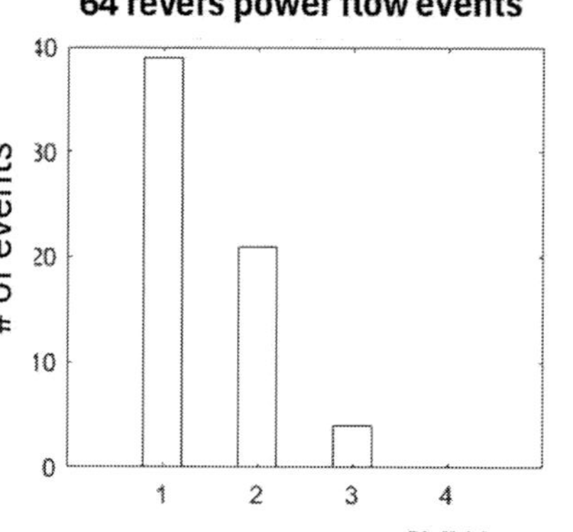

Results

The distribution of ramps is **practically restored** to the levels found in the absence of solar generation.

Ramps could be **further lowered with the use of PV power forecasting,** which would anticipate events and smooth out battery charging and discharging.

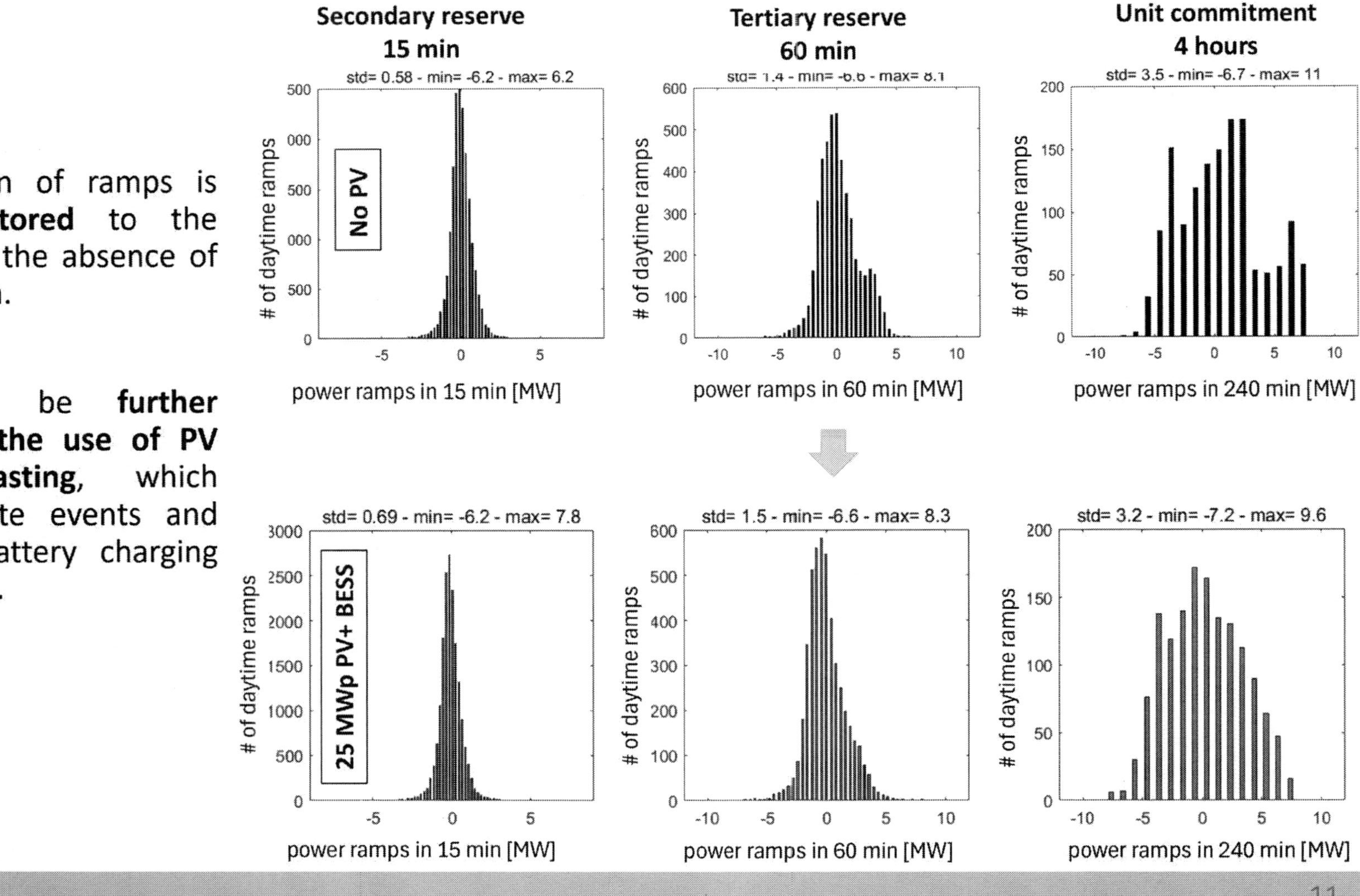

020489-011

Conclusions

1. This strategy allows:

- To **restore grid hosting capacity** when transformers are no more able to dispatch the PV DG peaks reverse feed-in;

- **To reduce the flexibility requirements of the transmission grid** by decreasing ramps at all time scales and restoring a residual load profile very similar to the electrical demand in the absence of distributed solar generation;

- **To provide flexibility services to the grid** through batteries: synthetic inertia (ultra fast reserve), frequency and voltage regulation etc.

2. **The strategy increases solar self-production in the control area** by locally increasing the fraction of demand covered by solar: in this case with 25 MW of PV installed it would increase from 20 % to 25 %.

3. **DG's self-generation is no longer an economic loss for Utilities but a gain.** The Utilities could buy some of the self-consumption and energy fed into the grid during the day (at low prices) and then resell this energy at night (at high prices).

Thank you for your attention

Marco Pierro

Marco.pierro@eurac.edu

www.eurac.edu

eurac
research

QUANTIFYING THE GAP: RULE-BASED VS. SMART ENERGY MANAGEMENT OF RESIDENTIAL PV SELF-CONSUMPTION WITH STORAGE

Carolina Crespo, Rodrigo Amaro e Silva, Miguel Centeno Brito
University of Lisbon, Faculty of Sciences, Instituto Dom Luiz, Lisboa, Portugal
Faculdade de Ciências da Universidade de Lisboa, Campo Grande Edifício C1, Piso 1, 1749-016 Lisboa

ABSTRACT: The growing adoption of residential photovoltaic (PV) and battery systems has led to an increasing interest in energy management strategies that optimize performance and maximize savings. These range from simple rule-based methods to advanced optimization and machine learning approaches. Among them, self-consumption maximization (SCM) stands out as a practical, low-cost, rule-based strategy requiring no external infrastructure or forecasting.

This work assesses the adequacy of SCM for residential PV and battery systems within collective self-consumption schemes. SCM performance is benchmarked against a MILP model with perfect foresight to quantify the gap between SCM and the theoretical optimum. A case study in Portugal shows that SCM achieves results within 1-7% of optimality, even for dynamic tariffs. Achieving optimality would correspond to maximum cost savings of €5 per household per month, when compared to SCM. Given the modest potential gains, the limits imposed by forecast uncertainty on practical performance, and the higher costs of implementing more complex methods, SCM is likely the most cost-effective solution for most residential applications, particularly in sunny climates like Portugal.

Keywords: Battery Energy Management, Home Energy Management System, Battery Energy Storage System, Residential PV, Collective Self-consumption

1 INTRODUCTION AND MOTIVATION

In recent years, the adoption of distributed photovoltaics (PV) has grown rapidly, often accompanied by the deployment of distributed energy storage, typically in the form of batteries. Batteries enable end-users to (i) store surplus PV generation for later self-consumption and (ii) shift demand in time by charging from the grid during low-price periods and discharging to cover consumption during high-price periods.

This evolution has fueled significant research interest in energy management strategies, which govern battery charging and discharging and, in some cases, the operation of controllable loads such as washing machines or HVAC systems. Proposed methods span from classical optimization techniques to the increasingly popular machine learning approaches [1]. However, deploying these advanced strategies in real-world systems entails costs for hardware, software, forecasting services (informing the expected load and generation), and, potentially, cloud-based infrastructure. For such approaches to deliver tangible benefits, the resulting savings must outweigh these expenses.

In contrast, many real-world PV-battery systems rely on simpler, rule-based approaches, most notably self-consumption maximization (SCM) [2]. SCM requires no external infrastructure and uses only instantaneous load and PV generation data to determine whether to charge or discharge the battery. Specifically, the battery charges during PV surplus (if not full) and discharges during load deficits (if sufficiently charged).

Many studies claiming improvements over baseline energy management strategies face a common issue: the lack of standardization in baseline definitions hinders comparability and the consistency of performance assessments. Beaudin and Zareipour highlighted this issue in 2015 [3], urging the adoption of common baselines, but more recent literature has yet to address this. Moreover, Azuatalam et al. [2] compared seven energy management strategies, including rule-based, classical optimization, and machine learning approaches, and found that simple rule-based methods such as SCM can achieve near-optimal results, especially under real-world conditions where forecast uncertainty degrades the performance of more complex methods, but does not affect SCM.

The objective of this work is to assess the suitability of SCM for energy management of distributed PV and battery systems, focusing on residential collective self-consumption schemes.

2 MEASURING THE POTENTIAL FOR INTELLIGENCE

Beyond the lack of standardized baselines, much of the literature on energy management strategies fails to quantify how distant the achieved performance is from the theoretical optimum. This work addresses this by explicitly measuring the performance difference between SCM and the optimal solution, providing a clear assessment of SCM's adequacy and the potential value of adopting more advanced strategies.

To this end, we introduce the Potential for Intelligence (PFI), defined in Eq. 1, as a metric to evaluate both the effectiveness of SCM and the remaining room for improvement. Installing a PV-battery system managed solely by a charge controller performing SCM delivers certain cost-saving benefits. However, in theory, an ideal energy management strategy with perfect foresight could further maximize these savings. PFI quantifies the gap between the outcome of SCM and this theoretical optimum, normalized by the maximum achievable savings compared to a scenario without a PV-battery system (illustrated in **Figure 1**).

$$PFI = \frac{c_{SCM} - c_{optimal}}{c_{no\ system} - c_{optimal}} \quad (1)$$

10.4229/EUPVSEC2025/5DO.15.2
020490-001

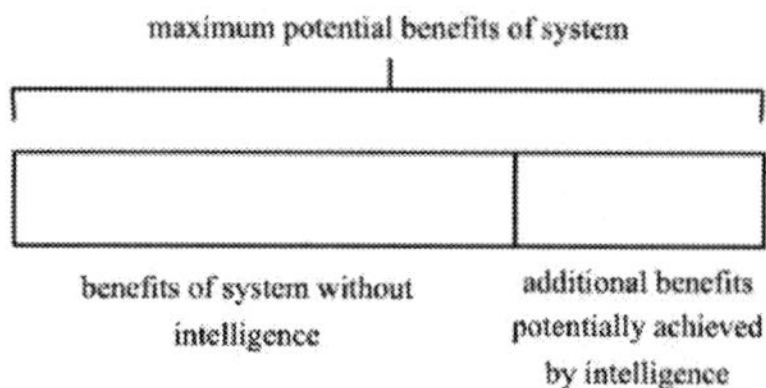

Figure 1: Of the total potential benefits of installing a PV-battery system, part can be achieved with a simple charge controller and SCM, while additional benefits require more sophisticated energy management strategies.

3 CASE STUDY DESCRIPTION

We apply the PFI metric to a case study involving a collective self-consumption scheme in Portugal, comprising 18 households. The analysis uses one full year of real energy consumption data alongside PV generation profiles obtained from PVGIS [4]. A sensitivity analysis was also conducted by testing different combinations of tariff schemes and installed PV and battery capacities.

Two tariff schemes were tested:

- **Dual tariff:** Electricity prices are €0.24/kWh between 9:00 and 22:00 (peak period) and €0.15/kWh during off-peak hours;
- **Dynamic tariff:** Prices vary hourly, following the fluctuations of the Iberian wholesale electricity market.

In both scenarios, surplus generation can be sold to the grid at a constant value of €0.045/kWh.

4 RESULTS AND DISCUSSION

The results are presented in **Figure 2**, which shows PFI heatmaps for different combinations of battery storage capacity and installed PV capacity. In most scenarios, SCM is found to perform well, with generally low PFI values. Even in scenarios with the highest remaining potential for improvement, the additional cost savings achievable with advanced energy management strategies are modest—approximately €5 per household per month, as shown in **Figure 3**.

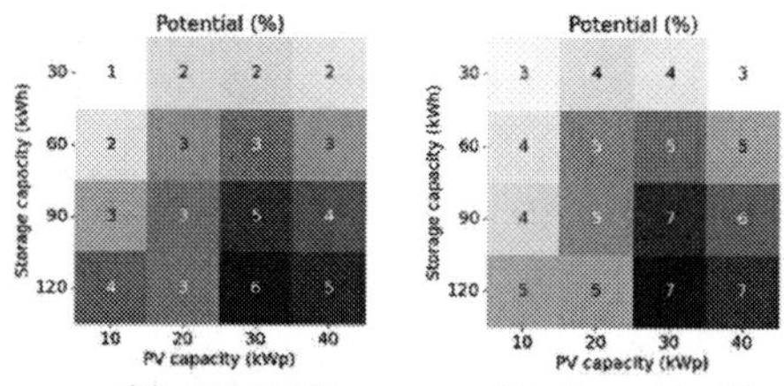

(a) Dual tariff   **(b)** Dynamic tariff

Figure 2: Heatmaps of PFI (%) for the case study, showing results under dual and dynamic tariffs across combinations of varying storage and PV installed capacities.

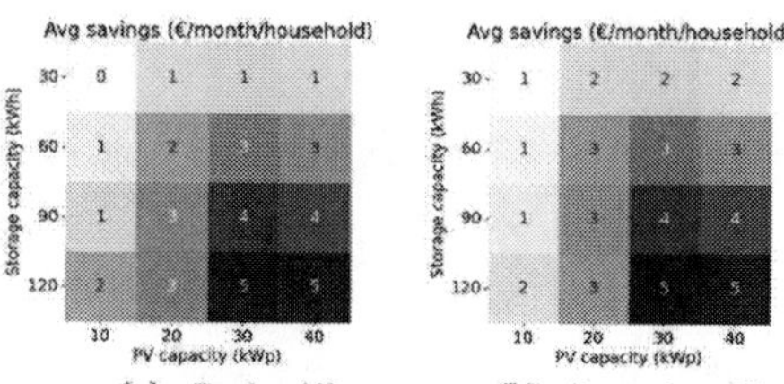

(a) Dual tariff   **(b)** Dynamic tariff

Figure 3: Heatmaps of average potential monthly savings per household for the case study achieved by an optimization with perfect foresight, when compared with SCM. Results are shown for a dual and a dynamic tariff, across combinations of varying storage and PV.

Two factors explain the robust performance of SCM in this context: abundant solar resource and favorable tariff alignment. This can be observed in **Figure 4**, which shows the energy management determined by SCM over three consecutive days for one of the scenarios.

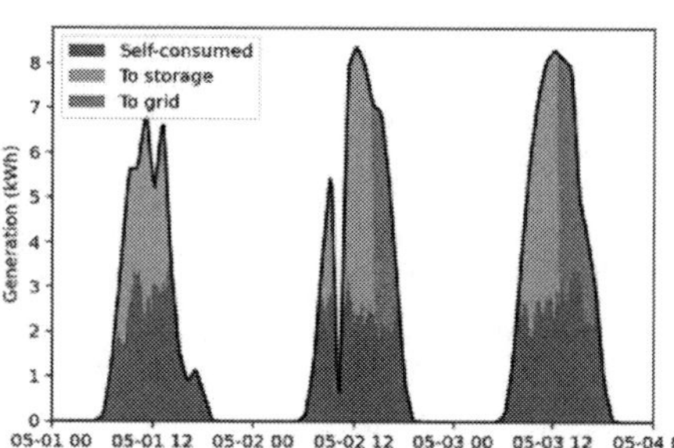

(a) PV generation

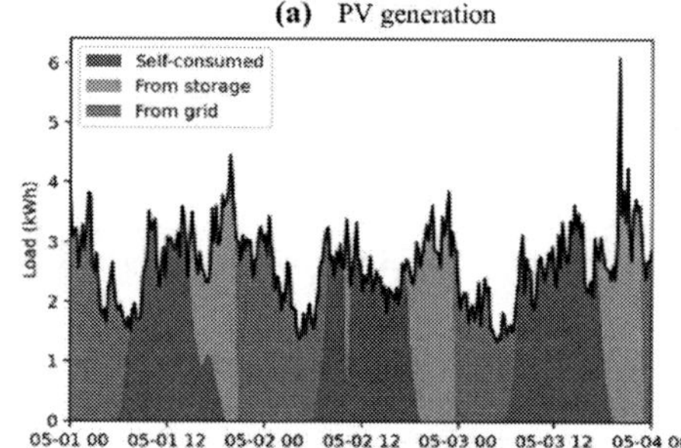

(b) Energy consumption

Figure 4: Energy management determined by SCM over a 3-day period. Figure 4a shows PV generation and its use, while Figure 4b shows the collective energy consumption and its source, in kWh over 15-minute periods.

The second and third days exhibit high solar production. SCM prioritizes immediate self-consumption and stores the surplus generation. Once the battery is full, surplus generation is injected into the grid. In the evening, the stored energy covers consumption, and by the time the battery is depleted, it is nearly midnight, when electricity prices are at their lowest. In such scenarios, SCM effectively minimizes energy costs, leaving little room for improvement through more advanced strategies.

In contrast, on days with lower solar generation, such as the first day shown in **Figure 4**, the surplus is insufficient to fully charge the battery, resulting in earlier reliance on grid energy during peak price periods. In these cases, price arbitrage – charging the battery with low-cost grid energy for later use – becomes critical for cost savings beyond what SCM can provide. It is in these situations that a smart strategy can outperform SCM. However, such days are relatively infrequent in Mediterranean climates. Additionally, hybrid approaches combining SCM with minimal forecasting and pre-set charging schedules could offer a cost-effective alternative to fully intelligent, high-cost solutions.

It is worth emphasizing that the optimal results reported here represent a theoretical upper bound, obtained under the assumption of perfect foresight. In reality, forecast errors inevitably lead to suboptimal decisions, preventing even advanced control strategies from fully realizing the theoretical potential. When these limitations are combined with the additional costs of forecasting services, cloud infrastructure, and more complex hardware, the economic advantage of intelligent energy management over simple rule-based control can be marginal. In contrast, SCM offers a robust, low-cost solution that is inherently resilient to uncertainty.

Future work could extend this analysis to other climates, assessing SCM's effectiveness under varying solar resource availability. An exploration of the impact of aggregation or diverse residential consumption patterns would also be valuable to generalize these findings.

5 ACKNOWLEDGEMENTS

This work is supported by the Portuguese Fundação para a Ciência e Tecnologia, FCT, I.P./MCTES through national funds (PIDDAC): UID/50019/2025 and LA/P/0068/2020 (https://doi.org/10.54499/LA/P/0068/2020), as well as the FCT Studentship UI/BD/154674/2023, and Project ATE: Aliança para a Transição Energética financed by IAPMEI - Agência para a Competitividade e Inovação, I. P.

6 REFERENCES

[1] Leitao, J., Gil, P., Ribeiro, B., & Cardoso, A. (2020). A survey on home energy management. *IEEE Access, 8*, 5699–5722.
https://doi.org/10.1109/ACCESS.2019.2963502

[2] Azuatalam, D., Paridari, K., Ma, Y., Förstl, M., Chapman, A. C., & Verbič, G. (2019). Energy management of small-scale PV-battery systems: A systematic review considering practical implementation, computational requirements, quality of input data and battery degradation. Renewable and Sustainable Energy Reviews, 112, 555–570.
https://doi.org/10.1016/j.rser.2019.06.007

[3] Beaudin, M., & Zareipour, H. (2015). Home energy management systems: A review of modelling and complexity. *Renewable and Sustainable Energy Reviews, 45*, 318–335.
https://doi.org/10.1016/j.rser.2015.01.046

[4] Huld, T., Müller, R., & Gambardella, A. (2012). A new solar radiation database for estimating PV performance in Europe and Africa. *Solar Energy, 86*(6), 1803–1815.
https://doi.org/10.1016/j.solener.2012.03.006

This presentation was selected by the Sc. Committee of the EU PVSEC 2025 for submission of a full paper to one of the EU PVSEC's collaborating peer-reviewed journals.

SOLUTIONS FOR OPTIMIZING SHARED PV INSTALLATIONS AT RENEWABLE ENERGY COMMUNITIES DRIVEN BY CITIZENS

Ana B. Cristóbal*[a,b] (0000-0002-4314-6160), Sergio Morales[a], Daniel Sierra[a], Laura Palomino[b], Luis Narvarte (0000-0002-6289-7605)[b].

a) Escuela Técnica Superior de Ingeniería de Sistemas Informáticos, Universidad Politécnica de Madrid, C/Alan Turing s/n, 28031 Madrid, Spain

b) Instituto de Energía Solar, Universidad Politécnica de Madrid, C/Nikola Tesla s/n, 28031 Madrid, Spain.

anabelen.cristobal@upm.es, sergio.morales.gonzalez@alumnos.upm.es, daniel.sierra@alumnos.upm.es, laura.palomino@upm.es, luis.narvarte@upm.es

ABSTRACT: The rapid emergence of Renewable Energy Communities (RECs) across Europe highlights the potential of citizen-led initiatives to accelerate the transition toward decentralized and sustainable energy systems. However, their effective operation requires digital tools capable of providing real-time data on consumption and production—resources often limited to company-driven projects with proprietary platforms. This work presents the design and implementation of an open, modular framework that empowers communities to autonomously monitor and manage shared photovoltaic installations. The system integrates low-cost Shelly EM devices, configured through the MQTT protocol, with a Docker-based backend deployed on AWS and a flexible data model supporting both public and private resources. Core functionalities include real-time visualization, hierarchical user roles, and integration with national data sources such as Spain's REData API. By lowering technical and administrative barriers, the platform strengthens citizen participation, enhances decision-making on energy allocation and surpluses, and offers a scalable digital infrastructure aligned with the original vision of community-driven renewable energy.
Keywords: Renewable Energy Communities (REC), IoT-based Energy Monitoring, MQTT Protocol, Citizen Participation, Dockerized Architecture

1 INTRODUCTION

Historically, the energy system has been dominated by large corporations, heavily dependent on fossil fuels and centralized distribution. However, technological advances, regulatory changes, the European energy crisis, and growing social commitment to sustainability have paved the way for the emergence of energy communities. European legislation distinguishes between two types: Citizen Energy Communities (CEC), defined in Directive (EU) 2019/944, and Renewable Energy Communities (REC), defined in Directive (EU) 2018/2001. While both frameworks coexist, in practice, the concept of REC has become the prevailing reference.

These communities can engage in a wide range of activities, including the production, consumption, sharing, storage, and sale of renewable energy, as well as initiatives for energy efficiency, sustainable mobility, and environmental awareness. Beyond reducing carbon footprints and energy costs, they foster social cohesion and empower citizens by directly involving them in energy management and decision-making.

According to the EC, there are more than 9,000 RECs in the EU, involving more than 1.5 million citizens in early 2024 [1]. Schwanitz estimated 10,540 initiatives involving more than 2 million people, an installed renewable capacity ranging from 7.2–9.9 GW and investments made 6.2–11.3 billion € for 30 EU countries [2]. Spain serves as a relevant example: 659 REC initiatives were registered by the end of 2024 [3] - twice as many as in 2023.

Despite their rapid growth, energy communities still face major challenges [4], particularly regarding digitalization. The effective management of collective self-consumption requires accurate, real-time data on both generation and demand; without it, participants cannot fully optimize the use of locally produced renewable

energy or make informed decisions on how to valorize surpluses and define allocation coefficients. In Spain, for example, DSOs allow adjustments of allocation shares from community installations up to four times per year, but most users remain unable to take informed decisions beyond fixed distributions typically based on their initial investment.

Many communities promoted by energy companies benefit from proprietary digital platforms that streamline these processes, but this model contrasts with the original vision of Renewable Energy Communities (RECs) as citizen-led initiatives aimed at empowering local actors. For grassroots projects, open-access digital tools are still lacking, limiting their ability to autonomously register, monitor, and manage energy flows, and ultimately hindering their potential for self-governance and scalability.

In this work, we present a digital framework designed to support citizen-led RECs in managing shared photovoltaic installations. The proposed solution combines open-access monitoring and data management tools to provide real-time insights on consumption and generation, enable more flexible allocation strategies, and facilitate collective decision-making. By lowering technical and administrative barriers, this approach aims to strengthen citizen participation, improve the economic performance of community energy projects, and contribute to the broader transition toward decentralized and sustainable energy systems.

2 TECHNICAL FRAMEWORK

2.1 Monitoring Demand

Electricity users are entitled to access the readings recorded by their smart meters. This information can be obtained either by physically inspecting the meter or through the application or website usually provided by the energy retailer, which connects to the distributor's metering infrastructure. As illustrated in Figure 1, daily consumption data are aggregated into three established periods (peak, flat, and off-peak), as well as the overall historical consumption profile.

Figure 1: Example of consumption data displayed by the regulated market retailer of the Naturgy group.

This approach presents two major limitations. First, implementing a data integration or extraction process individually for each retailer is unfeasible, particularly given that Spain has more than 400 energy retailers, each with its own interpretation of data access rights. Second, the aggregated data provided do not enable real-time consumption monitoring.

It is therefore logical that consumption data should be accessed directly from the distributor, which owns the smart meters and bears responsibility for providing such access. Since there are only five distribution companies in Spain, developing integrations with them may appear more manageable.

Figure 2 illustrates the access interface of Unión Fenosa Distribución. In practice, the application requires approximately two minutes to establish a connection before displaying real-time demand data. Although the system allows scheduled queries, these are limited to 30-minute intervals and cannot provide continuous real-time monitoring.

Figure 2: Data access through the distributor's application:
(a) user access panel; (b) real-time demand; (c) scheduled queries interface.

Attempts to develop external APIs capable of continuous calls to distributor systems have been blocked, as such activity is deemed potentially hazardous. In response, the five main electricity distributors in Spain created DATADIS, a centralized database designed to provide secure access to consumption data. As shown in Figure 3, DATADIS allows users to extract data from any smart meter, and also permits access to third-party data upon prior authorization.

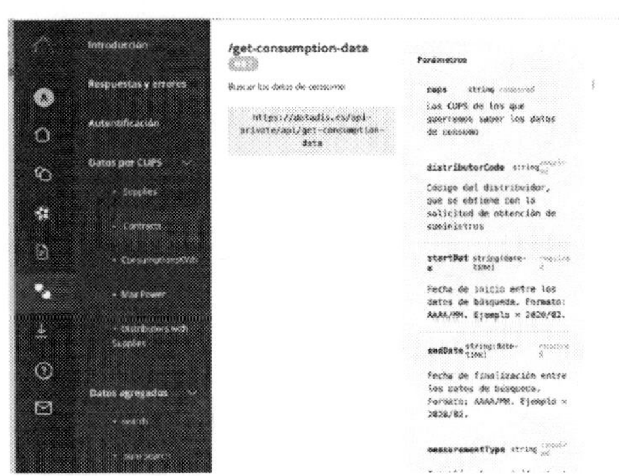

Figure 3: Overview of the DATADIS API platform.

2.2 Monitoring Production

Most distributed generation sources produce direct current (DC), which requires conversion to alternating current (AC) for domestic use. This task is performed by the inverter, which also provides the most relevant point for monitoring production. Inverters typically employ the Modbus protocol over TCP/IP or serial ports. Although robust, Modbus requires a dedicated server to query the inverter periodically and transmit data to users, which is impractical for non-expert citizens.

An alternative approach is to expose port 502 for remote Modbus access. However, because manufacturers implement Modbus differently, no universal solution exists. Moreover, configuring firewall exceptions requires technical expertise, rendering this option inaccessible for most communities.

A more viable solution is the deployment of universal electrical measurement devices capable of integrating with existing meters and inverters, while remaining non-intrusive. These devices should connect to an open-access platform, allowing all community members to monitor real-time energy flows.

2.2.1 Open Hardware

An initial attempt considered a custom ESP32-based device. While cost-effective, this solution remains a DIY approach, requiring technical knowledge beyond the capacity of most citizens. Consequently, commercially available alternatives were explored.

One promising option is the Shelly EM, a compact device that measures current, voltage, and other electrical parameters. It connects via Wi-Fi and can be operated remotely. Crucially, it supports the MQTT protocol, enabling integration with user-defined servers rather than relying solely on the manufacturer's cloud infrastructure. This flexibility, together with comprehensive documentation and backward compatibility, positioned the Shelly EM as the preferred choice for this study. Citizens can directly purchase and configure the device to connect with the **renew-net.com** open framework developed here.

2.2.2 Open Software

Currently, no open-source platform provides real-time visualization of energy community behaviour connected to IoT devices. Therefore, this study proposes the creation of such a platform.

Table I: Functional and Non-Functional Requirements of the Open Platform

ID	Name	Type	Description
RQF01	MQTT Connection with Shelly EM	Functional	Connectivity with Shelly EM meters via MQTT must be supported.
RQF02	MQTT to Database Proxy	Functional	Telemetry data must be stored in a persistent database.
RQF03	Configurable Graph	Functional	Users must be able to visualize data via configurable graphs.
RQF04	Hierarchical Roles	Functional	User roles with specific permissions must be defined.
RQF05	Sensor Integration	Functional	Users must select which sensors connect to the server.
RQNF01	Concurrency in MQTT Agent	Non-Functional	The system must ensure atomicity and resource exclusivity.
RQNF02	UX/UI Design	Non-Functional	The interface must be minimalist and user-friendly.
RQNF03	System Performance	Non-Functional	Responses must occur in <1s for up to 100 concurrent users.
RQNF05	Secure Sessions	Non-Functional	Sessions must expire after 1 hour; registration requires admin approval.
RQNF06	Secure Backend Requests	Non-Functional	Backend must use JWT authentication; no unauthenticated routes permitted.

3.2 General Architecture

The high-level architecture of the system is hosted on Amazon Web Services (AWS). The infrastructure is containerized using Docker, which ensures modularity, portability, and ease of deployment. Docker containers also enable scalability, allowing the system to adapt to higher loads when required.

- **Backend Container (Node.js + Express):** Provides REST APIs and serves the frontend application.
- **MSSQL Container (Database):** Manages relational data, including authentication, roles, and community resources.
- **MQTT Broker Container:** Handles telemetry ingestion, normalization, and database insertion.

While SQL Server supports structured data management effectively, telemetry data may be better served by migrating to a **NoSQL model** (e.g., MongoDB, Cassandra) or adopting **cloud-native time-series databases** such as Amazon Timestream or Azure Time Series Insights.

This modular, containerized design facilitates maintainability, supports scalability, and lays the foundation for real-time, citizen-driven monitoring of energy communities.

Currently, the entire system runs on a single EC2 virtual machine (1 vCPU, 4 GB RAM), which is sufficient for a pool of fewer than 100 users. The choice of containerization reflects the system's long-term goal of being continuously developed and extended, with Docker ensuring simplicity for collaborative work and future enhancements.

3 IMPLEMENTATION

3.1 Shelly EM Connection in the User's Internal Network.

The Shelly EM device can be connected to one or two current clamps (50A), depending on whether the user has an individual PV installation. Collective energy communities behave as users without self-consumption, therefore requiring only one clamp. Figure 4 illustrates the general connection scheme.

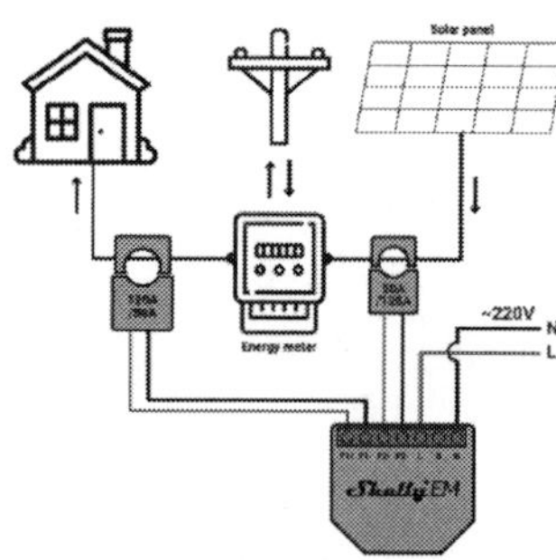

Figure 4: General connection scheme of Shelly EM devices (reproduced with permission from Shelly Spain).

Once the hardware is installed, the device must be paired with the Shelly mobile application (available on iOS and Android). The app requires the creation of a "room," which may represent an entire household or a single room. This design allows users to organize and manage multiple Shelly devices efficiently—up to 40 devices for non-premium users. Within the chosen room, the Shelly EM associated with consumption and/or production is added. If correctly installed, the application displays the detected energy flows in real time (Figure 5).

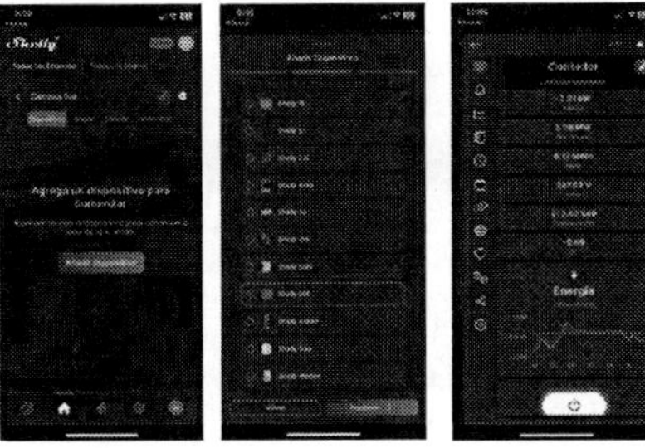

Figure 5: Process of linking a Shelly EM device to the Shelly mobile application.

3.2 Data and Resource Modelling (Business Logic)

The backend data model follows a decoupled design in which the primary entities are roles, devices, and resources, linked to users. The resources are the central elements of the system, shared across authorized users. Each resource has an optional owner_id field; when absent, the resource is considered public and accessible to all users (e.g., the national electricity price monitor).

Currently, three resource types are implemented:

- Electricity Price Monitor: Public resource displaying hourly electricity prices via the official REData API (National Grid Operator). Since data are fetched in real time from the API, no dedicated backend table is required (Figure 6).

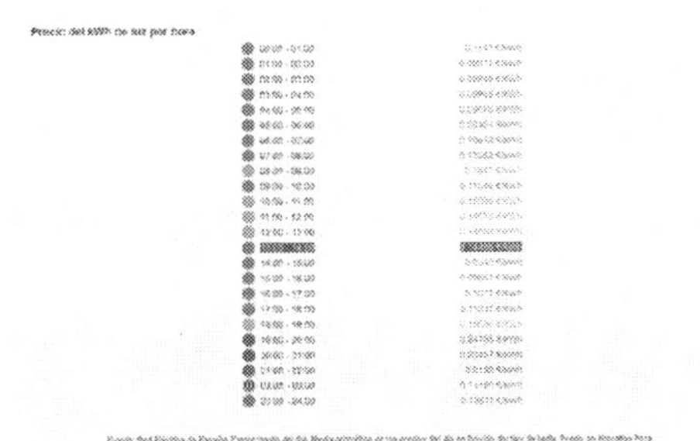

Figure 6: Hourly electricity price data provided by Red Eléctrica (REData API).

- Shelly EM Monitor: Private resource representing telemetry collected by Shelly EM sensors. Data are stored in the em_telemetry database table, aggregated over time, and presented to users as hourly graphs (Figure 7).

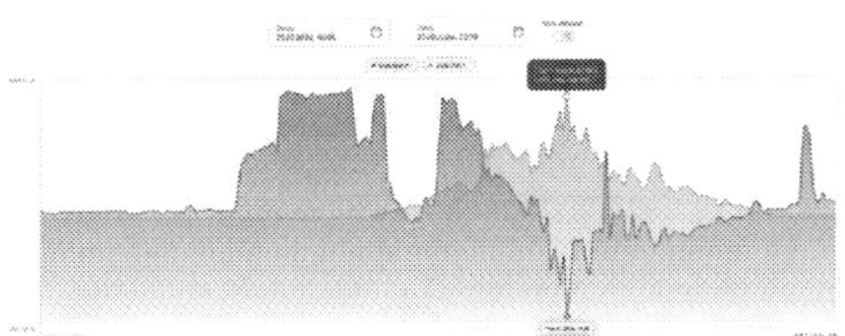

Figure 7: Monitoring resource displaying Shelly EM device telemetry data.

- Energy Community Resource: A collaborative resource with internal hierarchy. Two user roles are defined: administrators and regular members. Administrators can view all consumption and production data, while regular users only see their own. Aggregate community graphs are available to all participants. The database includes two dedicated tables to manage participants and their devices. Figures 8 and 9 show the community dashboard, including aggregated consumption/production, individual user balances, and hypothetical scenarios for collective PV installations.

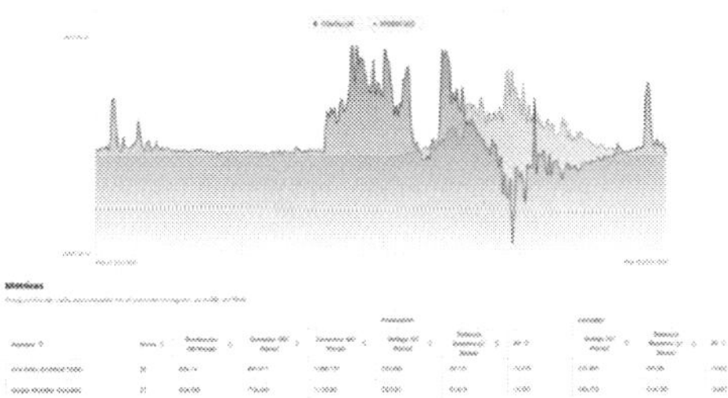

Figure 8: Example of the energy community dashboard from the administrator's perspective.

Figure 9: Energy community dashboard showing aggregated data, user balances, and hypothetical collective PV scenarios.

3.3 MQTT Broker Integration

Communication between devices and the platform relies on the MQTT (Message Queuing Telemetry Transport) protocol, widely adopted in IoT for its lightweight, publish–subscribe architecture. In this model, devices (clients) publish telemetry to specific topics, while other clients subscribe to those topics. A central broker manages message distribution, ensuring delivery to authorized subscribers.

In the proposed system, the broker also stores telemetry in the database, making it the central interface between IoT devices and the backend. MQTT was selected not only because it is an industry standard but also because Shelly EM devices support it exclusively.

3.4 Connecting a Shelly EM to the Telemetry Server

The integration of a Shelly EM with the telemetry server involves two main steps:

Step 1: Connect the device to the server. The user connects to the Shelly EM's default Wi-Fi network, which follows

the SSID format:
shelly<MODEL>-XXXXXXXXXXXX. Credentials must be provided to authorize telemetry publication (Figure 10).

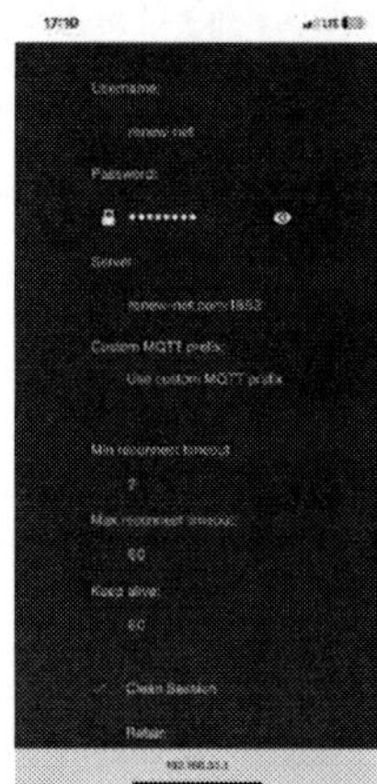

Figure 10. Shelly EM configuration interface for enabling MQTT and connecting to the telemetry server.

Step 2: Integrate the device into the application. Within the platform https://renew-net.com, users register their device under "My Devices" by entering the name, description, and unique identifier, which can be extracted from the Wi-Fi SSID. After this step, telemetry data are transmitted and visualized in the user account (Figure 11).

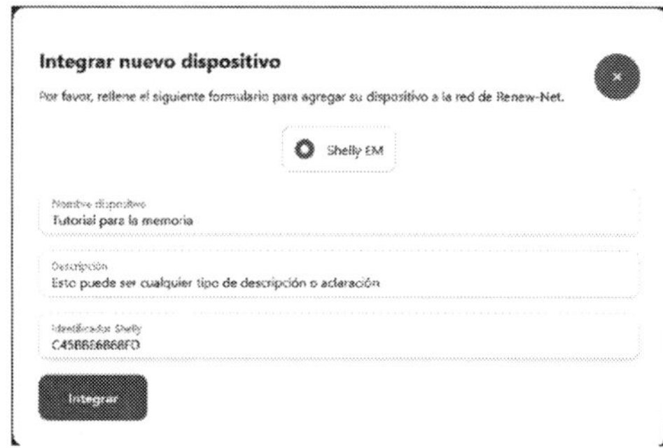

Figure 11. Device integration process within the renew-net.com application.

4 CONCLUSIONS

This work has presented the design and implementation of a modular, open platform aimed at enabling citizen-led energy communities in Spain to monitor both demand and production in real time. The system integrates low-cost hardware (Shelly EM devices) with an MQTT-based communication layer, a Dockerized backend infrastructure deployed on AWS, and a flexible data model that supports individual and collective resources.

The proposed solution addresses key barriers that energy communities currently face: the difficulty of accessing real-time consumption data through retailers or distributors, the lack of universal monitoring tools for production, and the absence of open platforms tailored to community needs. By combining commercial IoT devices with an open software architecture, the system offers an affordable and scalable approach that empowers citizens to actively participate in energy management.

Three main contributions can be highlighted:

1. **Practical integration of hardware and software**: The Shelly EM devices, when reconfigured to operate with MQTT, provide a universal and accessible entry point for collecting real-time telemetry.
2. **Modular and scalable architecture**: The use of Docker containers and AWS resources ensures that the system can evolve, scale, and be maintained collaboratively.
3. **Community-oriented data model**: The introduction of role-based access and shared resources allows for both individual monitoring and collective visualization within energy communities.

The results demonstrate that it is technically feasible for communities to deploy their own open, interoperable monitoring infrastructure without relying exclusively on proprietary or distributor-controlled systems.

Future work will focus on enhancing the scalability of the platform by integrating non-relational databases optimized for time-series telemetry, improving the user interface for broader accessibility, and exploring regulatory pathways that would allow community energy trading at the local level.

5 ACKNOWLEDGEMENTS

This research has been funded by the project "FOREVERPV-CM: For an Environmentally Friendly Photovoltaic Technology" (TEC2024/ECO72), granted by the Comunidad de Madrid.

6 REFERENCES

[1] Interreg Danube Region. (2024) Recent Survey Highlights Potential of Energy Communities in the EU. https://interreg-danube.eu/projects/nrgcom/news/recent-survey-highlights-potential-of-energy-communities-in-the-eu

[2] Schwanitz, V.J., et al., Statistical evidence for the contribution of citizen-led initiatives and projects to the energy transition in Europe. Scientific Reports, 2023. **13**: p. 1342.

[3] ECODES. (2024). Observatorio de comunidades energéticas. https://ecodes.org/biblioteca/documento?v=1&id=643-observatorio-de-comunidades-energeticas&descarga-documento=1&h=5160f5c50cd9e7fc57a8d9236a9640094015a7c59b22d1aa450f648c39166087

[4] European Commission, *Barriers and drivers report.* 2024, Energy Communities Repository. https://circabc.europa.eu/ui/group/8f5f9424-a7ef-4dbf-b914-1af1d12ff5d2/library/22055ff9-1f49-41f8-a321-cbf20ca3d316/details

ENHANCED VALUE OF GRID-CONNECTED PV WITH BATTERY STORAGE IN A NEGATIVE PRICE ENVIRONMENT

Djaber Berrian, Gaurang Chhapia, Rene vanBaal, Johannes Linder
Belectric Holding GmbH, Wadenbrunner Str. 10, 97509 Kolitzheim, e-mail: djaber.berrian@belectric.com

ABSTRACT: In recent years, the global installed PV system capacity has reached record levels, especially in the EU. This has led to more frequent negative prices due to overproduction. Consequently, utility-scale PV systems are often curtailed during these periods, reducing their value and attractiveness. Our study quantifies the value loss of PV systems during high negative price hours and explores solutions to enhance PV asset value by integrating battery storage. According to our models, PV systems can lose up to 11% of annual production due to negative price hours, while batteries can increase their production by up to 7% under these negative hours. Combining PV with battery storage shows greater resilience to negative price fluctuations, with almost no change in net energy production (PV + battery) during negative price hours.

Keywords: photovoltaic systems; negative electricity prices; battery energy storage systems; energy curtailment; economic valuation; grid flexibility; hybrid energy systems

1 INTRODUCTION

The deployment of photovoltaic (PV) systems has accelerated recently, with an additional 1 terawatt (TW) added between 2022 and 2024, bringing the global total to 2 TW. However, this rapid growth has led to challenges, particularly for grid-connected PV systems, as the number of hours with negative electricity prices has surged, reaching 457 hours in Germany and over 500 hours in Nordic countries [1]. This devalues PV assets and makes them less attractive investments. This study explores methods to increase PV system value by integrating them with battery energy storage systems (BESS) to enhance resilience against negative prices. We examine two market scenarios: low and high negative price environments and assess the benefits of co-locating PV with BESS.

It is widely recognized in literature that integrating a high proportion of renewable energy into the grid will eventually necessitate battery energy storage systems to stabilize the grid against the intermittent nature of these sources [2]. However, BESS can offer various grid services and financial advantages. Therefore, a thorough analysis of PV production and its net value in a negative price environment, as well as the extent to which BESS can enhance the PV net value in negative price environment, remain largely unquantified. This study employs advanced, bankable tools like PVsyst and COSMOS, utilizing 15–20-year price curves to simulate the intricate dynamics of a grid-connected hybrid PV + BESS system operating in a merchant market with access to day-ahead (DA) markets, automatic Frequency Restoration Reserve (aFRR), and Frequency Containment Reserve (FCR). Using these modeling tools, we will examine the extent to which PV value diminishes in negative price environments and how it interacts with BESS. The multiservice optimization approach also enables us to identify the market in which BESS is most productive under varying low and high negative price conditions.

2 METHODOLOGY AND KEY MATERIALS

We have modeled a hybrid PV + BESS plant in Germany based the summarized tools in Figure 1. PVsyst is known for its accuracy [3], it is used to model the energy production of a fixed-tilt bifacial n-type PV plant. We have used the price forecast for energy storage from Aurora research [4]. The energy production and prices

curves are then used in COSMOS [5] to model the dispatch of PV + BESS system. COSMOS Uses a multiple linear solver with constraints for dispatching a battery between day-ahead, intraday, and FCR and aFRR markets to optimize battery usage and maximize profits.

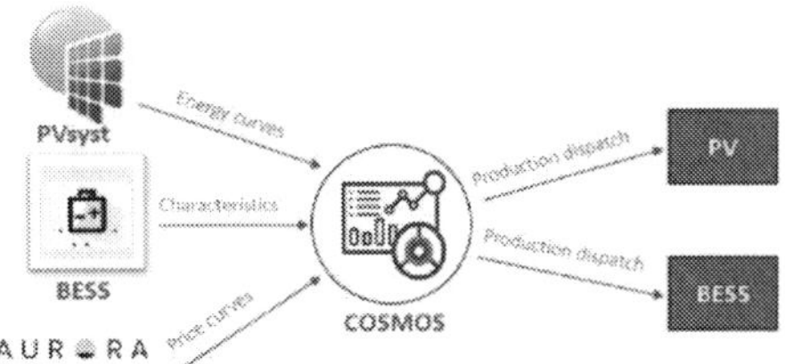

Figure 1 The structure of the modeling tool, inputs and outputs for

In our study we assume PV has priority over BESS, i.e BESS will work around PV production, BESS will deliver at times when PV production does not meet the grid capacity. We considered a 2-hour battery (45MW) with 1.5 cycles per day, and max yearly cycles of 547.5 cycles, and DoD 95%. The round-trip efficiency of BESS is assumed to be 82% including auxiliary losses. The battery and PV module yearly degradation are shown in Figure 2 and 3 respectively. The project is located in Germany and project lifetime is assumed to be 15 years from 2026 to 2040 for BESS and 20 years for PV. After 15 years only PV is assumed to be in operation, while BESS has reached the end of life.

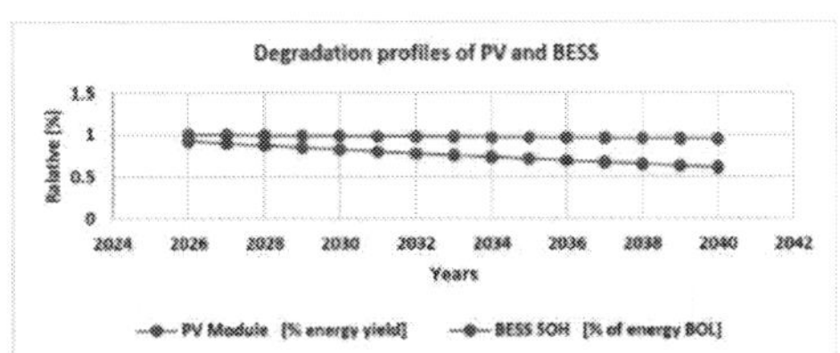

Figure 2 The degradation profiles of PV and BESS over the lifetime of the project used as input to the model

As can be seen in Figure 2, compared to PV modules, BESS degrades much faster than PV modules, after 15 years BESS will have a remaining capacity of 60%, whereas PV modules can deliver 94% of the initial specific energy yield. To assess the impact of negative price curves on the value of PV systems and determine how effectively BESS can enhance PV resilience against these curves, we examined two scenarios. Scenario 1 (S1) spans 15 years with a low frequency of negative price hours, while Scenario 2 (S2) covers 15 years with a high frequency of negative price hours. Negative hours are recorded in the day-ahead market. For instance, the yearly count of negative prices, as reported by Aurora research, is shown in Figure 3.

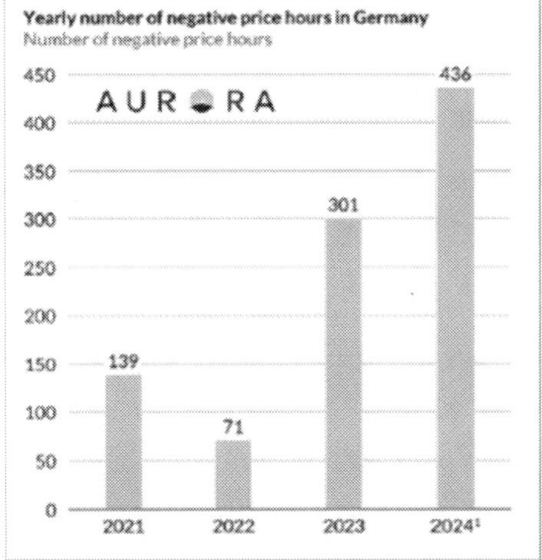

Figure 3 The negative hours measured in day

3 RESULTS & DISCUSSION

We simulated the energy production of PV and BESS over a 15-year period under both low and high negative price environments. The graph in Figure 4 illustrates the relative changes between (S1) and (S2). Over the 15 years, a clear trend emerges: PV production experiences a devaluation ranging from approximately -4% to -11%, while BESS production shows an improvement varying from around 4% to 7%, depending on the year. These results signify the fact that the energy or value lost for PV can be restored or gained again through BESS.

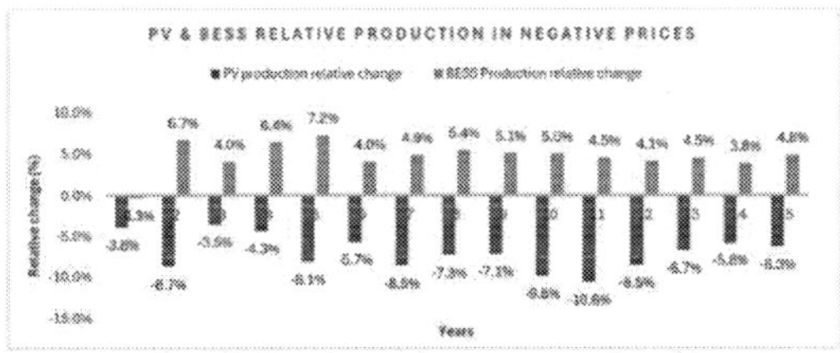

Figure 4 The relative change in energy produced by PV and BESS under high negative price environment

The decline in energy production from PV systems is primarily due to curtailment during periods of negative prices. When there is an oversupply of energy in the market, prices can drop significantly, even becoming negative in recent years. During these times, asset owners reduce PV production. The plot in Figure 5 illustrates the simulation of PV energy curtailed in both low and high negative price environments. As shown, more PV energy

is lost (curtailed) in a high negative price environment compared to a low negative price environment. This explains the loss in PV production seen previously in Figure 4

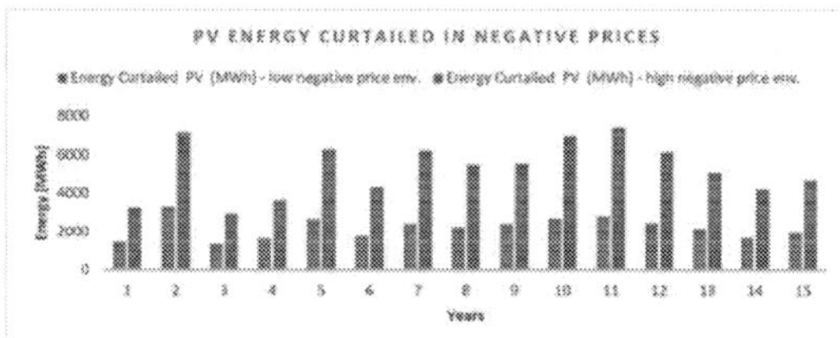

Figure 5 PV curtailed energy under high and low negative price environment

On the contrary, BESS has shown increased production in markets with high negative prices (Figure 4). We modeled and analyzed production across different markets to understand BESS behavior in both low and high negative price environments.

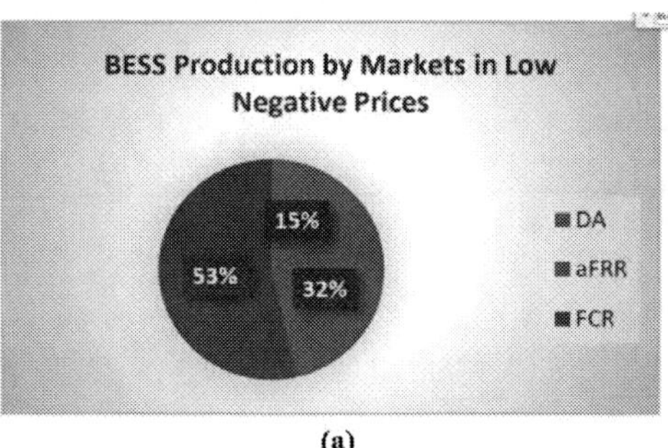

(a)

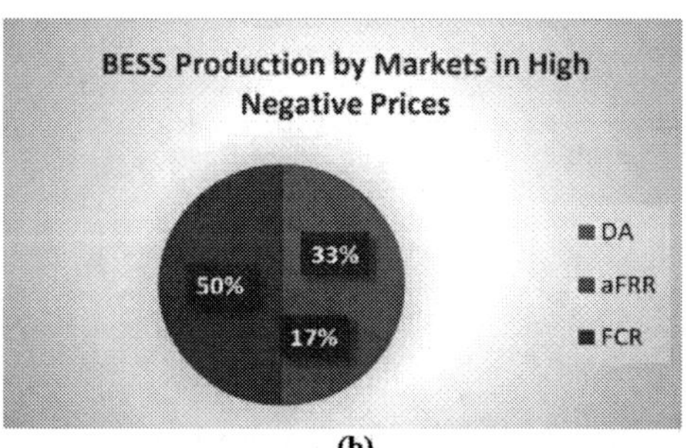

(b)

Figure 6 The distribution of BESS production per market over the project lifetime. (a) Low scenario, (b) high scenario.

The pie charts in Figure 6 summarize the relative production over 15 years across various markets (DA, aFRR, FCR) for both scenarios, S1 (a) and S2 (b). As can be seen, in a low negative price environment, BESS primarily operates in the FCR and aFRR markets, with the day-ahead (DA) market being secondary. However, in a high negative pric environment, BESS prioritizes the DA market over aFRR. This shift occurs because BESS can capitalize on negative prices in the DA market by charging during negative price hours and discharging during positive price hours, thus maximizing profits. In

10.4229/EUPVSEC2025/5DO.15.4
020492-002

the full abstract, we will explore the techno-economic implications of these behaviors and determine whether the revenue patterns align with the energy production trends of PV and BESS.

Finally, while earlier results indicated that PV systems lose value during periods of high negative prices, an interesting finding emerged when we examined the total production of PV and BESS (hybrid) in both low and high negative price environments. We discovered that the total production remains nearly unchanged, with only a 0.01% relative difference. This suggests that integrating BESS with PV enhances the robustness and resilience of PV systems against negative prices.

4 CONCLUSIONS

The analysis of energy output under varying price scenarios reveals contrasting impacts on PV and BESS systems. Under high-negative-price conditions, PV energy output experiences a notable decline - up to 11% - primarily due to increased curtailment. However, this effect diminishes over time and becomes negligible, reflecting the evolving market dynamics and system adaptations. In contrast, BESS energy output significantly increases under the same conditions. This surge is largely driven by enhanced participation in day-ahead and intraday markets, where BESS capitalizes on price volatility. These findings highlight the complementary role of BESS in mitigating curtailment losses and enhancing system flexibility in a high-renewable, price-volatile environment. The economic analysis reveals that integrating a BESS with a PV plant significantly enhances its financial performance under negative electricity price conditions. While standalone PV systems experience a decline in Net Present Value (NPV) due to curtailment and reduced market revenues; the addition of BESS not only mitigates these losses but also unlocks substantial economic gains. The hybrid system consistently outperforms the standalone PV configuration across scenarios, demonstrating both reduced downside risk and increased upside potential. Moreover, while PV revenues tend to decline under prolonged negative price conditions, BESS revenues improve markedly, driven by active participation in day-ahead and intraday markets. Over time, as market conditions stabilize and negative price events become less frequent, the economic gap narrows. These findings underscore the strategic importance of designing storage-ready PV systems, either through initial integration or future retrofitting, to maintain and enhance asset value in evolving electricity markets.

5 References

[1] Magazine, P. V. " Europe posts negative power prices for 2024 as renewables rise" PV Magazine (2025).
[2] T, Teh, Jiashen, and Ching-Ming Lai. "Reliability impacts of the dynamic thermal rating and battery energy storage systems on wind-integrated power networks." Sustainable Energy, Grids and Networks 20 (2019): 100268

[3] Nussbaumer, Hartmut, et al. "Accuracy of simulated data for bifacial systems with varying tilt angles and share of diffuse radiation." Solar Energy 197 (2020): 6-21.
[4] Aurora Energy Research. Chronos for Batteries. https://auroraer.com/software/chronos, 2025. Accessed July 21, 2025
[5] Clean Horizon, "Energy storage & Price forecast " https://www.cleanhorizon.com/about/, accessed 01.2025.

Enhanced Value of Grid-Connected PV
with Battery Storage in a Negative Price Environment

42nd EU PVSEC Conference, Bilbao
D. Berrian, G. Chhapia, R. VanBaal, J. Linder

September 25th, 2025

Content

01 Motivation

02 Methodology

03 Results & Discussion

04 Conclusions

Motivation

Motivation
The Solar PV Paradox: Growth & Cannibalisation

"It took the solar PV industry **68 years** to reach **1 TW** of installed capacity - from 1954-2022. It has taken only 2 **years** to reach **the next TW (2022-2024)**"
Global Solar Council and SolarPower Europe

Several EU countries face the challenge of increasing frequency of negative electricity hours

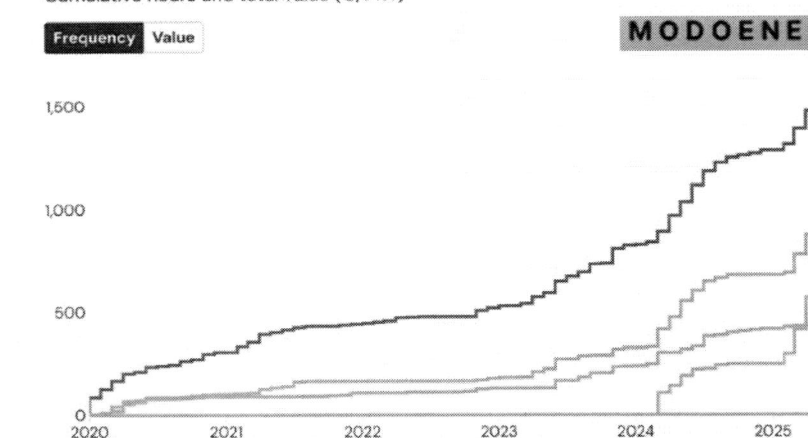

Day-ahead prices 27.04.2025 at 11am April 2025
Source: Nord Pool, OMIE, Iberian Electricity Market Operat

Exported from Germany
Cumulative hours and total value (€/MW)

Verband Deutscher Maschinen- und Anlagenbau. International technology roadmap for photovoltaic, 2023.
URL https://www.vdma.org/international-technology-roadmap-photovoltaic.

020493-004

Motivation
The Solar PV Paradox: Growth & Cannibalisation

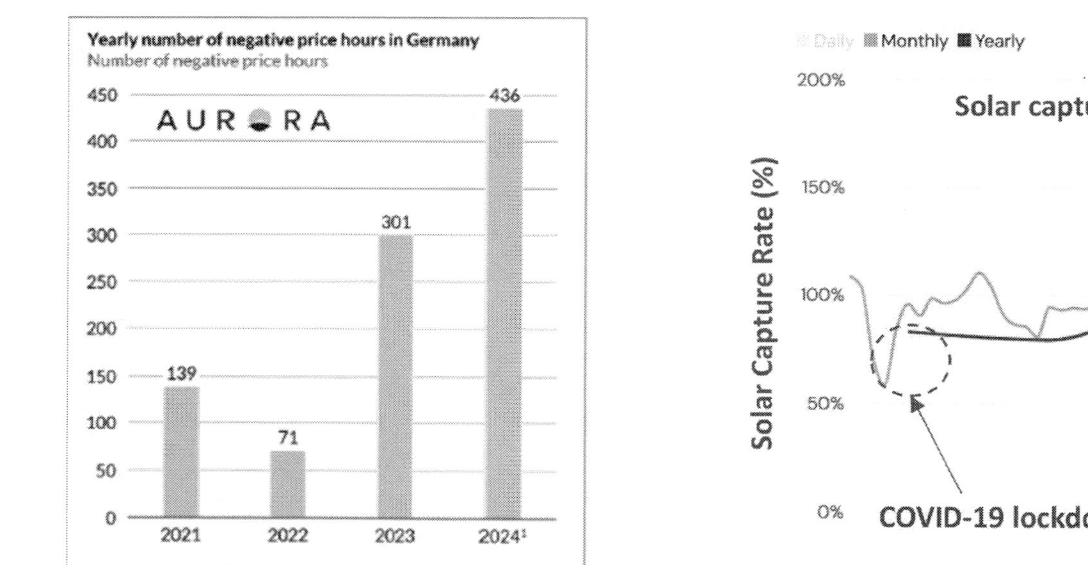

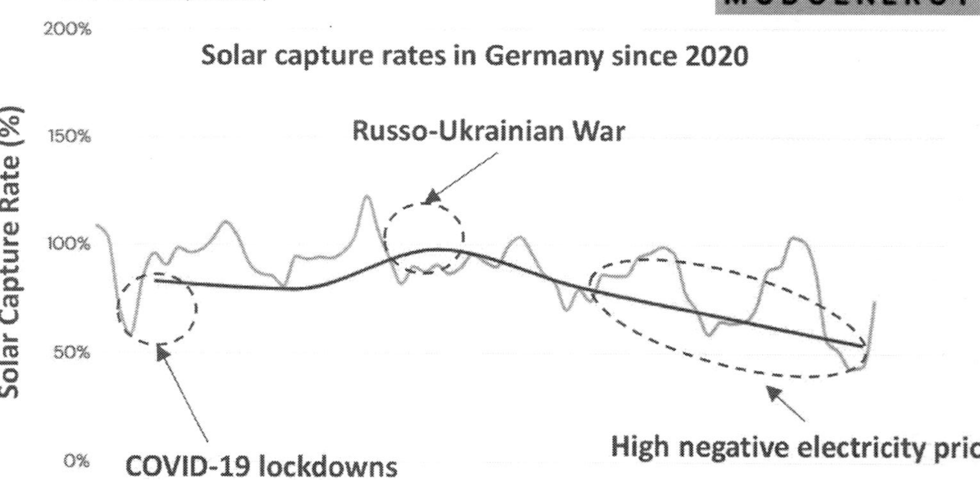

1. What behaviour do PV and BESS exhibit under high negative electricity prices?
2. How can BESS enhance the value of PV assets during periods of negative electricity prices?

020493-005

Methodology

⊙ BELECTRIC

020493-006

Methodology
Site Description

BELECTRIC® MEMBER OF ELEVION GROUP

Bifacial Solar Trackers + Battery Energy Storage (BESS)

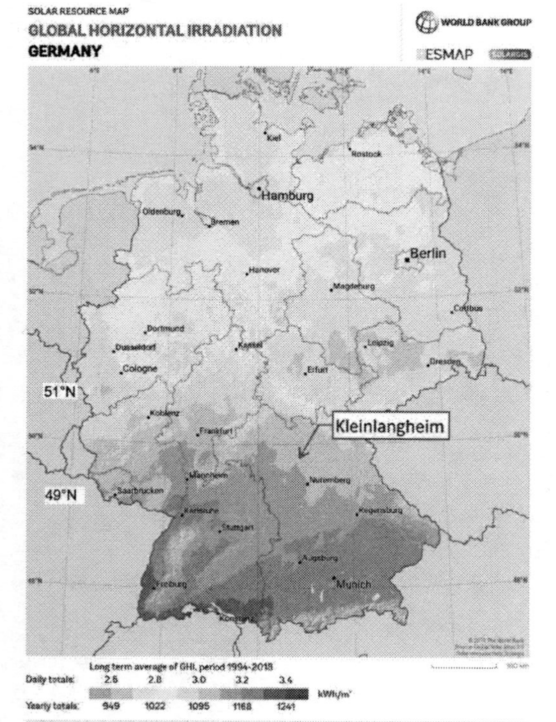

- 60 MWp PV with 1.2 DC/AC ratio, 2m RS, 50MW BESS, 50 MW Grid
- PV lifetime 30 years, BESS lifetime 15 years, 2H, 1.5 Cycle/day
- BESS + PV Sharing the same grid connection. Focus Front of the Meter applicaiton

Methodology
Modeling & Simulation

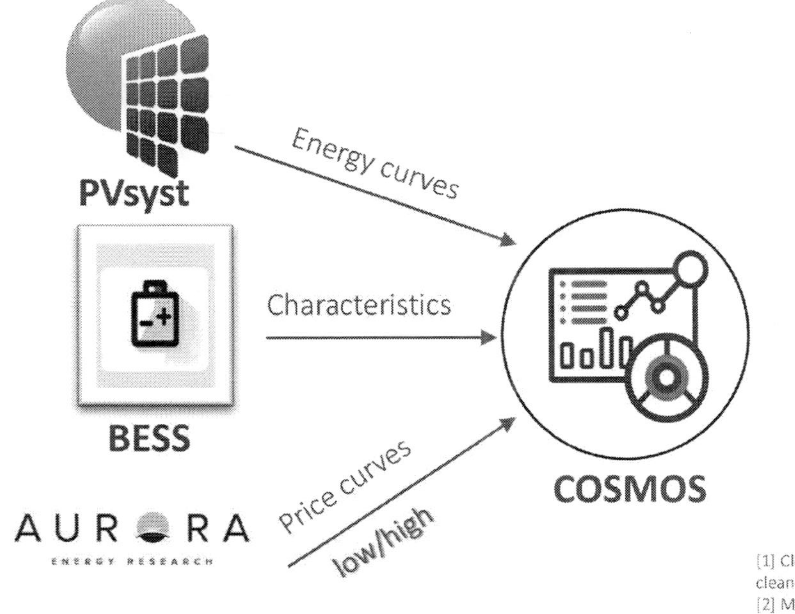

[1] Clean Horizon. Major Upgrade to Clean Horizon's COSMOS Tool. https://www. cleanhorizon.com/news/major-upgrade-to-clean-horizons-cosmos-tool/, 2025. Accessed July 21, 2025.
[2] Mermoud, André, and Bruno Wittmer. "PVSYST user's manual." Switzerland, January (2014).
[3] Aurora Energy Research. Chronos for Batteries. https://auroraer.com/software/chronos, 2025. Accessed July 21, 2025.

Methodology
Modeling & Simulation

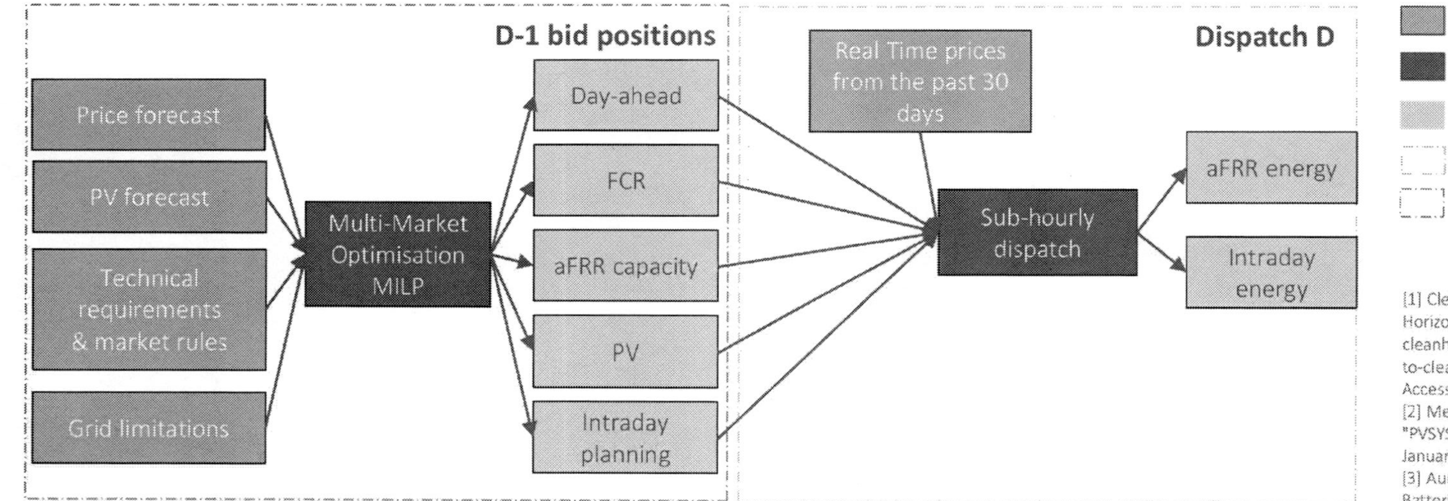

[1] Clean Horizon. Major Upgrade to Clean Horizon's COSMOS Tool. https://www.cleanhorizon.com/news/major-upgrade-to-clean-horizons-cosmos-tool/, 2025. Accessed July 21, 2025.
[2] Mermoud, André, and Bruno Wittmer. "PVSYST user's manual." Switzerland, January (2014).
[3] Aurora Energy Research. Chronos for Batteries. https://auroraer.com/software/chronos, 2025. Accessed July 21, 2025.
[4] Rachel Locquet. Unlocking bess revenues in europe's key markets. PVTech Magazine, 2025. Published by Clean Horizon, accessed via PVTech.

1. Perfect foresight for d-1 (based on forward looking price curves)
2. Imperfect foresight for real-time energy prices: aFRR energy, intraday (based on historical data)
3. PV generation was given priority over BESS for feeding electricity into the grid.
4. BESS can charge from the grid (grey storage)

Methodology
Modeling & Simulation

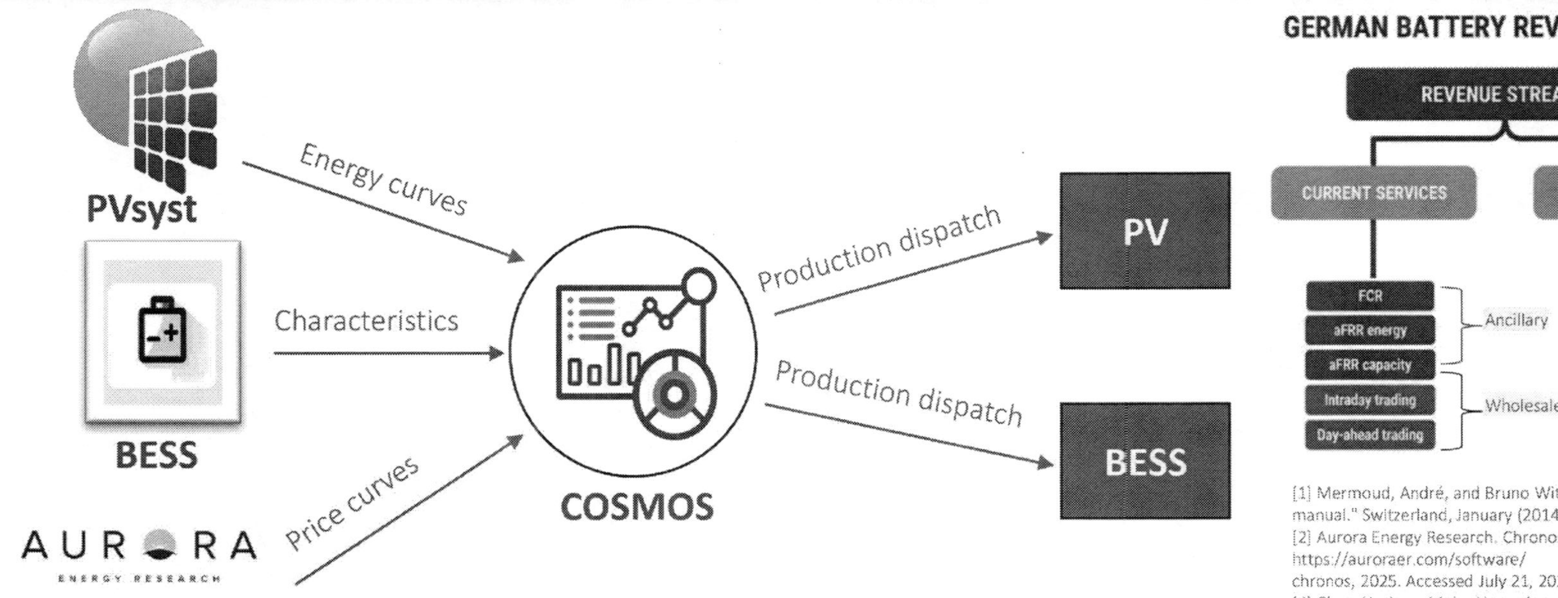

1. Perfect foresight for d-1 (based on forward looking price curves)
2. Imperfect foresight for real-time energy prices: aFRR energy, intraday (based on historical data)
3. PV generation was given priority over BESS for feeding electricity into the grid.
4. BESS can charge from the grid (grey storage)

[1] Mermoud, André, and Bruno Wittmer. "PVSYST user's manual." Switzerland, January (2014).
[2] Aurora Energy Research. Chronos for Batteries. https://auroraer.com/software/chronos, 2025. Accessed July 21, 2025.
[4] Clean Horizon. Major Upgrade to Clean Horizon's COSMOS Tool. https://www.cleanhorizon.com/news/major-upgrade-to-clean-horizons-cosmos-tool/, 2025. Accessed July 21, 2025.
[5] Rachel Locquet. Unlocking bess revenues in europe's key markets. PVTech Magazine, 2025. Published by Clean Horizon, accessed via PVTech.

Results & Discussion

Results & Discussion
Behaviour of PV Assets During Periods of Negative Electricity Prices

PV energy sold under low vs high scenario

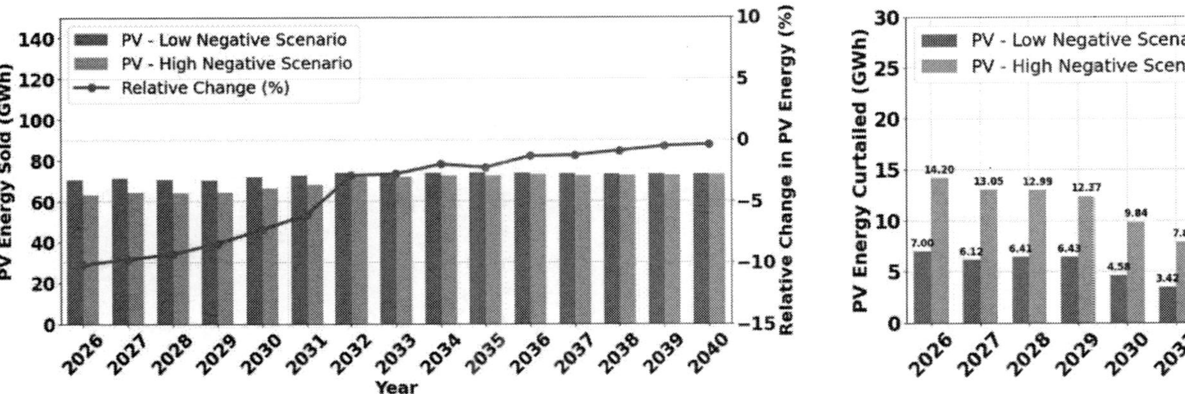

PV energy curtailed under low vs high scenario

- PV energy sold drops under high negative electricity price scenario
- Largest production drop in first 5 years
- Curtailment drives production decline
- Curtailment gap between high and low scenarios becomes negligible after 10 years

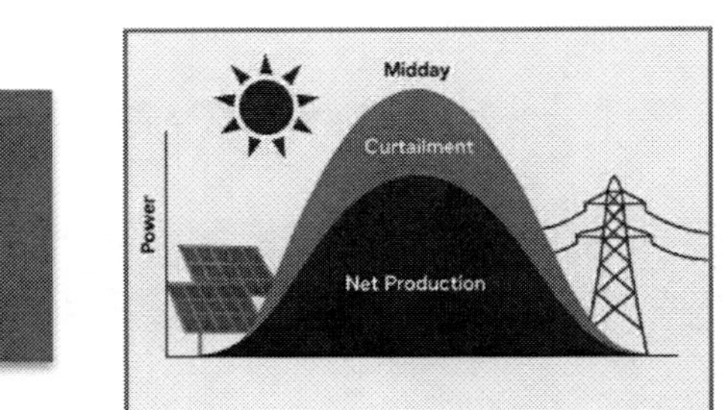

020493-012

Results & Discussion
Behaviour of BESS Assets During Periods of Negative Electricity Prices

BESS energy sold under low vs high scenario

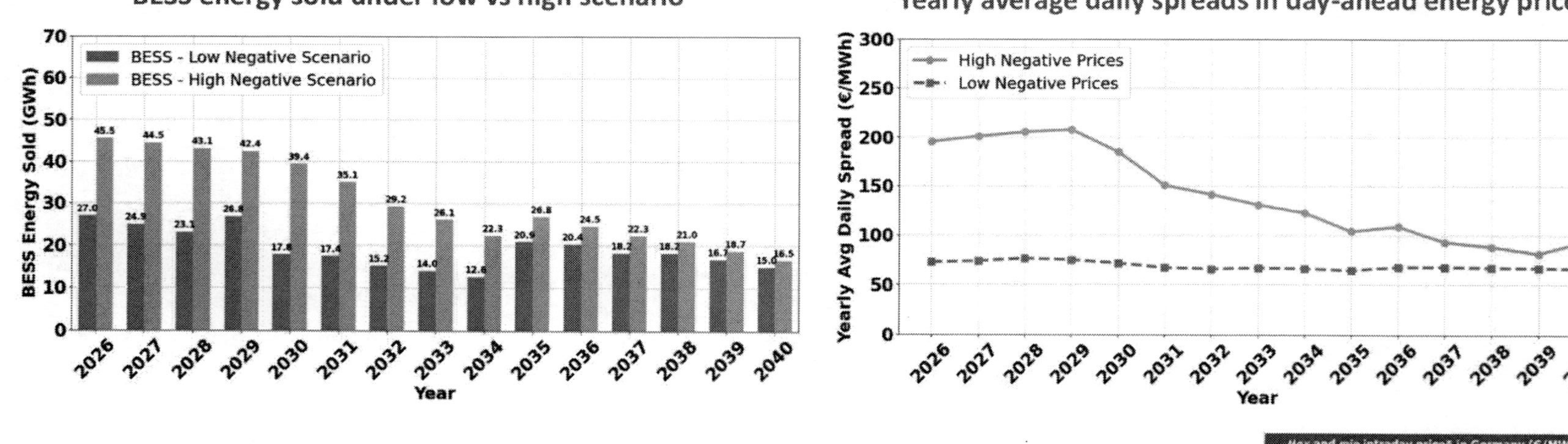

Yearly average daily spreads in day-ahead energy prices

- BESS output declines with aging, possibly market depth
- BESS has higher output under high negative price scenario
- Day-ahead spreads are much larger in high scenario, compared to low scenario
- Frequent negative prices widen spreads, boosting BESS output

Results & Discussion
Less Curtailment or Additional Revenue Streams?

PV + BESS (Curtailment vs Revenues) High neg. scenario

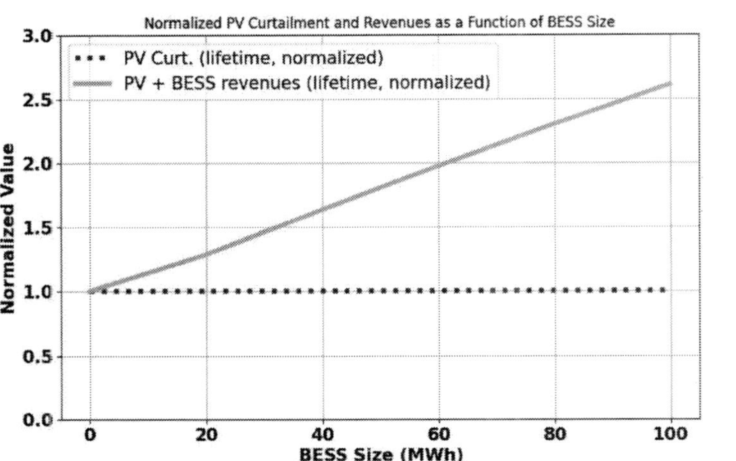

- BESS doesn't cut PV curtailment! (Grey Storage)
- Larger BESS capacity boosts lifetime revenues of the hybrid system (PV + Battery)
- The BESS improves the value of the PV asset by additional revenue stream through day ahead market

BESS energy production in day-ahead – Low Negative Scenario

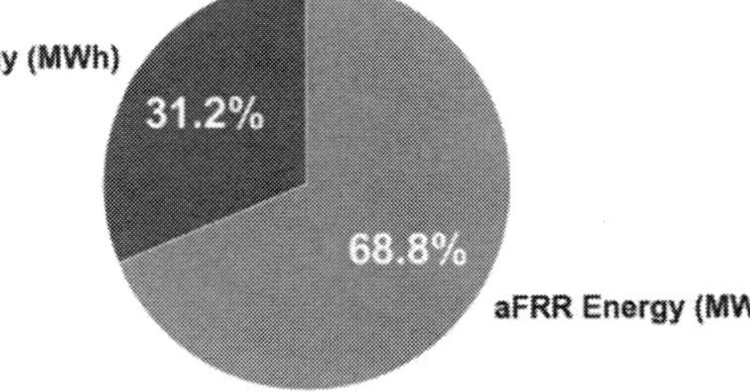

BESS energy production in day-ahead – High Negative Scenario

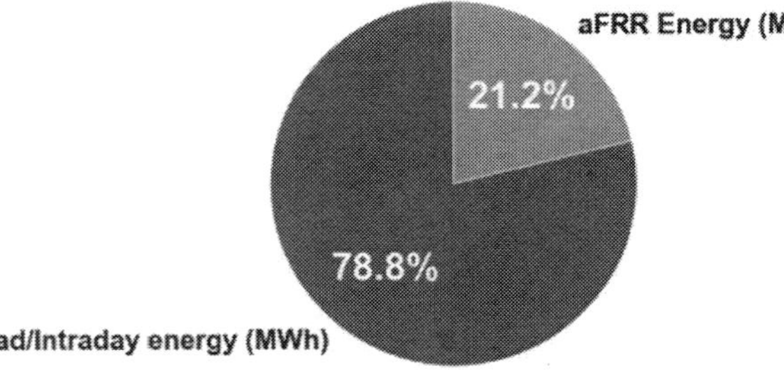

Results & Discussion
Robustness of PV economics with BESS Integration

Setup

- AC coupled Lithium Ion Battery
- 2h System, 1.5 cycles per day
- Market entry Jan 2027
- BESS Lifetime 15 years
- PV lifetime 30 years
- BESS to grid ratio, 1:1

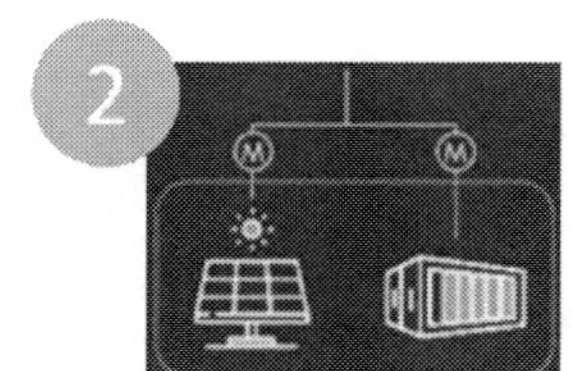

- PV asset value is vulnerable to negative prices
- Retrofitting PV with BESS on the same grid connection enhances project economics

Conclusions

Conclusions
Summary of key takeaways

- **PV value** declines under **negative electricity prices**, while **BESS benefits** from them

- **BESS boosts** PV value **not by reducing curtailment** (grey storage), but by **adding day-ahead trading**

- **Retrofitting** BESS to PV assets on the same grid connection **improves project economics**

- Recommendation to developers, investors: **develop/design** PV projects to be **battery-ready**

Thank you for your attention!

Dr. Djaber Berrian
Innovation & System Design

For any questions
djaber.berrian@belectric.com

Together, let's
take the chance
to change.
BELECTRIC GmbH
Wadenbrunner Str. 10
97509 Kolitzheim
T +49 9385 548-9000
F +49 9385 548-9040
info@belectric.com
www.belectric.com

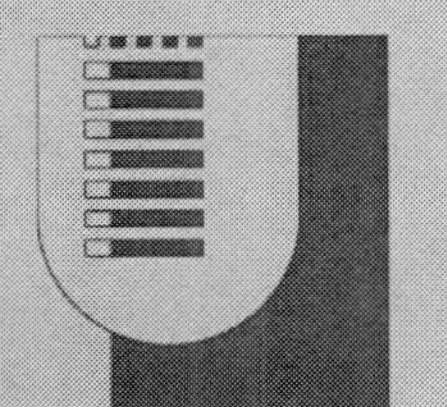

Infinity, a small-scale prototype for firm-PV generation

Federico Andreozzi

University of Rome Tor Vergata
Department of Enterprise Engineering

25 September 2025   42nd European Photovoltaic Solar Energy Conference and Exhibition   Bilbao Exhibition Center

020494-001

Agenda

- What is firm PV generation
- Firm PV for Tor Vergata – Simulation study
- The IN.FI.NI.TY. Prototype
- Experimental parameters
- Results
- Conclusions & future work

020494-002

What is firm PV generation

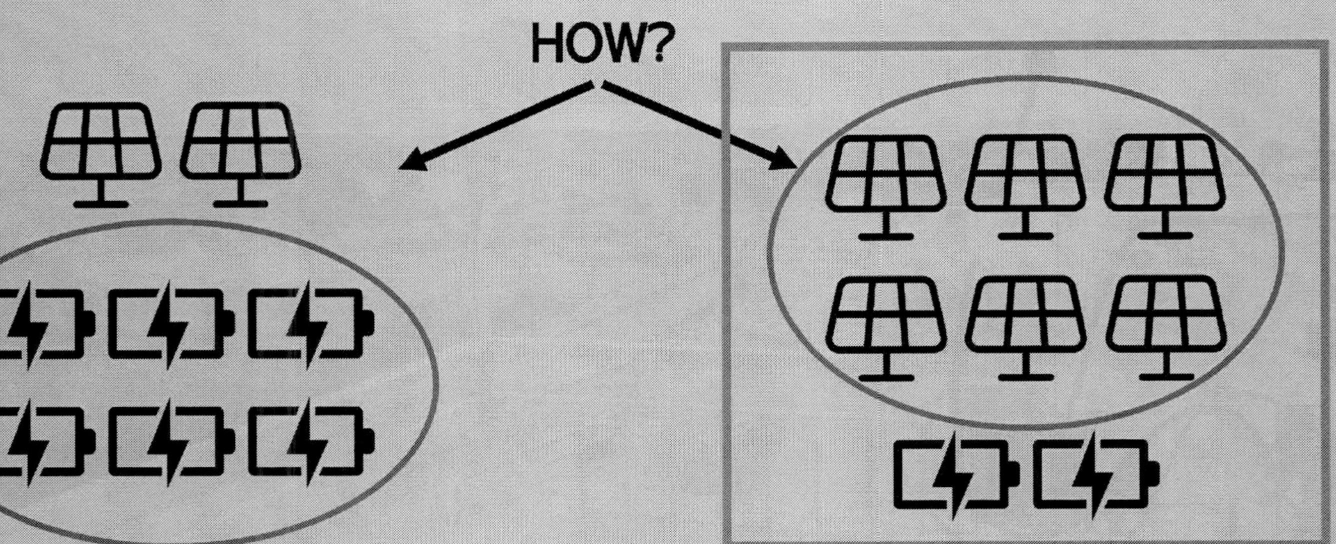

Firm-PV for Tor Vergata – Simulation study

Objective:

Finding the amount of **PV oversizing** and **battery storage** that **minimizes the LCOE** of a PV plant serving the **Engineering Macro-Area** of Tor Vergata University for increasing Self Production **(SP)**.

020494-004

Firm-PV for Tor Vergata – Simulation study

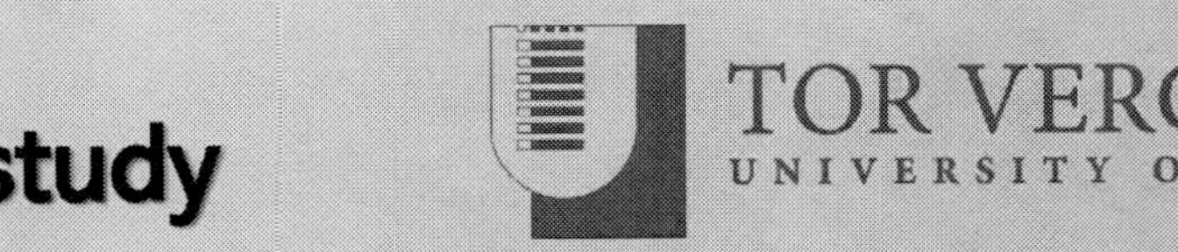

SP (%)	Installed capacity				Curt. (%)	LCOE (€/MWh)			
	PV (MWp)	BESS (MWh)	OVS[1]	NDY[2]		2023	2030	2040	2050
65	2.3	2.6	1.4	0.25	24	111.9	85.0	80.0	75.0
80	3.0	4.6	1.5	0.44	27	129.7	91.5	84.3	77.1
90	4.3	6.8	2	0.61	45	159.5	107.6	97.7	87.8
100	9.8	16.5	3.9	1.55	72	317.2	207.5	186.1	164.6

[1] Oversizing
[2] Number of days of electrical demand stored

Bovesecchi, G., Andreozzi, F., Petitta, M., Pierro, M., Perez, R., & Cornaro, C. (2025). Flexible photovoltaic generation strategy for Rome Technopole. *Energy Conversion and Management: X, 27*, 101204. https://doi.org/10.1016/J.ECMX.2025.101204

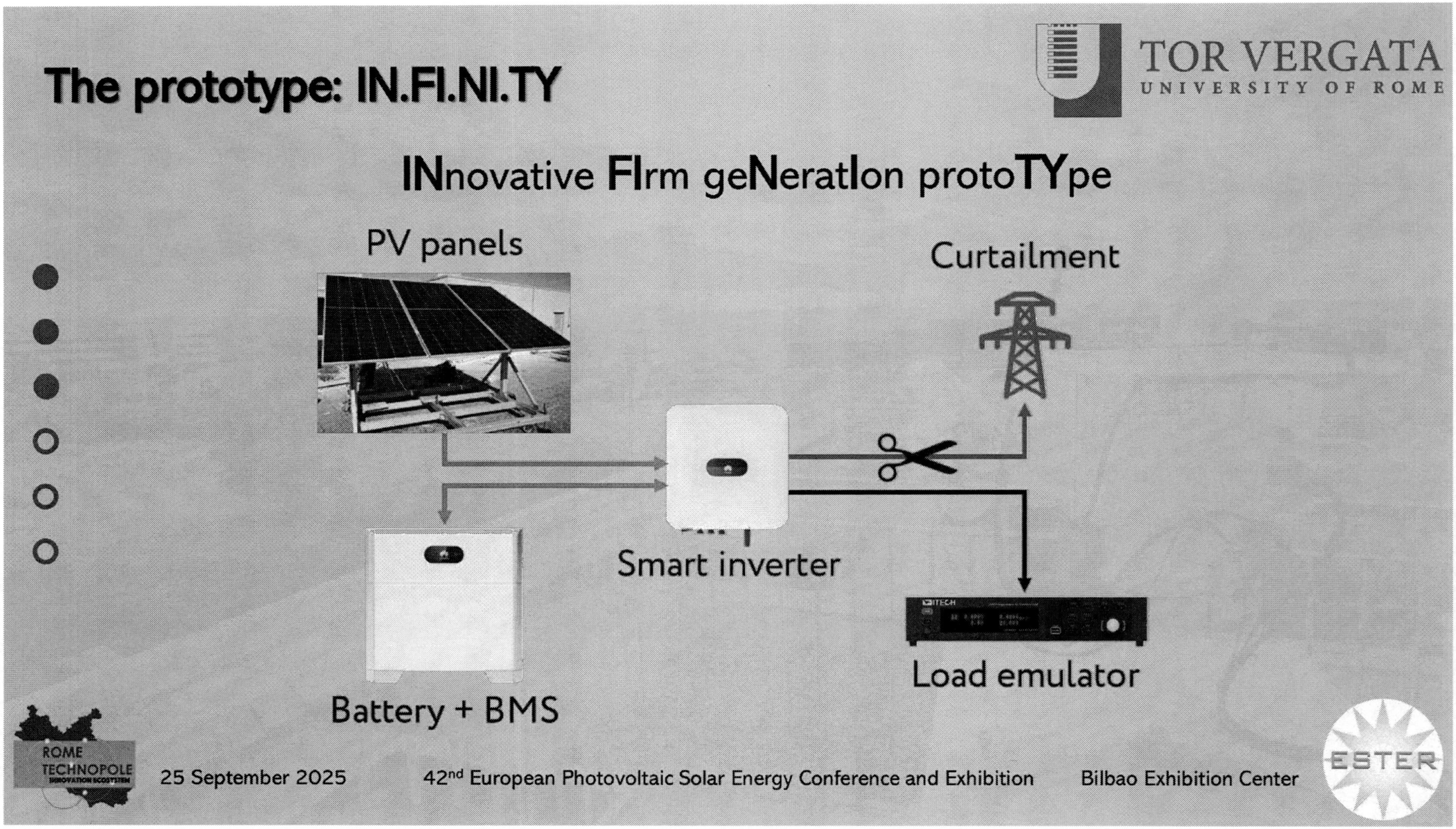

The prototype: IN.FI.NI.TY

The prototype: IN.FI.NI.TY

PV panels

3x 605-W bifacial modules from JA Solar.

Total peak power: **1815 W.**

South-oriented at **30°** tilt angle.

020494-007

The prototype: IN.FI.NI.TY

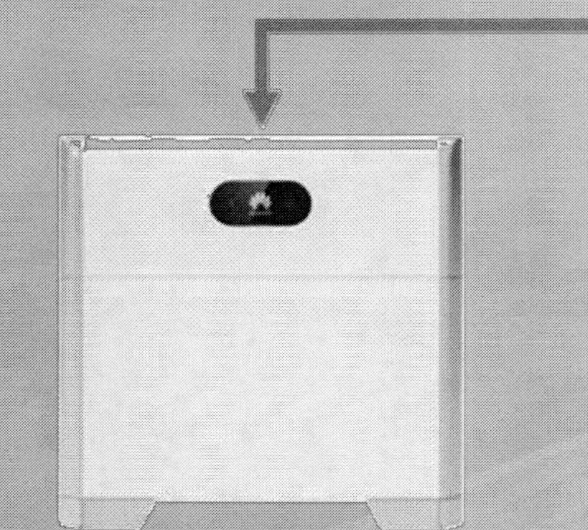

Huawei LUNA2000-5KW-C0

Battery capacity: **5 kWh.**

The Battery Management System (**BMS**) and the inverter manage **power flows to and from the battery**.

020494-008

The prototype: IN.FI.NI.TY

Huawei SUN2000-2KTL-L1

Controls all **power flows** in the plant.

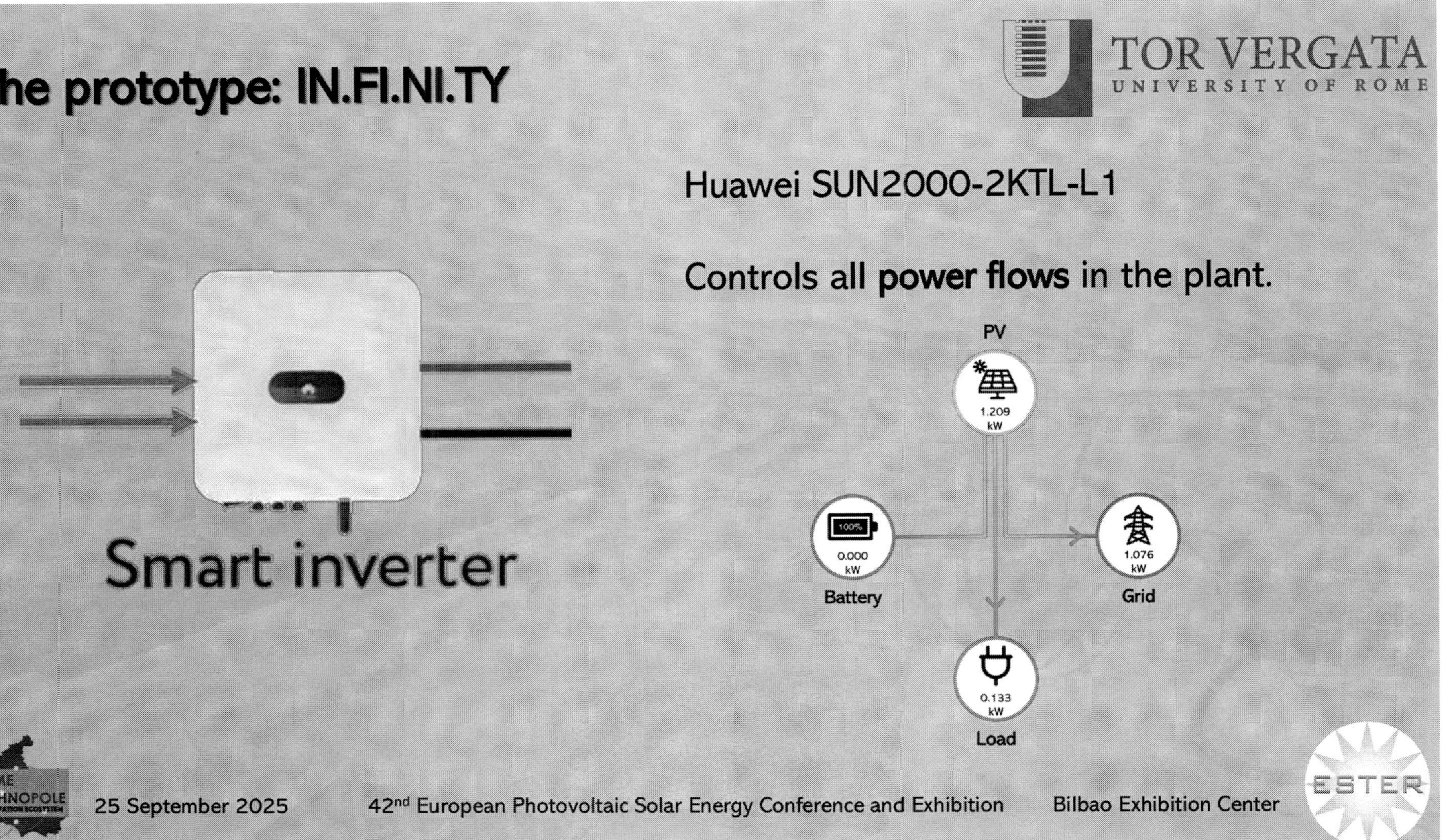

020494-009

The prototype: IN.FI.NI.TY

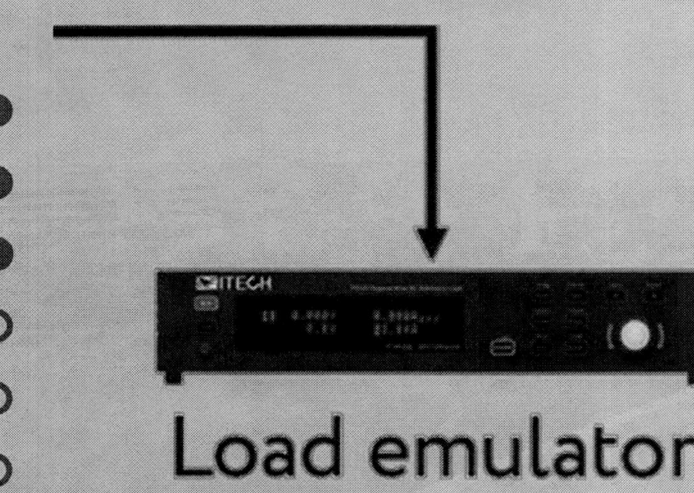

ITech IT-M3323

Provides **controllable DC power load**.

Power request value **updated live** via MatLab.

Connected to the inverter via a **AC/DC converter**.

020494-010

The prototype: IN.FI.NI.TY

Curtailment

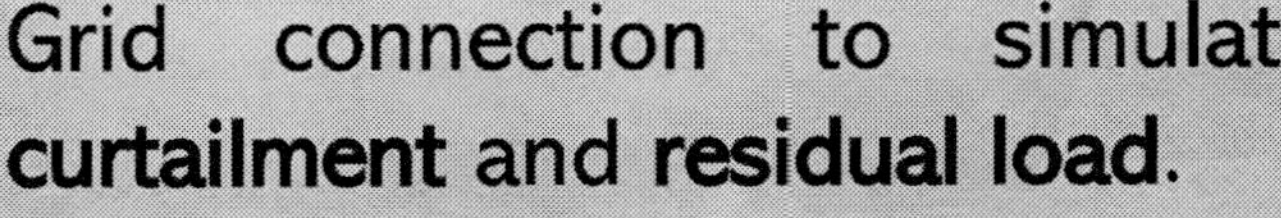

Grid connection to simulate **curtailment** and **residual load**.

Smart power sensor measures **energy to and from the grid** (curtailment and residual load).

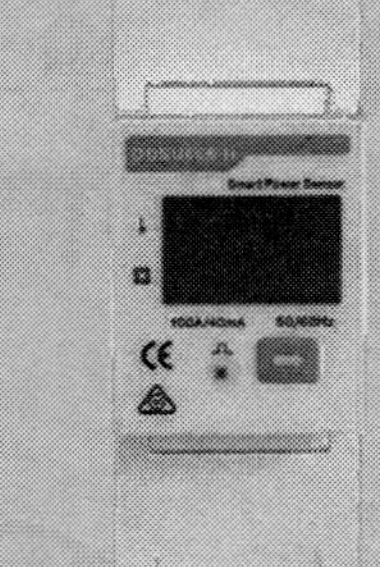

020494-011

Experimental parameters

Scaled-down load of the Engineering Macro-Area of Tor Vergata

Current parameters

Load scale factor: 6185
PV power installed: 1815 W

OVS = 4.56

Battery SOC ceiling: 100%
Battery SOC floor: 20%
Resulting battery capacity: 4 kWh

NDY = 2.51

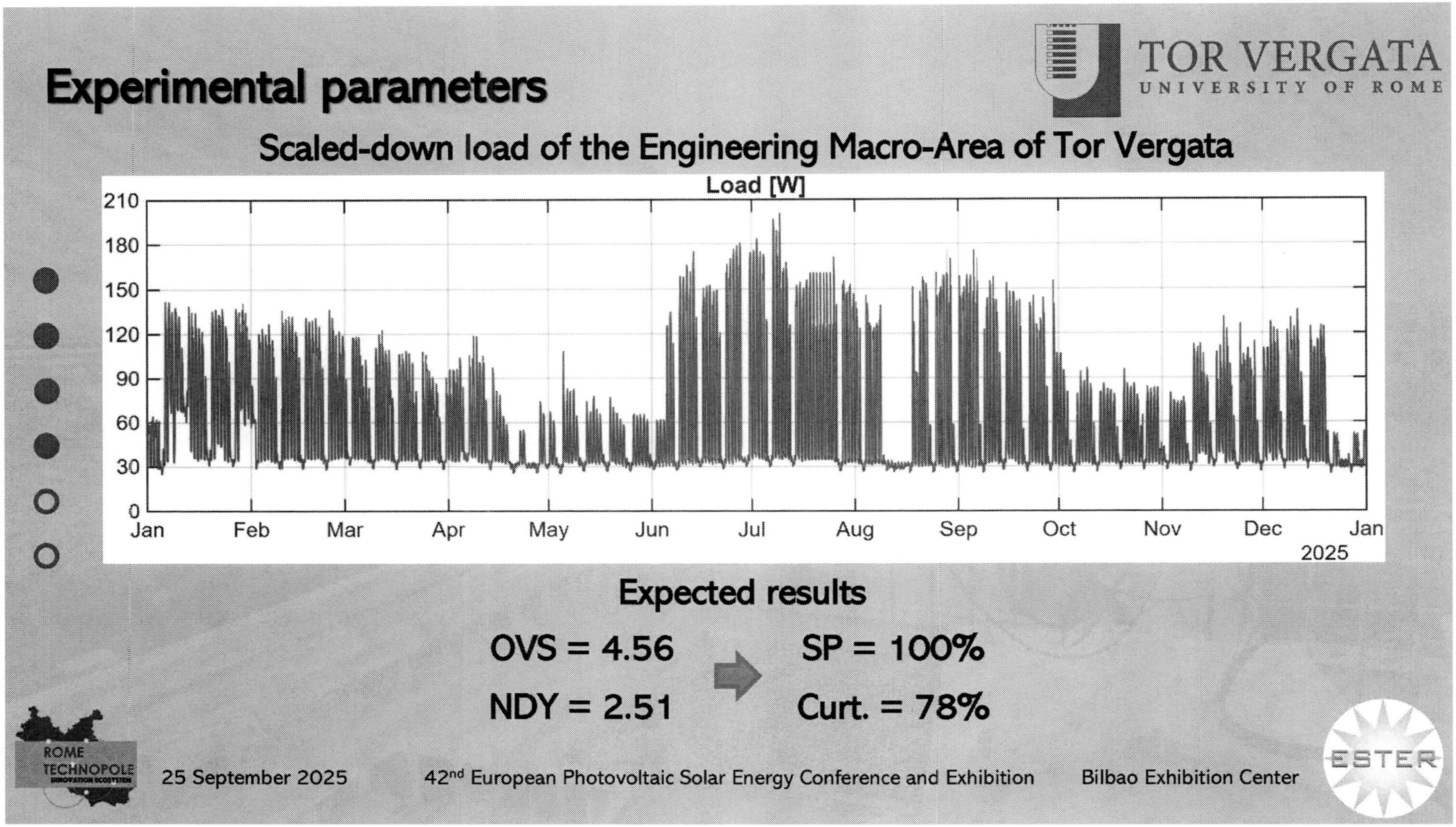

Experimental parameters

TOR VERGATA
UNIVERSITY OF ROME

Scaled-down load of the Engineering Macro-Area of Tor Vergata

Expected results

OVS = 4.56 → SP = 100%

NDY = 2.51 → Curt. = 78%

020494-013

Results

TOR VERGATA
UNIVERSITY OF ROME

Power flows for a **high-irradiance** day and for a **low-irradiance** one

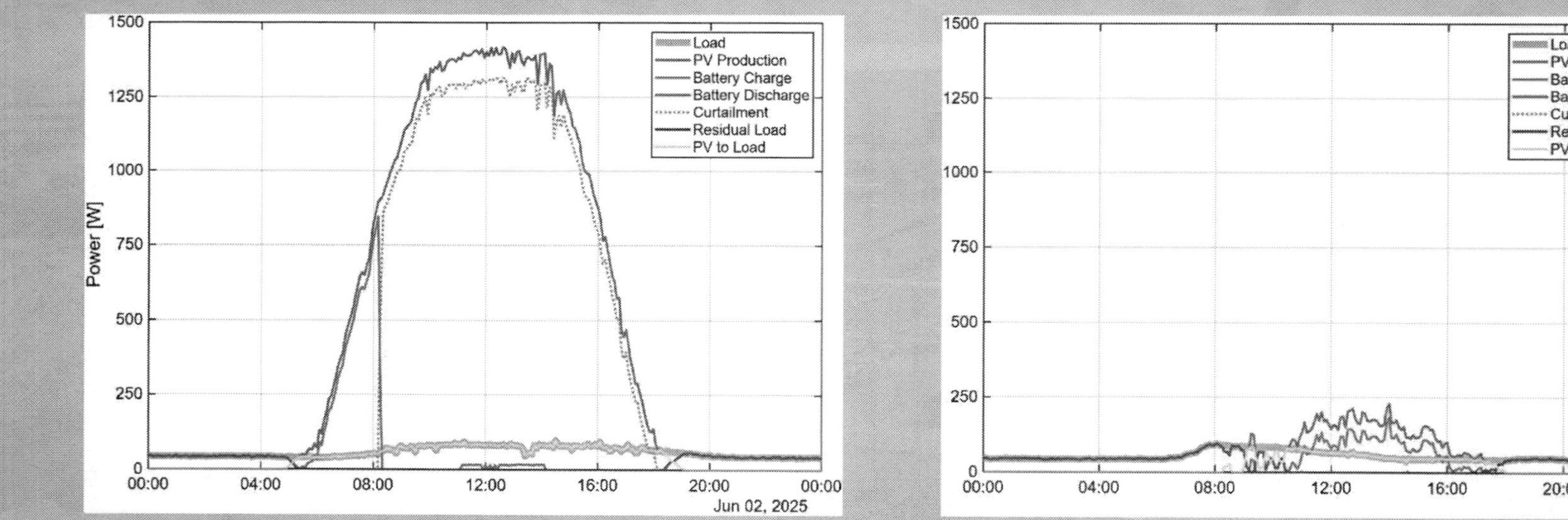

020494-014

Results

TOR VERGATA
UNIVERSITY OF ROME

High-irradiance day (02 June 2025)

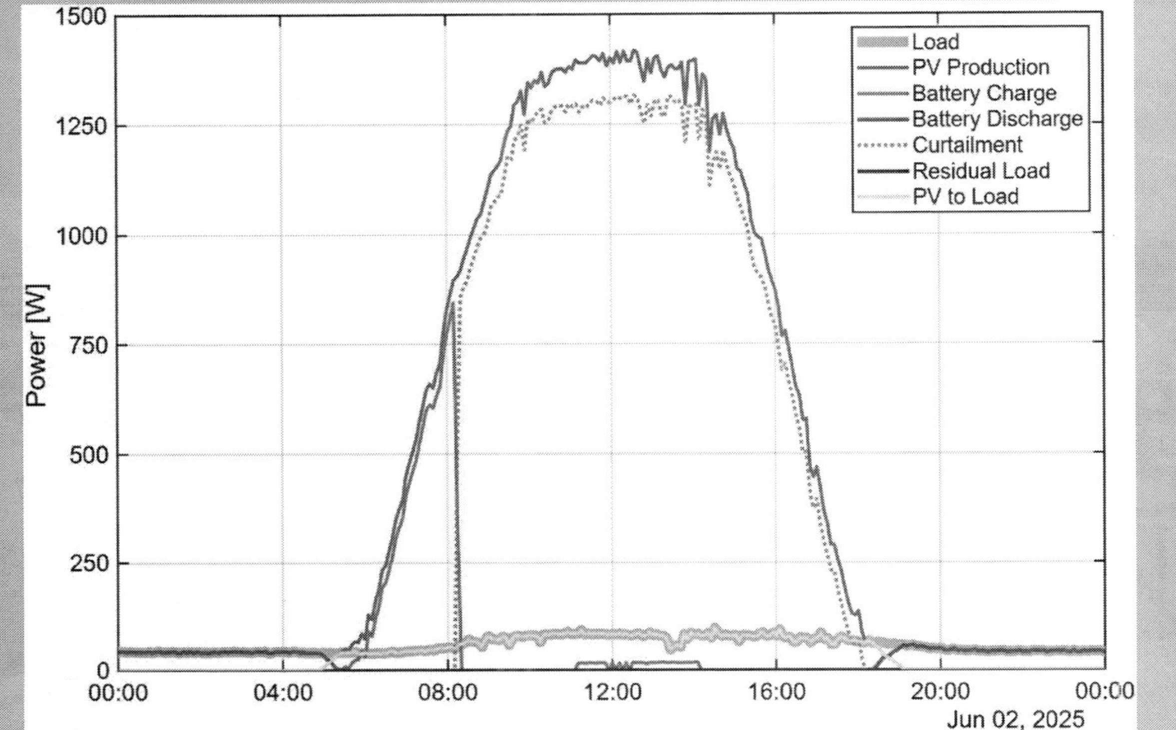

- > 1400 W peak power generation (11.9 kWh total)
- Battery fully charged at 8:00
- 83.4% curtailment
- Load during the day covered entirely by PV.

Results

Low-irradiance day (22 March 2025)

- < 250 W peak power generation (1.03 kWh total).
- **Battery** only charged from **70 to 76%**.
- **No curtailment.**
- **Load** during the day covered **mostly by PV**.

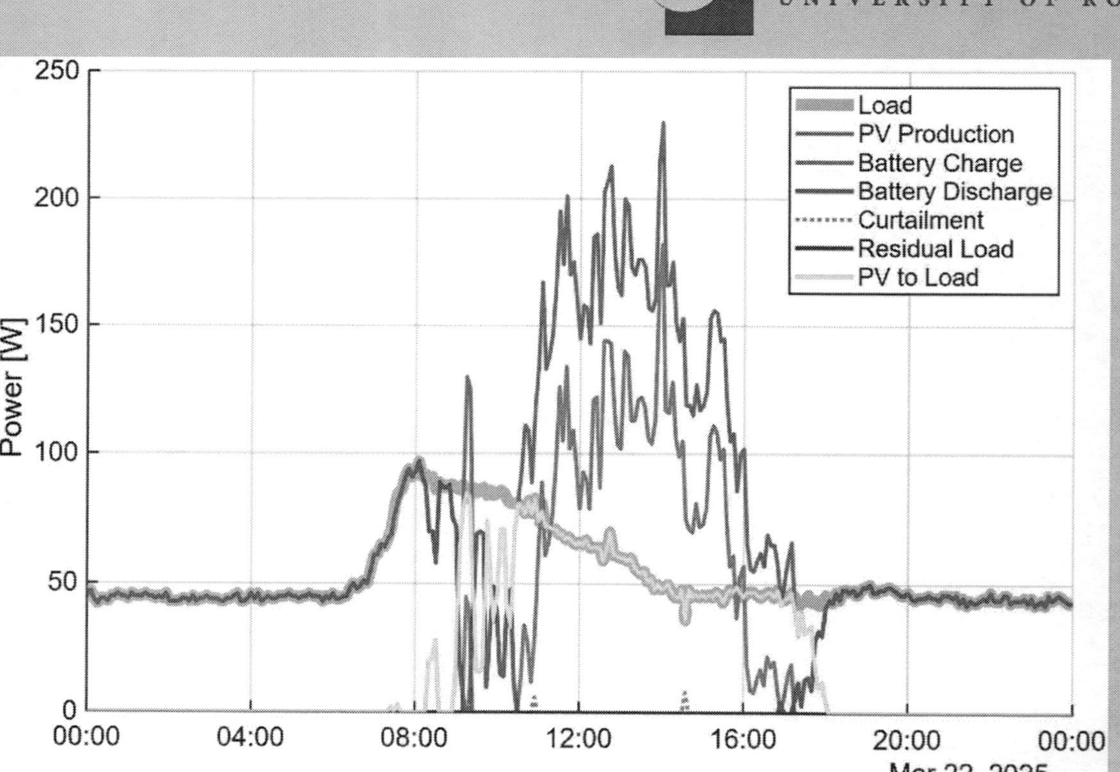

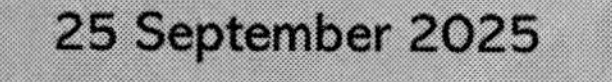

020494-016

Results

TOR VERGATA
UNIVERSITY OF ROME

Analysis of **load coverage** and **energy performance** from March to August.

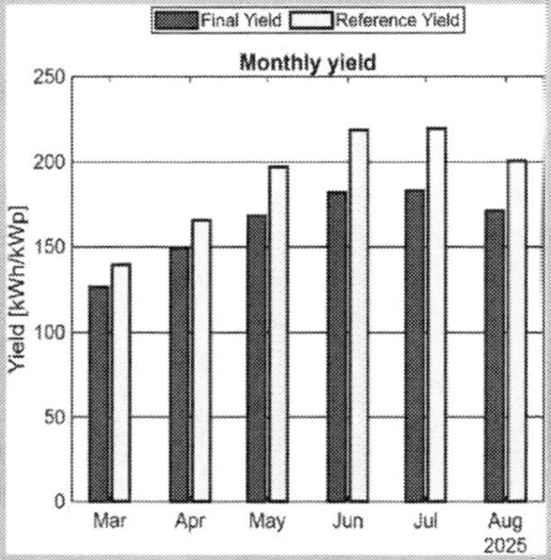

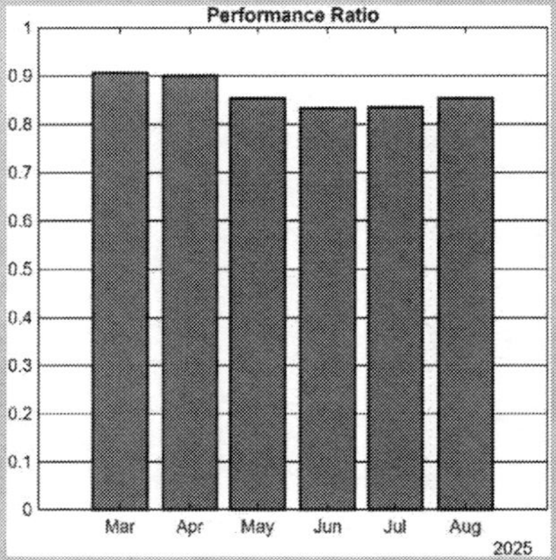

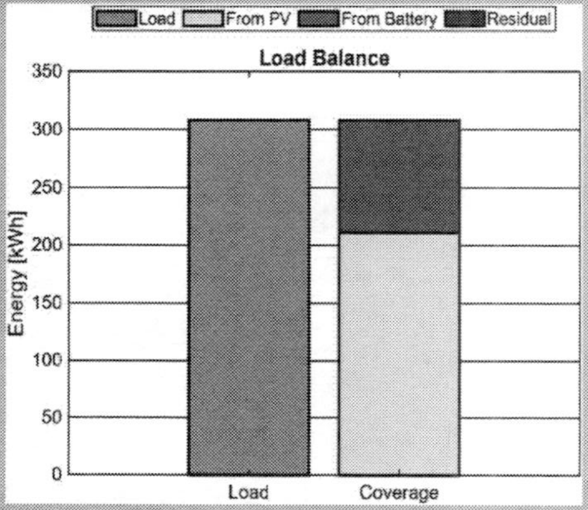

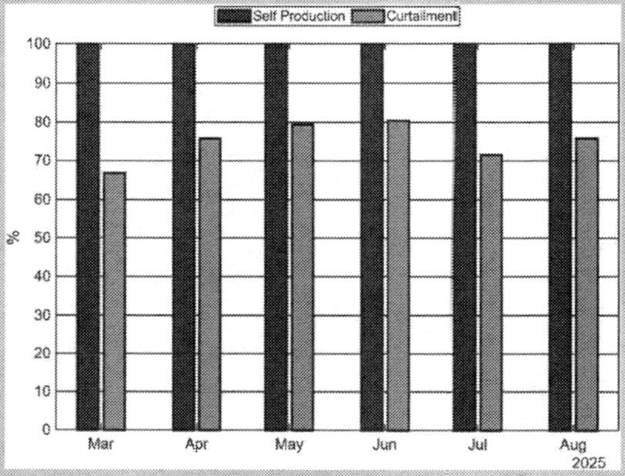

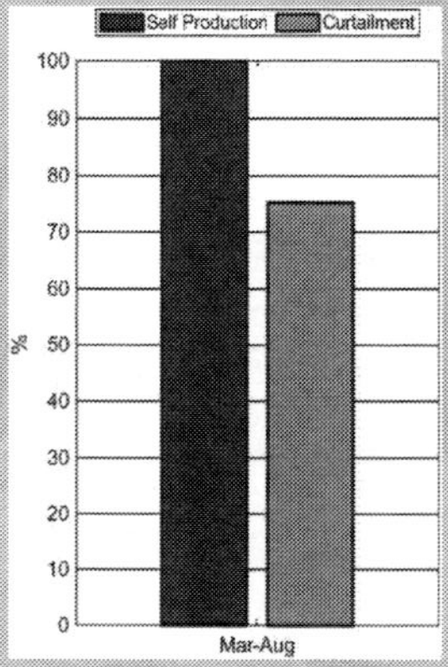

ROME TECHNOPOLE
INNOVATION ECOSYSTEM

ESTER

25 September 2025   42nd European Photovoltaic Solar Energy Conference and Exhibition   Bilbao Exhibition Center

Results

TOR VERGATA
UNIVERSITY OF ROME

PV performance

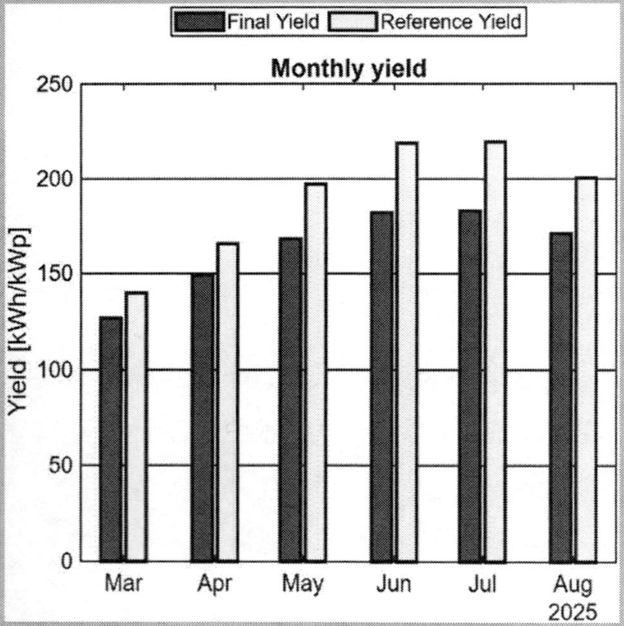

Yield ranging between **126.6 kWh/kWp** (March) and **183.1 kWh/kWp** (July).

PR between 0.8 and 0.9, peaking at **0.91** in March.

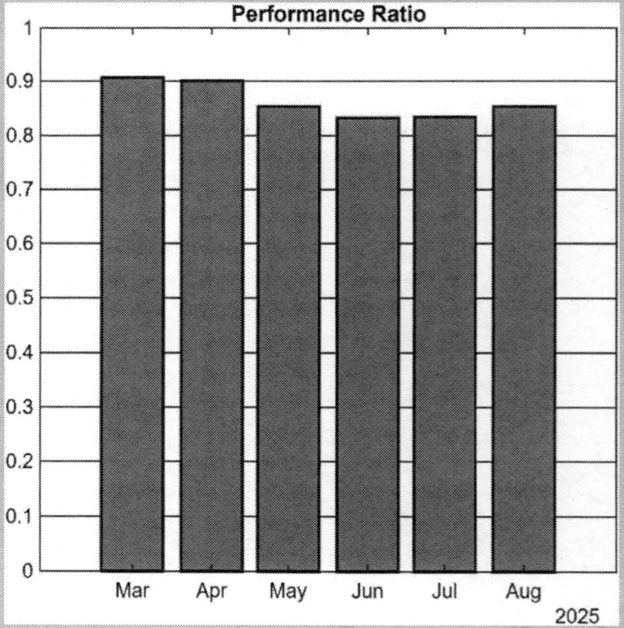

020494-018

Results

Load coverage

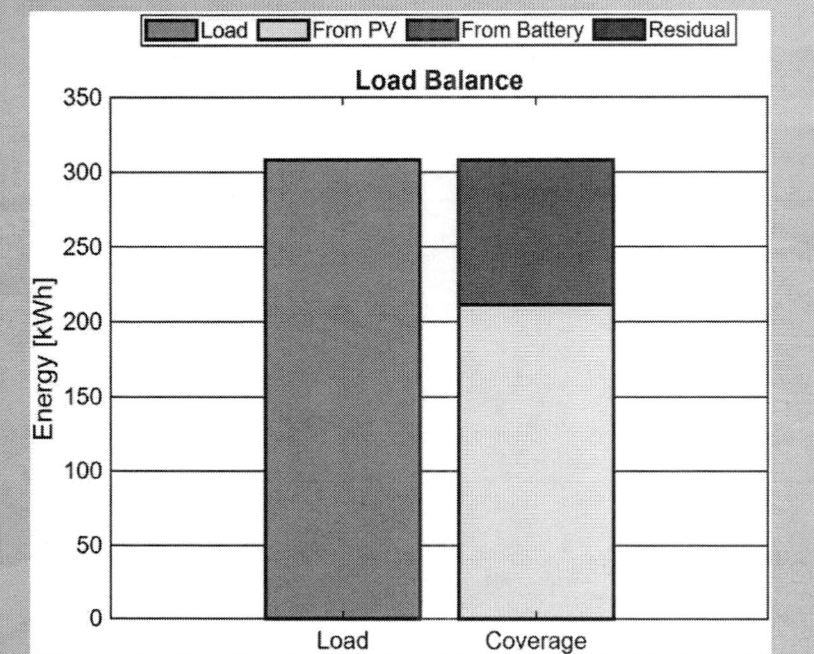

Load **fully covered** by the **PV+BESS** combination.

No grid support needed at any point.

020494-019

Results

TOR VERGATA
UNIVERSITY OF ROME

Plant percentage indicators

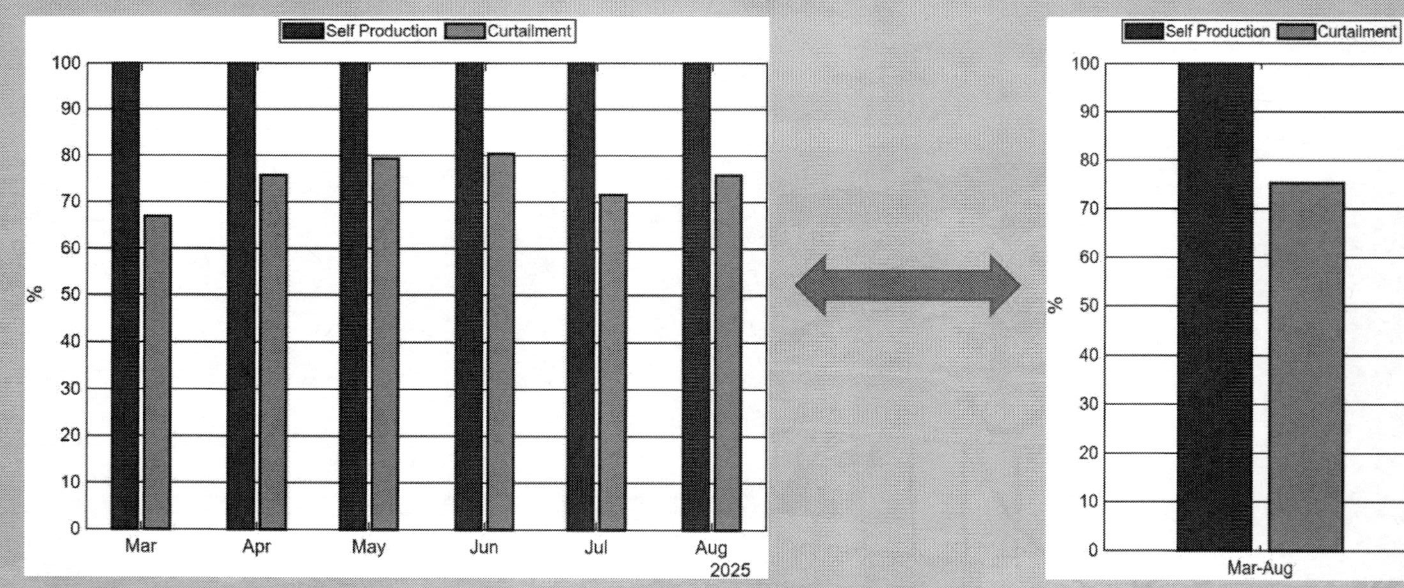

Self production stable at **100%** every month.

Curtailment peaked at **80.4% in June**, averaging at **75.3%** for the whole period.

020494-020

Results

TOR VERGATA
UNIVERSITY OF ROME

Analysis of the battery's State Of Charge (SOC)

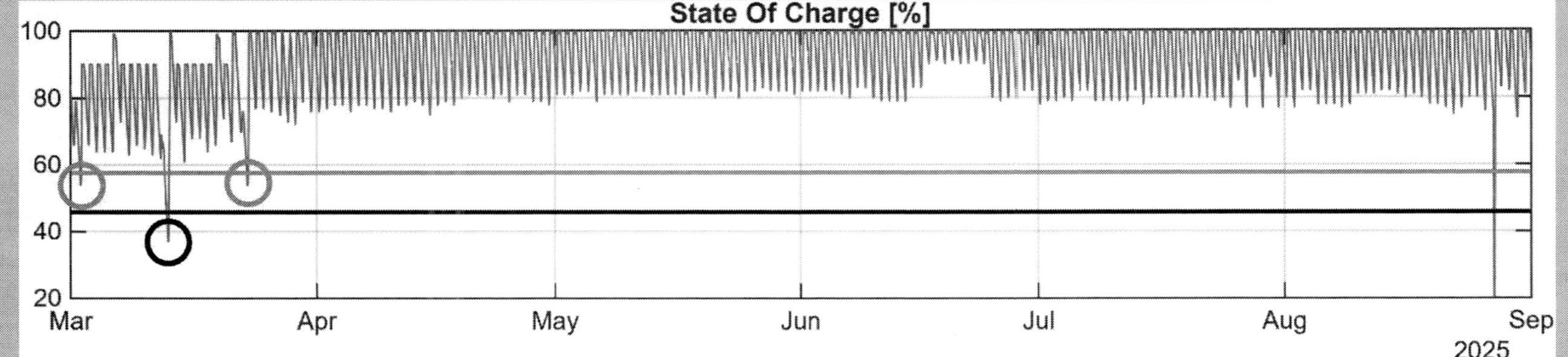

The battery **fully depleted** its charge only **once** (27-Aug).

This was due to a **communication error** that required inverter reset.

Lowering target SP to 99.5% reduces NDY to 1.76 (2.8 kWh – 100% to 44%).

SOC only went below 44% twice (13-Mar, 27-Aug).

Matching the simulation SP target (100% ± 1.5%) brings NDY down to 1.3 (2.1 kWh – 100% to 58%).

SOC only went below 58% four times (02-Mar, 13-Mar, 23-Mar, 27-Aug)

020494-021

Conclusions & future work

- The prototype was able to meet the electrical demand for the whole period, achieving the expected **100% Self Production**.
- Even on **low-irradiance days**, the **load was mostly covered** by the oversized PV during daylight hours.
- Average **curtailment** was **in line with expectations** (75.3% vs. 78%).
- **Battery capacity could be reduced** by 30-50 % without significantly hindering Self Production.

What's next?

- Testing during the **winter period**, when **less sunlight** is expected.
- **LCOE analysis** once enough data is available.
- Testing of **different load profiles**.
- **Upscaling** to a larger plant size.

020494-022

The EsterLab research group

Cristina Cornaro
Full Professor
Environmental
applied physics

Gianluigi Bovesecchi
RTDA
REGACE - Resilio

Emiliano Seri
Research Fellow
REGACE

Luca Rosati
Research Fellow
REGACE

Ali Sohani
Research Fellow
REGACE

Francesco Biso
Research Fellow
Resilio

Federico Andreozzi
PhD Student
Rome Technopole

Beatrice Bartolucci
Research Fellow
BEACON

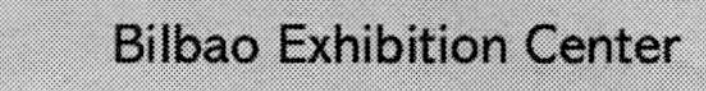

25 September 2025   42nd European Photovoltaic Solar Energy Conference and Exhibition   Bilbao Exhibition Center

TOR VERGATA
UNIVERSITY OF ROME
ESTER
Thank you!
My contact:
federico.andreozzi@uniroma2.it
Follow us on Instagram:
@esterlab.unitov
Visit our website:
www.ester.uniroma2.it
ESTERLAB.UNITOV

ECO-EFFICIENT PROCESSING AND REFINING ROUTES FOR SECONDARY RAW MATERIALS FROM SILICON INGOT AND WAFER MANUFACTURING

Martin Bellmann*[1], Berhane Darsene Dimd[1], Anne-Karin Søiland[2], Arne Dahle[3], C. Landaas[4], Victorien Iwaszko[5], Rene Peche[6], Wolfram Palitzsch[7], Philippe Lenain[8], Iratxe de Meatza[9], Theodora Kyratsi[10], Liu Huiping[11], Emanuele Milani[12], Guy Chichignoud[13], Stefan Fischer[14], Almut Schwenke[15], Eirik Nordboe[16], Marco Pieterse[17], Roland Riva[18]

[1]SINTEF, Trondheim Norway, [2]ReSiTec AS, Kristiansand Norway, [3]NorSun, Oslo Norway, [4]Northern Silicon, Meråker Norway, [5]ROSI Solar, Saint-Martin-d'Hères France, [6]bifa Umweltinstitut GmbH, Augsburg Germany, [7]LuxChemtech GmbH, Freiberg Germany, [8]benkei, Lyon France, [9]CIDETEC, San Sebastian Spain, [10]University of Cyprus, Nicosia Cyprus, [11]GRÄNGES, Finspång Sweden, [12]Marelli Europe SPA, Venaria Reala Italy, [13]Institut Polytechnique De Grenobl, Grenoble France, [14]SGL Carbon GmbH, Meitingen Germany, [15]SGL Battery Solutions, Meitingen Germany, [16]Fiven Norge AS, Lillesand Norway, [17]Chemconserve, Bussum The Netherlands, [18]Commissariat à l'énergie atomique et aux énergies alternatives, Le Bourget-du-Lac France

ABSTRACT: In the ICARUS project, 18 European partners collaborate to develop and scale innovative technologies for recovering and refining secondary raw materials from silicon photovoltaic (PV) ingot and wafer manufacturing. The production of PV modules generates significant quantities of waste, particularly silicon kerf, graphite, and silica residues. ICARUS aims to transform these waste streams into high-value secondary materials suitable for reintegration into the PV value chain and other industrial applications. Four industrial pilot-scale processes were developed, targeting the purification and reuse of these materials. Results from the pilots demonstrate both the technical feasibility and economic potential of substituting these recovered materials for virgin and critical raw materials. This work provides a viable pathway toward a more resource-efficient and circular PV manufacturing industry.

Keywords: Photovoltaics, Silicon, Silicon Kerf, Silica, Recycling, Circularity

1 INTRODUCTION

Global deployment of photovoltaic (PV) technology continues to accelerate, driven by declining module costs and net-zero emission targets. Alongside this growth, the silicon PV value chain generates substantial production wastes during ingot manufacturing and wafering. These include silicon kerf losses from wafering, as well as silica and graphite components from crystallization furnaces. A significant proportion of these wastes is either disposed of in landfills or diverted into low-value applications. Such practices not only result in the loss of potentially valuable materials but also conflict with sustainability and circular economy principles.

In general the literature demonstrates clear progress in recovering high-purity products from silicon kerf [1], silica waste [2], and graphite [3]. However, current methods generally yield secondary materials with limited recovery efficiency and insufficient quality for high-value reuse. In addition, significant recycling techniques are not yet scalable to industrial level due to their complexity and multi-stage approach. The ICARUS project addresses this challenge by developing and scaling industrially relevant routes for the recovery, refinement, and reintegration of secondary raw materials from ingot and wafer manufacturing.

The ICARUS project is a collaborative effort between 18 EU (European Union) partners. The work focuses on developing targeted technological solutions to refine and reuse silicon kerf, graphite, and silica wastes from PV manufacturing. Four industrial pilot technologies have been designed and tested at pilot scale to assess improved recycling processes, with the potential to outperform existing methods. The main goal is the production of high-purity, high-value secondary raw materials, thereby addressing the quality limitations often encountered in current recycling approaches. By 2027, the project aims to enable large-scale resource recovery, with projected capacities of 3.5 million tons of silicon kerf, 700 thousand tons of silica, and 480 thousand tons of graphite, demonstrating both scalability and economic viability. The work in ICARUS contributes directly to sustainability and circular economy goals by transforming waste into reusable raw materials, reducing environmental impacts, and improving the overall efficiency of the silicon PV value chain.

2 METHODOLOGY

This section provides a brief overview of the ICARUS project and PV waste volume estimates and characterization. It also discusses the four pilot-scale recycling technologies developed for silicon kerf, graphite, and silica.

2.1 Overview of ICARUS

The ICARUS project is organized into six work packages (WPs). WP1 addresses logistics, treatment, quality, quantity, and sourcing of silicon PV production waste. WP2 develops industrial routes for collecting and pre-treating silicon, silica, and graphite. WP3 reintroduces these wastes into silicon production, while WP4 focuses on controlled conditioning of purified silicon. WP5 upgrades a lab-scale reactor to semi-industrial scale for converting silicon waste into valuable materials. Finally, WP6 drives market uptake by demonstrating high-end prototypes that utilize recovered silicon, silica, and graphite.

2.2 Waste volume estimates and characterization

PV ingot manufacturing generates significant waste. To assess the potential of recycling pathways, it is essential to estimate waste volumes and characterize materials. Volume estimates provide context for the scale of the challenge, while characterization supports evaluation of technical feasibility and processing needs. In this work, silicon kerf waste was estimated using factors such as annual PV installations, the ratio of production to installations, crystalline PV production volumes, and the cell-to-wafer ratio. Estimates of crucible and pot scrap waste assumed multi-batch ingot pulling with M10 and G12 wafer dimensions, while graphite waste was estimated at 100 tons per gigawatt of PV capacity, as reported by [4].

The characterization of waste materials and produced silicon was carried out using several analytical techniques. Inductively Coupled Plasma Mass Spectrometry (ICP-MS) was applied to detect metallic and non-metallic impurities at trace levels, while LECO analysis was used to quantify carbon and oxygen contents. X-ray Diffraction (XRD) was employed to determine crystallographic structure and phase composition, and Scanning Electron Microscopy (SEM) was used to examine surface morphology. Together, these techniques assess chemical purity and morphology, ensuring recycled materials meet quality standards for high-performance applications.

2.3 Pilot technologies

The four industrial pilot technologies which are the core of the ICARUS project are:

- Pilot A: Collects and processes silicon kerf cake, graphite, and silica waste according to defined standards, delivering the material either to end-user groups for final applications or to other pilots for further refining.
- Pilot B: Aims to produce silicon with higher quality and at a lower cost than conventional metallurgical silicon processes. This pilot uses secondary materials such as graphite, silica, and silicon kerf in a pilot-scale submerged arc furnace (SAF).
- Pilot C: Scales up the annual controlled conditioning of silicon, based on material received from Pilot A to a capacity of 500 tons per year, aiming to improve the quality of granular silicon for PV applications.
- Pilot D: Will scale up a small-scale reactor to a semi-industrial level, targeting a capacity of 50–70 tons per year. The process is based on the reaction of free silicon in the kerf with a sodium hydroxide solution under controlled temperature and pressure conditions, producing hydrogen, sodium silicates, and reaction heat.

3 RESULT AND DISCUSSION

This section reports the key findings from waste volume estimates and material characterization, along with results from the four pilot projects, with emphasis on Pilot B.

3.1 Waste volume estimates and characterization result

The estimation of silicon kerf waste accounts for losses from wafering as well as cropping, squaring, chamfering, and grinding operations. Figure 1 shows the estimated global cumulative kerf generation from 2018 to 2027, indicating that annual volumes could reach about 700 kMT by 2027. Similarly, Figure 2 presents projected cumulative silica and graphite wastes from 2023 to 2027. Overall, these estimates highlight the substantial volumes of waste generated in ingot and wafer manufacturing. Although typically treated as waste, these materials represent a valuable opportunity for recycling and reintegration into the PV value chain and other applications.

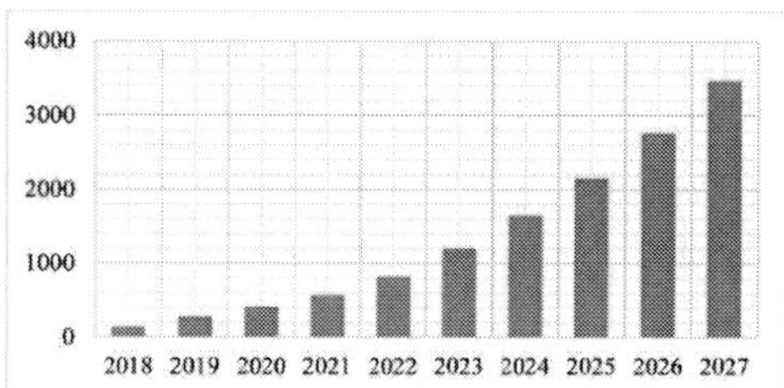

Figure 1: Cummulative silicon kerf waste in kMT.

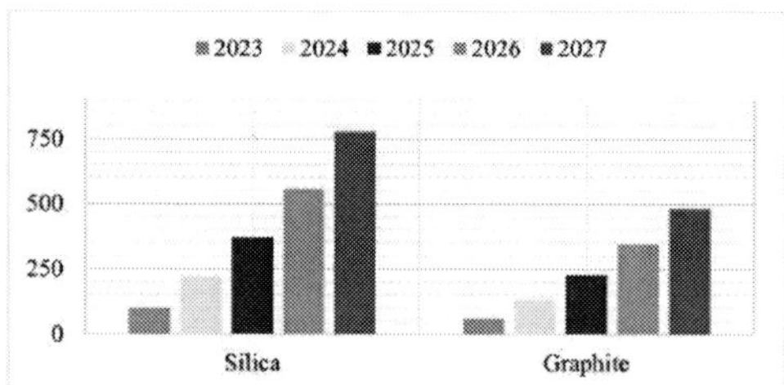

Figure 2: Cummulative silica and graphite waste in ton.

Impurity analysis of silicon kerf samples from different sources was conducted using ICP-MS. The results show that the main dopant impurities are boron, gallium, and phosphorus, with concentrations varying across samples. The main metallic impurities include aluminum, calcium, iron, and nickel. LECO analysis indicated carbon concentrations of 1–2 wt.% and oxygen content of 4–5 wt.% in most samples. SEM and XRD analyses revealed irregular morphologies, with the kerf consisting mainly of crystalline silicon and an amorphous phase.

LECO analysis of five graphite powder samples revealed significantly higher ash content compared to a virgin reference sample. ICP-MS analysis of the ash identified silicon, cobalt, and calcium as the main impurities. XRD results showed the presence of graphite 2H, SiC, and crystalline SiO2 phases, while SEM revealed multiple phases with distinct morphologies across different regions of the samples. Similar characterization was carried out on silica waste samples, which were found to consist mainly of amorphous silica and crystalline cristobalite, with calcium identified as the primary impurity.

3.2 Results from the pilots

The ICARUS project aims to transform silicon kerf, graphite, and silica waste into high-value secondary raw materials by developing and scaling four pilot technologies for efficient recycling. This section presents their results, with a more focus on Pilot B, chosen as the most representative of the overall processing chain, while summarizing key outcomes from the other pilots.

Pilot A: Industrial-scale processing routes for silicon kerf waste have been established at Technology Readiness Level (TRL) 7. A continuous drying system has been successfully commissioned as an alternative to the existing batch drying process for silicon kerf filter cake. This system achieves moisture levels of less than 1 wt%. Additionally, an industrial-scale post treatment process has been developed for material intended for use into lithium-ion batteries and thermoelectric modules. A pretreatment process has also been implemented to significantly reduce contaminants such as aluminum, nickel, and iron. For the silica waste, a processing route has been developed and a pilot line established, targeting raw material specification suitable for production of high purity silicon carbide.

Pilot B: This pilot aimed to reintroduce silicon kerf, graphite, and silica waste into the silicon value chain through carbothermic reduction. Two experimental campaigns were carried out in a pilot-scale SAF. The process began with the collection and pretreatment of raw materials, followed by agglomeration into self-reducing briquettes. Three types of briquettes were made, Type A (pure quartz and carbon black with binder and water), Type B (pot scrap, carbon black, binder, and water), and Type C (silicon kerf with binder and water). These briquettes were then subjected to pilot-scale carbothermic reduction in the SAF to produce silicon, which was subsequently analyzed to determine its purity. The two experimental campaigns which were run over a period of three days and three nights consisted of two experiments, totaling four experiments. These are:

- EXP 1: Type A briquettes and quartz lumps as charge.
- EXP 2: Type A briquettes, quartz lumps, and pot scrap lumps as charge.
- EXP 3: Type B briquettes and pot scrap lumps as charge.
- EXP 4: Type B and Type C briquettes and pot scrap lumps as charge.

Across two SAF campaigns, a total of 92 kg of silicon was produced through twelve tapping operations. In the first campaign (EXP 1 and EXP 2), 60 kg of silicon was obtained, while the second campaign (EXP 3 and EXP 4) yielded 32 kg. ICP-MS analysis of six samples from each tap (Tables I) confirmed that the produced silicon met metallurgical-grade purity requirements [5], with the second campaign achieving slightly higher purity than the first.

Table I: Purity of the tapped silicon measured by ICP-MS.

Sample	Purity (%)	
	Campaign 1	Campaign 2
1	97.87	98.43
2	98.27	98.16
3	98.47	98.01
4	98.39	98.47
5	98.34	98.78
6	98.79	98.05

Detailed ICP-MS analysis of Campaign 1 samples showed phosphorus as the dominant dopant, slightly above metallurgical-grade thresholds, while boron and gallium remained within limits. Aluminum exceeded the threshold in early tappings but stabilized later, iron was acceptable in half of the tappings, and titanium consistently exceeded limits; other metals were within range, confirming overall suitability for metallurgical-grade silicon. In Campaign 2, phosphorus and boron levels decreased, gallium increased, and aluminum and iron were well controlled, though calcium, titanium, chromium, and nickel exceeded thresholds. Despite these variations, it can be concluded that the produced silicon in this campaign met metallurgical-grade standards, an encouraging result given

that 70% of the feedstock came from recycled pot scrap and kerf.

Pilot C: A combined system for powder feeding, melting, solidification, and granulation has been developed and commissioned. The powder feeding unit has a capacity of 500 tons per year, while the melting and granulation units handle 50 tons per year. The process successfully demonstrated the production of recycled silicon at a flow rate of 1 kg/h, achieving 4N purity.

Pilot D: A chemical conversion process for silicon waste has been scaled up to 87 tons per year, producing waterglass and green hydrogen for diverse market applications. End-of-life PV panels and semiconductor industry residues were also shown to be valuable alternative sources for material recovery.

4 CONCLUSIONS

This study through the ICARUS project highlights the substantial volumes of silicon kerf, silica, and graphite waste generated during ingot and wafer manufacturing and demonstrates their huge potential as valuable secondary raw materials. Detailed characterization of these wastes confirmed the suitability of these wastes as substitutes for virgin materials, while the successful implementation of four pilot technologies within the ICARUS project validated the technical feasibility of their recovery and reuse. Together, these results provide a strong foundation for integrating recycling into the PV value chain, advancing both sustainability and circular economy objectives in the PV industry.

5 ACKNOWLEDGEMENT

This work is part of ICARUS project funded by Horizon 2020 research and innovation programme under grant agreement No 958365.

6 REFERENCES

[1] Li, J., Lin, Y., Wang, F., Shi, J., Sun, J., Ban, B., Liu, G. and Chen, J., 2021. Progress in recovery and recycling of kerf loss silicon waste in photovoltaic industry. Separation and Purification Technology, 254, p.117581. https://doi.org/10.1016/j.seppur.2020.117581.

[2] Yang, S., Han, S., Chen, J., Wei, K. and Ma, W., 2024. A sustainable mineral process for silicon and quartz recovery from quartz crucible waste ash via electrical separation. Minerals Engineering, 216, p.108887. https://doi.org/10.1016/j.mineng.2024.108887.

[3] Zhang, Y., Z. Chen, K. Xie, X. Chen, Y. Hu, and W. Ma. Purification of Waste Graphite from Crucibles Used in Photovoltaic Crystallization by an Alkali-Acid Method. Metals 2023, 13, 1180. 2023. https://doi.org/10.3390/met13071180.

[4] Brailovsky, P., Baumann, K., Held, M., Briem, A.K., Wambach, K., Gervais, E., Herceg, S., Mertvoy, B., Nold, S. and Rentsch, J., 2023. Insights into circular material and waste flows from c-Si PV industry. EPJ Photovoltaics, 14, p.5. https://doi.org/10.1051/epjpv/2022029.

[5] Metallurgical-Grade Silicon (MGS) - WikiChip. https://en.wikichip.org/wiki/metallurgical-grade_silicon#google_vignette.

ECO-EFFICIENT PROCESSING AND REFINING ROUTES FOR SECONDARY RAW MATERIALS FROM SILICON INGOT AND WAFER MANUFACTURING

M.P. BELLMANN*[1], B.D. DIMD [1], A.K SØILAND [2], ET AL.

[1] SINTEF, NORWAY AND [2] RESITEC, NORWAY

Content

1. Why recycling matters
2. ICARUS project
3. Pilot technologies
4. Results
5. Discussion & Outlook

Why recycling matters

- PV deployment is accelerating $\rightarrow$ huge silicon demand
- Ingot & wafer production generates large waste streams: kerf, crucible, and pot scrap and graphite.
- Current practice: landfill, low-value uses, and not industrial scale.
- Need for scalable, high value and circular recycling solutions: **ICARUS Project**

ICARUS project

- H2020 project with 18 EU partners.
- Goal: Recover, refine, reintegrate PV waste.
- Focus: Silicon kerf, Graphite, Silica.
- Develop 4 scalable pilot technologies (Pilot A-D).

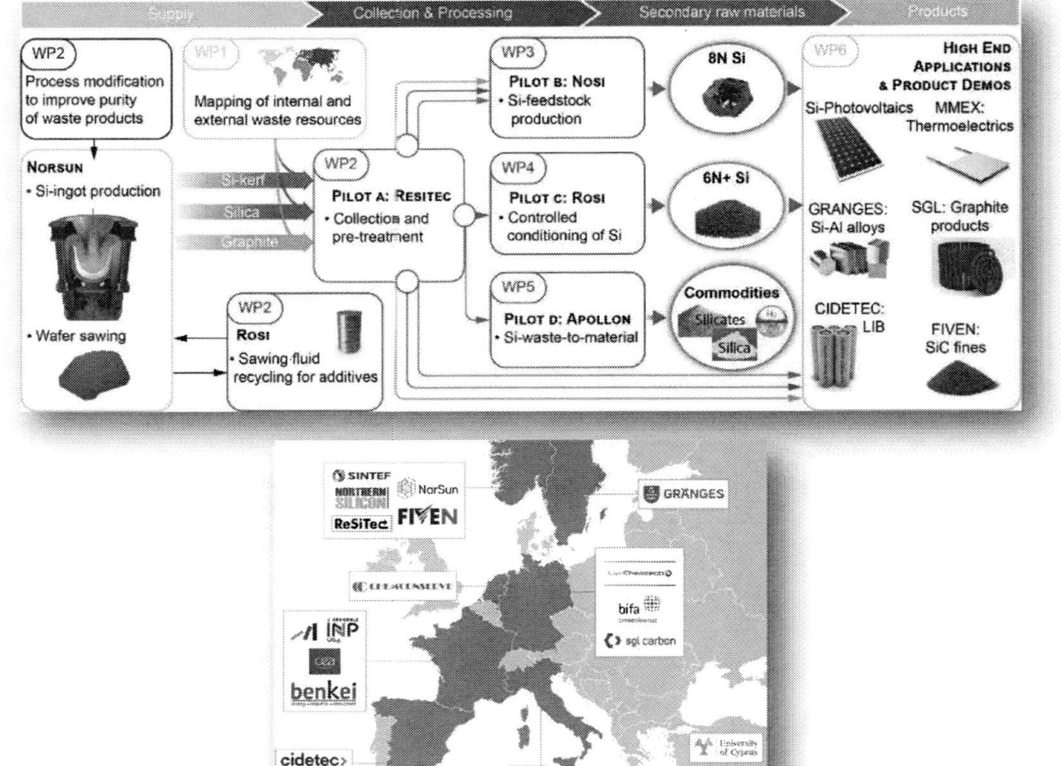

020496-004

Pilot technologies: Pilot A

Collects and processes silicon kerf cake, graphite, and silica waste according to defined standards.

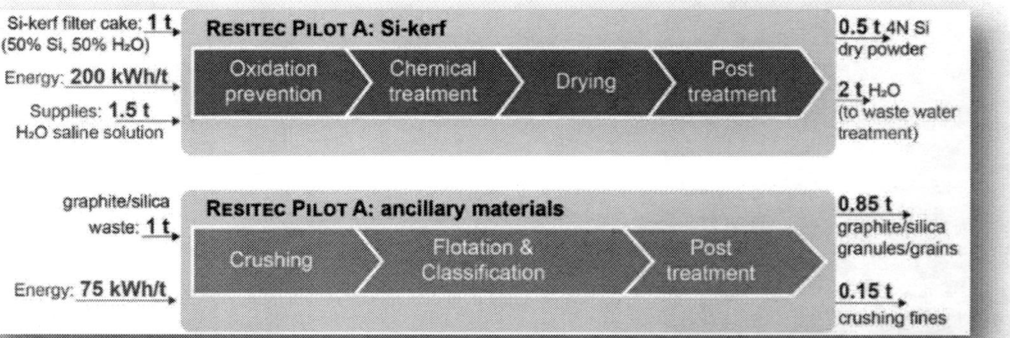

Pilot technologies: Pilot B

Silicon production via carbothermic reduction in SAF using waste materials

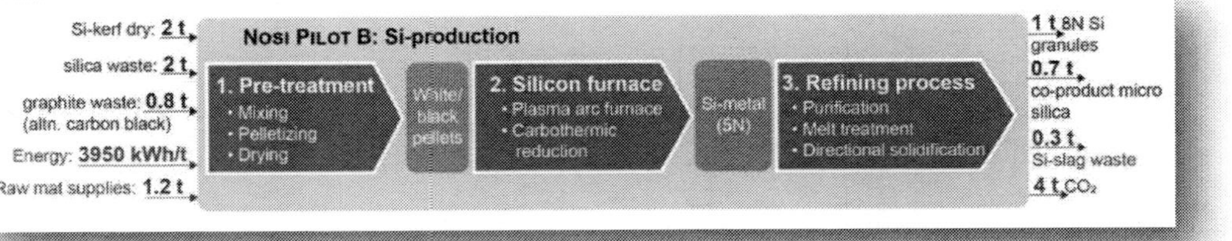

020496-006

Pilot technologies: Pilot C

Scales up the granulation & conditioning of silicon, based on material from PilotA.

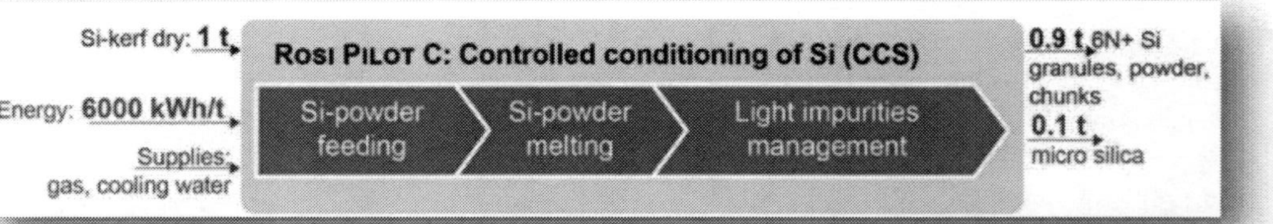

Pilot technologies: Pilot D

Scales up a reactor using a controlled reaction of free silicon in kerf with sodium hydroxide solution under controlled temperature and pressure conditions.

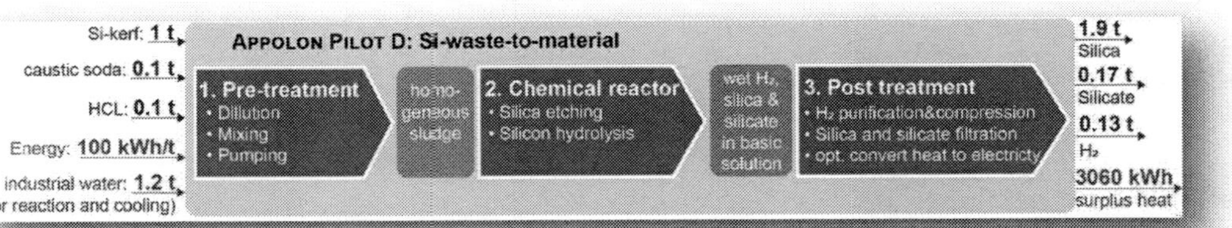

Results

Volume

Characterization

Pilot results

Results

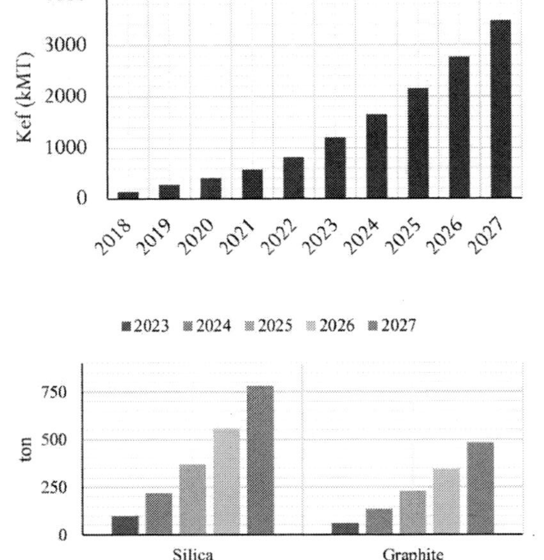

- Substantial volumes of waste are generated each year.

- With appropriate collection, purification, and processing strategies, there is strong potential to recycle and reintegrate these materials into the PV value chain.

Results

Volume

Characterization

Pilot results

Material	Characterization summary
Kerf	Impurities: B, Ga, P; Al, Ca, Fe, Ni C: 1-2 wt.% and O: 4-5 wt.% Phases: Crystalline + amorphous
Graphite	High ash vs virgin graphite Impurities: Si, Co, Ca Phases: Graphite 2H, SiC, SiO_2
Silica	Mainly amorphous silica + cristobalite Primary impurity: Ca

With proper pretreatment, these waste materials can substitute a significant share of virgin raw materials in PV ingot manufacturing.

Results

- TRL 7 industrial-scale routes for kerf & silica waste developed.

- Continuous drying system $\rightarrow$ <1 wt% moisture.

- Pretreatment process that removes Al, Ni, Fe contaminants.

- Post-treatment process that enables use in Li-ion batteries & thermoelectric modules.

Results

Volume

Characterization

Pilot B

- Reintroduce silicon kerf, graphite, and silica waste via carbothermic reduction in SAF.

- Agglomeration of waste into self-reducing briquettes.

- Three types of briquettes: Type A[1], Type B[2], and Type C[3].

- Two campaigns with 4 experiments:
  - EXP 1: Type A briquettes and quartz lumps.
  - EXP 2: Type A briquettes, quartz lumps, and pot scrap lumps.
  - EXP 3: Type B briquettes and pot scrap lumps.
  - EXP 4: Type B and Type C briquettes and pot scrap lumps.

[1] Type A: pure quartz and carbon black with binder and water

[2] Type B: pot scrap, carbon black, binder, and water

[3] Type C: silicon kerf with binder and water

020496-013

Results

Volume

Characterization

Pilot B

- Produced a total of 92 kg silicon.
  - 60 kg in Campaign 1 (EXP 1 & 2)
  - 32 kg in Campaign 2 (EXP 3 & 4)

- ICP-MS analysis confirmed metallurgical-grade purity.

Sample	Purity	
	Camp. 1	Camp. 2
1	97.87	98.43
2	98.27	98.16
3	98.47	98.01
4	98.39	98.47
5	98.34	98.78
6	98.79	98.05

020496-014

Results

Volume

Characterization

Pilot C

- Integrated system for powder feeding, melting, solidification & granulation commissioned.

- Achieved 4N purity recycled silicon.

- Significant reduction in carbon & oxygen impurities.

Results

Volume

Characterization

Pilot D

- Chemical conversion process for silicon waste scaled to 87 t/year.

- Produces waterglass and green hydrogen for multiple markets.

- Demonstrated alternative feedstocks: EoL PV panels & semiconductor waste.

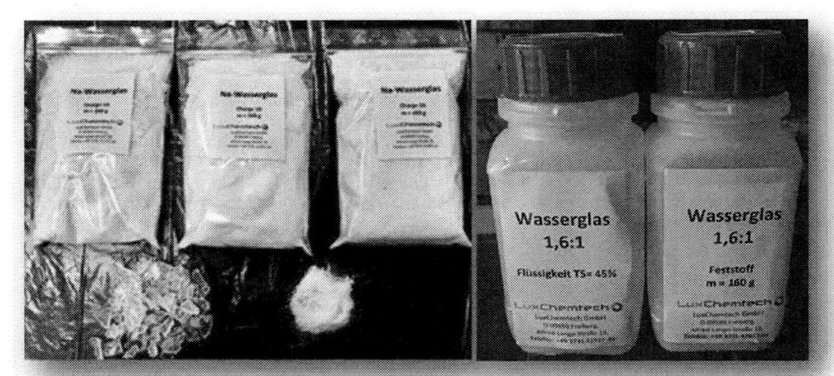

Discussion & Outlook

1. Pilot results prove feasibility of recycling kerf, silica, and graphite.

2. Recovered materials meet standards for PV and other industries.

3. Reduces reliance on virgin inputs $\rightarrow$ supports circular economy.

4. Next step:

   - Optimize recycling processes to control impurities.

   - Address operational inconsistencies between experiments.

   - Consider broad applications.

Thank you!! Questions?

martin.bellmann@sintef.no
berhane.dimd@sintef.no

This presentation was selected by the Sc. Committee of the EU PVSEC 2025 for submission of a full paper to one of the EU PVSEC's collaborating peer-reviewed journals.

NEW THERMOMECHANICAL TESTS TO ASSESS THE RECYCLABILITY INDEX OF PHOTOVOLTAIC MODULES

Cristina L. Pinto[1], Asier Murillo[1], Ana María Gracia[1], Felice Alfieri[2], Nieves Espinosa[3], Davide Polverini[4]

[1]National Renewable Energy Centre (CENER), Spain
[2]Viegand Maagøe A/S, København, Denmark
[3]University of Murcia, Spain
[4] European Commission, DG Internal Market, Industry, Entrepreneurship and SMEs, Brussels, Belgium
cpinto@cener.com

ABSTRACT: In the context of the increasing efforts to enhance the sustainability of photovoltaic (PV) technologies, recyclability has emerged as a critical aspect to address within the circular economy framework and EU regulatory directives. This study focuses on new thermomechanical tests developed to address the recyclability of PV modules. Specifically, new thermomechanical techniques have been designed to evaluate the dismantlability of PV modules, focusing on two critical processes: the removal of the aluminium frame and the separation of the PV laminate (back-sheet + encapsulant + solar cell) from the glass substrate(s) (or both substrates in the case of glass-glass modules). For the frame removal test, the required maximum force was measured to assess the dismantling efficiency. The separation of the PV laminate was achieved using a thermomechanical technique, ensuring precision, measurability and repeatability of the process. These techniques were applied to a set of 18 modules, comprising two units of nine distinct models representing various PV technologies.
Keywords: PV Recyclability index, aluminium frame removal, delamination, thermomechanical test

1 INTRODUCTION

The accelerated deployment of PV technology plays a crucial role in securing energy supply and combating climate change. However, this growth also leads to a significant increase in end-of-life PV module waste, with projections estimating between 78 and 200 million tons of industrial waste by 2050, representing a loss of approximately $80 billion in recoverable materials [1]. To address this challenge, the European Climate, Infrastructure and Environment Executive Agency (CINEA) launched an initiative to develop a standardised recyclability index for PV modules and PV inverters based on previous research findings [2]. This effort aimed to reduce waste generation, resource consumption, and environmental impacts.

Table I: Scoring parameters and aggregation of the recyclability index for PV modules

Type of parameters	N	Parameter		Aggregation
Service-related parameters	1	Technology identification		5%
	2	Dismantling of the information and conditions for access		10%
	3	3.1	Disclosure of material composition	10%
		3.2	Disclosure of the presence and location of Critical, Strategic and Environmental Relevant materials	10%
Dismantling-related parameters	6	6.2	Removability of the encapsulant after a heating process: peel-off test	15%
		6.3	Removability of the encapsulant from the glass after a heating process: hot knife test	15%
		6.4	Removability of the frame	15%
Material-based parameters	7	Level of concentration of hazardous substances and other substances affecting the recycling process		15%
	8	Selection of materials based on recyclability complexity		10%
	9	Combination of materials used / homogeneity		10%

This initiative focuses on developing and validating recyclability scoring systems for PV modules and PV inverters, ensuring they are cost-effective, rapid, and accessible for manufacturers and market surveillance bodies. Key aspects include identifying priority parts based on material relevance and recyclability, defining critical recycling parameters (service-related, dismantling-related, and material-based), establishing scoring criteria, and developing recyclability scores for PV products (

Table *I*). Introducing this recyclability index could represent a significant step toward fostering sustainability in the PV industry, particularly by promoting design-for-recycling principles.

The current study focuses on the technical evaluation of the dismantling processes for PV modules as part of the broader recyclability assessment, which covers the following parameters:

- 6.2. Removability of the encapsulant (delamination) after heating for glass-backsheet modules.
- 6.3 Removability of the encapsulant (delamination) after a heating process for glass-glass modules.
- 6.4 Removability (dismantling) of the frame.

The research activity presented in this paper is part of the overall initiative to develop the aforementioned recyclability index, with a specific focus on the development of thermomechanical testing for the assessment of the frame and encapsulant-cell laminate removability. Another paper, also submitted to EUPVSEC 2025 (5CO.6.3), elaborates in more detail on the architecture and general methodological approach of the recyclability index for PV modules, as well as on the policy implications.

By focusing on the dismantling phase, we isolate some of the key recycling-related aspects, such as design, providing critical data for the calibration of the recyclability index. Specifically, we designed and tested customised thermomechanical techniques developed to measure the dismantling-related parameters for the systematic evaluation of the dismantlability and recyclability of PV modules at the moment of placing them on the market. For this work, two main steps are going to be taken:

1. Removal of Aluminium Frames: Measuring the maximum force required for frame dismantling.
2. Separation of PV Laminates from Glass Substrates: Utilising a thermomechanical-based blade and measuring the force decrease between two temperatures needed to efficiently separate the PV laminate from glass substrate on glass-backsheet modules, and the force needed to separate both glasses from glass-glass PV modules, minimising material degradation.

2 METHODOLOGY AND MATERIALS

This section includes the specifications of the PV models used and the description of the various tests developed to assess, quantitatively, the dismantlability of PV modules to reach and separate, when possible, their main components.

2.1 Tested PV modules

The photovoltaic (PV) module models were selected to represent a wide variety of systems currently installed. Two units of each model were used to perform the tests. Table II provides the list of the 9 selected PV module models, supported by a reasoning for the selection of specific technologies/models.

Table II. List of PV models with their specifications

Product ID	Technology	Power (W)	Module type - Bifaciality
Model 1	mc-Si, n-BC	420	Monofacial
Model 2	mc-Si, non-encapsulant	550	Glass-glass
Model 3	Si, HJT	450	Monofacial
Model 4	mc-Si, PERC Shingled	430	Monofacial
Model 5	mc-Si, TOPCon	525	Glass-glass
Model 6	mc-Si, p-BC	610	Monofacial
Model 7	mc-Si, n-TOPCon, half cut	600	Glass-glass
Model 8	mc-Si, i-TOPCon	605	Glass-glass
Model 9	Thin-film	400	Glass-glass

The selection of PV models across a spectrum of established, emerging, and niche technologies, ranging from PERC and TOPCon to IBC, HJT, thin-film, and recyclable designs, ensures a comprehensive representation of the current PV module market and potential new designs. It not only reflects the dominant technologies in deployment today but also anticipates future trends, enabling a robust evaluation of recyclability that aligns with the evolving landscape of photovoltaic innovation.

2.2 PV module frame removal process

This section describes the experimental procedure used to dismantle the aluminium frames from commercial and newly manufactured PV modules. The process was designed to quantify the mechanical resistance of frame detachment and to study the structural characteristics of the frame, analysing the potential failure modes during dismantling under the condition that the module's glass should remain intact. Maintaining the integrity of the glass is critical, as breakage would compromise subsequent recycling processes

Each PV model unit was tested individually using a custom-designed rectangular test bench (Figure 1). This bench is equipped with lateral pressure units that can be repositioned along sliding rails to accommodate varying module sizes and ensure precise application of force. Each piston is fitted with a load cell at its end, and all load cells are connected to a central measurement device that records the sum of the forces applied by all pistons during the test. As a result, the maximum total detachment force exerted on the frame is captured and recorded as a single value.

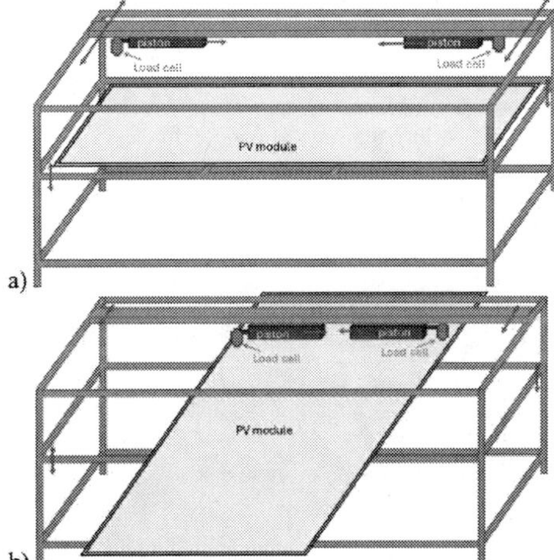

Figure 1. Test bench. a) bench configuration to remove short frames (denoted A-B); b) bench configuration to remove long frames (denoted 1-2)

The test procedure consists of five distinct steps aimed at removing both the long and short sides of the aluminium frame while maintaining the integrity of the glass. The complete methodology is described in [3].

The maximum total force recorded in each of the five steps is stored, and from these five values, an average detachment force is calculated. This average is then used to evaluate the recyclability performance of the PV module within the proposed index framework.

The scoring system for parameter 6.4 is defined as follows (Table III):

Table III. Scoring system of parameter 6.4

Force	Score
The glass has been broken in the process	1 point
$F > 14710\,N$	3 points
$9807\,N < F \leq 14710\,N$	4 points
$F \leq 9807\,N$	5 points

2.3 Delamination of glass-backsheet PV modules

The delamination tests were carried out using the same custom-built rectangular test bench employed for the frame removal procedure. However, in this configuration, the pneumatic pistons are not used. Instead, the setup is adapted with additional components specifically designed for thermal-mechanical delamination of PV modules.

The bench is equipped with a hot plate capable of reaching temperatures between 50 °C and 200 °C, which allows precise thermal conditioning of the module section to be tested.

A motorised horizontal arm is mounted on the bench, whose movement speed can be precisely adjusted. Attached to this arm is a load cell, which records the force applied during the delamination process. Fixed to the arm is a 10.00 cm wide steel blade, used to initiate and propagate the separation between the front glass and the laminate.

This configuration allows controlled, quantifiable and repeatable delamination testing by combining thermal softening of the encapsulant with mechanical cutting, while simultaneously recording the force required to perform the operation. Unlike shredding or crushing techniques—which destroy the module structure and mask design differences—this method allows assessment of how specific design choices affect dismantling performance. This is essential for this study, which aims to incentivise manufacturers to adopt more sustainable and circular design strategies for PV modules.

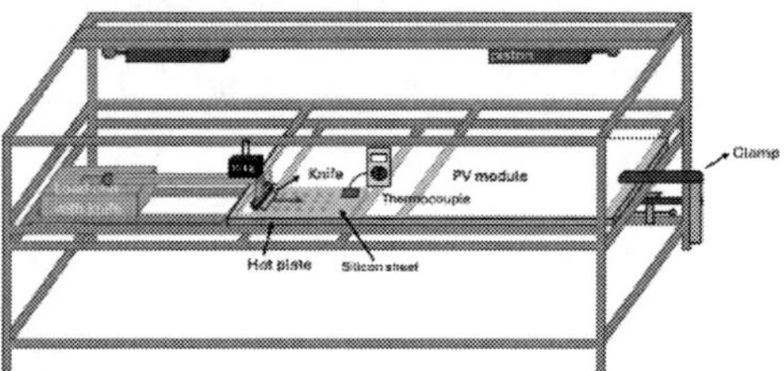

Figure 2. Scheme of the test bench equipped with the delamination test.

The delamination process is conducted at $T_1 = 70°C$ and $T_2 = 150°C$. The selected temperatures were chosen based on the thermochemical properties of the encapsulant materials. According to calorimetric analyses, the melting point of the most common encapsulants—EVA, POE, and TPO—lies within the range of 70–90 °C (although this may vary depending on the specific composition of the encapsulant). Therefore, a temperature of 70 °C was selected to remain below the melting point while still

representing a temperature that can realistically be reached by a PV module in normal working conditions. The second temperature chosen was 150 °C, as it is well above the melting point and far beyond the working temperatures that PV modules would normally experience. This approach allows for the analysis of the reduction in the force required for delamination between the two temperature conditions.

In order to account for possible local variations in adhesion strength across the PV module surface and to address the possible inhomogeneity of the adhesion force of the encapsulant to the glass in various regions of the module derived from the manufacturing process, each delamination test is performed in three predefined zones (Figure 3):

Zone A: Upper-left corner (or one corner)
Zone B: Centre of the module
Zone C: Lower-right corner (or the opposite corner to Zone A)

The complete methodology is described in [3].

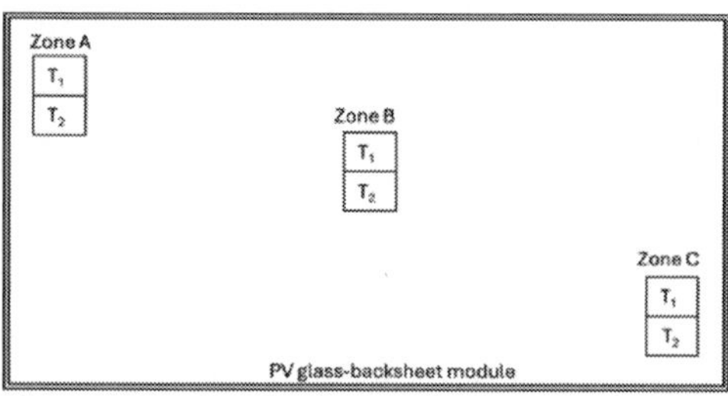

Figure 3. Locations for the delamination test.

Before the delamination procedure begins, the perimeter of each selected zone (A, B, and C) is carefully cut using a precision cutter with sufficient depth to reach the glass interface, ensuring that the entire laminate stack is fully separated along the border of the test area. Then the blade is manually positioned, and its movement is activated at a slow speed of 50 mm/min. Once the blade has penetrated between the glass and the remaining layers, the testing speed is set to 150 mm/min. The test width corresponds to the blade width: 10 cm. The total test length is 11 cm, although only 7.00 cm of constant force is considered for calculating the average force in N/mm, following the details defined in the standard peel-off test (IEC 61730-2). The decrease in the average delamination force will be a key criterion for assessing the recyclability of modules.

$$Force\ Reduction\ (\%) = \left(\frac{F_{T_1} - F_{T_2}}{F_{T_1}}\right) \times 100$$

Each module is evaluated based on the average percentage reduction across all three zones. The scoring system is defined as follows (Table IV):

Table IV. Scoring system of parameter 6.2

Force Reduction (%)	Score
< 30%	1 points
30% – 60%	3 points
> 60%	5 points

This scoring approach reflects the ability of the encapsulant and module design to facilitate separation at elevated temperatures. It rewards products that can be delaminated more easily under thermal conditions, thus promoting design strategies aligned with high-efficiency and low-contamination recycling processes.

2.4 Delamination of glass-glass PV modules

In contrast to glass-backsheet modules, glass-glass configuration makes it impossible to perform the delamination process; nevertheless, with a thin knife, it is feasible to enter between the two glasses and separate them.

The test is conducted on the same rectangular testing bench used in earlier tests. The test equipment consists of a motorised cutting device equipped with a load cell to monitor the applied force. A metal blade of 25.00 cm is mounted on the adjustable arm.

Before testing, the glass-glass modules are heated to a temperature of 160°C. This thermal conditioning ensures that the encapsulant becomes sufficiently softened to facilitate separation without damaging the structural integrity of the glass layers. A thermocouple is attached directly to the module to monitor the surface temperature. Once the target temperature is reached, the separation test begins. The blade is inserted between the two glass layers at a module corner while moving at a reduced speed of 50 mm/min, ensuring controlled and precise insertion. Once the blade tip has entered the module, the load cell is reset to zero, and the speed is increased to 150 mm/min. From this point, the test proceeds automatically, with the blade progressing deeper into the module structure until it enters 11.00 cm inside the module (Figure 4).

Figure 4. Photo of the glass-glass PV delamination test with a hot knife.

As the blade advances diagonally from the corner, the resistance gradually increases due to the enlarging interface area, resulting in a linear upward trend in the force profile. Thus, the slope of the force curve (in N/mm^2) is the main metric used in glass-glass modules; therefore, a mean value between the results obtained from the four corners will be the main result of this test. The scoring system is defined as follows (**Table V**)

Table V. Scoring system of parameter 6.3

Slope of Force Curve (N/mm²)	Score
< 5 N/mm²	5 points
5 – 15 N/mm² included	3 points
> 15 N/mm²	1 points

Lower slope values indicate a softer and more easily separable encapsulant at the test temperature, and thus

better recyclability potential. Conversely, higher slope values suggest stronger adhesion or less responsive encapsulants, which hinder separation and may result in glass contamination during recycling.

Take into account that the slicing direction significantly affects the measured force gradient; all modules must be positioned in a standardised orientation, such that the blade enters perpendicularly to the corner diagonal. This standardisation ensures the comparability of results across different samples

3   RESULTS AND DISCUSSION

The PV dismantling test encompasses the PV module aluminium frame removal test and the delamination of the modules, using a different technique for glass-backsheet and glass-glass devices, as explained above.

3.1 Aluminium frame removal test results

Starting from the frame removal test, 9 PV module models were tested, performing two tests per side, distinguishing between the long-side frames (Frame 1–2) and the short-side frames (Frame A–B). For each side, two tests were conducted per module, both applying pressure near the corners, and the average of the two measurements was considered. The force is expressed in Kgf, which is approximately equal to 9.8 N.

The results are depicted in Figure 5.

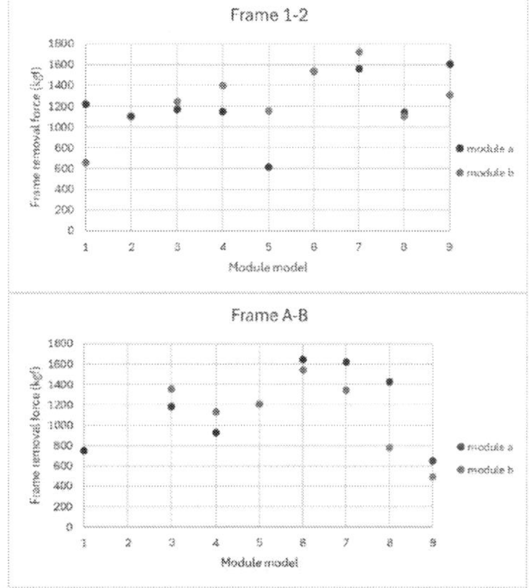

Figure 5. Frame removal test by module models 1 to 9, for the two devices tested per module type (a and b). top) test carried out between Frames 1-2, bottom) test carried out between Frames A-B.

The distribution of the recorded forces reveals a broad variability. The required forces span a range from below 800 kgf to values exceeding 1400 kgf. Despite being the same model from the same manufacturer, some intra-model variation is evident. For instance, in model 5, the removal force for Frame 1–2 varied from around 600 kgf to approximately 1200 kgf. Similar discrepancies appear in other models and for Frame A–B as well. For Model module 2, only one device was tested (module a) since the module glass and cells shattered while removing the Frame 1-2, therefore it was decided not to test the second device (module b). Similarly, for Model 1, unit b was damaged while changing the test bench configuration between frame removal and frame A-B could not be tested.

3.2 Delamination of glass-backsheet modules

Delamination tests were conducted on three types of PV modules: shingled, HJT (with multi-busbar contacts), and BC (with rear-side contacts only). These technologies enable the evaluation of differences in delamination resistance attributable to the various contact configurations.

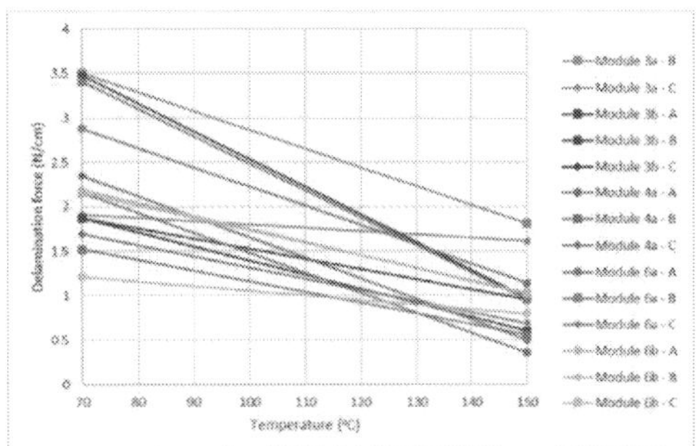

Figure 6. Results of the delamination of glass-backsheet modules

According to the results depicted in Figure *6*, significant discrepancies were observed in the delamination results between the two units of each PV module tested, and even between different zones of the same module (same colour in the graph). These variations are primarily attributed to the high sensitivity of the delamination process to the precise positioning and orientation of the blade during testing. Factors such as whether the blade crosses a single cell, multiple cells, or areas without cells, as well as the direction of delamination relative to the busbars, can have a major influence on the measured force. In particular, delamination performed perpendicular to the busbars may cause the blade to snag or encounter increased resistance, resulting in higher force values. Nevertheless, there is a clear tendency for the delamination force to decrease with increasing temperature, with a pronounced reduction from 70 °C to 150 °C. A more detailed discussion of the results is described in the recyclability index testing report [3].

3.3 Delamination of glass-glass modules

Following the methodology described above, the results of glass-glass modules are presented in Figure 7.

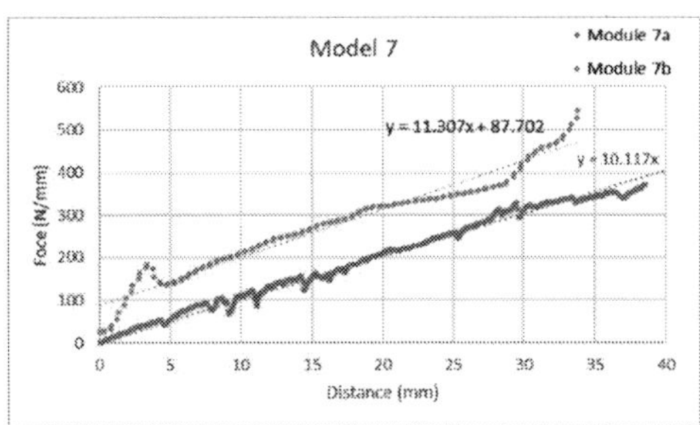

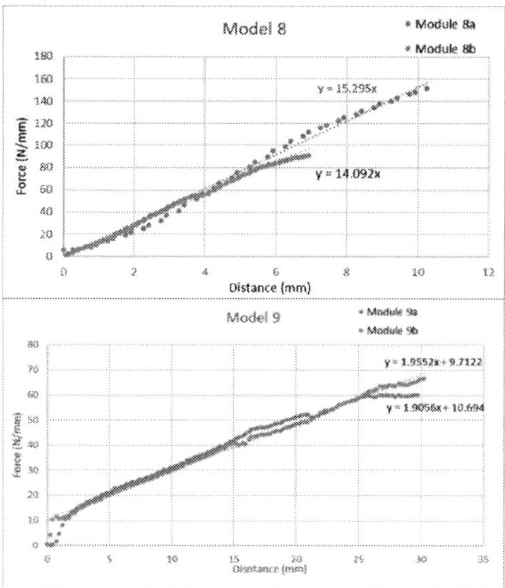

Figure 7. Delamination test results for glass-glass modules.

The delamination tests on the three glass-glass models reveal clear differences in behaviour. For Model 7, both units exhibit a similar trend, with comparable slopes of 10.12 N/mm² and 11.31 N/mm². Model 8 also shows consistent behaviour between units, with values of 15.30 N/mm² and 14.09 N/mm², although it should be noted that for unit 8a the penetration depth was limited to 10 mm due to positioning constraints, whereas a penetration of 110 mm would be required for a fully representative value. In contrast, the thin-film modules (Model 9) require significantly lower delamination forces, as expected from the absence of c-Si cells, with values of 1.91 N/mm² and 1.96 N/mm² for the two units tested.

3.4 Recyclability index of the PV nodules

In the following section, the recyclability index results are presented, focusing specifically on parameter 6 – dismantling-related parameters. To contextualise the results, the performance of the tested models is compared against a fictitious 'ideal module,' which is assumed to reach the maximum possible score for dismantling-related parameters. This comparison highlights the gap between current industrial designs and the best-case scenario, providing valuable insights into how different design choices influence recyclability.

The results are presented in **Figure 8**. The dismantling-related parameters reveal significant variability among the tested modules when compared to the fictitious ideal module. Frame removability shows relatively high values for most modules, with several reaching 0.75, close to the maximum score, although some designs (e.g., Model 2 and Model 6) display lower values, reflecting the fact that Model 2 did not pass the test as the glass got broken during the process, and potential difficulties in separating the aluminium frame for Module 6. In terms of delamination, glass–backsheet configurations generally achieve higher scores than glass–glass designs. Notably, Modules 7 and 8 exhibit measurable scores for glass–glass delamination, but these remain well below the ideal benchmark. On the contrary, Model 9 got the maximum punctuation in the glass-glass delamination process. The comparison with the virtual ideal module underscores the existing gap between current module designs and the maximum recyclability potential, especially in delamination processes. These findings emphasise that, while progress has been made in simplifying frame removal, further innovations are required in encapsulant and laminate design to significantly improve recyclability performance.

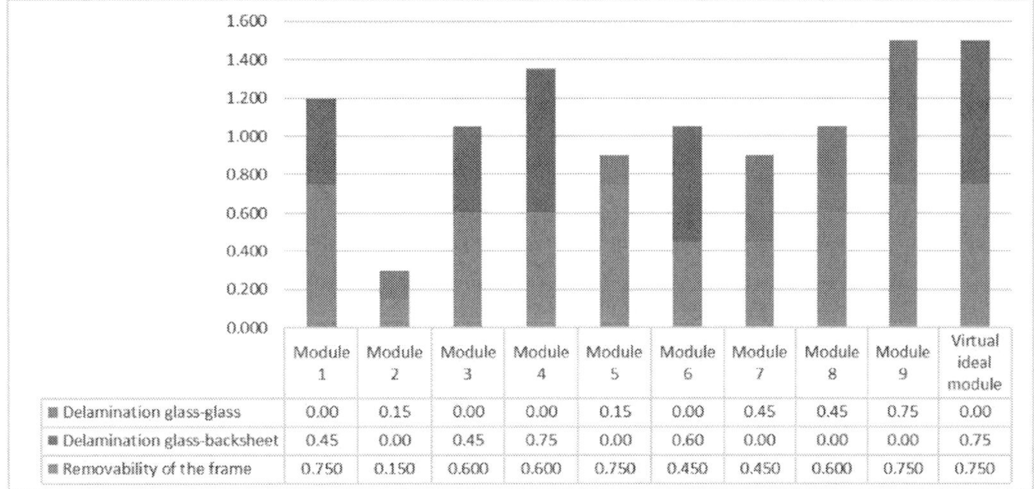

	Module 1	Module 2	Module 3	Module 4	Module 5	Module 6	Module 7	Module 8	Module 9	Virtual ideal module
Delamination glass-glass	0.00	0.15	0.00	0.00	0.15	0.00	0.45	0.45	0.75	0.00
Delamination glass-backsheet	0.45	0.00	0.45	0.75	0.00	0.60	0.00	0.00	0.00	0.75
Removability of the frame	0.750	0.150	0.600	0.600	0.750	0.450	0.450	0.600	0.750	0.750

Figure 8. Recyclability index of the PV modules, based only on the dismantling-related parameters.

4 CONCLUSIONS

This work presents the development and application of a novel 3-in-1 thermomechanical testing bench designed to assess dismantling-related parameters within the recyclability index for photovoltaic modules. The equipment enables a systematic and repeatable evaluation of three critical tests: the removal of aluminium frames, the delamination of glass–backsheet modules, and the delamination of glass–glass modules.

The results obtained across a representative set of PV technologies demonstrate that frame removal is generally less challenging than delamination, with several modules approaching the maximum score for this parameter. However, a considerable disparity was observed in the forces required to remove the aluminium frames. This variability is strongly influenced by multiple design aspects, such as the geometry of the profiles and the type of sealing materials (e.g., silicones) employed.

In contrast, delamination processes remain the main bottleneck. The delamination tests on glass-backsheet modules showed notable dispersion, largely due to the sensitivity of the results to the positioning of the blade, which strongly affects the measured force. The comparison with a fictitious ideal module highlights the significant design gap that still exists between current commercial products and the recyclability potential envisioned under circular economy principles.

These tests also represent the first application of this dismantling methodology, and their results have been instrumental in redefining and refining the overall procedure. The discrepancies observed, especially in delamination measurements, have provided valuable insights that allowed us to describe the methodology more precisely and establish clearer testing protocols, thereby reducing uncertainty and enhancing reproducibility for future evaluations.

Overall, the findings underline the importance of integrating design-for-recycling principles into PV module development. Improvements in encapsulant formulations, laminate configurations, and frame assembly strategies will be key to facilitating efficient dismantling, thereby supporting the broader objective of establishing a standardised recyclability index for PV products. This study provides a technical foundation that can guide both manufacturers and policymakers toward more sustainable photovoltaic systems.

REFERENCES

[1] IRENA, M. M. Aman, and K. H. Solangi, *End-Of-Life Management: Solar Photovoltaic Panels. International Renewable Energy Agency and the International Energy Agency Photovoltaic Power Systems*, vol. 47, no. 5. 2018. [Online]. Available: https://www.osti.gov/servlets/purl/1561525/%0

[2] Viegand Maagøe, Universidad de Murcia, and CENER, "Development of a recyclability index for photovoltaic products," 2025. https://www.pv-recyclability-index.eu/

[3] Viegand Maagøe, Universidad de Murcia, and CENER, "Technical support for the development of a recyclability index for photovoltaic products : Testing , calibration and validation," 2025. [Online]. Available: https://www.pv-recyclability-index.eu/documents/

SYNTHESIS AND ANALYSIS OF POLYANILINE PROPERTIES WITH VARIOUS COUNTERIONS FOR SILVER RECOVERY FROM TECHNOLOGICAL SOLUTIONS AFTER SILICON PV CELLS LEACHING

Hanna Rodziewicz[1], Anna Kuczyńska-Łażewska*,[1], Agnieszka Witkowska[2]
1 Gdansk University of Technology, Faculty of Chemistry
2 Gdansk University of Technology, Faculty of Applied Physics and Mathematics, Institute of Nanotechnology and Materials Engineering
ul. Narutowicza 11/12 80-233 Gdańsk, Poland
anna.lazewska@pg.edu.pl

ABSTRACT: In the presented work a one-step synthesis of polyaniline using four different organic acids and a hydrochloric acid solution was described. Polyaniline is a conductive polymer, so can be used for hydrometallurgical recovery of silver ions. Possible applications of the PAni/Ag composite were analysied. Fourier-transform infrared spectroscopy, UV-Vis spectroscopy and thermogravimetric analysis were carried out to evaluate the composition and structure of the synthesized materials. In addition, pH and specific conductivity were measured. The obtained spectra confirmed the presence of key functional groups, bonds and energy transitions for the analyzed substances. The specific conductivity values for all samples confirmed the ability of the materials to conduct electricity. The use of five different acids at the polymerization stage resulted in slightly different structures between the materials. The materials were placed in a solution of $AgNO_3$ to investigate the possibility of silver ions recovery on the polymer structure. The samples were subjected to X-ray spectroscopy and tested on the scanning electron microscope with Energy-dispersive X-ray spectroscopy, which made it possible to analyze the structure of the polymer and check for the presence of silver. In the future, the samples can be used for hydrometallurgical recovery of silver, and it will be examined how different counter-ions affect the efficiency of such a process and the final percentage of metal obtained.
Keywords: polyaniline, composites, silver recovery

1 INTRODUCTION

Composite materials are currently being applied on a wide scale across various scientific and engineering disciplines. Continuous efforts are directed toward the development of novel combinations of well-characterized components. In numerous reports, the fabrication of nanocomposites containing, among others, polyaniline and silver nanoparticles has been described. Owing to its advantageous properties, particularly electrical conductivity, polyaniline is frequently employed as a key element of such composites.

One of the applications reported in the literature involves the preparation of a material coated with silver, polyaniline, and aminated graphene oxide. This material was found to exhibit shielding effectiveness against electromagnetic interference across a broad frequency range. It was further demonstrated that the efficiency of the obtained fabrics remained high regardless of the frequency band. In addition, the composite containing silver, polyaniline, and aminated graphene oxide exhibited the highest antibacterial activity—97% against *Escherichia coli* and 99% against *Staphylococcus aureus*. Such results suggest that these materials may represent a breakthrough, as their shielding capacity against electromagnetic radiation can be utilized for the protection of human health [1]. A polyaniline/tungsten (V) phosphate/silver nanocomposite was subsequently employed for the fabrication of a selective membrane targeting hazardous heavy metal ions [2]. Selectivity studies indicated that the membrane responded to lead ions even at very low concentrations, down to 10^{-7} M. Another polyaniline-based composite, incorporating silver and gold nanoparticles, was synthesized with the aim of forming a buffer layer in polymer photovoltaic cells [3]. High electrical conductivity and optical

transparency (76–81%) were obtained in the resulting composites. Impedance spectroscopy measurements confirmed that charge transport was improved in solar cells containing nanocomposites with equal proportions of silver and gold. Enhanced light absorption by the active layer was also observed, and plasmonic coupling between the nanoparticles was suggested to further broaden the absorption range, thereby increasing device efficiency. These findings indicate that such a material may in the future replace the polymer blends currently used in polymer solar cells.

Current approaches to photovoltaic panel recycling are primarily focused on the separation of individual components. The efficiency of such processes is typically evaluated by the quantity and purity of the recovered element. Subsequently, the separated components are often directed to appropriate processing facilities and reintroduced into the production cycle through applications in various industrial sectors.

The application of conducting polymers may enable the recovery of elements such as silver from PV cells. The deposition of silver particles onto a conductive material results in the formation of a composite that can be further utilized. This approach eliminates the need for the direct separation of silver from photovoltaic cells, which is otherwise a complex and costly multi-stage process. Given that potential applications of polyaniline–silver composites are already documented, the recovery of silver using this polymer appears particularly promising. The resulting material could serve as a foundation for novel industrial solutions.

2 MATERIALS AND METHODS

2.1 Synthesis of Polyaniline

The initial syntheses were carried out according to

the procedure described by J. Laska and J. Widlarz. The process commenced with the preparation of an acid solution. Since the aim was to obtain polyaniline containing different counterions in its structure, the following five acids were employed: hydrochloric acid (HCl), 4-toluenesulfonic acid (TSA), 4-sulfanilic acid (SAA), sulfonobenzoic acid (SBA), polyphosphoric acid (PPA). Solutions of 0.02 mol concentration were prepared, and the flasks containing these solutions were placed in an ice bath. Upon cooling, 4.6 mol of aniline was added to each flask. While the reaction mixtures were cooling and the substances combining, a 0.066 mol solution of ammonium persulfate was prepared. After mixing the acid solution with aniline, five portions of 10 ml of the oxidant solution were added at 10-minute intervals in order to control the course of the reaction. The flasks were then left for approximately 5 hours. Once the synthesis was complete, the mixtures were filtered, washed with distilled water, and left to dry. Each synthesis, with the exception of TSA, was carried out twice to assess reproducibility. All used compounds were pure analitycal grade (Merck, Germany).

2.2 Fourier Transform Infrared Spectroscopy (FTIR)

Fourier transform infrared spectroscopy enables the analysis of a given substance in terms of its organic functional groups and hydrogen bonds. For solid-state samples, the material must be finely ground and mixed with a substance such as KBr, which exhibits low infrared absorption. Measurements were performed using a Thermo Scientific Nicolet iS50 FT-IR spectrometer (Thermo Scientific, USA).

2.3 Ultraviolet-Visible Spectroscopy (UV-Vis)

This analysis enables the determination of a wide range of compounds, including aromatic hydrocarbons, aldehydes, ketones, acids, amines, and rare earth elements, with particular sensitivity to conjugated bonds and aromatic groups. Sample preparation began with thorough grinding of the investigated material with barium sulfate (VI) in a mortar. The mixture was subsequently placed in a measurement cuvette and analyzed. Measurements were conducted using a Perkin Elmer Lambda 365+ UV/Vis spectrophotometer (PerkinElmer, USA).

2.4 Thermogravimetric Analysis (TG)

The resulting thermogram represents the change in sample mass (ordinate axis) as a function of either time or temperature (abscissa axis). The measurements were carried out using a Netzsch TG 209F3 thermogravimetric analyzer (NETZSCH, Germany).

2.5 Specific Conductivity Measurements

Conductometric studies were performed by dissolving 10 mg of polyaniline in 30 ml of dimethyl sulfoxide (DMSO). Conductivity was measured by immersing an electrode in the solution and recording the values on a conductometer. Both the electrode and the conductometer were manufactured by Elmetron, specifically models ECF-1 and CX-461, respectively (Elmetron, Poland).

2.6 pH measurement

The pH of the samples was determined by dispersing 10 mg of polyaniline in 20 ml of distilled water. The electrode was then immersed in the suspension, and the pH value was recorded. The analysis was performed using a Mettler Toledo pH meter (Mettler Toledo, Switzerland)

2.7 Silver recovery

In preliminary experiments, silver was recovered from a standardized solution prepared from 100 ppm silver nitrate ($AgNO_3$) and water. The samples were immersed in the solution, filtered, and the resulting powder was subjected to further analyses.

2.8 Synchrotron radiation-based investigation

With the support of the National Synchrotron Radiation Centre SOLARIS in Kraków, spectroscopic measurements were carried out for polyaniline samples as well as for polyaniline–silver composites at PIRX line. Metallic indium was used as a sample carrier, since it was crucial to obtain information on the carbon–nitrogen bonds, which can confirm the oxidation state of the polymer achieved during synthesis. During the experiment, high-quality near-edge soft X-ray absorption spectra were collected for most of the samples, mainly in the partial fluorescence yield (PFY) mode and also in the total electron yield (TEY) mode for samples with chloride counterions in the temperature of liquid nitrogen (around 80 K).

3 RESULTS AND DISCUSSION

3.1 Thermogravimetric

The thermogravimetric curves obtained for PAni Cl1 and PAni Cl2 differ markedly from one another (Fig. 1). The first significant mass losses for PAni Cl1 were observed already at around 80 °C. The peak at this temperature may suggest the presence of benzene or cyclohexane. At this stage, water loss from the analyzed sample undoubtedly also began. The decrease observed at 200 °C (Fig. 1) indicates polymer chain degradation, which continues until the end of the process, as reflected by the non-uniform shape of the curve [4]. In the case of PAni Cl2, the first slight mass loss occurs around 100 °C and corresponds to water evaporation from the analyzed material. Subsequently, starting at approximately 300 °C (Fig. 1), polymer degradation begins and persists up to 700 °C. The most pronounced mass loss for the first sample, recorded at 80 °C, suggests that a substantial fraction of the substrates remained unreacted during polymerization. Consequently, the small amount of polymer that formed likely exhibited an unstable structure. This explains why polymer chain degradation commenced at a lower temperature than expected.

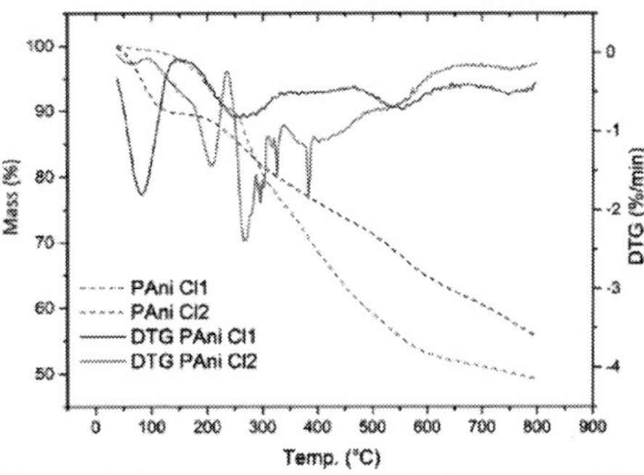

Figure 1: Thermogravimetric analysis curves – PAni Cl1, PAni Cl2

The comparison of curves obtained for PAni SAA1 and PAni SAA2 is presented in Figure 2. For both substances, the course of mass loss with increasing temperature is very similar. In the range of 90–100 °C, the first small band appears, indicating water evaporation. Subsequently, at approximately 250 °C (Fig. 2), polymer chain degradation begins [4]. A significant difference between the curves of the two samples is observed in the range of 300–350 °C (Fig. 5). At this point, PAni SAA2 exhibits a peak corresponding to as much as 45% mass loss, whereas PAni SAA1 does not display such a pronounced decrease. This difference may result from the presence of a greater amount of unreacted SAA in the synthesis of PAni SAA2. The peak may be attributed to the degradation of 4-sulfanilic acid, whose boiling point is 337 °C. Polymer degradation ends in the temperature range of 600–650 °C.

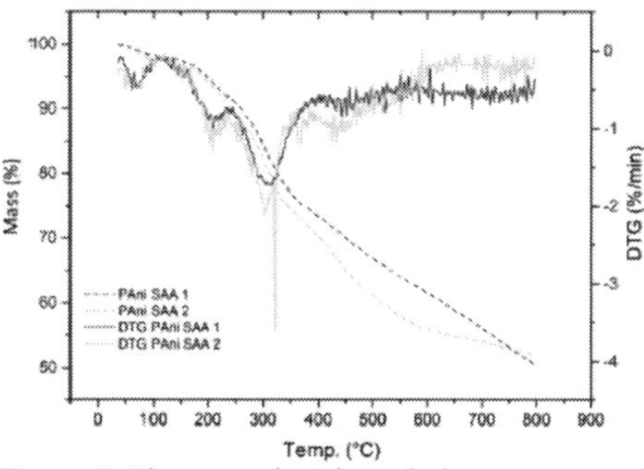

Figure 2: Thermogravimetric analysis curves – PAni SAA1, PAni SAA2

The curves for PAni SBA1 and PAni SBA2 exhibit identical profiles and overlap with each other (Fig. 3). At the beginning, as in other cases, a slight water loss is visible, followed by a peak at 200 °C. This peak can most likely be associated with the degradation of unreacted SBA acid. Subsequently, at approximately 300 °C (Fig. 3), polymer degradation begins and continues until reaching 600 °C [4].

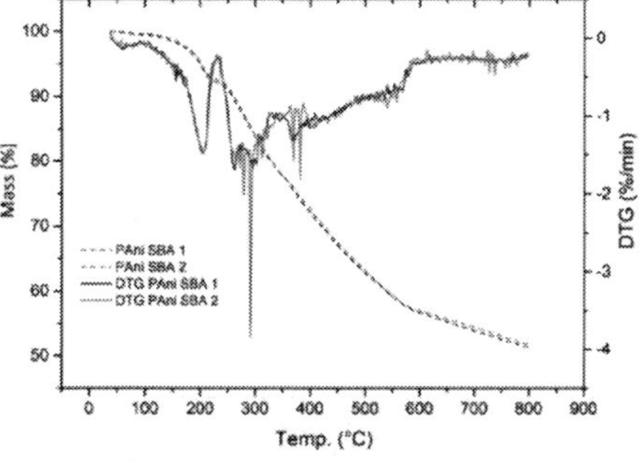

Figure 3: Thermogravimetric analysis curves – PAni SBA1, PAni SBA2

A comparison of all curves on a single plot reveals many similarities among the samples (Fig. 4). Against this background, PAni Cl1 stands out most distinctly, which can be attributed to unsuccessful synthesis. Apart from this exception, the remaining materials demonstrate good thermal stability.

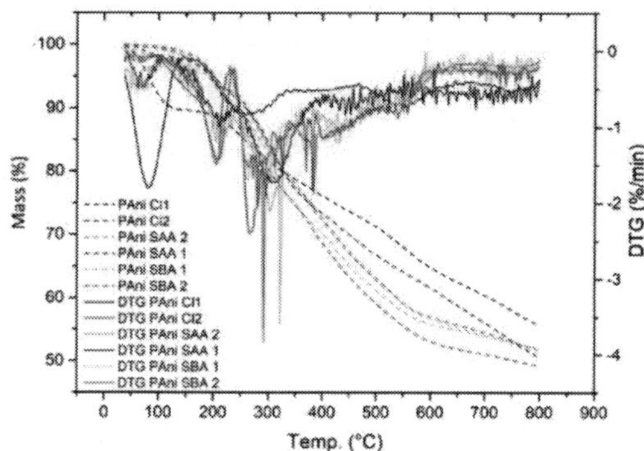

Figure 4: Thermogravimetric analysis curves – comparison of all substances

3.2 FTIR

The spectra obtained from Fourier transform infrared spectroscopy revealed that the individual spectra of the samples did not exhibit significant differences in most cases (Fig. 5). Several characteristic peaks were consistently observed, beginning with a broad band in the region of 3450–3230 cm⁻¹, attributed to N–H stretching vibrations (Jiang & Cui, 2006), indicative of amine groups. In this range, O–H stretching vibrations could also be identified. The peak at 1564 cm⁻¹ corresponds to the stretching vibrations of C=N and C=C bonds within the quinoid ring of polyaniline. Furthermore, bands between 1450–1610 cm⁻¹ (Fig. 5) confirm the presence of C=C stretching vibrations, consistent with the aromatic nature of the substance. The band at 1283 cm⁻¹ may be ascribed to C=N stretching vibrations, characteristic of amines or amine-containing functional groups. Additional C–H stretching vibrations were observed around 830 cm⁻¹ (Fig. 5), corresponding to aliphatic structures and present in all spectra. A distinct band at 1050 cm⁻¹ (Fig. 5), observed only in spectrum SAA1, is assigned to S=O stretching vibrations. Moreover, bands near 690 cm⁻¹, detected for SAA1 and SBA1, are associated with S–O stretching vibrations [5]. These two bands confirm the presence of sulfonic groups attached to the aromatic rings in the SAA1 and SBA1 samples. Minor differences in the 1000–1300 cm⁻¹ region may result from variations in oxidation state or protonation of the polyaniline salts. Additionally, differences in spectral stability could be linked to variations in conjugated system stability.

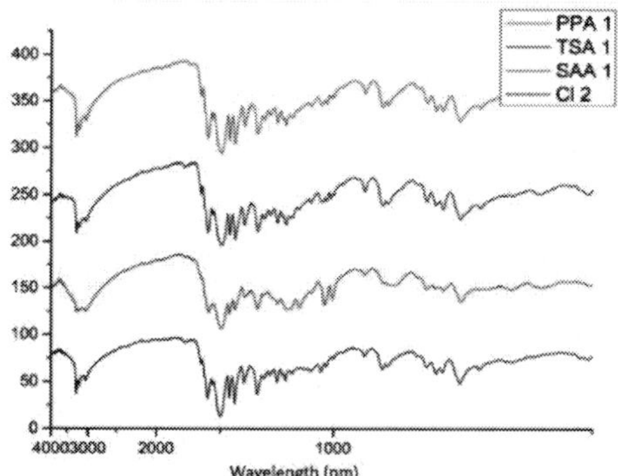

Figure 5: FTIR spectra for PAni PPA1, PAni TSA1,

PAni SAA1, PAni Cl2

3.2 UV-Vis

The comparison of spectra for all materials (Figs. 6-7) shows that they are highly similar, with no significant differences suggesting alternative electronic transitions. A peak around 260 nm (Fig. 6) is consistently observed across spectra, corresponding to $\pi \rightarrow \pi^*$ transitions. This transition reflects electron excitation from lower-energy multiple bonds to higher energy states due to strong absorption at 260 nm, confirming the presence of benzene structures [6]. Another absorption maximum appears around 430 nm (Fig. 6), associated with $n \rightarrow \pi^*$ transitions [4], characteristic of aniline. These maxima suggest that the studied substances possess potential for electrical conductivity. The absence of a distinct band in the 800–1000 nm range, typically indicative of polyaniline, may result from short polymer chain length and the presence of impurities in the samples.

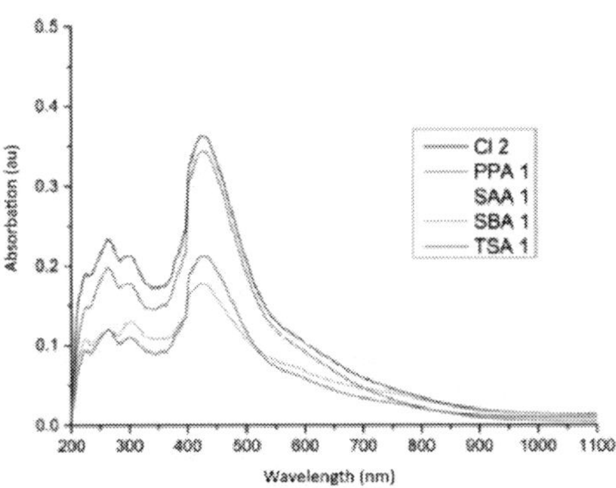

Figure 6: Absorbance as a function of wavelength for PAni PPA1, PAni TSA1, PAni SAA1, PAni Cl2

In the absorption versus energy spectrum, a band with a peak at approximately 2.8 eV is observed (Fig. 7). The pronounced absorption at this energy level corresponds to the transition of benzene rings into their quinoid form [6]. In practice, this indicates the formation of two carbonyl groups within the rings. Another absorption band exhibits a maximum at around 4.7 eV (Fig. 7), which suggests the excitation of benzene rings as a result of protonation of amino groups. The entire band is broad and inhomogeneous; however, as in the case of the previous spectrum, this effect can be attributed to the presence of impurities.

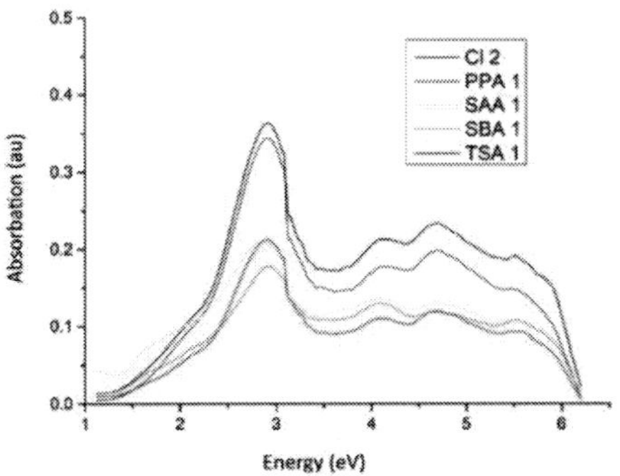

Figure 7: Absorbance as a function of energy for PAni PPA1, PAni TSA1, PAni SAA1, PAni Cl2.

3.4 Conductivity

The conductivity of undoped polyaniline at room temperature is approximately 0.5 µS/cm [7,8]. The analyzed samples exhibited higher conductivities (Table I), confirming the influence of incorporated counterions on enhanced conductivity. The conductivity values of the materials did not differ by orders of magnitude and remained comparable. Despite minor variations, the highest conductivity was observed for PAni Cl2 and PAni SAA1, whereas the lowest was recorded for PAni Cl1 (likely due to unsuccessful synthesis, as confirmed by TG analysis) and PAni SBA2.

3.5 pH measurement

The obtained pH values were generally consistent across samples, except for PAni Cl1 (where polymerization was unsuccessful). The substances exhibited pH values between 5 and 6 (Table I), indicating weakly acidic properties. The reduced pH is attributed to the incorporation of acidic groups into the polymer structure. The lowest pH value was recorded for PAni PPA2, likely due to the stronger acidity of PPA compared to the other acids. Conversely, the highest pH was observed for PAni SBA1.

Table I: Conductivity [µS/cm] and pH values.

Sample	Conductivity	pH
PAni Cl1	8.45	3.90
PAni Cl2	10.95	5.10
PAni SAA1	10.90	5.70
PAni SAA2	10.65	5.68
PAni SBA1	8.75	5.72
PAni SBA2	8.48	5.50
PAni PPA1	10.05	5.27
PAni PPA2	9.20	4.98
PAni TSA1	10.40	5.65

3.6 Synchrotron radiation-based investigation

The results will enable the investigation of the local structure (chemical coordination and electronic state) of the main elements constituting the polymer structure, such as N (K-edge: 409.9 eV), C (K-edge: 284.5 eV), and O (K-edge: 543.1 eV). Measurements of all samples were carried out at 80 K, as the samples proved to be unstable. In the TEY mode, only conductive samples were measured and analyzed. Unexpectedly, most of the samples were non-conductive, which made it impossible to collect TEY spectra for samples with P or S counterions.

Figure 8 presents the spectrum obtained during the analysis of measurements performed at the PIRX beamline. The spectra correspond to repeated measurements of the nitrogen K-edge in the PANI Cl2 sample. Distinct peaks at 399 eV and 402.8 eV are observed, confirming the emeraldine salt structure of polyaniline [9].

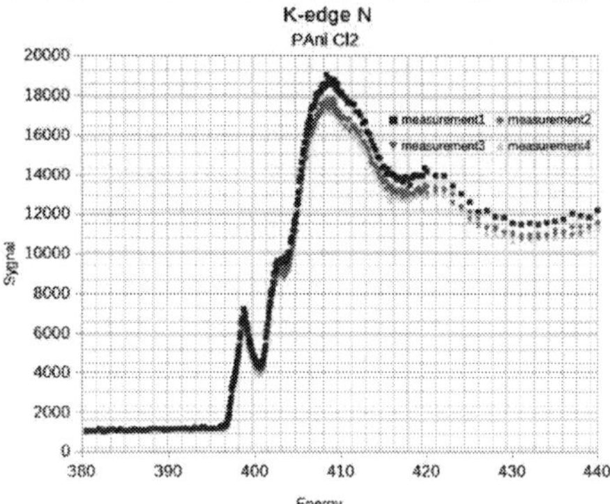

Figure 8: Nitrogen K egde XANES spectra for PAni Cl2

The signal originating from the recovered material, i.e., Ag ions, was very weak. The lines observed in the range of 360–400 eV were inconclusive regarding their possible origin from the silver M45 edges. The most probable explanation for this type of signal in this range is reflection from a chromium mirror.

4 CONCLUSION

The conducted studies demonstrated that the obtained polyaniline samples exhibit distinct properties depending on the acid used for doping. Thermogravimetric analysis confirmed generally good thermal stability of the materials, with PAni Cl1 standing out due to unsuccessful synthesis and the presence of unreacted substrates. FTIR spectroscopy revealed characteristic bands corresponding to N–H, C=N, C=C, and C–H vibrations, while sulfonic acid-doped samples additionally showed signals confirming the presence of sulfonic groups attached to aromatic rings. UV-Vis spectra displayed consistent absorption bands related to $\pi\rightarrow\pi^*$ and $n\rightarrow\pi^*$ transitions, typical of aniline and benzene structures, confirming the potential of the studied substances for electrical conductivity.

Electrical conductivity measurements further demonstrated the significant influence of counterions on material properties, with the highest values recorded for PAni Cl2 and PAni SAA1, and the lowest for PAni Cl1 and PAni SBA2. At the same time, pH measurements (typically within the 5–6 range) confirmed the weakly acidic nature of polyaniline, resulting from the incorporation of acidic groups into the polymer structure.

Synchrotron radiation-based investigations enabled detailed analysis of the local structure of key elements forming the polymer backbone, including N, C, and O. The results confirmed the presence of the emeraldine salt form in the PAni Cl2 sample. However, difficulties were encountered in collecting TEY spectra for samples containing P and S counterions due to their low conductivity. The signal attributed to the recovered silver ions proved to be very weak, while the observed lines in the 360–400 eV range were inconclusive and most likely originated from chromium mirror reflection.

Overall, the obtained results indicate that the synthesized materials exhibit favorable physicochemical properties and can be considered promising candidates for studies on the hydrometallurgical recovery of silver from silicon photovoltaic cells.

5 ACKNOWLEDGMENTS

Research at the National Synchrotron Radiation Centre SOLARIS is supported by the Ministry of Science and Higher Education , Poland, under contract no. 1/SOL/2021/2. This research was founded from the 233004 grant and performed with assist of Marcin Zając from NSRC SOLARIS.
Participation in EUPVESC 2025 is made possible through the PROM project funded by NAVA.

6 REFERENCES

[1] Akram, S., Aziz, H., Imran, A., Javid, A., Nosheen, A., Ashraf, M., Xue, Z., & Raza, M. (2023). Fabrication of silver/polyaniline/aminated graphene oxide coated textiles for electromagnetic interference shielding application within the different bands of frequency. Synthetic Metals, 298, 117440. https://doi.org/10.1016/j.synthmet.2023.117440

[2] Khan, A., Asiri, A. M., Rub, M. A., Azum, N., Khan, A. A. P., Khan, S. B., Rahman, M. M., & Khan, I. (2013). Synthesis, characterization of silver nanoparticle embedded polyaniline tungstophosphate-nanocomposite cation exchanger and its application for heavy metal selective membrane. Composites Part B: Engineering, 45(1), 1486–1492. https://doi.org/10.1016/j.compositesb.2012.09.023

[3] Babaei, Z., Rezaei, B., Pisheh, M. K., & Afshar-Taromi, F. (2020). In situ synthesis of gold/silver nanoparticles and polyaniline as buffer layer in polymer solar cells. Materials Chemistry and Physics, 248. https://doi.org/10.1016/j.matchemphys.2020.122879

[4] Ramalingam, R. J., Al-Lohedan, H., & T., R. (2016). Synthesis, surface and textural characterization of ag doped polyaniline-SiO2(Pan-Ag/RHA) nanocompositesderivedfrom biomass materials. Digest Journal of Nanomaterials and Biostructures, 11, 731–740.

[5] Chu, J., Li, X., Li, Q., Ma, J., Wu, B., Wang, X., Zhang, R., Gong, M., & Xiong, S. (2020). Hydrothermal synthesis of PANI nanowires for high-performance supercapacitor. High Performance Polymers, 32(3), 258–267. https://doi.org/10.1177/0954008319856664

[6] Padmapriya, S., Seshadri, H., Jaidev, K. J., Venkatachalam, S., Kumar, D., & Pal, S. (2017). Storage and evolution of hydrogen in acidic medium by polyaniline. International Journal of Energy Research, 42, 1196–1209. https://doi.org/10.1002/er.3920

[7] Catedral, M. D., Tapia, A. K. G., Sarmago, R. V, Tamayo, J. P., & Del Rosario, E. J. (2004). Effect of Dopant Ions on the Electrical Conductivity and Microstructure of Polyaniline (Emeraldine Salt) (T. 16, Numer 2).

[8] Chaudhari, H. K., & Kelkar, D. S. (1997). Investigation of Structure and Electrical Conductivity in Doped Polyaniline. W Polymer International (T. 42).

[9] Izumi, C. M. S., Constantino, V. R. L., Ferreira, A. M. C., & Temperini, M. L. A. (2006). Spectroscopic characterization of polyaniline doped with transition metal salts. Synthetic Metals, 156(9–10), 654–663. "https://doi.org/10.1016/j.synthmet.2005.12.023"

COMPARATIVE LCA ANALYSIS OF DELAMINATION METHODS FOR PHOTOVOLTAIC MODULES MADE OF CDTE

Anna Kuczyńska-Łażewska
Faculty of Chemistry, Gdansk University of Technology
Narutowicza 11/12, Gdansk PL-80-233, Poland

ABSTRACT: A key step in the recycling of photovoltaic modules is the delamination process, which can be carried out by thermal, chemical or mechanical methods. An analysis of the literature reveals a paucity of life-cycle analyses taking into account the different recycling processes for thin-film modules (CdTe), the completion of which is necessary to fully understand the issue.
The project included an assessment of the environmental impact of various delamination processes (thermal and chemical methods) of modules made with CdTe thin-film technology. In order to collect the data needed for the LCA analysis, experiments were carried out to determine the energy consumption, emissions and potentially harmful waste generated during the delamination process. The LCA analysis conducted on the collected primary data was compared with the analysis for secondary data based on scientific literature.
The data obtained during the project will provide a broader view of the recycling process and enable the identification of environmentally sensitive areas.
Keywords: photovoltaic module; recycling; CdTe; LCA

1 INTRODUCTION

Thin film photovoltaic cells encompass cells composed of:
• Amorphous silicon with an efficiency of 4-8% - a-Si,
• Tandem, a blend of amorphous and microcrystalline silicon with a yield of 9.8% - a-Si and μc-Si,
• Cadmium telluride with an efficiency of 11% - CdTe,
• Copper indium gallium disulfide/diselenide with an efficiency of 12% - CI(G)S [1].

Technologies related to renewable energy sources that are based on rare metals may have a negative environmental impact, despite the apparent benefits due to the rising demand for these raw materials. Hence, it's crucial to analyze environmental aspects of these processes. We need to monitor production, recycling processes and available new technologies that are developed to optimize the consumption of valuable raw materials. The estimated energy recovery time for CdTe modules is approximately 1 year [2]. However, this duration depends on the quantity of available raw materials and there is an environmental cost connected to that.

As the production technology of photovoltaic modules has advanced, so have the methods for material recovery from these processes. Consequently, with the introduction of new cells in the market, recycling techniques have been devised to reclaim the materials used in the manufacturing process and reintegrate them into the production cycle. When compared with traditional methods like incineration or fine grinding, the recycling process of CdTe-based modules is decidedly less environmentally intrusive, with the exception of the space required for the installation [3].

After technological review of available technologies, the environmental impact of known solutions was analyzed. Standard First Solar (FS) method significantly mitigates the adverse effects of used thin-film CdTe modules, for instance, by lowering the overall energy demand from 81 MJ/m² to 12 MJ/m² [3]. Moreover, it can decrease the detrimental environmental impact of this kind of module by approximately 10% in areas such as general energy demand, acidification, eutrophication, global warming, and photochemical ozone depletion [3].

The one of the newest and most complex life cycle assessment (LCA) was performed by Ravikumar et al. on 2020 [4] taking into consideration main First Solar technology and all other options available at that point in time (Figure 1).

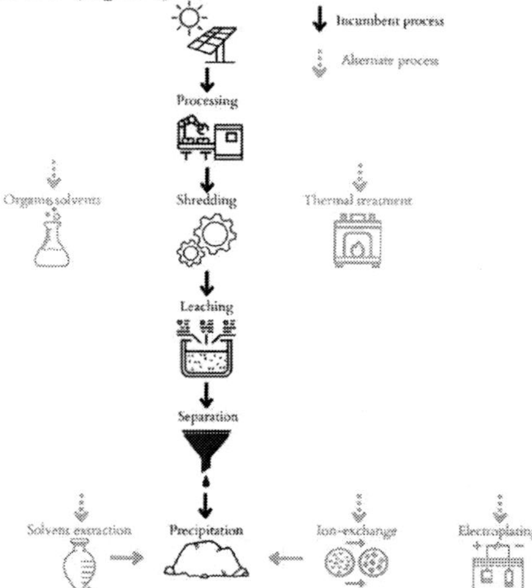

Figure 1: Scheme of alternative technologies in CdTe modules recycling (based on [4])

Four alternative delamination techniques: thermal delamination, organic solvent dissolution, bath sonification and probe sonification with two alternative methods of cadmium extraction: Cd ion-exchange resin and solvent extraction as well as tellurium precipitation. In total eight different combinations were analyzed. [4]

From the presented results they conclude that the lowest impacts are connected with First Solar technology. The thermal delamination+ leaching+ precipitation of unrefined semiconductor material (USM) process may be the competition, especially taking into account that the only difference is with the delamination process. Changing mechanical delamination to the thermal process seems to be a good alternative if we look from the environmental point of view. It does not bring as high energy consumption as it may seem but gives the benefit of better recovered glass

10.4229/EUPVSEC2025/5DV.2.7
020499-001

quality. Another alternative is mechanical delamination+ leaching+ icon exchange+ precipitation which gives an alternative to the recovery process by use of ion exchange columns. This technology is on the laboratory scale stage and may be a good alternative to USM precipitation and the opportunity of getting recovered materials of higher purity.

2 METHODOLOGY

The data for analysis came from secondary sources, publications based on data provided by companies involved in the recycling of photovoltaic modules and other electronic devices, and data collected as a result of laboratory tests. The list of secondary sources for the data used in the analysis can be found in Table I.

The LCA analysis was performed using the ReCiPe, Endpoint Egalitarian method in the SimaPro 7.1 program, using databases from the program itself.

2.1 Boundary conditions
The analysis was based on the following assumptions:
• The functional unit of analysis is 1 m² of a module (series 4 FirstSolar, US) weighing 16.667 kg.
• The recycling plant is located in the USA and serves most of the country in a centralized recycling system.

2.2 LCI for CdTe module recycling
Despite the many recycling methods described above, there are not many publications containing accurate data on the conditions and quantities of substances used. A review of existing LCA analyses for photovoltaic module recycling has identified three methods for separating the semiconductor from the glass and the same number of methods for recovering the semiconductor for which LCI data are available. All six are described in Table I.

Table I: CdTe panel recycling methods analyzed in part one

Name	Acronym	Source for LCI
Thermal delamination, leaching, and precipitation	TL	[2], [4]–[6]
Thermal delamination, leaching, organic solvent	TR	[2], [4]–[6]
Theraml delamination, leaching, ion exchange column and precipitation	TK	[2], [4]–[6]
Mechanical grinding, leaching, and precipitation	ML	[2], [4]–[16]
Solvent extraction, leaching, and precipitation	RL	[4], [6], [8], [10]
Thermal delamination, leaching, and precipitation	TL	[4], [6], [8], [10], [13]

3 RESULTS AND DISCUSSION

3.1 Literature review
Part one of the research was based on the use of secondary data from literature sources. There was the preferable scenario, pessimistic scenario, and a normalized one took into account while collecting data. At first three different approaches to the recovery process were analyzed (Table I – TL, TR, TK) and for the second part three different approaches to delamination were analyzed (Table I – ML, RL, TL). Example of results for single process is shown at Figure 2.

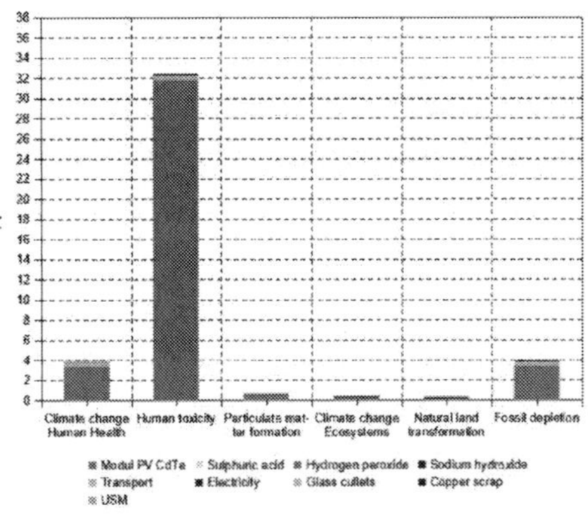

Figure 2. Selected results of LCA for TL recycling method after normalization and weighing.

Although the analysis (Fig. 2) indicates that the photovoltaic module is the input with the largest share in the final result of each analysis, it will not be discussed further, due to its identical presence in each of the methods. This means that it has no ultimate impact on the differences between the results for the subsequent recycling methods. The second input with the largest share in the analysis result varies depending on the method analyzed and the scenario considered.
For the ML method in the scenario containing normalized values, the input with the largest total contribution was transport, while for the other two scenarios, both optimistic and pessimistic, this input was electricity. The same situation was true for the TL method. In the analysis of the RL method, solvent (o-dichlorobenzene) was the second input with the highest influence in the total impact. For the scenario chosen as the most likely, its presence significantly increased the results for this method. The same is true for optimistic scenarios. For the pessimistic scenario, the input with the largest total share was electricity, because of the assumption the additional heating will be needed.
This means that the areas where improvement should be made according to the CdTe recycling process are efficiency of the energy use and the solvent substitution to the environmentally safe option. Also, the important seams are the PV waste collecting system which can be a big factor in the environmental impact of the recycling technology. In this work we will focus only on on-site technology process optimization.
The most sensitive and noteworthy risk points are human health and fossil fuel consumption and in these categories the uncertainty analysis was performed using Monte Carlo method with 1000 iterations.
Comparisons of the TL, TR, and TK recycling methods for all three scenarios were presented in Figure 3. The TR method had the biggest environmental impact, significantly higher than TK and TL method. The TL method achieved the lowest results and is the best option in terms of environmental impact, but it is not a big significant benefit in comparison to TK method.

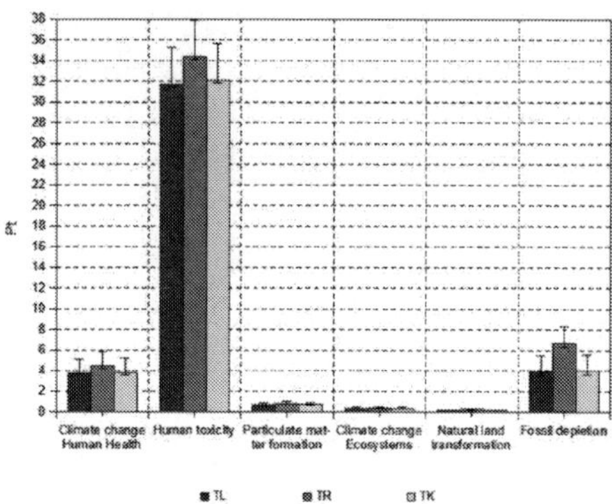

Figure 3. Selected results of LCA for different recycling methods (TL, TR, TK) after normalization and weighing.

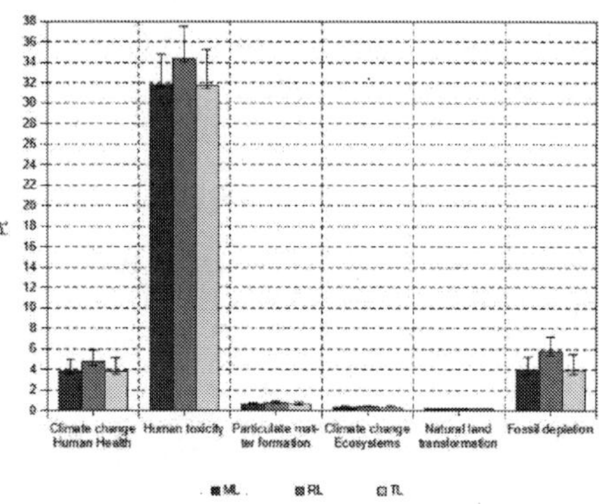

Figure 4. Selected results of LCA for different delamination methods (ML, RL, TL) after normalization and weighing.

The comparison results for the normalized values of the ML, RL, and TL methods indicate that in all six impact categories, the TL method consistently scores the lowest number of points (40.7 pt total) and is therefore the most environmentally friendly. The ML method came in second place. The differences in the results for both methods are small (Fig. 4.). In the Human Toxicity category, the difference between the two methods was only 0.3%. Similarly small differences between the results can be seen in the comparison of the most optimistic scenarios. In this comparison, but for pessimistic scenario the ML process must be identified as the most environmentally friendly process.

3.2 Experimental data
Primary data for the thermal delamination were collected during thermal decomposition of 5x5 cm CdTe module fragment in the tube furnace with air flow in different temperatures (400, 500, 600 °C). The emissions were collected to the Tedlar bags and analyzed using gas chromatography with thermal conductivity and flame ionization detector (GC-TCD+FID). The main groups of emissions were selected: hydrocarbons, aldehydes and ketones, acidic acid and polycyclic aromatic hydrocarbons (PAHs). The ratios in general gas mixture were determined and taken as a input to the LCA. And

the energy consumption during each 3h process was measured.

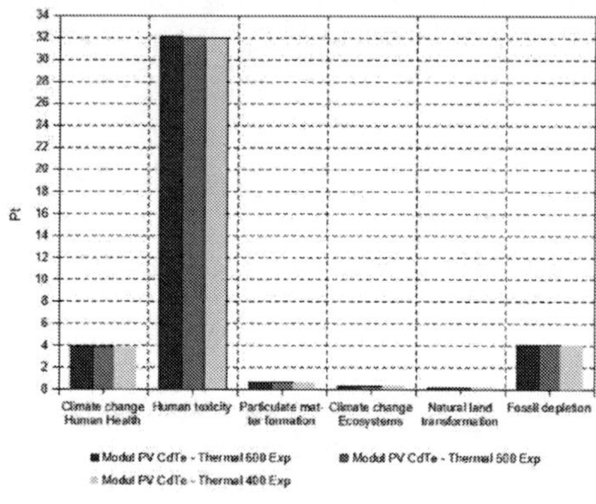

Figure 5. Selected results of LCA for thermal delamination method in different temperatures (400, 500, 600 °C) after normalization and weighing.

From the results (Fig. 5) we can conclude that with this equipment and size there is no significant difference with fossil fuel depletion connected to energy consumption. However, the temperature has a big impact on the gas emissions and the ratio between each faction and in connection with Human Toxicity.
Primary data for chemical delamination were collected during solvent bath of the 5x5 cm CdTe module fragment in different temperatures (25, 40, 60 °C). The electric power consumption, the evaporation rate and amount of solvent used were noted.

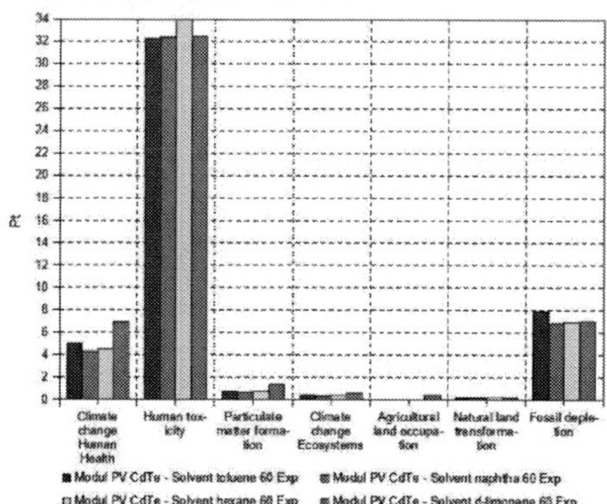

Figure 6. Selected results of LCA for chemical delamination method with different solvents (toluene, hexane, naphtha, d-limonene) at 60 °C after normalization and weighing.

From the obtained results (Fig. 6) the biggest difference is connected to the solvent type and not the temperature. Only for the hexane the evaporation rate was significant and greatly impacted the solvent consumption and the emissions, therefore also impacted the Human Toxicity. From the analysis we can conclude that naphtha and d-limonene have the lowest environmental impact were d-limonene has bigger share in the Climate Change than naphtha what may seem surprising. Even d-limonene seemed like an environmentally friendly option due to the production from citrus peels, the LCA results show that may not be the best option.

4 CONCLUSIONS

Based on a review of the literature the recycling process based on leaching and precipitation should be considered the most environmentally friendly. In addition to that it was found that the thermal delamination method has the least impact on the environment.

Therefore, it was recommended to collect more accurate data sets for the TL method for further comparative analyses. These data should include, in particular, emissions related to the thermal delamination process, because although the use of appropriate filters and scrubbers is assumed, it would be good to take into account their absence in a pessimistic scenario. In addition, the data on electricity consumption provided in the inputs for the TL method came from a process conducted in the laboratory conditions. For a larger scale of the process, this input may vary significantly, and research on this topic should be conducted.

Based on the recommendation during experimental part of data collecting focused was made on the impact of temperature in thermal delamination. Mainly on the gaseous emissions and energy consumption. There was not heat recovery conducted during the experiment, but it may be possible according to high caloric value of the EVA.

During the chemical delamination experiment the focus was on the solvent as a key factor. Most important was the type of the solvent, because it determined the source of the solvent and also the number of emissions to the atmosphere. Depending on the boiling point and how volatile the solvent was, the amount used was different what impacted the LCA.

From the results the conclusion may be made that from an environmental perspective, energy consumption is not a major concern. The crucial aspect is the temperature of the process. In the case of chemical delamination, it increases emissions and the amount of solvent used. During thermal delamination temperature plays a significant role because of the influence on the composition of waste gases.

5 ACKNOWLEDGMENTS

This publication is the result of research project No. 2023/07/X/ST4/00996 founded by The Polish National Science Centre (NCN). Author also would like to acknowledge Alicja Krawiecka (Eng. student) and Bartłomiej Malinowski (M.Sc. student) for participating in the research.

6 REFERENCES

[1] A. Paiano, "Photovoltaic waste assessment in Italy," *Renew. Sustain. Energy Rev.*, vol. 41, pp. 99–112, 2015, doi: 10.1016/j.rser.2014.07.208.

[2] W. Berger, F.-G. Simon, K. Weimann, and E. A. Alsema, "A novel approach for the recycling of thin film photovoltaic modules," *Resour. Conserv. Recycl.*, vol. 54, no. 10, pp. 711–718, 2010, doi: 10.1016/j.resconrec.2009.12.001.

[3] J. Tao and S. Yu, "Review on feasible recycling pathways and technologies of solar photovoltaic modules," *Sol. Energy Mater. Sol. Cells*, vol. 141, pp. 108–124, 2015, doi: 10.1016/j.solmat.2015.05.005.

[4] D. Ravikumar *et al.*, "Environmentally improved CdTe photovoltaic recycling through novel technologies and facility location strategies," *Prog. Photovoltaics Res. Appl.*, vol. 28, no. 9, pp. 887–898, 2020, doi: 10.1002/pip.3279.

[5] P. Sinha, M. Cossette, and J.-F. Ménard, "END-OF-LIFE CDTE PV RECYCLING WITH SEMICONDUCTOR REFINING," in *27th European Photovoltaic Solar Energy Conference and Exhibition*, 2012, pp. 4653–4656, doi: 10.4229/27thEUPVSEC2012-6CV.4.9.

[6] D. T. Ravikumar, P. Sinha, and M. Tao, "An Anticipatory-Lifecycle Approach Towards Increasing the Environmental Gains from Photovoltaic Systems Through Improved Manufacturing and Recycling," no. December, 2016.

[7] M. Held and R. Ilg, "Update of environmental indicators and energy payback time of CdTe PV systems in Europe," *Prog. Photovoltaics Res. Appl.*, vol. 19, no. 5, pp. 614–626, Aug. 2011, doi: 10.1002/PIP.1068.

[8] M. Raugei, M. Isasa, and P. F. Palmer, "Potential Cd emissions from end-of-life CdTe PV," *Int. J. Life Cycle Assess.*, vol. 17, no. 2, pp. 192–198, Feb. 2012, doi: 10.1007/S11367-011-0348-9/FIGURES/2.

[9] V. M. Fthenakis and H. C. Kim, "CdTe photovoltaics: Life cycle environmental profile and comparisons," *Thin Solid Films*, vol. 515, no. 15, pp. 5961–5963, May 2007, doi: 10.1016/J.TSF.2006.12.138.

[10] V. M. Fthenakis, P. Duby, W. Wang, C. Graves, and A. Belova, "Recycling of CdTe Photovoltaic Modules: Recovery of Cadmium and Tellurium," *21st Eur. Photovolt. Sol. energy Conf.*, pp. 2539–2541, 2006

[11] M. Held, "Life cycle assessment of CdTe module recycling," in *24th European Photovoltaic Solar Energy Conference*, 2009, pp. 2370–2375.

[12] P. Sinha, "Life cycle materials and water management for CdTe photovoltaics," *Sol. Energy Mater. Sol. Cells*, vol. 119, pp. 271–275, 2013, doi: 10.1016/j.solmat.2013.08.022.

[13] T. Maani, I. Celik, M. J. Heben, R. J. Ellingson, and D. Apul, "Environmental impacts of recycling crystalline silicon (c-SI) and cadmium telluride (CDTE) solar panels," *Sci. Total Environ.*, vol. 735, p. 138827, 2020, doi: 10.1016/j.scitotenv.2020.138827.

[14] G. Giacchetta, M. Leporini, and B. Marchetti, "Evaluation of the environmental benefits of new high value process for the management of the end of life of thin film photovoltaic modules," *J. Clean. Prod.*, vol. 51, pp. 214–224, 2013, doi: 10.1016/j.jclepro.2013.01.022.

[15] V. Fthenakis *et al.*, "Life Cycle Inventories and Life Cycle Assessments of Photovoltaic Systems," 2011. Accessed: Sep. 22, 2025.

[16] D. Ravikumar, P. Sinha, T. P. Seager, and M. P. Fraser, "An anticipatory approach to quantify energetics of recycling CdTe photovoltaic systems," *Prog. Photovoltaics Res. Appl.*, vol. 24, no. 5, pp. 735–746, May 2016, doi: 10.1002/PIP.2711.

Design for Repair of PV modules: A meaningful or crazy idea?

PCCL
Polymer Competence Center Leoben

Gernot Oreski[1], Sonja Feldbacher[1], Anika Gassner[2], Gabriele Eder[2], Ioannis Tsanakas[3], Timea Bejat[3]

[1] Polymer Competetence Center Leoben, Austria
[2] OFI Austrian Research Institute for Chemistry and Technology, Austria
[3] Univ. Grenoble Alpes, CEA, Liten, Campus Ines, 73375 Le Bourget du Lac, France

PV module design

- Standard PV module design: The current PV module design and packaging concept, with interconnected solar cells in between two transparent polymer films, a frontglass and a backsheet or backglass was developed over 40 years ago
- Design for Repair: Potential to extend the functional lifespan of modules, reduce waste, and enhance sustainability in the solar energy sector
- Current state: No comprehensive strategies addressing "Design for Repair" or the "Right for Repair" have been published for PV modules

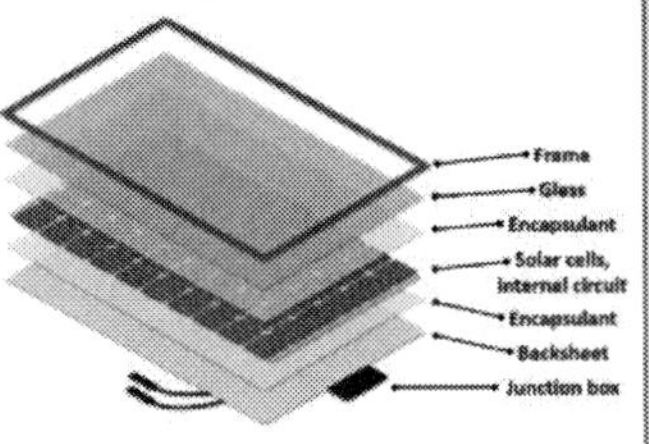

Figure 1: Most common configurations of PV modules for crystalline silicon cells https://doi.org/10.1016/j.rser.2022.112160

Durability-Repairability Paradox

General rule: the more permanently you attach materials the stronger and more durable it is, but the more difficult it is to repair and replace.

Objectives and Methodology

Main objective: To explore opportunities & challenges of Design for Repair (DfR) in PV modules through literature and market survey

Results

A few research groups and start-ups are working on new PV designs and module materials

Many of these innovations also enable easier repair

Focus is on improving recyclability of modules and components

Reversible adhesives for frames and junction boxes

Approach:

- **Modification** of existing silicone adhesive system by addition of functional fillers to the formulation to thermally trigger debonding of the adhesive connection after service life
- **Functional fillers** expand upon reaching a temperature threshold and facilitate debonding by overcoming the maximum strength of the adhesive joint

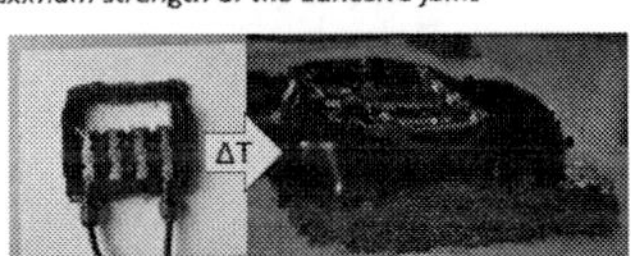

Figure 2: Adhesive connection containing thermally expanding fillers before (left) and after (right) thermally triggering the expansion; Wanghofer et al., 2023; https://doi.org/10.1016/j.ijadhadh.2023.103454

Benefit

- Enables removal of damaged frames or junction boxes **without harming the PV module**

Challenges

- **Prevent expansion** under normal operating conditions
- **Ensure** reliable functional **triggering** throughout the entire lifetime

Self healing polymer layers (for electrically conductive adhesives, encapsulants)

Approach:

- Introduction of **thermally responsive self healing polymers** based on reversible polymer networks that exploit daily temperature changes to repair micro-defects

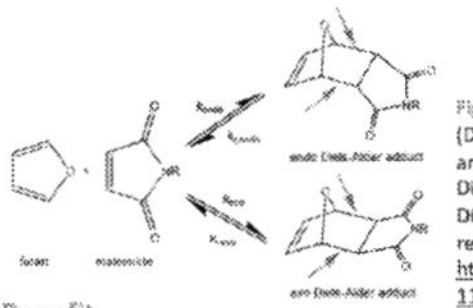

Figure 3: Reversible Diels–Alder (DA) reactions between maleimide and furan derivatives, forming Diels–Alder adducts. Reversible Diels–Alder bonds are indicated by red arrows. **Ehrhardt et al., 2020** http://dx.doi.org/10.3390/polym12112543

Benefit

- **Extending reliability** could be achieved if self-healing repairs microcracks/ delamination while maintaining adhesion and conductivity under thermal and mechanical stress

Challenges

- **Long-term stability:** Organic DA networks may degrade under 25+ years of outdoor exposure
- **Material compatibility:** Potential issues with other PV module materials or additives (e.g., fillers, crosslinkers, conductive particles)
- **Processing & performance trade-offs:** Dynamic networks may reduce mechanical strength and increase creep

Modular designs

Approach:

- **Encapsulant free module design:** Glass–glass construction sealed using a double edge-seal (e.g. N.I.C.E. Module Technology, Biosphere Solar)
- New concepts using liquid encapsulation (Biosphere Solar)

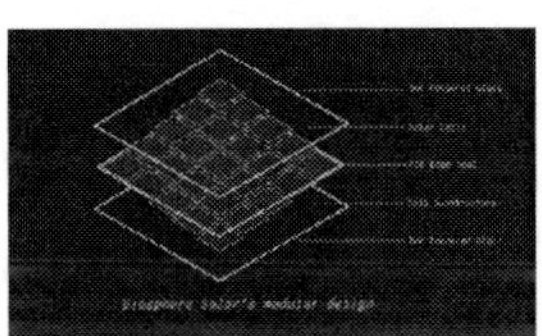

Figure 4: PV module concept without encapsulation. ©Biosphere Solar https://www.biosphere.solar

Benefit

- **Modular design** allowing for the replacement of individual components such as solar cells without damaging the entire unit
- **Absence** of traditional encapsulants may eliminate common degradation issues such as yellowing and delamination

Challenges

- **Performance:** Reflective losses due to lack of optical coupling between glass and cell
- **Long-term stability:** Butyl based edge seals provide excellent barrier to water vapor but not oxygen

CONCLUSIONS AND OUTLOOK

- No comprehensive strategies addressing "Design for Repair" or the "Right for Repair" have been published for PV modules
- Emerging Design for Repair Concepts: Current research explores reversible adhesives, self-healing materials, and encapsulant-free designs to enable easier repair and cell replacement in PV modules
- Low TRL Challenges: Most proposed approaches remain at low technology readiness levels and lack validation for long-term durability and reliability
- Future Outlook: Demonstrating robustness and performance is critical for advancing repair-friendly PV designs toward market adoption

- This work was done within the Austrian research project ReNewPV and as part of the IEA-PVPS Task 13 Subtask 1.2 "Performance and Reliability of Second Life PV"
- The final report of this activity will be published until the end of 2025 and can be downloaded for free from this website: https://iea-pvps.org/research-tasks/reliability-and-performance-of-pv-systems/

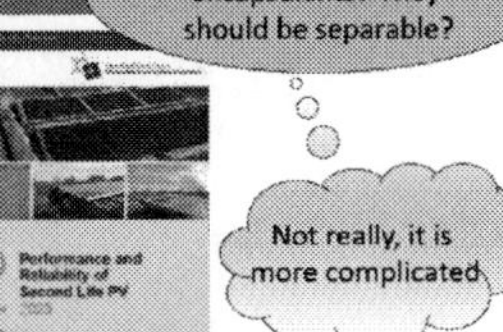

Polymer Competence Center Leoben GmbH (PCCL), Sauraugasse 1, 8700 Leoben, Austria
Corresponding Author: Gernot.oreski@pccl.at
ORCID ID

cea ofi 020500 IEA PVPS ReNewPV

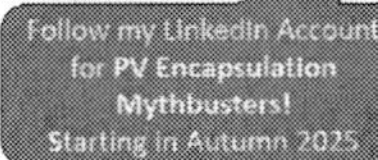

ADVANCING SOLAR ENERGY SUSTAINABILITY: TACKLING PHOTOVOLTAIC CELL UPCYCLING THROUGH METAL RECOVERY

Vázquez Adán, A.[1], López Cuéllar, J.M.[1], Ríos Moral, L.[1], Caballero L.J.[2], Dasilva-Villanueva N.[2], Fuertes Marrón D.[2], del Cañizo, C.[2], Díez Alcántara, E.[1], Rodríguez Rodríguez A.[1]
[1]Departamento de Ingeniería Química y de Materiales, Fac. Ciencias Químicas, Universidad Complutense de Madrid, Avenida Complutense (28040), Madrid, Spain.
[2]Instituto de Energía Solar, ETSI Telecomunicación, Universidad Politécnica de Madrid, Avenida Complutense 40 (28040), Madrid, Spain.

ABSTRACT: The rapid growth of photovoltaic (PV) installations around the world has led to a significant accumulation of PV end-of-life (EoL) cells. This paper aims to study the recycling process for these cells to recover valuable metals like silver and aluminium, as well as the silicon wafer while maintaining its quality to be reused. Two alternative routes were considered: a basic etching, with KOH/ethanol/water mixtures, and nitric acid leaching followed by electrolysis. The etching experiments enabled the physical separation of the contacts; however, rigorous control of the variables is important to minimize silicon loss. Silver and aluminium etched contacts could be separated thereof in a sieving process due to their difference in average size. Leaching experiments were performed with various nitric acid concentrations, with 3M as reference value. In this case, the silver contacts were extracted and transferred to the solution and subsequently recovered as native silver by means of electrodeposition. Usually, after delamination and encapsulant removal, the cells of an EoL PV-module are completely fragmented. Therefore, depending on the size of the fragments, one strategy may be more effective than another.
Keywords: Recycling, Solar Cells, Silicon, Metal Recovery

1 INTRODUCTION

Solar photovoltaic (PV) energy has a crucial role in the global effort to achieve decarbonization, becoming a priority for governments, businesses and society in general, with many entities aiming to be carbon neutral by 2050, with the aim of limiting global temperature rise to 1.5 °C [1]. The integration of solar energy, particularly through optimized PV systems, offers a viable solution to reduce CO_2 emissions, replacing traditional energy sources [2]. In this sense, according to the International Energy Agency [3], the cumulative global PV capacity reached 2.2 TW in 2024 (1.9 TW according to IRENA [4]), and the evolution of annual PV installations achieved a maximum growth of 554 GW, in 2024 (566 GW according to ITRPV, 2024 results [5]). ITRPV predictions [5] indicate that installed capacity is expected to increase to 63.4 TW in 2050 in a zero-greenhouse gas emission scenario.

However, due to the estimated lifetime of a PV module being between 25 to 30 years, the exponential growth of installations is generating a progressive accumulation of waste. This mainly affects devices, installed from the 1990s to the 2000s, crystalline silicon wafer based.

Even though it is true that solar PV can produce net zero-emission electricity for 25-30 years, the total environmental impact during the entire life cycle, including the manufacturing and waste management phases, must be considered. The former contributes to the total carbon footprint of the module, as it consumes water and raw materials, and the purification of silicon is energy intensive (according to the literature [6] approximately 40% of the overall costs associated with module manufacturing can be attributed to wafer production). Additionally, a fraction of off-specs solar cells is rejected during the manufacturing process without becoming part of a module, adding up to the waste.

Considering the number of discarded cells and the current accumulated capacity of photovoltaic waste, the purpose of this research is to study possible paths for the recycling process of these cells with the aim of recovering the metals (mainly silver and aluminium), as well as the silicon wafer, while maintaining its quality to be reused. Two possible ways have been explored: a basic etching

and an acid leaching followed by electrolysis, minimizing the environmental impact and contributing to effective recycling strategies. Usually, after delamination and encapsulant removal, the cells of an EoL panel are totally fragmented into small pieces. So, depending on the size of the fragments one strategy will be more adequate than the other.

Basic etching and acid leaching plus electrodeposition emerge as a critical innovation within this framework, offering several advantages. In the first case, it is possible to recover high purity metal contacts and to reuse the basic solution for several cycles. In the second case, by applying an electric current, silver ions in solution are reduced to metallic silver at the cathode. This process not only ensures a high-efficiency recovery, but also eliminates the need for additional purification steps, making it highly scalable for industrial applications. In addition, this study has identified optimal operating conditions for electrodeposition, including current density and electrode material, to maximize recovery rates and minimize energy consumption. On the other hand, in literature, other alternatives, such as selective adsorption, have also employed to selectively recover metals from CIGS cells leachates [7]. Figure 1 displays the complete recycling process of EoL solar modules, in which both processes would follow, just after the previous removal of backsheet and encapsulants.

This research presents a novel integration of chemical and electrochemical techniques that overcome the limitations of traditional metal recovery methods. The proposed methodologies minimize the generation of secondary waste and the consumption of chemical reagents and enables the extraction of silver with high purity.

2 EXPERIMENTAL PROCEDURES

Several chemical routes were explored, with different types of solar cells. In this paper, basic etching and acid leaching experiments were done on Al-BSF cells with SiN_x Antireflection Coating (ARC) manufactured in the nineties, and on more recent PERC solar cells. Some results are highlighted in this section; more details can be found in [8].

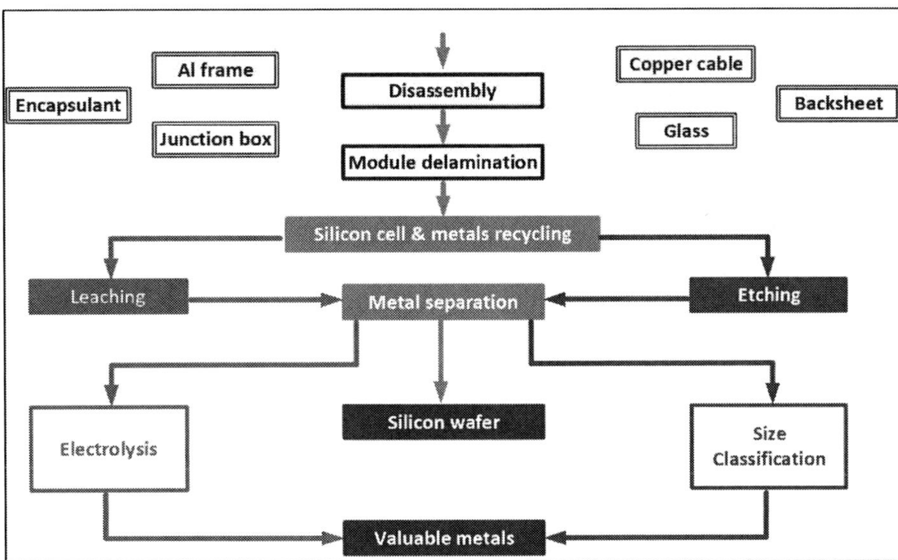

Figure 1. Flowchart of an overall EoL solar panels recycling process

2.1 Basic etching

The alkaline route is based on the physical separation of the metal contacts by etching the silicon layer immediately below, using aqueous KOH solutions, with ethanol added as a surfactant, facilitating the release of hydrogen bubbles generated in the process. Different compositions and different operational conditions (varying temperature, with or without stirring), were tested, while keeping the solution-to-solid ratio constant. Several analytical techniques were used to characterise the solid and liquid fractions resulting from the process: the solid fraction was examined by scanning electron microscopy (SEM) and X-ray fluorescence (XRF), while the liquid fraction was analysed using inductively coupled plasma (ICP) spectroscopy. This combination of techniques allowed to assess the purity of the metal contacts and the silicon wafer, as well as to quantify the transfer of solid material to the liquid phase during the etching process.

At the end of etching process, the silicon wafers were washed with distilled water and dried. Afterwards, the organics were cleaned with an RCA-1 treatment (5:1:1 v/v mixture of 27% ammonia (NH_3), 30% hydrogen peroxide (H_2O_2) and deionised water), and the ARC was removed with 2% HF.

2.2 Acid leaching + electrodeposition

Acid leaching was carried out by digestion of solar cell fragments with nitric acid solutions, being 3 M the acid concentration of reference.

The recovery of metals from the acid leaching processes was carried out by precipitation to recover silver in the form of silver chloride and by electrodeposition to recover silver in native form.

3 RESULTS AND DISCUSSION

3.1. Basic etching

As indicated, the etching experiments were developed with KOH/ethanol/water mixtures in all cases.

It is important to point out that as the concentration of potassium hydroxide increases, the etching time decreases and the loss of silicon from the wafer increases. This indicates that a rigorous control of the variables (concentration, time, temperature) is necessary. In the absence of ethanol, the process gives rise to foams that make the retrieval of the metallic contacts difficult. On the other hand, the incorporation of mechanical agitation has been shown to enhance the process, leading to a substantial reduction in etching time and reducing the loss of silicon. In this study, the potential reutilization of the etching solution for several etching cycles was examined. It was observed that agitation helped the reuse of the basic solution one or two additional cycles until the formation of very fine silica powder, which inhibits the etching process. The use of an etching solution of 35% KOH, and 5% ethanol at 65°C, with a solid/liquid ratio of 15 g/L, has been found effective to completely demetallize an Al-BSF cell fragment in less than 40 min. Additionally, the etching solution could be reused up to three etching cycles.

Concerning PERC cells, the best results were attained through the utilization of a basic solution composed of 25% KOH and 5% ethanol. These conditions facilitated the complete cell demetallization at a temperature of 65°C in less than 25 minutes. Figure 2 shows an example of demetallized Al-BSF (a) and PERC (b) cell.

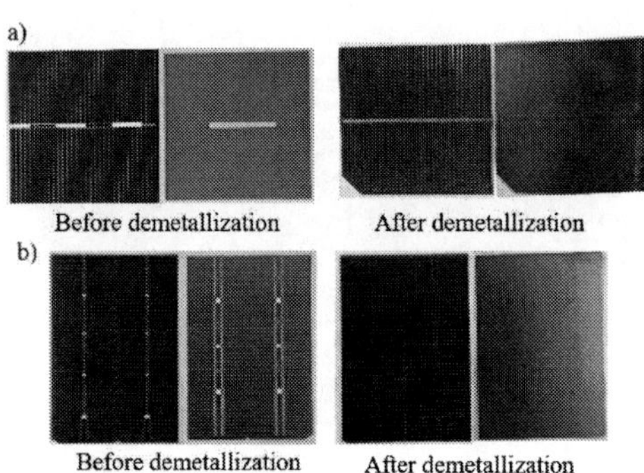

Figure 2. a) BSF cell before and after demetallization, b) PERC cell before and after demetallization.

Following the etching tests, the recuperation of the metal species in solid phase was conducted physically by filtration. The samples were then dried and sieved to separate aluminium from silver.

For this purpose, a granulometric analysis of the resulting metals was carried out to ensure an effective sieving process. In the case of Al-BSF cells it was possible to effectively separate silver and aluminium particles due to their different size and morphology, which was not the case of PERC cells.

After the etching process, a thorough cleaning of the contactless wafers was carried out in order to elucidate if these wafer fragments would be suitable for the fabrication of new devices. This is usually carried out by analysing the minority charge carrier lifetime of the wafers. As a quick reference, if this value exceeds 100 µs at an injection level of 10^{15} cm^{-3}, the silicon substrate could result in an efficient solar cell ($\eta > 20\%$) [6].

3.2. Acid leaching + electrodeposition.

When the size of the delaminated cell fragments is not large enough to efficiently separate the contacts after the etching step, the recovery of silver through acid leaching followed by electrodeposition has proved to be an efficient method yielding high purity silver. Regarding acid leaching efficiency, the use of nitric acid as a leaching agent has been demonstrated to facilitate the effective dissolution of silver. This reagent demonstrated high efficiency in isolating silver with a minimal impact on the structural integrity of the silicon wafer. In addition, analysis of the solid residue (demetallized solar cell fragment) revealed a complete metal elimination.

Electrodeposition was selected as a convenient recovery method, eliminating the need for subsequent silver purifying processes. The process was studied employing silver synthetic solutions in three distinct stages. Initially, the material of the cathode was selected, with stainless steel cathode as the most suitable option, as compared to copper, which suffered from lixiviation, thereby contaminating the medium. The study of the circulating current density as a function of applied voltage (in the range of 0.8 to 3.2 V) showed an increased recovery of silver with increasing current. Boron-Doped Diamond (BDD), Mixed Metal Oxide (MMO) and carbon filter were studied as anodes. Among them, BDD emerged as the most suitable option. The filter carbon process is rapid but causes iron leaching due to nitric acid capillarity. The MMO anode performance is too slow because of Oxygen Evolution Reaction (OER), and oxygen formation. In turn,

BDD offers a moderate rate without these drawbacks. Finally, the effect of the initial metal composition was investigated, by preparing synthetic solutions with an initial silver concentration ranging from 5 to 1000 ppm. The results of this study indicated that the process was effective in terms of selective silver recovery, even at the highest silver concentrations.

The results obtained with synthetic solutions were then extended to lixiviates from real solar cells. Figure 3 shows a drastic decrease in silver concentration in the solution over processing time, while the concentrations of other metals, such as silicon and aluminium, remained constant, indicating a selective removal of silver into the solid phase.

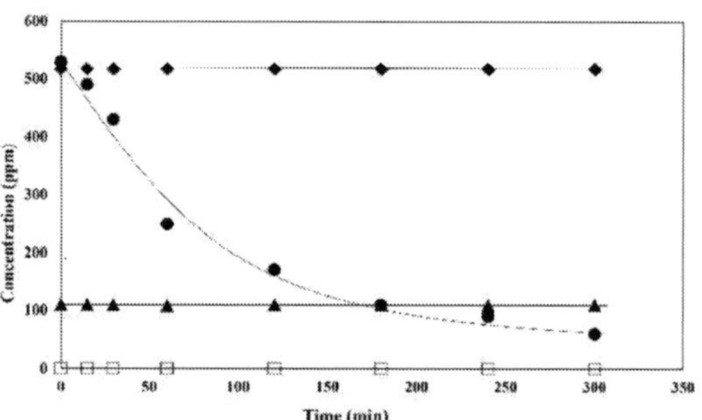

Figure 3. Concentrations of different metals, silver (●), copper (□), aluminium (▲) and silicon (◆) from real cell leachates as a function of processing time.

4 CONCLUSIONS

In summary, the KOH/ethanol/water etching process effectively demetallizes silicon wafers and recovers metallic contacts in solid phase. Careful control of KOH concentration, temperature, ethanol addition, and agitation is necessary to optimize etching rates, minimize silicon loss, and allow solution reuse. In this process, ethanol prevents foaming, and agitation improves efficiency. Demetallized Si-wafers must be cleaned and their minority carrier lifetime assessed to determine their reusability as substrates for new device fabrication. Recovered contacts can be efficiently separated by sieving due to the large difference between silver and aluminium particle sizes, and granulometric analysis can be used to ensure accuracy.

Stainless steel is a suitable cathode for silver recovery by electrodeposition after acidic etching of cell fragments. High current densities improve silver recovery, BDD offered the best balance as anode compared to carbon felt or MMO. Tests using real solar cells leachates demonstrated full silver recovery, confirming electrodeposition as an effective and selective method for the recovery of high-purity silver from PV-waste.

5 ACKNOWLEDGEMENTS

Grants No. TED2021-129624B-C41/C42 funded by the Spanish International Research Agency MCIN/AEI/10.13039/501100011033 and by "NextGenerationEU"/PRTR.

Grant No. PID2023-148369OB-C41 funded by the Spanish International Research Agency MCIN/AEI/10.13039/501100011033 and by "NextGenerationEU"/FEDER.

Grant No. TEC-2024ECO-72 funded by the

Directorate-General for Research and Technological Innovation of the Community of Madrid (Spain)

6 REFERENCES

[1] R. Basnet *et al.*, Sol. Energy Mater. Sol. Cells 292 (2025) 113816.
[2] IM. Peters *et al.*, Cradle-to-cradle recycling in terawatt photovoltaics: A vision of perpetual utility, Joule (2024).
[3] International Energy Agency, *Snapshot of Global PV Markets 2025 Task 1 Strategic PV Analysis & Outreach*, 2025.
[4] International Renewable Energy Agency, *Renewable Capacity Statistics 2025*, 2025.
[5] VDMA, *International Technology Roadmap for Photovoltaics: 2024 results*, 2025.
[6] J. Hofstetter *et al.*, Prog. Photov. 24 (2016) 122.
[7] V. Ramos *et al.*, Surfaces 8 (2025) 59.
[8] M. Tierno *et al.*, Solar Energy 274 (2024) 112533.

Sustainability strategies for optimising the use phase of photovoltaics: an overview from a Life Cycle perspective

Gamarra, A. R.*, Lechón, Y., Garraín, D.
Research Center on Energy, Environment and Technology (Ciemat). Av. Complutense, 40. 28040. Madrid.
anarosa.gamarra@ciemat.es, yolanda.lechon@ciemat.es, daniel.garrain@ciemat.es

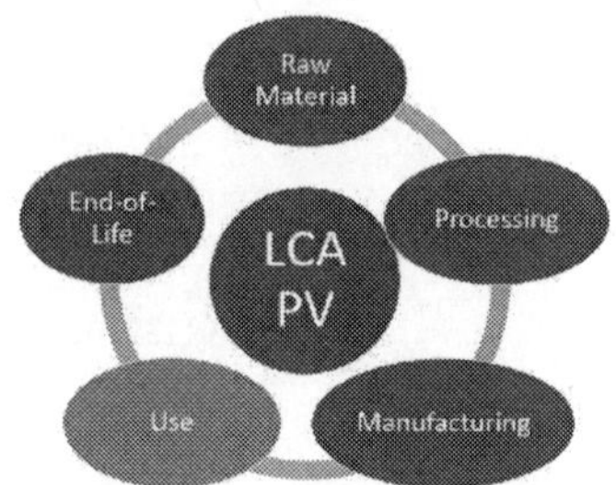

Introduction and methods

- The use phase, encompassing operational and performance factors, influences overall sustainability across different PV technologies.
- The Life Cycle Assessment (LCA) and the Life Cycle Costing analysis of photovoltaic (PV) systems have become essential to understanding their environmental impacts throughout their entire lifespan.
- The aim of this paper is to provide an up-to-date overview of the LCA/LCC of PV, focusing on the strategies for optimising the O&M phase, by reviewing the most recent literature and expected outcomes on the subject.
- The analysis of more than 25 scientific papers and grey literature reporting LCA and LCC of sustainability strategies undertaken in the O&M stage of PV published recently from 2022 allows to: 1) identify the best strategies proposed in the literature; and 2) identify which are the environmental and economic benefits associated along the life cycle of PV, and 3) to know which and how the benefits have been analysis by LCA and LCC and quantified.

Results

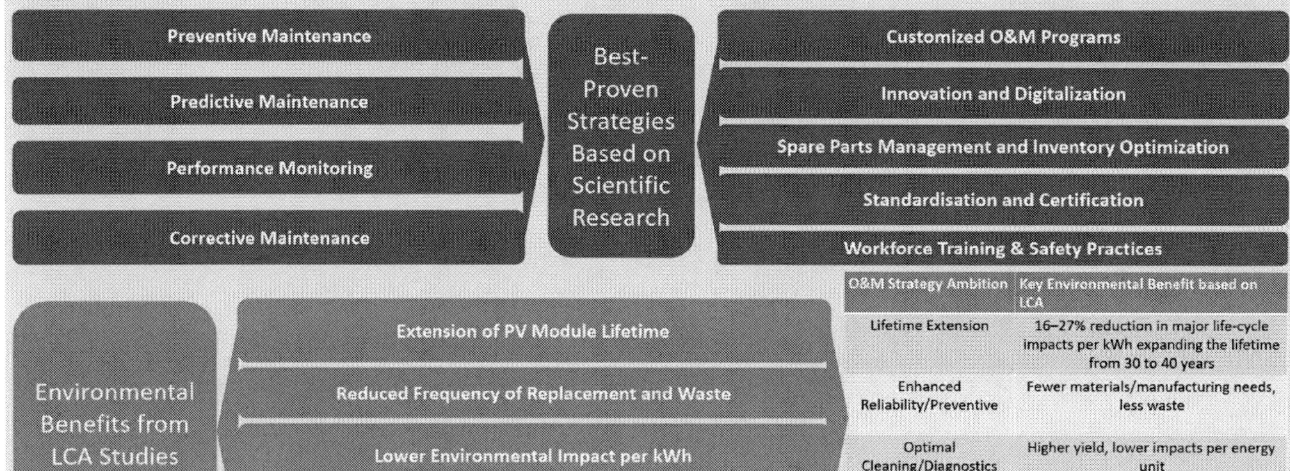

O&M Strategy Ambition	Key Environmental Benefit based on LCA
Lifetime Extension	16–27% reduction in major life-cycle impacts per kWh expanding the lifetime from 30 to 40 years
Enhanced Reliability/Preventive	Fewer materials/manufacturing needs, less waste
Optimal Cleaning/Diagnostics	Higher yield, lower impacts per energy unit
Digital Predictive/Drones/AI	Early issue detection, enabling longer asset use
Recycling-Focused Planning	Greater resource efficiency, less landfill waste

Cost Component	Description	Share LCC
Initial Cost	Solar panels, inverters, installation, mechanical & civil works	26%
Operation & Maintenance	Manpower, panel cleaning, regular inspections, system monitoring	63%
Failure Cost	Minor repairs, parts replacement (especially inverters and balance-of-system components)	11%

O&M Strategy Ambition	Key Economic Benefit based on LCC
Planned Maintenance	Reduces costs by 12-40%; extends asset life
Predictive Maintenance	Further savings beyond preventive (~8–12%)
Reactive/Corrective Maintenance	Up to 3-5 times more costly than planned
Performance Monitoring	Minimizes downtime and repair costs
Cleaning Management	Enhances yield, reduces degradation costs

Conclusions and ongoing developments

- The most scientifically validated and effective strategy is a combination of digital, data-driven predictive maintenance and robust performance monitoring, tailored to site-specific conditions. This maximizes reliability, minimizes both operating costs and downtime, and supports long-term profitability and sustainability in PV systems.
- LCAs confirm that the best O&M strategies—particularly those that extend service life, improve performance, and support recycling—substantially enhance the environmental profile of PV systems and help realize their sustainability potential.
- LCC studies consistently demonstrate that robust O&M strategies—especially those emphasizing reliability, preventive actions, and efficient resource allocation—can significantly reduce the lifetime costs and maximize the economic value of PV installations. In essence, shifting from reactive to planned and predictive maintenance, coupled with digital monitoring and proactive cleaning, produces the greatest measurable reductions in PV lifecycle cost.

ONGOING RESEARCH: **SOLARIS PROJECT** will provide an updated comprehensive assessment and quantification and comparison of benefits for sustainability by conducting the LCA, LCC and Socioeconomically Extended Input-Output Analysis (SEMRIO) of several solutions in a range of use-cases encountered (ground-mounted small- and utility-scale PVs, rooftop, floating PVs, AgriPV).
- Two groups of solutions:
  - Digital: Accurate weather and power generation forecasting; Energy trading tool for optimised energy selling and prolonged battery energy storage system BESS lifetime PV asset management software, relying on automated monitoring and inspection data gathering, for accurate fault detection, identification, predictive maintenance and decision-support to the operator.
  - Physical: Strategies against soiling for PV system increased performance and lower cleaning costs; Wind load sensing for adapted self-protection; Novel impedance sensing device for continuous, accurate and preventive fault detection and location & Novel inverter prototype for prolonged components lifetime and reconfiguration; Automated multi-imagery and high-resolution PV inspection using drones for fault location.

Acknowledgements

We thank the Solaris Project. This research is funded by the European Union under grant agreement no.101146377. Views and opinions expressed are however those of the author(s) only and do not necessarily reflect those of the European Union or CINEA. Neither the European Union nor the granting authority can be held responsible for them.

References

A detailed list of reference can be found in the link (QR)

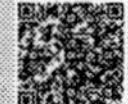

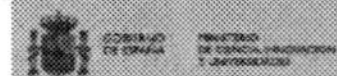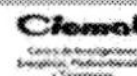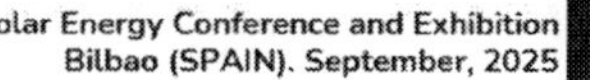

Recycling end-of-life PV modules
Pulsed lasers, light flashes and hot knives

Per-Anders Hansen*, Rune Søndenå
Institute for Energy Technology
Corresponding author: per-anders.hansen@ife.no

INTRODUCTION

The stream of discarded PV modules has previously been fairly small, but is rapidly increasing. It is expected that by 2050, 5-7 Mtons of discarded PV modules will have to be handled each year globally [1]. Still, there is no established method to recycle PV modules today. A major challenge is that neither old nor current PV modules were designed with recycling in mind. Separating a module back into its material components is difficult. Doing so in a way that preserves the various materials for further recycling while also being economically viable, even more so.

In this work, we have investigated three different method to separate the glass pane from the rest (metals, silicon and various polymers and laminate adhesives). The aim is to in one way or another sever the polymer bonding everything onto the glass, while at the same time keeping the glass intact in one piece.

Hot knife
A simple, electrically heated knife edge being pushed along the glass surface.

+ Simple and inexpensive
- Creates toxic fumes
- Hard work when done by hand

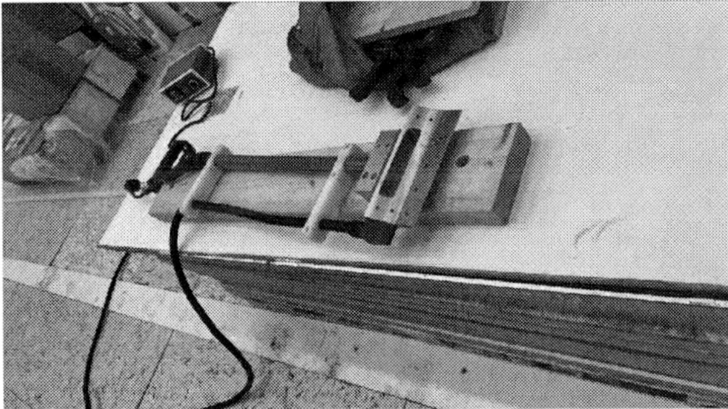

The electrically heated hot knife, used to separate the back sheet, cells and metals from the glass pane.

Flash lamp
Optically heating the silicon wafer beyond the charring temperature of the cell/polymer interface.

+ Does not (intentionally) heat the whole device
+ No fumes created
+ Cell was separated on both sides, resulting in a loose wafer
- Requires very expensive power / battery packs
- Metal was stuck on glass
- Did not separate the areas between and around cells, where only the white backsheet was visible

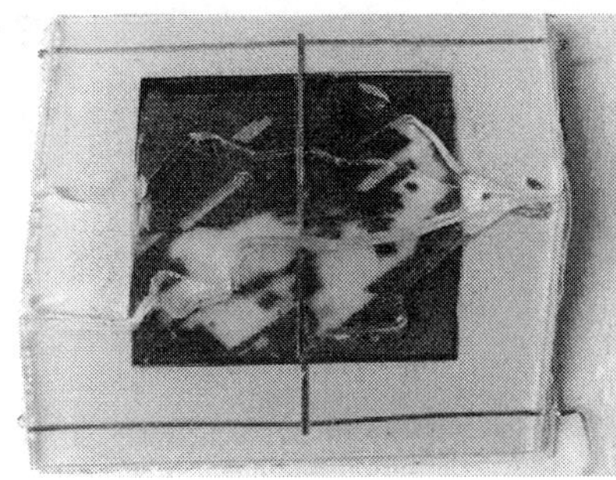

Mini-module after repeated Xe flashing, showing loose wafer fragments.

Pulsed laser
A more advanced form of Xe flash lamps, but bringing a spot above the interface charring temperature within the duration of a single laser pulse. Lasering was carried out by SYLSTAD AS and VDlaser AS.

+ No* fumes (some smell present)
+ Can shear the glass/metal and white glass/backsheet areas
- Only shears the irradiated side, as the while wafer isn't heated
• Exact mechanism depends on laser type and laser parameters

TOPCon lifetimes from different oxide routes and annealing

Conclusions
This work was carried out by hand. All three methods will benefit from proper automation and optimization. The hot knife resulted in relatively clean glass and a backsheet containing everything else. However, the two optical methods had major advantages by being fume-free*. The non-glass components are sent to further processing.

REFERENCES
[1] (2016) End-of-Life Management: Solar Photovoltaic Panels. I.R.E.A.a.I.E.A.P.P. Systems IRENA and IEA-PVPS.

020503-001

HYPERSPECTRAL IMAGING FOR ADVANCED MATERIAL IDENTIFICATION AND QUANTIFICATION OF PROCESSED PV MATERIALS

Authors

L. Neumaier[1]*, M. De Biasio[1], A. Gassner[2,3], G.C. Eder[2]

[1] SAL, Silicon Austria Labs GmbH, Villach, Austria
[2] OFI, Austrian Research Institute for Chemistry and Technology, Vienna, Austria
[3] TU Wien, Institute of Materials Science and Technology, Vienna, Austria
*Lukas.neumaier@silicon-austria.com; M:+43 664 88200146

This work was carried out as part of the Austrian project "PVReValue - Holistic Recycling of Photovoltaic Modules" (FFG No. 897767), which is funded by the Federal Ministry for Climate Action, Environment, Energy, Mobility, Innovation and Technology BMK as part of the Circular Economy - Energy and Environmental Technology Call 2022 and handled by the Austrian Research Promotion Agency (FFG).

Abstract

An advanced, layer-by-layer separation and recycling process for end-of-life (EoL) photovoltaic (PV) modules is developed, aiming for a material recovery rate of over 95% by weight. The workflow covers input characterization, component separation, fraction processing, and output analysis. Key recyclable groups are (i) front glass, (ii) metals/semiconductors (Si), and (iii) backsheet plastics. The main challenge is removing the crosslinked EVA encapsulant. Near-infrared hyperspectral imaging (HSI) is integrated for non-destructive material identification, detecting residual encapsulant on glass, solar cells, and backsheets. Machine-learning-based spectral analysis enables real-time classification and higher material purity. Early results confirm accurate material mapping in mixed streams, supporting scalable recycling and advancing a circular PV economy.

Keywords: recycling, circular economy, hyperspectral imaging, material classification, non-destructive analysis

APPROACH

PV recycling: Structured process under development to achieve >95 wt% recovery from EoL PV modules.

- **Multi-step workflow**

  (i) Input characterization, (ii) layer-by-layer component separation (waterjet cutting or milling), (iii) further processing of fractions, (iv) output characterization, (v) recycling of refined output fractions

- **Precise separation of main fractions**

  Glass, backsheet (+ residues of encapsulant), and solar cells + metallic connectors + wires with encapsulant

NIR spectroscopy & NIR HSI

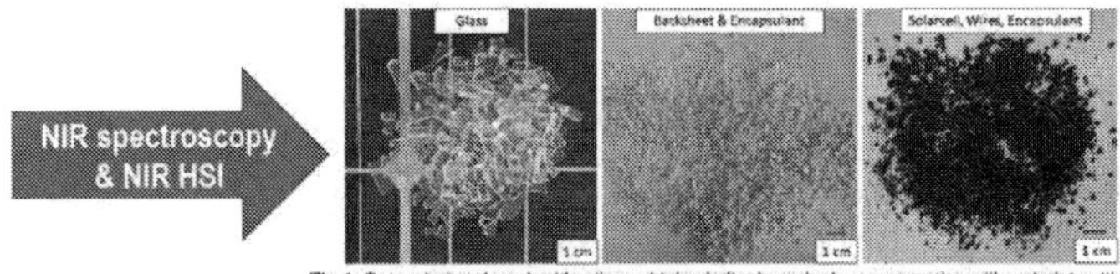

Fig.1: Separated and crushed fractions obtained after layer-by-layer separation with waterjet cutting

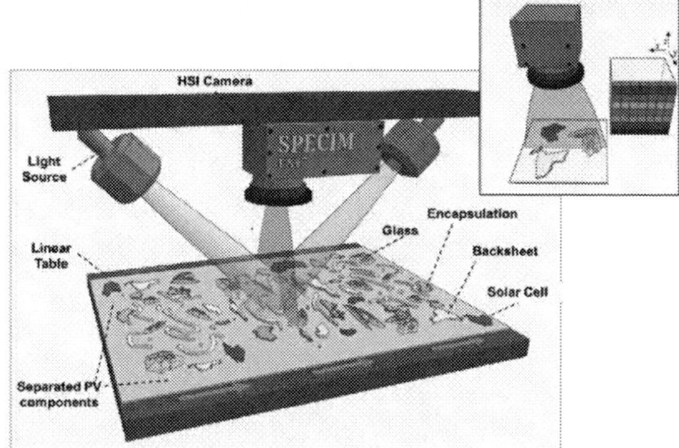

Fig.2: HSI setup to measure different components of PV materials after the separation process of EoL modules; *Insert*: spatial scanning via HSI

RESULTS

NIR spectroscopy & NIR hyper spectral imaging

- Rapid, non-destructive **material identification** of EoL PV modules and fractions
- Detection of **contaminants/residues** to ensure high-quality recovery
- Quantification of **material composition** in mixed fractions

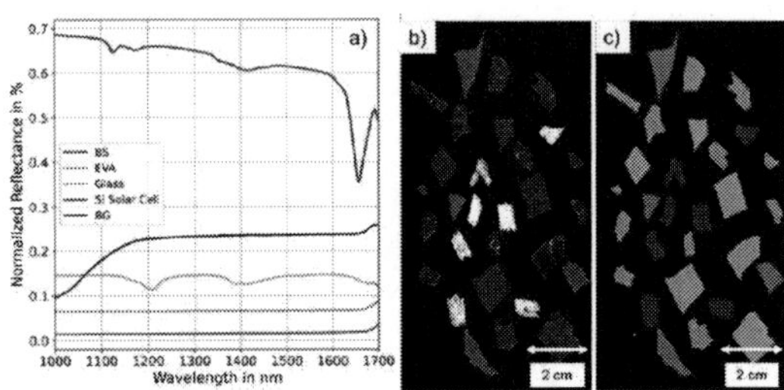

Fig.3.: (a) Reference spectra by class; (b) False-color sample image; (c) Color-coded HSI classification result of PV components

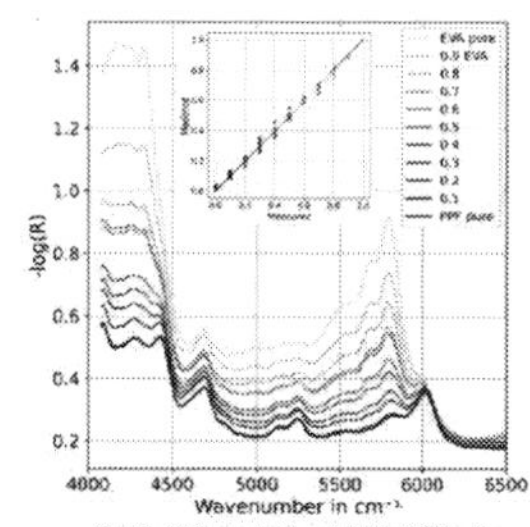

Fig.4: (a,b) False-color NIR images of measurement samples; (c) samples for reference spectra extraction (pure vs. EVA-contaminated); (d) EVA-covered glass (milling); (e) clean glass (waterjet).

Fig.5: NIR analysis of EVA–PET mix: reflectance spectra by ratio; *insert*: predicted vs. measured EVA content

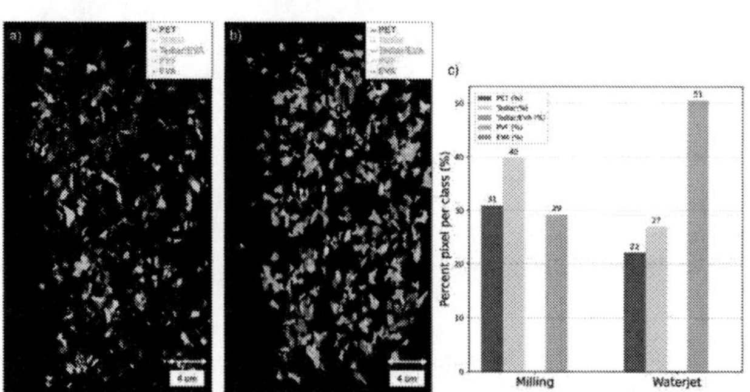

Fig.6: Classification of PET, Tedlar, Tedlar/EVA, PVF, EVA in rough BS fraction (1—4.3 mm): (a) milling, (b) waterjet, (c) Comparison of material type distribution (percent pixel per material class) after milling and waterjet cutting

SUMMARY

NIR spectroscopy and HSI were utilized for identifying and quantifying PV recycling fractions.

- HSI detects **EVA residues, classifies materials** in real time, and **improves separation accuracy**.
- **Waterjet cutting delivers cleaner** glass and separated backsheet layers than **milling**.
- **Flake sorter integration could enhance precision** for fine, transparent fractions (e.g., PET).

Future Work

Initial tests **confirm feasibility**, but **further optimization is needed** for complex material mixtures and small grain sizes (e.g.: adaption of detection algorithms).

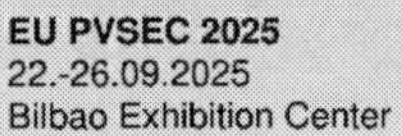

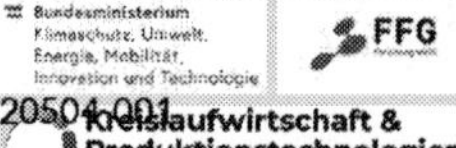

020504-001

Silicon Austria Labs GmbH
Sandgasse 34, 8010 Graz, Austria
www.silicon-austria-labs.com
contact@silicon-austria.com

SOCIAL LCA OF PEROVSKITES: INITIAL FINDINGS AND PATHS FOR IMPROVEMENT

Anna Barguès[1], Philippe Macé[2], Melodie de l'Epine[1], Damien Gautier[2]
[1]Becquerel Institute France, Lyon (France) [2]Becquerel Institute, Brussels (Belgium)
Rue Praetere 2, 1000 Brussels, Belgium. +32 493 451 720

ABSTRACT: Social Life Cycle Assessments (S-LCAs) evaluate the social impacts of products across their life cycle, from manufacturing to end-of-life. They consider aspects such as working conditions, human rights, gender equity, health and safety, and community engagement [1]. While Environmental LCAs (E-LCAs) are well-established with clear methods, databases like Ecoinvent and GaBi, and standardized frameworks such as ISO 14040 and ISO 14044, S-LCAs remain less mature due to the complex and context-specific nature of social issues. Limited data availability and regional differences further complicate evaluations [2]. In the photovoltaic sector, S-LCAs are still rare, as most studies focus on environmental aspects such as carbon emissions and resource use. Yet social impacts are critical for ensuring fair labour conditions and ethical supply chains. Although UNEP guidelines provide a foundation, further efforts are needed to refine methods and develop standardized indicators for meaningful assessments [3]. This publication presents preliminary results of the social assessment of an innovative silicon/perovskite tandem module. The study identifies key social impacts, explores alternative material provenance or processing sites, and highlights routes to reduce negative impacts. Conducted within the NEXUS project, it contributes to Europe's clean energy transition by supporting eco-designed, sustainable, and socially responsible PV production.
Keywords: Perovskites, social risks, value chain.

1 INTRODUCTION

The large-scale deployment of perovskite–silicon tandem (PST) photovoltaics offers significant potential for efficiency improvements and cost reductions, positioning these technologies as a key driver in the global transition to low-carbon energy. However, the rapid industrialization of PST modules also raises critical questions regarding the social impacts associated with their supply chains. From raw material extraction and processing to manufacturing and end-of-life management, each stage carries potential social risks, including labor conditions, community impacts, and equitable resource access.

To address these concerns, the NEXUS project conducted a comprehensive Social Life Cycle with two primary objectives: first, to systematically identify and quantify social risks across the PST value chain; and second, to evaluate opportunities for improvement through responsible sourcing, process optimization, and circular economy strategies, ensuring socially sustainable deployment alongside technological advancement.

2. METHODOLOGICAL APPROACH

UNEP Guidelines for Social Life Cycle Assessment of Products and Organizations, with the overarching aim of evaluating the social impacts associated with manufacturing PST technologies to ensure a responsible and sustainable energy transition.

The assessment was conducted in OpenLCA 2.2 using the PSILCA v3 database as the primary data source, which provides coverage of over 70 qualitative and quantitative social indicators organized into 25 subcategories across four stakeholder groups: workers, value chain actors, local communities, and society.

Given the complexity of analyzing all available indicators, a participatory approach was adopted to refine the scope, using a Best-Worst Scaling (BWS) survey administered to project partners. This method allowed experts to identify and prioritize the most relevant indicators while ensuring that all stakeholder categories were represented.

Through this process, the initial long list was reduced to eight key indicators: goods produced by forced labor and fatal accidents (workers), anti-competitive behavior and public sector corruption (value chain actors), indigenous rights and sanitation coverage (local communities), and illiteracy and education expenditures (society).

The system boundary for the analysis was cradle-to-cradle, encompassing raw material extraction, manufacturing, use, and end-of-life, with both baseline and optimized PST module configurations considered.

Following inventory compilation, the impact assessment phase applied PSILCA's risk characterization method, which assigns risk levels (from no risk to very high risk) to each indicator, translating them into numerical factors expressed in Medium Risk Hours per USD of output.

The interpretation phase consolidated results, highlighted key risks and opportunities, and provided

3. MAIN ASSUMPTIONS

The study focuses exclusively on the manufacturing phase of perovskite-silicon tandem photovoltaic modules, comparing a baseline and an optimized architecture. Both configurations share the same overall design, consisting of a perovskite thin-film top cell combined with a silicon heterojunction (SHJ) bottom cell in a two-terminal (2T) tandem structure. The module assembly and Balance of System (BOS) are identical in both cases.

The optimized configuration introduces several improvements at the cell level. Silicon wafers are sourced from Norway instead of China, reducing the social and environmental risks linked to supply. Wafer cleaning processes have been modified to use less water and solvents, lowering resource intensity. Cell metallization is performed using the advanced Electrically Conductive Adhesive (ECA) technique, which also allows a 40% reduction in silver consumption compared to the traditional multi-wire brazing approach. For the transparent conductive oxide (TCO) layer, aluminum zinc oxide (AZO) is adopted in place of the commonly used indium tin oxide (ITO), avoiding the reliance on indium. Finally, the deposition of the perovskite layer is carried out with a solvent-free evaporated process, replacing conventional solvent-based techniques and further reducing potential risks associated with hazardous materials.

4. RESULTS

The S-LCA focuses on the manufacturing phase of the baseline and optimized PST PV modules, with results expressed in medium-risk hours per 1 m² of module. This unit reflects the estimated working hours under medium social risk conditions associated with producing 1 m² of module.

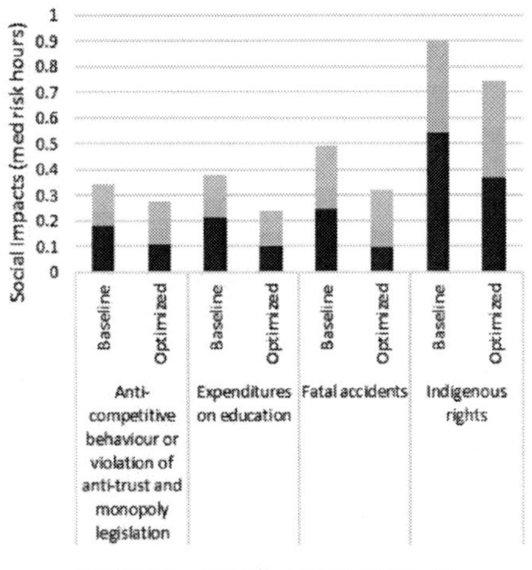

Figure 1: Social impacts of module manufacturing of Baseline and Optimized scenarios for the selected indicators

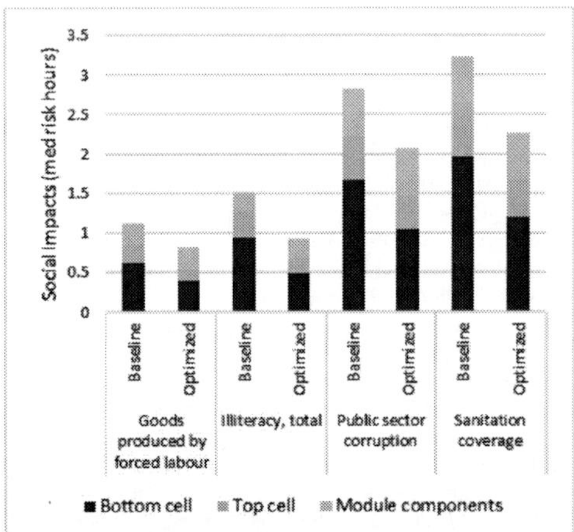

Figure 2: Social impacts of module manufacturing of Baseline and Optimized scenarios for the selected indicators

Table I: Social impact difference to produce baseline or optimized configurations

Social indicators	Reduction in impact (optimized vs. baseline)
Anti-competitive behavior or violation of anti-trust and monopoly legislation	-20%
Expenditure on education	-36%
Fatal accidents	-35%
Goods produced by forced labor	-27%
Illiteracy	-39%
Indigenous rights	-18%
Public sector corruption	-27%
Sanitation coverage	-30%

The largest contribution to social impacts comes from the silicon heterojunction (SHJ) bottom cell, since it represents the bulk of materials and costs.

A significant reduction in impacts is achieved in the optimized configuration thanks to changes in wafer production. Moving wafer manufacturing from China to Norway lowers risks across indicators due to stricter labor protections, better gender equality, higher health and safety standards, and a cleaner energy mix (mainly hydropower instead of coal) [4][5].

The perovskite top cell shows smaller but still meaningful improvements. The optimized design replaces traditional busbar brazing with Electrically Conductive Adhesives (ECA) and reduces silver use by 40%. Since silver mining is often linked to unsafe working conditions and community risks, this reduction directly lowers the social footprint of the module. In both baseline and optimized cases, the indicator with the largest weight is sanitation coverage, reflecting limited access to safe sanitation in some producing countries, which strongly drives overall social risk.

5. CONCLUSIONS

Key Findings: This study applied a Social Life Cycle Assessment to evaluate the potential social risks associated with the manufacturing of perovskite-silicon tandem photovoltaic modules. Results highlight that the silicon heterojunction bottom cell represents the largest contributor to overall social risks, emphasizing its central role in shaping the sustainability profile of these technologies. Nevertheless, the optimized configuration, featuring wafers sourced from Norway, reduced silver consumption through advanced metallization techniques, and solvent-free deposition processes, demonstrated clear improvements compared to the baseline, confirming the potential of targeted technological and sourcing strategies to mitigate social impacts.

Limitations: Despite providing valuable insights, the study is subject to limitations that must be acknowledged when interpreting results. A significant source of uncertainty arises from the reliance on secondary datasets and country-level averages, which may fail to capture local conditions or rapidly evolving supply chains. In particular, the lack of primary, industry-scale data for perovskite technologies introduces variability, as many inventory flows had to be modeled using proxy data not fully adapted to novel PV materials. Assumptions regarding sourcing locations, process configurations, and market dynamics further shape outcomes and can influence the magnitude of reported risks. These uncertainties underscore the need for caution in extrapolating results too broadly.

Paths for Improvement: Looking forward, several avenues for improvement emerge. Developing more accurate and geographically resolved datasets will be essential for refining S-LCA in the context of emerging PV technologies. Equally important is the adaptation of social indicators to the realities of globalized and fast-changing supply chains, ensuring assessments remain relevant and actionable. Strengthening methodological frameworks will reduce uncertainty and enhance robustness, while integrating S-LCA insights into sourcing strategies and policy development can help build more transparent and socially responsible supply chains. Ultimately, embedding social considerations into material choices and technology design will ensure that the PV sector contributes not only to climate goals but also to broader objectives of equity, transparency, and human rights.

6. ACKNOWLEDGEMENTS AND FUNDING

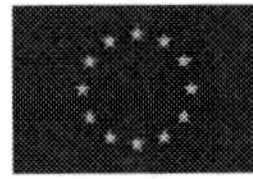 The work described has received funding as part of the NEXUS project from the European Union's Horizon Europe research and innovation program under grant agreement N° °101075330.

7. REFERENCES

[1] K. Maister, C. Di Noi, A. Ciroth, and M. Srocka, "PSILCA v.3 Database documentation," 2020.

[2] A. M. R. O. Chabrawi, J. M. de Andrade, C. M. L. Ugaya, and M. Traverso, "Towards reliable primary data collection and harmonized set of indicators in S-LCA on the stakeholder worker," International Journal of Life Cycle Assessment, pp. 1–19, Nov. 2024, doi: 10.1007/S11367-024-02400-Z/TABLES/8.

[3] Catherine. Benoît and Bernard. Mazijn, Guidelines for social life cycle assessment of products. United Nations Environment Programme, 2009.

[4] "Gender Gap Norway - Gender Equality - Red Yellow Blue The Gender Gap in Norway: A Comprehensive Analysis (RYB). (n.d.). from https://redyellowblue.org/data/no/gender-gap-norway/," 2025.

[5] "Electricity production - Norwegian Energy. (n.d.). from https://energifaktanorge.no/en/norsk-energiforsyning/kraftproduksjon/".

LIFE CYCLE ANALYSIS IN PHOTOVOLTAIC RECYCLING STRATEGIES: CHEMICAL AND THERMOMECHANICAL PROCESSES

J.A. Saura, N.Espinosa

University of Murcia, UM, Spain

1 INTRODUCTION

Solar photovoltaic energy is growing rapidly, surpassing 1 TW of installed capacity in 2021. This growth leads to an increase in waste, which could reach 60–78 million tons by 2050. To promote the circular economy, it is necessary to develop sustainable recycling strategies.[1]

2 GOAL

To compare two methods for recycling end-of-life photovoltaic modules: pyrolysis, which recovers high-purity materials, and thermomechanical processes, which require less energy. The analysis is performed using a Life Cycle Assessment (LCA).

3 METHODOLOGY

The functional unit of the study is 1,000 kg of end-of-life photovoltaic modules. OpenLCA software (v2.4) is used with the Ecoinvent database (v3.11), applying a Consequential LCA (CLCA) approach. Environmental impacts are assessed according to the EF 3.1 methodology, including climate change, toxicity, and eutrophication, among others.[2]

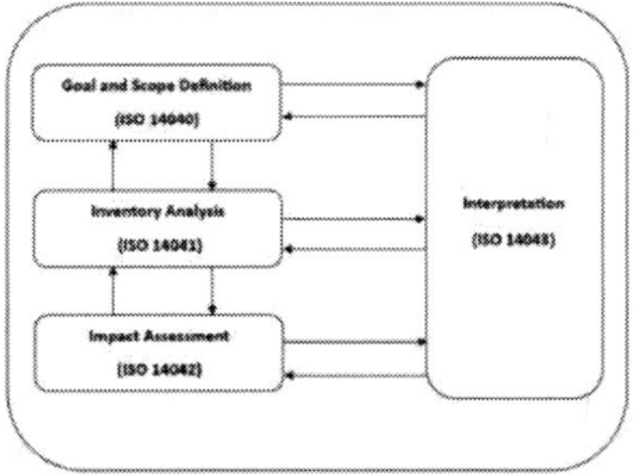

4 RESULTS

Pyrolysis offers greater material recovery, achieving silicon purity of 6–7N and high metal recovery rates, although it requires greater energy consumption and generates ionizing radiation impacts. Thermomechanical processes, on the other hand, consume less energy and have lower toxicity and radiation impacts, but produce lower purity materials. Both processes show net environmental benefits compared to the production of virgin raw materials.[3],[4],[5]

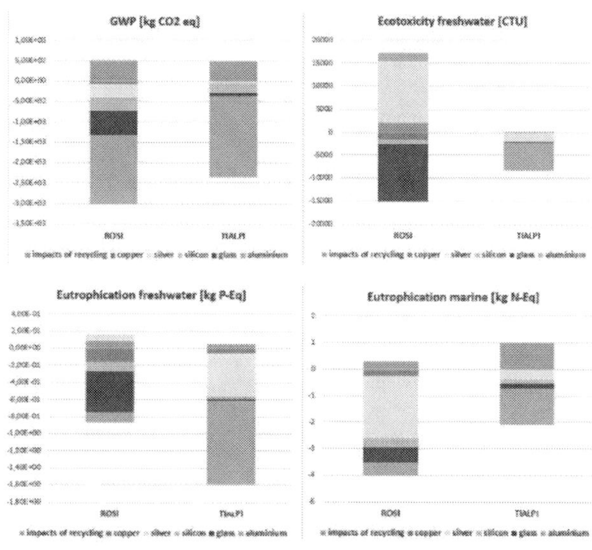

5 CONCLUSION

Both methods are sustainable, with distinct advantages. Pyrolysis is more suitable when seeking to maximize the quality and purity of materials, while thermomechanical recycling is more energy-efficient and better at reducing certain environmental impacts. The optimal choice will depend on the context: industry may prioritize purity, while public policies will tend to favor reducing overall impacts.

REFERENCES

[1] Sim, Y., Tay, A., Tay, Y. B., et al. (2025). Open challenges and opportunities in photovoltaic recycling. Nature Rev. Electr. Eng.
[2] Hauschild, M. Z., & Rosenbaum, R. K. (2018). Life Cycle Assessment: Theory and Practice. Springer.
[3] Fan, H. (2021). Life cycle assessment of an innovative recycling treatment for crystalline silicon PV modules. TU Eindhoven.
[4] Ardente, F., Latunussa, C., & Blengini, G. (2019). Resource efficient recovery of metals from PV panel recycling. Waste Management, 91, 156–167.
[5] Mazzi, A., Barbiero, C., Miserocchi, F., et al. (2024). Life cycle assessment of Al-C recycling from photovoltaic waste. Resour. Conserv. Recycl., 211, 107885.

CONTACT

ja.sauragarcia@um.es
nieves.espinosa@um.es

THE LANDSCAPE OF PV RECYCLING: CHALLENGES TO MAKE PV AN EXAMPLE OF CIRCULAR ECONOMY

del Cañizo C., Fuertes Marrón D.
Instituto de Energía Solar, ETSI Telecomunicación, Universidad Politécnica de Madrid,
Avenida Complutense 40 (28040), Madrid, Spain.

ABSTRACT: The recycling of PV modules has emerged as a topic of enormous relevance, driven by the urgent need to manage the decommissioning of millions of modules expected over the coming decades. The development of universal, effective, scalable, and environmentally responsible recycling pathways (either up- or down-cycling) for PV modules requires a holistic understanding of technological diversity, process engineering, regulatory support, and economic models. This paper offers a set of reflections on key questions that help outline the landscape of photovoltaic recycling. By identifying core issues and emerging trends, it aims to contribute to a clearer understanding of the opportunities and obstacles that lie ahead in the transition toward a circular solar economy.

Keywords: Recycling, PV Waste, Silicon, Circularity

1 INTRODUCTION

The recycling of photovoltaic (PV) modules has emerged as a topic of enormous relevance, driven by the urgent need to manage the decommissioning of millions of modules expected over the coming decades. As solar energy deployment accelerates globally, the end-of-life management of PV systems becomes a critical challenge for both environmental sustainability and resource recovery.

This concern has sparked a vast amount of research and development (R&D) activity aimed at supporting industrial initiatives in PV recycling. A clear upward trend can be exemplified by a quick survey of the scientific literature indexed in the Web of Science under the search terms "Photovoltaic" AND "Recycling": 562 papers were published between 2000 and 2020, while the period from 2021 to 2025 saw a significant increase to 980 publications. Notably, 16 articles including the term "review" in the title were just published in 2024 and 2025, underscoring the intensifying interest and complexity of the field [1-16].

A critical reading of these reviews highlights the difficulty in grasping and systematically organizing the diversity of source materials to be recycled, the wide range of process conditions, and the varying levels of technological maturity. These challenges reflect the multifaceted nature of PV recycling, which spans materials science, mechanical and chemical engineering, environmental policy, and industrial scalability.

This paper offers a set of reflections on key questions that help outline the landscape of photovoltaic recycling. By identifying core issues and emerging trends, it aims to contribute to a clearer understanding of the opportunities and obstacles that lie ahead in the transition toward a circular solar economy.

2 UPDATING ESTIMATIONS ON PV WASTE

To illustrate the huge amounts of PV waste to be handled in the next decades, the projections published in 2016 by IRENA/IEA PVPS are frequently referenced: between 1.7 and 8 million tonnes were expected to be decommissioned in 2030, and between 60 and 70 million tonnes in 2050 [17]. It has to be noted that these figures built up on an estimation of a cumulative PV capacity reaching 1632 GW in 2030, 4512 GW in 2050, while the 2000 GW landmark was already surpassed in 2024, and the annual installed capacities have been in the range of the hundreds GW since then [18].

This growth of PV installed capacity above expectations demands a continuous update of waste estimations. In Figure 1 we compare 2016 IRENA estimations with our own calculations. We have considered the projections in annual installed capacity until 2050 of the ambitious yet plausible "Verlinden scenario" presented in [19], which foresees a cumulative capacity in 2030 in the range of 7000 GW, and in 2050 of 71000 GW. We followed the methodology developed by researchers from CIEMAT [20]-[22] to model the generation of PV waste, for which two different Weibull distributions are proposed, one "Regular loss" representative of what is expected from conventional PV technology according to field experience, and another "Early loss", which introduces a corrected shape factor to take into account potential module failure during the early life stages.

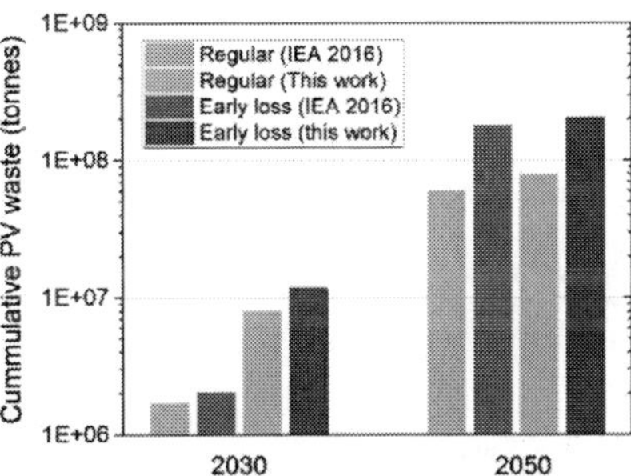

Figure 1: Comparison of PV waste estimations from IRENA/IEA PVPS in 2026 with our own.

It is clear how the increased deployment of photovoltaic capacity will cause the amount of PV waste to skyrocket well above the 2016 estimates. We are now talking about 2 to 12 million tonnes in 2030 (higher than initial estimates but in the same order of magnitude), and between 177 and 205 million tonnes in 2050 (approximately triple the initial estimates).

Additionally, we have included the initial loss of PV modules due to breakage during transport an installation, that neither the Regular nor the Early loss scenarios capture, which is of increasing importance along with the size of the new plants. We assume this additional loss to be in the range of 1% of the number of installed modules, according to the testimony of several EPC contractors that have been contacted. We show in Figure 2 how this additional source of losses sum up to the previous estimations.

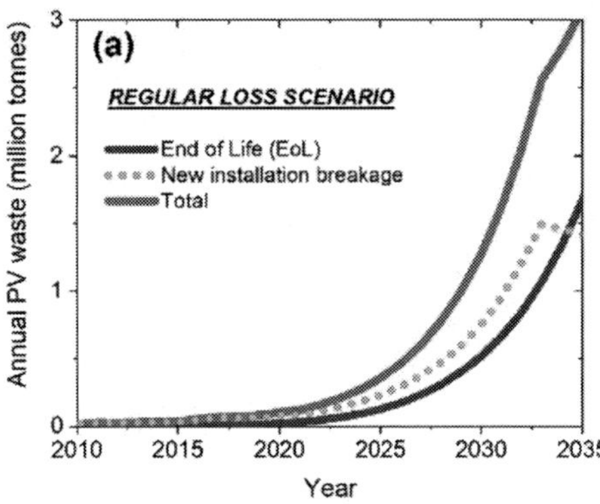

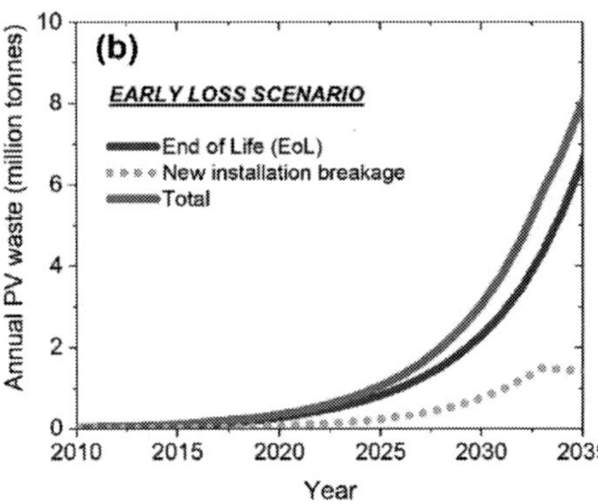

Figure 2: PV waste estimations when considering that 1% of PV modules break during installation and transport. (a) Regular loss scenario. (b) Early loss scenario.

The reduction of the PV waste due to the breakage during installation from 2033 on derives from the stabilisation of annual installed capacity according to the Verlinden scenario, which translates into a gradual reduction in terms of mass due to technological improvements.

Note that the installation breakage can be a concern in practical terms (mainly in the short term for the Regular loss scenario), as the large volume of broken new modules, even surpassing that of the old ones reaching their end-of-life, will arrive at the same time to the recycling plants. This will pose the relevant challenge of handling the technological differences between the old and the new modules, being the latter larger, with different metal contact schemes, and having glass-to-glass encapsulation, lower amounts of silver, etc.

3 RECYCLING METHODS

Figure 3 sketches the steps of a generic recycling process. There exists a wide variety of methods (mechanical, thermal, chemical, electrical, and combinations of them) to separate the components and recover the materials, which have been experimentally tested. The transition from laboratory-scale to industrial implementation requires a careful evaluation of several critical dimensions.

Among these, the *universality* of a given recycling pathway stands out as a major challenge due to the technological evolution among PV modules of different generations [23]: PV modules differ significantly in their construction, encompassing various configurations such as glass-backsheet and glass-glass architectures, the diversity in cell technologies—ranging from traditional aluminum back surface field (Al-BSF) cells to more advanced passivated emitter and rear cells (PERC) and tunnel oxide passivated contact (TOPCon) cells—, the transition from the universally used ethylene-vinyl acetate (EVA) encapsulant to other alternative ones such as polyolefin elastomer (POE), or similarly the variation in backsheet compositions including polyvinyl fluoride (PVF), polyvinylidene fluoride (PVDF), and polyethylene terephthalate (PET). Each variety requires tailored chemical or thermal treatments for effective separation and recovery.

Scalability is another critical issue. While many recycling techniques have demonstrated promising results at the laboratory level, scaling these processes to industrial capacities introduces new challenges. These include the need for robust automation, consistent feedstock quality, and economic viability under fluctuating market conditions. The transition often demands significant capital investment and process optimization to ensure throughput, reliability, and compliance with environmental regulations.

Environmental impact remains a central concern in evaluating recycling strategies. Some processes rely on toxic chemicals or generate hazardous emissions, including volatile organic compounds and acidic gases. The use of solvents, high-temperature treatments, and mechanical shredding must be assessed not only for their effectiveness but also for their ecological footprint. Life cycle assessments (LCAs) are essential tools to quantify these impacts and guide the development of cleaner, safer alternatives [24][25].

Cost is a decisive factor in the feasibility of PV recycling. Expenses arise from labor, energy consumption, chemical reagents, equipment maintenance, and logistics. Without sufficient economic incentives or regulatory frameworks, many recycling operations will struggle to achieve profitability. One promising approach to address this issue is the implementation of Extended Producer Responsibility (EPR), which shifts the financial burden of end-of-life management to manufacturers. Additionally, optimizing logistics—such as centralized module collection systems and minimum viable plant sizes—can improve economies of scale and reduce operational costs.

4 REINJECTION OF PV MATERIALS IN THE PRODUCTIVE SECTOR

The recovery of materials from end-of-life PV modules opens opportunities across several industrial sectors. Recycled metals, such as aluminum, copper, and silver, benefit from well-established markets, as metal recycling is already deeply integrated into global supply chains and industrial practices. In contrast, glass presents greater challenges, particularly in meeting the quality requirements of float or tempered glass industries, which

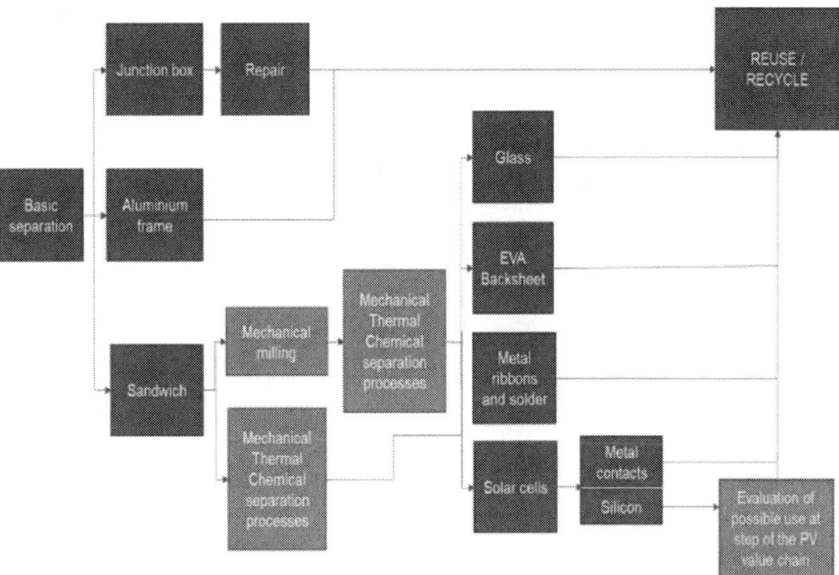

Figure 3: Steps in a generic recycling process.

demand specific physical and compositional properties. Polymers, including encapsulants and backsheets, are more difficult to valorize due to degradation and contamination; however, their calorific value offers potential for use as alternative energy sources through controlled thermal recovery processes. Silicon, depending on its purity but also on its resulting morphology (as powder, granulate or small/medium wafer pieces) after recovery, can serve diverse applications—from low-grade uses as an additive in construction materials or metallurgy, to high-purity feedstock for new solar cells, batteries or electronic devices [26] [27].

4.1 Downcycling or upcycling

The design of a recycling route should have in mind the achievable quality of the recovered materials, which will determine whether a "downcycling" or an "upcycling" approach can be followed to reinject them in the productive sector. By downcycling we refer to the conversion of the waste materials into new ones of lower intrinsic quality and reduced functionality with respect to their original application, while upcycling means that the original quality of the material is maintained or even improved after recovery.

Downcycling presents a practical advantage due to its relative simplicity, which translates into lower processing costs and easier implementation at scale. This approach typically involves less demanding separation and/or purification steps, making it attractive for early-stage or cost-sensitive operations. However, the reduction in quality and functionality can diminish the original value of the recovered materials and limit their appeal in secondary markets. In contrast, upcycling enables their reuse in high-performance applications, but it generally requires more complex and costly processes, often involving high energy input or hazardous chemicals, which may lead to increased environmental impacts.

4.2 Benefits of full circularity

The benefits that may come with a full circularity are exemplified in Table I by the new power capacity that could be served by the direct re-injection of the recovered silicon and silver in the PV-value chain from end-of-life PV modules, in case their quality is maintained. For these rough estimations, silicon is considered to be 3.5% of the total module mass, and silver 0.06%. For the new capacity, it is assumed that 2 g/W of silicon and 10 mg/W of silver are needed.

Table I: Cumulative power capacity that could be served by the usage of recycled silicon and silver by the solar industry from now on to year 2030 and 2050, depending on the scenario (Regular loss or Early loss) and considering the initial breakage during installation and transport.

	PV power (GW) covered by the recovered silicon	PV power (GW) covered by the recovered silver
	Accumulated up to 2030	
Regular loss	101	461
Early loss	271	1239
	Accumulated up to 2050	
Regular loss	3588	16404
Early loss	8113	37089

Even if these numbers are just taken as a starting point, as they do not incorporate the dynamism with which technological innovations are changing the configuration of the module, they show that at the short term (2030) between 1%-4% of the total power could be covered by recycled silicon, going to 5-11% in 2050. In the case of silver, the fractions move from 7-18% in 2030 to 23-52% in 2050.

5 CONCLUSIONS

The vertiginous growth of the installed PV capacity draws a scenario in which millions of modules will have to be decommissioned when they reach their end-of-life. The prospects of how much PV waste we will have to manage should be continuously updated, as the reality in the deployment of PV plants surpasses the expectations.

The development of universal, effective, scalable, and environmentally responsible recycling pathways for PV modules requires a holistic understanding of technological diversity, process engineering, regulatory support, and economic models.

The choice between downcycling and upcycling of recovered materials involves a trade-off between economic feasibility and material value preservation, with implications for both sustainability and industrial viability.

Addressing these interconnected challenges is essential for building a fully sustainable and circular photovoltaic industry.

5 ACKNOWLEDGEMENTS

The financial support from the Spanish International Research Agency MCIN/AEI/10.13039/501100011033 through the RESLIENS (TED2021-129624B-C41) and MORE-N (PID2023-148369OB-C41) projects is greatly acknowledged, together with that of the Directorate-General for Research and Technological Innovation of the Community of Madrid through Grant No. TEC-2024ECO-72.

6 REFERENCES

[1] E. Gerold et al., Advancements and Challenges in Photovoltaic Cell Recycling: A Comprehensive Review, Sustainability 16 (2024) 2542.

[2] PH. Chen et al., Comprehensive Review of Crystalline Silicon Solar Panel Recycling: From Historical Context to Advanced Techniques, Sustainability 16 (2024) 60.

[3] YR. Maghraby et al., Towards sustainability via recycling solar photovoltaic Panels, A review, Solar Energy 285 (2025) 113805.

[4] S. Song et al., Water treatment methods in heavy metals removal during photovoltaic modules recycling: a review, Resour. Conserv. Recycl., 208 (2024) 107701.

[5] S. Rout et al., Unlocking silver from end-of-life photovoltaic panels: A concise review, Renew. Sust. Energ. Rev. 210 (2025) 115205.

[6] R. Vinayagamoorthi, Recycling of end of life photovoltaic solar panels and recovery of valuable components: A comprehensive review and experimental validation, J. Environm. Chemical Engineering 12 (2024) 111715.

[7] R. Sanathi, A technical review of crystalline silicon photovoltaic module recycling, Solar Energy 281 (2024) 112869.

[8] M. Martínez, Technological Advancement in Solar Photovoltaic Recycling: A Review, Minerals 14 (2024) 638.

[9] S. Preet, A comprehensive review on the recycling technology of silicon based photovoltaic solar panels: Challenges and future outlook, J. Clean Prod. 12 (2024) 141661.

[10] AA. Vucinic, Recycling of photovoltaic cells – A review, Detritus 27 (2024) 47-65.

[11] M. Akhter, Sustainable Strategies for Crystalline Solar Cell Recycling: A Review on Recycling Techniques, Companies, and Environmental Impact Analysis, Sustainability 16 (2024) 5785.

[12] N. Mukwevho, Methodological approaches for resource recovery from end-of-life panels of different generations of photovoltaic technologies - A review, Renew. Sust. Energ. Rev. 207 (2025) 114980.

[13] A. Babaei, A Review of Photovoltaic Waste Management from a Sustainable Perspective, Electricity 5 (2024) 734-750.

[14] A. Ghaherami, Delamination Techniques of Waste Solar Panels: A Review. Clean Technol. 6 (2024) 280-298.

[15] ZA. Biyouki, Solar Photovoltaics Value Chain and End-of-Life Management Practices: A Systematic Literature Review, Sustainibility 16 (2024) 7038.

[16] MKH. Rabaia, Enabling the circular economy of solar PV through the 10Rs of sustainability: Critical review, conceptualization, barriers, and role in achieving SDGs, Sustainability 11 (2024) 100106.

[17] IRENA/IEA PVPS, EoL Management: Solar PV panels (2016).

[18] IEA Global Energy Review (2025).

[19] NM. Haegel et al., Photovoltaics at multi-terawatt scale: Waiting is not an option, Science 380 (2023) 39-42.

[20] JD. Santos et al., Projection of the photovoltaic waste in Spain until 2050, Journal of Cleaner Production 196 (2018) 1613-1628.

[21] JD. Santos et al., Update of the projection of the photovoltaic waste in Spain until 2050, European Photovoltaic Solar Energy Conference (2019).

[22] MB. Nieto-Morone et al., State and prospects of photovoltaic module waste generation in China, USA, and selected countries in Europe and South America, Sustainable Energy Fuels 7 (2023) 2163.

[23] International Technology Roadmap Photovoltaic 15th Edition (2024).

[24] Mao et al., Overview of life cycle assessment of recycling end-of-life photovoltaic panels: A case study of crystalline silicon photovoltaic panels, J. Cleaner Prod. 434 (2024) 140320.

[25] IEA PVPS, Advances in Photovoltaic Module Recycling (2024).

[26] IM. Peters et al., Cradle-to-cradle recycling in terawatt photovoltaics: A vision of perpetual utility, Joule (2024).

[27] R. Deng et al., Recent progress in silicon photovoltaic module recycling processes, Resources, Conservation & Recycling 187 (2022) 106612.

RECOVERY OF METAL CONTACTS AND REUTILIZATION OF SILICON SUBSTRATES FROM RECYCLED SOLAR CELLS

Dasilva-Villanueva N.[1], Fuertes Marrón D.[1], Caballero L.J.[1], Rodríguez A.[2], Díez E.[2], Vázquez, A.[2], Muñoz J.A.[2], Braña A.F.[3], Rodríguez Plaza J.L.[4], Cánovas E.[5], Menghini M.[5], Antoine C.[5], del Cañizo C.[1]
[1]Instituto de Energía Solar, ETSI Telecomunicación, Universidad Politécnica de Madrid,
Avenida Complutense 40 (28040), Madrid, Spain.
[2]Departamento de Ingeniería Química y de Materiales, Universidad Complutense de Madrid, Spain
[3]Grupo de Electrónica y Semiconductores, Departamento de Física Aplicada, Universidad Autónoma de
Madrid (28049), Madrid, Spain
[4]Laboratorio de Crecimiento de Cristales, Departamento de Física de Materiales, Universidad Autónoma de Madrid
(28049), Madrid, Spain
[5]Instituto Madrileño de Estudios Avanzados (IMDEA) Nanociencia (28049), Madrid, Spain

ABSTRACT: As the installed capacity of photovoltaic (PV) systems increases, so does the need to address the accumulation of waste from decommissioned modules, a challenge that requires the development of cost-effective and efficient recycling strategies. This work presents the main results in the research carried out within the RESILIENS project (funded by the Spanish National Research Agency) to develop a cost-effective and environmentally meaningful technological recycling process for silicon solar cells, that allows the recovery of precious metals and the reutilization of silicon substrates. On the one hand, three methods were evaluated for metal recovery: (i) acid leaching, for which 3 M HNO_3 was found to be the most effective, and an organic acidic medium, with Fe^{3+} as an oxidant and Cl^- to avoid Fe precipitation, was also explored; (ii) alkaline etching with KOH/ethanol/water, that allowed the separation of metal contacts and the removal of anti-reflection coatings with minimal silicon loss; and (iii) acidophilic and halotolerant bacteria, that effectively performed the bioleaching. On the other hand, p-type monocrystalline ingots with suitable electrical properties were obtained from the Czochralski growth of fragments of old boron-doped multicrystalline silicon wafers. Phosphorus gettering treatments were applied to p-type recrystallized wafers, achieving lifetimes in excess of 250 µs. Cells fabricated on recrystallised silicon showed only 5.2 % relative lower efficiency than reference ones, attributable to processing, not to the material quality. Conversion to n-type silicon was demonstrated when phosphorus emitters were present in the recrystallized material, Conversion to n-type silicon was demonstrated when phosphorus emitters were present, although challenges due to excessive doping were identified. The RESILIENS project has contributed to the reduction of the environmental footprint associated with solar photovoltaic energy, supporting the transformation of PV technology into a true example of circular economy.
Keywords: Recycling, Solar Cells, Silicon, Metal Recovery

1 INTRODUCTION

The recent and immediate record-breaking new PV installations will translate, with a time lag equivalent to the present useful life of the PV-modules of 25-30 years, into equally large amounts of PV-components waiting for disposal. Forecasts in this respect reveal that up to ten million tons of PV components will need recycling by 2030, a figure that goes up to the hundreds of million tons of accumulated weight by 2050 globally [1].

The existing infrastructures designed for PV-module recycling have been conceived to date for the recovery of massive (and passive) elements, like glass and aluminum frames, which are easily removable from old modules and reutilized for new products with minimal marginal costs associated. Approximately 74% of the total weight of a typical crystalline silicon (c-Si) PV module is contributed by the glass cover, while only a 3% is contributed by silicon (the actual solar cells), 1% by copper (electric connectors), and around 0.13% by silver (cell contact lines) and other metals (mostly tin and lead from contact pastes) [2]. These proportions adhere to the current normative, however, the social demand for a sustainable industrial production will shortly translate into more demanding requirements for clean energy technologies, PV in particular.

This reality urgently calls for the design and adoption of affordable and effective strategies for recycling and reutilization of all PV components, and particularly of those most energy-demanding in their manufacturing and thus responsible for the largest quote of environmental impact: the solar cells. To address this challenge, four institutions (IES-UPM, UCM, UAM, and IMDEA-Nano) have joined efforts in the research project RESILIENS, which explores an efficient approach to recycle the components of high intrinsic value in the PV module, specifically ultrapure silicon and precious metals, opening the door for the reutilization of such components into the manufacturing of new commercial products.

The approach of this work covers both the exploration of several chemical routes for the recovery of metal contacts (while preserving as much as possible the silicon substrates) and the recrystallization of old p-type wafers into monocrystalline substrates to reinject them in the PV value chain.

2 RECOVERY OF METAL CONTACTS

Several chemical routes were explored, based on alkaline etching, acidic leaching and bioleaching, respectively. Starting experiments were done on BSF solar cells with TiO_2 anti-reflection coating (ARC) manufactured in the eighties, and then to SiN_x ARC ones manufactured in the nineties. More recent PERC solar cells have also been processed. Some results are highlighted in this section, more details can be found in [3] and [4].

2.1 Alkaline route

The alkaline route is based on the physical separation of the metal contacts by etching the silicon layer immediately below, using aqueous KOH solutions, to which ethanol is added to act as a surfactant, facilitating

10.4229/EUPVSEC2025/5DV.2.32

the release of the hydrogen bubbles generated in the process. Different compositions and different operational conditions (varying temperature, with or without stirring), were tested, while keeping the solution-to-solid ratio constant. Several analytical techniques were used to characterise the solid and liquid fractions resulting from the process: the solid fraction was examined by scanning electron microscopy (SEM) and X-ray fluorescence (XRF), while the liquid fraction was analysed using inductively coupled plasma (ICP) spectroscopy. This combination of techniques allowed to assess the purity of the metal contacts and the silicon wafer, as well as to quantify the transfer of solid material to the liquid phase during the etching process.

For the samples with TiO_2 ARC, the front and back contacts (mainly Ag, determined by EDX measurements performed after detaching) were physically detached so that it was possible to recover them intact as solids. The underlying back side of the cell (mainly the aluminium-BSF layer), along with the antireflective coating and a tiny amount of Ag remnants were dissolved in the solution.

For the samples with SiN_x ARC, a two-step process was designed. The first one physically detached the Al layer from the back side and consisted of a solution of KOH and water. The second was intended to separate the metallic Ag contacts, and EtOH was added to the solution. Afterwards, Ag contacts were separated from Al contacts by sieving due to their difference in size. In contrast, for PERC cells, the alkaline etch was performed in a single step because these cells lacked the rear full Al layer. At the end of etching process, both the fragments and the silicon wafers themselves were washed with distilled water and dried. Afterwards, the organics were cleaned with an RCA-1 treatment (5:1:1 v/v mixture of 27% ammonia (NH_3), 30% hydrogen peroxide (H_2O_2) and deionised water), and the ARC was removed with 2% HF. The results of the two-step process for cells from five different manufacturers is shown in Table I.

Table I: Summary of the results obtained for the two-step etching processes optimized for solar cells coming from five different manufacturers.

St	Variables	Cell 1	Cell 2	Cell 3	Cell 4	Cell 5
1	[KOH] (% v/v)	5	5	5	5	25
	[EtOH] (% v/v)	0	0	0	0	5
	T(°C)	35	40	40	50	65
	t (min)	15	14	15	15	15
	Mass loss (%)	13,4	12,7	13,6	10,9	3,0
	Si loss (%)	0,2	11,2	12,2	9,9	1,3
	Ag (%)	0	0	0	0	1,6
	Al (%)	13,2	1,5	1,5	1,0	0
2	[KOH] (% v/v)	30	30	30	25	-
	[EtOH] (% v/v)	5	5	5	5	-
	T(°C)	65	70	70	65	-
	t (min)	12	16	20	15	-
	Mass loss (%)	6,3	6,4	2,7	2,4	-
	Si loss (%)	4,6	5,6	1,6	1,7	-
	Ag (%)	17,	0,8	1,1	0,7	-
	Al (%)	0	0	0	0	-

2.2 Acidic route

Acid leaching was carried out by digestion of solar cell fragments with nitric acid solutions, 3 M being the most suitable acid concentration. Acidic organic leaching was also tested, using Fe^{3+} as oxidant and a complexing agent (Cl^-) to avoid iron precipitation.

The recovery of metals from the acid leaching processes was carried out by precipitation to recover silver in the form of silver chloride and by electrodeposition tests to recover silver in native form.

2.3 Bioleaching route

An alternative procedure to demetallize the solar cells by means of microorganisms was also tested. Studies have been carried out using Acidithiobacillus ferrooxidans and Acidihalobacter prosperus as active agents. These microorganisms oxidize Fe^{2+}, generating Fe^{3+} which, in the presence of Al, causes its solubilization as Al^{3+} by a redox reaction. It has been observed that the ARC protects the metals against the action of these microorganisms, though.

3 RECRYSTALLIZATION OF Si FRAGMENTS

Regarding the reutilization of decommissioned Si substrates, the strategy has been to validate their reinjection at the crystallization step, using them as polysilicon feedstock. In the absence of sufficient quantities of demetalised silicon in our project, fragments of p-type multicrystalline wafers manufactured in the 2000s were used as a starting material for the growth of small Cz ingots. In some cases, conventional phosphorus emitters were diffused thermally in supersaturation conditions so that the starting material contained phosphorus and boron. Wafers were sliced from those ingots, and their optoelectronic properties were measured, mainly focusing on transport parameters, such as carrier lifetime and mobility.

3.1 Wafers grown from p-type multicrystalline material

During the crystallization process the dopant concentration along the ingot is expected to increase, due to the liquid-solid segregation coefficient of boron in silicon. This behavior is confirmed through 4-point probe resistivity measurements on wafers cut along the ingot, with resistivity values of recrystallized wafers ranging from 0.9 to 0.7 $\Omega\cdot cm$, whose evolution along the ingot is in good agreement with Scheil's model [5].

In order to determine the feasibility of processing new solar cells from the recrystallized wafers, the carrier lifetime was used as a metric [6]. Inductively-coupled photoconductance decay measurements yield carrier lifetime values between 5 and 45 µs at an injection level of 10^{15} cm^{-3}, values that increase up to several hundreds of microseconds after performing a phosphorus diffusion gettering (PDG) process to get rid of possible contaminants introduced during the recrystallization stage. Carrier lifetime measurements of the multicrystalline wafers before recrystallization, alongside the monocrystalline samples before and after the PDG are presented in Fig. 1. They show the efficacy of the gettering process for the elimination of spurious contaminants introduced during the recrystallization process, and with that the validation of recycled Si for the manufacturing of high-efficiency solar cells.

The minority carrier mobility of the recrystallized substrates is also analyzed. Through Time-of-flight measurements in a Haynes-Shockley setup, average

10.4229/EUPVSEC2025/5DV.2.32

020508-002

electron mobility values in the range of 1000 cm^{2}V^{-1}s^{-1} are obtained.

THz time domain spectroscopy (THz-TDS) measurements were made to interrogate in the AC limit the values of doping and mobility [7]. The measured samples provided Drude-like fingerprints in the frequency resolved complex conductivity. Fit to the data provided hole mobilities of approximately 400 cm^{2}V^{-1}s^{-1}, and doping in the range of 2×10^{16} cm^{-3}. The evolution of the doping content along the ingot was in good agreement with Scheil's model, validating the 4-probe measurement estimated in the DC limit.

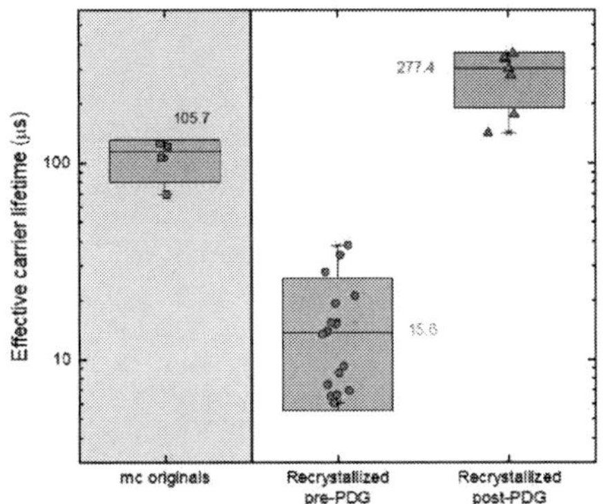

Figure 1: Effective carrier lifetime at an injection level Δn = 10^{15} cm^{-3} for the original multicrystalline wafers (grey) and the monocrystalline recrystallized wafers before (blue) and after (red) a P-diffusion gettering. Average values can be found in text.

3.2 Wafers grown from p-type multicrystalline material with diffused phosphorus emitters

In this case, after wafer cutting the hot probe indicated the wafers where n-type all along the ingot. Very low resistivities were measured with the four-point measurement, which corresponds to a distribution according to the Scheil equation of an initial phosphorus concentration of the order of 10^{18} cm^{-3} (see Fig. 2).

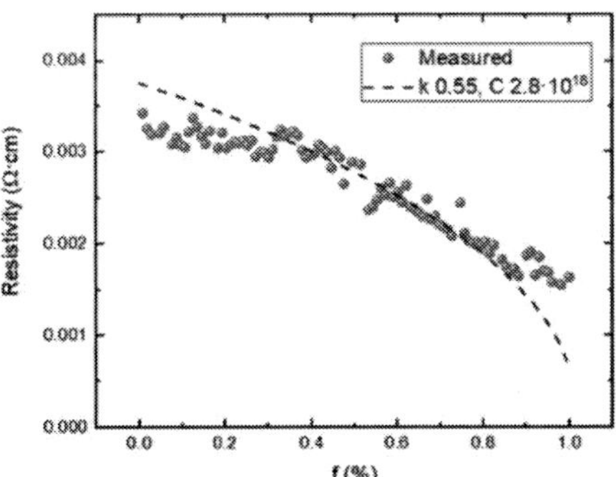

Figure 2: Resistivity measurement on wafers cut across the n-type compensated ingot, with estimation of the initial phosphorus concentration. f stands for the solidified fraction of the ingot.

Different hypotheses have been evaluated to explain why the phosphorus concentration in the material is much higher than expected. The two most plausible ones are the following. Firstly, we have to take into account that the phosphorus emitter has diffused on both sides of the wafer, so that the amount of n-type dopant is double what it would be in a conventional cell. Secondly, the diffusion under supersaturation conditions implies the incorporation of electrically inactive phosphorus [8], which dissolves in the molten silicon and occupies substitutional positions in the grown ingot, where it is electrically active and therefore contributes to the electrical properties of the substrates.

3.3 Solar cells on recrystallized silicon wafers

Conventional P-diffused emitter, Al-BSF solar cells were manufactured on some of the p-type recrystallized wafers, as well as on one of the original multicrystalline wafers and one demetallized substrate fragment. Further detail on the manufacturing of the solar cells can be found elsewhere [6].

Our findings suggest that the primary performance constraints observed in devices fabricated on recrystallized material and demetallized wafer fragments are not ascribed to material quality deterioration eventually incurred during the recovery and reuse phases of the silicon substrates. Rather, they stem from pitfalls encountered during cell manufacturing, notably highlighted by subpar BSF performance discerned in QE assessments and inadequate edge definition in the photolithography stage for front contact provisioning.

4   CONCLUSIONS

Three methods have been evaluated in the framework of the RESILIENS project for metal recovery from end-of-life silicon solar cells: alkaline etching, acidic leaching and bioleaching. Leaching with 3 M HNO$_3$ was the most effective acidic route, and a HALO medium with Fe^{3+} and Cl- was explored to avoid precipitation. In parallel, acidophilic and halotolerant bacteria were used for bioleaching. Alkaline etching with KOH/ethanol/water allowed the separation of metal contacts and the removal of ARC with minimal silicon loss. This strategy was optimised by design of experiments, and a selective sequence has been proposed to separate aluminium and silver.

The RESILIENS project has also proved that the recrystallization of silicon is feasible and that the distribution of dopants follows the expected behavior. In the case of using p-type silicon as starting material, resistivities and interstitial oxygen concentrations are within the expected values. The initial carrier lifetime values are modest, but after a gettering process they are within acceptable values for the fabrication of high efficiency solar cells, consistently exceeding 100 µs and reaching in the best cases more than 350 µs in some cases. In the case of using p-type silicon with n-type diffused emitters as starting material, n-type compensated wafers with a very high phosphorus concentration are obtained, possibly derived from the presence of electrically inactive phosphorus in the emitters diffused under supersaturation conditions.

The steps undertaken in the RESILIENS project towards the recycling of silicon solar cells support the idea that routes for the recovery and reutilization of their most valuable elements are technologically viable, and its establishment would lead the PV industry as a good example of circular economy.

5   ACKNOWLEDGEMENTS

We acknowledge Dr. Nikolay Abrosimov from Leibniz-Institut für Kristallzüchtung for crystal growth. Financial support from Grants No. TED2021-129624B funded by the Spanish International Research Agency MCIN/AEI/10.13039/501100011033 and by "NextGenerationEU"/PRTR is also acknowledged.

6   REFERENCES

[1] C. del Cañizo, D. Fuertes, "The landscape of PV recycling: challenges to make PV an example of circular economy, this conference.
[2] IM. Peters *et al.*, Cradle-to-cradle recycling in terawatt photovoltaics: A vision of perpetual utility, Joule (2024).
[3] M. Tierno *et al.*, Solar Energy 274 (2024) 112533.
[4] A. Vázquez *et al.*, Advancing solar energy sustainability: tackling PV cell upcycling through metal recovery, this conference.
[5] E. Scheil, Int. J. Mat. Research 34 (1942) 70.
[6] J. Hofstetter *et al.*, Prog. Photov. 24 (2016) 122.
[7] R. Ulbricht *et al.*, Rev. Mod. Phys. 89 (2017) 29901.
[8] H. Wagner *et al.*, J. Appl. Phys. 119 (2016) 185704.

Critical Review of Environmental LCA Methods and Their Representation of Current PV Market

Cristina Polacchi[1a], Atse Louwen[1b], Sandra Gallmetzer[1c], Luis André Pereira Fialho[1d], Denet Soler Toledo[2e]

[1]Eurac Research, Institute for Renewable Energy, Bolzano, Italy
[2]Centro de Desarrollo Energético CDEA-UA, Universidad de Antofagasta - Campus Coloso, Antofagasta, Chile
[a]cristina.polacchi@eurac.edu; [b]atse.lowen@gmail.com; [c]sandra.gallmetzer@eurac.edu; [d]luis.fialho@eurac.edu; [e]denet.soler@uantof.cl

Introduction

- The aim of this study is to evaluate existing **methods and inventories** used for environmental lifecycle assessments (E-LCA) of photovoltaic (PV) systems, in particular towards identifying gaps to perform **location-specific studies,** considering all the phases from manufacturing to operation and maintenance (O&M), to end-of-life operations.
- The **Atacama Desert in Chile** was chosen as a **case study**, since the study is part of the **CACTUS project,** which aims to enhance collaboration between European and Latin American countries in the field of PV development.
- The case study was also selected due to a **lack of representativeness** of studies in **desert contexts**.

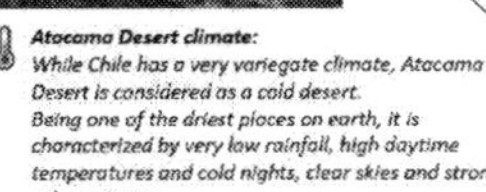
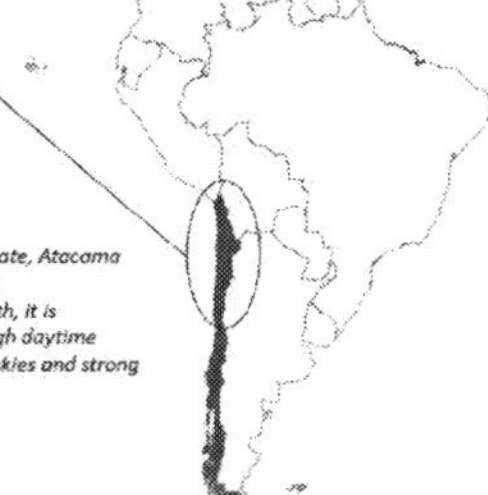

Atacama Desert climate:
While Chile has a very variegate climate, Atacama Desert is considered as a cold desert. Being one of the driest pieces on earth, it is characterized by very low rainfall, high daytime temperatures and cold nights, clear skies and strong solar radiation.

ENVIRONMENTAL LCA HOTSPOTS PER LIFECYCLE STAGE: ATACAMA DESERT CASE STUDY

Manufacturing and system design

- The majority of LCA studies are focused on PV technologies (Al-BSF, PERC) that are **non representative of the current market** (PERC, SHJ, TOPCon)
- Only a few LCA studies adequately address the **Balance of System (BOS)**.
- **Regionalization** of manufacturing processes in LCA studies is most often performed by only changing the **energy mix** of the country desired, in the manufacturing processes, without considering a **PV system design tailored** to the specific climatic conditions.
  In *Table 1*, the **stress factors** affecting the operating conditions and the resulting **design requirements** of a PV system in the Atacama Desert are summarized

Table 1. Summary of Atacama desert conditions that have an influence on PV design manufacturing requirements

	Atacama desert conditions
Köppen-Geiger classification	• Arid Cold Desert (BWk) [1]
PV stress factors	• Accelerated wear • High UV • Saline and corrosive soil • Limited water resources [2]
PV system design	• UV resistant encapsulant (PO over EVA) and backsheet • High anti-reflective coated glass • Hydrophobic or anti-soiling coatings to reduce particle adhesion • Compatibility with ad-hoc cleaning processes • High temperature resistant BOS components [3]

O&M

- **O&M is highly site-specific**, even in desert climates with similar characteristics (hot desert (BWh), foggy desert (BWn), cold desert (BWk)).
- Specific **degradation mechanisms** occurs depending on installation location climatic conditions: the **environmental impact** is depending on the climatic stress factors.
- **O&M phase** is often neglected in LCA studies, while it can be almost **as important as the PV design phase** in LCA, especially in remote areas (e.g., desert regions) due to transport operations and faster components replacement [2].
- **Water cleaning** remains the most adequate process, equipped with water **mitigation systems to reduce water stress**, due to limited water resources of the area (e.g., recirculation and filtering, adaptive cleaning based on monitoring soiling ratio)

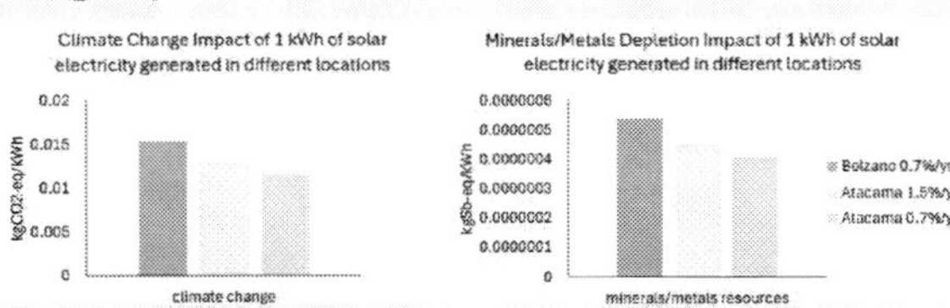

Figure 1. Cradle-to-gate Environmental impact results of 1 kWh of solar electricity, installed in different regions, reflecting the difference of results with different linear annual degradation rates assumed

End-of-life

- Different **LCA modelling methods** make LCA results difficult to compare:
  - **End-of-life approach:** evaluating the benefit from the avoided burdens thanks to the recycling;
  - **Cut-off approach:** using economic allocation to attribute the impact of the recycled co-products.
- LCA are not always reflecting the differences in **legislative requirements of different countries,** related to PV waste management and recycling processes. A summary of legislative requirements is presented for EU and Chile in *Table 2*.

Table 2. Comparison of legislative framework for PV waste management between Europe and Chile

	Europe	Chile
Law	WEEE Directive [4]	REP Law (20.920) [5]
Timeline	2003 first version 2012 new version 2014 PV included in the scope	2016 passed 2023 in force
Type of waste	Electrical and electronic equipment	General waste, including electric and electronic equipment
Producer responsibility	Yes: producers must deliver PV waste to an authorised centre	Yes: producers must deliver PV waste to an authorised centre
Quantitative collection target	85% of panels recovered and 80% prepared for reuse and recycled	Not specified

Conclusions and next steps

- **LCA inventories** reflecting up-to-date market situation and **geographical context, adequately including O&M and end-of-life stages,** are crucial to perform reliable and accurate LCA studies.
- **Social aspects,** addressing the significant lack of methodology harmonization and available inventories, will be discussed as a next step within CACTUS project.
- For future studies it would be beneficial to provide location specific **LCA guidelines** for **other regions of the world** with different climatic conditions.
- **Environmental Product Declarations (EPDs)** can be used as a future reliable source for LCA inventories and benchmark for results comparison.
- Ad-hoc lifecycle frameworks to **include circularity aspects** in lifecycle assessment and embrace the circular economy perspective needs to be improved.

References

[1] J. H. Schween, D. Hoffmeister, U. Löhnert, Filling the observational gap in the Atacama Desert with a new network of climate stations, Global and Planetary Change, Volume 184, 2020, 103034, ISSN 0921-8181, https://doi.org/10.1016/j.gloplacha.2019.103034.

[2] D. Soler, L. Rigamonti, N. Gazbour, E. Fuentealba, Environmental performance of a 1 MW photovoltaic plant in the Atacama Desert: A life cycle assessment study, Solar Energy, Volume 292, 2025, 113454, ISSN 0038-092X, https://doi.org/10.1016/j.solener.2025.113454.

[3] M. Mehdi, N. Ammari, A. A. Merrouni, S. Elhamaoui, M. Dahmani, Innovative design and field performance evaluation of a desert-adapted PV module for enhanced solar energy harvesting and reliability in harsh arid environments, Applied Energy, Volume 366, 2024, 123359, ISSN 0306-2619, https://doi.org/10.1016/j.apenergy.2024.123359.

[4] Directive 2012/19/EU of the European Parliament and of the Council of 4 July 2012 on waste electrical and electronic equipment (WEEE)

[5] Ley N°20.920 "REP": "Marco para la Gestión de Residuos, la Responsabilidad Extendida del Productor y Fomento al Reciclaje"

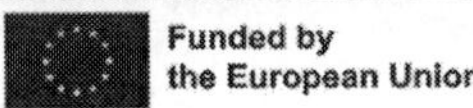

Funded by the European Union

This project has received funding from the European Union's Horizon Europe research and innovation programme under grant agreement No. 101132182.

020509-001

A MULTI-MODAL MACHINE LEARNING FRAMEWORK FOR IMPROVED HEALTH ASSESSMENT OF END-OF-LIFE PV MODULES

Berhane Darsene Dimd*[1], Martin Bellmann[1], and Christine Klos[2]
[1]Department of Sustainable Energy Technology, SINTEF Industry, Alfred Getz Vei 2, Trondheim, 7034, Norway
[2]Buhck Re.Energy GmbH & Co. KG, Liebigstraße 46 22133 Hamburg, Germany

ABSTRACT: The rapid increase in photovoltaic (PV) installations worldwide has raised growing concerns about the management of end-of-life (EOL) PV modules, with waste volumes projected to rise significantly in the coming decades. Robust and accurate health assessment of EOL PV modules is essential to enable their reuse as second-life products and to optimize recycling processes. Several studies have explored machine learning (ML) methods for assessing PV module health using current-voltage (IV) data and electroluminescence (EL) imaging. While successful, most of these techniques have been applied to single data sources, either EL images for crack detection or IV curves for failure classification. Such approaches fail to use the full potential of integrating multiple characterization methods. This paper proposes a conceptual framework for combining diverse data sources, such as EL images and IV curves, using ML approaches for EOL PV module health assessment at waste management facilities. It integrates both EL images and IV curves and uses the correlations between visual and electrical data to provide a more robust and reliable assessment of module health. This can identify degradation patterns and performance issues with better accuracy than single-data approaches, ultimately improving the sorting of EOL PV modules for reuse or recycling. The proposed framework can support circular economy objectives and sustainability in PV systems by reducing environmental impact and improving management of growing EOL module volumes.

Keywords: PV module, End-of-life PV, Machine learning, EL imaging, IV data, Circular economy

1 INTRODUCTION

The rapid global expansion of PV systems has driven installed capacity beyond 1.4 TW as of 2023, with further growth anticipated [1]. As PV modules near the end of their operational lifetimes, effective waste management has become imperative. A 2016 report by the International Renewable Energy Agency (IRENA) and the International Energy Agency Photovoltaic Power Systems (IEA-PVPS) projects that PV waste could reach 1.7 million tons by 2030 and 60 million tons by 2050 under standard failure scenarios, with worst-case scenarios seeing these figures increase to 8 million and 78 million tons, respectively [2]. This increasing wave of decommissioned PV modules underscores the urgent need for sustainable strategies to handle end-of-life (EOL) PV modules. Current PV waste management strategies focus on recycling materials and extending module lifespans through reuse. The principle of reuse, in particular, supports the circular economy by conserving resources and reducing energy intensive processing. However, second-life applications for decommissioned modules face challenges related to performance, safety, and financial viability [3]. This work focuses on the former, the performance aspect of EOL PV modules. Accurate and reliable health assessments are important for determining whether EOL modules are suitable for reuse or must be directed to recycling.

Manual inspections using IV curve testing and EL imaging are commonly used to evaluate module health condition. While effective, these techniques require specialized equipment, and demand a high level of human expertise, raising concerns about scalability as EOL PV volume increases. Machine learning (ML) based health assessments offer promising solution for automating and streamlining EOL module health monitoring. These methods can rapidly identify defects and performance issues and can process large volumes. Research in this domain remains in development, but findings suggest these approaches can improve decision-making and improve waste management efficiency. This shift toward automated health assessment could prove essential for handling the expected rise in EOL PV modules. This work focuses on evaluating ML-based techniques for PV module health assessment and proposing a conceptual framework of multi-modal ML approach to improve the accuracy and robustness of health assessments at waste management facilities.

Existing ML-based approaches predominantly analyze single data sources, such as EL imaging for crack detection or IV curves for classifying failure modes; however, each method alone provides only a partial view on the condition of EOL PV modules. In contrast, the multi-modal machine learning approach proposed in this work integrates both EL images and IV curves, using the correlations between visual and electrical data to provide a more robust and reliable assessment of module health. This multi-modal model can identify degradation patterns and performance issues with better accuracy than single-data approaches, ultimately improving the sorting of EOL modules for reuse or recycling in waste management facilities.

2 METHODLOGY

Health assessment of EOL PV modules is essential for determining their suitability for reuse or recycling. This section explores common defects in EOL PV modules and the detection methods used to identify them. It also reviews existing ML techniques for PV module health assessment, followed by a discussion of the proposed multi-modal ML approach.

2.1 Common defects and their detection

PV modules experience various defects over their operational lifetime, which can impact their performance. The most common defects include cell cracks, delamination, potential-induced degradation (PID), bypass diode failure, and hot spots. These defects vary in severity, ranging from minor defects (e.g., soiling and frame deformation) to moderate defects (e.g., snail trails and back sheet issues) and major defects (e.g., hotspots and

10.4229/EUPVSEC2025/5DV.2.35

cell cracks). Their detection methods also differ, including visual inspection (e.g., glass breakage and delamination), IV characterization (e.g., mismatches and degradation), and EL imaging (e.g., microcracks).

2.2 Existing ML approaches

Several studies in the literature have explored ML methods for assessing the health of PV modules using IV curve data and EL imaging. Authors in [4] used ML models for PV fault classification based on IV curves, employing convolutional neural networks (CNNs) to identify faults caused by soiling and cell cracks, achieving 96% accuracy on real-world test data. Similarly, authors in [5] implemented ML algorithms to classify PV module conditions into eight categories using IV curve data. On the other hand, authors in [6], [7] employed EL images for the automated detection and classification of defects in PV modules. In both approaches, a CNN is used as the base model. In summary, ML-based PV module health assessment relying solely on IV characterization or EL imaging has inherent limitations. IV curves lack spatial resolution, while EL imaging does not provide direct performance information. A multi-modal ML approach integrating both methods can improve health assessment by using their complementary advantages.

2.3 The proposed approach

The proposed multi-modal ML approach in this work integrates both EL images and IV curve data, using correlations between visual and electrical data to provide a comprehensive and reliable assessment of EOL PV module health. By combining these complementary data sources, the model improves the detection of degradation patterns and performance issues with better accuracy than single-data approaches. This improved health assessment method allows more effective sorting of EOL modules for reuse or recycling, contributing to a more efficient and sustainable EoL PV waste management process. The overall workflow of the proposed approach is shown in this Figure 1.

The proposed framework provides an end-to-end pipeline for assessing the health of EoL PV modules using EL imaging and IV characterization. The overall workflow consists of image processing (segmentation and data augmentation), feature extraction, classification, evaluation, and module-level decision making.

a) Image processing: EL images of entire PV modules are segmented into individual solar cell images. This allows cell-level defect detection and ensures that the classification model operates on consistent input regions. Since the dataset typically exhibits strong class imbalance, with certain defect categories (e.g., critical defects) underrepresented, image augmentation techniques including random rotation, zooming, and horizontal/vertical flipping are applied to increase their representation and improve classifier robustness.

b) Feature extraction: For each cell image, high-level features are extracted using a pre-trained convolutional neural networks (ResNet50, EfficientNetB0, MobileNetV2, and others). The classification head is removed, and the output of the final pooling layer is used to generate a feature vector. Each vector is paired with its ground-truth defect label for supervised learning.

c) Classification: The extracted features and labels are divided into training and testing sets using stratified sampling. A Support Vector Machine (SVM) is trained on the training data.

d) Model evaluation: The trained model is evaluated on the held-out test set. The performance is evaluated using standard classification metrics and the confusion matrix, which emphasizes the per-class classification accuracy.

e) Module-level decision: Following cell-level classification, results are aggregated to determine the condition of the entire module. A set of predefined decision rules is applied, which take into account the number and severity of defective cells. These rules are combined with information from IV characterization, which directly reflects the module's electrical performance. The combined assessment is used to determine whether a given module is suitable for second-life applications or should be directed to recycling pathways.

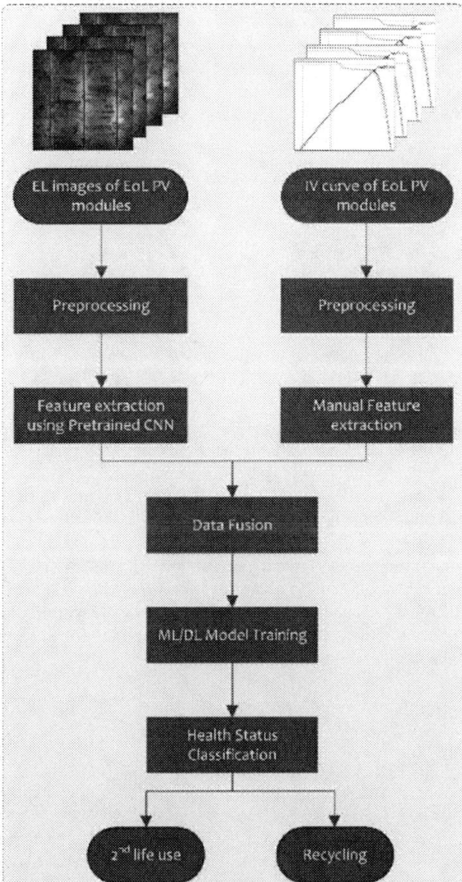

Figure 1: The proposed multi-modal ML approach.

3 PRELIMINARY RESULTS AND DISCUSSION

In this preliminary study, a total of 1200 cell-level EL images were used to evaluate the effectiveness of the proposed approach. The dataset was divided into 80% for training and 20% for testing. Within the training data, five-fold cross-validation was used to optimize model performance and reduce the risk of overfitting. Feature representations were extracted using five different CNN backbones: ResNet50, EfficientNetB0, DenseNet121, MobileNetV2, and InceptionV3. These features were then used to train a SVM classifier. Model performance was assessed in terms of the F1-score, the harmonic mean of precision and recall, which provides a balanced evaluation across classes and is particularly suitable in the presence of class imbalance.

Figure 2 presents the summary of the performance of the five backbone–SVM models based on the F1-score for three classes. As it can be seen from the result, all architectures showed consistently high performance especially for the major and normal defect classes. In contrast, all struggled on classifying the minor defect class. Among the tested backbones, EfficientNetB0 showed has the best performance, achieving an average score of 0.97 across all classes. These findings suggest that while defect detection is highly reliable for major and normal classes, classification of minor defects remains a challenge.

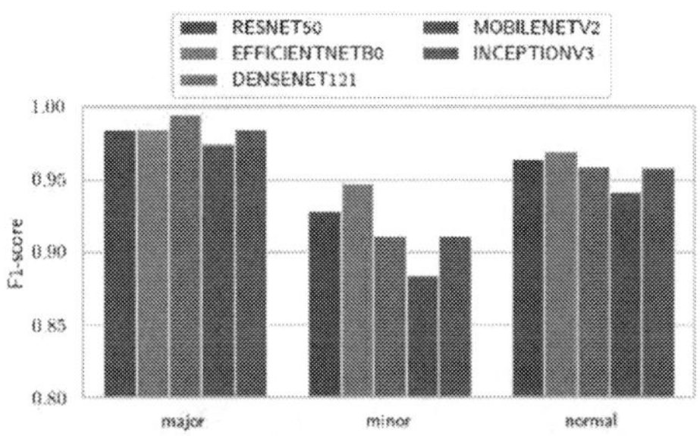

Figure 2: F1-score of the five models on the test data.

The confusion matrix (Figure 3) and t-SNE visualization (Figure 4) further support the above F1-score results for EfficientNetB0. The major class is clearly separable, achieving near-perfect classification with only 3 misclassifications. The normal class also performs well, though it is confused with the minor class. Overall, the results confirm that EfficientNetB0 provides robust and balanced performance.

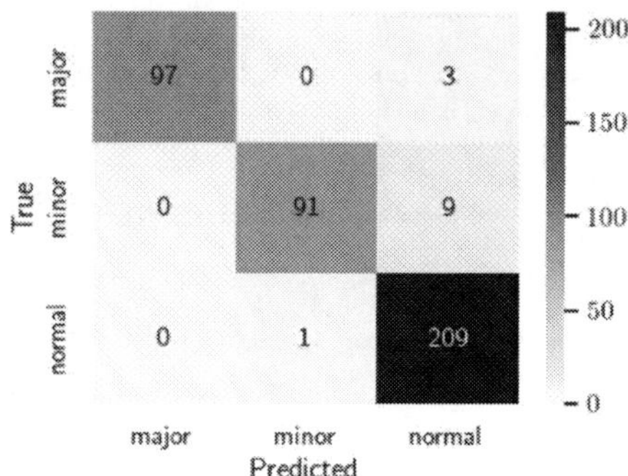

Figure 3: Confusion matix result for EfficientNetB0.

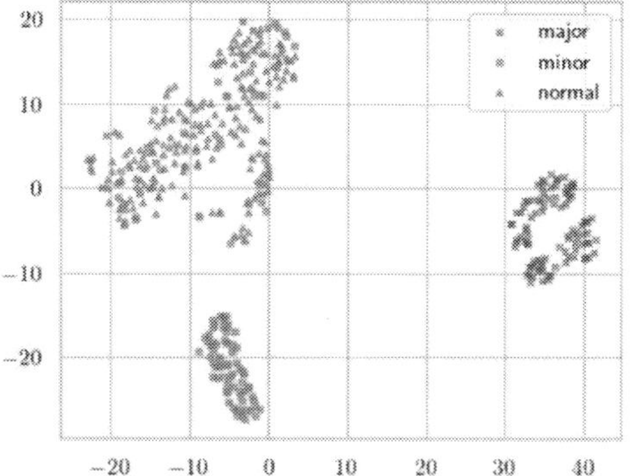

Figure 4: t-SNE result for EfficientNetB0.

4 CONCLUSION

The preliminary results indicate that a multi-modal ML approach gives promising improvements in EOL PV module health assessment, though several challenges remain. Limited availability of standardized datasets combining IV curves and EL images limits robust model training and validation. Moreover, fusing heterogeneous data and ensuring model generalization across diverse environmental conditions, degradation modes, and PV technologies add further complexity. Nevertheless, with the rapid growth of EOL PV modules, this approach has important implications for sustainable waste management. Reliable health assessment can facilitate reuse of functional modules and reduce premature disposal. At scale, such methods support more efficient PV waste processing, yielding both economic and environmental benefits.

5 ACKNOWLEDGEMENT

This work is part of the QUASAR project funded by the European Union's Horizon Europe research and innovation programme under grant agreement number 101122298.

7 REFERENCES

[1] "Solar energy." Accessed: Jan. 28, 2025. Solar energy
[2] "End-of-life management Solar Photovoltaic Panels." Accessed: Jan. 28, 2025. End-of-life management

Solar Photovoltaic Panels.

[3] "Re-use of pv modules: progress in standardisation and learnings from a real case study – trust pv." Accessed: Jan. 28, 2025. RE-USE OF PV MODULES: PROGRESS IN STANDARDISATION AND LEARNINGS FROM A REAL CASE STUDY – TRUST PV.

[4] M. W. Hopwood, J. S. Stein, J. L. Braid, and H. P. Seigneur, "Physics-Based Method for Generating Fully Synthetic IV Curve Training Datasets for Machine Learning Classification of PV Failures," Energies, vol. 15, no. 14, Art. no. 14, Jan. 2022. https://doi.org/10.3390/en15145085.

[5] B. Li, C. Delpha, A. Migan-Dubois, and D. Diallo, "Fault diagnosis of photovoltaic panels using full I–V characteristics and machine learning techniques," Energy Conversion and Management, vol. 248, p. 114785, Nov. 2021. https://doi.org/10.1016/j.enconman.2021.114785

[6] W. Tang, Q. Yang, K. Xiong, and W. Yan, "Deep learning based automatic defect identification of photovoltaic module using electroluminescence images," Solar Energy, vol. 201, pp. 453–460, May 2020. https://doi.org/10.1016/j.solener.2020.03.049.

[7] D. Korkmaz and H. Acikgoz, "An efficient fault classification method in solar photovoltaic modules using transfer learning and multi-scale convolutional neural network," Engineering Applications of Artificial Intelligence, vol. 113, p. 104959, Aug. 2022. https://doi.org/10.1016/j.engappai.2022.104959.

REMOTE FEASIBILITY ASSESSMENT OF PV PANEL REPAIRS AND REPLACEMENTS FROM A LIFE CYCLE PERSPECTIVE USING IRT AND HDR IMAGERY FROM UAV

Christoph Waibel[1,2], Pieter-Jan Baeck[1], Elias Hafidi[3]
[1]Flemish Institute for Technological Research (VITO), Boeretang 200, 2400 Mol, Belgium
[2]EnergyVille, Thor Park 8310, 3600 Genk, Belgium
[3]Inflights BV, Cantersteen 12, 1000 Brussels, Belgium
christoph.waibel@vito.be

This paper investigates the life cycle impact and carbon payback time (CPBT) of PV panel repairs and replacements in ground mounted farms. Using UAV captured RGB and IRT images, multiclass classification models are used to identify different anomaly types. Following, the parametric embodied impact calculator for PV panels, ACACIA, is used to assess CPBT from repair and replacement interventions in different scenarios. As case study, faulty panels in Spain, Bilbao, and Belgium, Brussels, are investigated. Results suggest that PV replacements need about 6 years to reach carbon break even. However, if sub components of a panel can be repaired, such as the backsheet or the junction box, CBPT can be down to 0.03 years. It suggests that full PV panel replacements need to be evaluated with the remaining operation time of the PV farm, especially towards its end of planned service time. Ideally, a 2nd life of a replaced PV panel should be foreseen, or partial repairs of sub components enforced, thus ensuring an environmentally beneficial repair and replacement.
Keywords: Remote Sensing, Life Cycle Assessment, Fault Detection, Computer Vision, Repair

1 INTRODUCTION

Ground-mounted PV plants consist of arrays of interlinked panels that can be damaged by various environmental factors. When damage occurs, an assessment is made to evaluate risks (e.g., fire or electrical hazards) and power loss, guiding decisions on whether to replace, isolate, or leave the panels in place. UAV-based remote inspection thereby has become an efficient and cost-effective method for anomaly detection. Captured images include high definition range (HDR) in RGB, infrared thermal (IRT) or Photoluminescence (PIL), and they should be used complementarily for the detection of various anomalies [1].

More recently, computer vision (CV) and deep learning (DL) techniques have been successfully implemented to automatically detect various defect types, using multiclass classification algorithms [2]. For the training of such classification models, large datasets are required, where images are labelled with their certain defect type, or as non-defect. Various large open datasets exist for different image types, ranging from RGB, IRT, PIL, and more [3], which eases developing own classification models.

However, in case a malfunctioning panel is detected, the question still remains on the exact intervention to partake: repair, replace, or keep. Especially in from the perspective of the environmental impact that a PV panel has, a context-dependent assessment is necessary to ensure a potential PV replacement contributes positively.

2 METHODOLOGY

In this paper, we propose a workflow where (i) unmanned aerial vehicles (UAV) equipped with RGB and IRT cameras are used to capture images of ground mounted PV farms, where (ii) these images are then used to autonomously detect various defect types and anomalies using multiclass classification algorithms trained on open datasets, and subsequently (iii) the embodied impact of different interventions are assessed,

including repair of the panel or complete replacement, using the open source parametric embodied impact configurator of PV panels called ACACIA [4] (see **Figure 1**).

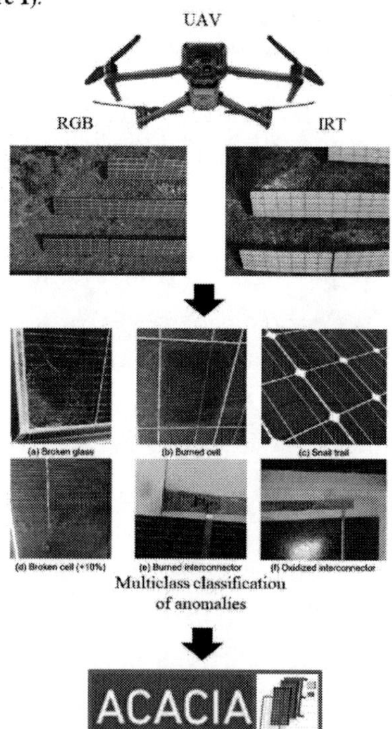

Figure 1: Proposed Workflow from UAV image capture to anomaly classification and LCA calculation for repairs.

The scientific novelty of this paper lies in the remote and autonomous quantification of the environmental impact of potential repairs, depending on the damage type (or affected panel component). This adds crucial information for making environmentally and economically conscious decisions on which interventions to take for the damaged panels. This first and easy to obtain estimation using UAV and defect classification combined with embodied impact calculations is important as it might influence the decision to employ a repair & replacement team on-site.

In the following, the methodology is further outlined in 2.1 Remote Sensing, 2.2 Defect Detection with Computer Vision, 2.3 Life Cycle Assessment using ACACIA.

2.1 Remote Sensing

Drones (i.e. UAV) are now commonly used for remote anomaly detection on PV farms [1]. Various imaging techniques are used, with the most popular and accessible techniques being visual (i.e., RGB) and infrared thermal (IRT) imaging. These can capture different defects and should be used complementarily. Using RGB images, surface related issues can be easily spotted, including glass and frame breakage, delamination, browning/yellowing, snail trails, or soiling. Using IRT, on the other hand, reveals hot spots on solar cells or entire panels, on cables, and junction boxes (**Table I**). It is thereby important to note that defects at different layers and components of a PV panel can be detected using different sensing techniques (**Figure 2**).

Table I: Overview of considered failure types detectable with RGB and IRT at each PV layer. Table adapted after Chen et al. (2025) [3] and Friesen et al. (2025) [5].

PV component	Failure modes	Imaging techniques
Frame, Front Cover	Breakage	RGB
Encapsulant	Yellowing, Delamination	RGB
Solar cells	Cracking, Hotspot	RGB, IRT
Backsheet	Delamination, Cracking	RGB
Junction box, connector	Breakage, poor sealing, hot	RGB, IRT

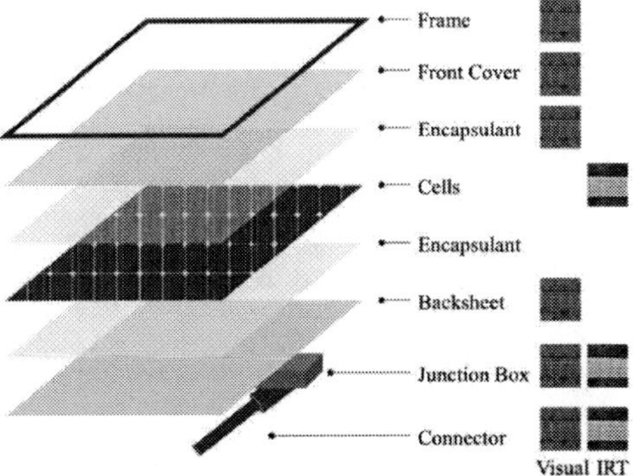

Figure 2: Defects detectable by IRT and/or RGB at each PV layer. Image modified after Chen et al. (2025) [3]

2.2 Defect Detection with Computer Vision

Common PV failure types are listed and described in the IEA technical report by Köntges et al. 2014 [6] and Friesen et al. 2025 [5], and it becomes apparent that many can be detected using vision based approaches. Using Computer vision (CV) and more recently deep learning (DL) models, such failures and defects can be recognized for autonomously using images of the panel to be inspected as input to the model [2]. Thereby, Convolutional Neural Networks (CNN) are employed and existing work has demonstrated their reliable and effective utilization to predict different faults using RGB and IRT images. Therefore, for this study, we assume a reliable classification from our input images and keep a demonstration for our own DL implementation for future work.

2.3 Life Cycle Assessment using ACACIA

In order to improve the cost efficiency and reliability of PV systems, it is crucial to obtain an understanding of common failures over the life time of a system [7]. Furthermore, from an environmental perspective, it is essential to ensure a proper end-of-life procedure of panels, and it has been shown that common monocrystalline and polycrystalline PV panels can be recycled to a high degree, regaining most of the materials [8].

Nevertheless, a major challenge remains in repairing defect PV panels. This is due to their design with laminated layers bond together (**Figure 2**). However, a major contribution to the environmental impact of a PV panel is from the solar cells. It is therefore of interest to identify the defect component in a panel and if possible conduct a repair maintaining the most environmentally intensive parts if those are undamaged.

In the workflow of this paper, we use an open-source browser-implemented life cycle assessment (LCA) configurator called ACACIA [4]. It offers a break-down of various PV panel components with configurable parts as shown in **Figure 2**.

3 CASE STUDY

We calculate the environmental impact, more specifically the global warming potential (GWP) and the resulting carbon payback time (CPBT), for following scenarios.

a) **Full PV replacement:** Any failure type requires full PV replacement
b) **Replacing junction box only:** Junction box and connectors can be replaced, anything else requires panel replacement.
c) **Replacing PET backsheet:** Junction box and connectors, backsheets, frame and front cover can be replaced, but defects in encapsulant and solar cells require panel replacement
d) **Replacing frame:** Same assumptions as c)
e) **Replacing front cover:** Same assumptions as c)

To test our workflow, we consider two PV farms, one in Belgium, Brussels, and one in Spain, Bilbao. Grid carbon emissions are obtained from ElectricityMaps [9] for the year 2024 (**Figure 3**). As lifetime of the PV farms and the panels, we assume 30 years. Annual electricity yield is calculated using PVGIS [10]. We further assume monocrystalline solar cells with an aluminum frame, tempered glass front cover, ethylene vinyl acetate (EVA) encapsulant, and polyethylene terephthalate (PET) backsheet. We also assume that the PV farms have a string layout with panels of 500 Wp with bypass diodes, such that faulty panels would not lead to a failure of the entire string.

While a comprehensive list of common failures and their associate risks, as well as appropriate response measures, are given in the technical reports from the IEA [5,6], they do not provide a quantification of failure occurrence. Therefore, since it is not clear, which failure type occurs how often, we list the environmental impact for each scenario, separately.

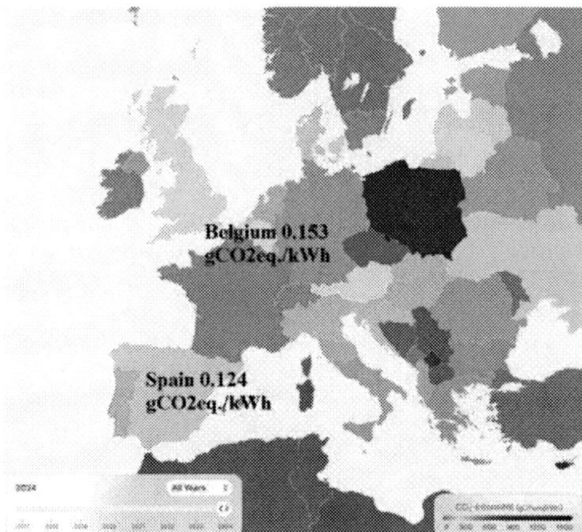

Figure 3: Grid carbon intensities for 2024 in Belgium and Spain. Image modified after ElectricityMaps [9]

4 RESULTS

Assuming a 35° South orientation for PV panels in both locations, Bilbao and Brussels, we can calculate the annual yield of a 500 Wp monocrystalline panel of 1.95 m² as follows: 659.86 kWh per year in Bilbao, or 338.39 kWh/m² per year, and 582.40 kWh per year in Belgium, Brussels, or 298.67 kWh/m² per year.

Considering the grid carbon intensities of both locations for 2024 (124 gCO2eq/kWh in Spain and 153 gCO2eq/kWh in Belgium), it translates to 42 kgCO2eq/m² carbon abatement per year in Spain, Bilbao, and 45.7 kgCO2/m² carbon abatement per year in Belgium, Brussels of a new PV panel.

The GWP of the configured PV panel for each component is shown in **Figure 4** and it sums to 266 kgCO2eq/m² total GWP. It means that the CBPT of a new panel is 6.3 years in Spain, Bilbao, and 5.8 years in Belgium, Brussels. Following the same calculation, we show CBPT for all scenarios a) to e) in **Figure 5**.

The results show that for all other scenarios, where we assume a repair of a defect panel by replacing only subcomponents of a panel, the CBPT is significantly reduced. Replacing the frame of a panel shows a CBPT of about 0.5 years, replacing the front cover has a CBPT of about 0.3 years, and replacing the backsheet or the junction box even has a CBPT of 0.1 years or less.

The differences between Spain and Belgium are marginal despite the higher yield possible in Spain. This is caused by lower grid intensities in Spain.

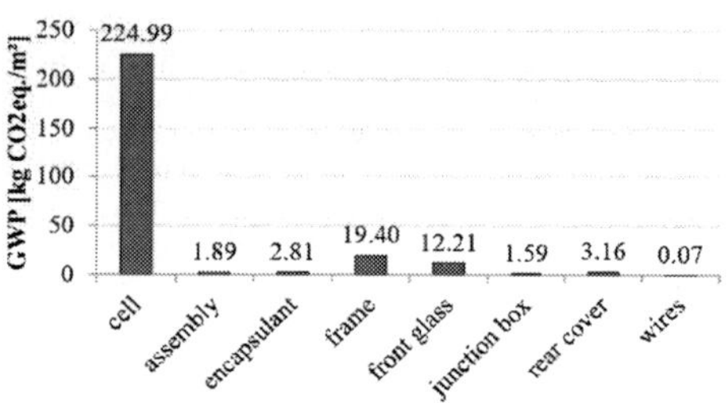

Figure 4: Global warming potential (GWP) per component of a monocrystalline PV panel using RER (European) data from ACACIA (Galimshina et al. 2024 [4]). Sum is 266.1 kgCO2eq./m²

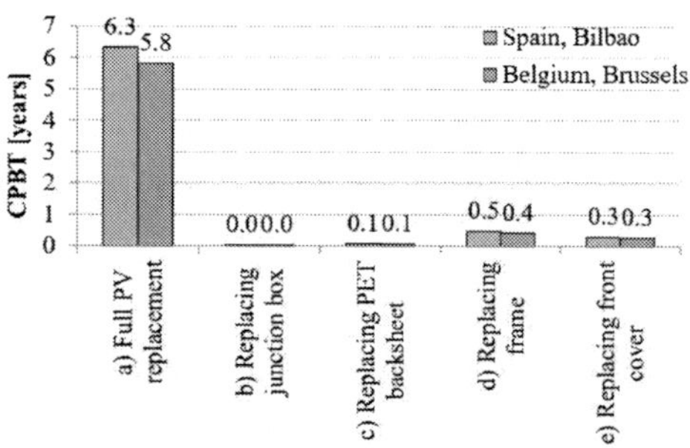

Figure 5: Carbon payback time (CPBT) in years for different repair / replacement scenarios.

5 DISCUSSION AND CONCLUSION

Using both RGB and IRT images in remote PV assessment complements the detectable fault types as they provide complementary information. With UAVs, a first estimation of the reparability of faulty PV panels can thus be done efficiently and effectively. With a following embodied environmental impact assessment, decisions can thus be made on the most economical and ecological interventions, whether be it repairing the faulty panel, replacing it, or leaving it in place. The workflow is a viable and efficient option for remote diagnostics of PV farms.

However, IRT and RGB images are evidently not able to detect all defects, and equipping UAVs with additional cameras and sensors, such as with daylight photoluminescence (PIL), should be considered [11,12]. Regarding the utilization of DL and CV models for the automatic detection of fault using images as inputs, large databases for established cell technologies (mono- and polycrystalline) are widespread, but newer cell technologies may likely need further development and model training [12,13].

With respect to the CBPT of PV panel replacements and component repairs, it is evident that the solar cell has the highest impact. Thus, it would be beneficial if only the damaged layers of a panel could be replaced and repaired while avoiding the replacement of the most carbon intensive components. Further research should investigate the feasibility of PV panel architectures with easier separability of the layers, and few related work is existing in the literature [14]. That way, frame, front cover, or backsheets, which all have minor impacts but are commonly involved in PV defects, could be more easily repaired, thus significantly reducing the environmental impact of interventions.

In conclusion, using the proposed workflow in this paper, from remote assessment of PV panel defects with UAVs, over autonomous defect classification using CV and DL, to an LCA assessment of different repair and replacement interventions, founded and informed decisions can be made, balancing between cost and environmental impact.

ACKNOWLEDGEMENT

This work has been funded by the European Union under Grant Agreement No 101138374. Views and opinions expressed are however those of the author(s) only and do not necessarily reflect those of the European Union or the European Health and Digital Executive Agency (HADEA). Neither the European Union nor the granting authority can be held responsible for them.

REFERENCES

[1] I. Høiaas, K. Grujic, A.G. Imenes, I. Burud, E. Olsen, N. Belbachir. "Inspection and condition monitoring of large-scale photovoltaic power plants: A review of imaging technologies". Renewable and Sustainable Energy Reviews 161 (2022) 112353.

[2] K. Masita et al. "Deep learning in defects detection of PV modules: A review." Solar Energy Advances (2025): 100090.

[3] X. Chen, B. Li, J.L. Braid, B. Byford, D.J. Colvin, A. Glaws, N. Jost, B. Pierce, S. Rabade, M. Springer, A. Jain. "Open data sets for assessing photovoltaic system reliability". Applied Energy 395 (2025) 126132.

[4] Galimshina, Alina, et al. "High-resolution parametric embodied impact configurator for PV and BIPV systems." Renewable Energy 236 (2024): 121404. https://acacia.arch.ethz.ch

[5] G. Friesen et al. "IEA-PVPS T13-30:2025: Photovoltaic Failure Fact Sheets (PVFS)". IEA Technical Report Task 13: Reliability and Performance of Photovoltaic Systems, International Energy Agency (2025).

[6] M. Köntges et al. "Performance and Reliability of Photovoltaic Systems". IEA Technical Report Subtask 3.2: Review of Failures of Photovoltaic Modules, International Energy Agency (2014).

[7] K.A. Weiß et al. "IEA-PVPS T13-16:2021: Service Life Estimation for Photovoltaic Modules". IEA PVPS Task 13: Reliability Performance, Operation and Reliability of Photovoltaic Systems, International Energy Agency (2014).

[8] G. Ansanelli et al. "A life cycle assessment of a recovery process from end-of-life photovoltaic panels." Applied Energy 290 (2021): 116727.

[9] ElectricityMaps, https://app.electricitymaps.com, website accessed [21.09.2025]

[10] PVGIS. https://pvgis.com/ , website accessed [21.09.2025]

[11] J.W. Weber et al. "Daylight photoluminescence imaging of photovoltaic systems using inverter-based switching". Prog Photovolt Res Appl. 2024;32:643–651.

[11] B. Doll et al. "Photoluminescence for Defect Detection on Full-Sized Photovoltaic Modules". IEEE Journal of Photovoltaics, Vol. 11, No. 6, November 2021

[12] M. Köntges et al. "IEA-PVPS T13-30:2025: Degradation and Failure Modes in New Photovoltaic Cell and Module Technologies". IEA Technical Report Task 13: Reliability and Performance of Photovoltaic Systems, Sandia National Laboratories.

[13] M. Aghaei et al. "Autonomous Intelligent Monitoring of Photovoltaic Systems: An In-Depth Multidisciplinary Review". Progress in Photovoltaics: Research and Applications, 2025; 33:381–409

[14] A. Majdi et al. "Fundamental study related to the development of modular solar panel for improved durability and repairability." IET Renewable Power Generation 15.7 (2021): 1382-1396.

Remote Feasibility Assessment of PV Panel Repairs and Replacements from a Life Cycle Perspective using IRT and HDR Imagery from UAV

Christoph Waibel[1,2], Pieter-Jan Baeck[1], Elias Hafdi[3]

[1] Flemish Institute for Technological Research (VITO), Boeretang 200, 2400 Mol, Belgium christoph.waibel@vito.be
[2] EnergyVille, Thor Park 3210, 3600 Genk, Belgium
[3] Inflighta BV, Centersteen 12, 1000 Brussels, Belgium

Abstract

This paper investigates the life cycle impact and carbon payback time (CPBT) of PV panel repairs and replacements in ground mounted farms. Using UAV captured RGB and IRT images, multiclass classification models are used to identify different anomaly types. Following, the parametric embodied impact calculator for PV panels, ACACIA, is used to assess CPBT from repair and replacement interventions in different scenarios. As case study, faulty panels in Spain, Bilbao, and Belgium, Brussels, are investigated. Results suggest that PV replacements need about 6 years to reach carbon break even. However, if sub components of a panel can be repaired, such as the backsheet or the junction box, CBPT can be down to 0.03 years. It suggests that full PV panel replacements need to be evaluated with the remaining operation time of the PV farm, especially towards its end of planned service time. Ideally, a 2nd life of a replaced PV panel should be foreseen, or partial repairs of sub components enforced, thus ensuring an environmentally beneficial repair and replacement.

Keywords: Remote Sensing, Life Cycle Assessment, Fault Detection, Computer Vision, Repair

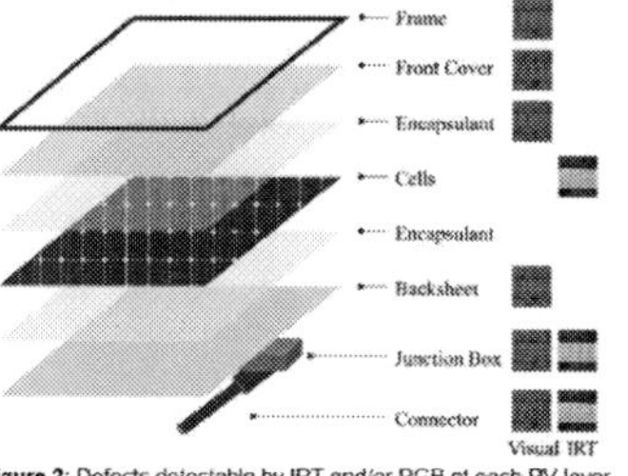

Figure 2: Defects detectable by IRT and/or RGB at each PV layer. Image modified after Chen et al. (2025) [3]

Table I: Overview of considered failure types detectable with RGB and IRT at each PV layer. Table adapted after Chen et al. (2025) [3] and Friesen et al. (2025) [5].

PV component	Failure modes	Imaging techniques
Frame, Front Cover	Breakage	RGB
Encapsulant	Yellowing, Delamination	RGB
Solar cells	Cracking, Hotspot	RGB, IRT
Backsheet	Delamination, Cracking	RGB
Junction box, connector	Breakage, poor sealing, hot	RGB, IRT

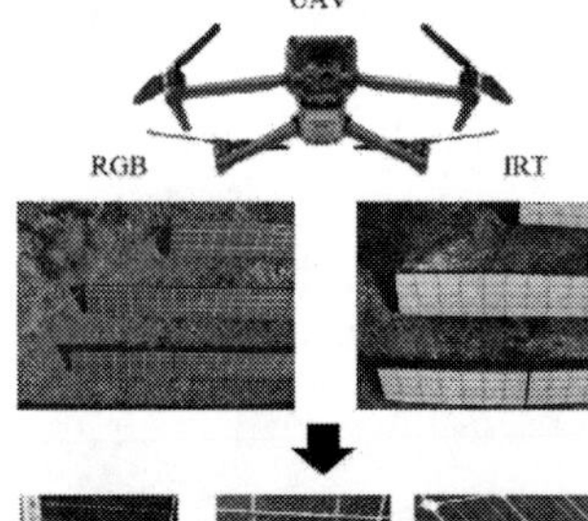

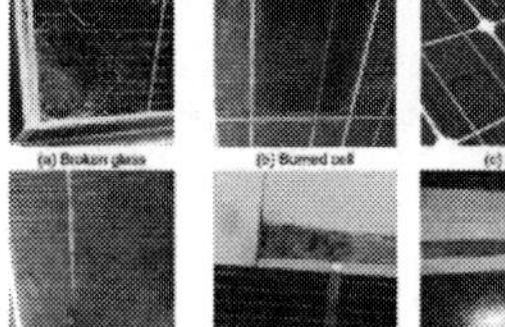

Multiclass classification of anomalies

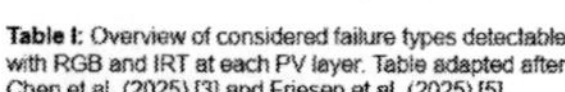

Figure 1: Proposed Workflow from UAV image capture to anomaly classification and LCA calculation for repairs.

Scenarios

a) **Full PV replacement:** Any failure type requires full PV replacement

b) **Replacing junction box only:** Junction box and connectors can be replaced, anything else requires panel replacement.

c) **Replacing PET backsheet:** Junction box and connectors, backsheets, frame and front cover can be replaced, but defects in encapsulant and solar cells require panel replacement.

d) **Replacing frame:** Same assumptions as c)

e) **Replacing front cover:** Same assumptions as c)

Calculated for Spain, Bilbao, and Belgium, Brussels, on 35° South tilt, with a 500 Wp panel of 1.95m².

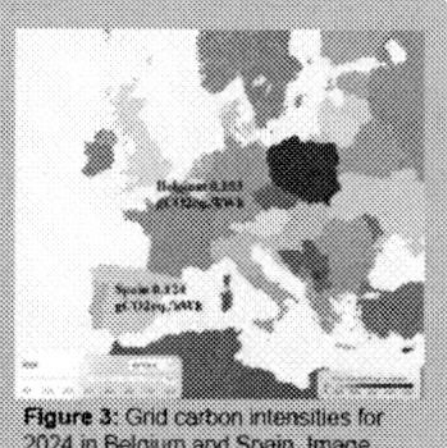

Figure 3: Grid carbon intensities for 2024 in Belgium and Spain. Image modified after app.electricitymaps.com

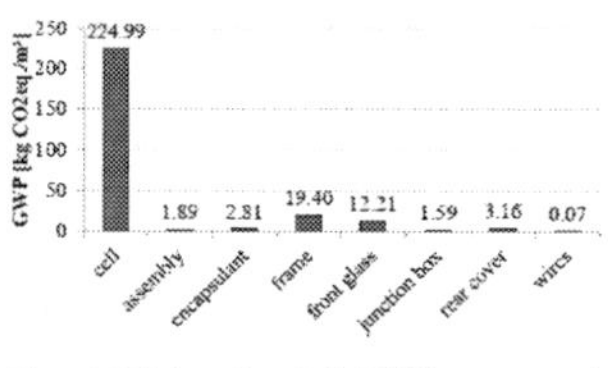

Figure 4: Global warming potential (GWP) per component of a monocrystalline PV panel using RER (European) data from ACACIA (Galimshina et al. 2024 [4]). Sum is 266.1 kgCO2eq./m²

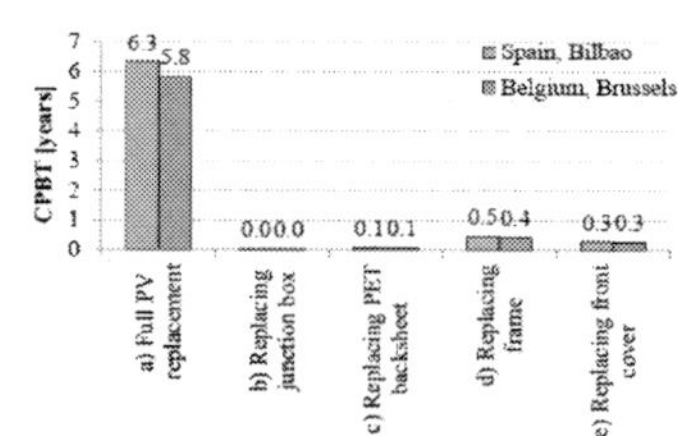

Figure 5: Carbon payback time (CPBT) in years for different repair / replacement scenarios

Results & Conclusion

- Carbon payback times (CBPT) are significantly lower when only repairing the damaged components in a a panel and not replacing the entire panel.
- The highest environmental impact stem from the solar cells. Other components have a marginal global warming potential (GWP)

- Infrared thermal (IRT) and visual (RGB) images provide complementary information and should both be used in remote fault detection
- Additional sensors and image techniques, such as daylight photoluminescence should be considered to detect further defect types
- Novel PV panel designs with easier separability of layers should be considered
- Novel cell technologies will require retraining of the classification algorithms

- Overall, the proposed workflow is an efficient approach towards a first estimate for PV panel repairs, balancing between environmental and economic considerations

Acknowledgement

This work has been funded by the European Union under Grant Agreement No 101138374. Views and opinions expressed are however those of the author(s) only and do not necessarily reflect those of the European Union or the European Health and Digital Executive Agency (HADEA). Neither the European Union nor the granting authority can be held responsible for them.

REFERENCES

[1] I. Høiaas, K. Grujic, A.G. Imenes, I. Burud, E. Olsen, N. Belbachir. "Inspection and condition monitoring of large-scale photovoltaic power plants: A review of imaging technologies". Renewable and Sustainable Energy Reviews 161 (2022) 112353.
[2] K. Masita et al. "Deep learning in defects detection of PV modules: A review." Solar Energy Advances (2025): 100090.
[3] X. Chen, B. Li, J.L. Braid, B. Byford, D.J. Colvin, A. Glaws, N. Jost, B. Pierce, S. Rabade, M. Springer, A. Jain. "Open data sets for assessing photovoltaic system reliability". Applied Energy 395 (2025) 126132.
[4] Galimshina, Alina, et al. "High-resolution parametric embodied impact configurator for PV and BIPV systems." Renewable Energy 236 (2024): 121404. https://acacia.arch.ethz.ch
[5] G. Friesen et al. "IEA-PVPS T13-30:2025: Photovoltaic Failure Fact Sheets (PVFS)". IEA Technical Report Task 13: Reliability and Performance of Photovoltaic Systems, International Energy Agency (2025).
[6] M. Köntges et al. "Performance and Reliability of Photovoltaic Systems". IEA Technical Report Subtask 3.2: Review of Failures of Photovoltaic Modules, International Energy Agency (2014).
[7] K.A. Weiß et al. "IEA-PVPS T13-16:2021: Service Life Estimation for Photovoltaic Modules". IEA PVPS Task 13: Reliability Performance, Operation and Reliability of Photovoltaic Systems, International Energy Agency (2014).
[8] G. Ansanelli et al. "A life cycle assessment of a recovery process from end-of-life photovoltaic panels." Applied Energy 290 (2021): 116727.
[9] ElectricityMaps, https://app.electricitymaps.com, website accessed [21.09.2025]
[10] PVGIS, https://pvgis.com/, website accessed [21.09.2025]
[11] J.W. Weber et al. "Daylight photoluminescence imaging of photovoltaic systems using inverter-based switching". Prog Photovolt Res Appl. 2024;32:643–651.
[11] B. Doll et al. "Photoluminescence for Defect Detection on Full-Sized Photovoltaic Modules". IEEE Journal of Photovoltaics, Vol. 11, No. 6, November 2021
[12] M. Köntges et al. "IEA-PVPS T13-30:2025: Degradation and Failure Modes in New Photovoltaic Cell and Module Technologies". IEA Technical Report Task 13: Reliability and Performance of Photovoltaic Systems, Sandia National Laboratories.
[13] M. Aghaei et al. "Autonomous Intelligent Monitoring of Photovoltaic Systems: An In-Depth Multidisciplinary Review". Progress in Photovoltaics: Research and Applications, 2025; 33:381–409
[14] A. Majdi et al. "Fundamental study related to the development of modular solar panel for improved durability and repairability." IET Renewable Power Generation 15.7 (2021): 1382-1396.

Enabling Innovation Through ESG:
A Roadmap for the European PV

Sustainability as a competitive advantage for Europe

Abeer Ali Khan[1*], Paula Sánchez-Friera[2], Sebastien Lizin[3], Samira Jama Aden[4], Pinar Derin-Gure[5], Jan Clyncke[6], John (Ioannis) A. Tsanakas[7], Marcello Passaro[8], Perine Louise Fleury[9], Cristina Polacchi[10], Veronese Elisa[10]

[1]First Solar Recycling GmbH, Germany, [2] Solkeys, Gijón, Spain, [3] Hasselt University, Belgium, [4] Helmholtz-Zentrum Berlin, Germany, [5] Middle East Technical University, Ankara, Turkiye, [6] PV CYCLE a.i.s.b.l., Belgium, [7] CEA, Liten, Univ. Grenoble Alpes, Campus INES, 73375 Le Bourget du Lac, France, [8] Sunzest Solar, Netherlands, [9] Biosphere Solar B.V., Netherlands, [10] Eurac Research, Italy

* e-mail: AbeerAli.Khan@FirstSolar.com

CONTEXT

Integrating ESG principles across the PV life cycle is essential. EU initiatives (e.g EUPI-PV and 2024 SRIA) stress sustainability in manufacturing, deployment, and recycling, addressing emissions, sourcing, equity, and circularity. Yet advancing further requires inclusive engagement, fair labor, and just transition measures, supported by robust metrics and governance to **boost innovation** and **ensure a resilient transition, and strengthen Europe's competitiveness and energy sovereignty.**

METHODOLOGICAL FRAMEWORK

This research examines the PV industry across its three life cycles -manufacturing, installation and operation, and end-of-life -assessing ESG impacts and priority areas. It draws on EU projects, expert insights, research, and policy to identify lessons learned and position ESG as a driver of innovation and EU competitiveness.

STRATEGIC RECOMMENDATIONS

For Policymakers
- Embed verifiable ESG criteria in solar-related regulations and funding
- Strengthen traceability and harmonize standards
- Support design for circularity beyond recycling
- Ensure policies are open to innovation in technology and system design

For Industry and Companies
- Adopt standardized ESG reporting and promote harmonization
- Innovate in sustainable manufacturing circular operations and maintenance (O&M) and supply chains
- Promote fair labor, diversity, equity, and inclusion
- Create community engagement plans

For Researchers and Technology Developers
- Advance interdisciplinary ESG research
- Focus on decarbonization, circularity, and critical and strategic material recovery
- Support innovation in deployment models
- Design PV to be resilient and durable in variable climatic conditions

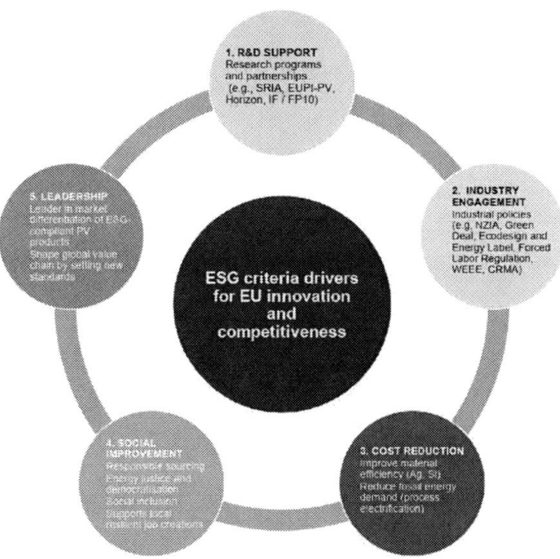

	Environmental Aspects	Social Aspects	Governance Aspects
Manufacturing	**Outcome:** •PV manufacturing is the **largest contributor to lifecycle emissions**, due to energy-intensive processes. •**Critical and strategic raw materials** are required in PV manufacturing (e.g., silver, indium) **Solution:** •**Decarbonizing** manufacturing •**Credible** ecodesign solutions with **improving material and energy use efficiency**	**Outcome:** •**Labor conditions** vary geographically, with documented risks of forced labor. •**Gender gaps** persist, and **Social Acceptance** is limited due to negative externalities. **Solution:** •Ensure **stakeholder engagement** •Expand job training programs •**Zero tolerance** to state-sponsored forced labor	**Outcome:** •Variability in ESG standards, reporting and gaps in global supply chain **transparency**. **Solution:** • Responsible sourcing in line with **UN Guiding Principles on Business and Human Rights** •**Enhancing verifiability** of ESG reported information
Installation and Operation	**Outcome:** •**Land use conflicts** for ground-mounted PV systems and **water consumption**, mainly for panel cleaning in arid regions. **Solution:** •Responsibly developed ground-mounted systems, **Agrivoltaics, floating PV, IPV and BIPV** represent promising strategies to optimize land use •**Dry cleaning** technologies and **self-cleaning** coatings.	**Outcome:** •PV supports local **job creation**, yet equitable access to training and quality employment remains uneven. •PV expands **energy access** but has high upfront costs. •Lack of **public acceptance** of PV solutions **Solution:** •**Transparent** planning and fair benefit-sharing •Innovative financing mechanisms •Proactive **community and stakeholder engagement.**	**Outcome:** •Deployment governance must ensure **responsible project siting** through effective environmental permitting •Inclusive **stakeholder consultation**, and the fostering of public-private partnerships. **Solution:** •Implement **best practices throughout the life cycle** of a solar project (from development to decommissioning)
End-of-Life	**Outcome:** •Current recycling technologies recover **bulk materials**. •Recovery of valuable materials like silicon and silver remains limited due to **lack of policy framework**. **Solution:** •Policy initiatives and research into **design-for-circularity** and promote **high value recycling** are key to scaling sustainable end-of-life management.	**Outcome:** •Recycling sector growth offers new **employment opportunities**. **Solution:** •**Occupational health and safety standards** to be enforced •**Public acceptance** of end-of-life initiatives. •**Training and education** throughout the value chain.	**Outcome:** •Regulatory frameworks mandate recycling, but **global harmonization is lacking** **Solution:** •Strengthening and harmonizing **standards for recycling** and circular economy policies. •**Streamline cross-boundary transportation** of PV waste destined for recycling.

020513-001

Funded by the European Union, under the Horizon Europe programme, Grant agreement number 101079394. Views and opinions expressed are however those of the author(s) only and do not necessarily reflect those of the European Union or European Climate, Infrastructure and Environment Executive Agency. Neither the European Union nor the granting authority can be held responsible for them.

A NOVEL TOOL FOR THE IDENTIFICATION OF SUSTAINABLE LOCATIONS OF MARINE FLOATING PHOTOVOLTAIC PLANTS

Gotzon Mandiola[1,2], Ibon Galparsoro[1], Iratxe Menchaca[1], María Jesús Belzunce[1], Iñigo Mendikoa[3], Juan Bald[1], Asier Sanz[3]*

[1] AZTI, Marine Research Division, Basque Research and Technology Alliance (BRTA), Herrera Kaia Portualdea z/g, 20110, Pasaia, Spain.
[2] University of the Basque Country (UPV/EHU), Plentzia, Bizkaia, Spain.
[3] Tecnalia, Basque Research and Technology Alliance (BRTA), Edificio 700, 48160, Derio, Bizkaia, Spain.

*Speaker
For more details, contact gmandiola@azti.es

INTRODUCTION

- Offshore floating photovoltaic (FPV) energy can help to diversify the renewable energy production capacity.
- The novel development status of this technology poses uncertainty regarding its potential environmental impacts.
- Blue economy maritime activities should be sustainable and must comply with the 'Do No Significant Harm' (DNSH) principles.

OBJECTIVES

- Investigate the environmental risk associated with the FPV technologies in the marine environment.
- Identify suitable locations for FPV deployment in Europe, developing a Bayesian Network (BN) model.
- Integrate the BN model into a decision-making tool.

METHODS

Study area

1. Identification of **environmental risk** associated with FPV technologies → Systematic Literature Review.
2. Capture **expert knowledge** of environmental risk associated with FPV technologies → Delphi method.
3. Develop and implement a BN model to **identify suitable locations** considering technical, activities and environmental assessment.
4. Integrate the model into **VAPEM tool** for user-friendly applicability (https://aztidata.es/vapem/).

RESULTS

Systematic Literature Review

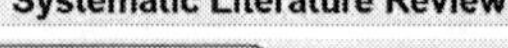

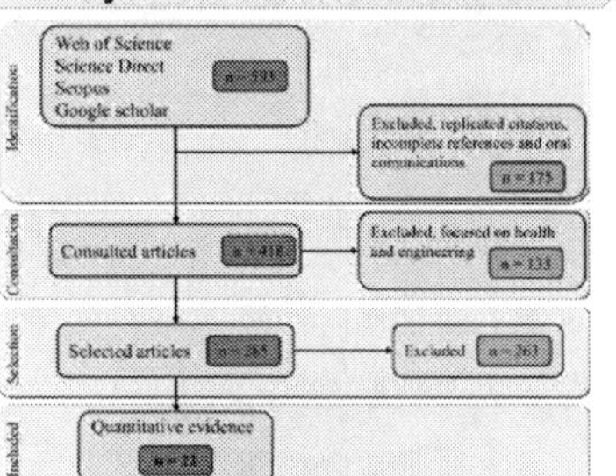

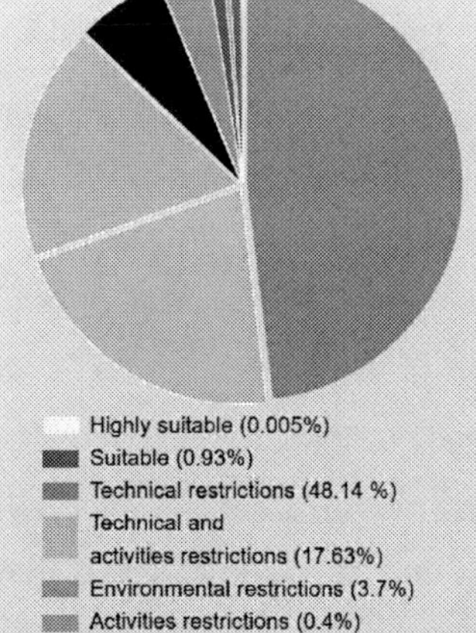

Expert knowledge (Delphi method)

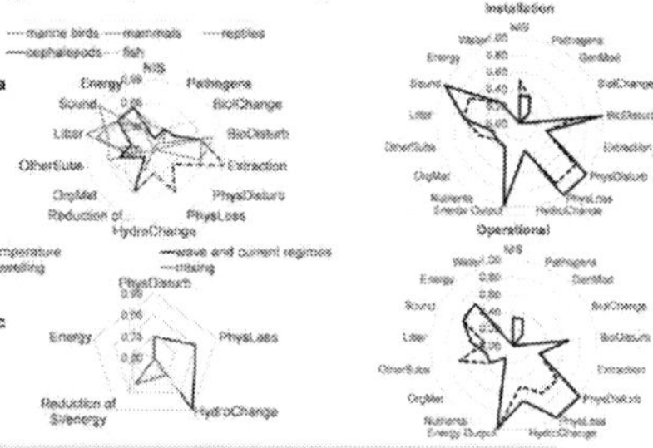

Integrated suitability

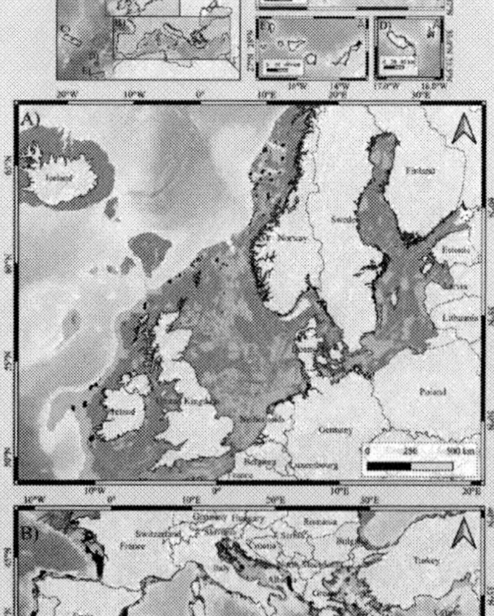

Bayesian Network modeling

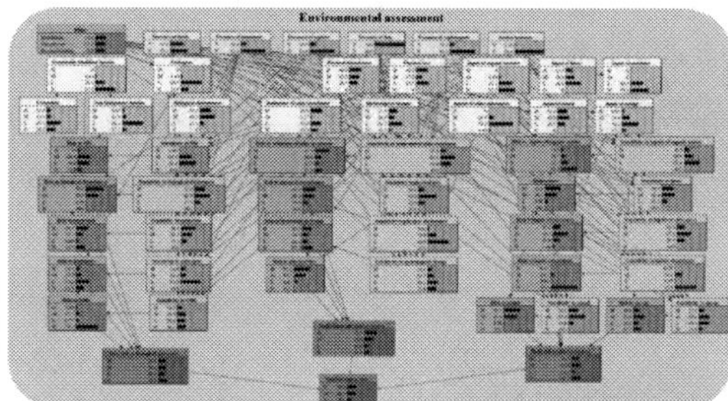

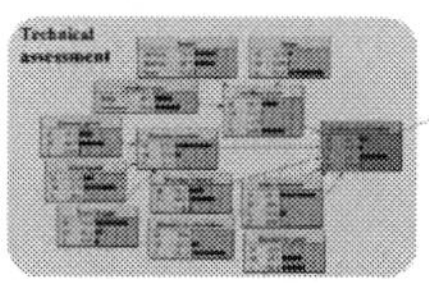

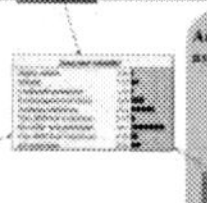

CONCLUSION

- A total of 154 km2 are highly suitable for offshore FPV.
- A total of 27,279 km2 are suitable for offshore FPV.
- The main limitation for offshore FPV development are related to technical restrictions.
- Useful results for industry, researchers, policy and decision-makers.

VAPEM

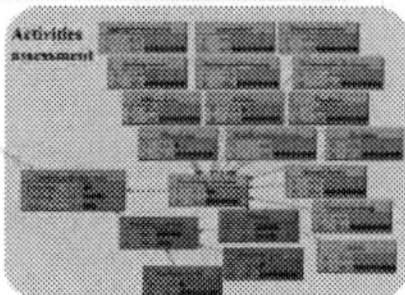

Ecological assessment and maritime spatial planning tool

https://aztidata.es/vapem/

Project founded by the Department of Economic Development, Sustainability and Environment of the Basque Government.

Research founded by:

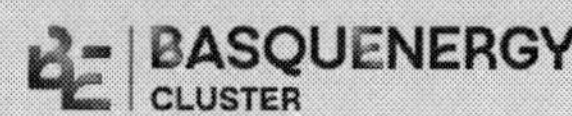

LIFE CYCLE ASSESSMENT OF A SILICON-HETEROJUNCTION-BASED PV SYSTEM

Arthur W. Weeber, Shashank Bhardwaj, Olindo Isabella, Malte R. Vogt
PVMD group Delft University of Technology
Mekelweg 4, 2628 CD Delft, The Netherlands

ABSTRACT: This paper presents a Life Cycle Analysis (LCA) of a silicon-heterojunction-based PV rooftop system produced and installed in the Netherlands in 2024. A prospective LCA (pLCA) for 2035 was carried out assuming different future scenarios (Integrated Assessment Models and Shared Socioeconomic Pathways). Future material consumption and efficiencies were taken from the ITRPV 2024. Material and energy input data were taken from the EcoInvent database and the LCA was performed using Brightway2.0. Since data from EcoInvent do not correspond to current technology we have adjusted these data. For example, in the database of EcoInvent wafer thickness and kerf loss are outdated and have been scaled down: wafer thickness from 270 to 120 µm and kerf loss from 180 to 55 µm. PECVD input data are based on TU Delft lab results and scaled to M10 wafer size. Metallization input data are based on the ITRPV 2024 data and other process parameters are taken from literature. Recycling and disposal are not included. For the 2024 reference rooftop system with performance ratio (PR) of 0.75, the Global Warming Potential (GWP1000) is 22 g CO_2-eq/kWh, which is lower than results presented in literature. For the 2035-SSP2-REMIND scenario the GWP1000 is 6.9 g CO_2-eq/kWh. With PR=0.85 the GWP1000 values will be respectively 19.4 and 6.1 g CO_2-eq/kWh.
Keywords: LCA, pLCA, Silicon, Heterojunction, PV system

1 INTRODUCTION

The progress made in efficiency, cost reduction and increase in production volume is huge and beyond expectation of many organizations. Nowadays the cumulative installed PV capacity is over 2 TWp [1] and expected to grow to about 75 TWp in 2050 [2]. With this enormous market size, the environmental impact profile and sustainability of PV is becoming more important. A life cycle analysis (LCA) can be used to quantify a set of environmental impact factors.

For an accurate LCA you need recent input parameters for material and energy consumption. These input parameters are hard to get mainly because of proprietary reasons. Furthermore, most PV LCA studies have not been carried out on the current high-efficiency Si PV technologies such as TOPCon and silicon heterojunction (SHJ) technology, but on PERC technology [3, 4], which is currently being phased out (or, is almost phased out).

In this study, we provide an LCA for a 22 m² rooftop PV system based on SHJ PV technology and using material input data from the ITRPV 2024 [5] and using the electricity mix of the Netherlands. Data from ITRPV 2024 will also be used for prospective LCAs (pLCAs) for 2035. The pLCAs for 2035 were done assuming different future scenarios involving Integrated Assessment Models (IAMs) and Shared Socioeconomic Pathways (SSPs) [6].

Recycling and disposal are not included in this study.

2 APPROACH AND METHODOLOGY

2.1 Rooftop PV system

The LCAs and pLCAs are based on a SHJ technology-based rooftop system. The module size is 2 m² consisting of 56 M10 SHJ solar cell and the system consists of 11 modules (22 m²). More accurately, the parameters are scaled to these sizes. As already stated: recycling and disposal are not included in this study.

The modules are assumed to be monofacial.

2.2 Input parameters and LCA software

For the input parameters the EcoInvent 3.9.1 database was used [7]. Since several input parameters are relatively old, some key parameters were scaled down. The ITRPV 2024 was used to obtain more recent data and for future data for the pLCA 2035. The wafer thickness and kerf losses were scaled down to 120 µm and 55 µm respectively for the 2024 reference, and to 100 µm and 40 µm for the 2035 scenarios. The Ag consumption was adjusted down to 4 g/cm² (front and rear) for 2024 and to 2 g/cm² for 2035. The calculations were scaled to M10 wafer size with which the Ag consumption would correspond to 140 mg/cell for 2024 and 80 mg/cell for 2035. The cell and module efficiencies are based on lab results of Zhao *et al.* [8] and on data from the ITRPV 2024.

Details about adjusted parameters can be found in Table I.

Table I: Adjusted input parameters for LCA 2024 and pLCA 2035

Input	LCA 2024	pLCA 2035
Cell thickness[5]	120 µm	100 µm
Kerf loss[5]	55 µm	40 µm
Ag consumption[5]	140 mg/cell	80 mg/cell
η_{cell}	24.2%[7]	26.6% [5]
η_{module}	22.2%[based on [7]]	24.4%[5]
Lifetime[5]	30 yrs	40 yrs
Degradation rate[5]	2% first year 0.6% next years	1% first year 0.5% next years

The consumption of precursor gases to deposit the amorphous layers is based on lab processing of Zhao *et al.* [8] and scaled to M10 wafers. For the other heterojunction specific layers data from Louwen [10] were used. For the standard processing, and the module and system components data from a IEA PVPS T12 report [3] were used.

Brightspace 2.0 [9] software was used for the LCA and pLCA. For the impact assessment the ReCiPe 2016 model [11] was applied using the so-called midpoint indicators. The assessment was done for all 18 LCA impact categories. The focus of discussion in this paper is on the Global Warming Potential (GPW1000). The LCA results of the other impact categories / indicators can be found in the appendix.

10.4229/EUPVSEC2025/5DV.2.43
020515-001

The electricity mix of the Netherlands in 2024 was assumed for the energy input parameter, meaning manufacturing is assumed to be in the Netherlands.

2.3 Scenarios prospective LCA

To determine potential future environmental impact parameters pLCA involving SSP IAMs REMIND (Regional Model of Investment and Development) and IMAGE (Integrated Model to Assess the Global Environment) were used [13]. The scenarios applied in this study are:

- 2035 SSP1 REMIND: Sustainable pathway in which economic growth is balanced with social equity and environmental goals.
- 2035 SSP2 REMIND: A pathway including incremental policy changes and technological improvements to address climate issues.
- 2035 SSP2 IMAGE: A pathway including incremental policy changes and technological improvements to address climate issues, but less strict than REMIND.
- 2035 SSP5: Pathway in which rapid economic growth is key and fossil fuel based, and resulting in climate change that needs to be mitigated (and therefore not meeting the Paris agreements).

From the descriptions it can be seen that the first one (2035 SSP2 REMIND) is the most sustainable one and the last one (SSP5) is not sustainable at all.

2.4 Energy output PV system

To calculate the energy output of the system the following simple equation is used:

$$E = I_{irrad} \cdot LT \cdot \eta_{mod} \cdot A \cdot PR \cdot DR$$

In which E is the energy generated, I_{irrad} the annual irradiation level per m^2 (kWh/m^2/yr), LT is the lifetime of the module (years), η_{mod} the module efficiency, A the area (m^2), PR the performance ratio and DR the degradation level.

For I_{irrad} we took 1000 kWh/m^2/yr which corresponds the Global Horizontal Irradiance in the Netherlands (a conservative number with respect to optimal orientation). The performance ratio PR is assumed to be 0.75. For the module efficiency η_{mod}, system area A, etc. we refer to previous paragraphs.

2.5 Sensitivity analysis PR and energy consumption for SoG Si and wafering

In this paragraph we show the sensitivity of the 2024 results on PR and on the energy consumption for production Solar Grade Si (SoG Si) and wafering.

As already stated PR=0.75 was used to determine the energy output of the PV system, which is a conservative number with respect to optimal orientation in the Netherlands. PR=0.85 was also used to show the impact of a more optimistic performance assumption and the LCA results with this current value will also be presented.

For the production of SoG Si and wafering EcoInvent contains data that are about 10 years old. In that period the cumulative installation capacity has grown with a factor of 16, meaning 2^4! The processing of SoG Si and wafering has certainly improved and will use less energy than 10 years ago. If we assume a learning rate of 5% it will mean that the energy consumption has decreased with a factor of 0.95^4=0.73. Of course this a simplified assumption because the wafer thickness and kerf losses have been reduced during that period and also saving material

consumption and energy. In our sensitivity analysis we evaluated an improved process for SoG Si production and wafering (all processes up to and including wafering) assuming a reduction in energy consumption of 20-70%.

3 RESULTS AND DISCUSSION

3.1 LCA GWP1000

The GWP1000 (Climate Change) for our reference (2024) rooftop system with 22.2% module efficiency is 22 g CO$_2$-eq/kWh and is lower than values presented in literature. Fig. 1 shows a comparison with results from Louwen [10] and Barrou [13]. Both studies resulted in about 35 g CO$_2$-eq/kWh, also for SHJ-based PV systems.

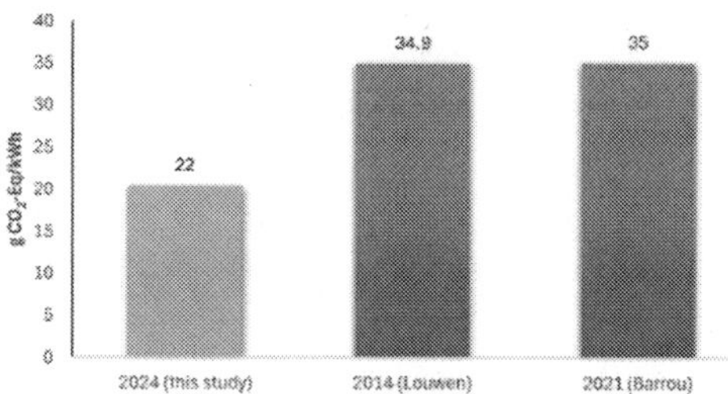

Figure 1: GWP results of our study on an SHJ-based system compared to results of Louwen and Barrou.

However, this comparison needs some more discussion about the parameters used. The main differences are described below. Louwen used an irradiation level of 1700 kWh/m^2 and Barrou 1391 kWh/m^2. Also different wafer thickness were used in both studies, 180 µm and 170 µm respectively. For the kerf losses it was 130 µm and 85 µm respectively. The same holds for η_{mod}, which were 18.4% and 21.8% respectively. In both cases a lifetime of 30 years and PR=0.75 were used, the same values as in our study. Another difference is the electricity mix used for determining the energy consumption. Louwen used the average European electricity mix of 2014 (UCTE, 531 g CO$_2$-eq/kWh) and Barrou assumed for production of cells, modules and systems and for the end-of-life processing the European electricity mix (2020, 418 g CO$_2$-eq/kWh), and for SoG Si and wafer production the Chinese electricity mix (2020, 1023 g CO$_2$-eq/kWh). Material transport and end-of-life measures were included by Barrou as well. We used the electricity mix of (and full production in) the Netherlands (2024, 370 g CO$_2$-eq/kWh), which has a lower carbon footprint than the ones used by Louwen and Barrou. It looks like comparing apples with pears, but we have performed some simple linear scaling on these parameters (irradiation level, efficiency and electricity mix on the total GWP1000, and for SoG Si and wafering on the part from raw SiO$_2$ material up to and including wafering) with respect to the Louwen study. Using this linear scaling on the GWP determined by Louwen (34.9 g CO$_2$-eq/kWh) to conditions and parameters used in our study (electricity mix 370 g CO$_2$-eq/kWh, 1000 kWh/m^2/yr, 22.4% efficiency, 120 µm wafer thickness, 55 µm kerf loss), we estimate a GWP of Louwen corresponding to 28-29 g CO$_2$-eq/kWh. With a more detailed analysis than this linear scaling and doing it for more parameters, the results might be even closer to each other.

In his 2014 study, Louwen [10] also performed a prospective LCA for 2020. He assumed for 2020 50 μm kerf free wafers, 23.5% module efficiency and progress on many other parameters. The GWP of that study resulted in a value of 21 g CO_2-eq/kWh, in the same range as our result.

A recent IEA PVPS Task 12 study on PERC showed a GWP of 26 g CO_2-eq/kWh for a system installed in Northern Italy (1361 kWh/m²/yr). Module manufacturing was assumed to be in China with a wafer thickness of 170 μm and $\eta_{mod.}$=21.2%. End of life and transportation were included in this study. The higher irradiation level will increase the energy output compared to our study, but the lower efficiency will slightly decrease it. However, the module manufacturing in China and the thicker wafers will increase the CO_2 emission compared to our study. A first estimate shows that these effects will more or less compensate each other keeping the GWP of this PERC technology in the same range as of our study.

3.2 pLCA GWP1000 for 2035

Fig. 2 shows the pLCA GWP1000 results 2035 compared to the current 2024 result. The 2035-SSP2-REMIND results in the lowest expected GWP1000 due to the incremental policy changes (more renewable energy in the energy mix) and technology improvements. It results in a significant decrease to 6.9 g CO2-eq/kWh. The reduction for the 2035-SSP5 scenario is the lowest because that scenario is still fossil fuel based.

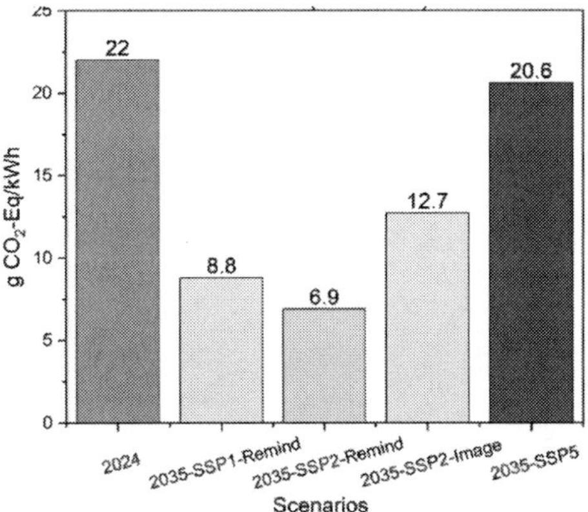

Figure 2: GWP1000 for SHJ-based rooftop system and the pLCA GWP1000 results for 2035.

Fig. 3 shows the share of the individual components / manufacturing steps for a module for 2024 and the 2035 results. In general module manufacturing step represents the largest fraction in GWP1000. Again the 2035-SSP2-REMIND shows the lowest GWP.

3.3 Ecotoxicity

Fig. 4 shows the impact on ecotoxicity potential for freshwater and marine for the LCA 2024 reference and pLCA 2035 SSP1 and SSP2 scenarios. The impact factors for the 2035 scenarios are significantly lower than for the 2024 reference, but do hardly differ from each other. In case of the implementation of policy changes on ecotoxicity for future scenarios the impact would be different for the different scenarios.

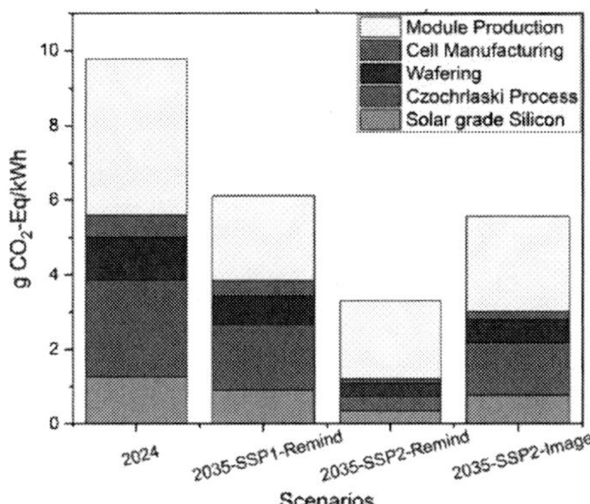

Figure 3: GPW1000 results of individual module components for pLCA 2035 compared to the 2024 reference.

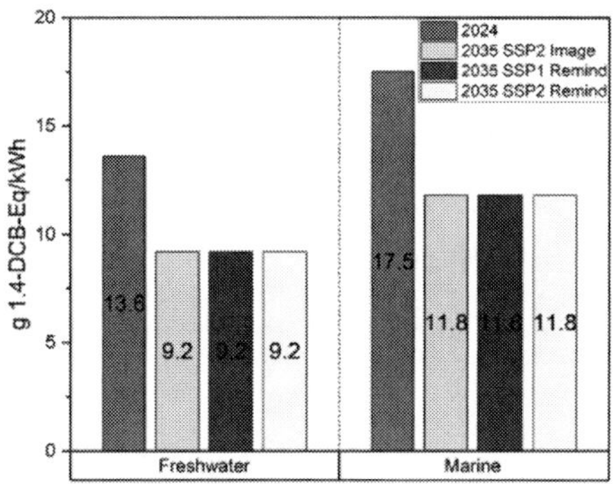

Figure 4: Ecotoxicity potential for fresh water and marine of a SHJ-based PV system for 2024 and pLCA for 2035.

3.4 Sensitivity analysis on *PR* and energy consumption for SoG Si production and wafering.

Fig. 5 shows the sensitivity analysis of the GWP1000 on *PR* for the 2024 reference and the 2035 SSP1 and SSP2 scenarios. Since the *PR* directly scales with the energy output of the system, the GWP1000 will also directly scale with *PR*. In fig. 5 the results for *PR*=0.75 and *PR*=0.85 are shown. The lowest GW1000 is for the 2035-SSP2-REMIND scenario with a value of 6.1 g CO_2-eq/kWh.

Fig. 6 shows the potential change in GWP1000 in case it is assumed that process development for SoG Si production and wafering has been improved (which is certainly the case but to the best of our knowledge not yet quantified in literature). The impact on GWP1000 for reducing the electricity consumption for SoG Si and wafering to 20-30% seems to have a minor impact on the overall GWP1000. Only the one of 70% shows a clear impact while this 70% corresponds to a learning rate of about 5%. So, it might be a realistic assumption.

3.5 Other LCA impact parameters

The LCA and pLCA results for all studied mid-point impact categories / indicators can be found in the appendix. The results of the other indicators show a similar trend as the ecotoxicity potential but will not be discussed further.

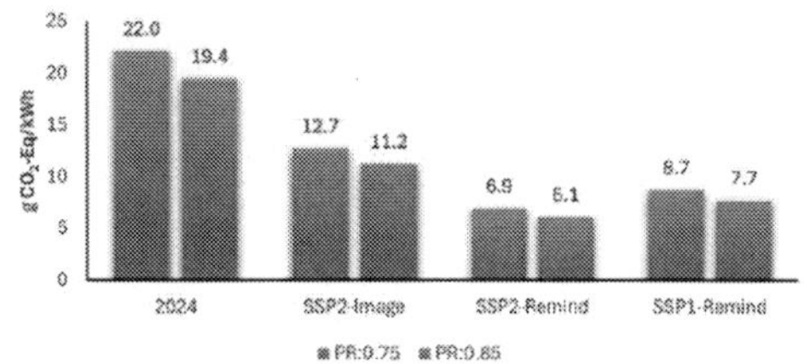

Figure 5: Sensitivity of *PR* on GWP1000 for the 2024 reference and 2035 SSP1 and SSP2 scenarios.

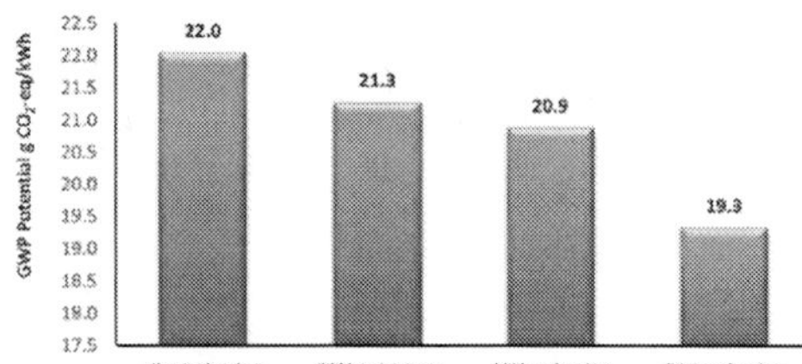

Figure 6: Sensitivity of the reduction of electricity consumption of SoG Si production and wafering on GWP1000 of the 2024 reference.

4 CONCLUSION

In our study the GWP1000 of a rooftop PV system based on SHJ PV technology, and produced and installed in 2024, is 22 g CO_2-eq/kWh. It is assumed that the system is produced in the Netherlands (Dutch electricity mix) and has an annual in-plane irradiation of 1000 kWh/m²/yr (Global Horizontal Irradiance in the Netherlands). Direct comparison with other studies is difficult because differences in production location (electricity mix, CO_2 emissions), irradiation levels during operation and module efficiency (kWh generation), etc. A first more detailed comparison shows that the GWP of our study is lower than the one from other studies on SHJ based PV technology. However, it seems to be in the same range as the results of an IEA PVPS Task 12 study on a PERC system in Northern Italy.

For pLCAs with different future scenarios and assuming *PR*=0.85, the GWP1000 can decline to about 6 g CO_2-eq/kWh (2035 SSP2 REMIND). Since input data on SoG Si and wafering for our reference PV system are from 2014, introducing a learning rate for electricity consumption for these process steps will further reduce the GWP1000 indicator.

5 REFERENCES

[1] A. Jäger-Waldau, EPJ Photovolt. 16 (2025) 22
[2] N. Haegel *et al.*, Science 380 (2023) 6640
[3] A. Danelli *et al.* IEA PVPS T12, https://doi.org/10.69766/EEMP5995
[4] A. Müller *et al*, SolMat 230 (2021) 111277
[5] ITRPV 15th edition Results 2023, May 2024 vdma.org
[6] R. Sacchi *et al.*, Renew. Sustain. Energy Rev. 160 (2022) 112311,
[7] EcoInvent, https://ecoinvent.org/
[8] Y. Zhao *et al*. SolMat 258 (2023) 112413
[9] Brightspace, https://docs.brightspace.dev/en/latest/
[10] A. Louwen, PhD thesis Utrecht University 2016 and A. Louwen *et al*. Prog. Photovolt.: Res. Appl. 23 (2015) 1406 (thesis and paper show slightly different results)
[11] M. Huijbregts *et al.*, Int. J. Life Cycle Assess., 22 (2017) 138
[12] Premise, Introduction to premise 2024 https://premise.readthedocs.io/en/latest/introduction.html
[13] A. Barrou, MSc thesis EPFL 2022, https://infoscience.epfl.ch/handle/20.500.14299/198917

APPENDIX

Table A1: Environmental impact assessment for an SHJ-based PV rooftop system produced and installed in the Netherlands. Data for the LCA 2024 and for pLCA 2035-SSSP REMIND are presented.

Indicator	Unit/kWh	SHJ 2024 reference	2035 SSP2-REMIND
Climate Change GWP1000	kg CO_2-eq	2.20E-02	6.9E-03
Terrestrial acidification potential (TAP)	kg 1.4-DCB-eq	9.0E-05	3.4E-05
Freshwater ecotoxicity potential (FETP)	kg 1.4-DCB-eq	1.4E-02	9.2E-03
Marine ecotoxicity potential (METP)	kg 1.4-DCB-eq	1.7E-02	1.2E-02
Terrestrial ecotoxicity potential (TETP)	kg 1.4-DCB-eq	1.1E-01	9.2E-02
Fossil fuel potential (FFP)	kg oil-eq	5.6E-03	1.7E-03
Freshwater eutrophication potential (FEP)	kg P-eq	2.5E-05	1.3E-05
Marine eutrophication potential (FEP)	kg N-eq	1.2E-06	5.6E-07
Human toxicity potential (HTPc)	kg 1.4-DCB-eq	3.5E-03	2.3E-03
Human toxicity potential (HTPnc)	kg 1.4-DCB-eq	1.7E-01	1.1E-01
Ionizing radiation potential (IRP)	kg ^{60}Co-eq	2.4E-03	9.3E-04
Agricultural land occupation (LOP)	m² crop-eq	1.6E-03	1.0E-03
Surplus ore potential (SOP)	kg Cu-eq	1.0E-03	7.0E-04
Ozone depletion potential (ODPinfinite)	kg CFC-11-eq	9.5E-09	3.5E-09
Particulate matter formation potential (PMFP)	kg PM2.5-eq	4.3E-05	1.2E-05
Photochemical oxidant formation: human health (HOFP)	kg NO_x-eq	6.8E-05	2.5E-05
Photochemical oxidant formation: terrestrial ecosystems (EOFP)	kg NO_x-eq	7.1E-05	2.7E-05
Water consumption potential	m³	3.5E-04	2.1E-04

Life Cycle Assessment of a Silicon Heterojunction based PV System

Arthur W. Weeber[*], Shashank Bhardwaj, Olindo Isabella, Malte R. Vogt

Photovoltaic Materials and Devices Laboratory, Delft University of Technology, The Netherlands (*Contact: a.w.weeber@tudelft.nl)

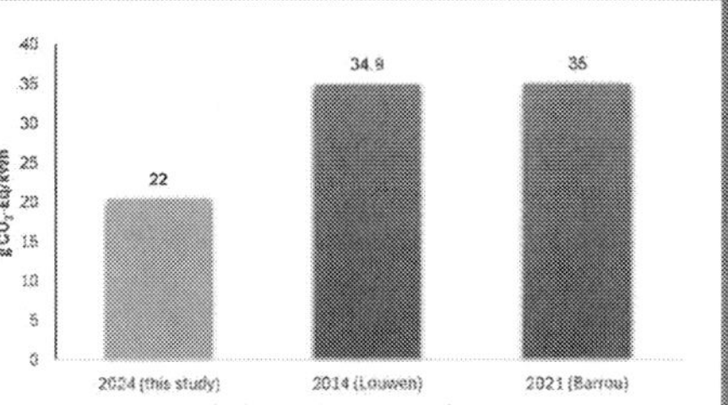

1. Motivation

- Environmental impact profile and sustainability of PV are becoming more important

- Old input data for LCA are generally used because actual data material and energy consumption are hard to get (proprietary reasons)

- Hardly any recent papers on LCA SHJ technology

- Prospective LCA studies hardly available

2. Approach – Method

- Input parameters from EcoInvent[1] v3.9.1 used

- Input data scaled down to more recent values, and based on ITRPV 2024[2] and recent lab results by Zhao et al.[3]

- Prospective LCA (pLCA) for 2035 based on projections by ITRPV 2024[2]

- Future energy scenarios applied involving Integrated Assessments Models (IAMs) IMAGE and REMIND and Shared Socioeconomics Pathways (SSPs):

  - 2035 SSP1 REMIND: Sustainable pathway in which economic growth is balanced with social equity and environmental goals

  - 2035 SSP2 REMIND: Pathway including incremental policy changes and technological improvements to address climate changes

  - 2035 SSP2 IMAGE: as SSP2 REMIND but less strict

  - 2035 SSP5: Pathway with rapid economic growth and not meeting Paris Agreements

- Brightway2.0[4] software used to perform LCAs and pLCAs

- Focus on carbon footprint GWP1000 (global warming potential)

- Sensitivity analysis based on performance ratio and on energy consumption up to and including wafer process

- System size: rooftop, 22 m²

3. Input data

- Input parameters scaled to M10 processing and based on Zhao et al., ITRPV 2024 (see table 1), Louen et al.[5] and IEA PVPS T12 report[6]. System components based on this IEA PVPS report[6].

- Electricity mix of / manufacturing in the Netherlands

- Energy output PV system based on simple calculations and in-plane irradiation of 1000 kWh/m² (GHI in the Netherlands), so conservative

- Performance ratio PR=0.75, also conservative

Table 1: Input data LCA 2024 and pLCA 2035

Input	Data 2024	Data 2035
Cell thickness[2]	120 μm	100 μm
Ag consumption[2]	140 mg/cell	80 mg/cell
η_{cell}	24.2%[3]	26.6%[2]
η_{module}	22.2% based on [3]	24.4%[2]
Lifetime[2]	30 years	40 years
Annual degradation rate[2]	2% first year, 0.6% remaining	1% first year, 0.5% remaining

4. Results LCA

- GWP1000 for 2024: 22 g CO_2-eq/kWh

- Comparison literature (see Fig. 1):

  - ~35 g CO_2-eq/kWh (also PR=0.75, 30 yrs lifetime) by:

    - Louwen et al. 1700 kWh/m² in-plane irradiation, η_{mod}=18.4%, 180 μm wafer[5]

    - Barrou, 1391 kWh/m² in-plane irradiation, η_{mod}=21.8%, 170 μm wafer[6]

  - ~26 g CO_2-eq/kWh for PERC in IEA PVPS T12 report on a plant in Italy with 1368 kWh/m² [7]

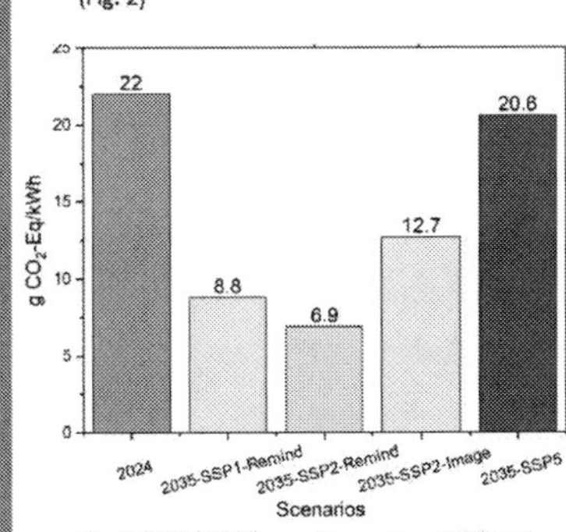

Fig 1. LCA result this study compared to literature

5. Results pLCA 2035

- Depending on the future scenario the GWP1000 could be reduced to 6.9 g CO_2-eq/kWh in 2035 (Fig. 2)

- Module production is largest fraction, especially for 2035 SSP2 REMIND (Fig. 3, only the module)

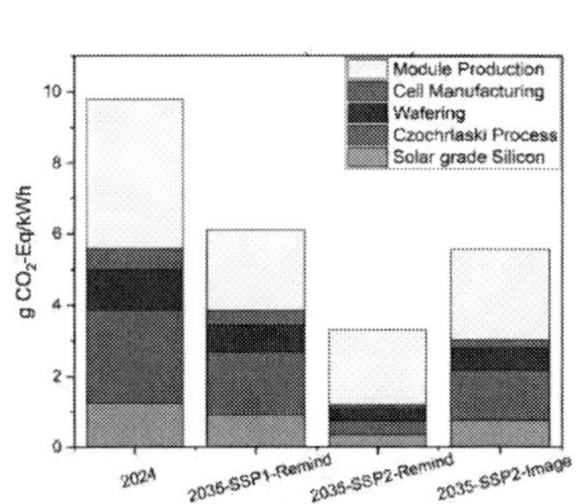

Fig 2. GWP1000 for rooftop system 2024 and pLCA result for 2035

Fig 3. GWP1000 for SHJ module components for 2024 and for pLCA 2035

6. Sensitivity results to PR and Si wafer

- GWP1000 scales directly with PR (Fig. 4)

- With 2035 SSP2 scenario GWP1000 could be reduced to 6.1 g CO_2-eq/kWh

- 2035 SSP5 not shown, but scales in the same way (about 18 g-CO_2-eq/kWh for PR=0.85)

- EcoInvent parameters for Si are based on data from 10 years ago. Lower energy consumption for SoG Si production and wafers expected.

- Fig. 5 shows impact on GWP1000 for 20-70% reduction in energy consumption from raw SiO_2 material up to and including wafering (2024 results)

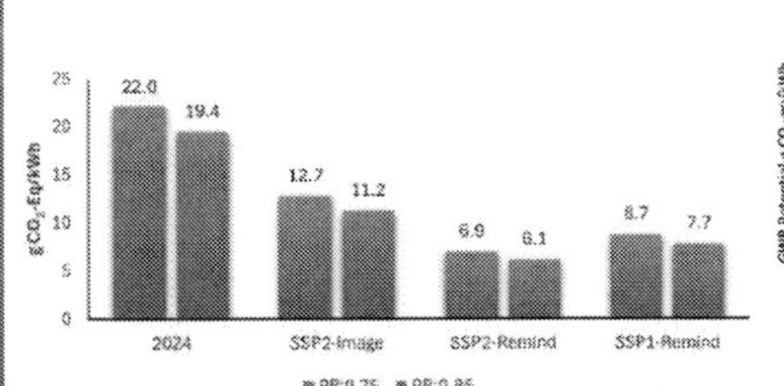

Fig 4. Sensitivity of PR on GWP1000 for 2024 and 2035

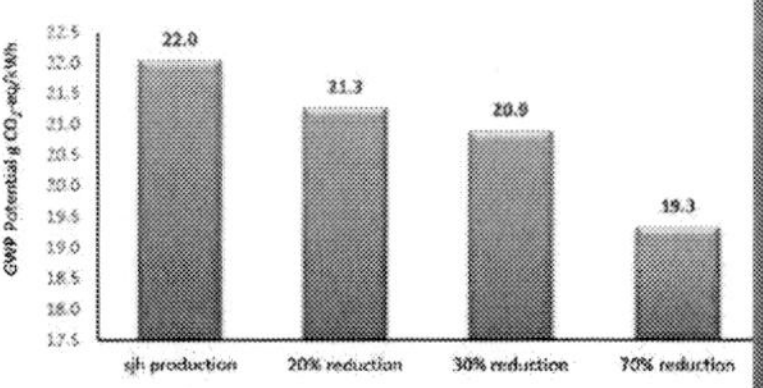

Fig 5. Sensitivity of reduction energy consumption for all production steps up to and including wafering (from SiO_2 -> wafer, 2024 results)

7. Conclusion

- The carbon footprint GWP1000 for SHJ-technology-based rooftop systems is about 22 g CO_2-eq/kWh as determined by using more recent data for processing and material consumption.

- Depending on future scenarios it can potentially be reduced to 6.9 g CO_2-eq/kWh and with assuming PR=0.85 even to about 6 g CO_2-eq/kWh in 2035.

- The carbon footprint GWP1000 for current SHJ technology from this study is significantly lower than data from literature, but in the same range as recent results on PERC technology. Note that this is despite this study assuming the lowest annual irradiation of 1000 kWh/m² due to being focused on the Netherlands.

- Assuming higher cell and module efficiencies for the future will reduce the carbon footprint GWP1000 to even lower values.

[1] https://ecoinvent.org/
[2] International Technology Roadmap PV ITRPV May 2024 - 2023 Results, vdma.org
[3] Zhao et al. SolMat doi:10.1016/j.solmat.2023.112413
[4] https://docs.brightway.dev/en/latest/
[5] Louwen et al. Progr. Photovolt. Res. Appl. doi:10.1002/pip.2540
[6] Barrou, MSc thesis EPFL 2022, https://infoscience.epfl.ch/handle/20.500.14299/198917
[7] A. Danelli et al., IEA PVPS T12 , 2024, https://doi.org/10.69766/EEMP5995

Photovoltaic Materials and Devices

REUSE, REDESIGN AND RECOVERY OF RESIDENTIAL SOLAR INSTALLATIONS COMPONENTS

Author(s): Y. Lara[1]*, R. Villén[1], R. Simón-Allué[1], G. Brun[1], I. Guedea[1]
Company / Institute(s): [1]ENDEF
Address(es): *yolanda.lara@endef.com

ABSTRACT: MUTABLE project is an industrial research initiative focused on applying circular economy principles in residential photovoltaic (PV) and photovoltaic-thermal (PVT or hybrid) installations. The overarching goal of MUTABLE is to define and develop an integral circularity strategy applicable to small self-consumption solar installations. This includes photovoltaic and hybrid installations, as well as complementary energy systems such as heat pumps, recovery devices, and storage systems. The project is structured around three interconnected pillars: reuse, redesign, and recovery, with the aim of defining methodologies to identify the most suitable route for each component of a solar installation and to determine maintenance needs to extend their lifespan.
Key activities within the project involve the disassembly and reassembly of photovoltaic, solar hybrid, and complementary installations, followed by monitoring their performance before and after these processes to validate operation and quantify reuse percentages.
This initiative is expected to provide valuable knowledge to develop new products, processes, and services with a reduced environmental footprint, ultimately increasing efficiency in solar residential energy use and minimizing waste generation. **Keywords:** Photovoltaics, Hybrid photovoltaic-thermal (PVT) collectors, circularity, second-life, circular economy, sustainability.

1 INTRODUCTION

Solar PV installations increased a 33% in 2024 over 2023, reaching a 2.2 TW cumulative installed solar PV capacity. It is estimated that by 2029, annual global solar installations may reach 930 GW [1]. Projected PV-related waste volumes are projected between 1.7 and 60 million tonnes, by 2030 and 2050, respectively [2]. This waste can be increased by material losses and damages during logistics stages, such as packaging, transportation, and storage [3]. The development of a circular mindset among the PV value chain is, therefore, critical to secure the availability of secondary raw materials and to prevent, delay, or mitigate environmental damage [4].

Europe adopted the Circular Economy Action Plan [5] seeking to include initiatives throughout the entire product life cycle, focusing on how products are designed and promoting circular economy processes.

To move to circular-based economy, both PV reuse and recycling need to be assessed. Current PV panel designs do not facilitate materials separation, leading these panels to low-value recycling or landfills. Similarly, current business models rarely allow for product maintenance, refurbishing, take-back, or recycling. PV reuse assessment is yet to be explored. There is a lack of reliable data on module degradation, yearly aging, as well as on business cases for reuse [4]. A survey among 3996 households in Flanders (Belgium) shown that PV reuse is considered interesting among younger, highly educated, migrant and less risk-averse customers segments [6].

Regarding PV recycling, the 2012/19/EU11 European Directive [7] requires the processing of photovoltaic panels at the end of their useful life (EOL) and establishes measures aimed at protecting the environment and human health by preventing or reducing the adverse impacts of the generation and management of waste electrical and electronic equipment (WEEE). Partly due to the implementation of this directive, associations such as PVCycle, carry out processes to separate the raw materials from photovoltaic panels during recycling.

MUTABLE project represents a significant leap in scientific innovation within the solar energy residential sector, particularly in its pioneering approach to circular economy principles.

- Integral Circularity Strategy: MUTABLE systematically focuses on reuse, redesign, and recovery as interconnected pillars, providing a holistic framework for extending the lifecycle of solar components. This shift from linear to circular processes is fundamental to increasing the sustainability of solar residential installations.
- Methodology for Component Routing: The project is developing specific methodologies to identify the "best route" for each individual component within a solar residential installation. This granular approach to material flow, considering direct reuse, redesign, or recovery, offers a framework for decision-making that optimizes resource utilization and minimizes waste.
- Redesign for Enhanced Reusability: The project's focus on redesigning hybrid panels (water and air) is highly innovative. By addressing inherent design flaws (e.g., hydraulic circuit breakage in water hybrid panels) and integrating recycled/second-life materials, MUTABLE directly contributes to increasing the reusability and prolonging the lifespan of these complex components. This includes the exploration of Building Integrated Photovoltaics (BIPV) for air hybrid systems, aiming to reduce material consumption by integrating panels directly into building envelopes.
- Best Practices Guide and Material Categorization: The creation of a formal "Best Practices Guide" for disassembly and assembly, specifically aimed at material recovery and reuse, is a significant practical innovation.

The primary aim of the MUTABLE project is to establish and implement a comprehensive circularity strategy within the solar energy residential sector, encompassing the entire lifecycle of solar installations and associated energy systems. This strategic approach is designed to be transversal, integrating circular economy principles. The project's global objective is broken down into four main outcomes:

- Increase reuse rate: by identifying the current reuse rate of materials and equipment across different types of solar residential installations, and characterizing improvement areas.

10.4229/EUPVSEC2025/5DV.2.44
020517-001

- Redesign hybrid solar panels: by identifying specific redesign needs for both water and air hybrid solar panels, as well as their associated installations, to enhance the reuse rate of their components.
- Assessing recovery paths: by defining the most appropriate recovery processes for materials that cannot be directly reused or redesigned.
- Develop a Methodology & Best Practices Guide: by designing a robust methodology for identifying the optimal path for each component of a solar installation to improve its sustainability, alongside creating a guide of best practices that applies across all company workstreams to ensure the highest levels of circularity in installations and equipment.

The work comprises the disassembly and assembly of four solar installations (one PV- and three PVT-based), as well as their ancillary systems, to define characterizing methodologies for the different elements. The disassembly and assembly processes will be documented and the newly assembled installations will be monitored to compare their performance after the disassembly and reassembly process.

2 METHODOLOGY & DEVELOPMENT

2.1 Analysis and planning.

As first step, comprehensive analysis of different solar PV and PVT installations was conducted, examining both their assembly and operational aspects to identify potential routes for reuse, recycling, and recovery of materials.

Four installation typologies were defined according to their components (see **Table I**). Each of these typologies was assessed separately. A manual for dismantling each one of the installations was prepared, to maximize components recovery, as well as a manual for reassembling the installations, taking into account the observations made during the dismantling process. These processes were applied in each one of the installations, allowing to iterate and refine the manuals.

This led to the development and continuous updating of a "Best Practices Guide" for disassembly and assembly, specifically designed to maximize material recovery and reuse. This guide represents a significant improvement, as no formal protocol for material recovery existed within the company prior to this project.

Table I: Installation typologies

Typology	Components	Connections
PVT water panels, type A	Hybrid panels	Electrical
	Inverters	
	Structures	Hydraulic
	Ancillary hydraulics	
PVT water panels, type B	Hybrid panels	Electrical
	Inverters	
	Structures	Hydraulic
	Ancillary hydraulics	
Photovoltaic panels	Hybrid panels	
	Inverters	Electrical
	Structures	
PVT air panels	Hybrid panels	Electrical
	Inverters	
	Structures	Pneumatic
	Ancillary pneumatics	

A methodology to classify the materials during disassembly was designed and tested. Two sticker-based methods were proposed: one based on colour codes and another combining shapes and colours. After practical application, the colour-code-only method (Method 1) was identified as the most efficient due to its simplicity and ease of use in the field, and it will be adopted for future phases.

Table II: Classification method 1

Item	Meaning
🔴	Good condition. Reuse directly
⚪	To be reviewed. Reuse or Redesign
⚫	Poor condition. Recycling or Recovery

By applying this method, three main routes were chosen for all the components assessed (Reuse, Redesign, Recycling). It is worth to say that a percentage of materials from each of the four disassembled installations were sent to recycling, due to different wearing conditions, installation age and in-the-field issues found during both dismantling and installing.

2.2 Disassembly, classification, and assembly of Installations.

Four types of solar installations were successfully disassembled, classified and re-assembled (if possible) in different locations, including water hybrid panels (Type A and Type B), simple photovoltaic panels, and air hybrid panels, along with their auxiliary components. From now on, the processes followed by each one of the installations is detailed.

2.2.1. Photovoltaic-thermal water panels, type A.

Figure 1: PVT water, type A. Initial installation.

This installation consists of 25 glazed PVT-water panels, south orientation, 45° tilt (**Figure 1**). During the disassembly process, the major part of the wiring as well as the structures (**Figure 2** d)) were classified to be reused. Nevertheless, the PV laminates, hydraulic connections, and insulating materials (see **Figure 2** a), b), c)) were found to be severely damaged, making them unsuitable for reuse, and were classified for recycling or potential recovery routes.

a) PVT panels   b) Removed conducts

c) Insulating material   d) Structures

Figure 2: PVT water, type A. Dissassembly.

2.2.2. Photovoltaic-thermal water panels, type B.

This second installation, **Figure 3**, comprises 8 PVT-water-based unglazed panels distributed in two benches, 30° tilt, south orientation, as well as an ancillary heat pump and inertia tanks.

Figure 3: PVT water, type B. Initial installation.

During disassembly, PVT panels and structures were classified to be directly reused (**Figure 4** a) and d)). Piping insulation was found in good condition, thus retained, and auxiliary hydraulic elements (heat pump, tanks) were carefully removed, with the working fluid recovered (**Figure 4** c)). Electrical components, wiring, and internal probes were also disassembled. Key elements like electrical panels, water tanks, and expansion vessels were categorized as directly reusable, while hydraulic circuits (**Figure 4** b)) and wiring required further review.

a) PVT panels   b) Retired conducts

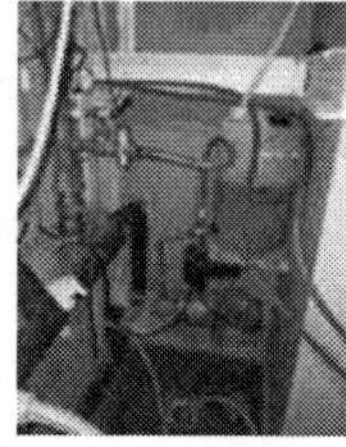

c) Water+glicol recovery   d) Structures

Figure 4: PVT water, type B. Dissassembly.

For the newly assembled installation, PVT panels, structures, inverters, hydraulic components and most of the pipes have been directly reused. Due to space restrictions, only 4 panels have been installed (**Figure 5**), while the rest have been stored. Also, the heat pump has been reused, adapting the hydraulic circuits to the new location. Those hydraulic circuits were kept as long as possible during the disassembly process in order to maximize their use during the reassembly.

Figure 5: PVT water, type B. Final installation.

2.2.3. Photovoltaic panels.

The photovoltaic installation has 4 half-cell panels, 320Wp each, **Figure 6**.

Figure 6: Photovoltaic panels. Initial installation.

Panels (**Figure 7** a)), structures (**Figure 7** b)), conduits and trays were classified as reusable, emphasizing the need for careful planning due to varying dimensions in new installations. Cabling and conduits (**Figure 7** c)) were disassembled, with MC4 connectors marked for functional review prior to be reused.

a) PV panels   b)   Structures

c) Wiring

Figure 7: Photovoltaic panels. Dissassembly.

The major part of the components (panels, inverter, wiring and trays) have been reused in the new installation. As the new installation is coplanar, former structures have been stored for later use.

Figure 8: Photovoltaic panels. Final installation.

2.2.4. Photovoltaic-thermal air panels.

Air-based hybrid panels consist of 5 PVT panels with 45° tilt, facing south, with a 5° west deviation, together with a fan for air circulation and ancillary ducts, **Figure 9**.

Figure 9: PVT air panels. Initial installation.

The disassembly process involved both exterior (cabling, conduits, probes, panels, structures, **Figure 10**) and interior (control system, inverter, fan…) components. Some cables showed damage from weather exposure and were marked for review.

a)   Panels, wiring, ducts. b)   Panels, wiring, ducts.
       Front view   Rear view

Figure 10: PVT air panels. Dissassembly.

In the reassembled installation, **Figure 11**, the mounting system had to be modified, including concrete blocks for the structures. One of the most delicate aspects was the connection between panels, that was carefully reinstalled, and has been pointed out as one of the redesign needs to be taken into account.

Figure 11: PVT air panels. Final installation.

All disassembled materials were catalogued, classified, and assigned to specific routes (reuse, review, or recovery) according to the newly defined methodology. Three of the four installation types were successfully reassembled at new locations using the reused materials.

2.3 Assessment of Redesign needs and Reuse rate.

Crucial redesign needs were identified for both water and air hybrid panels during the works.

For water hybrid panels type B (**Figure 12**), the primary redesign focus identified is to prevent hydraulic circuit breakage, both within the panel and at external connections. Solutions involve reducing the number of internal conduits/unions and minimizing external connections (e.g., through a single inlet/outlet design and larger panel sizes). Research has begun on larger glass-glass PV laminates and a redesigned thermal absorber to optimize heat transfer and robustness.

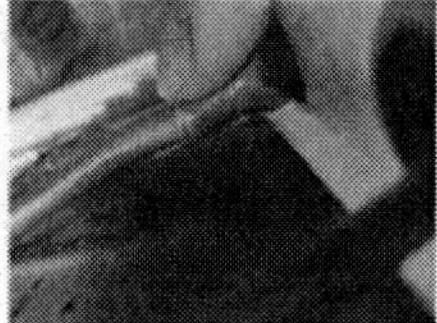

Figure 12: PVT water, type B. Redesign needs.

For air hybrid panels, critical elements identified for redesign include the air inlet filter, inter-panel connections, air outlet tube fixation, and the sealing of electrical wiring. Additionally, a global redesign effort has commenced for a new PVT air system concept integrated into inclined building roofs (BIPV), aiming to reduce material usage and expand applicability.

a) Inlet filter   b) Inter-panel connections

Figure 13: PVT air panels. Redesign needs.

Regarding the reuse route it is worth mentioning that the dismantling, classifying and storing processes for the large amount of material moved required a higher available workspace than expected (**Figure 14**), as many elements were installed in compact spaces.

Figure 14: Overview of components stored during classification process.

An estimated overall reuse rate of 30% of the material was achieved through the new processes defined in the project. The reuse rate varied significantly depending on both, component type and the specific requirements of the new assembly locations. For instance, plumbing elements from the PVT water type B installation, demonstrated a high reuse rate of approximately 70%. Components such as wiring, can be reused in their majority, although need to go through electrical safety and working tests prior to their reutilization. As mentioned before, for all the installations assessed there is always a percentage of the disassembled material that goes into recycling.

4 CONCLUSIONS

The experimental work described comprises the disassembly and assembly of photovoltaics, photovoltaic-thermal solar installations, as well as ancillary systems, together with the definition of methodologies to assign paths for the different elements (to be reused, redesigned or recycled). The main conclusions obtained from the work are summarized below.

- A methodology for material categorization, easy to use in the field, was designed and tested.
- Four types of solar installations were successfully disassembled, and all disassembled materials were assigned to Reuse, Redesign or Recovery routes.
- A "Best Practices Guide" for assembly and disassembly processes, designed to maximize material recovery and reuse, has been developed.
- Crucial redesign needs were identified for both water and air hybrid panels.
- Three of the four installation types were successfully reassembled at new locations using the reused materials, achieving an overall reuse rate of 30%.

As further work, the main immediate steps are focused on assessing the identified redesign needs as well as evaluation the performance of the three second-life installations.

5 ACKNOWLEDGEMENTS

This work was undertaken in the framework of MUTABLE project, funded by FEDER/Gobierno de Aragón/Project EC-35-2024.

6 REFERENCES

[1]. SolarPower Europe (2025): Global Market Outlook for Solar Power 2025-2029
[2]. IRENA. End-of-Life Management: Solar Photovoltaic Panels International Renewable Energy Agency. 2016.
[3]. Iseri, F. et al; A Circular Economy Systems Engineering Framework for Waste Management of Photovoltaic Panels; Ind. Eng. Chem. Res. 2025, 64, 14986−14997
[4]. Franco, M.A.; Groesser, S.N. A Systematic Literature Review of the Solar Photovoltaic Value Chain for a Circular Economy. Sustainability 2021, 13, 9615. https://doi.org/10.3390/su13179615
[5]. COMMUNICATION FROM THE COMMISSION TO THE EUROPEAN PARLIAMENT, THE COUNCIL, THE EUROPEAN ECONOMIC AND SOCIAL COMMITTEE AND THE COMMITTEE OF THE REGIONS A new Circular Economy Action Plan For a cleaner and more competitive Europe
[6]. Van Opstal, W.; Smeets, A.; When do circular business models resolve barriers to residential solar PV adoption? Evidence from survey data in Flanders; Energy Policy 182 (2023) 113761
[7]. DIRECTIVE 2012/19/EU OF THE EUROPEAN PARLIAMENT AND OF THE COUNCIL of 4 July 2012 on waste electrical and electronic equipment (WEEE)

Reuse, redesign and recovery of residential solar installations components

Y. Lara[1*], R. Villén[1], R. Simón-Allué[1], G. Brun[1], I. Guedea[1]

[1]ENDEF

*Corresponding author: yolanda.lara@endef.com

The goal of MUTABLE is to define and develop an integral circularity strategy applicable to small self-consumption solar installations. This includes photovoltaic and hybrid installations, as well as complementary energy systems such as heat pumps, recovery devices, and storage systems. The primary aim of is to establish and implement a comprehensive circularity strategy within the solar energy residential sector, encompassing the entire lifecycle of solar installations and associated energy systems.

Approach & classification methodology

Increase reuse rate

Identify the current reuse rate of materials and equipment across different types of solar residential installations, and characterize improvement areas.

Redesign hybrid solar panels

Identify specific redesign needs for both water and air hybrid solar panels, as well as their associated installations, to enhance the reuse rate of their components.

Assessing recovery paths

Define the most appropriate recovery processes for materials that cannot be directly reused or redesigned

Typology	Components	Connection
PVT water panels, type A	Hybrid panels	Electrical
	Inverters	
	Structures	Hydraulic
	Ancillary hydraulics	
PVT water panels, type B	Hybrid panels	Electrical
	Inverters	
	Structures	Hydraulic
	Ancillary hydraulics	
Photovoltaic panels	PV Panels	Electrical
	Inverters	
	Structures	
PVT air panels	Hybrid panels	Electrical
	Inverters	
	Structures	Neumatic
	Ancillary neumatics	

Four typologies were defined according to their components. Each typology was dismantled independently.

Methodology & Best Practices Guide

- Good condition — Reuse directly
- To be reviewed — Reuse or Redesign
- Poor condition — Recycling or Recovery

A **methodology** (color-coded, sticker-based) to classify the components while dismantling was developed. Easy to use and non-invasive to the components or the workers, to be used in roofs while working.

Best Practices Guide for disassembly and assembly installations to be able to reuse the most of material were prepared.

Main routes were chosen for the all the components. For all the installations, part of the materials were sent to recycling. Reuse ratio varies depending on both, type of components and new locations. Components such as wiring, able to be reused, needs to pass electrical safety and working tests prior to reuse.

Results and discussion

PV panels

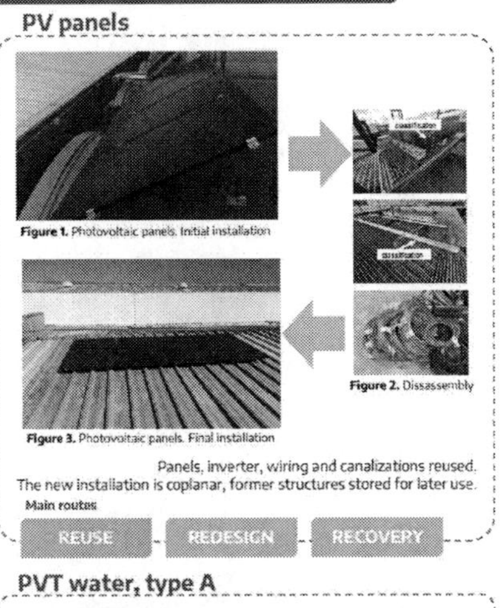

Figure 1. Photovoltaic panels. Initial installation

Figure 2. Dissassembly

Figure 3. Photovoltaic panels. Final installation

Panels, inverter, wiring and canalizations reused. The new installation is coplanar, former structures stored for later use.

Main routes

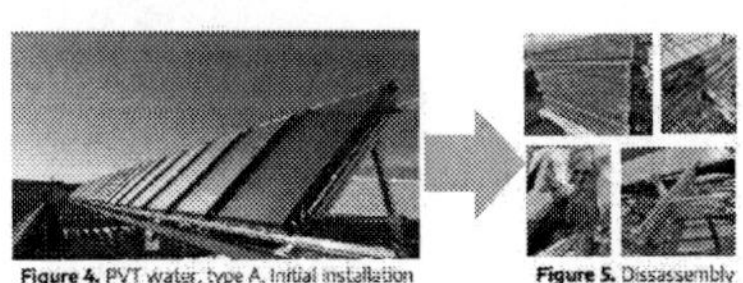

PVT water, type A

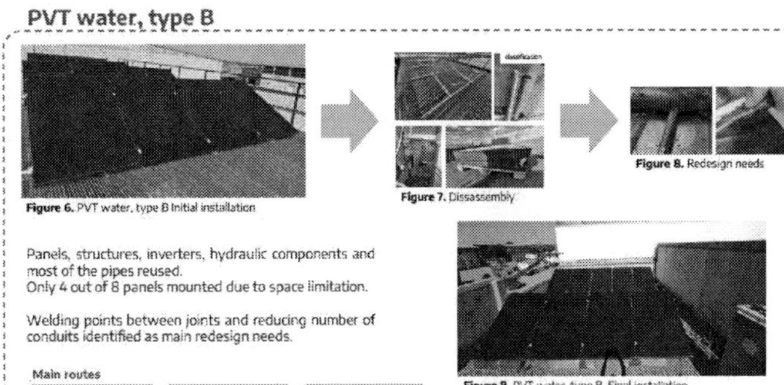

Figure 4. PVT water, type A. Initial installation

Figure 5. Dissassembly

Panels, insulating material and ducts were very damaged. Recycling route, no reassembly.

Main routes

PVT water, type B

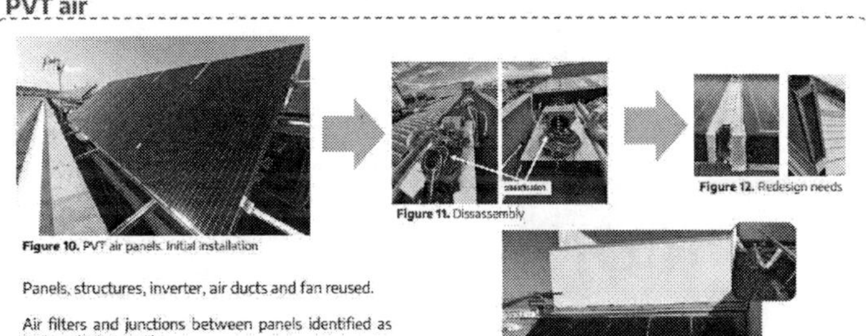

Figure 6. PVT water, type B Initial installation

Figure 7. Dissassembly

Figure 8. Redesign needs

Panels, structures, inverters, hydraulic components and most of the pipes reused.
Only 4 out of 8 panels mounted due to space limitation.

Welding points between joints and reducing number of conduits identified as main redesign needs.

Main routes

Figure 9. PVT water, type B. Final installation

PVT air

Figure 10. PVT air panels. Initial installation

Figure 11. Dissassembly

Figure 12. Redesign needs

Panels, structures, inverter, air ducts and fan reused.

Air filters and junctions between panels identified as main redesign needs.

Main routes

Figure 13. PVT air panels. Final installation

Conclusions

1. A **methodology for material categorization,** easy to use in the field, was designed and tested.

2. **Four types of solar installations were successfully disassembled,** and all disassembled materials were assigned to Reuse, Redesign or Recovery routes.

3. A **"Best Practices Guide"** for assembly and disassembly processes, designed to maximize material recovery and reuse, has been developed.

4. Crucial redesign needs were identified for both water and air hybrid panels

5. Three of the four installation types were **successfully reassembled at new locations** using the reused materials, achieving an **overall reuse rate of 30%.**

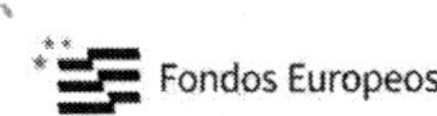

020518-001 Funded by: FEDER/Gobierno de Aragón/Project EC-35-2024

Rooftop Solar Explorer: Mapping the Rooftop Solar Potential of 100+ Cities in India

Shantanu Roy, Saptak Ghosh, and Mahesh Kalshetty

Center for Study of Science, Technology and Policy (CSTEP), Bengaluru, India

Contact: shantanu@cstep.in

020519-001

Introduction

In alignment with India's flagship rooftop solar scheme—PM Surya Ghar: Muft Bijli Yojana—aiming to solarise 10 million households, a potential assessment exercise is essential to accelerate rooftop solar adoption. It enables the accurate estimation of optimal system size, techno-economic viability, and shadow-free rooftop areas. By allowing easy visualisation of installations and identifying high-potential roofs and regions, it supports informed decision making, demand aggregation, and greater consumer awareness.

We undertook this assessment to deliver rooftop-level solar potential insights through an intuitive and user-friendly digital platform—the Rooftop Solar Explorer (RTSE) tool. The tool is designed to visualise shadow-free areas and estimate optimal system size, along with potential financial savings over a 25-year period.

Objectives

- To develop a user-friendly platform that estimates rooftop solar potential, optimal system size, and long-term savings
- To build a scalable, replicable, and automated model for rooftop solar mapping using high-resolution aerial imagery
- To support the large-scale implementation of PM Surya Ghar: Muft Bijli Yojana
- To assist government agencies, electricity utilities, and developers in identifying high-potential rooftops and ensuring efficient demand aggregation
- To contribute to India's renewable energy goals of 500 GW by 2030 and net-zero emission target by 2070 through decentralised solar deployment

020519-003

Methodology

The foundation of the Rooftop Solar Explorer (RTSE) tool lies in aerial data collection and preprocessing. The process begins with capturing raw aerial data, which are then transformed into precise geospatial layers enabling rooftop-level solar analysis.

1. True Ortho Imagery:

- High-resolution aerial imagery captured using drones/satellites
- Ensures accurate rooftop (50 cm × 50 cm grids) outlines
- AI/ML algorithms applied for automated rooftop digitisation

2. Digital Surface Modelling:

- Captures rooftop heights, slopes, and surrounding areas
- Used for shading analysis using ArcGIS hill-shade approach and solar potential mapping

3. 3D Point Cloud:

- 3D model generation and visualisation

4. Solar Radiation and System Sizing

- Data sourced from the National Solar Radiation Database (NSRDB) by the National Renewable Energy Laboratory (NREL) are used to compute grid-wise annual global horizontal irradiance (GHI)
- Panels placed in portrait/landscape layouts to optimise the capacity utilisation factor (CUF) and match demand

4. Development of RTSE tool:

- All datasets integrated into the RTSE platform
- Provides automated rooftop identification, shadow-free solar potential, optimal system sizing, and long-term financial savings

www.cstep.in

4

Methodology

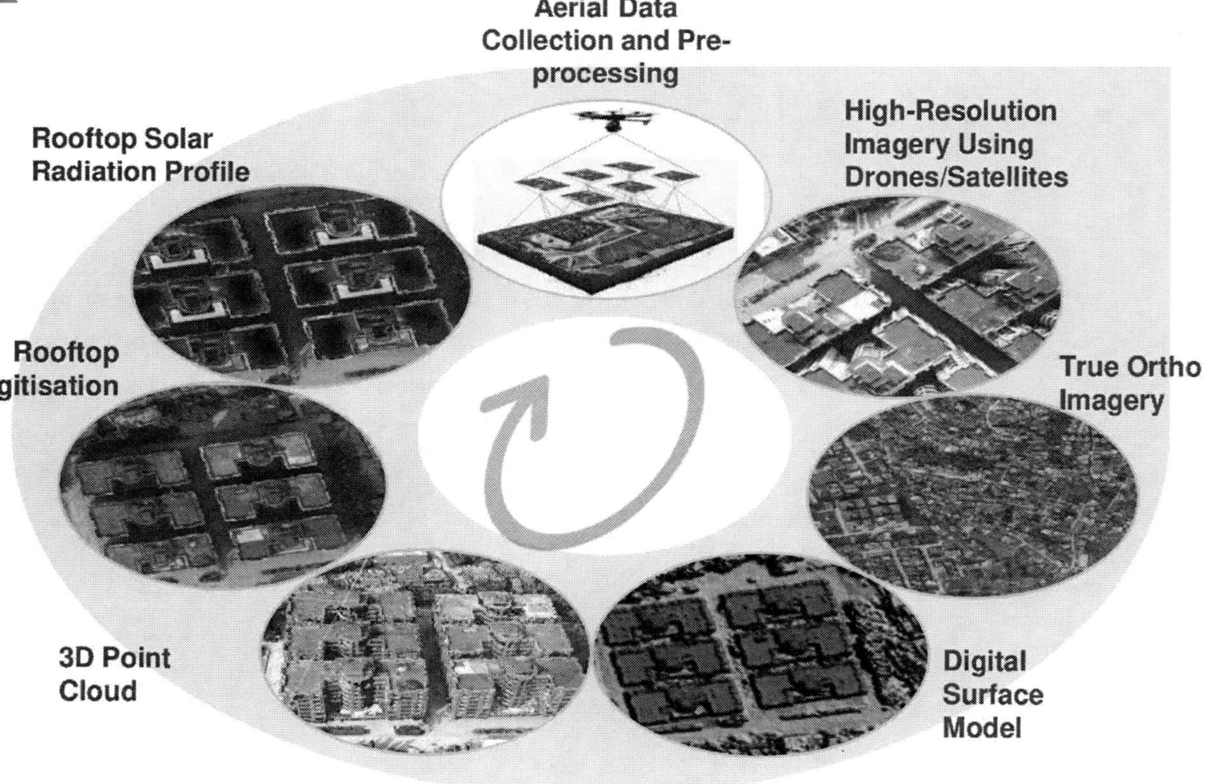

020519-005

Results

RTSE portals
Consumer portal
Multi-criteria analysis (MCA) portal
System size
Techno-economic estimation
Detailed project reports
Identification of high-potential rooftops and areas
City and Ward level Demand aggregation

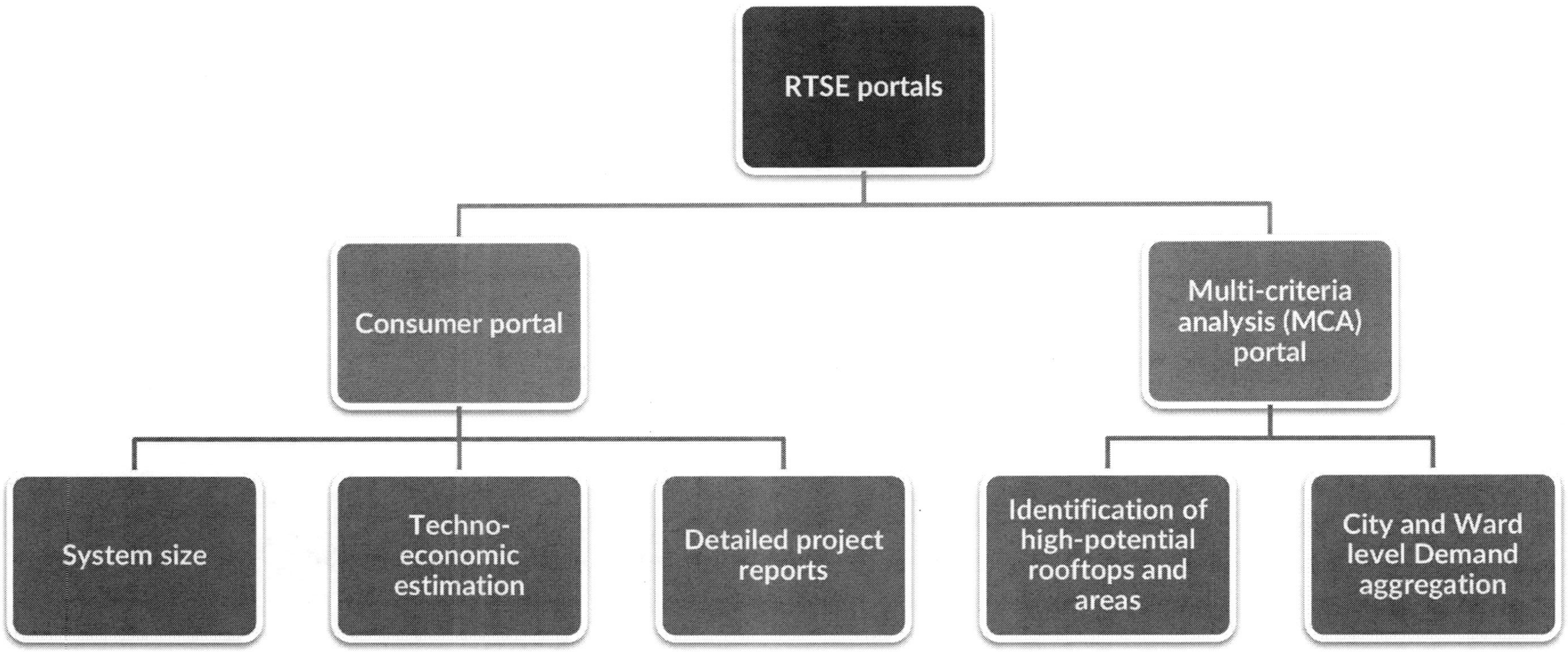

RTSE (Consumer Portal)

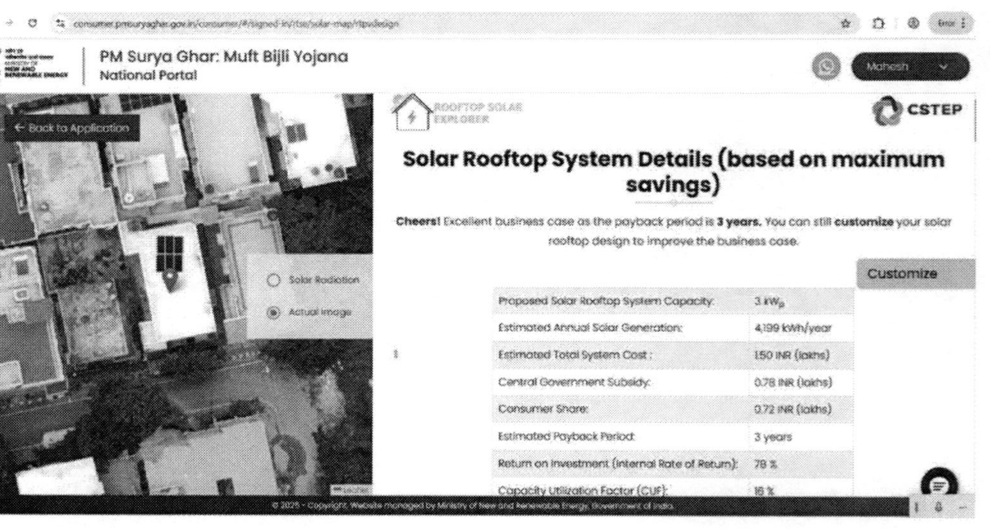

RTSE on Government of India's National Portal
for Rooftop Solar

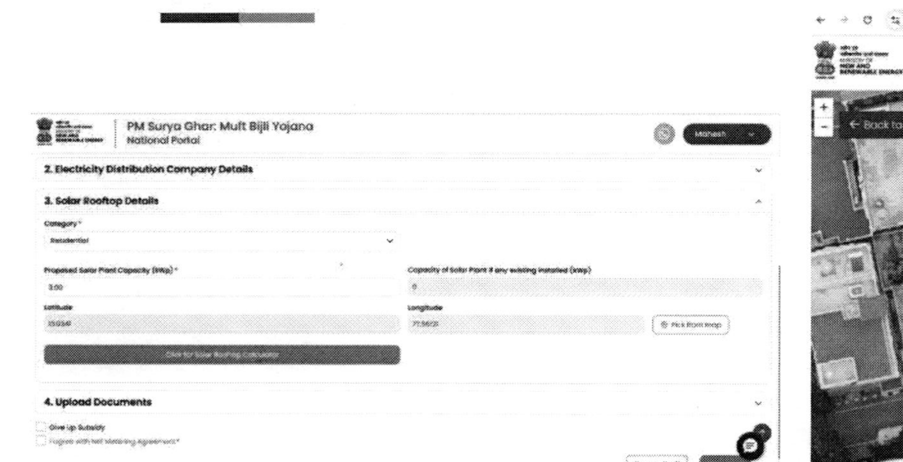
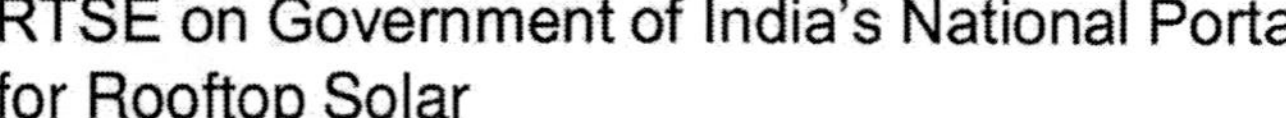

Information on the optimal system size, along with techno-economic details, based on available shadow-free rooftop area, the consumer's electricity consumption profile, and state-specific energy tariff, is provided and can be further customised

RTSE (MCA Portal)

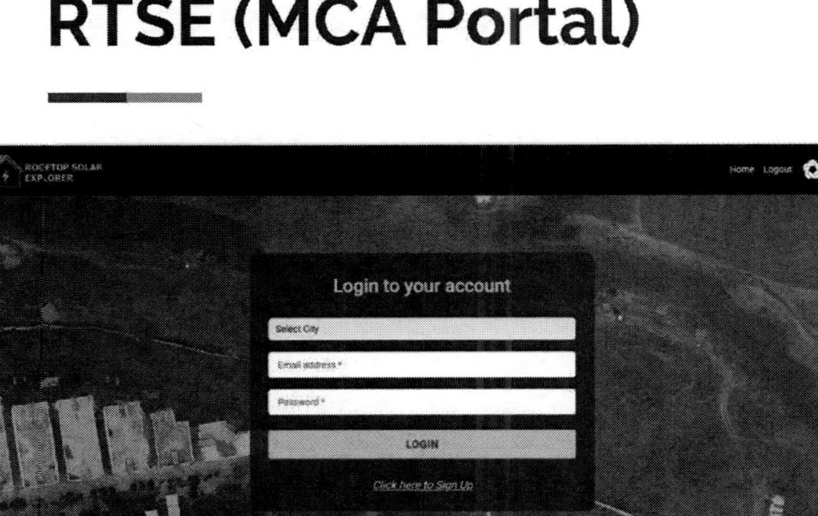

Select a city and enter credentials

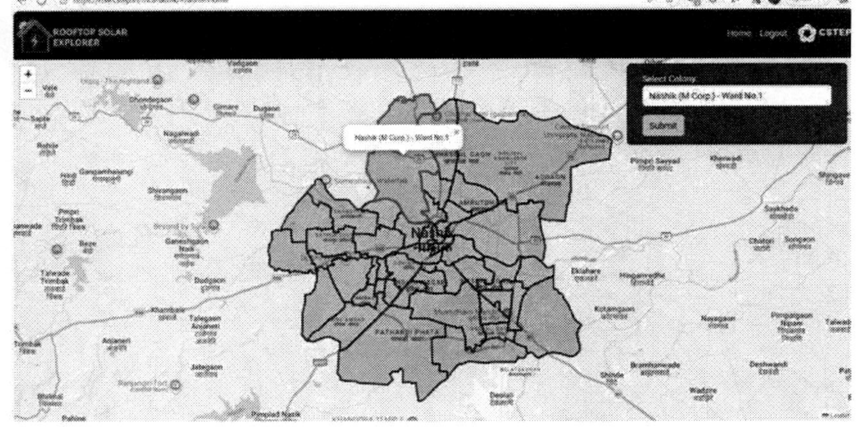

Select a ward within the city

020519-008

RTSE (MCA Portal)

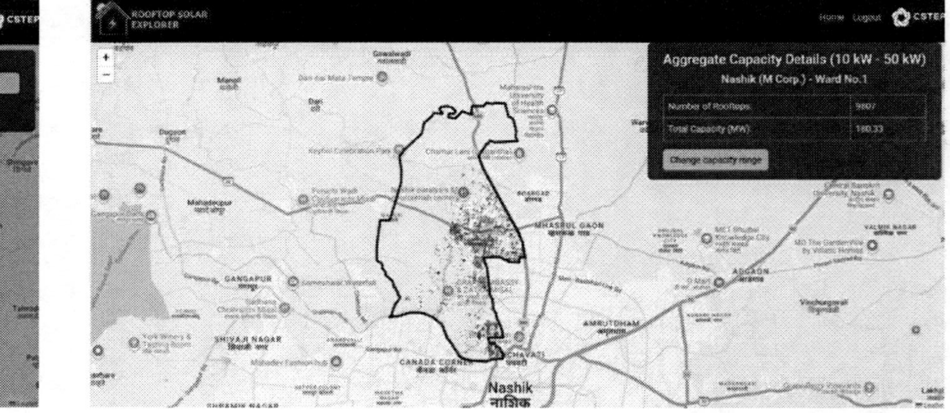

Different system size ranges in the ward will be shown

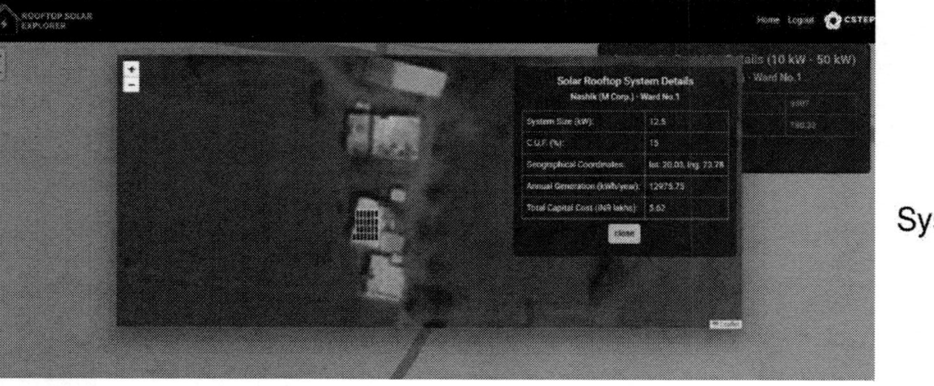

Choose any range to obtain a detailed view, with the option to further evaluate individual roofs

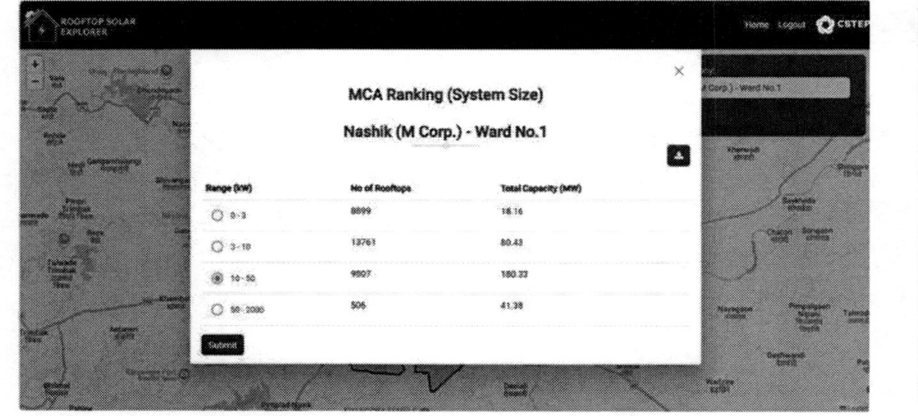

Systems details for a selected roof

Conclusion

- RTSE: First-of-its-kind geospatial rooftop solar potential assessment tool in India
- Piloted in 2020 in Bengaluru and then expanded to multiple cities across India
- Currently operational in 100+ cities in India
- Integrated into the Government of India's National Portal for Rooftop Solar (https://pmsuryaghar.gov.in/)
- Fully automated, scalable, and user-centric
- Optimal system sizing based on available shadow-free area and the consumer's electricity consumption
- Accessed by over 200,000 users
- Empowering consumers and accelerating adoption
- Providing policy and planning support
- Identification of high-potential rooftops for demand aggregation at the city/state level

Way Forward:
Expand to India's rural regions and other developing nations
Integrate advanced AI/ML for improved accuracy
Develop RTSE as a global model for rooftop solar adoption

Media Coverage and Recognition

- Shortlisted as an 'Innovator' in the Asia-Pacific region for 2025 Energy Heroes Awards organised by Sustainable Energy for ALL (SEforALL): https://www.seforall.org/news/announcing-the-2025-energy-heroes-award-shortlist
- RTSE presentation hosted on the official website of the Ministry of New and Renewable Energy, Government of India: https://solarrooftop.pmsuryaghar.gov.in/notification/160_notification.pdf
- Featured as a pioneering solution in rooftop solar adoption by The India Climate Collaborative (ICC): https://indiaclimatecollaborative.org/blog/voices-from-india-s-climate-ecosystem
- RTSE has received extensive coverage through state launch events in Madhya Pradesh, Chhattisgarh, Kerala, and Karnataka

References

https://saga-gis.sourceforge.io/saga_tool_doc/9.4.1/ta_lighting_2.html

https://www.researchgate.net/publication/2539232_The_solar_radiation_model_for_Open_source_GIS_Implementation_and_applications

https://developer.nrel.gov/docs/solar/nsrdb/suny-india-data-download/

https://developer.nrel.gov/docs/solar/nsrdb/meteosat-download/

https://developer.nrel.gov/docs/solar/nsrdb/himawari-download/

THANK YOU

INTERACTIVE LEARNING FOR PV SYSTEMS: A BOARD GAME-BASED TEACHING STRATEGY FOR OPERATIONS AND MAINTENANCE

Melodie de L'Epine[1], Yoselyn Walsh[2], Carlos Meza[3], Brian Azzopardi[4,5,6,7]

[1]ICARES Consulting (Becquerel Institute), Belgium [2]Costa Rica Institute of Technology, Cartago, Costa Rica, [3]Anhalt University of Applied Sciences, Koethen, Germany, [4]The Foundation for Innovation and Research – Malta, [5]The University of Malta, [6]The Malta College of Arts, Science and Technology, [7]Azzopardi and Associates, Malta. Corresponding author: carlos.meza@hs-anhalt.de

Challenge in PV education

- The global demand for skilled professionals in solar energy is rising.
- Traditional theoretical education often fails to prepare students for the complex, real-world challenges of Photovoltaic (PV) system operation and maintenance (O&M).

Learning objectives

- Understand the balance between initial investment and long-term costs.
- Identify common operational risks (e.g., weather, soiling) and their impact on performance.
- Learn the value of preventive strategies like insurance and system protection.
- Practice budgeting for operational expenses and strategic investments.

Work description and goals

- Apply gamification to support foundational and practical operation and maintenance skills.
- Developed two educational board games, SolarTycoon and a second case-study focused game, to simulate the technical and financial aspects of running a solar energy business.
- This study details the design, implementation, and reception of the games during an international training event for higher education students.

Methodology

Needs assessment
Surveys with educators & stakeholders

Platform development
Scenario simulations & multiplayer features

Content creation
Real-world PV challenges

Pilot testing
Across academia and industry

Impact evaluation
Mixed methods

Continuous Improvement
Iterative feedback integration

Board Games:

a) Facilitator-Guided Game

In-depth diagnostic and O&M tasks
Discussion-based, real-time decisions
Tested in 2025 and 2023

b) Solar Tycoon

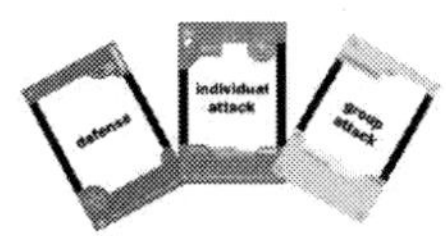

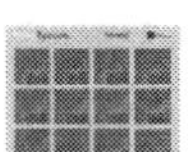

Tycoon gameplay: manage PV systems
Deal with equipment, weather events, and finance
Tested 2025

Preliminary results

↑ Engagement and motivation
↑ Knowledge retention (pre-post tests)
↑ Collaboration and problem-solving
Learners appreciated immersive, visual formats

Satisfaction survey

To what extent do you agree with the following statement: "The game was engaging and kept my attention."?

4.78
Average Rating

★ ★ ★ ★ ★

Future work

- Scale platform to more learners and contexts
- Add AI-based personalization
- Multilingual & region-specific localization
- Embed into curricula and training programs

Acknowledgments

Partly funded by the European Union under Grant 101079469 PROMISE "Photovoltaics Reliability Operations and Maintenance Innovative Solutions for Energy Alliance" project, under Grant 101075747 and UK Research and Innovation (UKRI) TRANSIT "TRANSiTion to sustainable future through training and education" project, European Union, Xjenza Malta under Grant REP-2023-061 ReOFFEVs.

"Robust Optimization Framework for PVs and EVs integration at Low Voltage Network" project.

Industrial Design Students in Costa Rican Institute of Technology for volunteer in the creation of Solar Tycoon.

Follow our Journey
@Promise
PvPromise.eu
info@pvpromise.eu

FOUNDATION FOR INNOVATION AND RESEARCH - MALTA
.MT

AUSTRIAN INSTITUTE OF TECHNOLOGY

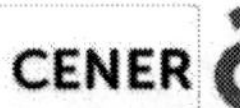
CENER

HOCHSCHULE ANHALT University of Applied Sciences

PIXAM

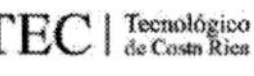
TEC | Tecnológico de Costa Rica

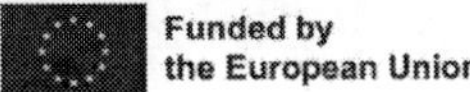
Funded by the European Union

This project has received funding from the European Union's Horizon Europe, Widening Participation and Spreading Excellence action, under grant agreement n°101079469.

020520-001

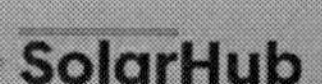

Gender Diversity in Photovoltaics: Experiences and Support Mechanisms

Pınar Derin-Güre*, Chiara Busto, Rita Ebner, Hande Eryılmaz, Perine Fleury, Nikoletta Fodor, Ivan Gordon, Eren Cihan Gülsoy, Ulrike Jahn, Delfina Munoz, Ezgi Pehlivanlı, Paula Sánchez-Friera, Ioannis Tsanakas, Busra Yılmaz.

Context

The PV sector remains highly gendered. Women and gender-diverse individuals are severely underrepresented in technical and leadership roles, hindering both innovation and a just energy transition. This study moves beyond numbers to explore lived experiences, identifying key barriers and support mechanisms, using a qualitative analysis techniques.

WHAT ABOUT YOU?

The Research Gap

Existing literature often focuses on quantitative gaps. This is the first qualitative study in PV to investigate the lived experiences of professionals from under-represented gender groups to identify the nuanced barriers they face and the support mechanisms that truly foster inclusion and advancement.

Methodology

This study adopts a qualitative research design based on **semi-structured interviews** with a diverse group of professionals from across the European PV sector. We use the snowball technique for interviews.

Participants: Diverse professionals across the European PV sector. (14 interviews completed, 35 planned).

Analysis: Thematic analysis of career pathways and workplace culture.

Interview Outcomes

Work–life balance remains a challenge for women in PV, who often face disproportionate care burdens, frequent travel, and burnout, mitigated mainly through supportive partners and outcome-focused work styles. Gender gaps persist in pay and promotion, with wage differences of up to 30%, slower advancement, and barriers in salary negotiation that can fuel imposter syndrome. Interviewees recommended solutions such as transparent pay structures, mentorship, flexible work policies, gender quotas, and recognition of diverse leadership styles.

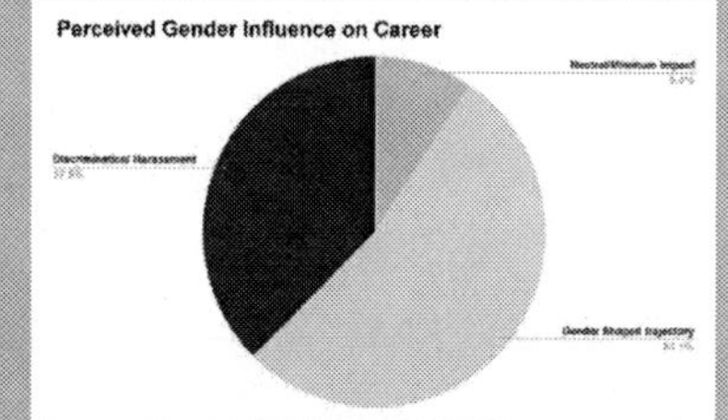

Perceived Gender Influence on Career

Pay & Promotion	
Theme	**Examples**
Wage gap	Up to 30% difference (interview 14)
Promotion bias	Women told they need more "experience" while men promoted sooner
Negotiation gap	Women negotiate less often, or seen as "aggressive" when they do
Positive discrimination & Tokenism	Women (accused of) being chosen for roles to "tick boxes" → imposter syndrome

Work-Life Balance	
Theme	**Finding**
Family care Burden	Mothers disproportionately responsible, career sacrifices
Travel demands	Difficult for mothers, easier for single/unmarried women
Burnout	Women with kids often 'exhausted, depleted'
Coping strategies	Simplifying personal life, relying on partner, focusing on results not hours

Recommendations for Change	
Level	**Recommendation**
Organisational	Transparent pay scales; mentorship; (non-gendered) parental leave; flexible hours
Cultural	Shift away from gender stereotypes; recognition of diverse leadership styles
Policy	Quotas; accountability in promotions; visibility for women experts
Personal advice (to newcomers)	"Negotiate early"; "find mentors/sponsors"; "don't be afraid to leave toxic workplaces"

Barriers and Support factors

Hindrances	Supports
Lack of role models, stereotypes, cultural conditioning	Mentorship, female professors, supportive colleagues
Male-dominated networks & decision-making	Growing diversity policies
Bias in assigning roles (pastoral vs technical)	Visibility of women leaders
Structural issues (pay opacity, hiring bias)	Flexible work arrangements, EU-funded equity pushes

Visibility and Leadership

Dimension	Findings
Conference invitations	Most women invited (esp. recently) but often tokenised or often the same small group
Leadership roles	~40% hold significant leadership roles but are still sidelined
Overall visibility	Technical leadership remains male dominated

POLICY RECOMMENDATIONS

Policy Area	Industry	Research
Leadership & Representation	Gender diversity targets in leadership; transparent promotions; equal pay; visibility in decision-making through gendered data.	Gender balance in conference speakers, panels, awards; track and report gender-disaggregated data.
Workplace Culture	Zero-tolerance harassment policies; unconscious bias training; value diverse leadership styles.	Supportive environments; standardized recognition systems to reduce bias.
Work–Life Balance	Flexible work models; equal parental leave; childcare support.	Recognize caregiving-related career breaks in evaluations; improve parental leave and support systems.
Career Support / Mentorship	Structured mentorship programs; women-focused networks; retraining and reskilling opportunities.	Formal mentorship networks; negotiation and leadership training; funding for women-led projects.
Long-Term Change	Partnerships with education systems; outreach to schools to promote PV careers.	Outreach to schools/universities; highlight female role models; cross-sector partnerships for inclusivity.

Funded by the European Union, under the Horizon Europe programme, Grant agreement number 101086110. Views and opinions expressed are, however, those of the author(s) only and do not necessarily reflect those of the European Union or European Climate, Infrastructure and Environment Executive Agency. Neither the European Union nor the granting authority can be held responsible for them.

*Corresponding Author. Email: pderin@metu.edu.tr

ADVANCED MACHINE-LEARNING-BASED ANALYSIS OF CRITICS AND THE SILENT MAJORITY REGARDING THE ENERGY TRANSITION AND PHOTOVOLTAICS ON TIKTOK

WHAT ALGORITHMIC APPROACHES ARE SUITABLE FOR SENTIMENT ANALYSIS AND STANCE DETECTION OF PUBLISHED VIDEO CONTENT AND COMMENTS?

Marc Schneider, Jannik Achenbach, Janek Gehrlein, Anne Maren Feldhof, Eva-Maria Grommes, Valérie Varney,
University of Applied Sciences Cologne
Faculty of Process Engineering, Energy and Mechanical Systems
Cologne Innovation and Transfer Lab
marc_gabriel.schneider@smail.th-koeln.de

Abstract—In this research project, several approaches of natural language processing are outlined to perform opining mining on the social media platform TikTok. The goal is to analyse the views of critics and the silent majority regarding the energy transition and photovoltaics. First, a dataset containing published TikTok videos with the hashtag #Energiewende, #Solarenergie and #Photovoltaik is created. After filtering out irrelevant content using an Ensemble Classifier model made up of a Random Forest and Support Vector Machine, the entities of the dataset undergo a sentiment analysis as well as a stance detection. Finally, the machine learning results are evaluated, revealing that there are slightly more videos in favour of the energy transition and photovoltaics. The engagement on the other hand is higher for neutral and negative videos. At last, the most used nouns by the critics are gathered and visualized with the aid of a word cloud. Although the word cloud does not show the context, in which the words are used, each word can be reviewed intuitively to gain a better idea of what aspects of the energy transition and photovoltaics are the most relevant to critics.

Keywords—machine learning, natural language processing, sentiment analysis, stance detection, ET, PV, TikTok, opinion mining

1 Introduction

With the human society facing the global warming crisis, transitioning from fossil fuels to renewable energies, a process called energy transition (ET), is a frequently discussed issue. In particular, photovoltaics (PV) play a central role in this transition and are increasingly debated in public discourse [1]. Especially social media platforms such as TikTok offer a place where political discourse takes place. This makes TikTok and social media in general an important aspect to consider when analysing the public's opinion toward the ET and PV [2]. However, due to the large amount of content available on TikTok today, machine learning (ML) is an essential tool to process and analyse the given data. A rapidly developing field within ML is natural language processing (NLP), which allows computers to understand and generate human language [3]. This study investigates different algorithmic approaches for sentiment analysis and stance detection. The underlying research question is to determine what approaches are suitable for on social media published videos and comments.

There are different ML models used in NLP including Logistic Regression (LR), Random Forests (RF) and Support Vector Machines (SVM) [4].

Additionally, multiple deep learning (DL) approaches, so called transformer models, are emerging. These models are expected to better understand natural language and more complex texts [3, 4]. One very popular model out of this field is called BERT [4, 5]. BERT stands for Bidirectional Encoder Representations from Transformers and was introduced in 2019. Because of its architecture, BERT can be easily adapted to different tasks such as sequence classification or sentiment analysis. The model can be fine-tuned by adding an additional output layer specialized to the performing tasks. As a result, BERT can create state-of-the-art ML models for NLP [5].

Using an approach based on ML and NLP, the goal of this research is to detect the sentiment, stance, and subjectively relevant topics of critics as well as the silent majority (SM) regarding the ET and PV. Furthermore, different technical approaches for these tasks are investigated and compared.

The SM refers to a large group of people within a population who do not publicly express their opinions, beliefs, or political preferences due to a lack of interest, fear of backlash, or a desire to avoid conflict. However, they can still have a significant influence on elections or policy decisions, which makes it crucial for political strategy, market research as well as social analysis to understand the group's sentiment [6]. In this paper, it is assumed that the SM's opinion on the

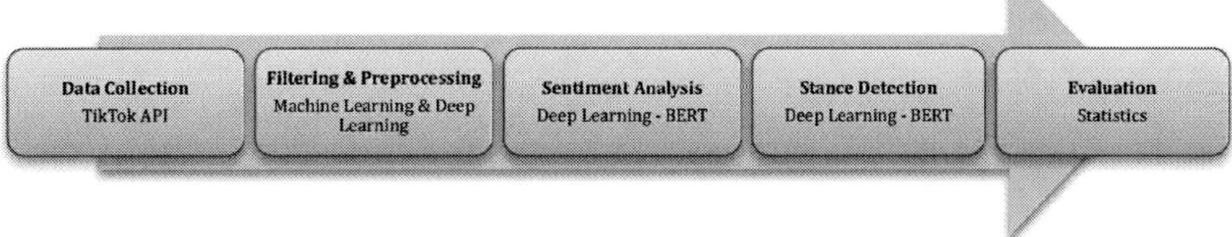

Figure 1: Software Pipeline

given subject cannot be reduced to being merely *positive, neutral,* or *negative.* Nevertheless, the group does hold an opinion, although it remains underrepresented in political discourse.

2 Machine learning pipeline

In this project, a pipeline was developed, that can also be applied to other subjects. The pipeline includes the steps data collection, filtering and preprocessing, and sentiment as well as stance prediction using ML models. The final step consists of evaluating and visualizing the results.

2.1 Data collection

To collect public data related to the ET and PV on TikTok, the official TikTok API was used [7]. It allows the user to create a dataset, made up of all the videos using a certain hashtag. In this project, all videos using #Energiewende (#energytransition), #Solarenergie (#solarenergy) and #Photovoltaik (#photovoltaics) (case-insensitive) in their video description were gathered leading to an initial dataset of 19274 entities. All entities have the following entries: *username, video_description, view_count, like_count, comment_count, share_count, create_time, video_id* and *voice_to_text,* the latter being only available for those videos, that have the appropriate option turned on. To extract the remaining *voice_to_text-files,* the respective videos were downloaded manually and then Google Speech Recognition was performed on those videos [8]. Additionally, the comments of all videos, that were labelled as relevant, were gathered using the entries *comment_username, video_id, comment_id, parent_comment_id,* and *creation_time.* The aspect of relevance as well as data filtering is explained in the next chapter.

2.2 Filtering and preprocessing

Filtering the dataset is a crucial step to ensure that its content aligns with the given topic. The content includes all videos tagged with *#Energiewende, #Solarenergie* and *#Photovoltaik* and contains both relevant content and irrelevant entries, such as spam, advertisements, or unrelated material. Since manual reviewing is impractical at the given scale, an automated ML approach was employed to classify videos into relevant and irrelevant classes.

The results confirm that traditional models like RF and SVM, when combined in an ensemble, can outperform transformer-based models like BERT in filtering tasks, possibly due to the limited size of the fine-tuning dataset and the overfitting risk in deep models.

2.2.1 Approach

Four primary classifiers were used: LR, RF, SVM and BERT. LR was chosen due to its simplicity, RF was used as it is another model suitable for text classification [4]. SVM, being a very popular model, was also picked and finally, BERT was chosen, given its promising performance [4, 5]. Furthermore, an Ensemble Classifier was developed, that combines LR, RF and SVM to predict together and therefore could improve the performance.

Data preprocessing involved tokenizing and normalizing the text in the *voice_to_text*-column as well as removing stop words and special characters. For traditional models such as LR, RF, and SVM, TF-IDF-vectorization was used to generate numerical representations of the texts. BERT was fine-tuned on the dataset over five epochs, leveraging its pre-trained embeddings for deep semantic understanding.

Feature engineering played a significant role in improving the models' performance by adding a manually designed keyword matching score in addition to TF-IDF-vectorization. This binary feature detected, whether specific keywords such as "energy", "climate", "heating policy", "wind", "nuclear", "coal", "electricity", or "sun" appeared in the respective video transcript. If at least one keyword was detected, the score was set to 1. Otherwise, it was set to 0. This feature, along with TF-IDF, was included in all models except BERT, which operated directly on embeddings. All models were trained and tested on a manually labelled dataset of 200 annotated entities, with an 80:20 training-validation split. Hyperparameter optimization using Grid Search was performed for the traditional models, while BERT was fine-tuned with a batch size of 16 over five epochs. After being trained, the models were evaluated using standard metrics including accuracy, precision, recall, and F1-score, to ensure a comprehensive assessment of their performance [4].

2.2.2 Results

The evaluation results of the optimized models are summarized below in Table 1:

Table 1: Accuracies of selected algorithms

Model	LR	RF	SVM	BERT	Ensemble Classifier
Accuracy	0.64	0.88	0.88	0.82	0.88
Precision (relevant)	0.69	0.91	0.91	0.79	0.91
Recall (relevant)	0.82	0.91	0.91	1	0.91
F1-Score (relevant)	0.75	0.91	0.91	0.88	0.91
Precision (irrelevant)	0.43	0.82	0.82	1	0.82
Recall (irrelevant)	0.27	0.82	0.82	0.45	0.82
F1-Score (irrelevant)	0.33	0.82	0.82	0.62	0.82

The results reveal key observations: LR achieved the lowest accuracy of 0.64 compared to the other models, possibly due to its simplicity [4]. Therefore, it was rejected for further use. RF, SVM, and the Ensemble Classifier, which combines predictions from LR, RF, and SVM, produced the best result for accuracy achieving a score of 88%, while also performing well regarding the other scores. The fine-tuned BERT model attained an accuracy of 0.82, while also excelling in precision for the irrelevant data, but underperforming in recall. This limited its overall effectiveness. The Ensemble Classifier was chosen for the final filtering, cropping down the dataset to 6715 entities, making up approximately 35% of the original dataset.

2.3 Sentiment Analysis

Sentiment analysis has become an essential tool for understanding public opinion on various topics [9]. By analysing text sequences, it predicts the underlying emotion without specifying a target or topic [10].

$$Sentiment(T) = \{Positive, Neutral, Negative\} \quad (1)$$

Sentiment analysis enables organizations and governments to assess attitudes toward specific topics, or policies, although being limited to only detecting the emotional tone of a text [11].

In this project, sentiment analysis was performed on videos as well as their comments. It focused on the transcribed text from the *voice_to_text* entries to uncover the emotional tone of the content and understand the communication culture on TikTok.

2.3.1 Approach

The sentiment analysis utilized the *german-sentiment-bert model* [12]. It is a fine-tuned BERT model that was trained on 1.834 million German-language samples from diverse sources, including Twitter, Facebook, and hotel reviews, making it very suitable for analysing social media content [12]. As a result, a general sentiment classification model specialized on German text was developed. The model takes text sequences as an input and predicts the sentiment class, being either *positive*, *neutral* or *negative*.

To evaluate the model's performance on the obtained dataset, 100 entities were manually assigned one of the three classes introduced above. The initial accuracy of the model was 61%. However, since the model was trained primarily on shorter text samples, whereas the dataset included many longer *voice_to_text* entries, there were still improvements to be made [12].

To address this issue, a Sliding Window Technique was implemented, meaning that long texts were divided into overlapping segments, each receiving an individual sentiment prediction [13]. The sentiment of the original text was then determined by the most frequently predicted sentiment class of the segments. It is a rather simple approach, expected not to claim much computational resources, while still considering the text's context thanks to the overlapping of half a segment length. To find the optimal segment length, a parameter optimization was performed, in which different text lengths were tested by calculating the respective model accuracy.

2.3.2 Results

Table 2 shows the results of the parameter optimization. Using this technique, the model's performance improved from an accuracy score of 61% to 67% (Table 2). This improvement demonstrates the effectiveness of segment-based analysis when encountering longer texts.

Table 2: Accuracy over segment lengths

Length	Accuracy
10	0.36
50	0.49
100	0.56
150	0.57
200	0.66
250	0.66
300	0.65
350	0.67
400	0.65
450	0.66
512	0.65

Table 3 displays the classification report of the sentiment analysis, showing different scores for each one of the three sentiment classes. The sentiment analysis model demonstrates consistent performance for the *negative*-class, achieving precision, recall, and F1-scores of 0.71. For the *positive* class, the model achieved a high precision score of 86%, indicating reliable predictions, but a lower recall score of 61% suggests some under-detection of *positive* sentiment. The neutral-class performed the weakest, with a precision of 55% and an F1-score of 61%, indicating difficulties in distinguishing *neutral* sentiment from other classes.

Table 3: Classification report sentiment analysis

	Precision	Re-call	F1-Score	Sup-port
positive	0.86	0.61	0.72	31
neutral	0.55	0.68	0.61	38
negative	0.71	0.71	0.71	31

2.4 Stance detection

Stance detection is a crucial task in NLP that aims to identify the position or attitude expressed in a text toward a specific target. Unlike sentiment analysis, which focuses solely on the emotional tone, stance detection determines whether the author supports, opposes, or remains *neutral* towards a given subject [14]. This means that stance detection differs from sentiment analysis in that it requires understanding the context and relationship between the text and the target. For instance, a *positive* sentiment of written content may not necessarily indicate support for the related topic [10, 14].

$$Stance(T, U|G) = \{Favour, Against, Neutral\} \quad (2)$$

Given the context of this research, the target G represents the ET and PV. The other model inputs are the text (T) or the user (U).

2.4.1 Approach

For model training, 100 entities were manually labelled regarding their stance towards the ET and PV, the three classes being *favour*, *neutral* or *against*. For the stance detection the *bert-base-german-cased* was chosen as the underlying architecture due to its robust performance in German sequence classification tasks [15].

The model itself is already an adapted BERT model for generating text embeddings of German-language contents. Therefore, the next step was to fine-tune the model by adding an additional output layer to classify texts into the three stance categories.

Since the model has a maximum sequence length of 512 words [15], the Sliding Window Technique, introduced in chapter 2.3.1, was used once again. Furthermore, the texts were split into shorter sequences of 256 words, to multiply the amount of labelled data for training. Based on the hypothesis that the stance of a text equals the stance of every one of its sequences, the sequences were then labelled according to the stance of their root *voice_to_text* entry. This hypothesis was later to be proven or rejected.

The labelled and enhanced dataset was split into training and testing sets, with 80% of the data used for training and 20% used for testing. The model was trained over three epochs using the Hugging Face Trainer API [16]. Since the labelling of 100 randomly selected videos led to class imbalance, oversampling was employed to compensate for this effect. To balance the three stance classes, random entries from the minority classes in the training set were duplicated until all classes contained an equal number of samples. The test set was not augmented and thus remained untouched, ensuring a fair evaluation of the model's performance. This approach helped stabilize the training process and ensured that the model did not become biased towards the majority class [17].

2.4.2 Results
Table 4 displays the classification report of the stance detection.

Table 4: Classification stance detection

	Precision	Recall	F1-score	Support
favour	0.75	0.81	0.78	22
neutral	0.85	0.66	0.75	18
against	0.82	0.87	0.84	32

The stance classification model demonstrates strong performance, made evident by the high precision, recall, and F1-scores across all three stance categories, especially the *favour*- and *against*-classes. The overall accuracy of the model was 81%. The model performed slightly worse regarding the *favouring*-class, which may be correlated to the fact that only very few videos in the dataset express a *positive* sentiment. Overall, the results indicate a high effectiveness of the model in accurately identifying stances. Therefore, the hypothesis from above has been proven, in that it is indeed a reliable way to multiply the training data without manual work and without impairing the results.

2.5 Comments
In this chapter, the as *relevant* categorized videos' comments are analysed. Because of their hierarchical structure, each comment has a *parent_comment_id*. A comment is either associated directly with the video itself (first-layer comment) or linked to the *comment_id* of another comment, in which case it represents a response (second-layer comment). Two different approaches were examined to maximize the performance of sentiment analysis and stance detection on this data. To measure the performance of each approach, 60 comments were manually assigned a sentiment and stance class.

For the sentiment analysis, the model, introduced in chapter 2.3, was used again and achieved an accuracy of 64%. For stance detection, a different approach to the one,

presented in chapter 2.4, was tested. This approach takes the predicted stance of the parent comment as well as the predicted sentiment of the comment itself to generate its stance class. This rule-based algorithm adopts the parent stance, if the sentiment is *positive* or *neutral* and takes the opposite stance, if the sentiment is *negative*. For a *neutral* parent stance, the comment stance equals the corresponding predicted sentiment.

The expectation, that this approach would lead to a higher accuracy was proven wrong. It achieved an accuracy score of 51%, whereas directly using the trained stance model, presented in chapter 2.4, led to a score of 62%. A reason for achieving a lower accuracy could be the suboptimal performance of the sentiment analysis, meaning a higher accuracy of the model used for sentiment analysis could lead to a higher accuracy with the approach presented above.

3   Evaluation
After the pipeline (Fig. 1, p.1) was run through, every *relevant* video entity as well as their corresponding comments had received a predicted sentiment and stance class. That data could then be evaluated.

At first the distribution of sentiment and stance classes over all entities was analysed:

Table 5: Sentiment distribution along videos and comments

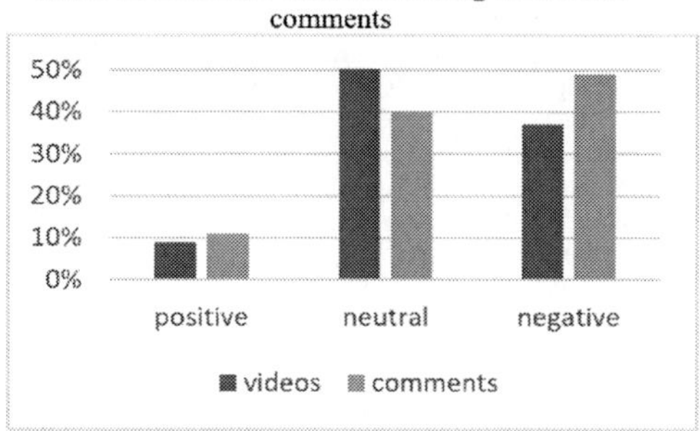

For the *positive*-class, both the videos and comments have almost similar scores with a difference of 2%. There were more *neutral* videos than comments, having received scores of 54% and 40%, respectively. On the other hand, the *negative*-labelled comments' score of 49% surpassed the videos' score of 37%.

Table 6: Stance distribution along videos and comments

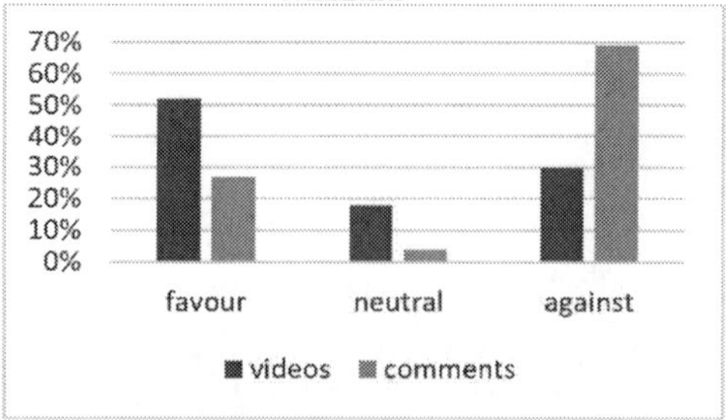

The results seen in Table 6 indicate a polarized stance distribution for both videos and comments, as only 18% and 4% of the *relevant* content was labelled *neutral*. While roughly half of the videos are in *favour* of the ET and PV, the stance distribution of the

evaluated comments leans strongly towards the *against*-class.

When comparing Table 5 to Table 6, one can observe that the content that was labelled *negative* or *against*, respectively, is very similar in frequency between both sentiment and stance distribution. However, the content with a *neutral* sentiment has shifted over to the *favour*-class regarding the stance. This suggests that content in *favour* of the ET and PV tends to be expressed with a more *neutral* sentiment compared to the content labelled as *against*. Furthermore, it was observed that 944 videos (making up 14% of all videos) received a *negative* sentiment but a *favour* stance. Additionally, 2249 videos (33% of all videos) received a *neutral* sentiment and *favour* stance. These two observations highlight the difference between sentiment and stance once again and underline the importance of considering them separately, as stated in literature [16, 15].

To infer the stance of the SM towards the ET and PV, the mean engagement statistics of the videos were analysed. The results are shown in Table 7. Since the SM typically refrains from expressing opinions through comments, it is assumed that their stance is most accurately reflected through passive engagement metrics such as view and like counts. Users who engage with content by viewing or liking without commenting may represent this group. Their behaviour thus provides an indirect but meaningful signal of general public opinion.

Table 7: Mean engagement statistics over stance

Mean Stance	Views	Likes	Comments	Shares
favour	10601	215	29	15
neutral	14363	215	18	35
against	12210	504	45	86

The mean engagement statistics over all stance classes of all videos show that videos with a *negative* stance receive by far the most likes, comments, and shares, while neutral videos are the most viewed. These observations suggest that the SM's stance lies somewhere between *neutral* and *against*.

Since the user engagement is not evenly distributed over all videos on social media, the ten most liked videos using with *#Energiewende*, *#Solarenergie* and *#Photovoltaik* were investigated separately, as they are assumed to be highly representative of the public's opinion. Regarding the stance, nine of those videos are labelled *against* and the one remaining is labelled as *neutral*. In terms of sentiment, seven of them are *negative* and three as *neutral*. These observations support the statement from above, that the SM is opposing the idea of transitioning to renewable energy sources using photovoltaics.

To gain a better understanding of what topics are relevant for the critics of the ET and PV, a word cloud was generated, containing the most frequently occurring words in *against*-classified content, though only the nouns were considered. The word cloud reveals that the most popular noun used by critics is *energy*, closely followed by *climate*, *gas*, *heating*, *price*, and *Federal*. Other commonly used words include *state*, *economic*, and *policy*. While the context, in which these words were used, is hardly accessible, each word can be manually reviewed and analysed. That way, it is still possible to gain an idea of what the critics could have meant when using these words.

4 Limitations

To better understanding the topics, that are of high importance for different groups of people on social media, the topic modelling could be further elaborated. A common technique, used for this task, is the Latent Dirichlet Allocation (LDA) [18]. In addition, although the developed software pipelines achieve respectable accuracy across the different submodules, they are still far from perfect. This needs to be kept in mind when interpreting the sentiment and stance detection results.

5 Conclusion

During the first step of the pipeline, the TikTok API proved to be a competent tool for collecting a large amount of published data to obtain a dataset. In the second part of the pipeline Filtering & preprocessing, several algorithms containing machine learning and DL classifiers were investigated and compared. Contrary to expectations, the DL model BERT, that promised great performance in understanding complex natural human language [4], was not able to achieve the best results compared to the other applied models. The presented Ensemble Classifier containing a RF and SVM model performed the best with an accuracy of 88%. However, that does not mean this behaviour will occur every time, it just shows that precisely engineered machine learning models can also outperform DL models, which have a higher grade of automatization.

Moving on to sentiment analysis, the goal was to implement a pre-trained BERT model, that can precisely detect the sentiment of a text. The model *german-sentiment-bert* achieved a good baseline accuracy of 61%, that could be further improved to 67% using the Sliding Window Technique. This proved sequence-based analysis of complex natural language to work accurately.

For the stance detection, another fine-tuned BERT model called *bert-base-german-cased* was introduced. To create a classification model, an additional output layer was added. The model achieved an accuracy of 81% on the test dataset, which can be considered a solid result for this task [10]. Finally, the results as well as the engagement regarding the stance and sentiment classes were analysed, revealing key insights on critics and the SM towards the ET and PV on TikTok.

The evaluation of publicly available TikTok content on ET and PV shows that the majority of videos have a *neutral* sentiment, followed by a *negative* one. However, a shift becomes apparent when examining the stance detection results. In this case, the *favour* class has the highest percentage, followed by the *against* class. This suggests that most videos supporting ET and PV adopt a more neutral tone and sentiment compared to those in the *against* class. A closer manual analysis confirms this: while 14% of all published videos have a *negative* sentiment combined with a *favour* stance, 33% of all videos show a neutral sentiment combined with a *favour* stance. These statistics indicate that most of the in-*favour* videos use a neutral or *negative* tone, which may reflect frustration while still supporting the topic.

The results of sentiment analysis and stance detection for the comments suggest a different interpretation. While sentiment analysis shows a considerable number of comments using a neutral tone, with the majority being *negative*, stance detection reveals a strong shift towards the *against* class. Around 69% of all comments were labeled as *against*, highlighting a strongly *negative* attitude towards ET and PV among the audience. To gain insights into the topics most important to the critics, the most frequently used nouns in the videos and comments labeled with an *against* stance were analyzed. Although this approach has a clear limitation, since the context in which these words are used is missing, it still provides a first impression of which topics might matter most to this group of users. Among the most frequently used nouns were, for example, *climate, gas, heating, price,* and *Federal,* indicating that the critics are dissatisfied with government actions related to heating, gas heating systems and associated costs, which may be connected to a transition toward renewable energy.

6   Acknowledgements

The study is part of the project MPower, which is funded by the German Federal Ministry of Research, Technology and Space (BMFTR). The authors thank their colleagues and students for their important contributions and discussions.

7   References

[1] I. Heras-Saizarbitoria, E. Cilleruelo, und I. Zamanillo, „Public acceptance of renewables and the media: an analysis of the Spanish PV solar experience", Renew. Sustain. Energy Rev., Bd. 15, Nr. 9, S. 4685–4696, Dez. 2011, doi: 10.1016/j.rser.2011.07.083.

[2] D. Amangeldi, A. Usmanova, und P. Shamoi, „Understanding Environmental Posts: Sentiment and Emotion Analysis of Social Media Data", IEEE Access, Bd. 12, S. 33504–33523, 2024, doi: 10.1109/ACCESS.2024.3371585.

[3] K. R. Chowdhary, „Natural Language Processing", in Fundamentals of Artificial Intelligence, K. R. Chowdhary, Hrsg., New Delhi: Springer India, 2020, S. 603–649. doi: 10.1007/978-81-322-3972-7_19.

[4] Y. Mao, Q. Liu, und Y. Zhang, „Sentiment analysis methods, applications, and challenges: A systematic literature review", J. King Saud Univ. - Comput. Inf. Sci., Bd. 36, Nr. 4, S. 102048, Apr. 2024, doi: 10.1016/j.jksuci.2024.102048.

[5] J. Devlin, M.-W. Chang, K. Lee, und K. Toutanova, „BERT: Pre-training of Deep Bidirectional Transformers for Language Understanding", 24. Mai 2019, arXiv: arXiv:1810.04805. doi: 10.48550/arXiv.1810.04805.

[6] „Silent Majority - ECPS". Zugegriffen: 8. August 2025. [Online]. Verfügbar unter: https://www.populismstudies.org/Vocabulary/silent-majority/

[7] „Research API | TikTok for Developers". Zugegriffen: 8. August 2025. [Online]. Verfügbar unter: https://developers.tiktok.com/products/research-api

[8] SpeechRecognition: Library for performing speech recognition, with support for several engines and APIs, online and offline. Python. Zugegriffen: 8. August 2025. Verfügbar unter: https://github.com/Uberi/speech_recognition#readme

[9] Z. Drus und H. Khalid, „Sentiment Analysis in Social Media and Its Application: Systematic Literature Review", Procedia Comput. Sci., Bd. 161, S. 707–714, Jan. 2019, doi: 10.1016/j.procs.2019.11.174.

[10]   A. ALDayel und W. Magdy, „Stance detection on social media: State of the art and trends", Inf. Process. Manag., Bd. 58, Nr. 4, S. 102597, Juli 2021, doi: 10.1016/j.ipm.2021.102597.

[11]   M. Wankhade, A. C. S. Rao, und C. Kulkarni, „A survey on sentiment analysis methods, applications, and challenges", Artif. Intell. Rev., Bd. 55, Nr. 7, S. 5731–5780, Okt. 2022, doi: 10.1007/s10462-022-10144-1.

[12]   O. Guhr, A.-K. Schumann, F. Bahrmann, und H. J. Böhme, „Training a Broad-Coverage German Sentiment Classification Model for Dialog Systems", in Proceedings of the Twelfth Language Resources and Evaluation Conference, N. Calzolari, F. Béchet, P. Blache, K. Choukri, C. Cieri, T. Declerck, S. Goggi, H. Isahara, B. Maegaard, J. Mariani, H. Mazo, A. Moreno, J. Odijk, und S. Piperidis, Hrsg., Marseille, France: European Language Resources Association, Mai 2020, S. 1627–1632. Zugegriffen: 8. August 2025. [Online]. Verfügbar unter: https://aclanthology.org/2020.lrec-1.202/

[13]   T. G. Dietterich, „Machine Learning for Sequential Data: A Review", in Structural, Syntactic, and Statistical Pattern Recognition, T. Caelli, A. Amin, R. P. W. Duin, D. de Ridder, und M. Kamel, Hrsg., Berlin, Heidelberg: Springer, 2002, S. 15–30. doi: 10.1007/3-540-70659-3_2.

[14]   S. E. Bestvater und B. L. Monroe, „Sentiment is Not Stance: Target-Aware Opinion Classification for Political Text Analysis", Polit. Anal., Bd. 31, Nr. 2, S. 235–256, Apr. 2023, doi: 10.1017/pan.2022.10.

[15]   „google-bert/bert-base-german-cased · Hugging Face". Zugegriffen: 8. August 2025. [Online]. Verfügbar unter: https://huggingface.co/google-bert/bert-base-german-cased

[16]   „Trainer". Zugegriffen: 8. August 2025. [Online]. Verfügbar unter: https://huggingface.co/docs/transformers/main_classes/trainer

[17]   R. Mohammed, J. Rawashdeh, und M. Abdullah, „Machine Learning with Oversampling and Undersampling Techniques: Overview Study and Experimental Results", in 2020 11th International Conference on Information and Communication Systems (ICICS), Apr. 2020, S. 243–248. doi: 10.1109/ICICS49469.2020.239556.

[18]   I. Vayansky und S. A. P. Kumar, „A review of topic modeling methods", Inf. Syst., Bd. 94, S. 101582, Dez. 2020, doi: 10.1016/j.is.2020.101582.

THE ROLE OF TARGET GROUPS AND GATEKEEPERS IN THE DEPLOYMENT OF MORE SUSTAINABLE PHOTOVOLTAIC SYSTEMS: A PARTICIPATORY APPROACH

Alexandra Tönies, Larissa Müller, Eva-Maria Grommes, Valérie Varney
University of Applied Sciences Cologne
Alexandra.toenies@th-koeln.de

ABSTRACT: In the challenge of supporting a sustainable energy transition, societal innovation is a powerful tool for enabling new technologies to reach their full potential. With the goal of designing effective action strategies, this paper argues for the relevance of participatory target group structuration in motivational approaches based on green purchase behavior research. Building on insights from environmental and marketing psychology, limitations of one-size-fits-all strategies are highlighted, and a workshop format designed for collaborative target group identification is introduced. In a use case on promoting more sustainable photovoltaic modules, researchers and practitioners jointly participated in the format, combining brainstorming and touchpoint mapping, in order to identify and prioritize relevant target groups. The workshop proved effective in structuring target groups for transdisciplinary cooperation, while also underlining the challenges of well-adapted stakeholder involvement. Findings revealed a focus on Business-to-Business dynamics for the present case, shaped by the gatekeeping role of organizational actors in the photovoltaic market. Since existing green purchase behavior models center mostly on individual consumers, the study concludes that further research on motivational factors in B2B contexts is essential for developing effective and context-specific strategies.
Keywords: Environmental Psychology, Green Purchase Behavior, Sustainable Energy Transition, Target Group Identification, Organizational Factors

1 INTRODUCTION

An impactful, sustainable energy transition requires not only technical innovations, but also the societal innovations that enable them to realize their full potential. Environmental psychology plays a significant role in identifying the most powerful factors that facilitate such a transition. Green Purchase Behavior research for example investigates the motivational factors involved in sustainable decision making concerning purchase situations. Especially given the at times higher costs of sustainable alternatives, the understanding of behavior drivers here is crucial. Some well-known influencing factors are attitudes, subjective norms, and perceived behavioral control, integrated in the famous theory of planned behavior introduced by Ajzen from 1985 [1], one of the best empirically researched and further developed models in environmental psychology. This model proposes attitudes, subjective norms, and perceived behavioral control as interdependent motivational factors, influencing behavioral intention, which then directly influences the behavior itself. However, while the model has been refined and enriched with more detail since its first introduction, and many more alterations as well as new models have been derived, green purchase behavior research suggests that there is a gap to be addressed in order to tackle universal societal challenges like climate change. Not every public and not every context is the same, with each of them providing different individual, social, and structural dynamics, which is why participatory target group analysis should play a central role in designing effective action strategies. This paper investigates this issue by introducing a workshop-based target group identification method that facilitates inter- and transdisciplinary collaboration, while remaining flexible and time-efficient. As part of the Green Solar Modules project, focused on the development and deployment of more sustainable photovoltaic modules, the workshop goal in the use case was to better understand relevant motivational dynamics in the field of photovoltaics for the stakeholders of this project specifically.

Research in environmental and marketing psychology shows that one-size-fits-all approaches do not achieve effective behavior change [2], [3], [4]. This is already evident in green purchase behavior models, mostly developed with private customers in mind, hereafter referred to as Business-to-Consumer (B2C). Research here highlights how motivational factors vary by country [4], product type [4], and between private and professional purchasing contexts [2]. Depending on the cultural background, local norms, regulations, and values might differ, for example, [5], [6]. Comparing different product types, such as fashion, food, and photovoltaic (PV), varying argument types have been found most important, ranging from peer perception and social norms [7], over health concerns [8], to financial incentives [9]. Concerning private and professional purchasing contexts, automatic spill-over effects from one context to the other have not been supported. Furthermore, empirical research has found unique motivational factors for organizations, such as supplier responsiveness, green compliance, corporate social responsibility [2], or perceived structural pressures [10]. When aiming for green purchase behavior, the necessity thus becomes clear to establish awareness of the context and potential target groups, as a base for all motivational strategies.

Despite this, target group identification is rarely addressed in PV adoption research. This may be due, in part, to the more advanced state of B2C green purchase behavior, compared to Business-to-Business (B2B), which shapes dominant approaches automatically. Another barrier, however, is the lack of standardized and easy-to-use identification methods. In marketing psychology, this typically involves the steps of segmentation – dividing populations into groups with similar, purchase-relevant traits – and positioning, which prioritizes the most promising segments for tailored outreach [11]. However, scientific literature offers no standard methodology for this [12]. Best practice examples use participatory workshops, but these are often lengthy, individualized, and poorly documented [13], making them impractical for most projects without a marketing specialization.

Equally important, inter- and transdisciplinary

10.4229/EUPVSEC2025/5DV.2.62
020523-001

collaborations are increasingly seen as essential for addressing the complexity of the energy transition, as they promise solutions with a more holistic understanding [14], which are therefore more effective [15]. At the same time, logistical and methodological challenges are typically inherent to these settings, given that they bring together stakeholders with different schedules, institutional backgrounds, and perspectives. For target group identification to be feasible and impactful in such contexts, tools must be resource-efficient, flexible, and accessible. The approach introduced by this paper – a participatory workshop design drawing from user experience and marketing research – responds directly to these constraints.

In response to the increasing prominence of inter- and transdisciplinary energy transition projects, this paper focuses on participatory collaboration as a means of developing target group insights. Since motivational strategies depend fundamentally on this context-sensitive knowledge, leveraging the rich perspectives of interdisciplinary teams is essential. Participatory research supports this notion, emphasizing that collective creativity can produce outcomes that exceed those of any single stakeholder [16].

2 METHODOLOGY

For the purpose of this study, a compact participatory workshop design was developed to support inter- and transdisciplinary collaboration. To enable efficient and inclusive target group identification, elements from user experience research were combined with participatory principles. The workshop was designed with the goal of remaining adaptable and time-efficient while enabling the identification of relevant target groups. This was considered crucial as to best support the integration of the various stake- and knowledge-holders in the project, with different localizations and schedules. The participants were representatives of the project partners in PV sales and interested project members with experience in PV sales. Both practitioners and researchers were included to ensure a mix of market expertise and academic perspectives.

The workshop was conducted remotely during a time frame of two hours and divided into the following parts: Introduction, Collective Brainstorming, Touchpoint Maps, and Closure and Feedback (Fig.1). For effective collaboration, an online workspace for drawing and mind mapping was used and a moderator guided through the format.

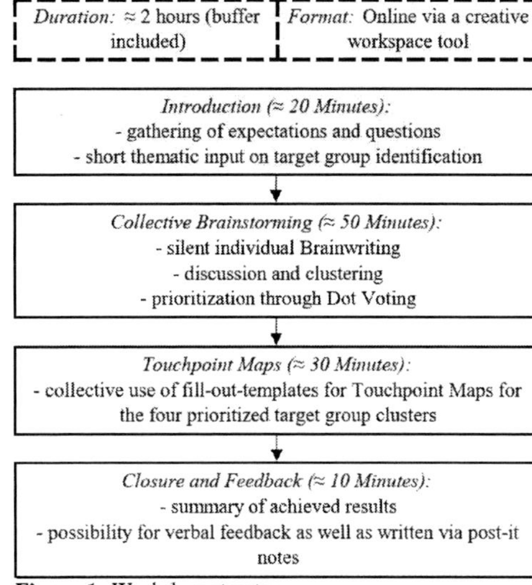

Figure 1: Workshop structure

Given the participants' diverse expertise backgrounds, a thematic introduction on target group work and its practical relevance, as well as the workshop goals, was essential to establish a shared conceptual foundation. To this end, questions and expectations were first collected, followed by a brief input on the topic of target group analysis. The input relied heavily on real life examples and recognizable case studies in order to make the approach tangible for non-specialists.

During the Collective Brainstorming part, various target group types from the perspective of the participants were silently collected (brainwriting), guided by the categories of current, potential and excluded target groups. Following, the gathered groups were discussed, clustered, and finally prioritized. While the discussion and clustering invited verbal exchange, the prioritization took place via a timed dot-voting. The four most important target group clusters were then transferred to the next step in the workshop, the Touchpoint Maps.

To identify relevant interaction dynamics for future intervention strategies concerning the prioritized target groups, touchpoint maps were adapted from user experience research for this stage. Such maps enable the participants to identify existing (or likely) points of contact with customer groups or stakeholders in a group setting, producing richer results. Templates of touchpoint maps structured through a timeline provided visual guidance to the participants, to be filled out based on their experience.

For the Closure and Feedback section, a brief overview of the achieved results was given, and next steps were briefly described. Feedback on the workshop was collected for the further development of such tools.

Despite a flexible appointment search via an online appointment scheduling tool, not everyone was able to attend the workshop in real time, which is why the results of another participant were subsequently integrated via written communication. This ensured that all voices were at least partially represented, and that the results reflected the input of all intended stakeholders.

To strengthen the reliability of the outcomes as a basis for future action strategies, the workshop results were later reviewed by the project coordination. This additional strategic evaluation validated the findings, pointing to an effective workshop conduction.

3 RESULTS

The workshop results show that large-scale buyers, like engineering, procurement, and construction companies (EPCs) or distributors, module manufacturers, standardization bodies, investors, and (solar) installers, in their function as decision-makers for the end-consumer, are perceived as the most important target groups (Fig. 2). Furthermore, the written retrospective integration also showed small-scale commercials and the public buildings sector as important target groups. In total, 22 current and potential target groups have been listed, which have subsequently been organized into a visual system of interactions, with the most important groups highlighted (Fig. 3).

The participatory workshop revealed a focus on B2B dynamics. Even if modules were ultimately meant for private use, B2B groups functioned as distributors.

The Touchpoint Maps segment of the workshop focused therefore on large-scale buyers, module manufacturers, standardization bodies, and investors as the most important target groups. Large-scale buyers and module manufacturers were addressed together, as their touchpoints were perceived by the participants to be very similar. As the results of the touchpoint maps were collected for future reference during the creation of action strategies and are not the subject of this paper, they will not be described in detail.

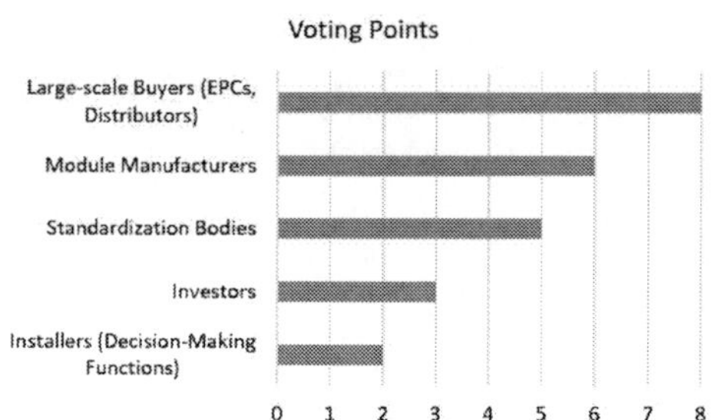

Figure 2: The perceived importance of identified target group clusters for the project. EPCs = Engineering, Procurement, and Construction companies

4 DISCUSSION

Based on the workshop results, a need to further develop purchase behavior research in the B2B sector is highlighted. With organizational actors occupying an in-between role, they function as gatekeepers to individual customers, influencing selection, as well as perception. They are hereby in a position to consciously and subconsciously limit the perceived options of choice for consumers and guide information flow as well as decision-making [17].

The term gatekeeper is used here as introduced by Kurt Lewin in 1947, who coined this concept when investigating food habits and household decision-making

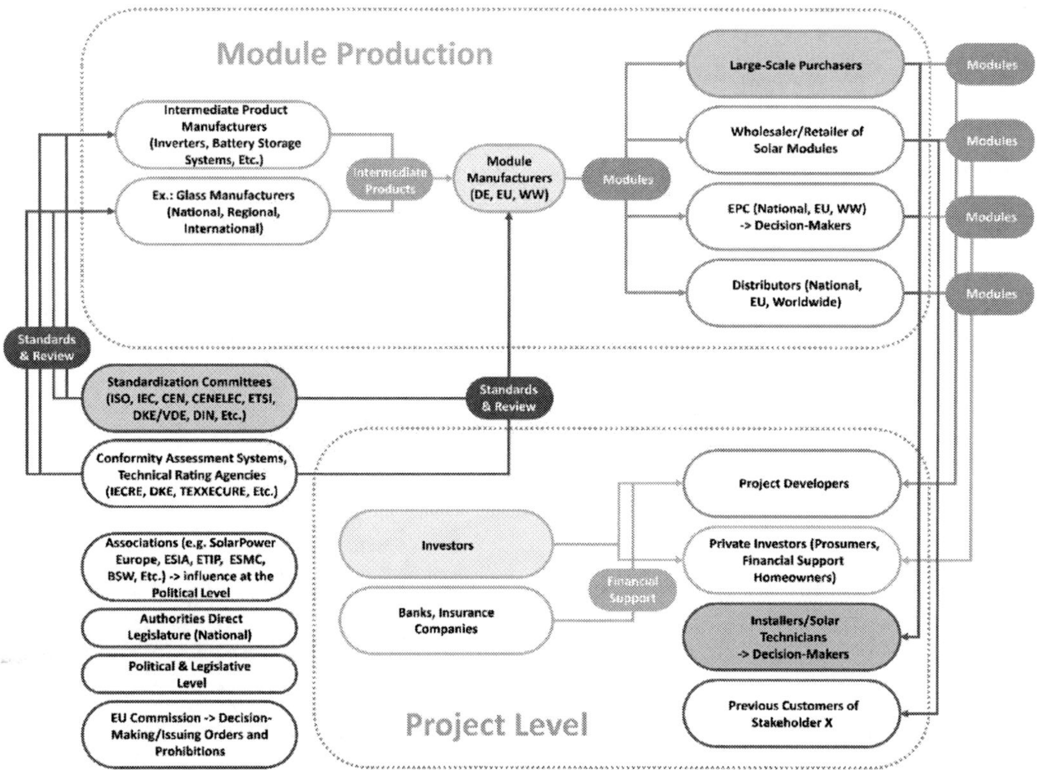

Figure 3: Structuration of the identified target groups on the PV market

[17]. Thereby, information flow does not occur automatically but is shaped through metaphorical gates it must pass through, with certain individuals or mechanisms acting as gatekeepers that can regulate, filter, or block this flow. At its core, gatekeeper theory postulates that the transmission of information is shaped by actors or processes that control what enters, what is delayed, and what is excluded, thereby influencing collective outcomes [18]. Gatekeepers do therefore not necessarily have to want to manipulate outcomes, but given the structural dependencies present, they will do so nonetheless. The model has since been extended from household decision making to various domains, including communication, journalism, and organizational studies [19].

If the goal is to foster the wider adoption of more sustainable solar panels, rather than only addressing private customers, the gatekeeper roles must therefore also be addressed. Such advancements would prove beneficial for supporting more systemic angles in environmental psychology as well. The individualization of responsibility for sustainable development is typically criticized in environmental psychology and calls for alternative solutions on a bigger scale [20]. Targeting B2B dynamics would contribute here, given the system of interactions on the photovoltaic market and resulting potential multiplier positions of gatekeepers (also see Fig. 3). To this date, such research remains mostly general and tends to focus on economic factors most instead of the likewise integration of psychological, contextual, and organizational variables. Given the empirical rejection of the homo economicus, such a focus would be incomplete and needs to be elaborated [21], [22]. Seeing that organizations are entities made up of human individuals and the empirical evidence for their potential for irrational decision-making, there is no reason why they should be treated differently [23]. Drawing on insights from B2C literature – where variations in motivational factors across countries, product types, and use contexts have been observed – the paper argues for a more nuanced development in B2B research as well.

Using target group analysis as the basis for effective motivational strategies is widely the norm in marketing and communication science, but typically overlooked in motivational research on green purchase behavior. Given the structure of the PV market and the insights gained through this workshop, this will be key in facilitating more sustainable buying behavior. In order to foster a citizen-centered energy transition, action initiatives must be strategically developed, with careful consideration given to the target groups of engagement and their specific needs.

The created workshop design itself received positive feedback and produced valuable results, which were also supported in a further validation by the project coordination, speaking to its effectiveness. By documenting the applied structure in sufficient detail to be reproduced, practical orientation for more targeted investigations in pursuit of creating powerful action strategies has been provided. While the workshop produced valuable results, such as the discovery and prioritization of relevant target groups, as well as the identification of meaningful points of contact, future approaches must consider certain constraints. The fact that an additional strategic evaluation was deemed necessary might suggest that not all relevant parties were involved in the workshop itself. This highlights the importance of careful evaluation of stakeholder involvement in participatory work [24].

Furthermore, this reflects a common dynamic in transdisciplinary work, where tangible results are often needed early on to encourage participation down the line. Initial differences in professional and experiential backgrounds require bridging efforts before meaningful collaboration can emerge. In such cases, a workshop like this can serve as a foot-in-the-door approach, laying the groundwork for deeper cooperation.

As demonstrated in the current study, for the goal of fostering the adoption of more sustainable energy systems, a participatory approach through collaborative, creative formats is not only useful with citizens, but also in inter- or transdisciplinary project settings. Thus, effective levers of action for the specific context become more visible. Functioning as an exploratory basis, the results of the current use case should further be validated across different green purchasing scenarios [4] and project structures.

4 REFERENCES

[1] I. Ajzen, 'From Intentions to Actions: A Theory of Planned Behavior', in *Action Control*, J. Kuhl and J. Beckmann, Eds, Berlin, Heidelberg: Springer Berlin Heidelberg, 1985, pp. 11–39. doi: 10.1007/978-3-642-69746-3_2.

[2] N. B. Bommenahalli Veerabhadrappa, S. Fernandes, and R. Panda, 'A review of green purchase with reference to individual consumers and organizational consumers: A TCCM approach', *Clean. Responsible Consum.*, vol. 8, p. 100097, Mar. 2023, doi: 10.1016/j.clrc.2022.100097.

[3] Y. Du and P. H. Kim, 'One size does not fit all: Strategy configurations, complex environments, and new venture performance in emerging economies', *J. Bus. Res.*, vol. 124, pp. 272–285, Jan. 2021, doi: 10.1016/j.jbusres.2020.11.059.

[4] X. Zhang and F. Dong, 'Why Do Consumers Make Green Purchase Decisions? Insights from a Systematic Review', *Int. J. Environ. Res. Public. Health*, vol. 17, no. 18, p. 6607, Sept. 2020, doi: 10.3390/ijerph17186607.

[5] A. Biswas and M. Roy, 'Green products: an exploratory study on the consumer behaviour in emerging economies of the East', *J. Clean. Prod.*, vol. 87, pp. 463–468, Jan. 2015, doi: 10.1016/j.jclepro.2014.09.075.

[6] B. Kumar, A. K. Manrai, and L. A. Manrai, 'Purchasing behaviour for environmentally sustainable products: A conceptual framework and empirical study', *J. Retail. Consum. Serv.*, vol. 34, pp. 1–9, Jan. 2017, doi: 10.1016/j.jretconser.2016.09.004.

[7] K. Peattie, 'Green Consumption: Behavior and Norms', *Annu. Rev. Environ. Resour.*, vol. 35, no. 1, pp. 195–228, Nov. 2010, doi: 10.1146/annurev-environ-032609-094328.

[8] R. S. Hughner, P. McDonagh, A. Prothero, C. J. Shultz, and J. Stanton, 'Who are organic food consumers? A compilation and review of why people purchase organic food', *J. Consum. Behav.*, vol. 6, no. 2–3, pp. 94–110, Mar. 2007, doi: 10.1002/cb.210.

[9] W. Poortinga, L. Steg, and C. Vlek, 'Values, Environmental Concern, and Environmental Behavior: A Study into Household Energy Use', *Environ. Behav.*, vol. 36, no. 1, pp. 70–93, Jan. 2004, doi: 10.1177/0013916503251466.

[10] X. Yu, Y. Tao, D. Wang, and M. M. Yang, 'Disengaging pro-environmental values in B2B green buying decisions: Evidence from a conjoint experiment', *Ind. Mark. Manag.*, vol. 105, pp. 240–252, Aug. 2022, doi: 10.1016/j.indmarman.2022.05.020.

[11] M. R. Czinkota, M. Kotabe, D. Vrontis, and S. M. R. Shams, *Marketing Management: Past, Present and Future*. in Springer Texts in Business and Economics. Cham: Springer International Publishing, 2021. doi: 10.1007/978-3-030-66916-4.

[12] R. Basu, W. M. Lim, A. Kumar, and S. Kumar, 'Marketing analytics: The bridge between customer psychology and marketing decision-making', *Psychol. Mark.*, vol. 40, no. 12, pp. 2588–2611, Dec. 2023, doi: 10.1002/mar.21908.

[13] J. K. Saint Clair, 'Consumer Identity: A Comprehensive Review and Integration of Contemporary Research', in *The Cambridge Handbook of Consumer Psychology*, 2nd edn, C. Lamberton, D. D. Rucker, and S. A. Spiller, Eds, Cambridge University Press, 2023, pp. 179–227. doi: 10.1017/9781009243957.009.

[14] H. Sanoff, *Participatory Environmental Design*. 2018.

[15] J. Bergold and S. Thomas, 'Partizipative Forschung', in *Handbuch qualitative Forschung in der Psychologie*, Springer, 2010, pp. 333–344. [Online]. Available: https://link.springer.com/content/pdf/10.1007/978-3-531-92052-8.pdf

[16] E. B.-N. Sanders and P. J. Stappers, 'Co-creation and the new landscapes of design', *Co-Des.*, vol. 4, no. 1, pp. 5–18, 2008.

[17] K. Lewin, 'Frontiers in Group Dynamics: Concept, Method and Reality in Social Science; Social Equilibria and Social Change', *Hum. Relat.*, vol. 1, no. 1, pp. 5–41, June 1947, doi: 10.1177/001872674700100103.

[18] K. Barzilai-Nahon, 'Toward a theory of network gatekeeping: A framework for exploring information control', *J. Am. Soc. Inf. Sci. Technol.*, vol. 59, no. 9, pp. 1493–1512, July 2008, doi: 10.1002/asi.20857.

[19] P. J. Shoemaker and T. Vos, *Gatekeeping Theory*, 0 edn. Routledge, 2009. doi: 10.4324/9780203931653.

[20] S. N. Jorgenson, J. C. Stephens, and B. White, 'Environmental education in transition: A critical review of recent research on climate change and energy education', *J. Environ. Educ.*, vol. 50, no. 3, pp. 160–171, May 2019, doi: 10.1080/00958964.2019.1604478.

[21] D. Ariely, *Predictably irrational: the hidden forces that shape our decisions*, 1st ed. New York, NY: Harper, 2008.

[22] A. Tversky and D. Kahneman, 'Judgment under Uncertainty: Heuristics and Biases: Biases in judgments reveal some heuristics of thinking under uncertainty.', *Science*, vol. 185, no. 4157, pp. 1124–1131, Sept. 1974, doi: 10.1126/science.185.4157.1124.

[23] H. R. Arkes and C. Blumer, 'The psychology of sunk cost', *Organ. Behav. Hum. Decis. Process.*, vol. 35, no. 1, pp. 124–140, Feb. 1985, doi: 10.1016/0749-5978(85)90049-4.

[24] P. Jones, 'Contexts of Co-creation: Designing with System Stakeholders', in *Systemic Design: Theory, Methods, and Practice*, P. Jones and K. Kijima, Eds, Tokyo: Springer Japan, 2018, pp. 3–52. doi: 10.1007/978-4-431-55639-8_1.

The Role of Target Groups and Gatekeepers in the Deployment of More Sustainable Photovoltaic Systems: A Participatory Approach

Alexandra Tönies, Larissa Müller, Valérie Varney

University of Applied Sciences Cologne

One Size-Fits-All Approaches and Target Group Analysis in Green Purchase Behaviour

- Achieving a sustainable energy transition requires more than technological advancement; it depends on societal innovation to ensure these technologies can be widely adopted. Green purchase behavior research focuses on factors influencing such purchase decisions.
- Empirical research shows different motivational factors for different contexts, which is important for designing effective action strategies [1], [2]. However, while target group analysis is typically encountered in marketing or communication science, it is not typically mentioned in green purchase behavior research.
- The majority of empirically investigated models in green behaviour research is focused on individual end consumers (e.g. Theory of Planned Behaviour), likely further shaping the nature of action strategies.

Cultural Context

- Motivational factors differ by country and cultural background [1].
- Local norms, regulations, and values are examples shaping purchasing decisions in green energy [3], [4].

Product Context

- Drivers of purchase behaviour vary by type of product [1].
- Product-specific attributes such as cost, durability, and performance perception influence decision-making for example as well as their respective target audiences, societal perceptions and surrounding ecosystems [5], [6], [7].

Private or Professional Context

- Green behaviour in private life does not automatically spill over into professional contexts. Empirical evidence shows partly distinct motivational drivers in private vs. workplace contexts [2]. Structural pressures can for example shape professional decisions [8].
- Organizations can neither solely be treated through a homo oeconomicus lense [9], as they are made up of people and demonstrate irrational decision fallacies as well (e.g. sunk cost fallacy) [10].

But How Does This Translate to Practical Interventions?

- Despite theory, practical methods for target group identification are lacking in PV adoption research.
- Marketing psychology suggests segmentation and positioning, but scientific literature does not mention a standardized methodology.
- Participatory workshops as best practice examples are promising but time-consuming, highly individualized, and vaguely documented.

An Adaptable Workshop Design for Participatory Target Group Identification

- A participatory remote workshop was developed for target group identification in the PV sector, involving sales partners and project members.
- The Structure consisted of three main parts (see also Figure 1):
  - Thematic introduction to establish a shared foundation with real-life examples and case studies.
  - Brainwriting/brainstorming to collect, cluster, and prioritize current, potential, and excluded target groups.
  - Touchpoint maps to identify points of contact with the four priority groups.
- Flexible participation was enabled, with absent participants contributing retrospectively via written communication.
- An additional strategic validation by the project coordination was requested, which confirmed the workshop results and at the same time highlights the importance of carefully evaluating stakeholder involvement.
- Considering typical transdisciplinary challenges in co-creation, the workshop can also function as a foot-in-the-door approach, bridging different professional backgrounds and building a basis for more meaningful collaboration.

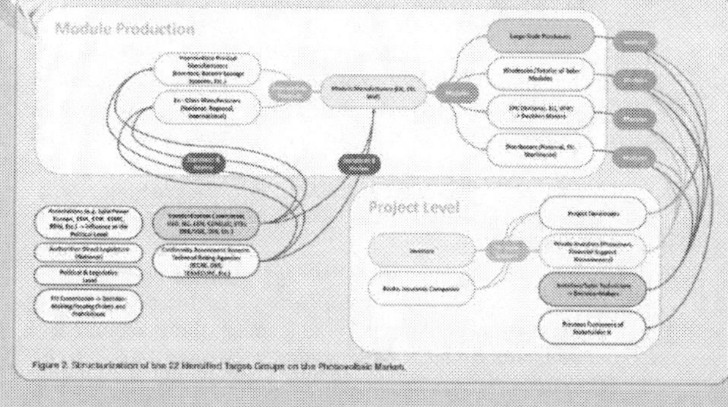

Figure 2. Structurization of the 22 identified Target Groups on the Photovoltaic Market.

Gathering of Questions and Expectations

Identification of Points of Contact Through Touchpoint Maps

Feedback

Short Thematic Input Regarding Target Group Identification

Collective Brainwriting of Current, Possible, and Impossible Target Groups, Followed by a Structurization through Discussion and Prioritization

Figure 1. Structure of the Target Group Identification Workshop

Workshop Results & Conclusions

- 22 target groups were identified and organized into a visual interaction system, with the 5 prioritized groups highlighted (see Figure 2).
- Primary groups identified: large-scale buyers, module manufacturers, standardization bodies, investors, and installers.
- Additional groups (retrospective inclusion): small-scale commercials and public buildings.
- Results revealed the central role of B2B dynamics, showing that organizational players functioning as gatekeepers are decisive for citizens' perceptions, information flows, and ultimate purchasing decisions.
- Findings support the need for expanded B2B research on green purchase behaviour, complementing B2C insights and at the same time addressing critiques in environmental psychology about overemphasizing individual responsibility by targeting systemic dynamics and enabling multiplier effects.

Literature:

[1] X. Zhang and F. Dong, 'Why Do Consumers Make Green Purchase Decisions? Insights from a Systematic Review', Int. J. Environ. Res. Public. Health, vol. 17, no. 18, p. 6607, Sep. 2020, doi: 10.3390/ijerph17186607.

[2] N. B. Bommenahalli Veerabhadrappa, S. Fernandes, and R. Panda, 'A review of green purchase with reference to individual consumers and organizational consumers: A TCCM approach', Clean. Responsible Consum., vol. 8, p. 100097, Mar. 2023, doi: 10.1016/j.clrc.2022.100097.

[3] A. Biswas and M. Roy, 'Green products: an exploratory study on the consumer behaviour in emerging economies of the East', J. Clean. Prod., vol. 87, pp. 463-468, Jan. 2015, doi: 10.1016/j.jclepro.2014.09.075.

[4] B. Kumar, A. K. Manrai, and L. A. Manrai, 'Purchasing behaviour for environmentally sustainable products: A conceptual framework and empirical study', J. Retail. Consum. Serv., vol. 34, pp. 9-1, Jan. 2017, doi: 10.1016/j.jretconser.2016.09.004.

[5] R. S. Hughner, P. McDonagh, A. Prothero, C. J. Shultz, and J. Stanton, 'Who are organic food consumers? A compilation and review of why people purchase organic food', J. Consum. Behav., vol. 6, no. 2-3, pp. 110-94, Mar. 2007, doi: 10.1002/cb.210.

[6] W. Poortinga, L. Steg, and C. Vlek, 'Values, Environmental Concern, and Environmental Behavior: A Study into Household Energy Use', Environ. Behav., vol. 36, no. 1, pp. 93-70, Jan. 2004, doi: 10.1177/0013916503251466/10.1177.

[7] K. Peattie, 'Green Consumption: Behavior and Norms', Annu. Rev. Environ. Resour., vol. 35, no. 1, pp. 228-195, Nov. 2010, doi: 10.1146/annurev-environ-004328-032609.

[8] A. Yu, Y. Tao, D. Wang, and M. M. Yang, 'Disengaging pro environmental values in 938 green buying decisions: Evidence from a conjoint experiment', Ind. Mark. Manag., vol. 105, pp. 252-240, Aug. 2022, doi: 10.1016/j.indmarman.2022.06.020.

[9] A. Tversky and D. Kahneman, 'Judgment under Uncertainty: Heuristics and Biases: Biases in judgments reveal some heuristics of thinking under uncertainty', Science, vol. 185, no. 4157, pp. 1131-1124, Sep. 1974, doi: 10.1126/science.185.4157.1124.

[10] H. R. Arkes and C. Blumer, 'The psychology of sunk cost', Organ. Behav. Hum. Decis. Process., vol. 35, no. 1, pp. 140-124, Feb. 1985, doi: 4-90049(85)6978-0749/10.1016.

Technology
Arts Sciences
TH Köln

POLYNOMIAL SURFACE MODEL-BASED BALANCING MARKET BID PLANNING AND EVALUATION FOR MULTI-SITE PV PLANTS

Jindan Cui[1], Xue Fang[1], Takashi Oozeki[2], Yuzuru Ueda[1]
[1]Tokyo University of Science, Japan, [2]National Institute of Advanced Industrial Science and Technology (AIST), Japan
cui_jindan@rs.tus.ac.jp

ABSTRACT: The Seventh Basic Energy Plan sets an ambitious target of expanding solar power generation beyond the current 7%, highlighting a strong national commitment to renewable energy. However, the large-scale deployment of photovoltaics (PV) faces two critical challenges: the inherent uncertainty of power generation due to weather variability, and the decline in profitability associated with daytime price drops under high renewable energy penetration. This study explores the creation of new value for PV systems through the provision of reserve power to address these challenges. Accurate management of prediction errors is essential to unlock this value and improve dispatchability. Building on our previous work, we applied kernel density estimation to model the probability distribution of historical prediction errors and constructed a polynomial surface model that incorporates PV-predicted values and the clearness index as features, with cumulative probability serving as the error threshold. In this study, the model is extended to multiple sites to demonstrate its general applicability and to evaluate the smoothing effect of aggregated prediction errors. The results show that aggregating PV reserve power can effectively reduce imbalances in balancing market operations, underscoring its potential to support the sustainable, large-scale integration of PV into the power grid.
Keywords: multi-site PV plant, polynomial surface, reserve power, headroom setting, balancing market bid planning

1 INTRODUCTION

The Seventh Basic Energy Plan released in December 2024, sets an ambitious goal to significantly increase solar power generation, beyond the current target of 7%. This signals a strong commitment to expanding the use of solar energy in Japan over the next few decades. However, the main challenge facing solar power as it strives to become a major source of electricity is the unpredictability of power generation due to weather fluctuations. The potential influx of renewable energy into the electricity market could also threaten to the profitability of solar power generation. If electricity prices plummet during the day, as a result of increased renewable energy supply, the business of generating solar power generation may become unsustainable, leading to a slower expansion of solar systems.

To overcome these challenges, this study investigates the creation of a new value for PV systems in the form of reserve power. Accurate management of prediction errors is essential for unlocking this value and enabling PV systems to provide both stable power supply and dispatch capacity. Over the past several years, we have explored various approaches to this problem, including a statistical model (quantile regression), a machine learning model (Support Vector Machine, SVM), a hybrid of the two [1], feature importance analysis using Random Forest (RF), multiple-initial-time modeling [2], and rare-event risk analysis of extreme prediction errors [3]. These studies have consistently highlighted the importance of accurately setting error-absorption headroom to mitigate the risks associated with prediction errors.

Building on this foundation, the present study develops a reserve-setting method that enhances error absorption capability and reduces imbalance events in the balancing market, particularly in contexts where individual PV plants face difficulty participating effectively. In Ref. [4], we employed a statistical approach based on kernel density estimation of historical prediction error distributions, followed by the construction of a polynomial surface model using cumulative probability as the error threshold, with PV-predicted values and the clearness index as explanatory variables. In this study, we extend this approach by validating the polynomial surface model across multiple sites. Furthermore, we investigate the smoothing effect of aggregated prediction errors, demonstrating that multi-site deployment can further reduce imbalances and improve the operational value of PV reserve power in balancing markets.

2 METHODOLOGIES

2.1 Approach

In this study, we applied the optimal polynomial surface model (Model 1 in Ref. [4]) to secure sufficient headroom for absorbing day-ahead prediction errors when six individual PV power plants provide reserve power to the balancing market without relying on batteries or intraday procurement. This approach was used to validate the model's applicability in practical market operations.

In day-ahead planning, it is essential to manage prediction errors of PV power plants—variable power sources—in order to formulate effective bidding strategies based on predicted power generation. To address this, we employed models that estimate the distribution of prediction errors using historical data, and then set error-absorption headroom according to the required cumulative probability. The headroom was determined as a function of two explanatory variables: predicted power generation and clearness index, an indicator of weather conditions.

2.2 Single site

The procedure for the building of a model is as follows:

Initially, at each site, the historical PV prediction errors are obtained in Eq. (1).

$$e(i,t) = P_f(i,t) - P_m(i,t), t \in \{19, 20, \cdots, 30\} \quad (1)$$

where P_f and P_m represent the predicted and measured PV power generation from the historical records, respectively; The subscript i denotes the site location; and t represents the 30-min time steps in accordance with market conventions. Only PV generation between 09:00 and 15:00 (bidding slots 19–30) was considered. Both the predicted and measured PV power generation values were normalized by the installed capacity.

Then, sample sets R_n of error e were created corresponding to P_n, where P_n represents a 0.01 kW unit of P_f. For each sample set R_n, outliers exceeding 1.5 times the interquartile range were excluded. The probability distribution and probability density function (PDF), denoted as $\hat{f}_h(e)$, were then estimated using kernel density estimation. A normal (Gaussian) kernel function with 0 mean and unit variance was employed.

$$(P_n, e) \in R_n, n \in \{0, 0.01, 0.02, 0.03, \cdots \cdots\} \quad (2)$$

$$\hat{f}_h(e) = \frac{1}{mh} \sum_{j=1}^{m} K\left(\frac{e - e_j}{h}\right) \quad (3)$$

where e_j denotes a random error sample obtained from the estimated probability distribution, m is the total number of samples, and $K(\cdot)$ representes the kernel smoothing function. In this study, we employed the Gaussian (normal) kernel, with h denoting the bandwidth parameter [4].

Second, for each set R_n the cumulative distribution function (CDF), $\hat{F}_h(e)$, was estimated using kernel density estimation. Based on $\hat{F}_h(e)$, the error threshold e_{th} corresponding to a cumulative probability μ was identified for each R_n.

$$\hat{F}_h(e) = \int_{-\infty}^{e_{max}} \hat{f}_h(e)de \quad (4)$$

$$e_{th} = \hat{F}_h^{-1}(\mu) \quad (5)$$

Third, the prediction error H_e in each sample set closest to e_{th} was identified, and the corresponding original predicted value, $P_{f,orig}$ and CI were retrieved. The CI was then calculated as follows.

$$CI(i, t) = \frac{H_g(i, t)}{H_O(i, t)} \quad (6)$$

where H_O and H_g represnt the extraterrestrial horizontal irradiance and global horizontal irradiance, respectively. CI ranges from 0 to 1, with lower values indicating overcast or rainy conditions, and values approaching 1 correspond to clear-sky conditions.

Fourth, a bivariate polynomial surface for cumulative probability μ was created using predicted PV generation P_f and CI as explanatory variables. Both predicted and measured CI values were considered in this analysis. The P_f variable was modeled as a quadratic term, while CI was treated as a linear term. The planned values were then updated using Eq. (8).

$$H_e^\mu = f_{py}\left(P_f, P_f{}^2, CI\right) \quad (7)$$

$$P_{rev}(t) = P_f(t) - H_e^\mu(t) \quad (8)$$

Fifth, measured data from the test period were used to evaluate imbalance. The main objective of this research was to develop planned market values that prevent shortages. The number of negative imbalance event, $ImbC^-$, was calculated using Eq. (9). In addition, the amounts of shortage (negative) and surplus (positive) were

calculated and evaluated based on the deviation from the planned values, as defined in Eqs. (10)–(12).

$$ImbC^- = \sum_t t, \; if \; P_m(t) < P_{rev}(t) \quad (9)$$

$$ImbA^- = \sum_t P_{rev}(t) - P_m(t), \; if \; P_m(t) \quad (10)$$
$$< P_{rev}(t)$$

$$ImbA^+ = \sum_t P_m(t) - P_{rev}(t), \; if \; P_m(t) \quad (11)$$
$$\geq P_{rev}(t)$$

$$ImbA = ImbA^- + ImbA^+ \quad (12)$$

where $ImbC^-$, $ImbA^+$, $ImbA^-$, and $ImbA$ represent the number of negative imbalance events, positive imbalance amount [kW · 30min], negative imbalance amount [kW · 30min], overall imbalance amount, respectively, with time spots defined as 12 intervals per day. The bid count ($BidC$) and bid amount ($BidA$) are defined in Eqs. (13) and (14), respectively.

$$BidC = \sum_t t, \; if \; P_{rev}(t) > 0 \quad (13)$$

$$BidA = \sum_t P_{rev}(t), \; if \; P_{rev}(t) > 0 \quad (14)$$

2.3 Multiple sites

The six locations are integrated to generate planned values and evaluate imbalances. For multi-site integration, the mean values of each feature, normalized by the PV capacity at each site, were first computed as follows:

$$\bar{P}_f(t) = \frac{1}{N} \sum_i^N \frac{P_f(i, t)}{P_{AS}(i)} \quad (15)$$

$$\bar{P}_m(t) = \frac{1}{N} \sum_i^N \frac{P_m(i, t)}{P_{AS}(i)} \quad (16)$$

$$\bar{H}_g(t) = \frac{1}{N} \sum_i^N H_g(i, t) \quad (17)$$

$$\bar{H}_O(t) = \frac{1}{N} \sum_i^N H_O(i, t) \quad (18)$$

where P_{AS} denotes the installed PV capacity per site and N represents the total number of sites. Subsequently, the aggregated prediction errors and clearness index were derived using Eqs. (1) and (6), the same procedure described in Section 2.2 was applied. The evaluation indicators were also computed using Eqs.(9)–(14), in addition, imbalances were evaluated on a monthly basis..

3 SIMULATION AND RESULTS

3.1 Datasets

We used the one-hour grid point value meso-scale model (GPV-MSM) forecast meteorological data [5] to predict PV power P_f by interpolating to 30-min intervals, and one-min meteorological observation data [6] to estimate PV power as measured data P_m, which were then accumulated into 30-minute values for each site. The meteorological values considered in this study included solar radiation, outdoor air temperature and wind speed. The initial value of the GPV-MSM was assumed to be 12:00 JST (03:00 UTC) on the previous day to satisfy the balance market bid (planned value) at 15:00.

PV power was calculated using the Erbs and Perez models [4], assuming an installation tilt angle of 20° and a south-facing tilt azimuth. The analysis period spanned from September 1, 2019, to August 31, 2022, focusing on data between 09:00 and 15:00 each day. The model was trained using a two-year period (September 2019 to August 2021), and its performance was evaluated over a subsequent one-year test period (September 2021 to August 2022). Six sites were selected for multi-site analysis: Utsunomiya, Choshi, Kofu, Maebashi, Tateno, and Tokyo. In this study, the headroom setting model was established by normalizing the values with respect to PV capacity, assuming a PV capacity of 1 kW.

3.2 Results and discussions

Figure 1 presents the polynomial surfaces for each location. The surfaces based on measured CI values of the explanatory variables ($\mu = 1.0$) are shown on the left, while those based on predicted CI values are shown in the middle ($\mu = 1.0$) and on the right ($\mu = 0.95$). In the measured CI model, the data points closely approximate a plane, whereas in the predicted CI model, they form a quadratic surface. This behavior reflects the correlation between CI values and prediction errors. For Kofu and Maebashi, the predicted CI model exhibits slightly different surface characteristics compared to other locations, with smaller errors observed where the correlation between the explanatory variables is stronger.

Figure 2 illustrates the polynomial surfaces representing different cumulative probabilities in the integration of multiple locations. As the cumulative probability μ increases, prediction errors decrease, the surface flattens, and the variation in prediction error with respect to the explanatory variables narrows.

Figures 3 and 4 show the standard deviation of historical errors. The error distribution and standard deviation at each individual location are approximately 0.13, whereas the deviation after integration is reduced to 0.08, indicating a smoothing effect. Table I summarizes the number of imbalance events, the imbalance amounts, the number of possible bids, and the bid amounts for each location and after integration. The predicted CI model notably reduces the frequency of negative imbalance events compared with the measured CI model. Out of 4380 spots per year (12 × 365), the average number of negative imbalances per location under the predicted CI model is 242, but this is reduced to 102 after integration— less than half. Due to missing data, the number of bids ($BidC$) for Maebashi, Tateno, and Tokyo is slightly reduced, although nearly all spots are still bid upon. Regarding the bid amount ($BidA$), Kofu yields the largest potential bid individually; however, after integrating six sites, the total bid amount is slightly reduced due to the smoothing effect.

Figure 5 presents the number and amount of negative imbalances, as well as the potential bids, for the integrated system using the predicted CI model. As the cumulative probability μ increases, the number of bids remains unchanged, while the potential bid amount decreases from 1872.5 kW ($\mu = 0.5$) to 1187.5 kW ($\mu = 1.0$). Concurrently, the number of negative imbalance events declines markedly from 1836 per year to 106.

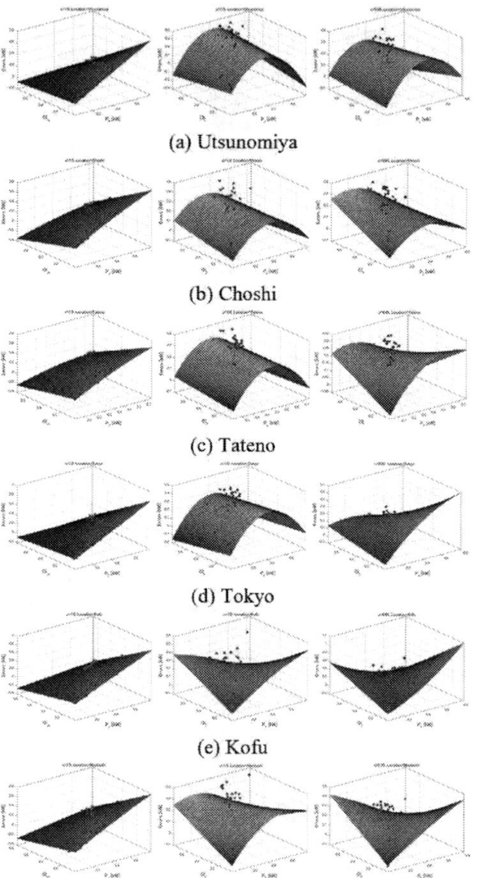

(a) Utsunomiya

(b) Choshi

(c) Tateno

(d) Tokyo

(e) Kofu

(f) Maebashi

Figure 1: Polynomial surfaces of single site

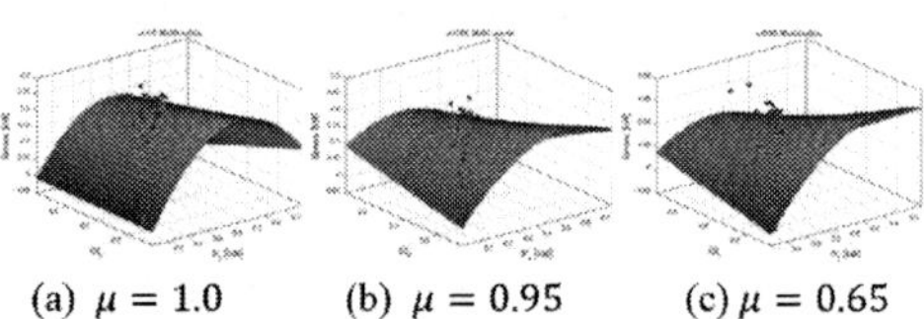

(a) $\mu = 1.0$ (b) $\mu = 0.95$ (c) $\mu = 0.65$

Figure 2: Polynomial surfaces of multi-site integration

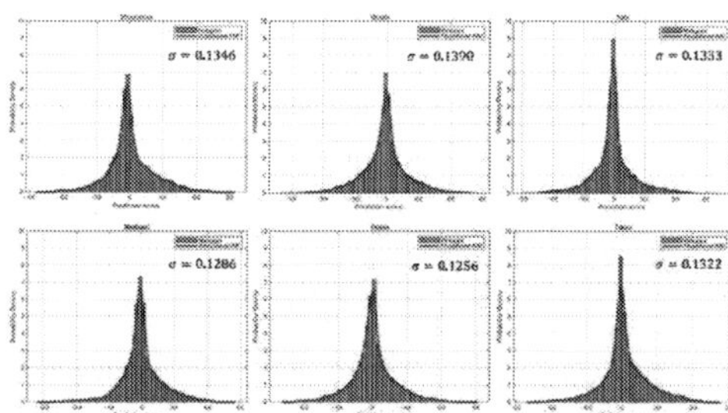

Figure 3: Frequency distribution and PDF of historical errors at each location

Figure 6 shows the average monthly headroom and available bid amounts. The smallest percentage of headroom relative to PV generation predictions is observed in April (30.2%), and the largest in September (45.6%). The black line indicates measured PV generation, while the monthly averages confirm that headroom settings successfully absorbed prediction errors across all months. On a spot-by-spot basis, the maximum number of negative imbalance events was 22 in January, 0 in July, September, and December, and within 11 in all other months (noting that a maximum of 12 reserve power spots could be offered per day).

Table II provides a comparison with several previously implemented models. Approaches based on importance analysis or different initial times reduced shortages by approximately half when prediction values were directly applied to planning. In contrast, the polynomial surface model reduced negative imbalance events to 281 events. Furthermore, when multiple locations were integrated under the same model, the number of negative imbalances was further reduced to 106 events—less than half the single-location result.

4 CONCLUSIONS

In this study, we employed a model that estimates the error threshold corresponding to a given cumulative probability by fitting a polynomial surface to the historical distribution of prediction errors at a single site. This threshold was then used to define the headroom required to absorb prediction errors. We extended this approach by validating the polynomial surface model across multiple sites and further evaluating its applicability in capturing the smoothing effect of site integration.

The standard deviation of prediction errors at individual sites was 0.1322, which decreased to 0.0839 after integrating six sites. Moreover, the number of negative imbalance events was reduced to 106 through multi-site integration. These significant reductions in error variability and imbalance events demonstrate the potential of PV power generation to provide balancing capacity.

ACKNOWLEDGEMENTS
This study was supported by NEDO "Demonstration study of photovoltaic power generation technology to create flexibility."

REFERENCES
[1] J. Cui, B. Jie, X. Fang, T. Oozeki and Y. Ueda, "Absorption of PV Power Prediction Errors with Headroom Control by Statistical, Machine Learning and Combined Models," IEEJ Transactions on Power and Energy (TEEE B), Vol.19 No.2, Dec. 2023. DOI: 10.1002/tee.23966

[2] J. Cui, X. Fang, T. Oozeki and Y. Ueda, "Absorption of PV Power Prediction Errors with Headroom Control by variable importance-considering SVR model with different initial values," 40th European Photovoltaic Solar Energy Conference and Exhibition (EU PVSEC), Lisbon, Portugal, Sept. 2023.

[3] J. Cui, X. Fang, T. Oozeki and Yuzuru Ueda, "Day-ahead Planning and Shortfall Risk Assessment in the Balancing Market for Sola power Plant," Journal of Japan Solar Energy System, Vol.51, No.5 (289), Sept. 2025. DOI:10.24632/jses.51.5_1 (in Japanes)

[4] J. Cui, X. Fang, T. Oozeki and Y. Ueda, "Development of Error Absorption Headroom Setting Algorithm using Polynomial Surfaces to Create Reserve Power in PV Power Plants," IEEJ Transactions on Power and Energy (TEEE B), Vol.20 No.12, July. 2025. DOI: 10.1002/tee.70086

[5] Japan Meteorological Business Support Center, "Grid Point Value Data from the Meso-Scale Model (MSM)." https://www.jmbsc.or.jp/jp/online/file/f-online10200.html.

[6] Japan Meteorological Agency, "Weather Services." https://www.jma.go.jp/jma/index.html.

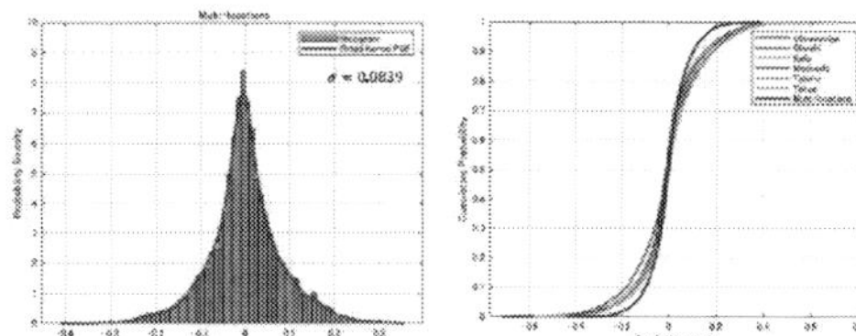

Figure 4: Frequency distribution and PDF of historical errors in multi-site integration

Table I: Imbalance evaluation ($\mu = 1.0$)

Predicted CI	Utsunomiya	Choshi	Kofu	Maebashi	Tateno	Tokyo	Integration
$ImbC^-$	222	237	229	246	281	238	106
	5.1%	5.4%	5.2%	5.6%	6.4%	5.4%	2.4%
$ImbA$	1002.8	1001.3	829.7	889.7	889.5	937.9	736.1
$BidC$	4380	4380	4380	4372	4379	4379	4370
$BidA$	952	961	1282	1085	1010	928	1188

Measured CI	Utsunomiya	Choshi	Kofu	Maebashi	Tateno	Tokyo	Integration
$ImbC^-$	952	1725	1912	1562	1583	1355	415
	21.7%	39.4%	43.7%	35.7%	36.1%	30.9%	9.5%
$ImbA$	518.3	536.2	436.1	440.0	466.9	450.3	476.8
$BidC$	4380	4380	4380	4372	4379	4379	4370
$BidA$	1568	1690	1917	1759	1640	1616	1474

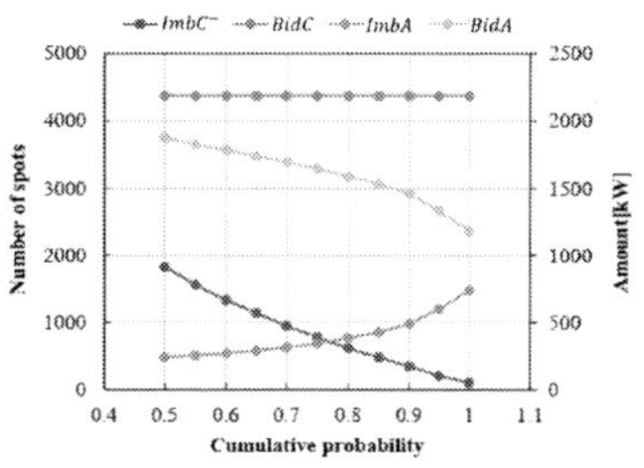

Figure 5: Evaluation results for multi-site integration (predicted CI model)

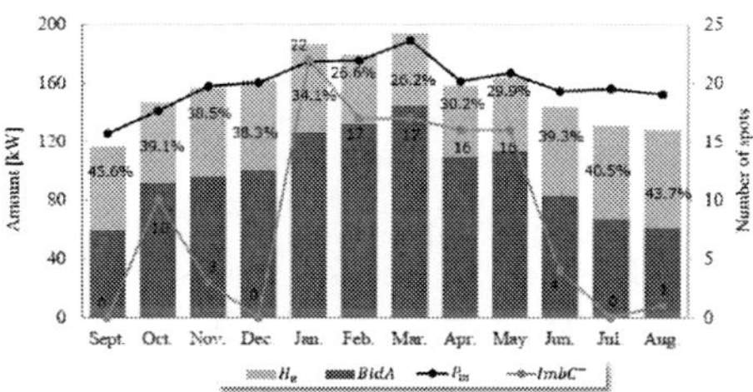

Figure 6: Monthly headroom (predicted CI model)

Table II: Comparison with different models (Tateno)

	Physical	SVR without importance	SVR with importance	SVR with importance	Polynomial surface	Polynomial surface (multi-site)
	The most recent initial values			8 different initial values	The most recent initial values	
$ImbC^-$	2570	2329	2154	1456	281	106
$ImbA$	514	500	500	604	890	736
$ImbA^+$	150	240	248	442	866	732
$ImbA^-$	364	260	252	162	23	4

INTEGRATION OF SOLAR ENERGY INTO ELECTRIC MOBILITY INFRASTRUCTURE

D.J. Rodriguez, J.F. Pantoja and J. Hernandez
Francisco José de Caldas District University
djrodriguezp@udistrital.edu.co

ABSTRACT: The transition to sustainable mobility requires comprehensive solutions that combine renewable energy sources, such as solar energy, with innovative urban planning strategies. Solar energy has established itself as one of the most promising technologies to drive this transformation, thanks to its ability to generate clean, decentralized, and low-environmental-impact electricity. In the context of electric mobility, solar-powered charging stations represent a strategic alternative to reduce dependence on the conventional electricity grid while optimizing the use of urban space. This integration not only responds to the growing energy demand of modern cities but also strengthens the resilience of electrical systems by leveraging local and sustainable resources. Furthermore, the incorporation of geolocation methodologies—such as cluster analysis, segmentation, and spatial correlation—is an essential tool for efficiently reorganizing the territory and planning electric charging infrastructure. These techniques make it possible to identify patterns in energy demand, identify areas of high solar irradiation, and locate urban areas with the highest density of electric vehicles. This facilitates strategic planning that ensures the proper allocation of resources to regions with the greatest potential impact in terms of energy efficiency, coverage, and sustainability.

Keywords: sustainable mobility, Solar energy, Electric vehicle charging infrastructure, Urban planning.

1 INTRODUCTION

The transition to sustainable mobility requires comprehensive solutions that combine renewable energy sources, such as solar energy, with urban planning strategies. Solar energy is emerging as one of the most promising technologies to drive this transformation, thanks to its ability to generate clean and decentralized electricity. In the context of electric mobility, solar-powered charging stations offer an opportunity to reduce dependence on the conventional electricity grid, limiting its impact on it, while maximizing the efficient use of urban space. This integration not only responds to the growing energy demands of modern cities but also strengthens the resilience of electrical systems through the use of local and sustainable resources.

In countries like Colombia, the accelerated incorporation of charging stations faces barriers associated with the reliability and capacity of the distribution network, [1]. Official reports show that, in 2023, the SAIDI (average interruption duration) exceeded the regulatory targets projected by CREG, while the SAIFI (interruption frequency) increased compared to previous years, although it remained close to the objectives, demonstrating that service continuity remains a challenge in several local distribution systems. These conditions, combined with episodes of system stress due to climate events such as El Niño and charging capacity restrictions in urban networks for new loads (such as fast EV charging), make connecting charging infrastructure complex without complementary measures.

The transition to sustainable mobility requires comprehensive solutions that combine renewable sources with urban planning and grid management. In this context, solar photovoltaic energy is consolidating as an ideal technology for supplying clean and decentralized electricity, reducing grid dependence and the environmental impact of transportation. In the context of electric mobility, charging stations powered (fully or partially) by on-site generation provide a strategic alternative for diversifying supply and cushioning peak demand in distribution circuits, [2].

Furthermore, the incorporation of geolocation methodologies such as cluster analysis, spatial correlation, and Voronoi zones offers a rigorous framework for organizing the territory and optimizing charging infrastructure. These tools make it possible to identify demand patterns, assess accessibility, and superimpose the available solar potential over each service area. The unit of analysis shifts from the city as a whole to each Voronoi polygon associated with a station, where investments can be prioritized based on expected load, grid constraints, and local irradiance, [3].

Faced with the reality of imperfect continuity indices and grids with limited capacity to absorb charging peaks, the integration of on-site photovoltaics at charging stations becomes a key enabler. By supplying part of the energy locally, the net power demanded from the feeder is reduced, transformer overloads are alleviated, and the risk of voltage dips during critical hours is limited. This approach is consistent with evidence on hosting capacity in urban grids: without management measures (local generation, storage, smart charging), the widespread use of EVs can strain the operating margins of the distribution network.

Overlaying irradiance maps (IDEAM/Global Solar Atlas, or simulations validated with PVsyst) on Voronoi polygons allows for the quantification of annual and seasonal solar resources for each service area. PV fields are then sized to cover target fractions of demand (e.g., 30–60% of energy), and peak demand reductions are estimated using diurnal generation profiles. This cross-layering converts Voronoi zones into energy planning units, prioritizing polygons with high EV density and higher GHI for the deployment of solar rooftops, PV canopies, and near-station PV micro-plants. (For Bogotá, recent public planning underscores that achieving adoption goals requires timely and strategic investments in charging infrastructure, which is further enhanced by local generation contributions), [4].

On-site generation is most effective when integrated with storage (batteries) and smart charging strategies (power management, scheduling, and pricing), and ideally

10.4229/EUPVSEC2025/5DV.3.2
020526-001

with V2G schemes where regulations allow. This technical package makes it possible to smooth demand at transformers, cover peaks with local power, and continue operating during short interruptions (station island mode or microgrid). Station standardization and interoperability, a framework already promoted at the regulatory level, reduces friction for users and facilitates operational coordination at the city/country level.

In short, the integration of charging infrastructure and solar radiation is not an optional extra, but a co-dependent design: Voronoi polygons allow for the alignment of demand and resources, on-site PV mitigates the chargeability of the local grid, and smart storage/charging increases resilience. All of this is especially pertinent in Colombia, where service quality still shows room for improvement, climate cycles can stress the system, and the EV/charger ratio highlights the need to accelerate deployment with technical solutions that free up grid capacity.

2   METHODOLOGY

The methodology employed in this research was based on a comprehensive approach combining geospatial analysis, statistical modeling, and energy infrastructure assessment techniques. First, data on solar radiation, vehicle density, and mobility patterns were collected and processed from official and collaborative sources. These data were integrated into a geographic information system (GIS), enabling clustering, territorial segmentation, and spatial correlation analyses to identify optimal areas for installing solar charging stations for electric vehicles.

To project the growth of the electric vehicle (EV) fleet in Colombia, data were collected from the Colombia Open Data platform, which offers official information on vehicle sales and registrations. Additionally, sector reports from Fenalco and ANDI, as well as statistics from the International Energy Agency (IEA), were used to compare national trends with the international landscape. These data sets cover the period from 2015 to 2023, including the evolution of pure electric vehicles (BEVs), electric hybrids (HEVs), and plug-in hybrids (PHEVs). The consolidation of these sources allowed not only to analyze the historical dynamics of the market, but also to establish the basis for the construction of a polynomial regression model that projects EV growth in the country toward 2030.

In parallel, georeferenced data related to the location of existing charging stations and road infrastructure were collected, primarily using the OpenStreetMap and Electromaps platforms. This information allowed the analysis to integrate the spatial distribution of charging infrastructure across the country, as well as its concentration in strategic urban areas such as Bogotá, Medellín, and Cali. Using geographic information systems (GIS) tools, analysis layers were generated that facilitated the identification of charging station accessibility, coverage, and density patterns. These inputs were essential for assessing the correlation between the location of charging points and the potential demand for electric vehicles, providing technical criteria for planning new stations and optimizing their distribution.

For the analysis of solar radiation conditions, official databases from IDEAM and the Global Solar Atlas were used, complemented by historical irradiance series obtained using PVsyst software. These sources provided average global horizontal irradiance (GHI) values ranging from 3.5 to 6.0 kWh/m²/day, depending on the region

analyzed. The data were processed to generate monthly and hourly radiation profiles, which allowed for a more accurate estimate of the photovoltaic potential available to power the charging infrastructure. Simulations were performed using PVsyst that integrated solar module efficiency parameters, system losses, and local climatic conditions, generating realistic scenarios to evaluate the energy contribution of solar stations in different cities across the country.

Planning the electric charging infrastructure in Colombia required the integration of solar radiation data, electric vehicle records, and the georeferenced location of existing charging stations. Based on this information, spatial analysis tools within a GIS environment were used, allowing the territory to be segmented into zones of influence around each station. To achieve this, the Voronoi diagram method was applied, with the goal of assigning exclusive service areas to each charging point, ensuring more equitable coverage and reducing infrastructure redundancies. This approach revealed inequalities in current distribution, especially in cities like Bogotá, where the concentration of stations in the north creates accessibility gaps in peripheral areas.

Spatial segmentation using Voronoi was key to assessing the correlation between vehicle density, charging demand, and solar radiation potential. In areas with a high concentration of electric vehicles, such as Chapinero and Suba, the polygons associated with each station had a higher user density, indicating the need to strengthen the infrastructure in these areas. This analysis also allowed for the identification of strategic areas for network expansion, prioritizing regions with high levels of solar irradiation and the availability of urban space suitable for the installation of photovoltaic systems. In this way, Voronoi zones become planning units that combine accessibility criteria, energy demand, and solar resources, facilitating more robust and sustainable decision-making.

Finally, a proposal was made to reinforce the electrical grid in the identified critical areas by integrating distributed photovoltaic systems and lithium-ion battery storage. These solutions would reduce overload at conventional grid nodes and improve the system's resilience to peak demand. By locating solar panels in Voronoi industrial estates with the highest user density, a hybrid model is created that combines existing infrastructure with local clean generation sources. This not only increases the autonomy of the charging stations but also contributes to the country's energy transition by optimally utilizing the solar resources available in each region.

3   RESULTS

3.1 Adoption of electric vehicles in Colombia.

Electric mobility is becoming established as a fundamental pillar in the search for a sustainable future with lower GHG emissions. The adoption of EVs in recent years has grown exponentially, driven by innovations, advances, and technological developments in batteries and charging stations, driven by responsible government policies committed to environmental protection, [5].

In the analysis of EV adoption in Colombia, information was collected from the Open Data Colombia platform, which provides official information on EV sales in Colombia. This information allows to identify trends in the Colombian market, analyze its evolution and evaluate the impact of government policies on EV adoption. In addition, the information available in OpenStreetMap was used to analyze the location and distribution of charging stations distributed throughout the national territory. These collaborative data sources allow a geospatial visualization of the charging infrastructure, identifying concentration patterns in strategic mobility areas in urban areas, [6], [7].

The data analyzed corresponds to EVs sold in Colombia with some degree of electrification, that is, BEV, HEV or PHEV. Within this group, EVs represent a significant part of the market. Figure 1 shows the distribution of EVs and hybrids sold in Colombia, classified according to fuel type. Hybrid vehicles represent 88.3% of the total, indicating that the majority of buyers opt for this type of vehicle. This suggests that, although the Colombian market is moving towards electrification, the current preference is more inclined towards hybrid solutions that allow a more gradual transition to electric mobility.

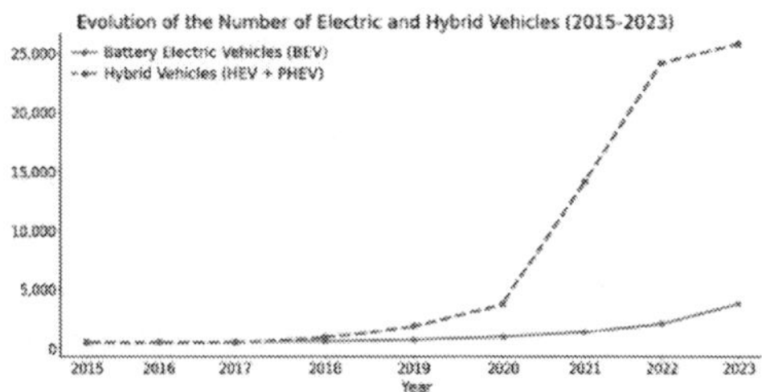

Figure 1: Distribution of EVs and hybrids by 2023. Source: Own elaboration.

Furthermore, analyzing the 2015 period, the number of EVs increased more than 30-fold, and by 2023, the growth was more than 250-fold, a significant increase in EVs. For every EV, there were approximately 7.6 hybrids. The trend indicates rapid progress toward sustainable mobility, with a clear current market preference for hybrid vehicles, possibly due to their lower cost, greater range, or more favorable support infrastructure. Click or tap here to enter text.

The temporal evolution of EV sales has been constant, with a notable increase in registrations starting in 2020. The departments with the highest sales levels are Bogotá D.C., Antioquia, Cundinamarca, and Valle del Cauca, due to a combination of factors, such as the economic capacity of the population, local incentive policies, and the charging infrastructure available in these regions. Figure 2 shows the distribution by department of EVs sold in Colombia as of January 2022, according to the joint report by Fenalco and ANDI. The departments with the highest number of EV registrations are Bogotá, representing 79.8%, Antioquia with 13.1%, Cundinamarca with 4%, and Valle del Cauca with 4%, reflecting a growing interest in zero-emission electric mobility, with the city of Bogotá leading the way.

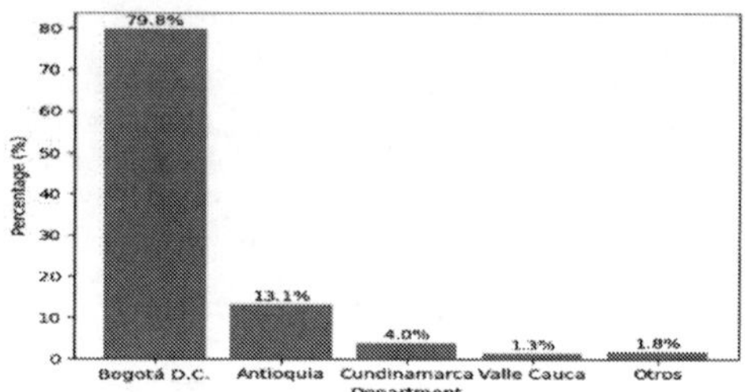

Figure 2: EVs by department in Colombia, as of February 2022. Source: Own elaboration.

Figure 3 shows the temporal evolution of EV registrations in Colombia between 2010 and 2022. During the period between 2010 and 2017, the number of annual registrations remained relatively low and stable, with fewer than 500 units per year. Since 2018, sustained growth in EV registrations has been evident, with particularly marked increases between 2020 and 2022. This accelerated increase can be attributed to multiple factors, such as the expansion of charging infrastructure, the implementation of government incentives, and greater environmental awareness among users. Law 1964 of 2019 played a key role by establishing benefits such as exemption from peak and plate charges, discounts on SOAT (Social Attention Tax) and technical-mechanical inspections, among other incentives aimed at encouraging the adoption of this technology.

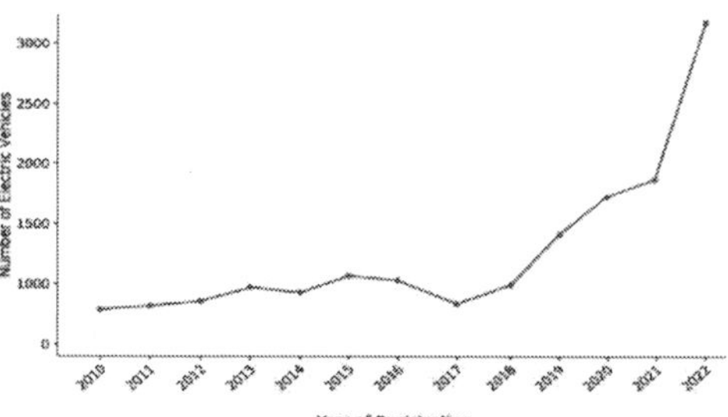

Figure 3: Temporal evolution of EVs in Colombia. Source: Transport Minister.

In 2022, the number of registrations exceeded 3,000 units. Specifically, between January and June of that year, 1,891 EVs were registered, with a monthly average of 315 registrations. This figure represents considerable progress compared to the goal established in the National Development Plan, which projected 6,000 EVs by the end of the government's term. Together, these data reflect a structural shift toward the electrification of the Colombian vehicle fleet, [8], [9].

3.2 Projection of its growth in Colombia.

The growth observed in EV sales in recent years reflects a significant shift towards the electrification of the vehicle fleet in Colombia. This recent boost suggests that the EV market in the country is in an expansion phase with projections of sustained growth in the short and medium term. Below, one of the possible methodologies to estimate the projection of EVs in Colombia until 2030 is presented. Based on the evolution shown in Figure 3, a trend is identified that can be modeled with a second-order polynomial regression, represented in equation (1).

$$\hat{y} = \beta_0 + \beta_1 x + \beta_2 x^2 \qquad (1)$$

With estimated values of β_0, β_1, β_2 using the least squares method, the model allows projecting EV sales in Colombia for the period 2023–2030, showing a trend of sustained growth in the adoption of Evs, [10].

The estimated coefficients of the second-order polynomial regression model are shown in equation (2):

$$\beta_0 = 126151352,33, \; \beta_1 = 125330,73, \; \beta_2 = 31,13 \qquad (2)$$

Therefore, the equation of the fitted model is shown in equation (3).

$$\hat{y} = 126151352,33 + 125330,73x + 31,13x^2 \qquad (3)$$

where, x represents the year and y^ the projected quantity of EVs, with coefficient of determination $R^2 \approx 0.872$, which indicates that approximately 87.2% of the variability in the historical VE data is explained by the 2nd-order polynomial regression model, a fairly adequate fit for projection purposes.

The accelerated growth of the EV market in Colombia has been driven by a combination of government incentives, environmental awareness among users, and technological innovations in these technologies. Recent statistics show a sustained increase in EV and hybrid sales, reflecting a progressive structural transformation in the country's mobility. This growth has been accompanied by the gradual expansion of charging infrastructure, which still presents coverage and capacity challenges.

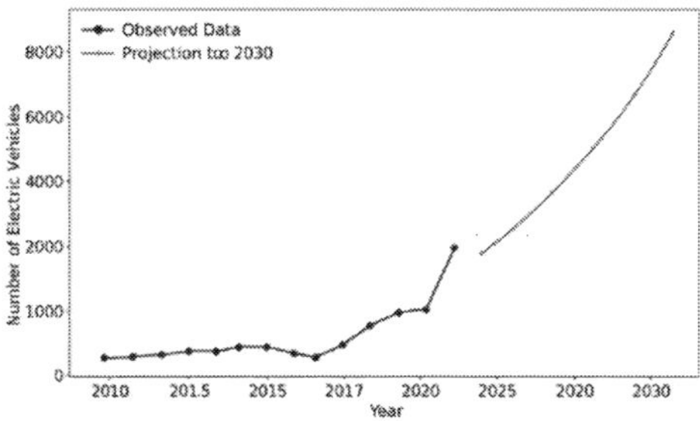

Figure 4: EV Projection to 2030 in Colombia. Source: Own elaboration.

Figure 4 shows the projection made with the model in equation (3), which indicates an accelerated and sustained trend through 2030. Based on historical data from 2010 to 2022, it is estimated that by 2030 the number of EVs registered in the country could exceed 8,900 vehicles, a growth that represents an approximate increase of 185% in 7 years, a significant expansion in the adoption of EVs in Colombia. The trend suggests that Colombia is moving towards a more widespread adoption of EVs, maintaining an accelerated growth rate. The boom in sales reflects a clear transition towards sustainable mobility.

3.3 Charging infrastructure for electric vehicles.

This trend goes hand in hand with the charging infrastructure, represented in Figure 5, where Bogotá leads with 80 charging stations, well above others and followed by cities such as Medellín and Cali. The Ministry of Mines and Energy, through its public policy, promotes electric mobility in Colombia. Through Resolution 40123 of 2024, users will be able to charge their EVs nationwide, without restrictions on access and payment. It seeks to facilitate

access to charging stations and requires users to be informed about charging prices and other associated costs. In this context, it is evident that Colombia faces great challenges in the transition to electric mobility, with the lack of charging infrastructure being one of the main research and development topics to achieve the transformation of the conventional vehicle fleet to electric.

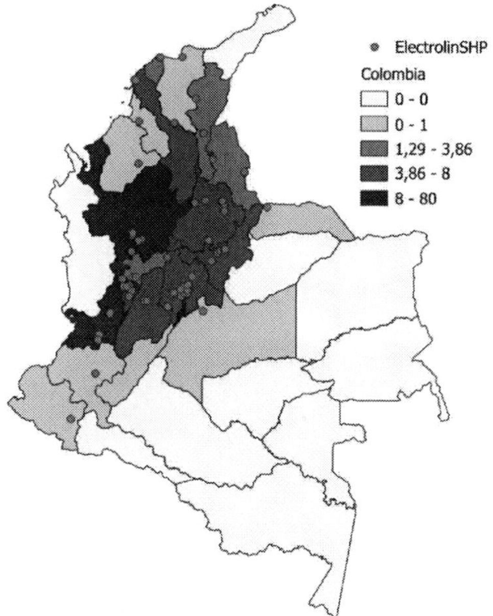

Figure 5: EV charging stations in Colombia by February 2024. Source: Own elaboration.

In Colombia, cities such as Bogotá, Medellín, and Cali already have public EV charging stations, driven by companies such as Celsia, Enel-Codensa, and Terpel, which have invested in infrastructure, including fast chargers. However, development has been limited. Carlos Ghosn, former CEO of Renault-Nissan, points out that the slow adoption of EVs is partly due to insufficient charging infrastructure and a lack of integration with urban planning. In 2020, the country had nearly 3,000 EVs, 47 charging stations, and 114 connectors, significant but insufficient figures given the growing demand. Although the NTC 2050 regulation governs technical aspects of charging systems, there are still no clear guidelines on their location, expansion, and strategic planning. This limits progress toward mass and sustainable electric mobility in the country, [11], [12], [13].

The 2018–2022 National Development Plan set a target of 6,600 registered EVs, which was surpassed with 8,128 units at the end of the period. By 2024, Colombia will have approximately 202 charging stations and 475 connectors, although Electromaps reports 311 charging points, mainly in Bogotá, Medellín, and Cali. The vehicle fleet exceeds 10,000 EVs, and according to the International Energy Agency, there should be at least 1,000 chargers, which shows a deficit of more than 50%. This gap limits the achievement of the goal of net-zero emissions by 2050. The lack of infrastructure can generate range anxiety in users, suggesting a rapid and planned expansion of charging stations in the country [14].

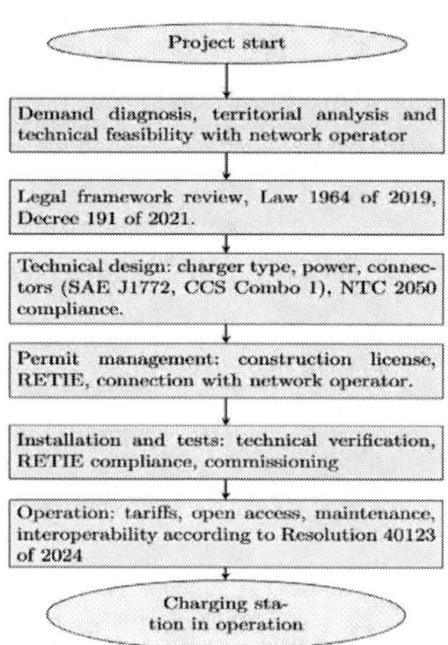

Figure 6: Projection and installation of an EV charging station in Colombia.Source: Prepared by the authors.

The installation of an EV charging station in Colombia requires compliance with a comprehensive process, structured under a legal and technical framework, which establishes clear guidelines to guarantee the safety, efficiency, and interoperability of the infrastructure. From a legal perspective, laws such as 1964 of 2019, decrees such as 191 of 2021, and MinEnergía resolutions (such as 40123 of 2024) define incentives, obligations, and conditions for access and interoperability. In parallel, the technical framework is supported by standards such as NTC 2050, SAE J1772, and resolutions 40405 and 40223, which regulate electrical aspects, connector types, and charging levels. The correct application of these frameworks allows for the design, licensing, installation, and operation of charging stations under safety, quality, and sustainability criteria. Figure 6 shows the process of installing a charging station, looking at the legislation, regulations and decrees established by local and national governments.

3.4 Solar radiation conditions in Colombia.

Colombia, due to its privileged location in the tropics and its geographic diversity, has abundant solar resources distributed relatively evenly throughout the year. Unlike countries with distinct seasons, its proximity to the equator allows solar radiation to vary less seasonally, although factors such as cloud cover, precipitation, and altitude significantly influence each region.

The regions with the highest average solar radiation are the Caribbean Coast, the Eastern Plains, and southwestern areas (Valle del Cauca, Huila, and Tolima), where daily averages reach 5.0 to 6.0 kWh/m²/day. In contrast, regions of the Andean region, particularly in areas with high cloud cover such as Antioquia, Nariño, and Cundinamarca, show more moderate levels, ranging from 3.5 to 4.5 kWh/m²/day.

Figure 7: Colombia solar radiation map. Source: IDEAM

Colombia has one of the highest solar potentials in Latin America, with a national average of nearly 4.5 kWh/m²/day. This represents a significant opportunity for the development of solar photovoltaic and thermal energy projects, contributing to the country's energy transition. Regional variability and the presence of areas with high cloud cover require a design adapted to local conditions, integrating storage and energy systems hybrids where necessary.

In the particular case of Bogotá, located at an altitude of 2,640 meters above sea level and with approximate coordinates of 4.7°N, 74.1°W, it presents a solar radiation pattern characterized by moderate values due to its tropical latitude and the influence of its high altitude. The city receives an average of between 3.5 and 4.5 kWh/m²/day of global horizontal irradiance (GHI), with seasonal variations marked by the rainy and dry seasons.

The solar radiation pattern in Bogotá (see Figure 8) is influenced by the bimodal rainfall cycle (typically in April-May and October-November), which causes decreased radiation levels due to cloudiness. In contrast, the months of December-March and July-August typically experience higher levels of solar radiation.

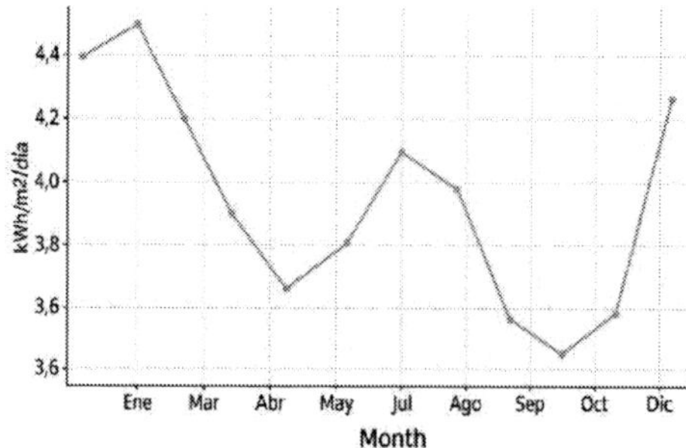

Figure 8: Bogotá—Monthly average daily global horizontal irradiance (GHI) (kWh·m⁻²·day⁻¹). Author's

calculations using representative climatological values. Sources: IDEAM – NASA.

The Moran index (see Figure 9) was used to evaluate the spatial distribution of demand and infrastructure using the city of Bogotá, Colombia, as a case study. Positive autocorrelation patterns were revealed in high-density traffic areas such as Suba and Chapinero. Furthermore, tools such as Voronoi diagrams were presented to divide the territory into optimal coverage regions around existing charging stations, maximizing access and minimizing operating costs. For example, it was indicated that stations in the north of Bogotá have more efficient coverage, while peripheral areas show uneven distribution.

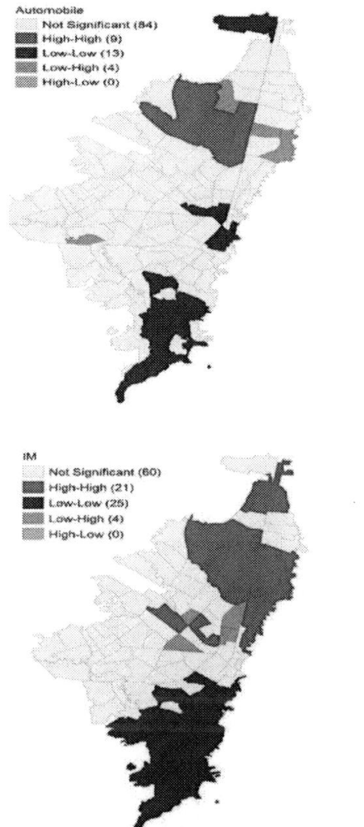

Figure 9: Spatial correlation index (Moran's Index) number of cars and mobility. Source: Own elaboration.

The planning of electric charging stations in urban areas was also analyzed using Voronoi zone segmentation, addressing key issues of accessibility, grid saturation, and sustainability. These zones divide the territory based on proximity to energy generating points, such as existing charging stations, allowing for maximizing coverage and minimizing infrastructure redundancies. This approach is particularly useful in cities like Bogotá, where the uneven distribution of energy resources and electric charging demand requires efficient solutions. This model

demonstrated that the strategic relocation of stations in areas with high vehicle density, such as Chapinero and Usaquén, could increase grid coverage by 20% without significantly increasing operating costs.

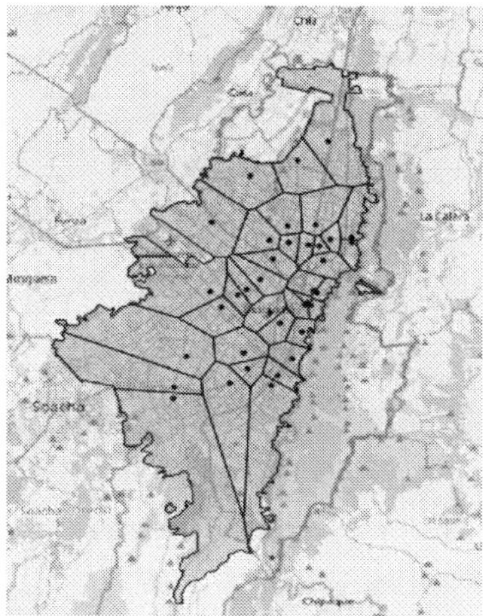

Figure 10: Voronoi zone segmentation based on EV charging stations and their area of influence. Source: Own elaboration.

The analysis of Voronoi polygons (see Figure 10) generated from the location of charging stations revealed marked heterogeneity in service coverage. In cities like Bogotá, polygons associated with stations located in central areas had small areas of influence due to the high density of charging points, while in peripheral areas, large polygons were identified, reflecting gaps in the existing infrastructure. This disparity highlights the need for more balanced planning, prioritizing the installation of new stations in areas with low coverage to improve equity in access to electric mobility.

Furthermore, the results showed that the polygons with the highest vehicle density coincided with the areas with the highest levels of saturation in the charging network. For example, in towns such as Chapinero and Usaquén, the Voronoi polygons concentrate the highest proportion of registered electric vehicles, placing significant pressure on the available infrastructure. This finding highlights the importance of using spatial segmentation not only as a visualization tool but also as a technical criterion for prioritizing investments and planning station expansion based on actual demand.

Finally, by integrating solar radiation data into the spatial analysis, polygons with high potential for the incorporation of supporting photovoltaic systems were identified. These results suggest that installing solar panels at stations strategically located within the most demanding polygons could reduce dependence on the conventional grid and increase local energy resilience. In this sense, Voronoi zones are established as a powerful tool not only for segmenting charging station coverage but also for guiding the transition toward a more sustainable, decentralized, and renewable-based electric mobility model.

4 CONCLUSIONS

The use of Voronoi zones allowed for the establishment of an analytical framework in which each charging station is directly associated with a catchment area determined by spatial proximity. This approach not only revealed the uneven coverage of infrastructure across urban areas but also provided a basis for superimposing other critical variables, such as solar radiation and electric vehicle density. In this way, each polygon became a planning unit that allows for the simultaneous assessment of charging demand and solar resource availability.

By integrating solar radiation maps obtained from IDEAM, the Global Solar Atlas, and PVsyst simulations within Voronoi polygons, it was possible to identify areas with a high correlation between energy demand and photovoltaic potential. For example, areas such as northern Bogotá showed polygons with high vehicle density and, at the same time, radiation levels close to 4.5 kWh/m²/day, making them prime candidates for reinforcement with distributed solar systems. In contrast, peripheral areas with low radiation and lower vehicle density require other types of support strategies, such as storage or grid interconnection.

This integrated analysis allows for a shift from purely spatial planning to a more robust energy model, where charging infrastructure is complemented by local renewable electricity generation. The incorporation of photovoltaic systems in strategic industrial parks not only reduces pressure on the conventional grid but also increases station autonomy and improves resilience to peak demand. In this way, the combination of spatial segmentation and solar resource assessment becomes a key tool for guiding investment decisions, maximizing coverage, reducing operating costs, and enhancing the sustainability of the electric mobility system in Colombia.

REFENCIAS

[1] J. Martínez-Gómez and V. S. Espinoza, "Challenges and Opportunities for Electric Vehicle Charging Stations in Latin America," *World Electric Vehicle Journal 2024, Vol. 15, Page 583*, vol. 15, no. 12, p. 583, Dec. 2024, doi: 10.3390/WEVJ15120583.

[2] T. Khatib and L. Sabri, "Grid Impact Assessment of Centralized and Decentralized Photovoltaic-Based Distribution Generation: A Case Study of Power Distribution Network with High Renewable Energy Penetration," *Math Probl Eng*, vol. 2021, no. 1, p. 5430089, Jan. 2021, doi: 10.1155/2021/5430089.

[3] S. Boonprong, N. Punturasan, P. Varnakovida, and W. Prechathamwong, "Towards Sustainable Urban Mobility: Voronoi-Based Spatial Analysis of EV Charging Stations in Bangkok," *Sustainability 2024, Vol. 16, Page 4729*, vol. 16, no. 11, p. 4729, Jun. 2024, doi: 10.3390/SU16114729.

[4] N. A. Díaz Meza, "An interactive tool for visualization and prediction of solar radiation and photovoltaic generation in Colombia," 2021, *Universidad de los Andes*. Accessed: Sep. 09, 2025. [Online]. Available: https://hdl.handle.net/1992/53603

[5] F. Kogan, "Remote sensing land surface changes: The 1981-2020 intensive global warming," *Remote Sensing Land Surface Changes: The 1981-2020 Intensive Global Warming*, pp. 1–462, Feb. 2023, doi: 10.1007/978-3-030-96810-6/COVER.

[6] IDECA, "Transporte - Temáticas - Datos Abiertos Bogotá." Accessed: Sep. 11, 2025. [Online]. Available: https://datosabiertos.bogota.gov.co/group/transporte?organization=sdm

[7] OpenStreetMap, "OpenStreetMap." Accessed: Sep. 11, 2025. [Online]. Available: https://www.openstreetmap.org./#map=5/4.63/-74.30

[8] C. Xue, H. Zhou, Q. Wu, X. Wu, X. X.- Sustainability, and undefined 2021, "Impact of incentive policies and other socio-economic factors on electric vehicle market share: A panel data analysis from the 20 countries," *mdpi.comC Xue, H Zhou, Q Wu, X Wu, X XuSustainability, 2021•mdpi.com*, Accessed: Sep. 11, 2025. [Online]. Available: https://www.mdpi.com/2071-1050/13/5/2928

[9] K. S. Giraldo Florez and D. A. Moreno Gomez, "Estrategias para impulsar la demanda y oferta de vehículos eléctricos en Bogotá en los estratos sociales 4, 5 y 6 para mejorar la calidad del aire," Jul. 07, 2023. Accessed: Sep. 11, 2025. [Online]. Available: http://hdl.handle.net/10726/5211

[10] M. Islamovic and T. Lind Supervisor Trudy-Ann Stone Karlskrona, "Development of a new forecasting equation simulating EV sales globally A combination approach," 2021, Accessed: Sep. 11, 2025. [Online]. Available: www.bth.se/mba

[11] I. Avellaneda Bolívar, Y. N. Cárdenas Zipa, and J. C. Rodríguez Sanguino, "Estrategias para impulsar el desarrollo de los sistemas de carga de vehículos eléctricos en Colombia.," Nov. 06, 2024, *Universidad Ean*. Accessed: Sep. 11, 2025. [Online]. Available: http://hdl.handle.net/10882/14149

[12] C. Blum, C. Correa Escaf, J. F. Charry, A. Luis, O. Rodriguez, and S. Aparicio, "Socios del Proceso: E2050 Colombia 2 Estrategia Climática de Largo Plazo de Colombia para Cumplir con el Acuerdo de París (E2050) REPÚBLICA DE COLOMBIA Presidente de la República: Iván Duque Márquez Ministerio de Relaciones Exteriores Ministra de Relaciones Exteriores", Accessed: Sep. 11, 2025. [Online]. Available: www.cambioclimatico.gov.co;

[13] I. Avellaneda Bolívar, Y. N. Cárdenas Zipa, and J. C. Rodríguez Sanguino, "Estrategias para impulsar el desarrollo de los sistemas de carga de vehículos eléctricos en Colombia.," Nov. 06, 2024, *Universidad Ean*. Accessed: Sep. 11, 2025. [Online]. Available: http://hdl.handle.net/10882/14149

[14] La República, "'Hay un déficit de 40% de puntos de carga para el parque automotor de vehículos eléctricos.'" Accessed: Sep. 11, 2025. [Online]. Available: https://www.larepublica.co/empresas/hay-un-deficit-de-40-de-puntos-de-carga-para-vehiculos-electricos-3541949

Integration of Solar Energy into Electric Mobility Infrastructure

Diego J. Rodriguez [1]   Jaime F. Pantoja [1]   Johann A. Hernandez [1]

[1]Universidad Distrital Francisco José de Caldas
Faculta de Ingenieria
Bogota - Colombia

Motivation

- The shift toward sustainable mobility demands integrated solutions that merge renewable energy, especially solar, with advanced urban planning.
- Solar-powered charging stations reduce dependence on traditional grids, generate clean and decentralized electricity, and bolster urban energy resilience.
- Geolocation tools such as clustering and spatial analysis enable identification of high-demand areas, optimal solar irradiation zones, and regions with dense electric-vehicle use, ensuring efficient resource allocation and sustainable infrastructure planning.
- Combining solar generation with smart grid strategies supports peak-demand management and enhances the reliability of urban energy systems.
- This holistic approach accelerates the decarbonization of transport and strengthens cities' ability to adapt to future growth and climate challenges.

Methodology

METHODOLOGY

DATA COLLECTION AND PROCESSING
- Oficirial Solar Atlas, PVyst, Oipen Data Colombia, Fenalco/ANDi, OpenStreetMa, Fenalcomaps
- Polynomial regression for projection EV adoption

GEOSPATIAL ANALYSIS
- Voronoi diagrams for territory segmentation
- Clustering and spatial correlation identify EV demand zones

SOLAR INTEGRATION
- Irradiance profiles and PVyst simulations quantify photovoltaicc potential
- Sizing PV systems and estimating peak-demand reduction

GRID REINFORCEMENT PROPOSAL
- Distributed photovoltaics and battery storage

Voronoi Zones and Their Application to Electric Mobility

Solar Potential and Voronoi-Based Planning

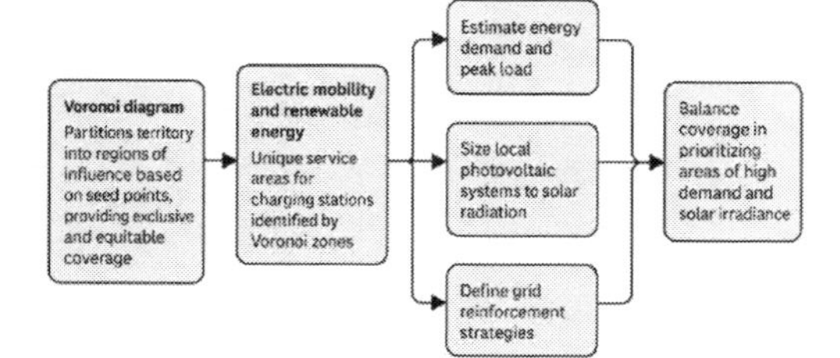

Projected EV Expansion (2030)

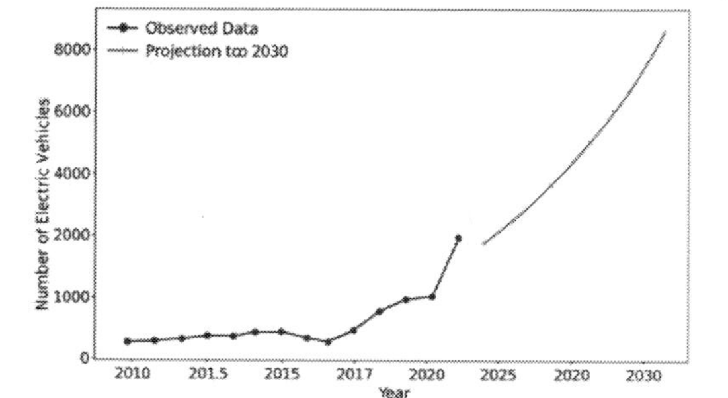

Figure 1. Observed electric vehicle (EV) registrations in Colombia (2010–2023) and second-order polynomial regression projection through 2030, showing an estimated growth exceeding 8,900 units by the end of the decade.

Based on 2010–2023 data and a second-order polynomial regression ($R^2 \approx 0.87$), Colombia's electric vehicle (EV) fleet could exceed 8,900 units by 2030—about 185% above 2023 levels. This growth, driven by incentives, battery and charging innovations, and rising environmental awareness, underscores the need for well-planned charging networks supported by local renewable energy.

Optimizing Charging Infrastructure with Voronoi and Solar Data

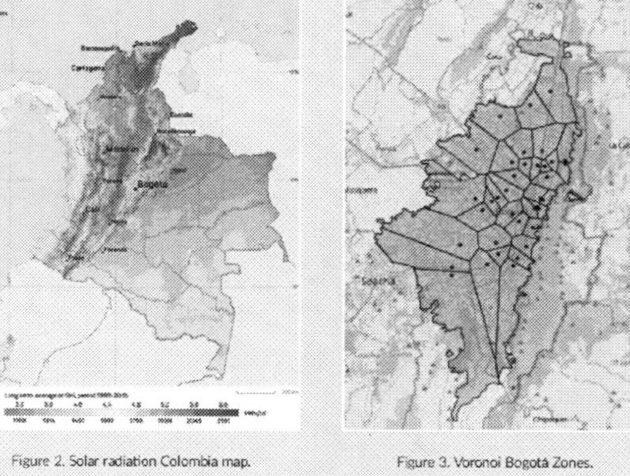

Figure 2. Solar radiation Colombia map.

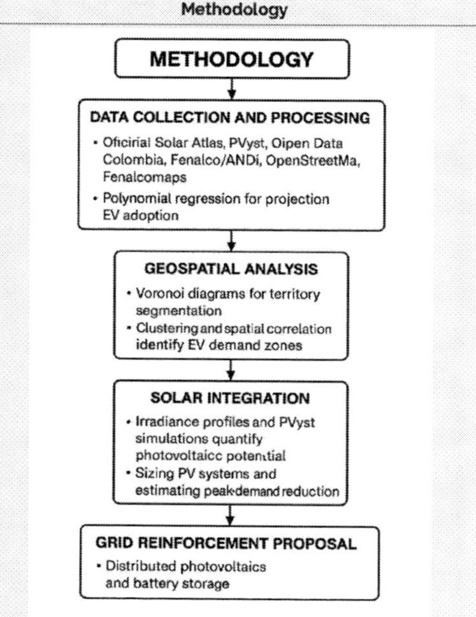

Figure 3. Voronoi Bogotá Zones.

Conclusions

- The combination of **Voronoi zones** with solar irradiance and electric vehicle (EV) density data enabled precise definition of service areas for each charging station, optimizing location and reducing infrastructure redundancies.
- Overlaying solar radiation maps with energy demand revealed that regions such as northern Bogotá have high potential for integrating distributed photovoltaic generation, fostering a more autonomous and resilient charging network.
- The integration of **photovoltaic systems and energy storage** into charging stations decreases dependence on the conventional grid, mitigates transformer overloads, and improves service continuity, particularly in urban networks with limited capacity.
- This approach provides a strategic tool to guide investments, maximize EV charging coverage, and accelerate the transition toward a more **sustainable and decentralized electric mobility** model in Colombia.

References

[1] J. Martinez-Gomez and V.S. Espinoza, "Challenges and Opportunities for Electric Vehicle Charging Stations in Latin America," World Electric Vehicle Journal 2024, Vol. 15, Page 583, vol. 15, no. 12, p. 583, Dec. 2024, doi: 10.3390/wEVJ15120583.

[2] T. Khatib and L. Sabri, "Grid Impact Assessment of Centralized and Decentralized Photovoltaic-Based Distribution Generators: A Case Study of Power Distribution Network with High Renewable Energy Penetration," Math Probl Eng, vol. 2021, no. 1, p. 5430089, Jan. 2021, doi: 10.1155/2021/5430089.

[3] S. Boonpeng, N. Pornsuwan, P. Vanaloudda, and W. Prachathomwong, "Towards Sustainable Urban Mobility: Voronoi-Based Spatial Analysis of EV Charging Stations in Bangkok," Sustainability 2024, Vol. 16, Page 4729, vol. 16, no. 11, p. 4729, Jun. 2024, doi: 10.3390/SU16114729.

[4] R. A. Diaz Meza, "An interactive tool for visualization and prediction of solar radiation and photovoltaic generation in Colombia," 2021, Universidad de los Andes. Accessed: Sep. 09, 2025. [Online]. Available: https://hdl.handle.net/1992/53603

[5] F. Kogan, "Remote sensing land surface changes: The 1981-2020 intensive global warming," Remote Sensing Land Surface Changes: The 1981-2020 intensive Global Warming, pp. 1-462, Feb. 2023, doi: 10.1007/978-3-030-96810-6/COVER.

ESTIMATING PHOTOVOLTAIC POWER RAMP RATES USING SINGLE POINT IRRADIANCE MEASUREMENT

Micke Talvi[1], Jan Kleissl[2] and Kari Lappalainen[1]
[1]Tampere University, Electrical Engineering, P.O. Box 692, FI-33101 Tampere, Finland
[2]University of California, San Diego, Center for Energy Research and Department of Mechanical and Aerospace Engineering, CA 92093-0411, United States
micke.talvi@tuni.fi, jkleissl@ucsd.edu, kari.lappalainen@tuni.fi

ABSTRACT: Generation power of photovoltaic (PV) power plants can fluctuate drastically. In this paper, it is studied how accurately different PV power modeling methods that can be executed using single point irradiance measurement estimate the PV power ramp rates (RR). 4 PV power modeling methods are compared to each other and to the measured generation power of a PV power plant. The investigation is done with 4 PV power plant sizes. The main quantities investigated are the highest observed power RRs and the distribution of the power RRs. The study is based on measured irradiance and PV power. It was found that there can be significant differences among the PV power modeling methods, and in contrast to the measured PV power when the variability of PV power was considered. Based on the results, the R2021 method performed the best, and the M2011 method performed the worst.
Keywords: Photovoltaic power, Power fluctuations, Photovoltaic power modeling, Irradiance fluctuations

1 INTRODUCTION

International Energy Agency has estimated the share of global electricity produced with variable renewable energy power plants to be 30% in 2030. Solar power alone would generate roughly 20% of the global electricity in 2030 [1]. One downside of solar photovoltaic (PV) power is that the power generation of PV power plants can fluctuate drastically. The highest observed ramp rate (RR) caused by irradiance variability for a 48 MW PV power plant was 176 %/min in [2]. These power fluctuations should be mitigated, as with the significantly increasing share of PV power in the power grids, the power fluctuations are likely to cause issues. Some solutions to this are increasing the amount of regulative power in the power grids and implementing stricter grid rules. For example, Puerto Rico has set an RR limit of 10 %/min [3]. The RR limit is a threshold that the output powers of power plants may not exceed. However, the PV power fluctuations easily exceed the commonly applied RR limits.

When studying the amount of regulative power needed for mitigation of the PV power fluctuations, accurate PV power modeling methods are necessary if measured PV power data cannot be acquired. Highly accurate PV power modeling methods exist, but they often require comprehensive climate measurements to be executed, which are generally not available in the studied PV power plant locations. Modeling methods that take timeseries measurements at a single point can produce PV power that is usually sufficiently accurate to project daily or annual generation. However, when considering the highest observed power RRs and the variability of PV power, the PV power modeled with simple methods may differ significantly from the real produced PV power.

For instance, in [4], where the PV power was simulated using the PV modeling method proposed in [5] (referred to as M2011 method), the highest observed upward and downward power RRs were found to be significantly smaller compared to those of the real produced PV power. In [6], a wavelet variability model (WVM) was proposed for PV power modeling. The WVM method was found to compare well against the other simulation methods of the time. In [6] it was also found that a moving average method for PV power modeling was

found to underestimate the highest power RRs. In [7], a cloud advection model (referred to as R2021 method) was proposed for PV power modeling. The R2021 method was tested against 2 other methods (the M2011 and WVM methods), and the R2021 method was found to perform well against the methods. However, the highest power RRs during short timescales were not presented in sufficient detail to clearly see the differences and the accuracies of the methods.

As the PV power fluctuations can be extremely fast, the use of high temporal resolution of power data would be necessary when conducting a study involving PV power variability. The fastest PV power fluctuations may not be detected if the sampling frequency is lower than 1 Hz [8]. Thereby, this study uses a high temporal resolution of PV power and irradiance data to precisely investigate the PV power variability.

In this study, various PV power modeling methods are compared considering the variability of PV power. The aim of this study is to investigate how well the PV power modeling methods model power variability and spatial smoothing of actual PV power plants. We studied how power modeled with various methods correspond to the measured power of different size PV power plants when PV power variability is considered. The PV power modeling methods of this study were chosen to be methods that model PV power smoothing using only a single point irradiance measurement. The study is conducted using 1 s temporal resolution for the measured irradiance and PV power.

2 DATA AND METHODS

2.1 Data

This study is based on power and plane of array (POA) irradiance measurements from the 48 MW Copper Mountain Solar 1 PV Plant at Boulder City, Nevada (35.78° N, 115.00° W). The PV power plant is composed of fixed-tilt thin-film CdTe PV modules which are manufactured by First Solar [9]. The POA irradiance was measured using a reference cell. The PV modules and the reference cell are facing south, and their tilt angle is 25°. The main parameter values used for the simulations are presented in Table I. The typical cloud speed and the

Table I. Parameter values used for the simulations.

Plant area 0.5 MW	12478 m²
Plant area 6 MW	160104 m²
Plant area 10 MW	268354 m²
Plant area 20 MW	544788 m²
Typical cloud speed	23 m/s [10]
Typical movement direction of cloud shadows	49.5° (north-east-ward) [10]
Normal operating cell temperature (NOCT)	45 °C [9]
Temperature coefficient of power, β	-0.25 %/°C [9]

movement direction of the cloud shadows determined in [10] are from the same PV power plant location. Hourly temperature data of North Las Vegas was used to calculate the temperature correction for the modeled PV powers. North Las Vegas was chosen, as it was the closest location to the Copper Mountain PV power plant with sufficient temperature data. The temperature data was provided by CustomWeather, Inc [11]. The period investigated consists of 4 months: March, April, May, and June 2012. The temporal resolution of the power and irradiance data was 1 s.

The PV power plant was artificially regulated during 33 days of the studied period. These short regulation periods included multiple extremely fast upward and downward power ramps and maintaining power at a certain level which would have significantly affected the results. Thereby, these 33 days were excluded from the study. Thus, a total of 89 days were used for the study.

2.2 PV power modeling

The investigation was done using 4 different PV power plant sizes: 0.5, 6, 10 and 20 MW. For each PV power plant size, a section of the Copper Mountain 1 PV Plant with that nominal power was selected and its power was modeled based on irradiance and temperature measurements. The area of each modeled PV power plant was determined based on the PV array area of the corresponding section of the Copper Mountain 1 PV Plant. The shapes of the studied PV power plants were kept close to a square. Figs. 1 and 2 present satellite photographs of the Copper Mountain 1 PV Plant showing the studied sections of the plant [12].

4 PV power modeling methods that can be executed with a single point irradiance measurement were used for the study. The results of the methods were compared among each other and against the measured PV power. The chosen methods were the R2021 method [7], the M2011 method [5], the average irradiance method (AIM) that is used for example in [13], and the WVM method [6]. The WVM method was executed using the WVM model in the pvlib library [14].

After the smoothed irradiances were calculated for the 4 methods, the effect of temperature on power production was taken into account. First, the average temperature of the PV modules T_{PVM} was calculated using the equation of [15] which can estimate the T_{PVM} using ambient temperature T_{amb} and smoothed POA irradiance G_S as

$$T_{PVM} = T_{amb} + (NOCT - 20)\frac{G_S}{800}. \qquad (1)$$

Once the T_{PVM} was calculated, the generated PV power P_{PV} of each method was calculated using an equation [16] that takes into account the effect of the T_{PVM} on P_{PV} as

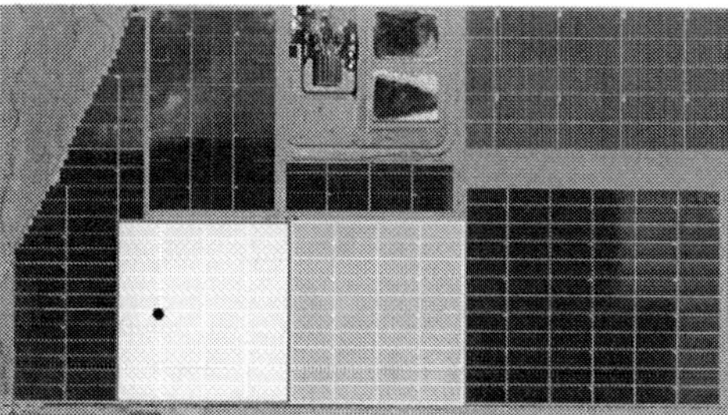

Figure 1: Satellite photograph of the Copper Mountain Solar 1 PV Plant [12]. The imaginary 10 MW and 20 MW PV power plants are indicated with red and yellow rectangles, respectively. The black dot indicates the location of the reference cell.

Figure 2: Satellite photograph of a part of the Copper Mountain Solar 1 PV Plant [12]. The imaginary 0.5 MW and 6 MW PV power plants are indicated with blue and green rectangles, respectively. The black dot indicates the location of the reference cell.

$$P_{PV} = \frac{P_{nom,\,PV}}{G_{STC}} G_S[1 - \beta(T_{PVM} - T_{STC})], \qquad (2)$$

where $P_{nom,\,PV}$ is the nominal power of the PV power plant, G_{STC} is the irradiance in standard test conditions (STC), β is the temperature coefficient of power, and T_{STC} is the temperature in STC. The main quantities that were investigated in this paper are the highest observed power RRs and the distribution of the power RRs.

3 RESULTS AND DISCUSSION

3.1 Example

Fig. 3 presents an example of the behavior of the measured POA irradiance and the modeled and measured PV powers of the 0.5 MW PV power plant during a highly fluctuating period. The figure shows that all the PV powers modeled with different methods follow the measured PV power and irradiance closely, but their lines are smoother. The PV power modeled with the M2011 method seems to be significantly smoother than the other lines. Moreover, the small upward ramps in irradiance roughly at 13:46:10, 13:47:05 and 13:48:45 seem to be nearly neglected with the M2011 method. Fig. 3 shows that the measured PV power had sharp power ramps that were often faster than those of the measured irradiance. These sharp ramps in measured PV power were caused by the combined effect of changing environmental conditions and the operation of the inverter including maximum power point tracking (MPPT).

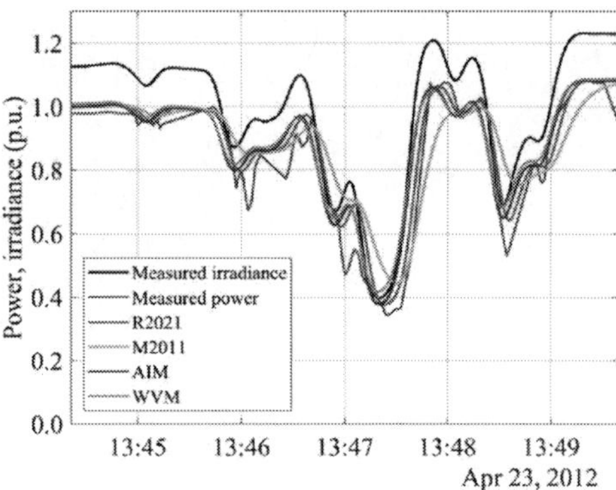

Figure 3: Example of the measured irradiance, the measured PV power and the modeled PV powers during a highly fluctuating period for the 0.5 MW PV power plant.

Table II: Highest observed upward and downward irradiance RRs during 1 s for the measured single point irradiance and the smoothed irradiances for the 0.5 MW and 6 MW PV power plants.

	0.5 MW		6 MW	
	Up	Down	Up	Down
Measured irradiance (%/min)	444.1	468.7	444.1	468.7
R2021 (%/min)	424.7	446.2	284.3	287.0
M2011 (%/min)	261.6	260.0	39.4	36.1
AIM (%/min)	409.0	429.1	219.8	216.7
WVM (%/min)	372.5	391.9	266.0	277.2

3.2 Smoothed irradiances

Table II presents the highest observed upward and downward irradiance RRs during 1 s for the measured and smoothed irradiances for the 0.5 MW and 6 MW PV power plants. The R2021 method performed best among the modeling methods when the highest irradiance RRs are considered. The M2011 performed the worst among the methods, and its highest irradiance RRs were significantly lower than those of the other methods or the measured irradiance.

Figs. 4 and 5 present the shares of time when the irradiance RRs for the measured and smoothed irradiances of the 0.5 MW and 6 MW PV power plants exceeded certain RR magnitudes as a function of that magnitude. Figs. 4 and 5 show that the R2021, AIM and WVM methods yielded quite similar results among each other and compared to the measured irradiance. With the M2011 method, the RR magnitudes higher than 5 %/min were slightly more infrequent compared to the other methods for the 0.5 MW PV power plant, but there was a significant difference when considering the results of the 6 MW PV power plant. It seems that a clear performance difference emerges between the M2011 method and the other methods already at a PV power plant size of 6 MW when the variability of the smoothed irradiance is considered.

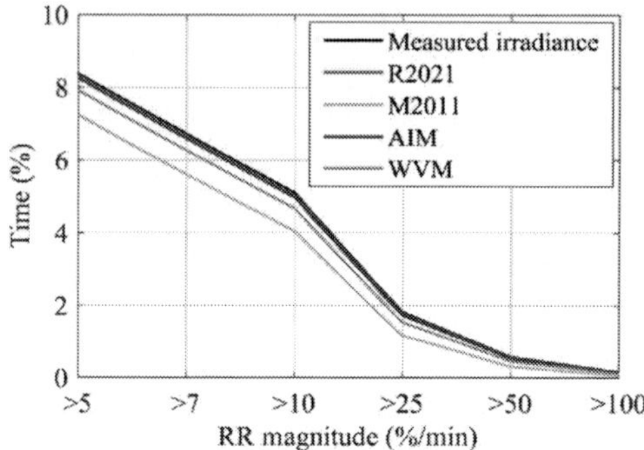

Figure 4: Share of the time when the RRs of the measured and smoothed irradiances of the 0.5 MW PW power plant exceeded certain RR magnitude as a function of the RR magnitude exceeded.

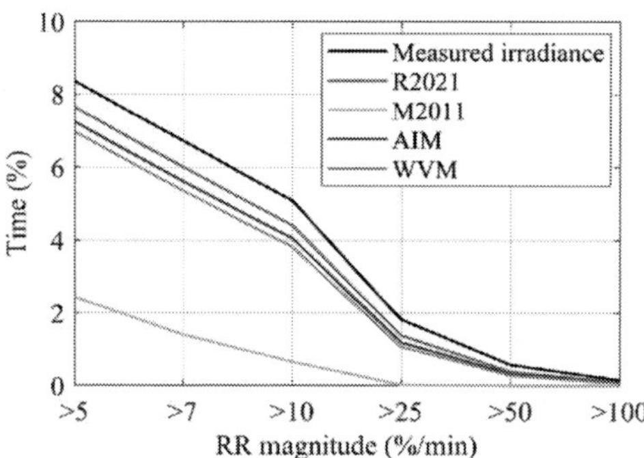

Figure 5: Share of the time when the RRs of the measured and smoothed irradiances of the 6 MW PW power plant exceeded certain RR magnitude as a function of the RR magnitude exceeded.

3.3 Modeled PV powers

Table III presents the highest observed upward and downward power RRs for the 0.5 MW, 6 MW, 10 MW and 20 MW PV power plants with the measured and modeled PV powers. The highest power RRs of the measured PV power of the 10 MW PV power plant are well in line with the highest power RRs recorded for a 9.5 MW PV power plant in [17] (300 %/min). The highest observed upward and downward power RRs of the measured PV power were significantly higher than those recorded with the modeled PV powers especially for small PV power plant sizes. In general, the difference in the highest observed power RRs of the measured and modeled PV powers decreased as the size of the PV power plant increased. The R2021 method achieved the closest values to the measured PV power for PV power plant sizes of 0.5 MW, 6 MW and 10 MW. For the 20 MW PV power plant, the WVM method achieved the closest values to the measured PV power. The M2011 method differed most from the measured PV power, and the relative difference increased significantly as the size of the PV power increased.

It is interesting how small the errors were between the highest observed RRs of the WVM method and the measured PV power for the 20 MW PV power plant. In general, the highest observed RRs yielded with the modeled PV powers were quite different from the measured PV power. This is reasonable as the fastest

Table III: Highest observed upward and downward power RRs during 1 s for the 0.5 MW, 6 MW, 10 MW and 20 MW PV power plants with the measured and modeled PV powers.

	0.5 MW		6 MW		10 MW		20 MW	
	Up	Down	Up	Down	Up	Down	Up	Down
Measured power (%/min)	1196.5	1369.1	416.8	340.0	280.5	251.1	200.4	223.9
R2021 (%/min)	372.7	395.6	250.4	254.0	228.7	231.5	140.4	142.7
M2011 (%/min)	235.1	225.5	37.0	30.4	21.7	19.3	11.6	9.8
AIM (%/min)	360.0	378.5	194.6	193.3	160.1	159.3	104.5	106.0
WVM (%/min)	329.9	346.9	234.1	245.0	214.5	223.8	179.1	185.7

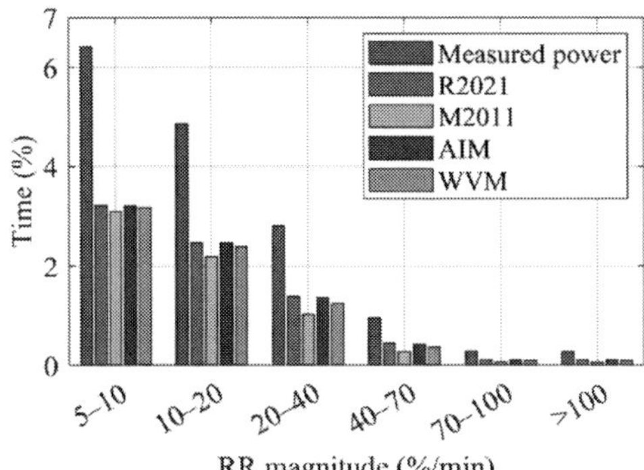

Figure 6: Distribution of the power RRs that exceeded 5 %/min during 1 s time windows for the measured and modeled PV power of the 0.5 MW PV power plant.

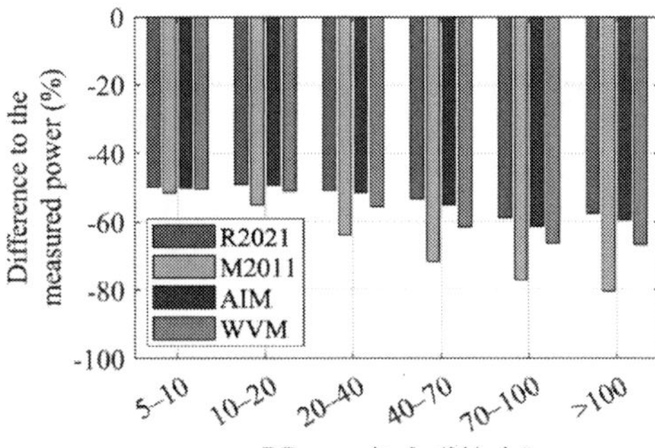

Figure 7: Differences in the power RR distributions of the modeled PV power and the measured PV power of the 0.5 MW PV power plant.

power fluctuations of the measured PV power are extreme occasions, and it is very challenging to model them reliably using only single point irradiance measurements.

When comparing the highest RRs of the measured irradiance and the measured PV power of the 0.5 MW PV power plant, those of the measured PV power were more extreme than those of the measured irradiance. The highest observed irradiance RRs during 1 s in [17] and [18] were 3840 %/min and 4230 %/min, respectively, which are significantly larger than the one recorded in this study. In [17], the highest observed irradiance RR during 10 s was 408 %/min. In this study, the highest observed upward and downward RRs during 10 s for the measured irradiance were 378.6 %/min and 393.0 %/min, respectively. These

values are well in line with the corresponding value of [17] (408 %/min). For the measured PV power of the 0.5 MW PV power plant, the highest observed power RRs during 10 s were 474.0 %/min and 456.8 %/min, respectively for the upward and downward RRs. When comparing the highest irradiance RRs observed in this study and in [17] and [18], the PV power plant location may have caused the major difference in the values — the locations of the PV power plants studied in [17] and [18] may produce extreme irradiance transitions depending on the highest cloud optical depth, highest speed of cloud formation, and/or highest cloud speed at the site.

However, there may be also other factors considering the highest irradiance RRs observed between these studies. One factor could be the different irradiance measurement and data collection devices. The use of reference cells for measuring irradiance might not enable capturing the fastest irradiance transitions in contrast to the pyranometers used in [18]. The sampling rate used for the irradiance measurements is likely to affect the variability of the recorded irradiance as well. In [19], a sampling rate of 0.1 s was used for the irradiance measurements, and the highest observed upward and downward irradiance RRs during 1 s were 22296 %/min and 19554 %/min, respectively. These values are significantly larger than the corresponding ones of [17] and [18] which both had a sampling rate of 1 s for the irradiance measurements.

The reason why the highest RRs of the measured PV power were extreme in contrast to the measured irradiance, is that the operation of the inverter, especially the MPPT algorithm, may have escalated some of the fastest power ramps. This effect was the strongest with the 0.5 MW PV power plant, as it had only 1 inverter, whereas the studied larger PV power plants had multiple inverters. An example of the fast power ramps that are likely caused by the inverter can be seen in Fig. 3 roughly at 13:45 and 13:46. However, the highest observed power RRs of the 0.5 MW PV power plant are in line with the fastest observed power RRs of the 0.143 MW and 0.958 MW PV power plants studied in [17] (1980 %/min and 600 %/min, respectively).

Figs. 6, 8, 9 and 10 present the distributions of the power RRs that exceeded 5 %/min during 1 s time windows for the measured and modeled PV powers of the 0.5 MW, 6 MW, 10 MW and 20 MW PV power plants, respectively. Figs. 7 and 11 present the differences in the power RR distributions of the modeled and measured PV power for the 0.5 MW and 20 MW PV power plants, respectively. Fig. 6 shows that the measured PV power had significantly more power RRs that exceeded the RR magnitude level of 5 %/min compared to the modeled PV powers for the 0.5 MW PV power plant. One reason that caused this difference can be explained by the shadows of

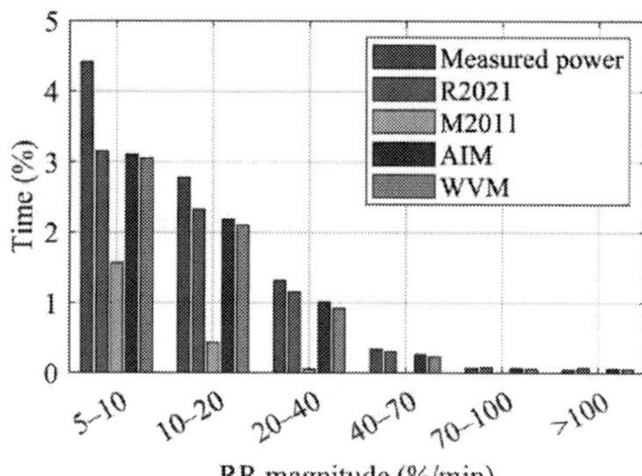

Figure 8: Distribution of the power RRs that exceeded 5 %/min during 1 s time windows for the measured and modeled PV power of the 6 MW PV power plant.

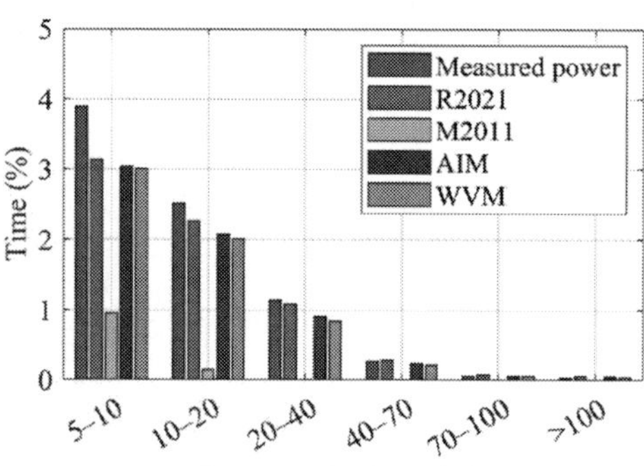

Figure 9: Distribution of the power RRs that exceeded 5 %/min during 1 s time windows for the measured and modeled PV power of the 10 MW PV power plant.

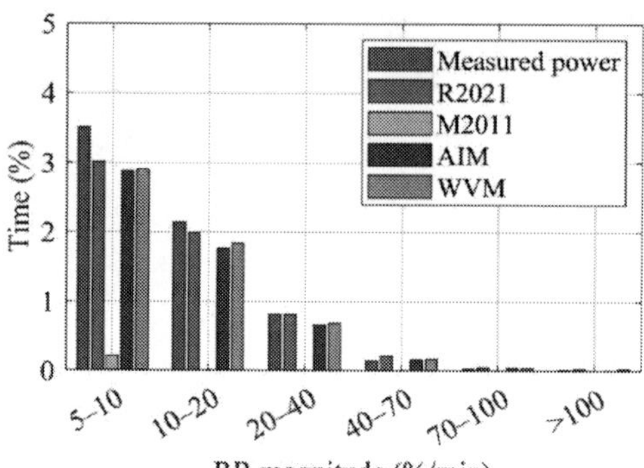

Figure 10: Distribution of the power RRs that exceeded 5 %/min during 1 s time windows for the measured and modeled PV power of the 20 MW PV power plant.

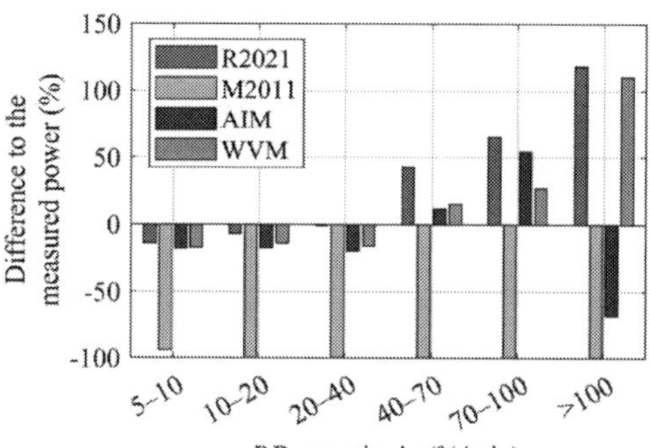

Figure 11: Differences in the power RR distributions of the modeled PV power and the measured PV power of the 20 MW PV power plant.

small clouds that covered the PV power plant partially but did not cover the reference cell. The shadows of small clouds can cause significant power fluctuations for a small PV power plant, but for a larger PV power plant, their effect is not as strong. The power RR distributions for the modeled PV powers of the 0.5 MW PV power plant were similar to each other. Considering Figs. 6 and 7, the values of the M2011 method were smaller in contrast to the other methods, and the difference to the other methods gradually increased with increasing RR magnitude.

Figs. 8 and 9 show that the distributions of the power RRs of the R2021, AIM and WVM methods were quite similar with those of the measured PV power for the 6 MW and 10 MW PV power plants. The distributions of the methods were also very similar to each other. The reason why the total amounts of power RRs that exceeded the RR magnitude of 5 %/min were lower for the 6 MW and 10 MW PV power plants than for the 0.5 MW PV power plant is that the PV power fluctuations become smoother with increasing PV power plant size [5]. This effect can be seen also when comparing the results of the 20 MW PV power plant (Fig. 10) to the results of the smaller PV power plants. The M2011 method differed clearly from the other methods. Considering the results of Figs. 8 and 9, the R2021 method yielded the closest results to the measured PV power. The R2021, AIM and WVM methods slightly overestimated the amount of power RRs above the RR magnitude of 70 %/min with the 6 MW and 10 MW PV

power plants. An interesting finding is that even the RR distributions of the R2021, AIM and WVM methods did not change that much between the 6 MW and 10 MW PV power plants, the RR distribution of the M2011 method changed significantly.

Figs. 10 and 11 show that the R2021, AIM and WVM methods modeled the measured PV power of the 20 MW PV power plant quite accurately when the RR magnitude was smaller than 70 %/min. With larger RR magnitudes, the relative difference to the RR distribution of the measured PV power started to increase with the R2021, AIM and WVM methods. The R2021 method performed best for RR magnitudes below 40 %/min, the AIM method performed best for RR range from 40 to 70 %/min and the WVM method performed best for RR magnitudes above 70 %/min. The RR distribution of the M2011 method was far off the RR distribution of the measured PV power.

Considering all the results presented, the M2011 performed the worst among the methods studied. With the 0.5 MW PV power plant, the results of the M2011 method were similar to the results of the other methods to some extent. However, for the larger PV power plants, the difference between the M2011 method and the other methods grew significantly. It seems that the smoothed irradiance produced with the M2011 is oversmoothed. Oversmoothing of the measured irradiance can be seen also in Fig. 3. Oversmoothing of the irradiance using the M2011 method was suspected also in [4]. The M2011 method may perform better when long-term variability of

PV power is considered, as stated in [7]. It can be concluded that the M2011 method should not be used to model PV power when the short-term variability and the highest RRs of PV power are of importance, for example in studies of smoothing PV power fluctuations by energy storage systems.

Considering all results, overall the R2021 method performed the best. However, the WVM method performed slightly better than the R2021 method when considering the RR magnitudes larger than 70 %/min with the 10 MW and 20 MW PV power plants. This means that the WVM method might be the best one among these methods to estimate the highest power RRs of large-scale PV power plants. The AIM method yielded surprisingly accurate results in contrast to the other methods and measured PV power, even though the AIM method is fundamentally the simplest and the easiest to implement among the studied methods. This means that the AIM method is a solid choice when simplicity and low computing time are the desired features.

All methods except for M2011 depend on the cloud speed. Neglecting cloud formation and dissipation, PV power ramps are caused by the translation of cloud shadows across the PV plant area (or vice versa). If the cloud is large enough, this movement transitions the PV plant from a completely unshaded to a completely shaded condition with the time between the states derived from the ratio of PV plant length in the direction of cloud motion (x) divided by the cloud speed (v). The ramp rate is then given by RR $= (P_{clear} - P_{cloudy})\, v\, /\, x$, where P_{cloudy} mostly depends on the optical depth of the cloud. This equation shows that the RR is directly proportional to the cloud speed. In this study for simplicity a constant cloud speed of $v = 23$ m / s is used. However, in the real world cloud speeds vary with atmospheric wind speeds [20]. Therefore, especially extreme RRs are expected to occur under conditions of extreme cloud speeds. Therefore, in this paper the modeled maximum RRs are likely underestimated as a result of the constant cloud speed assumption.

The days excluded from the study due to power management / curtailment may have contained periods during which the measured irradiance or the measured PV powers could have fluctuated with higher RRs than those reported. It should be noted that actual PV power plants are likely to yield higher power RRs than the ones reported here because of power management.

4 CONCLUSIONS

This paper estimated PV power variability using PV power modeling methods that can be executed using single point irradiance measurement. The study was executed using the measured irradiance and PV power data of 1 s temporal resolution, thus creating an accurate basis for studying PV power variability. The study period consisted of 89 days. The highest observed power RRs, distributions of the RRs by the RR magnitude and power graphs of the methods were analyzed.

It was found that there can be significant differences between the measured and the modeled PV powers when the highest observed RRs and the RR distributions are considered. Moreover, there can be a significant difference between the different PV power modeling methods. It was found that the R2021 method performed best among the studied methods. The M2011 method performed the worst.

The results of this study are valuable for future research into mitigation of PV power variability as well as for planning and sizing of PV power plants and their energy storage systems.

ACKNOWLEDGMENTS

M. Talvi was funded by KAUTE foundation and Business Finland (grant number 1191/31/2022) and K. Lappalainen was funded by the Research Council of Finland (funding decision 348701).

REFERENCES

[1] International Energy Agency, 2024. Available online: https://www.iea.org/reports/renewables-2024 (accessed on 23.8.2025).

[2] K. Lappalainen, J. Kleissl, Proceedings of the 40th European Photovoltaic Solar Energy Conference and Exhibition, Vol. I (2023) 020522. https://doi.org/10.4229/EUPVSEC2023/5DV.2.6.

[3] V. Gevorgian, S. Booth, National Renewable Energy Laboratory Technical Report (2013), NREL/TP-5D00-57089.

[4] M. Talvi, K. Lappalainen, Proceedings of the 41st European Photovoltaic Solar Energy Conference and Exhibition, Vol. I (2024) 020510. https://doi.org/10.4229/EUPVSEC2024/5DV.2.4.

[5] J. Marcos, L. Marroyo, E. Lorenzo, D. Alvira, E. Izco, Progress in Photovoltaics: Research and Applications 19 (2011) 505. https://doi.org/10.1002/pip.1063.

[6] M. Lave, J. Kleissl, J. S. Stein, IEEE Transactions on Sustainable Energy 4 (2013) 501. https://doi.org/10.1109/TSTE.2012.2205716.

[7] J. Ranalli, E.E.M. Peerlings, Journal of Renewable and Sustainable Energy 13 (2021) 033704. https://doi.org/10.1063/5.0050428.

[8] D. Torres Lobera, A. Mäki, J. Huusari, K. Lappalainen, T. Suntio, S. Valkealahti, International Journal of Photoenergy 2013 (2013) 837310. https://doi.org/10.1155/2013/837310.

[9] First Solar FS Series 2 PV Module. Available online: https://www.firstsolar.com/Resources/Downloads (accessed on 26.8.2025).

[10] J.L. Bosch, J. Kleissl, Solar Energy 95 (2013) 13. https://doi.org/10.1016/j.solener.2013.05.027.

[11] CustomWeather, Inc. https://customweather.com/. (accessed on 22.5.2025).

[12] Google Earth (2025) https://earth.google.com/web/ (accessed on 24.8.2025).

[13] K. Lappalainen, J. Kleissl, Journal of Renewable and Sustainable Energy 12 (2020) 043502. https://doi.org/10.1063/5.0007550.

[14] K. Anderson, C. Hansen, W. Holmgren, A. Jensen, M. Mikofski, A. Driesse, Journal of Open Source Software 8 (2023) 5994. https://doi.org/10.21105/joss.05994.

[15] R.P. Kenny, E.D. Dunlop, H.A. Ossenbrink, H. Müllejans, Progress in Photovoltaics: Research and Applications 14 (2006) 155. https://doi.org/10.1002/pip.658.

[16] E. Skoplaki, J.A. Palyvos, Solar Energy 83 (2009) 614. https://doi.org/10.1016/j.solener.2008.10.008.

[17] J. Marcos, L. Marroyo, E. Lorenzo, D. Alvira, E. Izco, Progress in Photovoltaic Research and Applications 19 (2011) 218. https://doi.org/10.1002/pip.1016.

[18] T. Tomson, Solar Energy 84 (2010) 318. http://dx.doi.org/10.1016/j.solener.2009.11.013.

[19] K. Lappalainen, S. Valkealahti, Solar Energy 112 (2015) 55. https://doi.org/10.1016/j.solener.2014.11.018.

[20] M. Lave, J. Kleissl, Solar Energy 91 (2013) 11. https://doi.org/10.1016/j.solener.2013.01.023.

Tampere University

UC San Diego

ESTIMATING PHOTOVOLTAIC POWER RAMP RATES USING SINGLE POINT IRRADIANCE MEASUREMENT

Micke Talvi and Kari Lappalainen
Jan Kleissl

Tampere University, Electrical Engineering
University of California, San Diego

Data and methods

- Single point irradiance measurements were used to simulate produced photovoltaic (PV) power. The temperature correction was considered.
- 4 PV power modeling methods were compared:
  - Method proposed by Ranalli and Peerlings 2021 ("R2021")
  - Method proposed by Marcos et al. 2011 ("M2011")
  - Average irradiance method (AIM)
  - Method proposed by Lave et al. 2013 (wavelet variability model, WVM)
- Measured PV power of 48 MW Copper Mountain Solar 1 PV Plant at Boulder City, Nevada
- Simulation period of 4 months: March–June of 2012 (89 days)
- Measurements of PV power productions and plane of array irradiance with a 1 s time resolution

Table I: *Parameter values used for the simulations.*

Typical cloud speed	23 m/s
Typical movement direction of cloud shadows	49.5° (north-east-ward)
Normal operating cell temperature	45 °C
Temperature coefficient of power	−0.25 %/°C

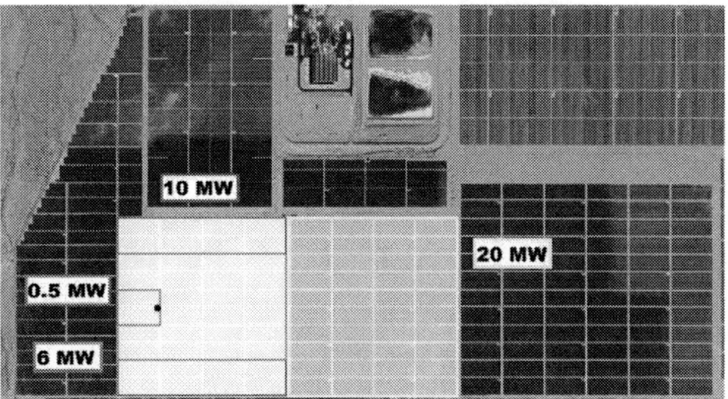

Figure 1: *Satellite photograph of the Copper Mountain Solar 1 PV Plant indicating the imaginary PV power plants and their nominal powers with rectangles. The black dot indicates the location of the irradiance measurement.*

Results

- The main quantities investigated were the highest observed power ramp rates (RR) and the distribution of the power RRs.
- The measured PV power had periods during which it was regulated, these days were excluded. The sharp ramps in measured power were caused by changing conditions and operation of the inverter (Fig. 2).
- The smoothed irradiance produced with the M2011 method is oversmoothed (Fig. 2).

Table II: *The highest observed upward and downward power RRs during 1 s for the 0.5 MW, 6 MW, 10 MW and 20 MW PV power plants with the measured and modeled PV powers.*

	0.5 MW		6 MW		10 MW		20 MW	
	Up	Down	Up	Down	Up	Down	Up	Down
Measured power (%/min)	1196.5	1369.1	416.8	340.0	280.5	251.1	200.4	223.9
R2021 (%/min)	372.7	395.6	250.4	254.0	228.7	231.5	140.4	142.7
M2011 (%/min)	235.1	225.5	37.0	30.4	21.7	19.3	11.6	9.8
AIM (%/min)	360.0	378.5	194.6	193.3	160.1	159.3	104.5	106.0
WVM (%/min)	329.9	346.9	234.1	245.0	214.5	223.8	179.1	185.7

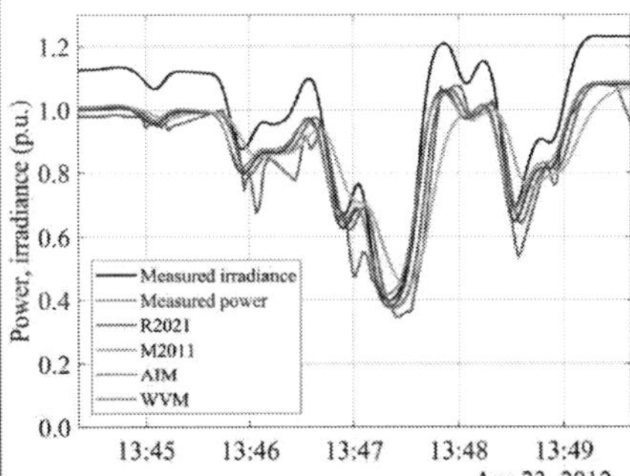

Figure 2: *Example of the measured irradiance, the measured PV power and the modeled PV powers during a highly fluctuating period for the 0.5 MW PV power plant.*

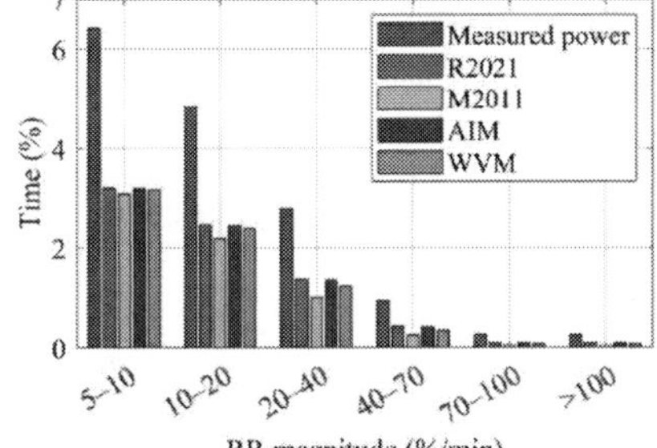

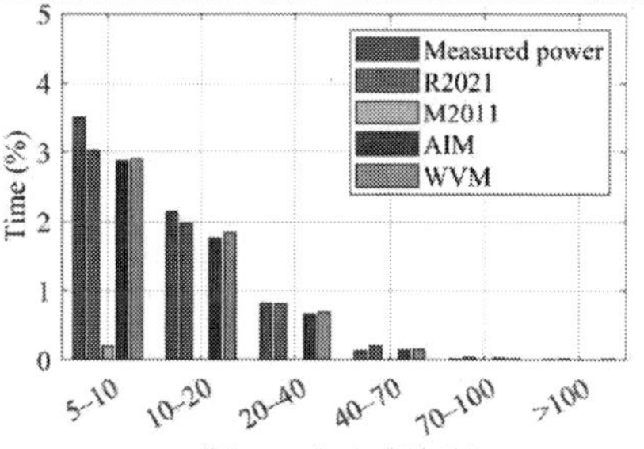

Figure 3: *Distributions of the power RRs that exceeded 5 %/min during 1 s time windows for the measured and modeled PV power of the 0.5 MW (left) and 20 MW (right) PV power plants.*

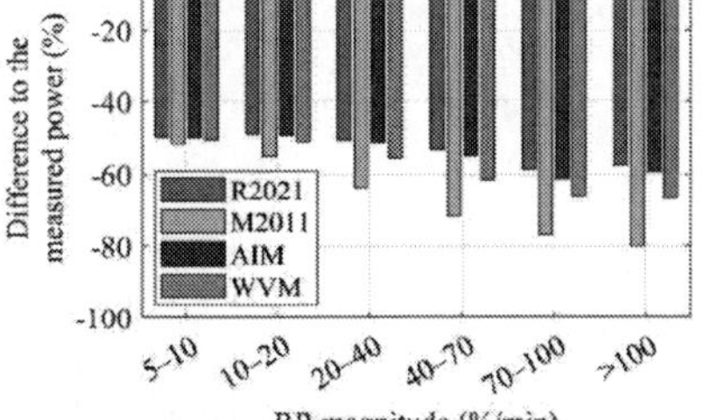

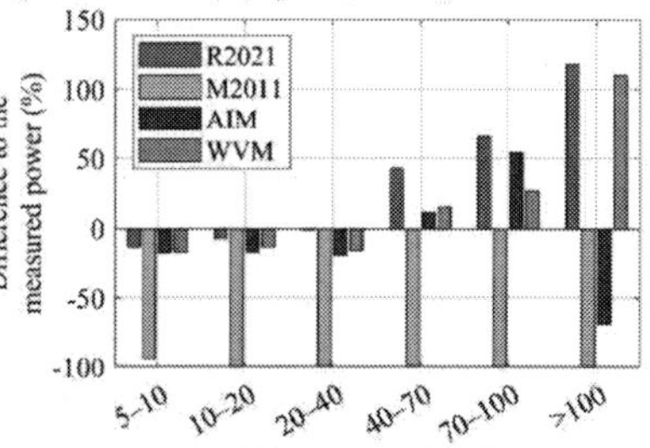

Figure 4: *Differences in the power RR distributions of the modeled PV power and the measured PV power of the 0.5 MW (left) and 20 MW (right) PV power plants.*

- On overall, the R2021 method performed best. The WVM method might be better than the R2021 method when larger PV power plants are considered.
- The M2011 method performed worst. The AIM method yielded surprisingly accurate results, even though it is fundamentally simple and very easy to implement.

Conclusions

- There can be significant differences among the PV power modeling methods, and in contrast to the measured PV power, when the variability of PV power is considered.
- The R2021 method performed the best, and the M2011 method performed the worst.

Related journal articles

- M. Talvi, T. Roinila, K. Lappalainen, Energies 16 (2023) 4313. https://doi.org/10.3390/en16114313.
- K. Lappalainen, S. Valkealahti, Renewable Energy 198 (2022) 1366–1375. https://doi.org/10.1016/j.renene.2022.07.069.

Contact information

- M.Sc. Micke Talvi
- Doctoral Researcher
- Tampere University, Finland
- **micke.talvi@tuni.fi**

OPTIMIZING HYBRID WIND-SOLAR PLANTS IN BRAZIL: ADDRESSING CURTAILMENT AND CONSTRAINED-OFF CHALLENGES

Letícia Vasconcelos[1, a], Luiz Reis[1, b], Lúcio Paiva[1, c], Luis Castro[1, d] and Rodrigo Santos[1, e]

[1]Casa dos Ventos Energias Renováveis

[a]leticia.bezerra@casadosventos.com.br

[b]luiz.reis@casadosventos.com.br

[c]lucio.paiva@casadosventos.com.br

[d]guilherme.castro@casadosventos.com.br

[e]rodrigo.raimundo@casadosventos.com.br

Hybrid wind-solar plants in Brazil offer significant advantages due to resource complementarity and shared infrastructure. However, their operation faces two key power generation restrictions. The first is curtailment, an internal power reduction to respect contracted transmission limits when combined output is high, typically affecting the solar plant. The second, constrained-off, is a less predictable reduction imposed by the National Electric System Operator (ONS) due to systemic grid constraints, severely impacting the project's economic viability and revenue predictability. This article presents a methodology to analyze the combined impact of curtailment and constrained-off on the optimal sizing of a solar plant in a hybrid complex. Through a case study of a new photovoltaic plant being added to an existing wind farm, we calculate and compare the resulting generation losses across different installed capacity scenarios to support decision-making.

Keywords: hybrid power plants, curtailment, constrained-off, sizing optimization, grid integration

1 INTRODUCTION

1.1 The Context of Brazil's Energy Transition

Brazil is in a decisive phase of its energy transition, seeking to diversify its electricity matrix beyond traditional sources. In this scenario, the expansion of power generation from unconventional renewable sources has gained significant prominence. The first large-scale wind farms were implemented around 2007, followed by the first large solar photovoltaic plants in mid-2015. This expansion has been driven by the abundance of these resources in the country and the need to increase the security and sustainability of the energy supply. In 2024, according to [1], wind and solar sources accounted for 14.1% and 9.3% of the internal electricity supply, respectively.

The growing penetration of these renewable sources, however, introduces significant challenges for the operation of the National Interconnected System (SIN). The SIN is a complex and massive transmission grid, according to [2], with over 174,000 kilometers of transmission lines and substations with a combined capacity of over 414 GVA in 2024. For reference, the sections connecting Porto Alegre and Manaus are equivalent to interconnecting Lisbon, Portugal, and Stockholm, Sweden, as shown in Figure 1, which was extracted from [3].

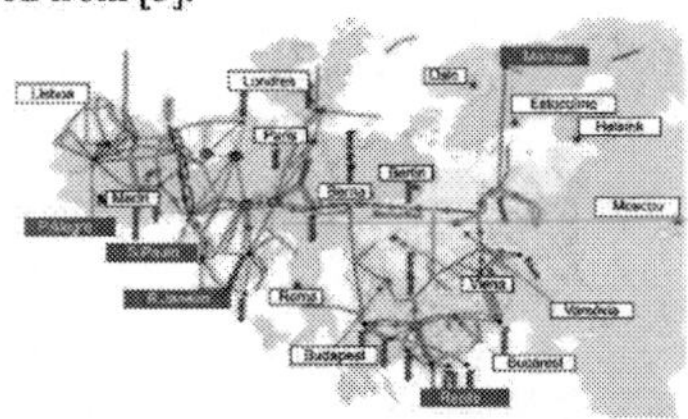

Figure 1: Brazil-Europe Comparison. Source: [3]

Operating an electrical system on this scale is inherently complex, requiring continuous effort to ensure reliability and continuity. In the context of the urgent transition to a cleaner energy matrix, this complexity is heightened by the intermittency of wind and solar sources and the uncontrollability of Micro and Mini Distributed Generation (MMDG) plants. The growth of MMDG is reshaping grid behavior, with daytime solar production leading to a high supply of generation. This shifts the net demand peak to the early evening, a new challenge that, without proper management, can lead to systemic constraints such as constrained-off during peak generation hours. Given this context, the electricity sector has sought solutions that maximize the economic efficiency of generation and transmission assets. This is where the association of different generation sources in the same project becomes a strategic alternative.

1.2 The Rise of Hybrid Wind-Solar Power Plants

In Brazil, energy generation projects that exploit more than one source, such as wind and solar, were only regulated in 2021 through Normative Resolution (REN) 954/2021, [4], established by the National Electric Energy Agency (ANEEL). This resolution defined four ways to associate power plants with different generation sources that share the same connection point in the SIN.

Among these modalities, the possibility of connecting a new plant to an existing one stands out, allowing the sharing of the transmission system usage contract. In this case, the Transmission System Usage Amount (MUST) must be defined between the total installed power of the largest plant and the sum of the installed power of both plants. This enables the addition of a new plant with a fraction of the installed power of the existing one, without the need to contract additional transmission capacity.

Given this regulatory scenario, the association between wind and solar plants has become an attractive business model, especially in regions with good resource complementarity. Since wind generation occurs predominantly at night, adding a smaller solar plant to an existing wind farm brings significant advantages compared to operating only the wind plant.

Among the main benefits are: optimized energy delivery to the grid, reduced uncertainties, and lower modulation costs for flat energy supply ; financial gains from sharing transmission system usage contracts and common infrastructure ; and more efficient use of the transmission system, which reduces operational costs.

1.3 The Problem: Generation Constraints

The variability of wind and solar resources can lead to situations where combined generation exceeds the capacity of the substation and the contracted transmission limits. To avoid surpassing these limits, it becomes necessary to reduce the generation of one of the sources, a process known as curtailment. Typically, solar plants are more affected, as interrupting wind turbines is more complex. A high curtailment rate is undesirable, as it directly impacts solar energy production. Thus, the optimal sizing of the solar plant requires rigorous analysis to minimize power reductions and uncertainties.

Additionally, the growth of MMGD has changed the electrical system's demand profile in recent years. Previously, the system experienced a rapid increase in demand between 2 PM and 4 PM. However, with the high penetration of MMGD , this period now shows a demand valley. Peak demand, however, still occurs after 6 PM, a factor that has contributed to the increase in constrained-off events, as highlighted in [5].

According to ANEEL Normative Resolutions REN 1030/2022 and REN 1073/2022 [6], [7], constrained-off is defined as the forced reduction of generation from centrally dispatched wind plants or wind plant clusters included in the scheduling by the National Electric System Operator (ONS) due to external factors unrelated to the plants. These events occur for three main reasons: external unavailability, when essential transmission equipment, such as transmission lines, transformers, and circuit breakers, are out of operation; compliance with electrical reliability requirements, when the system cannot operate normally due to technical limitations of equipment or transmission lines; and energy-related reasons, when generation must be reduced due to low system demand.

The ONS is responsible for notifying plants about the need of power reductions. In cases of constrained-off due to unavailability or reliability, the reduction affects plants located in the interference region. For energy-related constrained-off, priority is given to constrained-off where the economic impact on consumers is minimized. Since there are no well-defined regulatory criteria for selecting which plants will have their generation reduced, constrained-off is a much less predictable event than curtailment.

1.4 Objective of the Study

Given this scenario, new associations of solar plants with wind farms that already face constrained-off make the sizing of the solar plant even more challenging. The solar plant will be subject to two types of generation restriction: curtailment, applied to photovoltaic generation when the total power exceeds the MUST, and constrained-off, imposed by the ONS. In view of this, the article addresses the optimization of a solar plant in a hybrid complex, presenting a case study with different scenarios of installed solar power to analyze how curtailment and constrained-off impact the decision on the size of the solar plant.

2 METODOLOGY

2.1 Case Study Description

The objective of this study is to analyze the impact of grid operational constraints, such as curtailment and constrained-off events, on the performance of a large-scale hybrid wind-solar power plant. The base case consists of a wind plant with an installed capacity of 817 MW associated with a solar photovoltaic (PV) power plant.

To determine the optimal configuration of the solar component, its installed alternating current (AC) capacity is parameterized, varying from 50 MW to 500 MW in 50 MW increments. For each capacity level, the analysis explores different inverter loading scenarios by evaluating a DC/AC ratio ranging from 1.052 to 1.333. This approach allows for an investigation into how both the injection capacity (MWac) and the PV array sizing (MWp) influence the technical and financial outcomes under operational constraint conditions.

2.2 Data Source

The generation assets analyzed are pre-operational projects. Consequently, the electricity generation time series for the wind source was obtained through computational simulations based on references [8] and [9], which provided hourly production estimates. The solar time series was generated using the PVsyst software. To simulate the impact of operational constraints, historical constrained-off data from an existing hybrid wind-solar plant already in operation within the SIN was used. This data was collected directly from the ONS open data portal. The selection of this reference asset was based on its systemic proximity to the project under analysis, with its connection point located in the fourth electrical neighborhood of the target substation, which indicates a network relevance and a similar technical behavior.

The data used for the simulation covers a full one-year period, from September 1, 2024, to August 31, 2025. The analysis methodology does not forecast future changes in the constrained-off profile. The dataset did not require any handling of missing data, as no gaps were identified within the analyzed period.

2.3 Simulation and Analysis Process

The simulation process was designed to quantify two distinct layers of generation constraints: constrained-off, a physical limitation imposed by the grid, and curtailment, a contractual restriction. The methodology applies a historical constraint profile from a reference plant to the potential generation of the hybrid project under analysis.

2.3.1 Step 1: Determining the Grid Export Factor

Considering that constrained-off represents the grid's inability to export generated energy, the first step is to derive a "Grid Export Factor" from the reference plant's data. This factor normalizes the grid's export capacity relative to the reference asset's installed capacity. To prevent the factor from being skewed by non-grid-related outages (e.g., scheduled maintenance), it is calculated exclusively for time intervals where constrained-off events were recorded.

A single, unified Grid Export Factor (*ref_hybrid_export_factor*) is calculated for all periods. This factor is defined as the ratio of the total actual generation (wind + solar) from the reference plant to the total installed capacity of the reference complex. This ensures that the factor consistently represents the overall grid's export capability, regardless of the time of day.

2.3.2 Step 2: Simulating Constrained-off on the Target Project

This unified export factor is then transferred to the project under analysis to estimate the dynamic power injection limit (*estimated_grid_limit_kW*) at the target substation. The application of this factor is conditional on the target plant's operational state to correctly scale the limit.

During periods with solar generation: The limit is calculated by multiplying the *ref_hybrid_export_factor* by the total installed capacity of the target hybrid complex (wind + solar).

During periods without solar generation: The limit is calculated by multiplying the same *ref_hybrid_export_factor* by the installed capacity of only the wind component of the target plant.

The hybrid plant's generation after this grid constraint (*hybrid_production_after_cof_kW*) is defined as the minimum value between its potential generation (*hybrid_potential_kW*) and the estimated grid limit. The amount of energy not injected due to this constraint is quantified as constrained-off (*coff_kW*).

2.3.3 Step 3: Pro-rata Allocation of Constrained-off

Once the total constrained-off amount (*coff_kW*) is determined, it is allocated between the wind and solar sources. The allocation follows the principle of equal treatment for sources of the same priority, as detailed in [10]. Since wind and solar sources share the same hierarchical priority in restriction-based dispatch, the cut is proportionally distributed based on the potential generation of each technology at the moment of the constraint, as shown in the equations below:

$$\text{wind_ratio} = \frac{\text{wind_potential_kW}}{\text{hybrid_potential_kW}}$$

$$\text{solar_ratio} = \frac{\text{solar_potential_kW}}{\text{hybrid_potential_kW}}$$

$$\text{coff_wind_kW} = \text{coff_kW} \times \text{wind_ratio}$$

$$\text{coff_solar_kW} = \text{coff_kW} \times \text{solar_ratio}$$

The final generation of each source after constrained-off is the difference between its potential generation and the allocated cut.

2.3.4 Step 4: Applying the Contractual Limit (MUST)

The total plant generation, already adjusted for constrained-off (*hybrid_production_after_cof_kW*), is then subjected to the contracted transmission system usage limit (MUST), which for this study corresponds to the installed capacity of the wind component (817 MW).

The surplus amount, defined as curtailment (*curtailment_kW*), is entirely allocated to the solar

component of the hybrid complex, which is a premise of the project's business model.

The methodology used is summarized in the following flowchart.

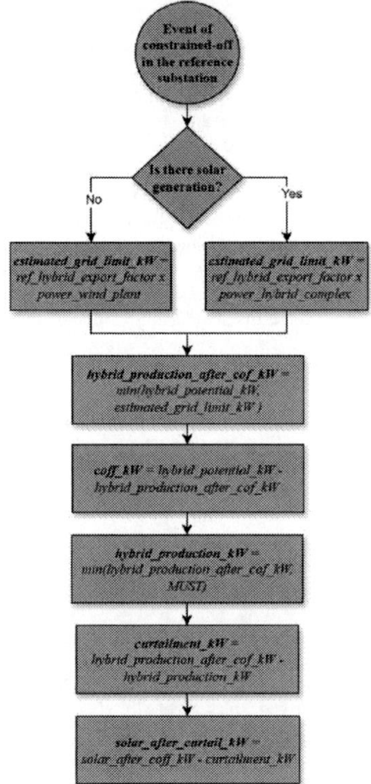

Figure 2: Flowchart of the constrained-off and curtailment calculation process

2.4 Analysis Metrics

Based on the calculated results for constrained-off, affecting both wind and solar sources, and for curtailment, applied exclusively to the solar generation, the following metrics are calculated to analyze and compare the scenarios:

$$\text{solar_coff_loss} = \frac{\text{coff_solar_kW}}{\text{solar_potential_kW}}$$

$$\text{wind_coff_loss} = \frac{\text{coff_wind_kW}}{\text{wind_potential_kW}}$$

$$\text{solar_curtail_loss} = \frac{\text{curtailment_kW}}{\text{solar_after_coff_kW}}$$

$$\text{solar_total_loss} = \frac{\text{curtailment_kW} + \text{coff_solar_kW}}{\text{solar_potential_kW}}$$

$$\text{hybrid_coff_loss} = \frac{\text{coff_kW}}{\text{hybrid_potential_kW}}$$

$$\text{hybrid_total_loss} = \frac{\text{coff_kW} + \text{curtailment_kW}}{\text{hybrid_potential_kW}}$$

3　RESULTS

3.1 Profile and Seasonality of Constrained-Off

The analysis of historical data demonstrates that, despite the inherent uncertainty regarding future constrained-off levels for a plant at a specific point in the system, it is possible to identify clear patterns of days, times, and months with the highest curtailments. This occurs because constrained-off events for energy-related and reliability reasons are driven by surpluses of renewable generation, which coincide with the overlap between high wind production and the onset of solar production. Additionally, the lack of controllability of MMDG plants, which cannot be curtailed by the grid operator, also contributes to the high percentage of curtailment that solar energy experiences. Figure 3 illustrates the daily constrained-off profiles for the reference substation of this study, compared to the generation of the respective energy sources.

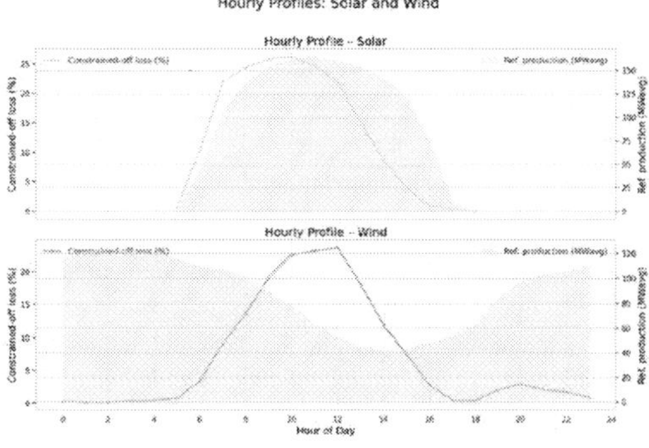

Figure 3: Hourly constrained-off profiles and potential solar and wind power generation of the reference hybrid plant.

The distribution of curtailments throughout the week can be explained by the consumption profile. Energy demand tends to be lower on weekends due to reduced consumption in factories and commercial units, which generates a surplus of generation and can lead to more constrained-off events for energy-related reasons. Figure 4 presents the hourly constrained-off profiles for each day of the week for the reference hybrid plant.

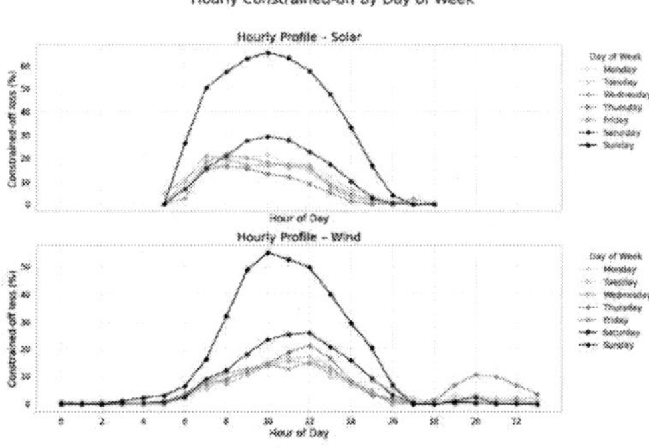

Figure 4: Hourly profiles of constrained-off for each day of the week of the reference hybrid plant.

The analysis of the monthly profile, presented in Figure 5, corroborates the conclusions from figures 3 and

4. It shows that the largest volumes of constrained-off occur in the months with high production, confirming that generation surpluses are the main cause of losses. This correlation between peaks in generation and peaks in operational restriction is consistent with the hourly dynamics already identified.

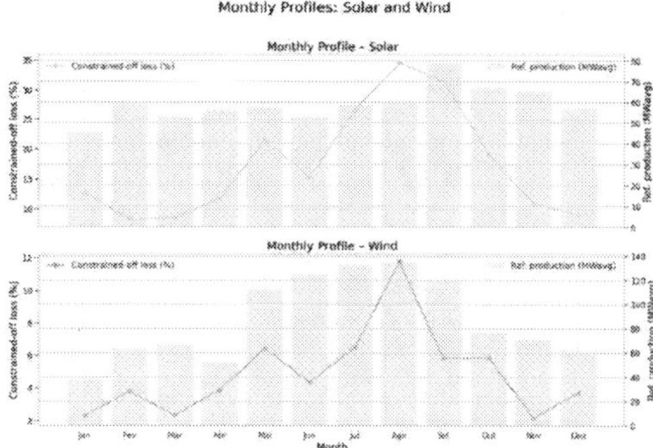

Figure 5: Monthly profiles of constrained-off and potential generation of solar and wind energy.

3.2 Quantitative Loss Analysis

The correlation between constrained-off events and moments of high generation is crucial for understanding the results presented. Given that curtailment events also occur during these peak generation periods, the overlap of both restrictions requires an integrated analysis. Evaluating losses in isolation, whether due to curtailment or constrained-off, can underestimate or distort the total loss profile, as one event can impact the other.

To demonstrate this effect, two simulations were conducted, both with a 200 MWac solar plant and the same DC/AC ratio. The first considered only curtailment events, assuming the absence of constrained-off. The second included the occurrence of both effects. Figure 6 illustrates the hourly and monthly loss profiles for each scenario. When comparing the curves, it is observed that the constrained-off loss in the second scenario absorbs a significant portion of the loss that, in the first scenario, would be categorized as curtailment in an isolated evaluation.

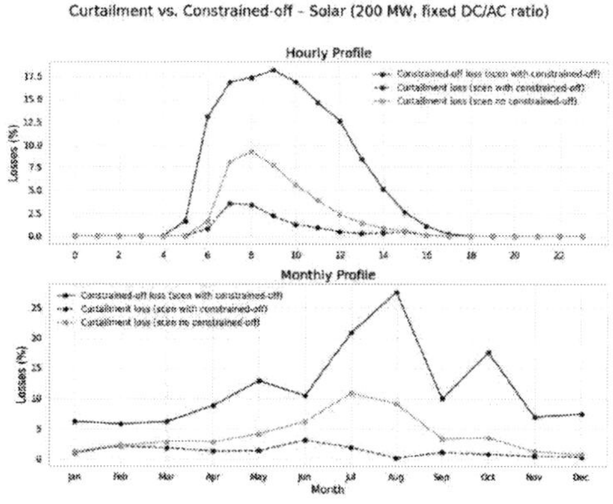

Figure 6: Comparison of loss profiles in a scenario that includes only curtailment versus a scenario that considers both events.

4 DISCUSSION

4.1 Analysis of Results

The two types of generation restrictions, curtailment and constrained-off, behave in distinct ways due to their natures. Curtailment is a direct function of the plant's installed capacity in relation to its internal and contractual export capacities. On the other hand, constrained-off is a function of the regional or national grid state, imposed by the ONS due to external factors.

The result of this dynamic is evidenced in Figure 7, which presents the relationship between the installed capacity of the solar plant and the percentage of losses. The bottom curve, "Curtailment only," which considers only curtailment losses, shows an almost linear growth as solar capacity increases, reflecting the saturation of the internal export limit. In contrast, the top curve, "Effective total loss," which includes the effect of constrained-off, shows a less pronounced total loss growth. This highlights the main implication of the study: the resilience of larger-scale projects to constrained-off. Although they lose more energy in absolute terms due to this restriction, the percentage loss does not increase proportionally, making the risk more manageable compared to smaller projects.

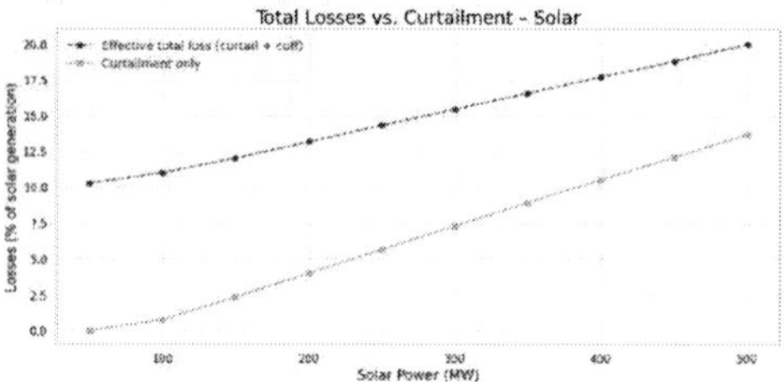

Figure 7: Comparison of losses in scenarios that include only curtailment versus scenarios that consider both events.

As expected, the total solar loss, which considers both curtailment and constrained-off, varies directly with the DC/AC ratio, as illustrated in Figure 8. The behavior of the curve for each DC/AC ratio is consistent, indicating that scenarios with higher photovoltaic panel overloads result in greater losses. This is due to a higher DC/AC ratio increasing the total generation of the hybrid complex, causing more curtailment or constrained-off events. The slope of the curves in the figure demonstrates that the increase in losses is more pronounced at higher solar capacities, confirming the need for a careful analysis when sizing the project.

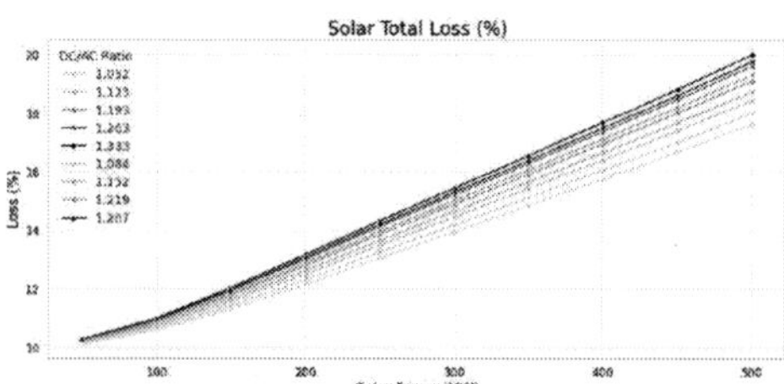

Figure 8: Total solar loss as a function of installed power for different DC/AC Ratio values.

Another crucial point for decision-making is the impact of increased constrained-off on the wind project, as detailed in Figure 9. Given that the *estimated_grid_limit_kW* depends on the total installed capacity of the hybrid complex, scenarios with higher solar capacity will result in a greater curtailment limit. This curtailment, when necessary, is apportioned between the two sources based on their potential generation at that moment. Although the increase in solar capacity may, in some cases, lead to more constrained-off events that affect the wind project, the percentage impact on wind production is minimal. It is even possible, in some cases, for the wind project to benefit if the increase in the *estimated_grid_limit_kW* is greater than the increment in photovoltaic generation, resulting in more headroom for wind energy export.

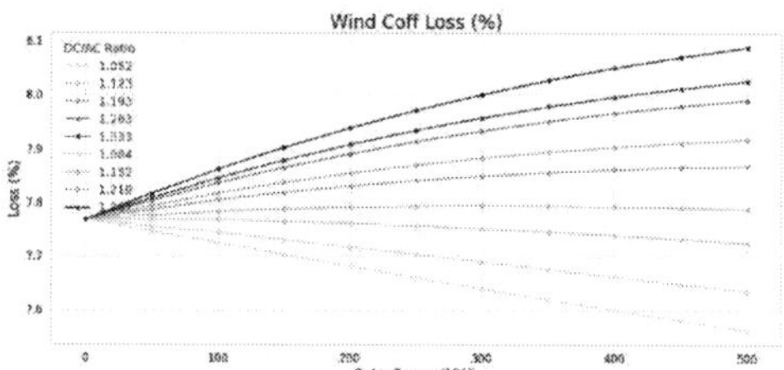

Figure 9: Wind constrained-off loss as a function of solar scale for different DC/AC Ratio values.

4.2 Implication for Investors

Figure 10 illustrates the impact of constrained-off on the economic viability of different solar project configurations, expressing the percentage difference in LCOE relative to a scenario that considers only curtailment. As expected, the LCOE is always higher when constrained-off is included, as the revenue loss from grid restrictions reduces the project's competitiveness. However, the analysis demonstrates that the increase in LCOE is less pronounced as the installed capacity of the solar plant grows. This trend suggests that, in scenarios with constrained-off risk, the ideal configuration points to larger solar capacities. This is due to the fact that larger-scale projects are able to dilute the losses caused by this effect more effectively, reducing the percentage impact on LCOE and making them more resilient to grid restrictions.

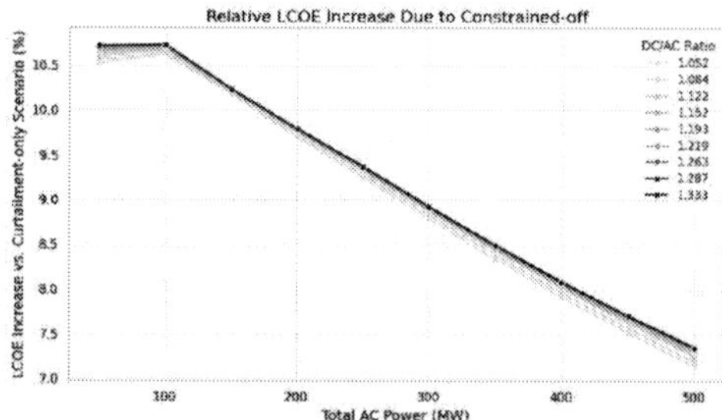

Figure 10: Percentage difference in LCOE between scenarios that consider only curtailment and scenarios that include the effects of constrained-off.

As constrained-off events often happen during the same periods, a portion of the energy that would have been lost to curtailment is instead attributed to constrained-off. This analysis underscores the importance of treating constrained-off as a key variable in the sizing and design phase, rather than merely a discount factor in a Power Purchase Agreement (PPA).

5 CONCLUSION

In a scenario with increasing grid operational restrictions, this study aimed to analyze the impact of total losses, comprising curtailment and constrained-off, on the optimal sizing of a solar plant associated with a wind farm. The results demonstrated that an isolated evaluation of each type of restriction can lead to erroneous conclusions, highlighting the importance of a methodology that integrates both effects for an accurate analysis.

The main contribution of this work is the clear demonstration that curtailment is intrinsically sensitive to project scale, growing as the installed solar capacity increases. In contrast, constrained-off losses are a function of the regional/national grid state and do not depend on the project scale to the same extent. Although larger-scale projects lose more energy in absolute terms due to constrained-off, the percentage impact on the total project is less pronounced, making larger projects more resilient and economically viable under these conditions.

For future work, it is suggested that the proposed methodology be applied to other regions of Brazil to verify how the constrained-off dynamic behaves in different subsystems of the electrical grid. Furthermore, the research can be enhanced by incorporating predictive models for constrained-off, aiming for greater analytical precision. Another important step would be to analyze the impact of energy storage solutions (batteries) to mitigate the effects of curtailment and constrained-off, thereby optimizing energy delivery and project profitability.

6 REFERENCES

[1] Empresa de Pesquisa Energética. (2025). *National energy balance 2025: Base year 2024*. Rio de Janeiro: EPE. Retrieved from https://www.epe.gov.br/sites-pt/publicacoes-dados-aberto s/publicacoes/PublicacoesArquivos/publicacao-885/topic o-771/Relat%C3%B3rio%20Final_BEN%202025.pdf

[2] Operador Nacional do Sistema Elétrico. (2024, December 27). *PARPEL Magazine* [2024 issue]. Rio de Janeiro: ONS. Retrieved from https://www.ons.org.br/AcervoDigitalDocumentosEPubli cacoes/Revista%20PARPEL%20_2024_VF_27.12.24.pdf

[3] Oliveira, F. J. A. de (Ed.). (2020). *Energy operation planning in Brazil's National Interconnected System: Concepts, mathematical modeling, generation and load forecasting* [Portuguese: O planejamento da operação energética no Sistema Interligado Nacional: conceitos, modelagem matemática, previsão de geração e carga]. São Paulo: Artliber. Retrieved from https://www.ons.org.br/AcervoDigitalDocumentosEPubli cacoes/O%20Planejamento%20da%20Operacao%20Ener g%C3%A9tica%20no%20Sistema%20Interligado%20Na cional%20conceitos,%20modelagem%20matem%C3%A 1tica,%20previs%C3%A3o%20de%20gera%C3%A7%C 3%A3o%20e%20carga.pdf

[4] Agência Nacional de Energia Elétrica. (2021, November 30). *Normative Resolution No. 954/2021: Regulation of hybrid and associated power plants*. Brasília, DF: ANEEL. Retrieved from https://www2.aneel.gov.br/cedoc/ren2021954.html

[5] Operador Nacional do Sistema Elétrico. (2024, February). *Revista PARPEL* [Issue 2023-3]. Rio de Janeiro: ONS. Retrieved from https://www.ons.org.br/AcervoDigitalDocumentosEPubli cacoes/Revista%20PARPEL%202023-3-Fev24%20VF.p df

[6] Agência Nacional de Energia Elétrica. (2022, July 26). *Normative Resolution No. 1,030/2022: Consolidation of regulatory acts related to demand response, ancillary services, generation restrictions, and energy settlement mechanisms*. Brasília, DF: ANEEL. Retrieved from https://www2.aneel.gov.br/cedoc/ren20221030.pdf

[7] Agência Nacional de Energia Elétrica. (2023, September 12). *Normative Resolution No. 1,073/2023: Amendment to Normative Resolution No. 1,030/2022 regarding procedures for constrained-off of wind power plants*. Brasília, DF: ANEEL. https://www2.aneel.gov.br/cedoc/ren20231073.pdf

[8] Caldas, J., Delmiro, T., & Ferrer, V. (2022). *Time series energy calculation for wind power projects*. In *Proceedings of Brasil Windpower 2022*.

[9] Lazar, M., & Oliveira, D. (2022). *Long-term analysis and annual energy forecast for different wind measurement periods*. In *Proceedings of Brasil Windpower 2022*.

[10] Operador Nacional do Sistema Elétrico. (2019, August). *Submodule 26.2: Criteria for classification of power plants' operation modality* (Revision 2019.08, effective September 4, 2019). Rio de Janeiro: ONS. Retrieved from https://www.ons.org.br/ProcedimentosDeRede/Módulo% 2026/Submódulo%2026.2/Submódulo%2026.2%202019. 08.pdf

Optimizing Hybrid Wind-Solar Plants in Brazil: Addressing Curtailment and Constrained-off Challenges

Letícia Vasconcelos, Luiz Reis, Lúcio Paiva, Luis Castro and Rodrigo Santos

CdV Desenvolvimento

The overlap with curtailment reveals that constrained-off is a key variable in the design phase, not just a loss factor to be applied in the final feasibility analysis.

Abstract & Introduction

Brazil's energy transition presents challenges for grid operation. Hybrid wind-solar projects offer advantages but face two generation constraints: **curtailment** (internal limitation) and **constrained-off** (grid-imposed restriction). This work proposes a methodology to analyze the combined impact of both losses on the optimal sizing of solar projects associated with wind plants.

Methodology

Data Source: Historical constrained-off data from September 2024 to August 2025 of an operating hybrid plant in the SIN.

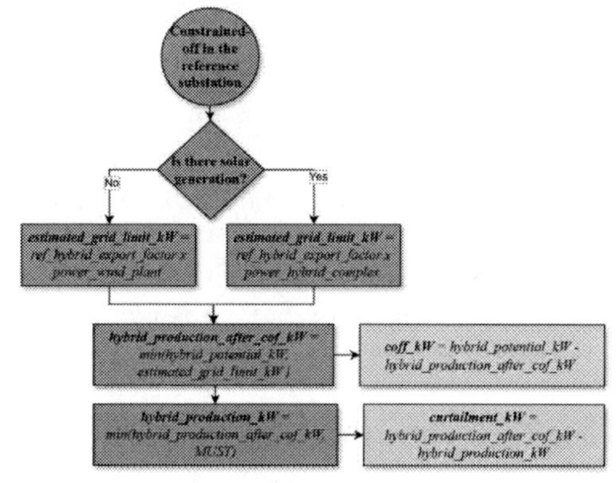

Figure 1: Flowchart of the constrained-off and curtailment calculation process.

Simulation: Comparing two scenarios:

1) Curtailment only.

2) Curtailment + constrained-off.

Analysis: Evaluating percentage losses and the impact on LCOE (Levelized Cost of Energy) for different solar power capacities and DC/AC ratios.

Loss Profiles: Daily and Monthly

Data analysis reveals that constrained-off losses are highest during peak generation periods when high wind and solar production overlap.

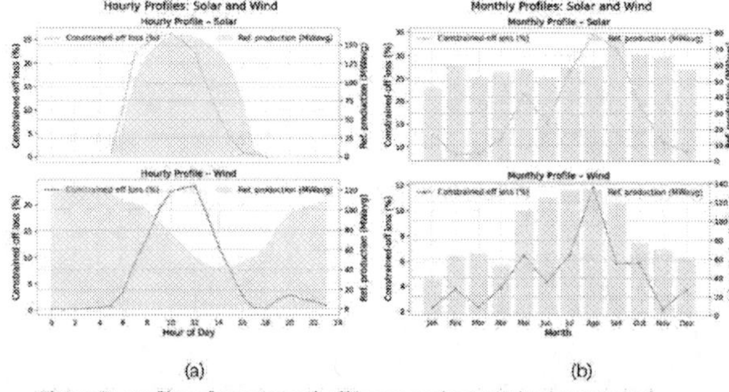

Figure 2: profiles of constrained-off losses and potential solar and wind power generation for the reference hybrid power plant. (a) Hourly; (b) Monthly.

Impact Analysis

Loss overlap shows that constrained-off absorbs a significant portion of what would be lost to curtailment alone. The resilience of larger projects to constrained-off is a key factor.

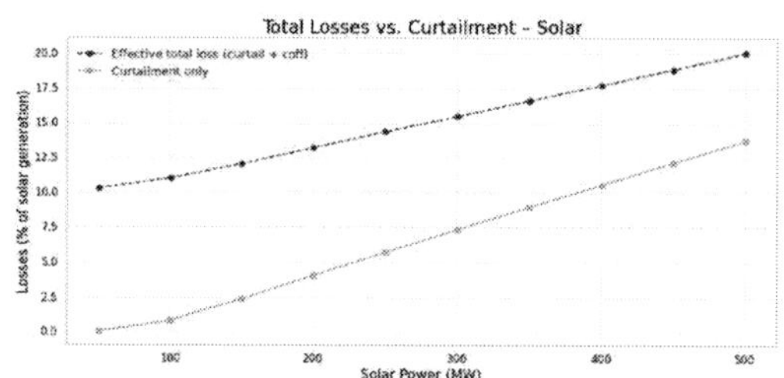

Figure 3: Comparison of losses in scenarios that include only curtailment versus scenarios that consider both events.

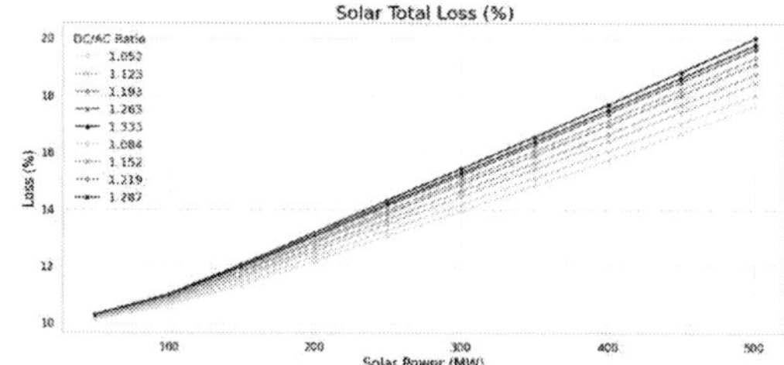

Figure 4: Total solar loss as a function of solar scale for different DC/AC ratio values.

Financial Implications

Constrained-off increases LCOE, but larger solar projects are more efficient at diluting this percentage loss.

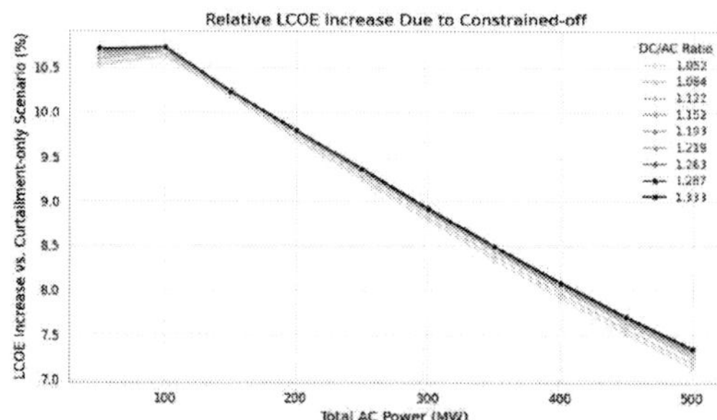

Figure 5: Percentage difference in LCOE between scenarios that consider only curtailment and scenarios that include the effects of constrained-off.

Conclusion and future work

- Isolated loss evaluation for curtailment or constrained-off is insufficient.
- For the site analyzed, larger-scale solar projects associated with wind plants demonstrate greater resilience to constrained-off, making them more attractive.
- Next steps: Predictive models, application in other Brazilian regions and analysis of storage solutions (batteries).

COMPARING APPROACHES FOR ESTIMATING RESIDENTIAL PV SYSTEM ORIENTATIONS

Johan Lindahl[a], Joakim Munkhammar[b] and Gustav Öhgren[a]

[a]Becquerel Sweden AB, Staffansvägen 14, SE-74142 Knivsta, Sweden, johan.lindahl@becquerelsweden.se
[b]Department of Civil and Industrial Engineering, Uppsala University, SE-751 21 Uppsala, Sweden,
joakim.munkhammar@angstrom.uu.se

ABSTRACT: Accurate knowledge of photovoltaic (PV) system orientations—tilt and azimuth—is crucial for forecasting generation, assessing self-consumption, and managing distributed solar power. Yet, orientation data are often missing or unreliable in PV databases. This study compares three approaches for determining the orientation of residential PV systems in Sweden: (i) self-reported values from the national capital subsidy program, (ii) statistical orientation distributions based on PV penetration, and (iii) a LiDAR-based method using aerial imagery and linear regression. Validation was performed against a manually derived ground truth dataset of 104 PV polygons across three municipalities. Self-reported orientations proved highly inaccurate, primarily because the application form allowed only a single entry for a system's azimuth and tilt and lacked clear guidance on azimuth conventions, compounded by imprecise or careless estimations from applicants. In contrast, the LiDAR-based method closely matched the ground truth, with R^2 values of 0.96 for azimuth and 0.82 for tilt and captured the diversity of real-world orientations more accurately than the statistical model. These results demonstrate that LiDAR-based remote sensing provides a reliable, scalable, and high-accuracy approach for determining PV system orientations, supporting improved generation forecasts, grid operation planning, and the integration of distributed solar power at high penetration levels.
Keywords: Photovoltaics, Orientation methods, Azimuth, Tilt, Remote Sensing

1 INTRODUCTION

Solar power is growing rapidly worldwide. In 2024, photovoltaic (PV) systems made up 75% of all newly installed power generation capacity globally, adding an estimated 600 GW [1]. Within the European Union, solar now accounts for 14% of total electricity generation, of which about half is distributed PV systems [1].

Integrating large shares of PV power into the power grid is challenging due to weather variability [2], which affects system stability and requires effective management [3], [4]. As distributed PV adoption grows, accurately forecasting both generation and self-consumption [5] at local and regional levels becomes crucial for optimizing grid operation and energy management [6], [7].

The orientation, i.e., tilt and azimuth, of a PV system highly influences the PV power output profile. Although installed capacity is often reported in PV databases, tilt and azimuth are most often not reported [8]. For instance, a global study by Killinger et al. [9] found that among 14.8% of the world's installed PV capacity analyzed (as of 2017), tilt and azimuth data were available for only 1.7%.

To address this gap, several approaches have been proposed: (1) collect the azimuth and tilt through manual self-reporting — usually connect to different subsidy schemes, (2) assuming optimal tilt and azimuth for maximum power generation at each location [10], [11], (3) estimating a single representative orientation by minimizing discrepancies between simulated and observed regional PV power output [7], (4) using statistical models based on existing PV system orientations [12] or rooftop solar potential [13], (5) applying machine learning or parameterization models to infer orientation from reported PV generation [14], (6) employing remote sensing techniques, such as aerial image analysis combined with 3D building data [15] or calibrating tilt based on nearby systems in non-profit PV databases [16] and (7) using LiDAR data and linear regression to estimate the orientation [17], [18], [19], [20].

This study presents a novel comparison of three of these approaches that has been applied in Sweden for assessing the orientation of PV systems. The first approach evaluates orientation data reported by PV system owners or installers to the Swedish direct capital subsidy program registry [21], [22]. The second approach applies to the model by Ramadhani et al. [13], which estimates statistical orientation distributions based on PV penetration levels. The third approach leverages the method developed by Lingfors et al. [17], which uses Light Detection and Ranging (LiDAR) data to derive tilt and azimuth angles of solar energy systems.

The aim of this study is to evaluate and compare the three distinct approaches for assessing the orientation of residential PV systems, focusing on their accuracy and practical applicability.

2 DATA

2.1 Data from the Swedish Capital Subsidy Program

In mid-2009, a subsidy program was launched in Sweden in which actors could apply for direct capital support for PV installations [21]. The scheme remained in place until 2021, though it was revised several times — for example, lowering support levels in response to declining technology prices and rising market demand [22].

Applications for the capital subsidy had to include project location, applicant details (e.g., address and contact information), planned start and completion dates, and a project description. Moreover, the description needed to specify the type of PV system, whether it would be grid-connected, the estimated total rated power of the modules (kW), and the planned installation site. In the application form, applicants could also enter the azimuth and tilt of the system in two dedicated fields, following the exact instruction in Swedish directly translated to:

"Orientation – azimuth and tilt must be specified as degree values, with azimuth ranging from 0–360 and tilt from 0–90."

This information was recorded and stored in the subsidy program database by the Swedish Energy Agency. Although many applications omitted orientation data, a considerable share did include it. In this study, those entries represent approach (1) described in the introduction

— i.e., the collection of azimuth and tilt through manual self-reporting.

In this study, azimuth is defined such that −90° corresponds to East, 0° to South, and 90° to West and consequently the azimuth data from the direct capital subsidy database was recalculated to match this definition.

3 METHODOLOGY

3.1 Manually Created Ground Truth Dataset

To create a ground truth dataset, residential PV systems first need to be located. For this purpose, the *Alfrödull* [23] remote sensing pipeline was applied to the latest aerial orthophotos from the Swedish Land Survey to identify residential PV installations within the Swedish municipalities of Fagersta (May 2024), Falun (June 2024) and Karlshamn (May 2024).

In the first step of the *Alfrödull* pipeline, a Convolutional Neural Network (CNN) deep-learning model, developed in [24], is used to detect PV systems in aerial imagery across the target area. When applied in Sweden, the CNN algorithm has been shown to accurately identify over 95% of all existing solar energy systems at the municipal level [24].

In the second step, polygons of the identified PV systems are generated, either manually or preferably using the U-net segmentation method described in [25]. These polygons provide the coordinates and orthographic (top-down) area of each PV module cluster. This enables the extraction of LiDAR data for the rooftops hosting the PV systems, which is then used to calculate tilt and azimuth, as further described in section 3.2 and in detail in [17]. A residential PV system containing two PV polygons, generated using the above-mentioned remote sensing pipeline, is illustrated in Figure 1.

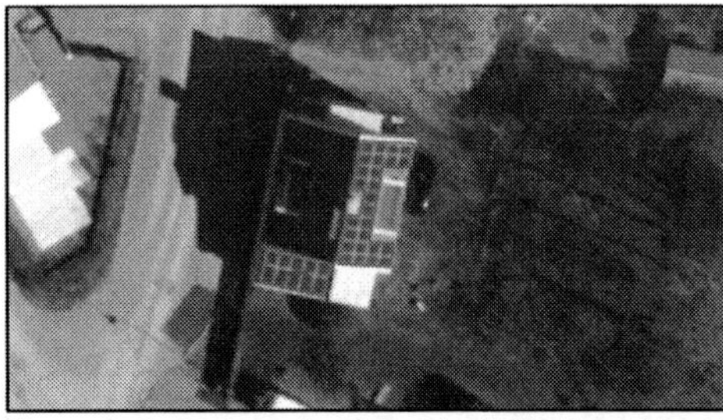

Figure 1. Orthophoto showing a single-family residential house with two distinct clusters of PV modules, each outlined by blue polygons. © Lantmäteriet, 2024. The dark red line indicates the azimuth measurement performed in QGIS for the polygon marked with a bright red cross.

Two different methodologies were applied to manually determine the orientation of the generated residential PV polygons in the ground truth dataset. Azimuth was obtained through manual measurements in QGIS using the "Azimuth Measurement" plugin, as illustrated in Figure 1. Tilt was determined by extracting Google Street View images of the building containing the PV polygon, selecting views taken at an estimated ~85–95° angle relative to the measured azimuth of the polygon, i.e. close to perpendicular. An online angle measurement tool was then applied to these images, as illustrated in Figure 2.

Figure 2. Google Street View image taken approximately perpendicular to the PV polygon marked with a red cross in Figure 1. Image © Google, 2024. The overlay illustrates the online angle measurement tool and the manually derived tilt of the PV system.

The manual derivation of both azimuth and tilt angles is subject to uncertainties. Firstly, the Swedish orthophotos are not orthorectified orthophotos — i.e., they are projected relative to terrain without accounting for building heights — which means that some buildings appear tilted or skewed. Moreover, it is not always possible to obtain Google Street View images that are perfectly perpendicular to the roof being measured. Both factors contribute to slightly distorted measurements. In addition, there is the risk of human error when performing measurements based solely on screenshotted street view images. Overall, the authors estimate that the accuracy of manual tilt and azimuth determinations for the manual ground truth is within ±3° for both angles.

While manually derived azimuths could be collected for all 4,817 residential PV polygons across the three municipalities, only 1,012 of these had a corresponding subsidy application, and just 249 of those applications included both tilt and azimuth values provided by the applicant. The availability of Google Street View images taken close to perpendicular to the polygons' azimuth further reduced our dataset to 104 polygons.

When analyzing the database of the Swedish subsidy scheme, a major drawback was identified: applicants could only enter a single azimuth and tilt value in the submission form. For PV systems consisting of multiple clusters of modules with different orientations, this restriction inevitably introduces errors in the reported orientation. For example, in Figure 1, the marked southernmost smaller PV polygon has a tilt of approximately 8° and an azimuth of 13°, whereas the adjacent larger polygon has a tilt of 45° and an azimuth of −79°. The applicant for this system reported a tilt of 45° and an azimuth of −90°, which reasonably represents the larger polygon but completely misrepresents the smaller one. To assess how widespread this application form and database design limitation was, the authors classified systems with more than one polygon into *primary* and *secondary polygons*, assigning the *primary* status to the cluster whose tilt and azimuth values were closest to the established ground truth. In the example of Figure 1, the larger east-facing polygon was designated as the *primary polygon*, while the smaller southernmost polygon was considered secondary. If two polygons are installed on the same roof facet, both are assigned as *primary* or *secondary*.

3.2 The LiDAR Data and Linear Regression Method

As demonstrated by Lingfors et al. [17], the tilt and azimuth of a solar energy system can be derived from

LiDAR point cloud data. Since Swedish orthophotos are not orthorectified orthophotos PV polygons may be spatially misaligned. To overcome this, Lingfors et al. [17] developed and described in detail an orthorectification procedure to align PV polygons with the LiDAR data.

The results in [17] showed that for most PV polygons detected by the *Alfrödull* remote sensing pipeline in municipal scans, the available Swedish LiDAR data contained a sufficient number of points to enable reliable orientation estimation. However, in cases where LiDAR data could not be used with confidence, a set of special cases and rules was defined to assign a plausible and realistic orientation. These include:

1. **Insufficient LiDAR points** → no regression performed; tilt fixed at $26°$[1], azimuth set to the southernmost long edge the polygon.
2. **Ground-mounted systems (>2 m from buildings)** → tilt set to $30°$, azimuth set to the southernmost long edge of the polygon, panels assumed to be 0.75 m above ground.
3. **Vertical systems** (not identifiable from aerial images) → added manually with tilt $90°$, azimuth set to the southernmost long edge of the polygon.
4. **Flat-roof systems (tilt <5°)** → tilt adjusted to $10°$[2], azimuth set to the southernmost long edge of the polygon.
5. **Flat-roof systems oriented east–west** → treated as bi-directional by splitting the PV polygon. Tilt adjusted to $10°$, two different azimuths set based on the southernmost long edge of the polygon with $180°$ difference.
6. **Unrealistically high tilts from LiDAR** (caused by outdated or misleading data) → treated as in case 1.

These special cases are also relevant for some of the PV systems included in this study.

In [17], the method was evaluated on 3,500 Swedish solar energy systems using a manually derived ground truth azimuth dataset, following the same procedure described in Section 3.1. For 91–95% of the systems, the model accurately estimated the azimuth within the stated uncertainty margin of $±3°$ [17].

3.3 The Statistical Model Based on PV Penetration

The Ramadhani et al model [13], can be used to estimate the distribution of residential PV tilt and azimuth angles based on penetration level — defined in this study as the number of residential PV systems divided by the total number of residential buildings. Flat roofs ($0°$ in tilt) are first excluded, and then the tilt and azimuth distributions of non-zero tilt roofs are estimated according to the stochastic variables:

$$\mathbb{X}_{Tilt} \sim \mathcal{N}[\mu(x), \sigma(x)],$$

for tilt and:

$$\mathbb{X}_{Azimuth} \sim \mathcal{U}[-180(x), 180(x)],$$

for azimuth. Here $x \in [0, 1]$ is the penetration level defined as the number of roofs with PV installations divided by

total amount of roofs. In [13], the parameters were determined to be $\mu(x) = -0.078x + 26.295$ and $\sigma(x) = 0.028x + 6.429$. The complete Ramadhani et al model is then based on using these distributions with an addition of a degenerate distribution at zero for the tilt distribution for the flat roofs, see [13], [26] for more detailed information.

It should be mentioned that the model settings were determined in [13] based on a PV model with the hypothesis of best-roofs-first (in terms of yearly solar energy yield) for PV installations.

In this study the Ramadhani statistical model is tested on the three municipalities of Knivsta, Uppvidinge and Falun and compared to a model which fits normal distributions to both tilt and azimuth using the Matlab function "fitdist". According to a remote sensing-based study on PV penetration levels [27] Knivsta reached a residential penetration level of $x = 0.0375$ in 2023, while Uppvidinge reported $x = 0.0231$ in 2022 and Falun $x = 0.0232$ in 2020.

To assess the goodness-of-fit between the produced distributions of the model and the distribution of the observations, the Kolmogorov-Smirnov (K-S) test statistic was used. Formally, the K-S test statistic $K \in [0, 1]$ is based on the maximum deviation between two distributions [28]:

$$K = \max_x |F_1(x) - F_1(x)|,$$

where F_1 and F_2 are cumulative density functions (CDFs) of the probability distributions to be tested. The K-S test statistic is a negatively oriented score such that lower values mean higher goodness-of-fit.

3.4 Model evaluation

The accuracy of two methods, the LiDAR-based method and database-derived parameters, in estimating tilt and azimuth of PV systems was evaluated using the metrics shown in Table 1.

Table 1. Evaluation metrics and their definitions.

Evaluation metric	Definition
Coefficient of determination	$R^2 = 1 - \dfrac{\sum_{i=1}^{n}(y_i - x_i)^2}{\sum_{i=1}^{n}(y_i - \bar{x})^2}$
Root Mean Square Error	$RMSE = \sqrt{\dfrac{1}{n}\sum_{i=1}^{n}(y_i - x_i)^2}$
Mean Absolute Error	$MAE = \dfrac{1}{n}\sum_{i=1}^{n}|y_i - x_i|$

In the evaluation metric formulas presented in Table 1, y_i represents the estimated value of a datapoint, x_i the corresponded measured value, $\bar{x}$ the overall mean of the measured values, n the number of observations. The variables thus refer to either tilt or azimuth.

---

[1]Based on a sample of 100 PV systems with correctly identified azimuths, the mean tilt was $26°$, which appears to be the most common roof inclination for single-family houses in Sweden [17], confirmed in Figure 4 in this study.

[2]The prevailing practice in Sweden for PV installations on large commercial and industrial (C&I) flat roofs is to mount the modules in rows with a tilt of $10°$ [29].

4. RESULTS AND DISCUSSION

4.1 Comparing Manual Self-Reporting and the LiDAR based Method with the Manually Created Ground Truth Dataset

As described in Section 3.1, a complete-case total data set of 104 PV system polygons in the three municipalities could be created for which applicants for the Swedish capital subsidy program had filled in both azimuth and tilt estimations, and for which it also was possible to manually derive both azimuth and tilt values from the orthophotos and Google Street view images, respectively. In addition, the LiDAR data and linear regression method of [17] could also generate both azimuth and tilt values based on either the sufficient LiDAR data or the six special cases specified in section 3.2.

When comparing the results of the three methods it became evident that many applicants for the capital subsidy used inconsistent definitions. The application form instructs that azimuth values should range from 0° to 360°, and when azimuth data from the subsidy database was analyzed, the authors concluded that different applicants appear to have used either of the two conventions:

- Clockwise from North (0°–360°): East = 90°, South = 180°, West = 270°, North = 0°.
- Clockwise from South (0°–360°): East = 270°, South = 0°, West = 90°, North = 180°.

To enable a more fair comparison of the methods, the authors therefore adopted for each PV system a generous interpretation of which of the two azimuth convention the applicant likely have used — to bring them as close as possible to the ground truth — and then recalculated that value to the definition used in this study, i.e., that −90° corresponds to the East, 0° to the South, and 90° to the West.

Figure 3 shows the distribution of azimuth angles for each PV polygon derived by the three methods (after the generous interpretation modification of the subsidy scheme data) while Figure 4 presents the corresponding distribution of tilt angles.

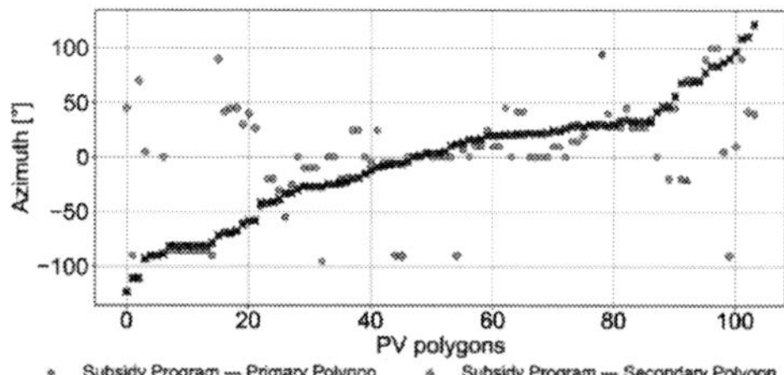

Figure 3. Distribution of azimuth angles derived by three different methods for each PV polygon. Yellow markers show values reported in the Swedish direct capital subsidy program (circles = *primary polygons*, squares = *secondary polygons*). Orange markers represent results from the LiDAR-based method (circles = sufficient LiDAR points, triangles = special-case estimations). Black crosses indicate manually measured azimuth angles from QGIS.

As shown in Figure 3, there is a strong correlation between the manually derived ground truth and the LiDAR-based methodology for azimuth angles: only 2 out

of 104 PV polygons (1.9%) differed by more than ±3°. In contrast, applications submitted under the capital subsidy program showed much poorer accuracy, with 86 polygons (82.7%) deviating by more than ±3° from the ground truth. Not only were errors more frequent in the self-reported data, but the magnitude of the deviations was also often substantial, as seen in Figure 3.

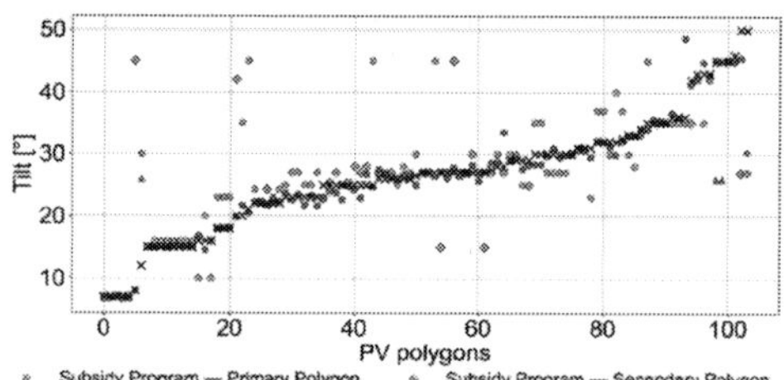

Figure 4. Distribution of tilt angles derived by three different methods for each PV polygon. Yellow markers show values reported in the Swedish direct capital subsidy program (circles = *primary polygons*, squares = *secondary polygons*). Orange markers represent results from the LiDAR-based method (circles = sufficient LiDAR points, triangles = special-case estimations). Black crosses indicate manually measured tilts from Google Street View.

Figure 4 shows a similar pattern for tilt angles. Here too, the LiDAR-based method aligns closely with the ground truth: only 7 out of 104 PV polygons (6.7%) differed by more than ±3°. By comparison, 35 polygons (33.7%) from the subsidy database deviated by more than ±3°. Again, the self-reported data show both more errors and larger discrepancies.

Furthermore, the accuracy of the subsidy database and the LiDAR-based method in estimating tilt and azimuth as compared to the ground truth dataset is summarized in and Table 2 (azimuth) Table 3 (tilt), showing R², MAE, and RMSE.

Table 2. Accuracy of the LiDAR-based method and the self-reporting method of the Swedish subsidy database as compared to the manually derived ground truth dataset in estimating azimuth, illustrated by R², MAE, and RMSE.

Case / Method	R^2	MAE [°]	RMSE [°]
LiDAR	0.96	2.17	10.82
Database	0.06	31.38	52.55

Table 3. Accuracy of the LiDAR-based method and the self-reporting method of the Swedish subsidy database as compared to the manually derived ground truth dataset in estimating tilt, illustrated by R², MAE, and RMSE.

Case / Method	R^2	MAE [°]	RMSE [°]
LiDAR	0.82	1.49	3.91
Database	0.30	4.21	7.76

When interpreting the results in Tables 2 and 3, it should be noted that the ground truth dataset is not absolute, as the manual measurements of azimuth and tilt angles are subject to uncertainties, estimated by the authors to be within ±3°. Nevertheless, the trends observed in Figures 3 and 4 are corroborated by the statistical measures presented in Tables 2 and 3. The LiDAR-based method demonstrates superior accuracy compared to the database-derived values. For instance, considering R^2, the LiDAR-based method achieves 0.96 for azimuth and 0.82 for tilt, whereas the database-derived parameters yield 0.3 and 0.06, respectively.

As mentioned earlier, a major source of discrepancy in both tilt and azimuth between the direct capital subsidy data and the ground truth or LiDAR-based method is that applicants could only enter a single value for each parameter in the submission form. Figures 3 and 4 show, however, that this limitation does not fully explain the deviations: 21 *primary* polygons differed by more than ±10° in azimuth, and 6 by more than ±10° in tilt. When accuracy was assessed using only the *primary polygon* values (as defined in Section 3.1), the results were R^2, MAE, and RMSE values of 0.57, 3.27°, and 5.73° for tilt, and 0.81, 13.92° and 20.14° for azimuth. Even under this favorable assumption, the database accuracy remains substantially lower than that of the LiDAR-based method, most likely because applicants were imprecise or careless when estimating roof orientations.

For the LiDAR-based method, 3 of the 104 polygons could not be reliably assessed due to insufficient LiDAR points (special case 1). In these cases, a fixed tilt of 26° was assigned and the azimuth was set perpendicular to the southernmost long edge of the polygon. This simplification introduced substantial errors, including one case where the southernmost edge did not align with the module cluster's lower boundary, leading to an azimuth offset of –90°. The second major azimuth error came from a non-special-case polygon that deviated by +64°, properly due to noise in the LiDAR data. All three special-case polygons also appeared among the seven polygons with tilt deviations greater than ±3°, with actual errors of –19°, –19°, and +14°. The remaining four non-special-case polygons showed tilt deviations of –19.7°, –4.6°, +5.5°, and +12.7°.

Overall, the LiDAR-based method demonstrated a stronger fit for azimuth than for tilt, as indicated by the higher R^2 value. At the same time, higher MAE and RMSE for azimuth suggest that occasional large errors can occur, as seen in the two polygons with –90° and +64° deviations.

4.2 Comparing the Statistical Model and the LiDAR based Method

The formal K–S test statistics for the agreement between modeled and observed distributions are presented in Table 4 for both the Ramadhani et al. model and the fitted normal distributions, separately for tilt and azimuth. For tilt, the K–S statistics are similar for the two models, indicating comparable performance. In contrast, for azimuth there is a pronounced difference: the Ramadhani et al. model departs much more strongly from the observed distribution than the fitted normal model. Keeping in mind that the K-S test statistic score is a negatively oriented score, the normal distribution model outperforms the Ramadhani model for the azimuth angle distribution estimation.

Table 4. Kolmogorov-Smirnov test statistics for Ramadhani model / normal distribution.

Variable	Knivsta	Falun	Uppvidinge
Tilt	0.19/0.16	0.14/0.22	0.19/0.15
Azimuth	0.49/0.07	0.50/0.07	0.46/0.06

This comparison is not entirely a fair comparison from a modelling and general perspective, since the normal distribution models were in fact trained on the data sets given, and not another data set and generalized as instructed for the Ramadhani model case. However, the mean value for the fitted normal distributions ranged from 3.87 to 4.48 and the standard deviation from 52.17 to 61.83, which shows a close universal fit to these distributions for these data sets, albeit both for Swedish towns and for similar low penetration levels. A proposal could be that the distribution of the azimuth is in fact universal regardless of penetration level and, based on the mean value of this data, that μ=4.263 and σ=52.335 are suggested parameters for this distribution. Investigating the universality of this proposition is left for future work.

It should also be mentioned that while the Ramadhani model as a statistical method is testable on the distributions of orientations of an aggregate of buildings in this study, it lacks the detailed system-to-system comparison features that are inherent to the self-reporting and LiDAR-based methods, such as the results in Section 4.1.

Moreover, since the majority of applications in the direct capital subsidy scheme lack reported orientation values, a direct comparison of general distributions is also not feasible.

However, as the LiDAR-based method generates both azimuth and tilt angles for all polygons of all PV systems within a scanned area, it enables a comparison of the overall distribution of orientations. Figure 5 presents such a comparison of the azimuth distributions obtained from the Ramadhani statistical model [13] and the LiDAR-based method [17] for all actual residential PV systems in the three Swedish municipalities of Knivsta, Uppvidinge and Falun in 2022.

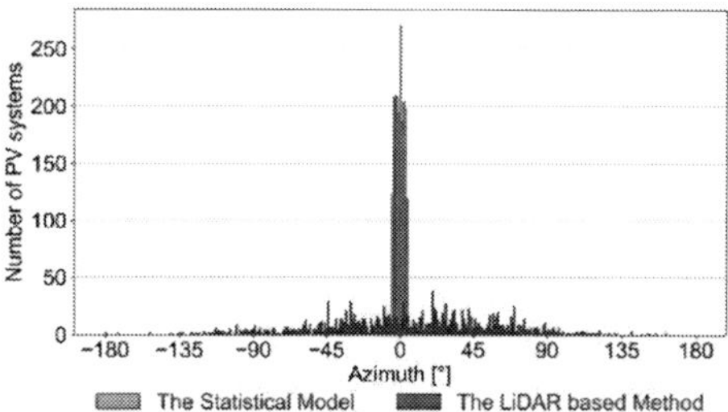

Figure 5. Histograms of the azimuth distribution from random samples using the Ramadhani et al. [13] model, which estimates orientation based on PV penetration levels, and the Lingfors et al. [17] method, which derives tilt and azimuth angles using LiDAR data, for 1922 actual residential PV systems in three Swedish municipalities in 2022.

As shown in Figure 5, the Ramadhani statistical model — assuminh that the "best" roofs are utilized first — produces a much narrower distribution of azimuth angles than the LiDAR-based method, which explain the high K-S test statistic values. While this result was expected from the probability distribution fit estimates, the difference is substantial in system azimuth orientation diversity. The LiDAR-based method is highly accurate in deriving azimuth angles for PV polygons, both in our dataset (where it produced only 2 erroneous azimuths out of 104 polygons) and in previous work [17], which demonstrated accurate azimuth estimation within a ±3° uncertainty margin for 91–95% of systems in these three municipalities. We therefore conclude that the assumption underlying the statistical model — that PV systems are installed on the best-oriented residential roofs — does not reflect reality and leads to erroneous estimates of the actual orientation distribution of residential PV systems.

5 CONCLUSIONS

This study compared three approaches for assessing the orientation of residential PV systems in Sweden: (i) self-reported values from the national capital subsidy program [21], (ii) statistical orientation distributions based on PV penetration levels [13], and (iii) a LiDAR data and linear regression method [17].

The results demonstrate that self-reported values are highly unreliable. During the analyses, two major design flaws were identified in the application form of the Swedish direct capital subsidy scheme. Firstly, the form provided only a single field for azimuth and tilt angles. In practice, many PV systems consist of multiple clusters of modules installed with different orientations. Restricting applicants to one entry per system has therefore proven to be a significant flaw, leading to substantial errors in capturing the true orientation of PV systems. Second, the instructions for reporting azimuth angles were insufficient. It became evident that applicants had used at least two different conventions — where an azimuth of 0° was taken to represent either north or south.

Since it is impossible to know which azimuth convention was applied in each individual case without a ground truth for comparison, the entire subsidy database becomes unreliable for analyzing azimuth data in isolation. Combined with the restriction of allowing only one orientation value per system, these design flaws render the Swedish capital subsidy program database practically unusable for orientation statistics. This serves as an important lesson for the design of future self-reporting systems.

However, because a ground truth was established in this study, it was possible to filter out these form-related issues and assess the accuracy of the self-reporting method. The results show that substantial errors arise not only from database design, but also from imprecise or careless estimations by applicants.

By contrast, the LiDAR-based approach [17] showed strong agreement with the manually derived ground truth, for both tilt and azimuth. Although occasional large errors occurred in special cases with insufficient LiDAR data or noise, overall performance was far superior to the database values. This suggests that LiDAR offers a robust and scalable means to derive system-level orientations at high accuracy.

The statistical model by Ramadhani et al. [13] provided some insight into aggregate distributions but failed to capture the diversity of real-world orientations. Its underlying assumption — that PV installations preferentially occupy the "best" roofs — led to a much narrower azimuth distribution than observed with LiDAR and it is concluded that the statistical approach cannot substitute for detailed system-level information.

In conclusion, LiDAR-based methods currently provide the most accurate and comprehensive option for determining PV system orientations at scale, while self-reported databases and statistical models are of limited reliability. For researchers and actors such as grid operators and aggregators, the adoption of remote sensing approaches based on LiDAR-derived system orientations will be essential for improving PV generation forecasts, enabling more effective network planning, and supporting the transition to high shares of distributed solar power.

6 ACKNOWLEDGEMENTS

The author gratefully acknowledges financial support from the Swedish Energy Agency (Project number P2023-00440). The Agency had no role in the study's design, execution, or interpretation.

7 REFERENCES

[1] IEA PVPS task 1 *et al.*, "Trends in Photovoltaic Applications — 2024," 2024.

[2] R. Luthander, D. Lingfors, and J. Widén, "Large-scale integration of photovoltaic power in a distribution grid using power curtailment and energy storage," *Solar Energy*, vol. 155, pp. 1319–1325, 2017, doi: 10.1016/j.solener.2017.07.083.

[3] N. Etherden and M. H. J. Bollen, "Increasing the hosting capacity of distribution networks by curtailment of renewable energy resources," in *Proceedings ot the 2011 IEEE PES Trondheim PowerTech*, IEEE, 2011, pp. 1–7. doi: 10.1109/PTC.2011.6019292.

[4] G. Barchi, M. Pierro, and D. Moser, "The impact of photovoltaic power estimation modeling on distribution grid voltages," in *2021 IEEE International Conference on Environment and Electrical Engineering and 2021 IEEE Industrial and Commercial Power Systems Europe (EEEIC / I&CPS Europe)*, 2021, pp. 1–6.

[5] R. Luthander, J. Widén, D. Nilsson, and J. Palm, "Photovoltaic self-consumption in buildings: A review," *Appl Energy*, vol. 142, pp. 80–94, 2015, doi: 10.1016/j.apenergy.2014.12.028.

[6] M. Pierro *et al.*, "Photovoltaic generation forecast for power transmission scheduling: A real case study," *Solar Energy*, vol. 174, no. October, pp. 976–990, 2018, doi: 10.1016/j.solener.2018.09.054.

[7] M. Pierro *et al.*, "Impact of PV / Wind Forecast Accuracy and National Transmission Grid Reinforcement on the Italian Electric System," 2022.

[8] Å. L. Sørensen, J. Hole, D. Bjerkehagen, and H. T. Walnum, "From customers to prosumers: PV systems impact on residential load profiles, peak power, and coincidence," in *CIRED 2025 Conference*, 2025, pp. 1–5.

[9] S. Killinger *et al.*, "On the search for representative characteristics of PV systems: Data collection and analysis of PV system azimuth, tilt, capacity, yield and shading," *Solar Energy*, vol. 173, no. August, pp. 1087–1106, 2018, doi: 10.1016/j.solener.2018.08.051.

[10] E. Hartvigsson, M. Odenberger, P. Chen, and E. Nyholm, "Estimating national and local low-voltage grid capacity for residential solar photovoltaic in Sweden, UK and Germany," *Renew Energy*, vol. 171, pp. 915–926, 2021, doi: 10.1016/j.renene.2021.02.073.

[11] D. Lingfors and J. Widén, "Development and

validation of a wide-area model of hourly aggregate solar power generation," *Energy*, vol. 102, pp. 559–566, 2016, doi: 10.1016/j.energy.2016.02.085.

[12] Y. M. Saint-Drenan, G. H. Good, M. Braun, and T. Freisinger, "Analysis of the uncertainty in the estimates of regional PV power generation evaluated with the upscaling method," *Solar Energy*, vol. 135, pp. 536–550, 2016.

[13] U. H. Ramadhani, D. Lingfors, J. Munkhammar, and J. Widén, "On the properties of residential rooftop azimuth and tilt uncertainties for photovoltaic power generation modeling and hosting capacity analysis," *Solar Energy Advances*, vol. 3, no. February, p. 100036, 2023, doi: 10.1016/j.seja.2023.100036.

[14] S. Killinger, N. Engerer, and B. Müller, "QCPV: A quality control algorithm for distributed photovoltaic array power output," *Solar Energy*, vol. 143, pp. 120–131, 2017.

[15] K. Mayer *et al.*, "3D-PV-Locator: Large-scale detection of rooftop-mounted photovoltaic systems in 3D," *Appl Energy*, vol. 310, no. December 2021, p. 118469, 2022, doi: 10.1016/j.apenergy.2021.118469.

[16] G. Kasmi, L. Dubus, P. Blanc, and Y. M. Saint-Drenan, "Towards unsupervised assessment with open-source data of the accuracy of deep learning-based distributed PV mapping," in *CEUR Workshop Proceedings*, 2022.

[17] D. Lingfors, R. Johansson, and J. Lindahl, "Deriving the orientation of existing solar energy systems from LiDAR data at scale," *Solar Energy*, vol. 291, no. 113344, 2025, doi: 10.1016/j.solener.2025.113344.

[18] J. Martín-Jiménez, S. Del Pozo, M. Sánchez-Aparicio, and S. Lagüela, "Multi-scale roof characterization from LiDAR data and aerial orthoimagery: Automatic computation of building photovoltaic capacity," *Autom Constr*, vol. 109, no. September 2019, p. 102965, 2020, doi: 10.1016/j.autcon.2019.102965.

[19] B. Tian, R. C. G. M. Loonen, R. Valckenborg, and J. L. M. Hensen, "A fully automated urban PV parameterization framework for improved estimation of energy production profiles," 2025. doi: https://doi.org/10.48550/arXiv.2505.19876.

[20] D. Lingfors, J. Bright, N. Engerer, J. Ahlberg, S. Killinger, and J. Widén, "Comparing the capability of low- and high-resolution LiDAR data with application to solar resource assessment, roof type classification and shading analysis," *Appl Energy*, vol. 205, no. June, pp. 1216–1230, 2017, doi: 10.1016/j.apenergy.2017.08.045.

[21] Sveriges Riksdag, *Svensk författningssamling — Förordning (2009:689) om statligt stöd till solceller*. Sweden, 2009.

[22] H. Rydehell, B. Lantz, I. Mignon, and J. Lindahl, "The impact of solar PV subsidies on investment over time — the case of Sweden," *Energy Econ*, vol. 133, no. April, p. 107552, 2024, doi: 10.1016/j.eneco.2024.107552.

[23] L. Molin, S. Ericson, D. Lingfors, J. Munkhammar, and J. Lindahl, "Validation of a PV generation model for simulation of wide area aggregated distributed PV power generation that takes individual systems location and orientation into account," in *40th European Photovoltaic Solar Energy Conference and Exhibition (EUPVSEC)*, 2023, pp. 020527–001. doi: http://dx.doi.org/10.4229/EUPVSEC2023/5DV.2.10.

[24] J. Lindahl, R. Johansson, and D. Lingfors, "Mapping of decentralised photovoltaic and solar thermal systems by remote sensing aerial imagery and deep machine learning for statistic generation," *Energy and AI*, vol. 14, p. 100300, 2023, doi: 10.1016/j.egyai.2023.100300.

[25] Â. Frimane, R. Johansson, J. Munkhammar, D. Lingfors, and J. Lindahl, "Identifying small decentralized solar systems in aerial images using deep learning," *Solar Energy*, vol. 262, 2023, doi: 10.1016/j.solener.2023.111822.

[26] U. H. Ramadhani, F. Johari, O. Lindberg, and J. Munkhammar, "A city-level assessment of residential PV hosting capacity for low-voltage distribution systems considering rooftop data and uncertainties," *Appl Energy*, vol. 371, no. February, p. 123715, 2024, doi: 10.1016/j.apenergy.2024.123715.

[27] E. Ekstrand and F. Hermodsson, "Assessing Rooftop Solar Energy Adoption — The remaining potential across market segments and the impact of socio-economic factors," Master Thesis, Uppsala University, 2024.

[28] W. J. Conover, *Practical Nonparametric Statistics*, Third Edit. New York: John Wiley & Sons, 1999.

[29] S. Liljeroth, "A techno-economic study of commercial and industrial PV systems in Sweden," Master Thesis, Uppsala University, 2025.

Comparing Approaches for Estimating Residential PV system Orientations

Johan Lindahl[a], Joakim Munkhammar[b], Gustav Öhgren[a]
[a]Becquerel Sweden AB, Sweden, johan@becquerelsweden.se
[b]Department of Civil and Industrial Engineering, Sweden, joakim.munkhammar@angstrom.uu.se

Introduction

Solar power is expanding rapidly, with PV now the dominant source of new global power capacity. However, integrating distributed PV into electricity grids requires accurate data on system orientation (tilt and azimuth), which strongly affects generation profiles but is rarely reported. To address this discrepancy, we compare three approaches for estimating PV orientations in Sweden against a manually created ground-truth dataset.

A Manually Created Ground-truth Dataset

To build a ground-truth dataset:

- Residential PV systems were identified using the Alfrödull remote sensing pipeline [1], applied to aerial orthophotos in three Swedish municipalities.
- Manual orientation measurements (see images) were used for validation, with an estimated measurement error of ±3° for both tilt and azimuth.
- Out of 4,817 detected PV polygons, only 104 had both matching subsidy applications that included tilt and azimuth values and suitable Google Street View coverage close to perpendicular to the polygon.

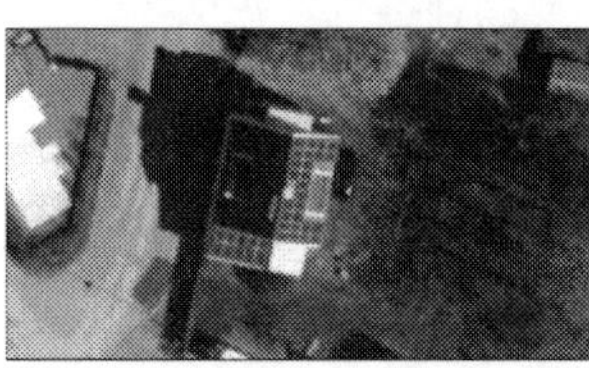

Orthophoto showing a single-family residential house with two distinct clusters of PV modules, each outlined by blue polygons. The dark red line indicates the azimuth measurement performed in QGIS for the polygon marked with a bright red cross. © Lantmäteriet, 2024.

Google Street View image taken approximately perpendicular to the PV polygon marked with a red cross in Figure 1. Image © Google, 2024. The overlay illustrates the online angle measurement tool and the manually derived tilt of the PV system.

(1) Data from the Swedish Capital Subsidy Program

Sweden's capital subsidy program for PV ran from 2009–2021:

- Applicants were required to provide project details, including rated capacity and location; tilt and azimuth could be entered optionally.
- Optional orientation values were entered manually in the application form and stored in the national database.
- The subsidy application form only allowed single azimuth and tilt values, causing errors for multi-cluster systems. Multi-polygon systems were classified into primary and secondary polygons, with the primary chosen as closest to the ground truth.

(2) The LiDAR Data and Linear Regression Method

Following Lingfors et al. [2], PV tilt and azimuth can be derived from LiDAR point cloud data:

- For most systems, LiDAR points allow reliable orientation estimates.
- When LiDAR data are insufficient, pre-defined rules are applied: fixed tilts and azimuth aligned with the polygon's southernmost long edge are used for ground-mounted, flat-roof, vertical, or misaligned PV systems.

Orthophoto showing a single-family residential house with two distinct clusters of PV modules. © Lantmäteriet, 2024. Building footprint polygons are outlined in yellow, and the two PV polygons are shown in red.

LiDAR point clouds corresponding to the two buildings. Points within the building footprint polygons are shown in yellow, while points within the PV system polygons (in red) are shown in dark blue and framed in dark blue rectangle to illustrate the final derived orientation.

(3) The Statistical Model Based on PV Penetration

The Ramadhani et al. model [3]:

- Predicts PV tilt and azimuth based on penetration level, defined as the number of residential PV systems divided by the total number of residential buildings.
- The model assumes PV is installed on "best" roofs first, i.e., those with highest annual solar yield.
- The model was tested in three municipalities — Knivsta, Uppvidinge, and Falun — where residential PV penetration levels were 3.75% (2023), 2.31% (2022), and 2.32% (2020), respectively.

Results

The LiDAR-based method demonstrated substantially higher accuracy than the self-reported subsidy database in estimating both tilt and azimuth. For tilt, the LiDAR-based method achieved an R^2 of 0.82 with a mean absolute error (MAE) of 1.49° and a root mean square error (RMSE) of 3.91°, compared to the database values of 0.30, 4.21°, and 7.67°, respectively. For azimuth, the LiDAR demonstrated an accuracy of R^2 of 0.96, MAE of 2.17°, and RMSE of 10.82°, whereas the database values were at 0.06, 31.38°, and 52.55°.

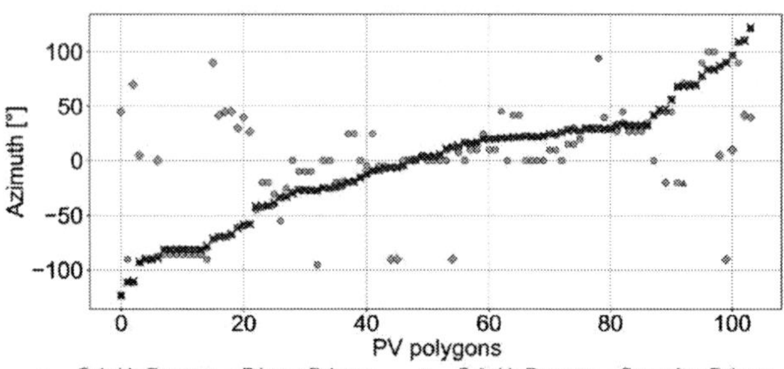

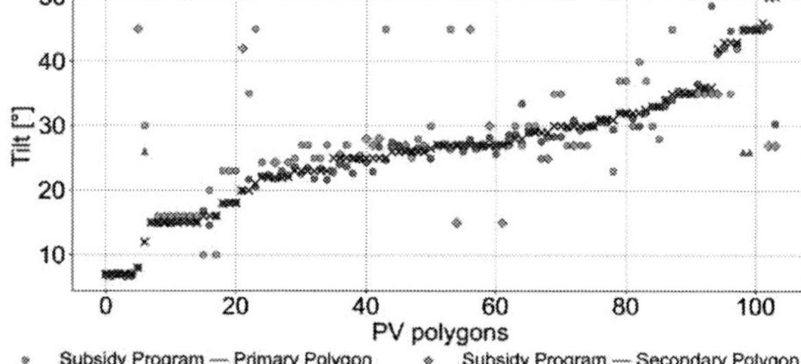

Distribution of azimuth and tilt angles derived from the Swedish capital subsidy database and the LiDAR-based method, compared with manually created ground truth.

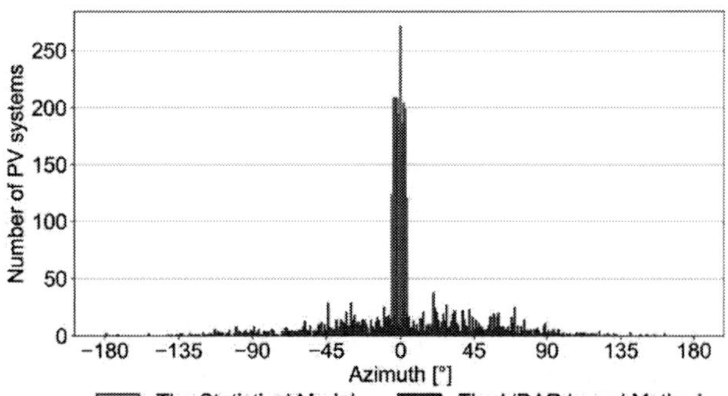

Azimuth distribution for 1922 residential PV systems in three Swedish municipalities, from the Ramadhani et al. statistical model [3] (based on PV penetration levels) and the Lingfors et al. method [2] (derived from LiDAR data).

Conclusions

This study compared three approaches for determining residential PV system orientations in Sweden.

- <u>Self-reported data</u> were found to be highly unreliable due to:
  - Only one azimuth respective tilt entry allowed per system, which fails for multi-cluster PV installations.
  - Inconsistent azimuth conventions where 0° was interpreted as either North or South by applicants.
  - Additional errors from imprecise applicant estimates of their roof orientation.
- <u>The statistical model</u>, which assumes PV systems are installed on the "best" roofs first, produced a much narrower azimuth distribution than what is observed in reality.
- <u>The LiDAR-based method</u> showed strong agreement with the manually derived ground truth, achieving high accuracy for both azimuth and tilt.

This study demonstrates that the LiDAR-based method developed in [2] is a robust, scalable, and reliable approach for obtaining PV system-level orientation data.

References:
[1] L. Molin, B. Ericson, D. Lingfors, J. Munkhammar, and J. Lindahl, "Validation of a PV generation model for simulation of wide area aggregated distributed PV power … actual systems location and orientation into account," in 40th European Photovoltaic Solar Energy Conference and Exhibition (EUPVSEC), 2023, pp. 020527–001.
[2] D. Lingfors, R. Johansson, and J. Lindahl, "Deriving the orientation of existing solar energy systems from LiDAR data at scale," Solar Energy, vol. 291, no. 113344, 2025.
[3] U. H. Ramadhani, D. Lingfors, J. Munkhammar, and J. Widén, "On the properties of residential rooftop azimuth and tilt uncertainties for photovoltaic power generation modeling and hosting capacity analysis," Solar Energy Advances, vol. 3, no. February, p. 100036, 2023.

ADVANCED ENERGY MANAGEMENT SYSTEM FOR SOLAR-PLUS-STORAGE SYSTEMS

Marangis Demetris[1], Herodotou Panayiotis[1], Livera Andreas[1], Makrides George[1], Georghiou George E.[1]
University of Cyprus, 2109 Nicosia, Cyprus
[1]PHAETHON Centre of Excellence for Intelligent, Efficient and Sustainable Energy Solutions,
2109 Nicosia, Cyprus
*Corresponding authors: Demetris Marangis (marangis.demetris@ucy.ac.cy)

ABSTRACT: A major challenge in the energy transition is the effective integration of renewable energy sources into the electrical grid, while optimizing power flow and reducing costs through advanced energy management system (EMS) controllers. Although recent advancements have improved EMS controllers, significant gaps remain in their validation under dynamic conditions, such as fluctuating loads and storage constraints. This study addresses these challenges by developing an optimized controller using linear programming, that minimizes costs and optimizes power flow among the grid, photovoltaic (PV) modules and battery storage. The proposed model utilizes historical load data from the University of Cyprus nanogrid, which features a 40 kWp PV system and a 50-kWh battery, and is benchmarked against a reference rule-based controller across various prediction horizons and operational scenarios. The results demonstrated that the advanced controller consistently reduces grid dependence and operational expenses, with the day ahead prediction horizon yielding mean daily savings of €6.90/kWh. Furthermore, in scenarios with sudden drops in PV output (such as during curtailment events), the advanced controller achieved cost savings of up to €24.04/kWh compared to the rule-based alternative, demonstrating its superior performance.
Keywords: controller, energy management system, energy storage, optimization, photovoltaic.

1 INTRODUCTION

Reducing dependence on fossil fuels is crucial for addressing global warming. Transitioning to renewable energy sources (RES), such as photovoltaic (PV) systems, provides a sustainable solution and is vital for building a greener future. RES promote a more decentralized approach to electricity generation, play a key role in reducing greenhouse gas emissions, and help mitigate the environmental impacts associated with conventional energy production [1].

Integrating a high share of RES into the energy mix presents significant challenges due to their intermittent and unpredictable nature. These technical obstacles can adversely affect the reliability and power quality of the utility grid [2], [3]. Moreover, the daily and seasonal variability of PV power generation leads to pronounced imbalances between energy supply and demand, increasing overall grid instability [4]. Consequently, the introduction of energy storage technologies is crucial for maintaining a consistent supply of renewable energy and for bridging the gap between fluctuating demand and supply. Integrating battery energy storage systems (BESS) provides an effective means of enhancing the stability, reliability, and flexibility of the utility grid [5], [6]. Specifically, combining BESS with PV systems allows surplus energy to be stored for later use during periods of low solar generation (e.g., evenings or cloudy days). This integration not only helps to smooth out fluctuations in power output but also supports grid stability and increases the overall share of renewable energy within grid networks [7], [8].

To optimize the integration of PV and storage systems within modern grid networks, the development and deployment of advanced Energy Management System (EMS) controllers are crucial. These sophisticated EMS controllers enable the creation of optimal charging and discharging schedules for BESS, thereby increasing the utilization of renewable energy through demand-side management while simultaneously reducing operational costs [9], [10].

Researchers have explored numerous EMS strategies, including load shifting, integrating energy storage for peak shaving, and applying advanced algorithms such as genetic algorithms, Extreme Learning Machine (ELM), k-means clustering, and Support Vector Regression (SVR) to reduce costs [8,9]. In this domain, Babu et al. [11] employed a multi-objective genetic algorithm, that utilized forecasted solar PV and wind generation data, to optimize grid and battery power usage in a 2.5 MW microgrid. This method enabled efficient renewable energy integration and economically optimal operation under both fixed and dynamic tariff conditions. Similarly, in [12], an EMS controller based on the modified grey wolf optimizer was developed for PV-based microgrids, achieving cost reductions of 23.34% on sunny days and 45.55% on cloudy days compared to a mixed linear programming approach.

Although advanced EMS controllers have already been developed, they often lack validation under dynamic optimization conditions that consider storage constraints, fluctuating load demands, and variable electricity pricing. Addressing this gap is a critical industrial requirement, particularly for nanogrid and microgrid operations, where analyzing historical load data across various seasons is essential. The proposed work tackles this challenge by developing an advanced EMS controller based on the revised simplex method (i.e., a linear programming algorithm). The proposed solution enhances grid flexibility by promoting cost-effective strategies for renewable integration and optimizing battery operation. The controller considers various parameters and constraints, including dynamic grid pricing, varying load demands, and upper and lower limits on the battery's state of charge (SOC).

2 METHODOLOGY

The approach followed to design the EMS controllers consisted of the following steps: (a) experimental setup and data acquisition (b) development of the rule-based and advanced EMS controllers (c) development of forecasting algorithms, (d) performance evaluation and validation of EMS controllers and (e) test scenarios.

2.1 Experimental setup and data acquisition

The first step included the acquisition of load data from the nanogrid of the University of Cyprus. Historical load data (at hourly intervals) were collected over a yearly period (01/06/2019-01/06/2020). During this evaluation period, the average hourly load was 14.3 kWh, with a peak load of 105.11 kWh. The nanogrid included a 40 kWp PV system and a battery with a usable capacity of 50 kWh. Dynamic time-of-use electricity prices were incorporated to simulate realistic fluctuations in energy costs. These prices were based on Cyprus's electricity tariffs [13], and were adjusted to reflect current rates. Extremely high load data were identified from 29/04/2020 to 01/06/2020, which were not representative of the seasonal behavior of the nanogrid, and were excluded from the analysis.

2.2 Development of the rule-based and advanced EMS controllers

The two controllers were developed during this stage: a rule-based controller and an advanced EMS controller. The rule-based controller operates as a state machine, using predefined rules to manage the battery's charging and discharging behavior. When PV production exceeds load demand, the surplus energy is used to charge the battery. During peak demand periods in the evening, the battery discharges stored energy to supply the load.

The advanced EMS controller is designed to optimize power flow among the grid, the PV system, and the battery, with the objective of minimizing costs using a linear programming-based algorithm, known as the revised simplex method [14]. This method is chosen for its efficiency and robustness in solving large-scale linear programming problems, which align well with the mathematical formulations of EMS. Its reliable convergence and computational efficiency make it a widely adopted approach in energy system optimization applications [15], [16].

PV system, load, and battery data were used as inputs to the model. The optimization problem is described below (Eq. 1):

$$\min \sum_{t=1}^{N} C_{grid,t} \times P_{grid,t} \tag{1}$$

where $C_{grid,t}$ represents the electricity price at a given time t, N denotes the total number of hourly intervals in a day, $P_{grid,t}$ is the energy drawn from the grid at time t, occurring when the combined supply from the PV system and the battery is insufficient to meet the demand.

Various constraints were used to control the state of charge (SOC) limits, as well as the battery's discharging rate and power flow from the grid ($P_{grid,t}$, $P_{curtail,t}$). Specifically, the battery's lower and upper SOC limits were set at 20% and 100%, respectively, to prolong battery lifespan and improve grid frequency regulation [17], [18]. A round-trip efficiency of 96% was assumed, accounting for typical conversion and charging losses that usually range between 1% and 5% per cycle. The complete set of equations defining these constraints for the optimization problem is provided below (Eq. 2-7).

$$C_{bat} \geq SOC_t \geq 0.2 \times C_{bat} \tag{2}$$
$$P_{max\ charge} \geq P_{bat,t} \geq -P_{max\ discharge} \tag{3}$$
$$SOC_t = SOC_{t-1} + \eta_{bat} \times P_{bat,t} \tag{4}$$
$$P_{load,t} - P_{PV,t} + P_{bat,t} = P_{grid,t} + P_{curtail,t} \tag{5}$$
$$P_{grid,t} \geq 0 \tag{6}$$
$$0 \leq P_{curtail,t} \leq P_{PV,t} \tag{7}$$

where $P_{curtail,t}$ represents the surplus energy fed back into the grid at time t in times of excess supply, C_{bat} is the maximum battery capacity, SOC_t and SOC_{t-1} is the state

of charge of the battery at time t and t-1 respectively, $P_{max\ charge}$ and $P_{max\ discharge}$ represent the maximum charging and discharging power that can be drawn from the battery at each time t (in this case it is 25 kWh), $P_{bat,t}$ represents the power flow from the battery (positive is discharging, negative is charging), η_{bat} is the charging and discharging efficiency, $P_{load,t}$ is the load power at time t, and P_{PV} is the PV generated power at time t.

The algorithm iteratively updates the parameters until the objective function converges to a value within a minimum tolerance close to zero. The optimization variable is the battery power flow (i.e., $P_{bat,t}$), which represents the rate of charging or discharging of the battery at each time step. The developed EMS controller adjusts this variable to determine the optimal daily charging and discharging schedule, with the goal of minimizing the total electricity cost.

2.3 Development of forecasting algorithms

To simulate real-life applications, PV generation and load were forecasted using machine learning algorithms. In this paper, the extreme Gradient Boosting method (XGBoost) [19] method and the linear regression (LR) [20] were employed, both of which have demonstrated high accuracy in forecasting tasks [21], [22]. Each algorithm was applied to forecast PV generation and load over different prediction horizons (i.e., 2, 12 and 24 hours ahead corresponding to forecasts at time t+2, t+12 and t+24). For each horizon and forecast data (PV or load), the better-performing algorithm was selected as input for the advanced EMS controller.

The forecasting algorithms used as inputs the PV and load data from one week and one day prior to the current measurement, as well as the most recent measurement (at time t) before the forecast. The dataset was divided into 70% for training (01/06/2019-19/01/2020) and 30% for testing (20/01/2020-29/04/2020).

2.4 Performance evaluation and validation of EMS controllers

The accuracy of the forecasting algorithms across different test cases was evaluated using the normalized Root Mean Square Error (nRMSE). For PV forecasting, the error was normalized by the nominal capacity of the PV plant (i.e., 40 kWp), while for load forecasting, normalization was based on the maximum hourly load value of 105 kWh. The formula for the nRMSE metric can be found in [23].

The performance of the optimization model was also benchmarked against the rule-based controller using the daily energy cost and daily cost savings as evaluation metrics. Eq. 8-9 below detail the calculations used for each metric.

$$Daily\ energy\ cost = \frac{\sum_{t=1}^{N} E_{grid,hour} \times C_{grid,t}}{\sum_{t=1}^{N} E_{load,hour}} \tag{8}$$

$$Daily\ cost\ savings = \frac{C_{O,day} - C_{RB,day}}{\sum_{t=1}^{N} E_{load,hour}} \tag{9}$$

where $E_{grid,hour}$ is the hourly energy imported by the grid, N is the number of hours in each day (i.e., 24), $E_{load,hour}$ is the hourly energy demanded by the microgrid, $C_{O,day}$ and $C_{RB,day}$ represent the daily price costs of the advanced EMS controller and the rule-based controller.

2.5 Test scenarios

Two different test scenarios were considered in this study. The first scenario simulated real-life applications and it included the optimization of the EMS controller using forecasted data and the tuning of the rule-based controller using actual data. The assessment was conducted over the test set period.

In the second scenario, a curtailment event was introduced during midday hours (12:00 to 14:00) on a randomly selected day in each of the four seasons (spring, summer, autumn, and winter). In this scenario, the developed controller was optimized based on data that did not include the curtailment event, in contrast with the reference rule-based controller, which accounted for this event. This scenario was designed to assess the algorithm's effectiveness in responding to unforeseen curtailment events and to evaluate its robustness in managing sudden fluctuations in PV generation.

For each scenario, the effectiveness of the EMS controllers was evaluated across various prediction horizons: (i) 2 hours ahead, (ii) 12 hours ahead, and (iii) 24 hours ahead – day ahead. The different prediction horizons were used to further optimize and evaluate the ability of the advanced EMS controller to reduce operational costs.

3   RESULTS

3.1 Accuracy of forecasting algorithms

The PV generation forecasting algorithms were developed using a sequential 70:30% train and test set approach. Both algorithms (i.e., the XGBoost and LR) were employed to forecast PV generation 2, 12 and 24 hours ahead and the results are summarized in Fig. 1. The XGBoost algorithm achieved the lowest error of 8.93% at 2 hours ahead prediction horizon, compared to 9.71% achieved by the LR. In contrast, the LR outperformed slightly the XGBoost algorithm when forecasting 12 hours and day ahead.

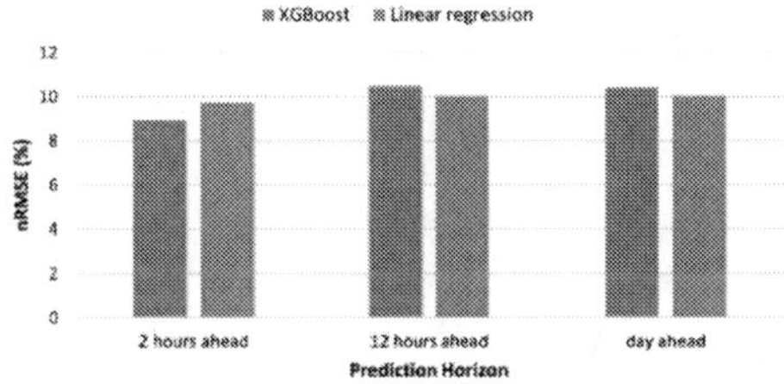

Figure 1: Test set nRMSE values achieved by the XGBoost and LR for PV generation forecasting.

Fig. 2 shows the results obtained by the XGBoost and LR for load forecasting across the different prediction horizons. The XGBoost outperformed LR for 2 and 12 hours ahead prediction horizons, while the LR has shown better accuracy for the day ahead prediction horizon.

It is worth noting that the accuracy of both models decreased when forecasting longer prediction horizons. In addition, both algorithms have consistently shown low forecast errors across all prediction horizons, indicating their robustness and suitability for forecasting applications.

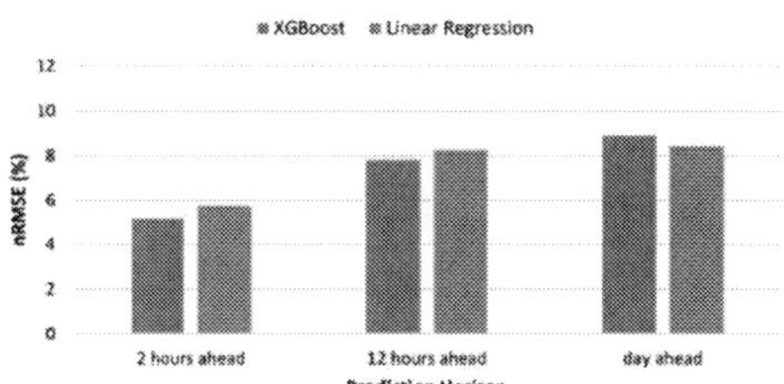

Figure 2: Test set nRMSE values achieved by the XGBoost and LR for load forecasting.

Overall, the XGBoost algorithm demonstrated superior accuracy for 2 hours ahead forecasts, while for day ahead forecasts, the LR method yielded better accuracy (see Table I). Therefore, a combination of both algorithms is proposed to achieve the lowest forecasting error.

Table I: Best performing algorithm for each prediction horizon and forecast data.

Prediction horizon	PV	Load
2 hours ahead	XGBoost	XGBoost
12 hours ahead	LR	XGBoost
day ahead	LR	LR

3.2 Scenario 1 – Real-life conditions

The first scenario simulated real-life applications and it included the optimization of the EMS controller using forecasted data and the tuning of the rule-based controller using actual data.

The performance of the EMS controllers was evaluated based on the mean daily energy cost over the test set period, with the results across different prediction horizons illustrated in Fig. 3. The advanced EMS controller with the day ahead prediction horizon achieved the best performance, yielding a mean daily energy cost of €41.28/kWh. This corresponds to a cost reduction of €6.90/kWh compared to the rule-based controller, which achieved a mean daily energy cost of €48.18/kWh. In contrast, the advanced EMS controller was less cost effective at shorter prediction horizons; for the 2 hours horizons, the mean daily energy costs increased to €94.74/kWh, while at the 12 hours ahead horizon, it rose to €54.44/kWh.

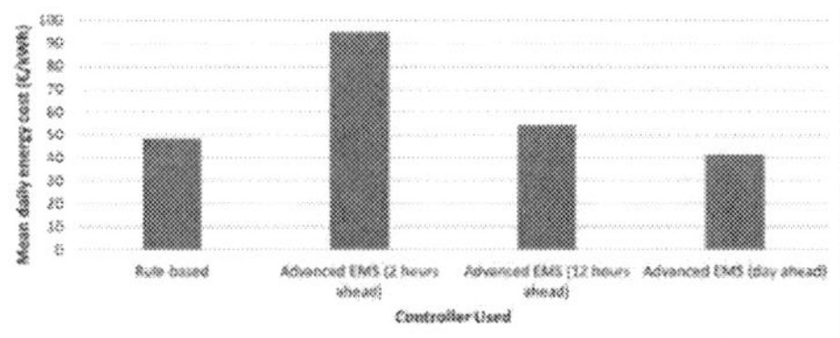

Figure 3: Mean daily energy cost achieved by rule-based and advanced EMS controllers.

To further analyze the controllers' behavior, Fig. 4 presents the comparison of power flows and the battery's SOC over a day ahead prediction horizon. The results show that the advanced EMS controller effectively manages the battery SOC, allowing for nearly autonomous operation with no grid imports during the observed day.

This strategy maximizes cost savings and reduces dependence on the grid. In contrast, the rule-based controller charged the battery during high-price periods and utilized the PV generated power less efficiently, leading to higher grid costs.

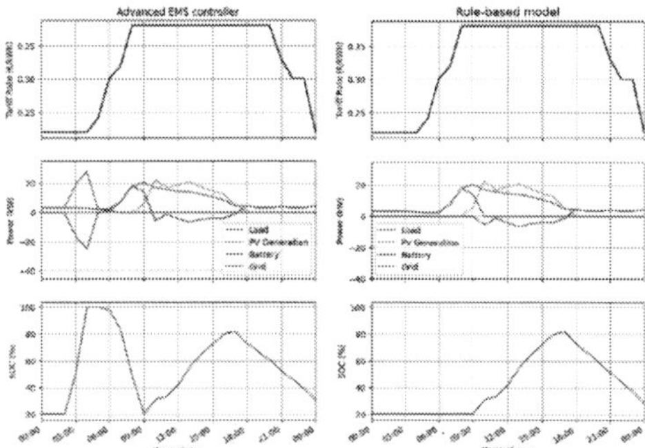

Figure 4: Hourly tariff rates (top), power flow between load, PV, battery and grid (middle) and SOC of the battery during a day for the rule-based (right) and advanced EMS controllers (left).

Fig. 5 illustrates the daily energy costs (€/kWh) achieved by the rule-based controller (orange) and the advanced EMS controller (blue) over the test set period. The advanced EMS controller consistently yields lower daily energy costs compared to the rule-based controller. The cost difference between the two controllers is most pronounced during periods of high load and relatively low PV production (i.e., December - February). During such periods, the advanced EMS controller achieved significant savings when compared to the rule-based controller. Conversely, the difference was noticeably smaller in March and April, when the PV generation was significantly higher than the load demand. The results indicate that in cases of positive net load (PV > load), both the advanced EMS controller and rule-based controller performed relatively well, whereas in cases of negative net load (PV < load), the advanced EMS controller outperforms the rule-based controller.

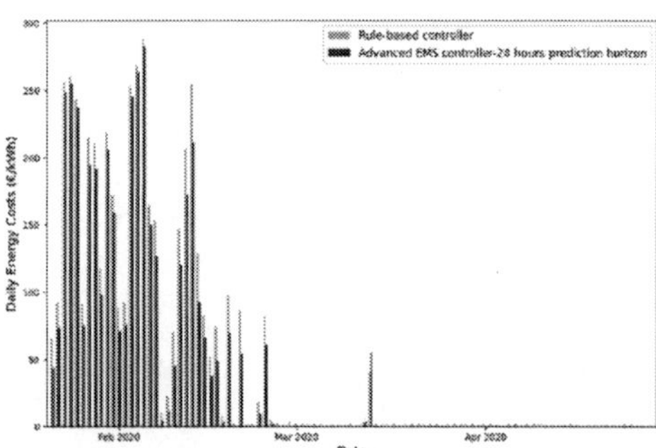

Figure 5: Daily energy costs of the rule-based controller (orange) and advanced EMS controller (blue) over test set period.

Fig. 6 presents the daily energy cost savings (€/kWh) achieved by the advanced EMS controller relative to a rule-based controller over the test set period. The mean daily savings were €6.90/kWh, highlighting the substantial cost efficiency improvement delivered by the advanced EMS controller. The most significant cost reductions were observed in mid-February, with daily energy cost savings reaching up to €45/kWh. Notably, the advanced EMS controller demonstrated significant savings under high demand conditions (e.g., January and February), whereas less savings were observed during low demand conditions (e.g., March and April). This adaptability underscores its potential to enhance operational performance and reduce costs in demand-intensive environments, such as the University of Cyprus nanogrid.

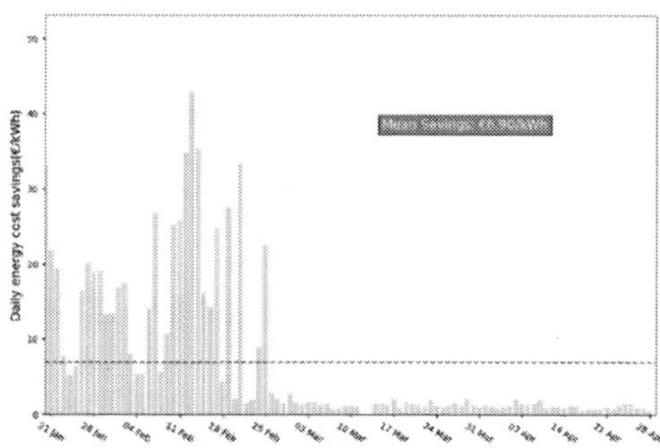

Figure 6: Daily energy cost savings achieved by the advanced EMS controller when compared to the rule-based model over the yearly period.

3.3 Scenario 2 – Curtailment event

In this scenario, a curtailment event was introduced during midday hours (12:00 to 14:00) on a randomly selected day in each of the four seasons (spring, summer, autumn, and winter). Fig. 7 illustrates the daily energy cost savings achieved by both the rule-based and advanced EMS controllers across various prediction horizons and different seasons, during an unexpected curtailment event.

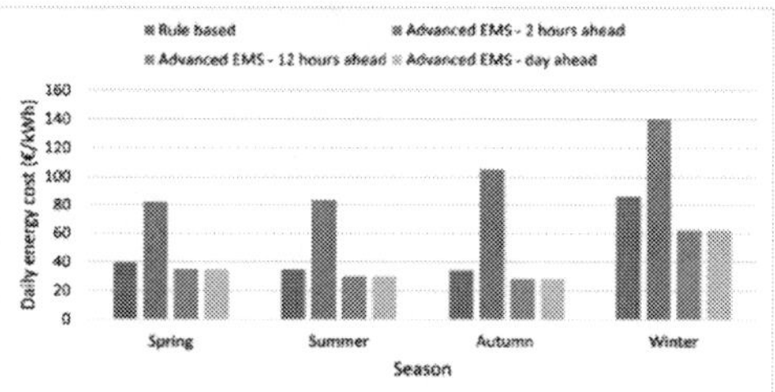

Figure 7: Daily energy cost of the two controllers over the four seasons and across various prediction horizons during a random curtailment event.

The results highlight clear differences in performance and cost efficiency between the two controllers. Specifically, the advanced EMS controller with 2 hours ahead prediction horizon showed limited robustness to abrupt changes in PV output, leading to higher daily energy costs ranging from €82/kWh to €140/kWh. In contrast, the advanced EMS controller for 12 and 24 hours ahead exhibited greater resilience, delivering superior performance (daily energy costs ranging from €28.51/kWh to €62.21/kWh). Finally, the rule-based controller achieved significant lower costs when compared to the 2 hours ahead horizon. The 12 hours ahead and day ahead prediction horizon achieved equal daily energy cost savings between €4.75/kWh and €24.04/kWh. The seasonal analysis showed that the highest savings occurred in winter, which is characterized by high energy demand and low PV generation.

Overall, the 12 hours and day ahead prediction horizons consistently provided the most reliable and cost-effective results across all seasons, highlighting the developed EMS controller's capability to balance forecast accuracy with operational flexibility. In contrast, the advanced EMS controller with the 2 hours ahead prediction horizon limited adaptability to sudden PV output fluctuations significantly undermined its performance.

4 CONCLUSION

To increase the share of RES in the grid, it is essential to integrate EMS controllers to optimize power flow between systems, reduce costs, and enhance overall system reliability. Despite recent advancements in EMS development, a major challenge remains the lack of validation of these algorithms' robustness under dynamic conditions, including storage limitations, fluctuating load demand, and variable electricity pricing.

In this paper, an advanced EMS controller based on linear programming was developed and evaluated using various prediction horizons and across different seasons. Additionally, the controller's robustness was tested in scenarios involving unexpected curtailment events. Its performance was also compared against a rule-based controller. Both controllers were tested using historical data from the University of Cyprus nanogrid system, incorporating a 40 kWp PV plant and a 50 kWh battery.

The results demonstrated that the advanced EMS controller with the day ahead prediction horizon effectively manages power flows, particularly during periods of high energy demand, reducing reliance on the grid and achieving mean cost savings of €6.90/kWh. When curtailment events were introduced, the 12 hours and day ahead prediction horizons achieved the best performance, with cost savings ranging from €4.75/kWh to €24.04/kWh.

Future work will focus on comparing the proposed approach with other optimization algorithms, improving the accuracy and robustness of forecasting models, and conducting further benchmarking in commercial and industrial settings to evaluate the generalizability and performance of the EMS controller.

5 ACKNOWLEDGMENTS

This work was funded by the EMS4PVBEV project. The EMS4PVBEV project is financed by the Recovery and Resilience Facility of the NextGenerationEU instrument through the Cyprus Research and Innovation Foundation (ENTERPRISES/ENERGY/1123/0011).

6 REFERENCES

[1] M. Adham, S. Keene, and R. B. Bass, "Distributed Energy Resources: A Systematic Literature Review," Energy Reports, vol. 13, pp. 1980–1999, 2025, doi: 10.1016/j.egyr.2025.01.026.

[2] A. Q. Al-Shetwi, M. A. Hannan, K. P. Jern, M. Mansur, and T. M. I. Mahlia, "Grid-connected renewable energy sources: Review of the recent integration requirements and control methods," J Clean Prod, vol. 253, p. 119831, 2020,

doi: 10.1016/j.jclepro.2019.119831.

[3] H. Jafarizadeh, E. Yamini, S. M. Zolfaghari, F. Esmaeilion, M. E. H. Assad, and M. Soltani, "Navigating challenges in large-scale renewable energy storage: Barriers, solutions, and innovations," Energy Reports, vol. 12, pp. 2179–2192, 2024, doi: 10.1016/j.egyr.2024.08.019.

[4] S. D. Ahmed, F. S. M. Al-Ismail, M. Shafiullah, F. A. Al-Sulaiman, and I. M. El-Amin, "Grid integration challenges of wind energy: A review," Ieee Access, vol. 8, pp. 10857–10878, 2020, doi: 10.1109/ACCESS.2020.2964896.

[5] A. H. Nebey, "Recent advancement in demand side energy management system for optimal energy utilization," Energy Reports, vol. 11, pp. 5422–5435, 2024, doi: 10.1016/j.egyr.2024.05.028.

[6] A. Azarhooshang, D. Sedighizadeh, and M. Sedighizadeh, "Two-stage stochastic operation considering day-ahead and real-time scheduling of microgrids with high renewable energy sources and electric vehicles based on multi-layer energy management system," Electric Power Systems Research, vol. 201, p. 107527, 2021, doi: 10.1016/j.epsr.2021.107527.

[7] M. Hasan and H. Serra Altinoluk, "Current and future prospective for battery controllers of solar PV integrated battery energy storage systems," Front Energy Res, vol. 11, p. 1139255, 2023, doi: 10.3389/fenrg.2023.1139255.

[8] A. Jain and S. Bhullar, "Design and performance analysis of solar PV-battery energy storage system integration with three-phase grid," J Power Sources, vol. 640, p. 236486, 2025, doi: 10.1016/j.jpowsour.2025.236486.

[9] M. Darwish, S. Ioannou, A. Janbey, H. Amreiz, and C. C. Marouchos, "Review of battery management systems," in 2021 International Conference on Electrical, Computer, Communications and Mechatronics Engineering (ICECCME), IEEE, 2021, pp. 1–6. doi: 10.1109/ICECCME52200.2021.9590884.

[10] H. Abouobaida, L. de Oliveira-Assis, E. P. P. Soares-Ramos, H. Mahmoudi, J. M. Guerrero, and M. Jamil, "Energy management and control strategy of DC microgrid based hybrid storage system," Simul Model Pract Theory, vol. 124, p. 102726, 2023, doi: 10.1016/j.simpat.2023.102726.

[11] V. V. Babu, J. P. Roselyn, and P. Sundaravadivel, "Multi-objective genetic algorithm based energy management system considering optimal utilization of grid and degradation of battery storage in microgrid," Energy Reports, vol. 9, pp. 5992–6005, 2023, doi: 10.1016/j.egyr.2023.05.067.

[12] A. Kumar, M. Alaraj, M. Rizwan, and U. Nangia, "Novel AI based energy management system for smart grid with RES integration," IEEE Access, vol. 9, pp. 162530–162542, 2021, doi: 10.1109/ACCESS.2021.3131502.

[13] V. Venizelou, G. Makrides, V. Efthymiou, and G. E. Georghiou, "Residential consumption responsiveness under time-varying pricing," in 2018 IEEE International Energy Conference (ENERGYCON), IEEE, 2018, pp. 1–6. doi: 10.1109/ENERGYCON.2018.8398735.

[14] Q. Huangfu and J. A. J. Hall, "Novel update techniques for the revised simplex method," Comput Optim Appl, vol. 60, no. 3, pp. 587–608, 2015, doi: 10.1007/s10589-014-9689-1.

[15] M. Mohammadi, Y. Noorollahi, B. Mohammadi-ivatloo, M. Hosseinzadeh, H. Yousefi, and S. T. Khorasani, "Optimal management of energy hubs and smart energy hubs A review," Renewable and Sustainable Energy Reviews, vol. 89, pp. 33–50, 2018, doi:

10.1016/j.rser.2018.02.035.

[16] L. Olatomiwa, S. Mekhilef, M. S. Ismail, and M. Moghavvemi, "Energy management strategies in hybrid renewable energy systems: A review," Renewable and Sustainable Energy Reviews, vol. 62, pp. 821–835, 2016, doi: 10.1016/j.rser.2016.05.040.

[17] S.-M. Cho, J.-C. Kim, and S.-Y. Yun, "Optimum State-of-Charge Operating Range for Frequency Regulation of Energy Storage Systems Using a Master–Slave Parallel Genetic Algorithm," Electronics (Basel), vol. 9, no. 8, p. 1298, 2020, doi: 10.3390/electronics9081298.

[18] M. Darwish, S. Ioannou, A. Janbey, H. Amreiz, and C. C. Marouchos, "Review of battery management systems," in 2021 International Conference on Electrical, Computer, Communications and Mechatronics Engineering (ICECCME), IEEE, 2021, pp. 1–6. doi: 10.1109/ICECCME52200.2021.9590884.

[19] T. Chen and C. Guestrin, "Xgboost: A scalable tree boosting system," in Proceedings of the 22nd acm sigkdd international conference on knowledge discovery and data mining, 2016, pp. 785–794. doi: 10.1016/j.eswa.2025.129449.

[20] G. James, D. Witten, T. Hastie, R. Tibshirani, and J. Taylor, "Linear regression," in An introduction to statistical learning: With applications in python, Springer, 2023, pp. 69–134. doi: 10.1007/978-1-0716-1418-1_3.

[21] D.-J. Bae, B.-S. Kwon, and K.-B. Song, "XGBoost-based day-ahead load forecasting algorithm considering behind-the-meter solar PV generation," Energies (Basel), vol. 15, no. 1, p. 128, 2021, doi: 10.3390/en15010128.

[22] M. AlShafeey and C. Csáki, "Evaluating neural network and linear regression photovoltaic power forecasting models based on different input methods," Energy Reports, vol. 7, pp. 7601–7614, 2021, doi: 10.1016/j.egyr.2021.10.125.

[23] S. Theocharides, G. Makrides, G. E. Georghiou, and A. Kyprianou, "Machine learning algorithms for photovoltaic system power output prediction," in 2018 IEEE International Energy Conference (ENERGYCON), 2018, pp. 1–6. doi: 10.1109/ENERGYCON.2018.8398737.

AN OPEN VIRTUAL POWER PLANT FOR RENEWABLE ENERGY COMMUNITIES - STRATEGIES FOR CENTRALIZED BATTERIES

Rita Hogan Almeida, Luis Miguel Carrasco, Javier Ramírez Ledesma, Javier Martín Rueda, Ana Belén Cristóbal, Laura Palomino, Kiane Alves e Silva, Luis Narvarte
Instituto de Energía Solar, Universidad Politécnica de Madrid, Spain
rita.hogan@upm.es

ABSTRACT: An open Virtual Power Plant designed for rural Renewable Energy Communities (REC) is presented, considering centralized batteries associated with photovoltaic (PV) generators. To evaluate different possibilities of battery allocation among self-consumers, three strategies have been considered: i) priority-based distribution, ii) fixed proportional distribution, and iii) variable proportional distribution. The model has been applied to a real REC located in the Calatayud Region (Spain), composed of 22 end-users. Results show that the variable proportional distribution achieves the best performance in terms of self-consumption and self-sufficiency, while the priority-based distribution presents the lowest indicators. The analysis confirms the relevance of centralized batteries to increase local use of solar and stored energy, although some strategies are not possible under current legislation.
Keywords: Energy Communities, Photovoltaics, Storage, Virtual Power Plants

1 INTRODUCTION

A virtual power plant (VPP) combines distributed energy resources (DER) with advance management systems to, for example, balance generation and consumption [1]. A renewable energy community (REC) consists of end-users (individuals, households, businesses, local authorities) that collaborate to generate and manage renewable energy, typically using self-consumption photovoltaic (PV) systems sized based on self-consumption rate (SCR) and self-sufficiency rate (SSR) [2]. Merging VPP and REC means building a VPP that integrates DER, end-users and advance management systems to control electricity generation and consumption.

In the current state-of-the-art, there are a huge variety of VPPs [3], but there is no specialized version for REC. Accordingly, we are developing an open VPP tailored specifically for rural and distributed REC, using existing components to interoperate with inverters, batteries and manageable devices, developing data management systems and specialized local optimization algorithms, as well as different strategies (algorithms to maximize SCR and SSR and local energy resilience).

Particularly, this paper describes three preliminary strategies for centralized batteries associated with PV generators for collective self-consumption: i) priority-based distribution, supplying energy by predefined sequence; ii) fixed proportional distribution, based on total fixed shares; and iii) variable proportional distribution, based on hourly consumption shares.

In the priority-based distribution, end-users are ranked according to a predetermined priority order; in the fixed proportional distribution, all end-users are assigned a fixed percentage of available energy; and in the variable proportional distribution the allocation of available energy is done on an hourly basis according to the end-users' demand profiles.

In the three strategies, the final objective of the model is to know the use of energy from the PV plant and the centralized battery to reduce costs and enhance the use of solar and stored energy, while minimizing surpluses that go outside the self-consumer network.

The model is then applied to a case-study: a small village in Calatayud Region, Spain

2 MODEL AND STRATEGIES DESCRIPTION

This section provides a detailed overview of the strategies, beginning with the main inputs and outputs, followed by an in-depth explanation of the three distinct strategies.

2.1 Inputs
The model considers the following inputs:
- PV peak power
- Hourly PV production (8760 values)
- Hourly consumption for each end-user (8760 values per user)
- Battery storage capacity
- Minimum depth of discharge
- Maximum depth of charge

2.2 Outputs
The following hourly outputs are obtained:
- PV energy consumed directly by end-users (E_{PV})
- PV energy used to charge the battery (E_{bat})
- Battery state of charge
- Unmet energy demand (this is, energy not covered by PV or battery)

By summing the previous values, monthly and annual values are used to better understand the VPP network performance. In addition to the aggregated data, the following annual values are calculated:
- Self-consumption rate (SCR)
- Self-sufficiency rate (SSR)

The SCR reflects the proportion of PV-generated energy that is directly consumed by the load or through stored energy, as opposed to being exported to the grid. Similarly, the SSR measures the extent to which the total energy demand is met by self-generated energy from the PV and storage systems. These metrics are defined as follows [4]:

$$SCR = \frac{E_{PV} + E_{bat}}{E_{PV_available}} \cdot 100 \quad [\%] \qquad (1)$$

10.4229/EUPVSEC2025/5DV.3.9

$$SSR = \frac{E_{PV} + E_{bat}}{E_{load}} \cdot 100 \quad [\%] \qquad (2)$$

where E_{PV} and E_{bat} correspond to the self-consumed energy from PV and battery, respectively, $E_{PV_available}$ is the available PV energy and E_{load} refers to the total energy demand of all self-consumers.

A high SCR indicates efficient local energy use, minimizing reliance on grid exports. A higher SSR indicates greater self-sufficiency, reducing the system's dependence on the grid.

2.3 Scenarios

Three allocation scenarios are considered (a detailed explanation is presented in the next sections):

- **Priority-based distribution:** PV and battery-stored energies are supplied to end-users according to a predefined sequence of priority.
- **Fixed proportional distribution:** PV energy and battery-stored energy are allocated based on each end-user's predetermined share of total energy usage.
- **Variable proportional distribution:** PV energy and battery-stored energy are allocated based on each end-user's predetermined share of hourly energy usage.

2.3.1 Priority-based distribution

Initially, end-users are ranked according to a predetermined priority order.

Thereafter, the following criteria are applicable for each hour:

1. Surplus PV production: If PV energy generation exceeds the total consumption of all end-users, their energy needs are fully met by PV. Any excess energy is then directed to charge the battery, or exported to the national grid if battery is completely charged.
2. Insufficient PV production: If PV generation falls short of total demand, the system attempts to discharge the battery to cover the deficit. If the battery cannot supply enough energy, some demand remains unmet.

   In this case, PV energy is first allocated to the highest-priority users. Then, battery is used to supply the next group in the priority order. Lower-priority users may experience partial or complete energy shortfalls.

2.3.2 Proportional distribution

In the fixed proportional distribution, end-users are firstly assigned a fixed and uniform allocation of available energy.

On the other hand, in the variable proportional distribution, end-users are initially allocated available energy on an hourly basis according to their demand profile.

In the two proportional distribution scenarios, the following conditions shall apply on an hourly basis:

1. Surplus PV production: If PV energy available for each end-user exceeds its individual consumption, energy needs are fully met by PV. Any excess energy is then directed to charge the battery, or exported to the national grid if battery is completely charged.
2. Partial sufficiency of assigned PV shares: When the allocated PV energy is sufficient for some users but not for all, two cases appear:
   a. If an end-user's assigned PV share is sufficient: They consume their portion of PV energy. Any remaining PV energy after all allocations is used to charge the battery.
   b. If an end-user's assigned PV share is insufficient: The battery is discharged considering the shares to supplement the shortfall (if stored energy is available).
3. Insufficient PV production: If PV generation falls short for all end-users (for example during night-time), the system attempts to discharge the battery considering the shares. This is, if allocated energy in the battery for each end-user is enough, demand for this end-user is fulfilled, if not some demand remains unmet.

The difference between fixed and variable proportional distributions lies in the fact that the former applies a constant percentage throughout the year, while the latter assigns an hourly percentage to each self-consumer based on their previous annual energy consumption profile.

3 CASE-STUDY DESCRIPTION

A REC made up of a static south-oriented 68 kWp PV generator installed at 25° inclination, a 370 kWh battery capacity, and with 22 self-consumers has been used to validate the strategies developed. From the 22 end-users, 17 are individual households and 5 belong to a cultural association. This system, apart from the battery, represents a real installation in a small village in Calatayud Region, Spain.

Based on a previous simulation of the PV system in SISIFO [5], annual PV energy production is 1,530 kWh/kWp.

The battery capacity is determined based on the average daily energy demand. Operational limits are defined such that the minimum and maximum state of charge correspond to 20% and 80% of the total battery capacity, respectively. Real consumption data of the 22 self-consumers are available and used as input. Annual energy consumption per end-user is presented in Figure 1, in which one (number 18, representing a cultural association) stands out due to its high consumption.

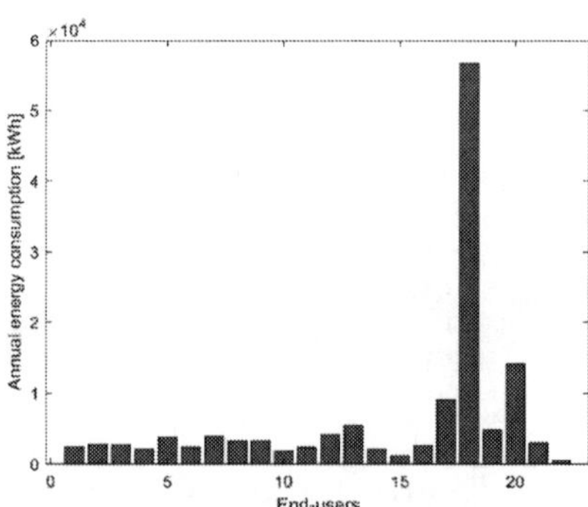

Fig. 1. Annual energy consumption per end-user

Annual consumption is 135 MWh, and Figure 2 shows the monthly distribution of the total consumption (as the sum of the 22 end-users).

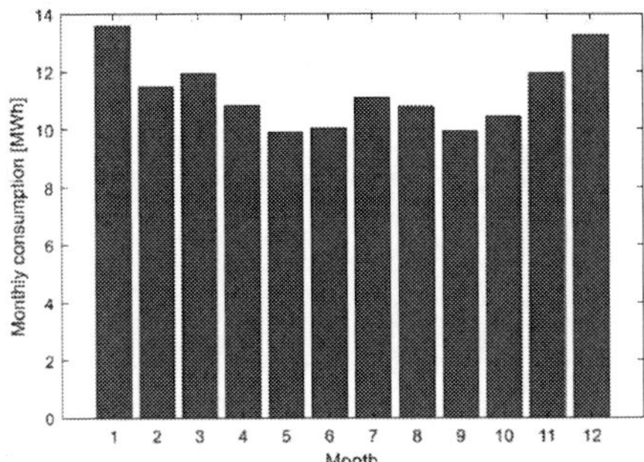

Fig. 2. Monthly distribution of the total consumption

4 RESULTS

This work presents a VPP made up of a PV plant, a centralized battery and different self-consumers.

For presentation clarity, the different scenarios will be enumerated as follows:

- Scenario 1: Priority-based distribution
- Scenario 2: Fixed proportional distribution
- Scenario 3: Variable proportional distribution

The PV energy produced by the PV generator is 104,070 kWh (obviously the same for three scenarios). Table I shows the annual outputs obtained in terms of PV energy used, and Table II the unmet energy demand. As expected, PV used reaches its maximum in scenario 3 (90,596 kWh), while the lowest value is obtained in scenario 1 (78,215 kWh). PV energy consumed directly is equal in scenarios 1 and 3 in total, However, this equal total does not reflect uniform consumption across individual end-users—each user consumes PV energy differently depending on the scenario.

Table I: PV energy used for the 3 scenarios under study

Scenario	1	2	3
PV energy consumed directly [kWh]	57,101	32,631	57,101
PV energy used to charge the battery [kWh]	21,114	51,895	33,495

Table II: Unmet energy demand for the 3 scenarios under study

Scenario	1	2	3
Unmet energy demand [kWh]	57,009	50,699	44,628

Unmet energy demand is 42% in the first scenario, 37% in the second one, and 33% in the third scenario.

Table III includes the two rates considered for the 3 scenarios: as expected, lowest values are always obtained in scenario 1 and highest ones in scenario 3.

Table III: SCR and SSR for the 3 scenarios under study

Scenario	1	2	3
SCR [%]	75%	81%	87%
SSR [%]	58%	63%	67%

In no-batteries scenarios equivalent to these ones, SCR and SSR are obviously lower. Particularly, SCR in scenario 1 and 3 would be 55% and SSR 42%. For scenario 2, SCR 31% and SSR 24%.

5 CONCLUSIONS AND FUTURE WORK

This work presented a VPP made up of a PV generator, a centralized battery and different self-consumers/end-users.

Three allocation scenarios had been considered: priority-based distribution, fixed proportional distribution and variable proportional distribution.

The application of the different scenarios to a particular village showed the expected results: scenario 3 (variable proportional distribution) is the one who presents higher values of both self-consumption and self-sufficient rates, with values of 87% and 67% respectively. Although, this scenario, as well as the first one, is not possible in some countries due to current legislation.

The next phase in the development of this VPP will involve the following steps:

- Modelling of a new variable proportional distribution: by feature dynamic, real-time management of power distribution based on current PV production, battery state-of-charge, demand and usage patterns, and grid energy prices.
- Modeling of grid interconnection: by integrating mechanisms for simulating energy exchange with the national grid, including bidirectional power flows, grid constraints, and regulatory frameworks.
- Integration of economic constraints: by incorporating parameters such as electricity tariffs, market price dynamics, and battery costs.
- Inclusion of electric vehicles [6]: to extend the system modeling framework to account for electric vehicles as dynamic assets, considering their charging behavior, and mobility patterns.
- Migration to python and open-source deployment: with the goal of enhance scalability, maintainability, and fostering community collaboration through open-source.

6 ACKNOWLEDGEMENTS

JALON: Funded by the European Union. Views and opinions expressed are however those of the author(s) only and do not necessarily reflect those of the European Union or CINEA. Neither the European Union nor the granting authority can be held responsible for them.

7   REFERENCES

[1] N. Naval, J. M. Yusta, Virtual power plant models and electricity markets - A review, Renewable and Sustainable Energy Reviews, Volume 149, 2021, 111393, https://doi.org/10.1016/j.rser.2021.111393.

[2] European Union. Directive (EU) 2018/2001 of the European Parliament and of the Council on the Promotion of the Use of Energy from Renewable Sources; European Union: Brussels, Belgium, 2018.

[3] M. Esfahani, A. Alizadeh, B. Cao, I. Kamwa, M. Xu, Bridging theory and practice: A comprehensive review of virtual power plant technologies and their real-world applications, Renewable and Sustainable Energy Reviews, Volume 222, 2025, 115929, https://doi.org/10.1016/j.rser.2025.115929

[4] R. Luthander, J. Widén, D. Nilsson, J. Palm, Photovoltaic self-consumption in buildings: A review, Applied Energy, Volume 142, 2015, Pages 80-94, https://doi.org/10.1016/j.apenergy.2014.12.028

[5] Universidad Politécnica de Madrid, "SISIFO: An online simulator of PV systems," 2025, v3.3. Accessed: Jul. 31, 2025. [Online]. Available: https://www.sisifo.info

[6] C. Sanz-Cuadrado, L. Narvarte, A. B, Cristóbal, Energy Valorization Strategies in Rural Renewable Energy Communities: A Path to Social Revitalization and Sustainable Development. Energies 2025, 18, 2561. https://doi.org/10.3390/en18102561

VALIDATION OF A MULTISTRATEGY ENERGY MANAGEMENT SYSTEM FOR BATTERY IN PV PLANTS

Celena Lorenzo[a], Laura Barrutia[a], Luis Narvarte[a], Jesús Heras[b], Carlos Awadallah[b]
[a]Instituto de Energía Solar - Universidad Politécnica de Madrid, 28031 Madrid, Spain
[b]Wattkraft España, 28046, Madrid, Spain

c.lorenzon@upm.es

ABSTRACT: The integration of Li-ion batteries with photovoltaic (PV) plants is crucial for enhancing grid stability and maximizing renewable energy utilization. However, advanced Energy Management Systems (EMS) are required to optimize battery operation for both performance-oriented and regulation-oriented services. This paper presents the preliminary validation of a smart EMS for a grid-connected PV-battery system, tested at the UPM facilities. The EMS implements five control strategies: Time-of-Use arbitrage, Peak Shaving, Maximization of Self-Consumption, Frequency Regulation, and Capacity Market participation. Preliminary results demonstrate accurate power tracking (RMSE < 0.25 kW) and rapid response times (<650 ms) for the first three strategies, confirming the system's readiness for grid services. While current performance is suitable for capacity markets, faster response times are needed for ancillary services. Future work will integrate an AI-based market predictor to enable dynamic strategy selection and improve economic returns.

Keywords: Li-ion batteries, Energy Management System (EMS), photovoltaic systems, grid services

1 INTRODUCTION

The mitigation of climatic change and the depletion of fossil fuels are leading to a very fast energy transition, where electrification is playing a key role [1]. Electrification goes hand in hand with the large-scale deployment of renewable energy. However, the increasing penetration rates of intermittent energy sources (mainly wind and solar) are putting at risk the stability of the electric grids [2]. A recent example was the blackout that affected the interconnected electrical grid of Spain and Portugal on April 28, 2025, where the lack of sufficient operational energy reserves for frequency regulation was one of the key causes that led to the grid's collapse [3].

The integration of energy storage systems is one of the most powerful tools for strengthening the power grid. In particular, the use of Li-ion batteries integrated with PV systems is one of the solutions to this problem to receive more attention [4], [5], [6]. Although a lot has already been done [7][2], [8], [9] , advanced Energy Management Systems (EMS) are necessary for better optimization of the system performance and of the energy trading of PV plants.

Furthermore, one of the main barriers to the massive deployment of Li-ion batteries is still their high cost [10]. Control strategies that improve the performance of the PV plant will increase its economic revenue. In addition, control strategies related to grid regulation (i.e. frequency regulation, contingency market, capacity market...) have a great economical potential, as the grid operators pay considerable amounts just for availability [11]. To amortize the initial investment cost of the battery in a reasonably short period of time, it is necessary to combine both types of strategies (performance-oriented and regulation-oriented).

This paper presents the preliminary results for the validation of a smart EMS system for the integration of batteries in PV plants. This validation is taking place with an outdoor demonstrator at the UPM facilities. The smart EMS will be able to integrate different control strategies, attending to different objectives. Some of these strategies are already commercially available (for example, the Maximization of Self-Consumption) and others are more innovative (for example, Grid-Ancillary Services). There will be two operation modes: manual (where a certain control strategy is selected) and automatic (where the EMS itself will be able to decide which one of the control strategies is more convenient, depending on several external factors like the market prices for different services).

2 METHODOLOGY

2.1 Objectives and validation planning

This work is part of a European research project called PVOP [12], that aims at the innovative digitalization of the PV sector. One of the central lines of work is related to the control of PV plants to optimize their performance. The main objectives of this line of work are:

- To develop and demonstrate technical solutions for the control of PV plants to maximize their performance.
- To optimize the energy trading of PV plants with batteries.

For achieving these objectives, the smart EMS for a Li-ion battery will be implemented in two phases:

1. An alpha version is being currently developed, integrated and validated in an outdoor demonstrator at the UPM facilities. This demonstrator is composed of a Li-ion battery (model LUNA 97kWh/100kW), powered by a 16 kW$_p$ PV generator and connected to the electric grid (although capable of stand-alone operation), according to Figure 1:

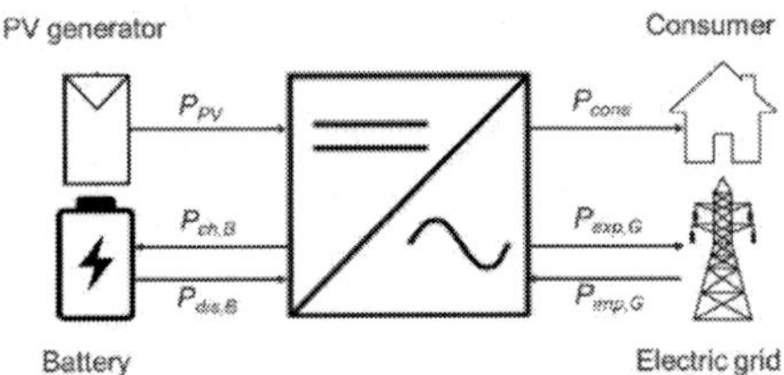

Figure 1: Schematic of the demonstrator at the UPM facilities.

2. Using the lessons learnt during the alpha version validation, a beta version will be implemented and validated in a real PV power plant, under real operation conditions.

This paper presents the preliminary results for the validation of the alpha version, including some of the control strategies that will be implemented in the smart EMS.

2.2 Control strategies

There are five different control strategies that will be implemented in the smart EMS: three of them are performance-oriented (TOU, PS and MSC) and two, regulation-oriented (FR and CM). They are described in Table I:

Table I: Battery control strategies to be implemented in the smart EMS.

Operating modes	Revenue Generation	Return on Investment
Time of Use (TOU) Arbitrage	TOU arbitrage involves charging the battery during off-peak hours when electricity prices are low and discharging during peak hours when prices are high. This process allows the BESS to capitalize on price differentials by buying low and selling high	Consistently leveraging daily market fluctuations generates regular income, contributing to the overall revenue stack and shortening the payback period.
Peak Shaving (PS)	Peak shaving reduces the demand charges on electricity bills by lowering the peak demand during high-consumption periods. By discharging the battery during peak times, businesses can avoid the highest tariff rates associated with their peak usage.	A significant reduction in demand charges, which can constitute a large portion of industrial and commercial electricity bills, directly improves net income. This cost-saving measure adds to the revenue stack, accelerating the return on investment. This operation mode can avoid Grid reconstruction (AGR).
Maximization of Self-Consumption (MSC)	This mode ensures that energy generated by a PV system is used as much as possible on-site rather than being exported to the grid at lower rates. The BESS stores excess solar energy during the day for use during the night or periods of low generation.	Maximizing self-consumption reduces dependency on grid electricity, leading to substantial savings on energy bills. These savings contribute to the revenue stack, resulting in a faster recovery of the BESS investment.
Frequency Regulation (FR) and Ancillary Services	Providing grid services such as frequency regulation, voltage support, and spinning reserve can generate additional income. Utilities and grid operators often pay for these ancillary services to maintain grid stability and reliability.	Participating in these markets provides a steady revenue stream, adding to the revenue stack and ensuring a quicker payback period.
Capacity Market (CM)	Capacity markets allow BESS owners to receive payments for being available to supply energy during high-demand periods, ensuring sufficient capacity for grid stability.	By participating in these markets, the BESS earns additional income simply by being available, which adds to the revenue stack and contributes to faster investment recovery.

The three performace-oriented strategies (TOU, PS and MSC) have already been validated for two different consumption profiles (during two complete days for each profile). These profiles were simulated in order to be representative of a typical residential and industrial consumptions. The real PV production of the PV generator was scaled-up in order to be of a similar magnitude as the consumption.

The FR and CM strategies do not require of a specific control validation: it is only necessary to assure that the battery can deliver/absorb a certain amount of energy (with high accuracy) in a short period of time (as demanded by the grid operator). Both metrics (accuracy when following a power setpoint and response time) have been characterized during the validation of the three other strategies.

3 RESULTS

3.1 Time of Use (TOU)

The objective of this strategy is to set a charge and a discharge period for the next day, depending on the electricity prices announced by the grid operator. When the prices are lower, the battery will charge from the grid; when the prices are higher, it will sell the electricity to the grid. For the validation of this strategy, the PV energy was directly self-consumed by the university.

Figure 2 presents the power profiles (commands sent to the battery, loads consumption, PV inverters active power, charge and discharge battery power and energy at the Point of Injection -POI-) for a complete day with the TOU control implemented. It can be observed that the battery is charged between 13-15h (when electricity prices were lower) and discharged between 21-23h (when electricity prices were higher).

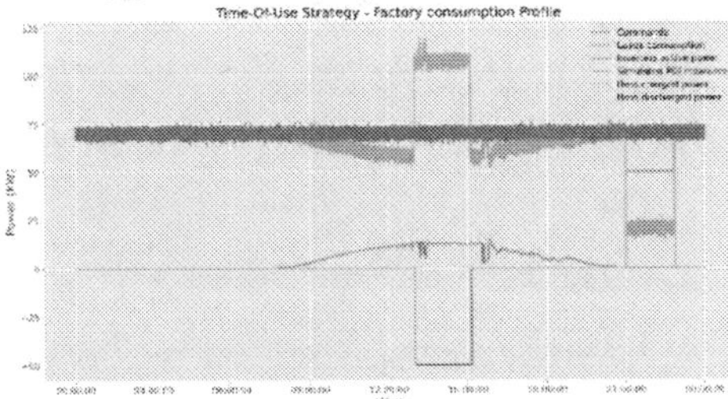

Figure 2: Power profiles during the validation of the TOU control strategy.

The KPIs obtained during the TOU validation are the following:

- RMSE ($P_{SetPoint,Battery}$ - $P_{measured,Battery}$) $< \mathbf{0.25\ kW}$
- $t_{transition} < \mathbf{600\ ms}$
- $\dfrac{\text{Energy trade during TOU hours}}{\text{Total energy trade}} = \mathbf{100\%}$

3.2 Peak Shaving (PS)

The objective of this strategy is to use the battery to stop the system from going over the contracted power limit. This happens when consumption is too high and the avilable PV power isn't enough.

Figure 3 presents the power profiles (commands sent to the battery, loads consumption, PV inverters active power, charge and discharge battery power) for a complete day with the PS control implemented. It can be observed that the battery is charged with the PV surplus and discharged when the loads consumption exceeds the PS threshold. The result is that the POI measures exceed this threshold but very briefly. Actually, when calculating the total energy consumed for every 15-minutes period (which is the period that the grid operator considers for detecting

an excess in consumption), the grid limitation was always respected.

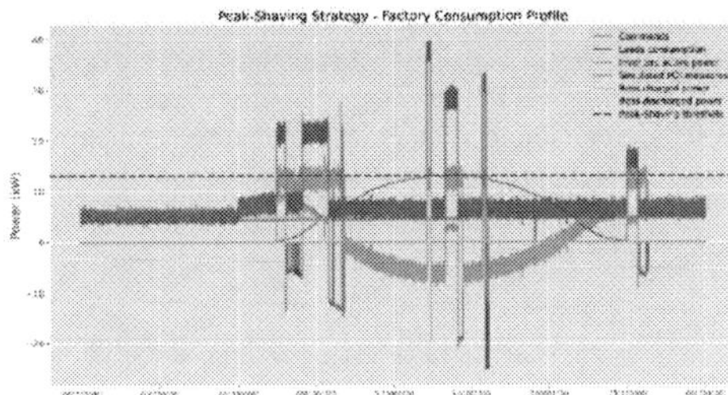

Figure 3: Power profiles during the validation of the PS control strategy.

The KPIs obtained during the PS validation are the following:

- RMSE ($P_{SetPoint,Battery}$ - $P_{measured,Battery}$) $< \mathbf{0.2\ kW}$
- $t_{transition} < \mathbf{500\ ms}$
- $\int_{t1}^{t2} P_{imp/exp,G} \leq P_{max,G} \times 15min : \mathbf{100\%}$

3.3 Maximization of Self-Consumption (MSC)

The objective of this strategy is to use the battery for storing PV energy when it exceeds the loads consumption, and discharging when the consumption exceeds the PV production. This way, the PV self-consumtpion is maximized.

Figure 4 presents the power profiles (commands sent to the battery, loads consumption, PV inverters active power, charge and discharge battery power) for a complete day with the MSC control implemented. It can be observed that the battery is charged when the PV production is high (during the central hours of the day) and discharged when the PV production decreases in the morning and in the evening. This way, the excess of PV energy at midday is later used for covering the evening consumption. In consequence, less PV energy is sold to the grid, and less electricity is bought from it. This does not only represent an economic advantage, but also avoids the congestion of the transmission electric lines.

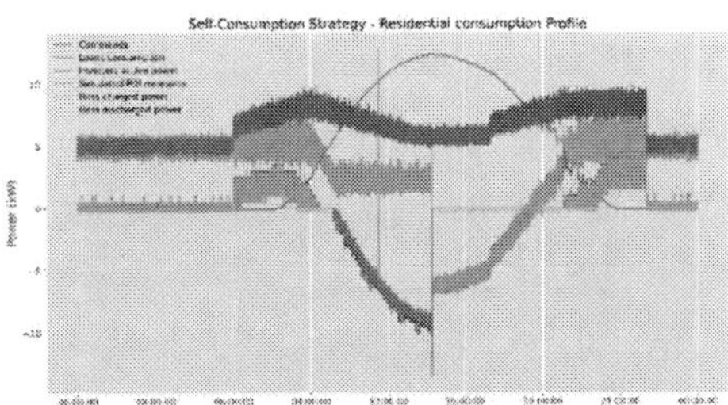

Figure 4: Power profiles during the validation of the MSC control strategy.

The KPIs obtained during the PS validation are the following:

- RMSE ($P_{SetPoint,Battery}$ - $P_{measured,Battery}$) $< \mathbf{0.25\ kW}$
- $t_{transition} < \mathbf{650\ ms}$
- $Self - Consumption\ Rate = 82 - 100\%$

4 CONLUSIONS

-The three control strategies -TOU, PS and MSC- have been correctly implemented. The different control logics have fulfilled their objectives: charging/discharging when indicated depending on the electricity market prices (TOU), avoiding that the energy at the Point of Injection exceeds a certain power limit (PS) and maximizing the PV self-consumption for reducing the PV surplus sold to the grid (MSC).

-The EMS fulfils the power commands with good accuracy: the mean RMSE is lower than 0.25kW, while the power commands range between 5-100kW.

-Response times are sufficient for normal FR and CM, where batteries need to be able to act in 2-3s [8].

-Response times might be insufficient for contingency markets, which are part of Ancillary Services, where batteries need to be able to act in 200-300ms [13].

The next step is to integrate these three control strategies into a single smart EMS, that will decide which one is the most convenient at every moment (mainly from an economic point of view, although degradation will also be considered). This smart EMS will also consider possible revenues from participating in Capacity Markets. However, the response times still need to be lowered before considering participating in the FR and Ancillary Services markets. This implies both hardware and software improvements.

Finally, an AI-based electricity market predictor will be integrated into the smart EMS. This way, the electricity prices will be estimated for longer periods than one day, potentially improving the battery management.

REFERENCES

[1] IEA, "World Energy Outlook 2023," 2023. [Online]. Available: www.iea.org/terms

[2] IRENA, "Renewable Power Generation Costs in 2022", 2023. [Online]. Available: www.irena.org

[3] Red Eléctrica, "Incidente en el Sistema Eléctrico Peninsular Espanol el 18 de junio de 2025". [Online]. Available: chrome-extension://efaidnbmnnnibpcajpcglclefindmkaj/ https://d1n1o4zeyfu21r.cloudfront.net/WEB_Inc idente_SistemaElectricoPeninsularEspanol_18ju nio2025.pdf

[4] H. C. Hesse, M. Schimpe, D. Kucevic, and A. Jossen, "Lithium-ion battery storage for the grid - A review of stationary battery storage system design tailored for applications in modern power grids", *Energies*, vol. 10, no. 12, 2017, doi: 10.3390/en10122107.

[5] C. A. Hill, M. C. Such, D. Chen, J. Gonzalez, and W. M. K. Grady, "Battery energy storage for enabling integration of distributed solar power generation," *IEEE Trans Smart Grid*, vol. 3, no. 2, pp. 850–857, 2012, doi: 10.1109/TSG.2012.2190113.

[6] P. Ferreira Torres *et al.*, "Energy Storage as a Transmission Asset—Assessing the Multiple Uses of a Utility-Scale Battery Energy Storage System in Brazil," *Energies (Basel)*, vol. 18, no. 4, Feb. 2025, doi: 10.3390/en18040902.

[7] M. Pinho Almeida, A. R. Arrifano Manito, G. Figueiredo Pinto Filho, and R. Zilles, "Optimization tool for operating isolated diesel-photovoltaic-battery hybrid power systems using day-ahead power forecasts," *Journal of Renewable and Sustainable Energy*, vol. 15, no. 4, Jul. 2023, doi: 10.1063/5.0156371.

[8] Y. Shi, B. Xu, D. Wang, and B. Zhang, "Using Battery Storage for Peak Shaving and Frequency Regulation: Joint Optimization for Superlinear Gains," *IEEE Transactions on Power Systems*, vol. PP, Feb. 2017, doi: 10.1109/TPWRS.2017.2749512.

[9] S. Tibude, G. Goyal, A. Ranjan, and S. Bodkhe, *Advanced Energy Management Strategies for Hybrid Energy Storage Systems in Electric Vehicles: A Comprehensive Review*. 2025. doi: 10.1109/ICPC2T63847.2025.10958756.

[10] O. Schmidt, S. Melchior, A. Hawkes, and I. Staffell, "Projecting the Future Levelized Cost of Electricity Storage Technologies," *Joule*, vol. 3, no. 1, pp. 81–100, Jan. 2019, doi: 10.1016/j.joule.2018.12.008.

[11] AEMO, "Ancillary Services Market Report. Australian Energy Market Operator." Available: https://www.aemo.com.au/energy-systems/electricity/national-electricity-market-nem/system-operations/ancillary-services

[12] "PVOP Project: Digitalization of Photovoltaic Systems. Horizon Europe Programme." Available: https://pvop.eu/

[13] ENTSO-E, "Market Report 2023", Available: https://www.entsoe.eu/about/

PHOTOVOLTAIC HOSTING CAPACITY IN NORDIC DISTRIBUTION GRIDS

Lauri Aaltonen and Kari Lappalainen
Tampere University, Electrical Engineering Unit, P. O. Box 692, FI-33101 Tampere, Finland
lauri.aaltonen.tuni.fi, kari.lappalainen@tuni.fi

ABSTRACT: Due to the ongoing energy transition, distribution grids are experiencing a rapid change. Centralized power production is being replaced by variable, distributed electricity production such as wind and solar power. Many consumers have been installing photovoltaic (PV) power production at their premises. The variability of PV generation and its impact on grid performance poses challenges. Understanding these challenges is crucial for optimizing PV system integration. This research aims to investigate the factors affecting PV hosting capacity in Nordic distribution grids using real measurement data for PV modules as well as real Finnish distribution grid data. The findings will prove insights on different types of low voltage grids in Finland and compare them.
Keywords: hosting capacity, energy transition, photovoltaic power production, distribution grid

1 INTRODUCTION

Photovoltaic (PV) installations are on the rise in Europe but also in Nordic countries such as Finland. According to the Energy Authority of Finland, grid-connected PV production capacity rose over 300 MW during the year 2023 [1]. In the neighboring country, Sweden, the amount was even higher, around 1600 MW [2]. A large portion of the installed PV production is micro production, i.e., it is connected to the low voltage (LV) distribution grid. Also, electric vehicles are increasing in popularity for newly registered cars.

The components in electrical grids can have a lifetime of even many decades which means that many sections of the grids were designed a long time ago with only consumption customers in mind. A high penetration of distributed generation such as PV may create issues in the grids that the distribution system operators (DSOs) need to solve. Some of these solutions, like grid reinforcements, can be costly and time consuming. In the end, the grid customers are the ones paying for it via subscription fees.

When the PV penetration increases enough in the grid, some grid constraint will be exceeded. Hosting capacity (HC) is defined as the maximum amount of new distributed generation or load that the grid can handle before any of the selected constraints are exceeded. Reverse power flow results in overvoltage, instead of undervoltage as in forward power flow. Similarly, also the thermal limits, e.g., line ampacity or transformer loading, can be exceeded. Other factors that limit the HC can be unbalance issues if the PV installations are single phase. Power quality can also be an issue with cloud movements causing rapid voltage changes as well as grid connected inverter injecting harmonic currents. According to a literature review by Fatima et al. [3] the most pronounced limiting constraint used in PV HC studies was voltage violations, followed by ampacity and unbalance. According to [4] in LV grids those were power quality and feeder threshold limits. In Nordic grids unbalance is not generally an issue since most LV customers have three phase connections to the grid.

Generally, DSOs have solved the issues with classical grid reinforcement measures. For example, if line section ampacity is a limiting factor or the customer voltage is out of bounds, changing the size of the cabling changes the impedance and therefore mitigates the severe load flow case.

Many studies of PV hosting capacity have been done for low voltage grids [5–6]. Unfortunately, most of the studies used a test grid instead of a real grid. Few studies [7–8] have been done using real grid values, but those studies usually focused on a single grid type, and none have been done for Nordic distribution grids.

This paper studies PV HC in three real Nordic LV distribution grids. The next chapter focuses on data and methods of this study. The 10 second interval PV production data is formed from power plant measurements, sun position and aerial imagery. Grid data is collected from a DSO. The customer load data from hourly energy meter readings is utilized. Chapter 3 presents and discusses the results from the grids based on the time-based simulations from summer months of 2024. Finally, in Chapter 4 some concluding remarks are made. The results of this study are applicable for distribution grids in the Nordic countries, since they share similar grid structure, climate, electricity market etc.

2 DATA AND METHODS

2.1 Data

The data used in this study is from four summer months in 2024: May, June, July and August. As the goal is to study PV hosting capacity, the nighttime hours, 18:00–06:00 EEST, were omitted from the data.

This study uses LV grid data from one of the Finnish DSOs, Tampereen Energia Sähköverkko Oy. This data includes grid component information, topology and customer load profiles. Load profiles are on a 1-hour measurement interval.

The data used to model PV power production is from Tampere University Solar PV Power Station Research Plant [9] that is in the same area as the DSO. The solar data used was in 10-second intervals. Backsheet temperature of a PV module was measured with a National Instruments Pt100 thermocouple. Global and diffuse horizontal irradiances were recorded with Kipp & Zonen CMP22 and CMP21 pyranometers, respectively.

2.2 Modelling of PV power production

PV power production was modelled using the irradiance measurements and the module backsheet temperature measurement. The diffuse irradiance is measured with a pyranometer (CMP21) that has a shading ring to block the direct irradiation. To calculate the irradiance that a PV module with an arbitrary tilt and orientation receives the direct irradiance needs to be known. Direct irradiance G_{direct} can be calculated by subtracting the diffuse irradiation G_{diffuse} from the global one G_{global}, i.e., $G_{\text{direct}} = G_{\text{global}} - G_{\text{diffuse}}$.

Since all the production is assumed to be installed at rooftops, the roof orientation and tilt play a central role when determining the unique production profile for each rooftop. To know the irradiance that the PV modules receive, one must know the installation tilt and azimuth angles as well as the position of the Sun in addition to the irradiance.

The position of the Sun, i.e., the zenith and azimuth angles, were calculated for every timestamp using the algorithm of [10]. The algorithm takes GPS-coordinates and timestamps as inputs. It does not consider other things impacting the local observed sun position such as air pressure among other things. The position of the Sun was calculated for a single GPS-point selected in central Tampere area as all the studied grids for the study were nearby. The resulting estimate of the Sun elevation from the horizon, in the city of Tampere for one day is presented in Fig. 1. and azimuth in Fig. 2.

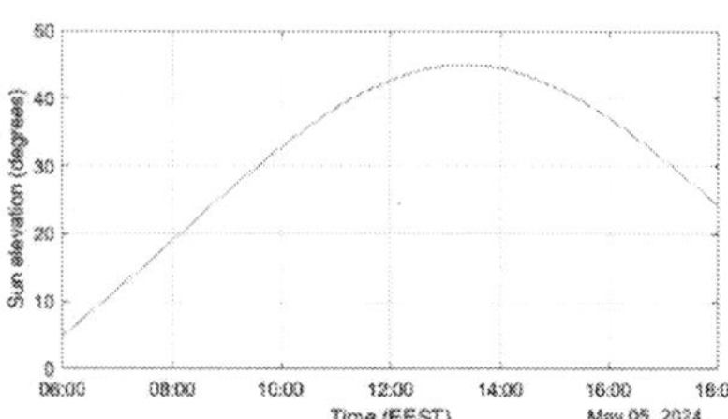

Figure 1: Local sun elevation from the horizon as a function of time for May 5th, 2024.

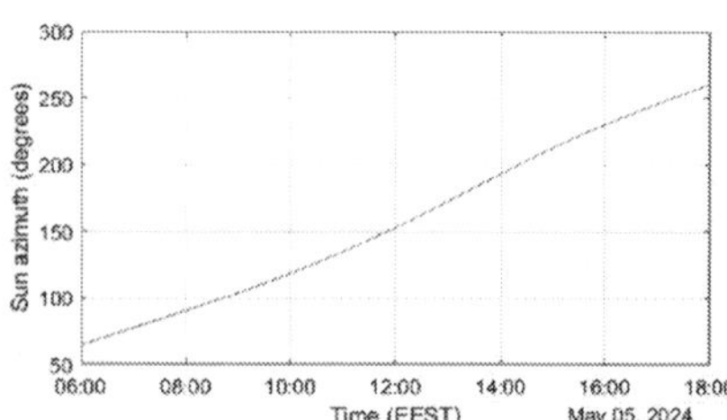

Figure 2: Local sun azimuth clockwise from north as a function of time for May 5th, 2024.

As the tilt and azimuth angle of a PV module are known, as well as Sun position in the sky for every timestep, the direct irradiation arriving at the module can be calculated as

$$G_{\text{Direct, module}} = \cos(\text{AOI})\, G_{\text{Direct}}, \qquad (2)$$

where AOI is the angle-of-incidence meaning the angle between the sunrays and the normal of the module. The total irradiance of the module is therefore

$$G_{\text{Module}} = G_{\text{Direct, module}} + G_{\text{Diffuse, module}}. \qquad (3)$$

This means that even if the position of the Sun goes behind the module, i.e., Eq. (2) goes to zero, the module will still receive some diffuse irradiation and produce some, although small, power. In this study the measured diffuse horizontal irradiance was used as $G_{\text{Diffuse, module}}$, i.e.,

$$G_{\text{Diffuse, module}} = G_{\text{Diffuse}}.$$

As the PV plant size increases, i.e., the plant is utilizing a larger land area, the irradiance fluctuations become smoother. A spatial irradiance method proposed in [11] was used to smooth out the irradiance measurement. The spatial irradiance G_S was calculated as

$$G_{\text{s}}(t) = \frac{G_{\text{Module}}(t)}{\left(\dfrac{\sqrt{A_{\text{PV}}}}{2\pi \cdot 0.0204 \cdot A_{\text{PV}}^{-0.4997}} \right) s + 1}, \qquad (4)$$

where A_{PV} is the area in hectares that is occupied by the PV plant and s is the Laplace-variable.

The generated PV power was obtained using an equation [12] that takes the PV module temperature into account, as temperature greatly affects the current–voltage characteristics of the PV modules. The generated power of the PV plant is

$$P_{\text{Gen, PV}} = \frac{P_{\text{nom}}}{G_{\text{STC}}} G_{\text{S}}[1 - \beta(T_{\text{PVM}} - T_{\text{STC}})], \qquad (5)$$

where P_{nom} is the nominal power of the PV system, G_{STC} is the irradiance in standard test conditions (STC), β is the temperature coefficient estimated to be 0.0045 1/°C based on average value from [11], T_{STC} is the temperature in the STC and T_{PVM} is the PV module temperature measured from the backsheet.

In this study, PV power production for the roofs of flat roofed buildings and the south-facing roofs of gabled buildings was formed using Eqs. (1–5) and an aerial image tool [13] illustrated in Fig. 3 along with its production curve in Fig. 4.

Figure 3: PV plant size selection example using the aerial image tool [13] for a tilted roof of a detached house.

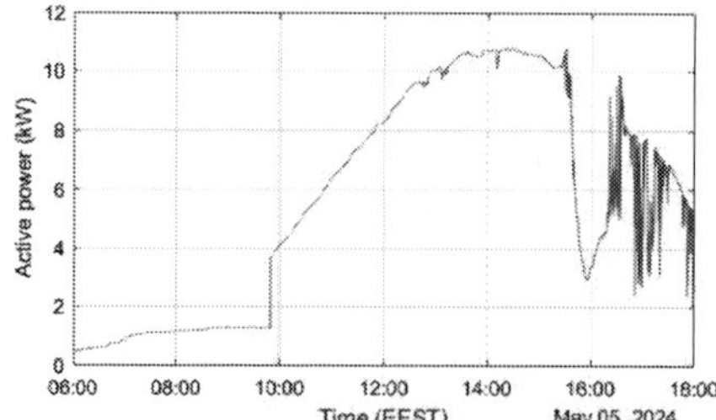

Figure 4: Simulated PV power production of the house in Fig. 4 for May 5th, 2024.

As can be seen from Figs. 3–4, the roof azimuth

deviates 26 degrees from South to West. This means that the peak production happening during the solar noon at approximately 13:15 in Fig. 1 is shifted in the production figure to the right, to around 14:00. The sudden boost in production just before 10:00 is due to the Sun moving from the backside and side of the panel to the front of the panel, geographically. This can be verified by inspecting Fig. 2. The evening of that day was cloudy so that can be seen as the high variation of power at the end of the production curve.

Although the PV power plant is operating at unity power factor, the possible inverter filter might produce reactive power to the grid. The produced reactive power was modelled as

$$Q_{\text{Gen, PV}} = d_0 + d_1 P_{\text{Gen,PV}}, \qquad (6)$$

where d_0 and d_1 are coefficients determined to be 0.072 and 0.034, respectively. [14]

For houses with a tilted roof, a 45° tilt angle was assumed for the installation of PV modules and the whole south facing roof area was assumed to be utilized. For flat roofed houses, a tilt angle of 45° was assumed with a row spacing of 1.5 m to prevent self-shading during the peak hours. Self-shading effect was not considered, as it does not typically occur at the highest production hours. P_{nom} was calculated by multiplying the area occupied by the modules by a typical PV power density of 200 W/m². Only the habited houses were utilized, i.e., no sheds or garages were considered. If the orientation of a gabled house deviated over 80° degrees from South, i.e., it was not very suitable for a PV installation, it was omitted.

2.3 Low voltage grids

Three example low voltage grids were chosen: rural, suburban and urban. The rural grid, presented in Fig. 5, was a countryside grid comprising mostly of overhead lines with some of the consumer connection lines being cabled connections. The area had mostly farms and summer cottages as customers. The suburban grid, in Fig. 6, was chosen from the outskirts of Tampere city with a mix of detached houses and townhouse complexes. The urban grid, shown in Fig. 7., included several big apartment buildings, a small store, a bar and a few detached houses. The urban grid was fully underground cabled and the suburban one was mostly underground cabled with a small exception of the northernmost feeder having a relatively short amount of overhead line.

The suburban grid features the highest amount of connection points while the urban and rural ones have clearly fewer. A connection point may have one or more customers: a connection point of a detached house has typically one customer, but an apartment building can have several. For example, a connection point with main fuses of 3x320 A may have several 3x25 A fused customers who are all metered individually. These customers of each connection point are summed together to form the grid connection point power. As the customers are LV customers, only their hourly active power consumption is measured. For the study, all customers were assumed to have a 0.95 power factor. Grid data, e.g., cable lengths and types, were fetched from the same system that the DSO uses to design and document the grids, network information system (NIS).

2.4 Hosting capacity determination

The factors that were used to determine the hosting

Figure 5: Topology of the rural grid.

Figure 6: Topology of the suburban grid.

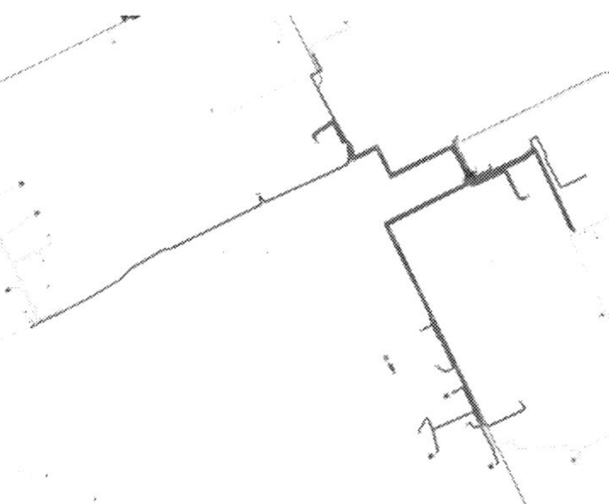

Figure 7: Topology of the urban grid.

capacity were transformer rating, line continuous ampacity and customer connection point under-/overvoltage. The transformer rating and line ampacities were collected from the NIS.

The customer voltages need to be within agreed limits that vary between regions and countries. USA uses the ANSI-standard which defines the limits as ±5% from the nominal. Germany has set a +3% limit for overvoltage on top of the European one [15] which sets limits to be ±10%. [3] For this study, the European standard was applied.

PV penetration was increased in increments and simulations in Matlab-Simulink were performed. The increment steps were the roofs, which were selected to adopt PV production at a random order.

There are many ways to define HC. For this study the HC is defined with transformer rating as a reference. This means that HC is the maximum amount of PV penetration that the grid can handle without breaking the constraints presented by nominal active power of the PV in the grid compared to the nominal apparent power of the distribution transformer.

3 RESULTS AND DISCUSSION

The simulations were performed in Matlab-Simulink environment. The maximum and minimum voltages that each customer experienced during the 4 months simulation time were saved. Fig. 8. presents the extreme customer voltages for all three grids as a function of PV penetration.

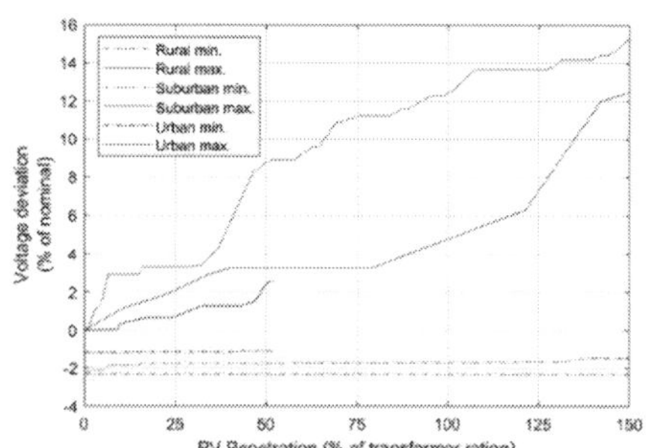

Figure 8: Customer extreme voltages for the three grids as a function of PV penetration in the grid.

The suburban grid has most roofs, so it has many smaller PV penetration increments. The rural grid has low number of customers but a weaker grid and less consumption as many of the summer cottages are used only for a few days a year, resulting in bigger impact on every added PV plant to the grid. The urban grid maximum customer voltage did not exceed the set limit even when all the available roof space was used.

The recorded maximum line ampacities for the grids are presented in Fig. 9 as a function of the PV penetration. The urban grid seems to be heavily loaded, and the PV penetration increments do hardly any harm. The relative maximum currents in the suburban and rural grid increased rapidly with large steps. For the suburban grid, not every added PV system contributed to the highest observed current but only a few.

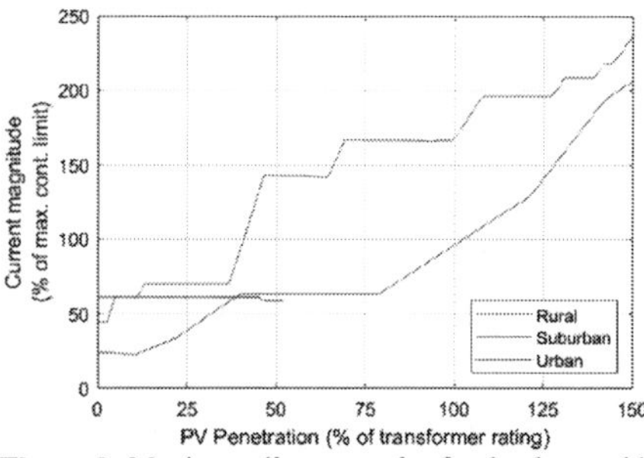

Figure 9: Maximum line ampacity for the three grids as a function of PV penetration in the grid.

The highest transformer loading is presented in Fig. 10 as a function of the PV penetration. The urban grid transformer experienced benefit from high PV penetration. This means that the time of the highest consumption

occurred when there was significant amount of PV production and the consumption was much larger than the PV production. For the suburban and rural grids, the transformer loading stayed the same or lowered slightly before the increasing PV penetration started to make it higher.

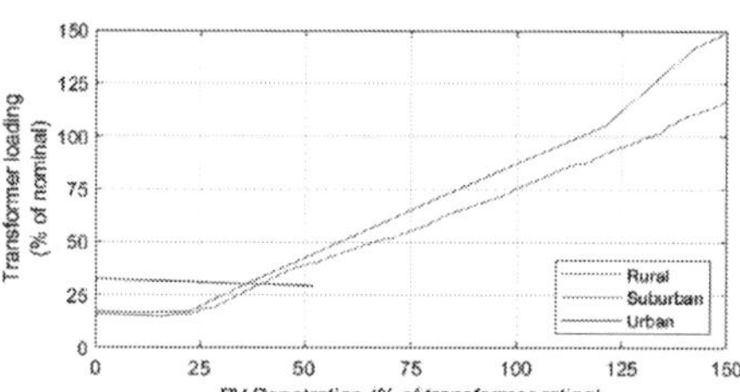

Figure 10: Transformer loading for the three distribution transformers as a function of PV penetration in the grid.

The hosting capacity results are gathered to Table I. The rural grid HC was 102.59% and suburban grid 41.04%. Both had the same limiting factor: line ampacity.

Depending on the voltage profile along the medium voltage feeder, which was not considered in the study, a different limit could be used. The results would have changed if a 5% overvoltage limit had been used. The urban grid did not reach that limit either. The rural grid would still have had the same limiting factor. For the suburban grid, the overvoltage would have become the limiting factor and the HC would have decreased slightly below 40%.

Table I: Hosting capacity with the transformer rating as a reference and the HC limiting factor.

	HC	Limiting factor
Rural	102.59 %	Line ampacity
Suburban	41.04 %	Line ampacity
Urban	-	-

There are only few previous studies made with a time series method for real life LV grids. In real Brazilian LV grids the HC was 38.2% of transformer rating [16]. For a residential LV grid in Zürich, Switzerland HC was determined to be 43% when comparing PV production to the load energy of the grid [17]. A Danish study using real LV grid data from a DSO and 24-hour field measurements found the HC to be 40% of the customer PVs [18].

A study [19] made with example LV grids using Monte Carlo method indicates that the rural HC will be reached at a lower penetration rate than for the urban and intermediate types. A study in Australia [20] using a suburban radial LV grid indicates PV HC to be 35% of the transformer rating. This is closely in line with the results obtained with the Finnish grid in this study. For an urban grid, an earlier study [21] focusing on a part of a real grid in Perth, Australia indicates that the HC will be around 31.9%. For the urban grid in this study, any violations of the factors limiting the HC were not achieved due to insufficient roof space available.

There are several factors in the methodology used that have caused some level of inaccuracy in the results. The sun position used in the study is slightly inaccurate due to the earth rotation speed variance, atmospheric conditions etc. but most importantly the actual GPS coordinates are slightly different for every house. Also, elevation from sea level plays a role in sun observation.

The PV power modeling holds some simplifications and assumptions. The module temperature in tilted roof installations could be slightly higher than the test plant measured module temperature used due to the hot roof being more near and air not flowing as freely. The diffuse irradiation will be slightly different with different installations. For example, flat roofs will have a lower diffuse component due to the nearby panel rows blocking the hemisphere seen by the module. In addition, self-shading and shading from nearby structures were not included in the study.

The customer's consumption was known only from the hourly energy meter readings. For future, a more detailed consumption profile should be studied.

4 CONCLUSIONS

This paper studied photovoltaic hosting capacity in Nordic distribution grids. Three different low voltage grids were chosen: rural, suburban and urban. A time-based simulation was performed in Matlab/Simulink for four summer months of 2024.

The data for grid components and hourly customer consumption was received from a local DSO Tampereen Energia Sähköverkko Oy. The PV production was considered for the roofs of flat roofed buildings and the south-facing roofs of gabled buildings. The roof size, tilt and orientation were considered individually using aerial imagery. Irradiance and PV module temperature measurements were used together with sun position and the unique roof data to form individual production profiles with a 10-second resolution.

The HC was the lowest for the suburban grid with line ampacity as a limiting factor. The rural grid experienced the same situation with a higher HC. The increasing PV penetration caused the urban grid transformer to be under less load. The customer voltages were increased in the urban grid but only to a relatively low level compared to the limit.

There were small uncertainties in the study related to PV production formulation, mainly due to shading not considered. As the time passes and new energy meters get installed, the study should be revised using consumption data with a higher temporal resolution.

ACKNOWLEDGEMENTS

This work used grid and customer data of Tampereen Energia Sähköverkko Oy. L. Aaltonen was funded by Tampereen Energia Sähköverkko Oy and K. Lappalainen was funded by the Research Council of Finland (funding decision 348701).

REFERENCES

[1] Energy Authority of Finland. Available online (accessed on 11.9.2025): https://energiavirasto.fi/en/-/solar-power-production-capacity-rose-to-1-000-megawatts.

[2] IEA. Available online (accessed on 11.9.2025), https://iea-pvps.org/national_survey/national-survey-report-of-pv-power-applications-in-sweden-2023-2.

[3] S. Fatima, V. Püvi, M. Lehtonen, Energies 13 (2020) 4756. https://doi.org/10.3390/en13184756.

[4] W. Martin, Y. Stauffer, C. Ballif, A. Hutter, P.J. Alet, 2018 IEEE PES Innovative Smart Grid Technologies Conference Europe (2018) 1–6. https://doi.org/10.1109/ISGTEurope.2018.8571427.

[5] B. Navarro, M. Navarro, 2017 IEEE PES Innovative Smart Grid Technologies Conference Europe (2017) 1–6. https://doi.org/10.1109/ISGTEurope.2017.8260210.

[6] M.-T. Do, A. Bruyere, B. Francois, IEEE Manchester PowerTech (2017) 1–6. https://doi.org/10.1109/PTC.2017.7981041.

[7] M. Bartecka, G. Barchi, J. Paska, Energies 13 (2020) 2524. https://doi.org/10.3390/en13102524.

[8] D. Schwanz, S. Ronnberg, M. Bollen, IEEE Manchester PowerTech (2017) 1–6. https://doi.org/10.1109/PTC.2017.7981274.

[9] D. Torres Lobera, A. Mäki, J. Huusari, K. Lappalainen, T. Suntio, S. Valkealahti, International Journal of Photoenergy 2013 (2013) 837310. https://doi.org/10.1155/2013/837310.

[10] M. Blanco, K. Milidonis, A. Bonanos, Solar Energy 212 (2020), 339–341. https://doi.org/10.1016/j.solener.2020.10.084.

[11] J. Marcos, L. Marroyo, E. Lorenzo, D. Alvira, E. Ezco, Progress in Photovoltaics: Research and Applications 19 (2011) 505. https://doi.org/10.1002/pip.1063.

[12] E. Skoplaki, J.A. Palyvos, Solar Energy 83 (2009) 614. https://doi.org/10.1016/j.solener.2008.10.008.

[13] Tampere city map service. Available online (accessed on 4.9.2025): https://kartat.tampere.fi/oskari/.

[14] A. Woyte, V. Van Thong, R. Belmans, J. Nils, IEEE Transaction on Energy Conversion 21 (2006) 202–209. https://doi.org/10.1109/TEC.2005.845454.

[15] Finnish Standards, SFS-EN 50160: Voltage characteristics of electricity supplied by public electricity networks (2022).

[16] R. Torquato, D. Salles, C. Oriente Pereira, P.C.M. Meira, W. Freitas, IEEE Transactions on Power Delivery 33 (2018) 1002–1012. https://doi.org/10.1109/TPWRD.2018.2798707.

[17] M.J. Weisshaupt, B. Schlatter, P. Korba, E. Kaffe, F. Kienzle, IFAC-PapersOnLine 49 (2016), 336–341. https://doi.org/10.1016/j.ifacol.2016.10.714.

[18] J. Hu, M. Marinelli, M. Coppo, A. Zecchino, H.W. Bindner, Electric Power Systems Research 131 (2016) 267–274. https://doi.org/10.1016/j.epsr.2015.10.025.

[19] A. Arshad, M. Lindner, M. Lehtonen, Energies 10 (2017) 1702. https://doi.org/10.3390/en10111702.

[20] M.M. Rahman, A. Arefi, G.M. Shafiullah, S. Hettiwatte, International Journal of Electrical Power & Energy Systems 99 (2018) 11–27. https://doi.org/10.1016/j.ijepes.2017.12.034.

[21] X. Su, M.A.S. Masoum, P.J. Wolfs, IEEE Transactions on Sustainable Energy 5 (2014) 967–977. https://doi.org/10.1109/TSTE.2014.2313862.

Tampere University

TAMPEREEN ENERGIA SÄHKÖVERKKO

DSII Doctoral School of Industry Innovations

PHOTOVOLTAIC HOSTING CAPACITY IN NORDIC DISTRIBUTION GRIDS

Lauri Aaltonen and Kari Lappalainen

Tampere University, Electrical Engineering

Data and methods

- Data from the solar PV power research plant of Tampere University
  - Module temperature
  - Global horizontal irradiance (GHI)
  - Diffuse horizontal irradiance (DHI)
  - Four summer months (May–August 2024) with a 10 second resolution
- Grid data from the local DSO (Tampereen Energia Sähköverkko Oy)
  - Grid information, e.g., line lengths, line types, topology
  - Customer hourly consumption data from summer months of 2024
- Identification of hosting capacity (HC)
  - Criteria for HC used was continuous ampacity and voltage violation (± 10%).
  - PV plants were inserted to the grid randomly, roof-by-roof, to cover the south-facing roof areas.
  - PV penetration was expressed with respect to the nominal transformer power.
- Simulation model
  - Simulations were performed using Matlab/Simulink.
  - PV power production was modelled based on measured temperature and irradiances.
  - The house orientation, south-facing roof area and roof type (tilted/flat) were considered individually for every roof.

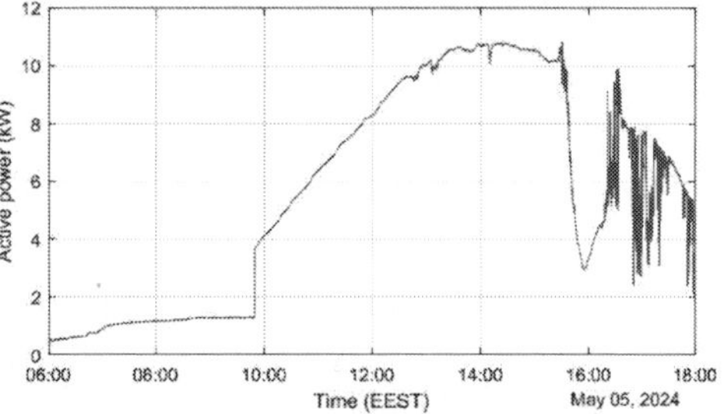

Figure 1: One roof area selected for the study and its modelled active PV power production for May 5th 2024.

Results

- Three examples of different kind of low voltage grids were chosen for the study
  - Rural, Suburban and Urban
- Rural grid
  - Mostly farms and summer cottages
  - Overhead lines and underground cables
  - Number of connection points: 16
  - Number of roofs with PV: 16
  - HC: 102.59%
  - Limiting factor: Line ampacity
- Suburban grid
  - Mix of detached houses and townhouses
  - Underground cables
  - Number of connection points: 59
  - Number of roofs with PV: 73
  - HC: 41.04%
  - Limiting factor: Line ampacity
- Urban grid
  - Mix of detached houses, apartment buildings, a supermarket and a local pub.
  - Underground cables
  - Number of connection points: 16
  - Number of roofs with PV: 16
  - HC: No limit achieved
- Future considerations
  - Façade installations
  - In rural grids, the utilization of near by space such as cropland
  - Secondary batteries may be utilized along the PV installations.

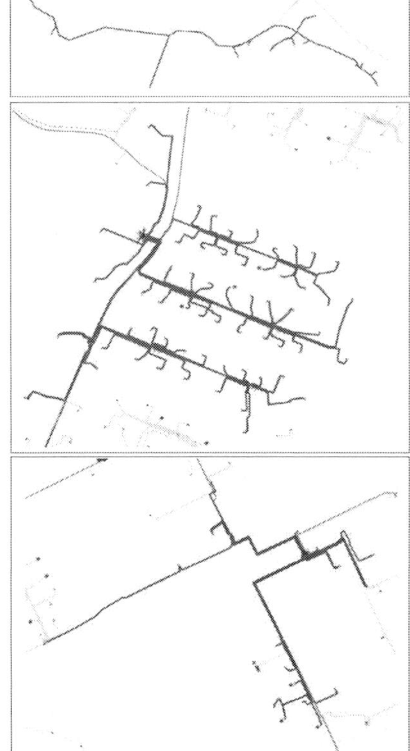

Figure 2: Low voltage grids studied: Rural (top), Suburban (middle) and Urban (bottom) highlighted in bold red.

Figure 3: The customer voltage minimum and maximum (top), the maximum line loading (middle) and the maximum transformer loading (bottom) as a function of PV penetration.

Conclusions

- Line ampacity was the limiting factor for rural and suburban grids.
- Limits of hosting capacity are hard to achieve in urban grids due to the high power consumption compared to the available roof area.

Related journal article

- D. Torres Lobera, et. al., International Journal of Photoenergy (2013) 837310. https://doi.org/10.1155/2013/837310

Contact information

- Lauri Aaltonen
- Researcher
- Tampere University, Finland
- lauri.aaltonen@tuni.fi

MAXIMIZING MARKET VALUE IN SOLAR POWER PLANTS
USING BATTERY STORAGE SYSTEMS

Hossein Rafiee[1], Rasoul Manochehrian[1], Dr. Sebastian Schäfer[1]
[1]Frankfurt University of Applied Sciences, Faculty of Computer Science and Engineering
Nibelungenplatz 1, 60318 Frankfurt am Main, Germany
Corresponding author: hossein.rafiee@stud.fra-uas.de

ABSTRACT: The more an electricity market is supplied by solar power, the lower the electricity price will be in times of high sun irradiation. For instance, in Germany prices at noon on sunny days are often close to zero. Therefore, the performance of a solar power plant should not be evaluated by its electricity output alone. In fact, the market value of electricity generation is more important since power plant operators seek to maximize their profits.
Battery storage can increase the market value by unbundling the timing of generation from the timing of sales. The success of this strategy mainly depends on three variables: the cost of the solar power plant, the cost of the battery system, and the electricity market conditions, particularly price levels and volatility. These variables are highly dynamic in the context of energy transition.
In this paper, we simulate a realistic solar power plant in Mainz using PVsyst program with adjustable plant capacity. We then develop an algorithm to increase the market value of solar electricity using battery storage. Based on mentioned variables, we calculate the optimal ratio of solar generation to battery capacity, enabling operators to select the most suitable configuration respective market conditions.
Keywords: Market Value, Solar Power Plant, PV Systems, Storage System, Optimal Capacity of Battery Storage

1 INTRODUCTION

The rising need for energy and international desire to reduce carbon emissions and apprehensions over climate change drive the expansion of renewable energy [1]. The two most popular types of renewable energy are solar and wind, a trend which is likely to be sustained in future energy systems [2]. The share of these variable renewable energy sources in power generation has been increasing rapidly. This trend has been mainly supported by government policies and further boosted by falling costs, as technologies improved and production expanded. Today, renewables can already compete with conventional energy sources in terms of generation cost [3]. They have almost negligible marginal costs. Consequently, their revenue depends on the covariance of market price developments and weather patterns [4, 5].

In order to measure and describe variations in renewable energy generation, a framework known as "Energy Quality" was most recently emerged [6]. While energy quality addresses the technical challenges associated with power fluctuations and grid stability. This article focuses on the economic dimension of renewable integration—specifically the concept of "market value."

The full integration of wind and solar power into electricity markets can be challenging. This is mainly because of two key reasons: on the one hand, their output depends on weather conditions, on the other hand, they have almost no cost for producing extra electricity. As a result, when wind and solar energy are available, they can offer electricity with low marginal cost, which lowers the overall electricity price. This leads to lower earnings for these same producers, a situation known as "self-cannibalization," first introduced in 1991 [7]. More recent studies confirm this effect, showing that the market value of wind and solar energy decreases as their output increases, especially when their production patterns do not match electricity demand. [8]. Thus, as more variable renewable energy is used, concerns about the need for flexibility and the volatility of electricity prices are increasing [9].

In [10] authors have analyzed the factors that can affect the market value. [11] aims at optimizing PV power plants, including components arrangements within the installation site, the inverter topology, cables, PV modules, the number of inverters, PV module tilt angle and shading effect result in increasing energy injected to the grid. In [12] the focus is on developing a better understanding of how the market value interacts with penetration and how policies and prices affect the market value. In this paper, we focus on improving the revenue (market value) of a PV power plant. The idea is to find better times to sell electricity production instead of increasing energy injected into the grid (E-g).

2 BATTERY STORAGE

2.1 Role and Cost Trends

When solar energy continues to expand its share in electricity generation, the role of energy storage technologies becomes increasingly important. Among various options, lithium-ion batteries are one possibility.

Lithium-ion batteries have become a major player in the energy sector, especially as storage technologies gain importance in balancing renewable generation. In the first half of 2024, global energy storage installations reached 64.9 GWh, marking a 93.8% year-on-year increase. Besides, the global battery technology market was valued at USD 213.36 billion in 2024 and is projected to grow from USD 252.13 billion in 2025 to around USD 431.65 billion by 2030 [13,14,15].

One of the key reasons for this rapid adoption is the continuous decline in battery prices. Between 2007 and 2014, lithium-ion prices dropped by roughly 14%, followed by annual reductions of 6–9% in the years that followed. Much of this progress has been driven by innovation in the automotive sector and the large-scale production of batteries for consumer electronics [13].

This steady cost reduction opens up new opportunities for the power sector. However, despite the lower investment costs, battery systems still require a

10.4229/EUPVSEC2025/5DV.3.16
020539-001

combination of technical and economic benefits to justify deployment. Stacking multiple value streams is often necessary to make battery storage financially viable in utility-scale applications [13].

The Levelized Cost of Electricity (LCOE) is commonly used to compare power plants that have different cost structures and generation profiles. It is calculated by dividing the present value of total life time cost of building and running a plant by the discounted total lifetime energy production. This makes it possible to fairly compare different technologies, even if they vary in size, investment costs, or operational lifespans [16].

$$LCOE = \frac{Total\ Life\ Cycle\ Cost}{Total\ Lifetime\ Energy\ Production} \quad (1)$$

One of the biggest challenges in increasing the share of renewables in electricity generation is dealing with their variable output. Among the available solutions, cost-effective energy storage remains a key requirement. For any storage system, the Levelized Cost of Electricity Storage (LCOES) is a useful metric that reflects the minimum average price per kilowatt-hour that would be needed for the system to recover its total lifetime costs [13]. This value helps investors understand whether a storage installation is financially viable under specific market conditions.

2.2 Market Value

In order to determine the revenues of the feed-in electricity in the market, the market value concept has been introduced. The average revenue earned per unit of energy is defined as the 'market value' or 'absolute market value' of renewables [10]. The mathematical representation is given as follows:

$$MV_{abs} = \frac{\sum_{h=1}^{n} p_h \times f_h}{f_m} \quad (2)$$

Where,
MV_{abs}: absolute market value
h: hour
n: number of hours in respective month
m: month
p: electricity market price
f: feed-in/generation of renewable plant

The absolute market value compared to LCOE indicate how far renewables will be able to pay for themselves at regular electricity markets. However, even if renewables can pay for themselves in conventional energy markets on average, this may not result in high deployment rates without support due to the greater risks associated with investing in RE, as demonstrated by Tietjen et al. [17] and Bunn and Yusupov [18]. They contend that the risk-return profile of renewables gets progressively less appealing over time as the merit order impact lowers market income. Their participation in balancing markets and other market segments could be a solution (see for example [19]).

The market value of variable renewable energy sources (VRES), such as wind and solar, can be assessed by comparing the price they receive in the electricity market to the average market price over the same period.

This comparison is expressed through a metric known as the value factor.

The value factor is calculated as the ratio between the generation-weighted average electricity price (based on the hourly output of the renewable source) and the time-weighted average market price, which already includes the contribution of the source under examination. In other words, it reflects how well the timing of renewable electricity generation aligns with higher or lower market prices. Alternative definitions exist, such as comparing to an average price that excludes the source itself or excludes all renewables, but these rely on non-observable counterfactual prices. Therefore, the comparison with the observed average market price is the practical and most widely applied definition.

$$VF = \frac{MV}{\bar{p}} \quad (3)$$

Where,
VF: is the Value Factor
$\bar{p}$: is the average wholesale day-ahead price

A value factor above 1 means that the energy is mostly generated during high-price hours while a value below 1 indicates that the generation occurs when electricity prices are lower on average [20].

This metric is essential for evaluating the economic competitiveness of renewables, especially as their share in the energy mix increases and their market value becomes more sensitive to the timing of production.

The variability of renewable generation influences its market value in two main ways, commonly referred to as the correlation effect and the merit-order effect [20].

The correlation effect occurs when the generation profile of a renewable source aligns positively with periods of high electricity prices, typically driven by high demand or external factors. In such cases, the renewable source benefits from selling electricity at a higher-than-average price.

On the other hand, the merit-order effect becomes relevant when the installed capacity of renewables is large enough to influence market prices. During hours with high wind or solar output, the supply of electricity from renewables shifts the residual load curve to the left, pushing down the market-clearing price. As more renewable capacity is added, the resulting downward pressure on prices becomes stronger, thereby reducing the market value of additional renewable output [20]. This effect is particularly pronounced in capacity-constrained thermal systems. However, it should be noted that this effect only applies in the short and medium term, since, in the long run, an adaptation of the power plant mix will cancel the merit-order effect.

At the core of the merit-order effect lies the structure of short-term electricity supply [20]:

Firstly, generation section technologies have different variable and fixed cost structures which lead to a supply curve that increases with quantity.

Secondly, the cost of storage and the lack of sufficient installed capacity limit the ability to shift surplus renewable generation to periods of higher market value.

As mentioned, in contrast to MV, the Levelized Cost of Electricity (LCOE) represents the average cost per unit of electricity produced, calculated based on all expenses over the lifetime of the asset [21]. While this definition aligns well with dispatchable generators, a slight adjustment is needed for variable renewable sources like wind and solar. For these technologies, LCOE is more accurately calculated by dividing total costs by the actual energy output, not the theoretical potential before curtailment. As a result, the LCOE for wind and solar tends to rise at high penetration levels, where curtailment becomes more frequent.

Each generation of technology has its own value factor, shaped by its production profile, variability and how well it aligns with electricity demand and market prices. Technologies that consistently deliver power during high-price hours tend to have higher market values while those producing during low-demand periods may receive lower prices. As a result, each technology fits into a different role within the system and contributes optimally to a different share of total generation.

At high levels of VRE penetration, curtailment becomes a major factor, especially in systems lacking flexibility. Without sufficient storage or transmission capacity, excess renewable generation during low-demand periods cannot be absorbed, which leads to a drop in market value. In contrast, when the system includes additional flexibility options—such as battery storage, hydrogen storage, or enhanced grid interconnection—market value can be maintained or even improved. This highlights the importance of coordinating storage investment with the expansion of renewable generation.

3 METHODOLOGIES

3.1 PVsyst Modeling

In this paper, we employed PVsyst to calculate the electricity injected into the grid by a photovoltaic power plant. The hourly PV generation profile of the power plant was simulated using PVsyst. Additionally, hourly day-ahead electricity market prices for Germany (year 2024) were obtained from Enerdata [22]. A specific geographical location was defined for the simulation: Mainz; a city near Frankfurt, one of Europe's major economic hubs. Mainz is a promising candidate for the installation of a solar power plant due to its proximity to Frankfurt and its comparatively lower land costs.

We then used Meteonorm data and incorporated important location-specific parameters into PVsyst, such as irradiation, temperature and system orientation.

A 750-kW solar power plant was considered in this study. Although the plant size is set to 750 kW, the impact of system size will be neutralized in later stages of the analysis, as the focus shifts to relative economic indicators, such as the change in market value relative to the change in LCOE (ΔMV / ΔLCOE).

The selected PV module and inverter used in the system design are shown below. PVsyst automatically suggests suitable inverter power based on the I-V curve of the selected module. Following this, we selected the most appropriate inverter and PVsyst generated a complete system configuration including the number of inverters, strings and modules in series.

The main output of PVsyst is the hourly electricity production over a full year, representing the energy that can be injected into the grid.

After simulating energy production in PVsyst and calculating the generated electricity, we determine the average market value of a certain year which represents the average revenue per unit of energy. This metric is then

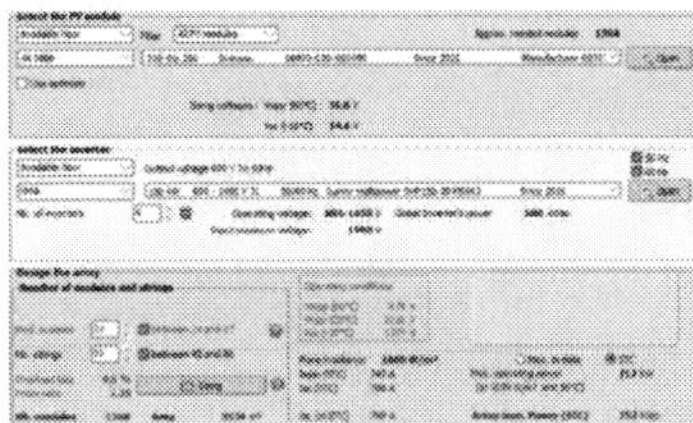

Figure 1: PV module and inverter in the system

Table I: Calculated optimum tilt for 6 meters pitch

	Tilt=20	Tilt=21	Tilt=22	Tilt=23
Eg (Kwh/year)	823065.6	823626.6	823935.3	823940.3
MV (Cent/Kwh)	3.4973	3.49650	3.4957	3.4948
Eg x MV (€/year)	28785.97	28798.1	28802.31	28795.07
Area (m2)	8100	8100	8100	8100
Price for area (€/year)	2430	2430	2430	2430
Total (€/year)	26355.97	26368.1	26372.31	26365.07

used to optimize the dispatch strategy with the goal of maximizing revenue. A key observation is that the point of maximum energy injection into the grid does not necessarily coincide with the point of maximum market value. This discrepancy arises due to variations in hourly electricity prices in the day-ahead market. Since battery storage allows energy injections to be shifted to higher-priced hours, different battery sizes result in variations in both produced and injected energy. Therefore, maximizing grid injection does not always maximize market value.

If we use PVsyst's optimization tools, the software provides the optimal pitch and tilt angle that maximizes the annual energy yield injected into the grid. Based on the selected optimum configuration, we then calculate the following parameters:

Market value (MV) of the electricity generated, Injected energy into the grid (E-g), Required land area for the power plant, estimated land cost, Ground Coverage Ratio (GCR)

The ground coverage ratio (GCR) is defined as the ratio between the active PV area and the total ground area occupied by the same PV system:

$$GCR = \frac{Area_{PV}}{Area_{Ground}} \qquad (4)$$

In many real-world scenarios, the available ground area is constrained, such as in rooftop systems or when the PV system must be installed on a plot of land with limited area. So, if we decrease the pitch, we can install more rows of panels within the same area which increases the active PV surface and consequently the GCR. The lower the pitch, the more sheds can be fitted on a given plot of land.

Since we consider a regular, shed-based PV layout, the GCR can be approximated by the ratio of the module length to the pitch distance. However, we have to also consider mutual shading. Mutual shading occurs when one row of panels casts a shadow on the adjacent row, especially during low solar angles. This trade-off between compactness (high GCR) and shading losses must be carefully evaluated in the optimization process.

To better illustrate this issue, the following table presents the results for different tilt angles. In this analysis, the land cost is assumed to be €0.30 per square meter per year.

By comparing the "Total" row in the results table, the optimal combination is identified: a tilt angle of 22 degrees with a row spacing (pitch) of 6 meters.

While other combinations could also be considered, our choice corresponds to the investor's optimum, which makes it the appropriate reference point for the following analysis.

3.2 Dispatch Strategy

We model a battery storage system to increase the market value by storing energy when the price is low and inject it into the grid when the price is high. While this part is very straightforward, there are also several disadvantages to a battery which need to be considered: first of all, its investment cost. We start by considering variable Levelized Cost of Electricity (LCOE) for the power plant and a variable surcharge for the battery, then generalizing the specific values by using relative values. For simplicity, we ignore inverter consumption and assume a battery efficiency of 97%.

In the next step, we develop an algorithm to manage battery storage and electricity dispatch with the objective of maximizing the market value — without the assumption of an unrealistic perfect foresight.

This strategy is based on day-ahead market data and aims to make use of limited and realistic forecasts, as typically available in actual electricity markets.

To define this strategy, we impose the following constraints on the charging and discharging behavior of the battery:

Lower Price Threshold:

This threshold determines when the system should store energy instead of injecting it into the grid. It is calculated as

$$((mean\ (S1)\text{-}min(S1))/2) + min(S1)$$

Where,

S1: represents the vector of hourly electricity prices for each day. If the price at a given hour is below this limit, and battery capacity is available, the energy will be stored rather than sold.

Upper Price Threshold:

Energy stored in the battery will only be discharged to the grid when the electricity price reaches the daily maximum. In this way, we ensure that stored energy is utilized at the most economically favorable time of day.

These thresholds are designed to reflect realistic operational conditions, assuming that market participants have access to day-ahead electricity price forecasts, as is commonly the case in most European markets. Thus, the strategy relies on limited foresight (one-day lookahead), making it applicable to real-world systems.

This approach allows for improved utilization of the battery by exploiting daily price fluctuations, without relying on hypothetical or unrealistic assumptions about long-term market behavior. The resulting control logic can be easily implemented and adapted to other systems with similar data availability.

3.3 Optimization Approach

The primary objective of this study is to identify the optimal combination of a solar power plant and battery storage system at which the rate of increase in market value closely matches the rate of increase in the Levelized Cost of Electricity (LCOE) induced by expanding battery capacity.

This condition, where the ratio between the relatives change leading to the optimum where the relative increase

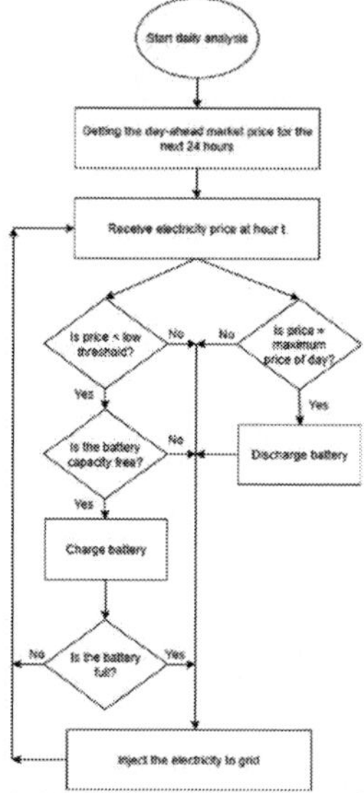

Figure 2: Battery dispatch logic based on day-ahead prices and battery state

of the market value is equal to the relative increase in LCOE approaches one, indicates that each unit of additional market value is offset by an equal increase in cost. These points mark the economically optimal configuration of the system.

To reach this point, we conduct a systematic analysis by varying two key input parameters: battery price and battery size, both expressed in relation to the PV power plant.

The analysis begins with a baseline scenario featuring a battery price of 0.1 cents per kWh and a battery size equivalent to 1% of the total installed PV capacity. These values are then incrementally increased to cover the entire solution space, and for each case, the corresponding market value, LCOE, and their ratio are calculated and evaluated. By expressing both parameters as percentages, we eliminate the dependency on absolute system size. This allows the results to remain scalable and applicable across different PV plant capacities, irrespective of their specific dimensions in the PVsyst model.

The approach ensures that the findings are generalizable and can inform decision-making for a broad range of system scales and investment conditions.

4   RESULTS

The results clearly show that as the relative battery capacity increases compared to the installed PV capacity, the ratio of market value to LCOE gradually approaches unity, particularly at lower battery price levels. Conversely, at higher battery prices, the optimal ratio can only be achieved with smaller storage capacities, since the economic benefit of additional storage decreases relative to its cost. This highlights the dual dependence of economic viability on both battery size and battery price, and the importance of identifying a balanced configuration under different cost scenarios.

In simpler terms, when the ratio between market value and LCOE reaches around 1, any extra benefit from storing and shifting energy is balanced out by the extra cost of adding the battery. This creates a point where the system reaches economic balance — where including the battery neither improves nor worsens the overall cost-effectiveness.

Moreover, the results indicate that once the battery capacity becomes large enough to cover all the storable energy of a given day, further capacity increases no longer change the amount of energy sold during peak-price hours. From this point onward, the market value reaches its ceiling and remains constant ($\Delta MV = 0$). This saturation effect repeats across all battery price levels, since MV is determined by market prices and dispatched electricity (E-grid) rather than battery cost.

This balance is especially important in electricity markets with fluctuating prices or high solar shares, where the role of batteries is not to increase production, but to make the timing of energy injections smarter and more profitable. For project developers and investors, identifying this point helps ensure that battery systems are not only technically useful, but also financially reasonable.

This relationship is visually confirmed in Figure 3, which presents a 3D plot mapping battery price, battery size (as a percentage of PV capacity), and the resulting market value-to-LCOE ratio.

In this visualization, red points represent scenarios where the ratio is approximately equal to 1, marking optimal combinations where the economic value gained matches the cost incurred.

Conversely, the surrounding blue region illustrates a wide range of non-optimal configurations, where the ratio diverges substantially from unity. These are either scenarios in which the battery is too expensive to justify economically, or too small to contribute meaningfully to market value optimization.

To highlight the critical configurations more clearly, Figure 4 presents a two-dimensional plot of battery price versus battery capacity. Red points indicate the cases where the market value to LCOE ratio is close to unity. The concentration of these points along a narrow diagonal zone emphasizes that the economic optimum is confined to a small and well-defined region. Within this region, the balance between cost and value of battery integration is achieved, and even small changes in battery pricing have a strong impact on the outcome.

This focused representation reveals a level of detail that was not easily detectable in the broader 3D plot, where the critical region appeared only as a thin strip. By isolating the relevant configurations, the figure makes it evident that the system is highly sensitive to modest changes in price or capacity. Such sensitivity means that even small adjustments can quickly shift the system from an optimal to a non-optimal configuration, underscoring the importance of precise sizing in real-world applications. Moreover, it should be noted that the optimum itself is not static but will evolve over time as market conditions and technology parameters change.

These results also reinforce the earlier observation that the optimal balance between cost and value is achieved only at specific combinations of battery price and capacity. Beyond this point, increasing the battery capacity does not lead to significant additional gains and will even reduce the overall economic efficiency of the system.

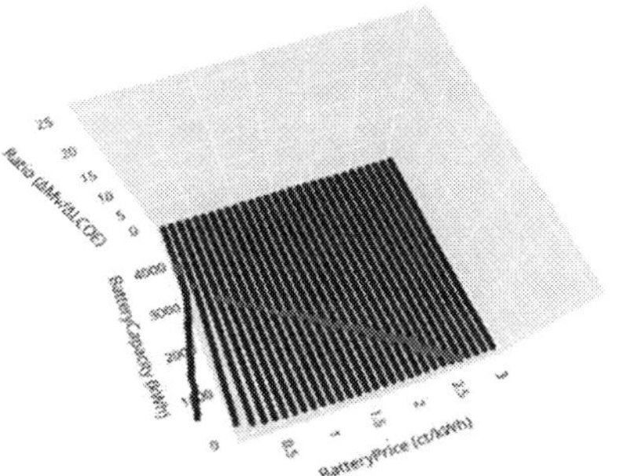

Figure 3: Market value to LCOE (ratio) across battery prices and capacities

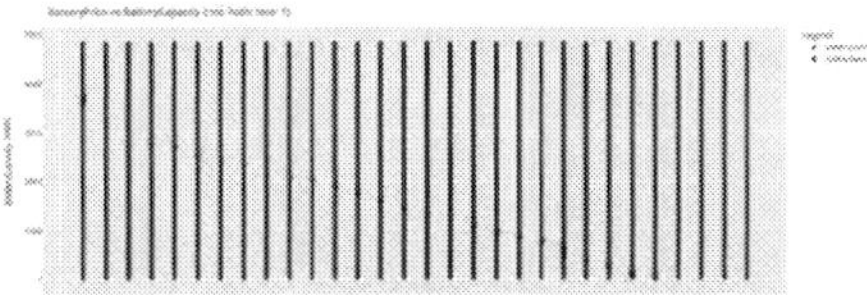

Figure 4: Battery price vs. battery capacity, red points mark ratio ≈ 1

Overall, the figure complements the quantitative analysis by offering a clear graphical representation of the economic optimum for battery integration. It visually demonstrates the limited and sensitive nature of the feasible zone and highlights the importance of careful sizing and realistic pricing to achieve viable outcomes for renewable energy projects, without relying on assumptions of perfect foresight.

5 CONCLUSIONS

While renewable energy generation inherently faces challenges such as uncertainty and intermittency, our analysis demonstrates that the economic outcome depends not only on the presence of storage but also on its careful sizing and operation. Simply adding a battery is not sufficient; rather, the way it is dimensioned and managed makes a decisive difference in financial performance.

Previous studies have primarily focused on integrating battery storage with solar power plants to mitigate periods of low solar availability [2,11,13], often emphasizing the technical role of storage rather than its economic implications. While such approaches have typically emphasized energy production alone, they often neglect the impact of day-ahead market prices and the associated fluctuations in market value.

In contrast, this study shows that the financial benefit of battery integration crucially depends on the interplay between battery price and battery size, with each price level corresponding to a specific capacity that maximizes profitability. By modeling battery behavior (charging and discharging) based on price thresholds rather than generation patterns alone, this research presents a more realistic and economically grounded approach for managing storage dispatch.

A key contribution of this research is the introduction of hourly price-based optimization for battery charging and discharging. This dynamic scheduling approach ensures that energy is stored and sold during the most profitable hours, which directly increases the market value of the system. This methodology sets the study apart from earlier work by explicitly linking technical storage behavior to economic indicators.

Additionally, the analysis of the ratio between market value increase and LCOE increase provides a practical and scalable method for identifying the optimal battery size for any solar plant and cost condition. This approach does not rely on unrealistic assumptions of perfect foresight and is applicable across different project sizes and market environments.

These findings offer a valuable framework for more informed and economically sound decision-making by investors, system designers, and plant operators, highlighting how optimized storage integration can significantly improve the financial viability of solar projects.

6   REFERENCES

[1] Wennersten, R., Q. Sun, and H. Li, The future potential for Carbon Capture and Storage in climate change mitigation–an overview from perspectives of technology, economy and risk. Journal of cleaner production, 2015. 103: p. 724-736.

[2] Wang, W., B. Yuan, Q. Sun, and R. Wennersten, Application of energy storage in integrated energy systems—A solution to fluctuation and uncertainty of renewable energy. Journal of Energy Storage, 2022. 52: p. 104812.

[3] Jansen, M., et al., Offshore wind competitiveness in mature markets without subsidy. Nature Energy, 2020. 5(8): p. 614-622.

[4] Sensfuß, F., M. Ragwitz, and M. Genoese, The merit-order effect: A detailed analysis of the price effect of renewable electricity generation on spot market prices in Germany. Energy policy, 2008. 36(8): p. 3086-3094.

[5] Würzburg, K., X. Labandeira, and P. Linares, Renewable generation and electricity prices: Taking stock and new evidence for Germany and Austria. Energy Economics, 2013. 40: p. S159-S171.

[6] Zhang, X.-P. and Z. Yan, Energy quality: A definition. IEEE Open Access Journal of Power and Energy, 2020. 7: p. 430-440.

[7] Grudd, M. Value of variable sources on power systems. in IEE Proceedings C (Generation, Transmission and Distribution). 1991. IET.

[8] Hirth, L. and A. Radebach, The market value of wind and solar power: an analytical approach. 2016.

[9] Shimomura, M., et al., Beyond the merit order effect: Impact of the rapid expansion of renewable energy on electricity market price. Renewable and Sustainable Energy Reviews, 2024. 189: p. 114037.

[10] Winkler, J., M. Pudlik, M. Ragwitz, and B. Pfluger, the market value of renewable electricity–Which factors really matter? Applied energy, 2016. 184: p. 464-481.

[11] Zidane, T.E.K., et al., Grid-connected Solar PV power plants optimization: A review. IEEE Access, 2023. 11: p. 79588-79608.

[12] Hirth, L., The market value of variable renewables: The effect of solar wind power variability on their relative price. Energy economics, 2013. 38: p. 218-236.

[13] Arteaga, J. and H. Zareipour, A price-maker/price-taker model for the operation of battery storage systems in electricity markets. IEEE Transactions on Smart Grid, 2019. 10(6): p. 6912-6920.

[14] Global energy storage market: H1 2024 installation figures, Robin Song

[15] Markets and markets – Battery technology market size, share and trend.

[16] Foster, J., L. Wagner, and A. Bratanova, LCOE models: A comparison of the theoretical frameworks and key assumptions. Energy Economics and Management Group Working Papers, 2014. 4.

[17] Tietjen, O., M. Pahle, and S. Fuss, Investment risks in power generation: A comparison of fossil fuel and renewable energy dominated markets. Energy Economics, 2016. 58: p. 174-185.

[18] Bunn, D. and T. Yusupov, The progressive inefficiency of replacing renewable obligation certificates with contracts-for-differences in the UK electricity market. Energy Policy, 2015. 82: p. 298-309.

[19] Fernandes, C., P. Frías, and J. Reneses, Participation of intermittent renewable generators in balancing mechanisms: A closer look into the Spanish market design. Renewable Energy, 2016. 89: p. 305-316.

[20] Hirth, L., The market value of variable renewables. 2012.

[21] Brown, T. and L. Reichenberg, Decreasing market value of variable renewables can be avoided by policy action. Energy Economics, 2021. 100: p. 105354.

[22] Enerdata. Global Energy & CO_2 Data. Available at: https://yearbook.enerdata.net

Maximizing Market Value In Solar Power Plants Using Battery Storage Systems

Hossein Rafiee, Rasoul Manochehrian, Dr. Sebastian Schäfer

Frankfurt University of Applied Sciences, Faculty of Computer Science and Engineering

Introduction

Background

The rapid growth of renewable energy especially solar PV, is crucial to reduce carbon emissions and combat climate change. The battery storage of a PV power plant can increase the market value by unbundling the timing of generation from the timing of sale.

Problem

However, solar power has very low marginal costs and depends on weather conditions. When PV capacity increases, it pushes electricity prices down during sunny hours resulting in reducing the revenues of PV producers. This effect is known as self-cannibalization; The market value of wind and solar energy decreases when their output increases, especially when their production patterns do not match electricity demand [1].

Objective

This study aims to improve the economic performance (market value) of PV power plants by shifting their electricity output to the hours with higher market prices using an optimal battery storage system instead of only increasing total energy production [2].

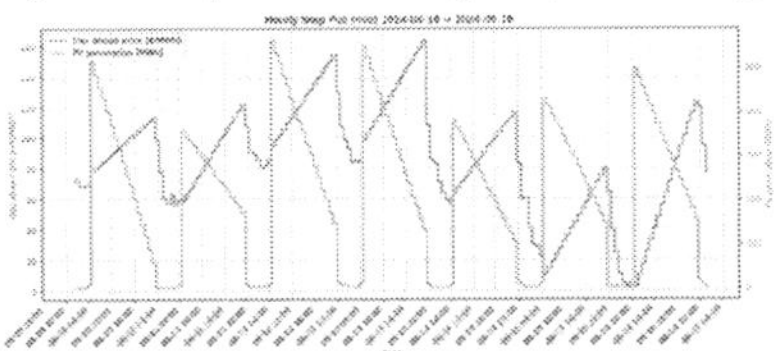

Battery Storage

Role

As PV penetration rises, storage becomes essential for smoothing variability and time-shifting energy to higher-price hours that causes mitigating self-cannibalization.
Nowadays, Lithium-ion is the most practical option for short-to-medium duration applications due to maturity, scalability and efficiency.

Trends

In the first half of 2024, global energy storage installations reached 64.9 GWh, marking a 93.8% year-on-year increase. Li-ion has the majority share.
The global battery technology market was valued at USD 213.36 billion in 2024 and is projected to grow from USD 252.13 billion in 2025 to around USD 431.65 billion by 2030 [3].

Economics

Falling costs has opened new opportunities but stacking revenue streams (arbitrage + ancillary services) is often required. We benchmark economics with LCOE for generation and LCOE_S for storage to compare technologies consistently [4].

$$LCOE = \frac{\text{Total Life Cycle Cost}}{\text{Total Lifetime Energy Production}}$$

$$LCOE_S = \frac{\text{Total Lifetime Cost of Storage}}{\text{Total Lifetime Discarged Energy}}$$

Market Value & Value Factor

Concept

The market value (MV) is the average revenue per kWh that a technology earns [5]:

$$MV_{abs} = \frac{\sum_{h=1}^{n} P_h \times f_h}{f_m}$$

The value factor (VF) compares MV to the average market price:

$$VF = \frac{MV}{\bar{p}}$$

VF > 1 → generation matches high-price hours
VF < 1 → generation during low-price hours (self-cannibalization risk)

Effects

Correlation effect: When renewable output aligns with high prices → MV ↑

Merit-order effect: High renewable output shifts supply curve → lowers market prices → MV ↓

Challenges

As VRE penetration grows, curtailment increases, which raises LCOE and reduces MV.
Storage and grid flexibility are key to maintain MV at high penetration levels.

Methodology

PVsyst Modeling

Hourly PV generation for a 750 kW plant was simulated in PVsyst using Meteonorm weather data for Mainz (near Frankfurt).

PVsyst provided annual hourly electricity output, which we combined with hourly day-ahead market prices (Germany, 2024).

We varied tilt and pitch to maximize energy yield (Eg) and calculated market value (MV), required land area, land cost, and ground coverage ratio (GCR).

The tilt that results in the highest Eg is not necessarily the one with the highest MV.

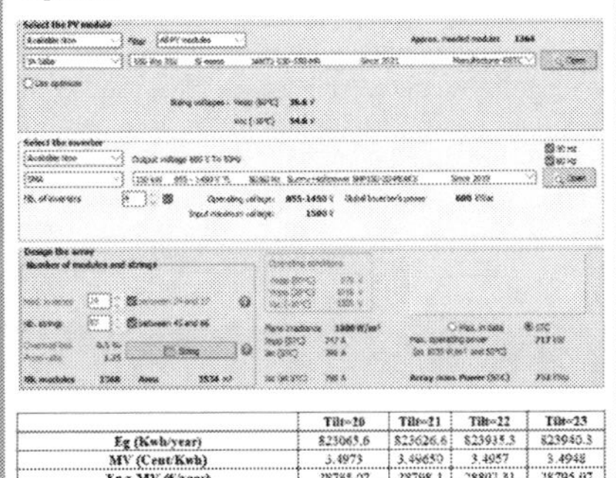

	Tilt=20	Tilt=21	Tilt=22	Tilt=23
Eg (Kwh/year)	823065.6	823626.6	823935.3	823940.3
MV (Cent/Kwh)	3.4973	3.49650	3.4957	3.4948
Eg x MV (€/year)	28785.07	28798.1	28802.31	28795.07
Area (m2)	8100	8100	8100	8100
Price for area (€ /year)	2430	2430	2430	2430
Total (€/year)	26355.07	26368.1	26372.31	26365.07

Dispatch Strategy

A battery storage system was added to shift energy from low-price hours to the daily peak-price hour.

Thresholds are calculated daily from day-ahead prices:
Lower threshold = ((mean(S1)-min(S1))/2)+min(S1)
Upper threshold = max(S1)

The control algorithm only uses 1-day foresight to reflect real market conditions.

Logic:
If price < lower → charge (if capacity free)
If price = daily max → discharge
Otherwise inject directly to grid

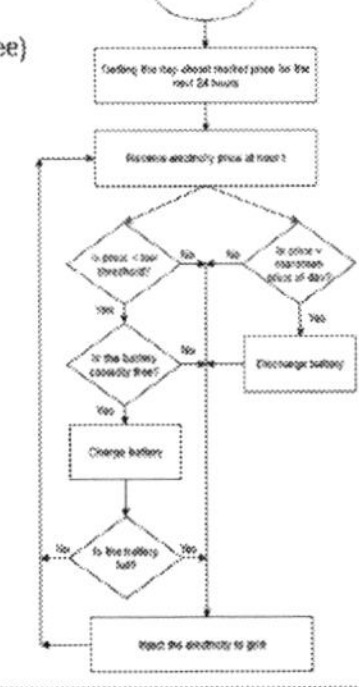

Optimization Approach

Goal
Finding the **economic balance point**
Where battery size-price is:

$$\frac{\Delta MV}{\Delta LCOE} \approx 1$$

This means the added revenue matches the added cost.

We varied battery size (1–644% of PV capacity) and battery price (0.1–3 cent/kWh), calculated MV, LCOE and their ratio for every scenario.

Once battery capacity exceeds the storable daily energy, market value saturates (ΔMV = 0) and no further benefit is achieved.

Using relative values makes results scalable and system-size independent.

Results

Across scenarios, increasing battery capacity tends to move the market-value-to-LCOE ratio toward unity at lower battery prices, while higher prices shift the optimum to smaller capacities as marginal cost overtakes marginal value.

A clear saturation appears once capacity can cover the day's storable energy: market value plateaus and additional capacity no longer increases revenue.

The economically attractive solutions form a narrow band; small deviations in price or size quickly push the system off-optimal, highlighting the need for precise sizing.

These patterns are consistent under the one-day-ahead dispatch used here.

The left plot maps the full design space; the right zoom reveals the narrow optimum band where PV + battery configurations are near economic balance (red = near-neutral, blue = off-optimal). The band is highly sensitive to battery price and size, and once daily storable energy is covered, market value saturates—larger batteries add no further revenue.

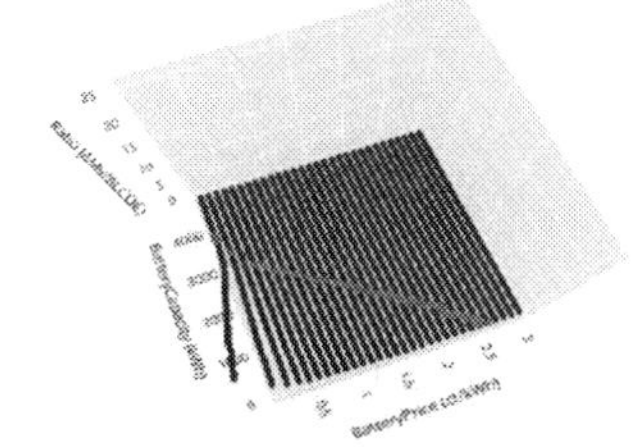

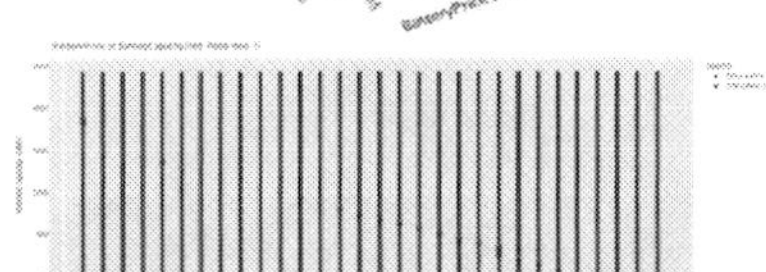

Conclusions

Optimized storage adds value not by increasing energy, but by shifting timing: price-based, day-ahead dispatch (with one-day foresight) is financially decisive.

Our results show a narrow, price-sensitive band where PV + battery reaches economic balance (MV rises in step with LCOE). Beyond the daily storable-energy point, market value saturates and larger batteries no longer improve revenues.

This price-driven control (rather than generation-only scheduling) links storage behavior directly to market value and avoids unrealistic perfect foresight. The ΔMV vs ΔLCOE perspective provides a practical, scalable way to size batteries across projects and cost conditions.

Implication: precise sizing and price-aware dispatch are essential; at higher battery prices, smaller capacities are favored, while lower prices can justify larger storage, always within the narrow band where added value matches added cost.

Acknowledgements

Data: Enerdata (2024) day-ahead prices; Meteonorm weather inputs.

Simulations with PVsyst; data processing and analysis in Python.

No external funding; no conflicts of interest.

Travel support was provided by Frankfurt University of Applied Sciences.

References

[1] Hirth, L. and A. Radebach, The market value of wind and solar power: an analytical approach. 2016
[2] SMARD (Bundesnetzagentur), Day-ahead market prices (DE-LU bidding zone). 2024-01-2024-12; accessed 18 Sep 2025.
[3] Global energy storage market: H1 2024 installation figures, Robin Song
[4] Brown, T. and L. Reichenberg, Decreasing market value of variable renewables can be avoided by policy action. Energy Economics, 2021. 100: p. 105354.
[5] Winkler, J., M. Pudlik, M. Ragwitz, and B. Pfluger. The market value of renewable electricity–Which factors really matter? Applied energy, 2016. 184: p. 464-481

Contact Information

Hossein Rafiee — hossein.rafiee@stud.fra-uas.de
Rasoul Manochehrian — rasoul.manochehrian@stud.fra-uas.de
Dr. Sebastian Schäfer — sebastian.schaefer@fb2.fra-uas.de

ROAD TO ECOLOGICAL TRANSITION: THE ITALIAN PERSPECTIVE OF THE AGRIVOLTAICS DEVELOPMENT

Alessandra Scognamiglio, Celeste Mellone and Giulia Guidetti, Valeria Viti, Lorenzo Massaro and Cesare Gatti, Fabio Salis

AIAS and ENEA, Green Horse Legal Advisory, PedersoliGattai, Iberdrola Renovables Italia

presidente@associazioneitalianagrivoltaicosostenibile.com; celeste.mellone@greenhorseadvisory.com; giulia.guidetti@greenhorseadvisory.com; vviti@pglex.it; lmassaro@pglex.it; cgatti@pglex.it; fsalis@iberdrola.it

ABSTRACT: This paper has been jointly prepared by the authors, as experts, researchers and players of the renewable energy sector and in their quality of members of AIAS (Italian Association for Sustainable Agrivoltaic), as the most relevant association in Italy for the development of a sustainable way of doing agrivoltaics.

As Agri-PV represents nowadays the most sustainable way to combine the agricultural land use and the renewable energy production, a multidisciplinary and cross-sectoral approach is necessary to demonstrate its value, avoiding any type of misconception about land use and making the Agri-PV social accepted.

For that purpose, energy-law experts, together with policymakers and researchers, can together validate the operational feasibility of Agri-PV to gain public and institutional support. On one hand, the technical support is crucial for implementing technical innovations to the plant and, on the other hand, the role of legal experts is necessary for clearly understanding the regulatory framework in the context of which the industry stakeholders operate. Awareness of the values of Agri-PV needs to be preserved, along with the need to achieve European targets, and requires a correct interpretation of the regulations and an evolving vision of the renewable energy market.

In the ecological transition context, a multi-sectoral approach deriving from associations between professionals and players in the energy, environment and agricultural sectors, can certainly support the correct development of Agri-PV in Italy.

Keywords: cooperation, innovation, cross-lateral approach, energy transition, agrivoltaic.

1 INTRODUCTION

Dealing with daily and global challenges regarding the energy transition has made real the necessity to improve and implement innovative solutions in order to ensure energy security, environmental sustainability, and food production. As Agri-Photovoltaics (Agri-PV) can combine the renewable energy production with the agricultural land use, they can represent the best solution to these interconnected challenges. Italy has recently implemented a detailed legal and regulatory framework to regulate the way of developing Agri-PV, by introducing certain principles that can be emulate by other EU member states. This paper will be focused on Italy's legal advancements in Agri-PV and its practical challenges and criticalities and on the crucial support that the associations together with the renewable energy sector experts may give to implement the proper approach and way of doing Agri-PV in Italy.

2 ITALIAN LEGAL FRAMEWORK: AGRI-PV FUNDAMENTALS

The development of Agri-PV in Italy became real and regulated following the adoption in June 2022 by MASE – Ministry of Environment and Energy Security jointly with CREA – Council for agricultural research and for the analysis of agricultural economy and GSE – Operator for energy services, of the national guidelines on Agri-PV (the "**Italian Guidelines**"), that have the purpose to establish the essential requirements necessary to define a plant as Agri-PV. Italian Guidelines are not binding in nature, but merely provide guidance in the Agri-PV sector.

Based on the objective requirements listed under the Italian Guidelines (*e.g.* thresholds of minimum occupied agricultural surface and electrical producibility; panels minimum height, depending on the agricultural activity

carried out; implementation of monitoring system), a distinction between the standard Agri-PV technology – on one side – and the advanced one – on the other side - has been defined in order to make the latter eligible for certain advantages. In general terms, (i) the standard Agri-PV is a PV system that adopts solutions to preserve the continuity of agricultural and pastoral cultivation activities at the installation site; (ii) the advanced Agri-PV is a PV system that, in accordance with the provisions of article 65, paragraph 1-*quater* and 1-*quinquies*, of Decree-Law No. 1/2012, adopts innovative integrative solutions with assembly of the modules elevated from the ground, also providing for the rotation of the modules themselves, in any case in such a way as not to compromise the continuity of agricultural and pastoral cultivation activities, also possibly allowing the application of digital and precision agriculture tools; moreover, it provides for the simultaneous implementation of monitoring systems to verify the impact of the photovoltaic installation on crops, water savings, agricultural productivity for different types of crops, continuity of the activities of the farms involved, recovery of soil fertility, microclimate, and resilience to climate change.

Only advanced Agri-PV are eligible to receive incentives tariffs and PNRR capital grants, according to the Ministerial Decree No. 436/2023, that supports the construction and operation in Italy of new agrivoltaic plants for a total capacity of 1.04 GW and an electricity production of at least 1300 GWh/year (the "**Agrivoltaic Decree**"). Eligible Agri-PV may access such public incentives through direct access (i.e. direct application to a register, in case of Agri-PV having a nominal power capacity lower than 1 MW) or through the participation to public auctions (for Agri-PV higher than 1 MW).

Agrivoltaic Decree – together with its operating rules – set precise criteria for accessing the tariff incentives on the energy production and the PNRR capital grants up to 40% of the eligible costs related to the development and construction phase. As deeper detailed in the following section, the most practical criteria to be investigated regards the subjective requirements of the beneficiaries, that shall be – or shall have a strict contractual relationship with – agricultural companies or entrepreneurs. Otherwise, from the technical standpoint, most of the support to the implementation of Agri-PV eligible for the Agrivoltaic Decree is granted by the operating rules (that firmly establish the definition of PLV – *Produzione Lorda Vendibile*, as a benchmark to measure the effective agricultural production and the surface dedicated to the agricultural activity) and technical guidelines that have been *medio tempore* enacted (*e.g.* CREA-GSE guidelines on the monitoring systems; CEI-PAS 82-93, setting the technical rules on Agri-PV (CEI - Italian Electrotechnical Committee); UNI/PdR 148/2023 aimed at providing the reference practice for realizing Agri-PV (Italian Standards Organization - UNI).

3 CURRENT REGULATORY FRAMEWORK – WHERE WE ARE

3.1 Prohibition to install PV systems on agricultural lands

Before delving into the most recent authorization procedure updates, it is crucial to summarize the recent prohibition of installing traditional PV systems on agricultural lands, even if they are considered suitable for RES plants installation in accordance with the current legal framework in Italy (cfr. Legislative Decree No. 199/2021). Such prohibition has been introduced by Italian Government through the Law Decree No. 63/2024 (subsequently converted into Law No. 101/2024 – the **"Agricultural Decree"**) in order to avoid the agricultural soil consumption, exclusively allowing the installation of Agri-PV on agricultural lands. Even if this type of prohibition slows down the energy transition process, it may be considered coherent with the needs of safeguarding the agricultural landscape and its value. Nonetheless, the relevant strict application is causing several critical between RES operators and requires an innovative approach that makes real and usable the harmonization between the renewable energy production with agricultural activities, delivering environmental and socio-economic benefits. This is the primary challenge that the legislator shall understand and deal with in ensuring – through the adoption of a specific legislation – the sustainable transformation of the landscape.

Indeed, a prudent a more literal interpretation of the prohibition at hand requires that advanced Agri-PV are exclusively allowed on agricultural areas, without taking in consideration that the continuity of agricultural activity can be ensured also through the installation of standard Agri-PV as well. This is the main reason why the Agricultural Decree has been challenged before the Italian Constitutional Court, that is going to rule on the constitutional lawfulness of such strict prohibition.

3.2 The new RES Code

In order to summarize and encompass all the national regulation that came across over the years in the renewable energy sector, the Italian legislator has recently enacted the Legislative Decree No. 190/2024 (the **"RES Code"**), aimed at simplifying and regulate the authorization regimes for the construction and operation of RES plants, by envisaging three main administrative procedures that RES projects undergo, based on power, type, location. The construction of new RES plants, repowering and revamping interventions are now efficiently summarized in sole and comprehensive code, that regulates the different developments of RES project and the technical modifications of RES plants in operation, by envisaging different authorization regimes (i.e. free building activity, PAS – *Procedura Abilitativa Semplificata* and AU – *Autorizzazione Unica*). From the authorization perspective, relevant updates and administrative simplifications have been introduced by the RES Code in relation to Agri-PV:

- Agri-PV $\geq$ 12 MW in agricultural areas shall demonstrate the "compatibility and integration with agricultural activity" to qualify for certain authorization regimes;
- RES Code includes Agri-PV within the list of cases where ordinary thresholds are adjusted;
- Agri-PV up to 5 MW may undergo to free building activity (with no need of starting any authorization procedures) if certain pre-requirements are met and they are located on suitable areas, in accordance with the law.

Landscape constraints remain strongly safeguarded even where Agri-PV are allowed and this contributes to make the coexistence of agricultural and landscape values with renewable energy production effective.

Nonetheless, the effective application of such simplified procedure and the way to ensure the continuity of agricultural activity shows practical issues that need to be addressed to the public authority. In detail, such practical issues are currently managed on a case-by-case basis, depending on the access of Agri-PV to the public incentives under the Agrivoltaic Decree or on the standard development of Agri-PV in order to avoid the general ban of installation of photovoltaic system on agricultural lands.

4 THE EVOLVING REGULATION OF AGRI-PV: LEGAL INSTRUMENTS AND ORGANISATIONAL MODELS

The regulation of the relationship between agricultural operators and electricity operators remains in an evolving state, as the legislator has not yet enacted a definitive and comprehensive set of rules.

Against this background of regulatory uncertainty, it is particularly important to frame the matter from two complementary perspectives, each one highlighting different aspects of the interaction between the parties.

The first perspective concerns the rights which must necessarily be held by both operators to validly and effectively carry out their respective activities.

The second perspective is not underpinned by a fixed and predetermined framework of rules, but instead develops in practice through contractual negotiations, sectoral guidelines and the gradual emergence of best practices. It is therefore characterised by a degree of flexibility, requiring careful case-by-case assessment to balance agricultural productivity with energy generation objectives.

In conclusion, while the definitive regulatory discipline has yet to crystallise, the dual focus on such perspectives provides a useful analytical framework for understanding and structuring the complex relationship between agricultural and electricity operators, as will be illustrated in the following sections.

4.1 Rights required for the exercise of agricultural and energy activities

As mentioned above, the structure of Agro-PV projects requires, as a preliminary step, careful consideration of the co-existence of two entities whose interests are distinct yet necessarily convergent.

On the one hand, the agricultural entrepreneur, whose primary concern lies in maintaining and, where possible, enhancing farming activities. On the other hand, there is the energy operator, whose focus is directed towards the construction and long-term management of the photovoltaic installation.

As of today, the legal system does not lay down a comprehensive set of provisions specifically governing the relationship between these two parties. Accordingly, reference must first be made to the general categories of civil law and to the legal instruments capable of ensuring:

- the lawful availability of land for the development of the project and,
- the continued exercise of agricultural activities on the same site.

In the case of ground-mounted photovoltaic plants, the widespread use of surface rights (Articles 952 et seq. of the Italian Civil Code) became established as the most appropriate legal instrument, given the specific and limited needs of such projects.

However, the scope of surface rights is expressly limited by Article 956 of the Italian Civil Code, which excludes their extension to cultivation rights. This limitation acquires particular significance in the context of Agri-PV projects, where the coexistence of agricultural and energy activities is of the essence and where the surface rights alone cannot adequately regulate the continuity of farming on the same land.

It therefore becomes necessary to identify alternative or complementary legal instruments capable of reconciling both dimensions. In the context of Agri-PV, surface rights, taken alone, do not ensure the exercise of agricultural activity. Yet the latter constitutes not only an essential and qualifying element for the lawfulness of the intervention itself, but also a requirement for access to the incentives established by the legislator.

This context has therefore given rise to the widespread need to identify and implement alternative or complementary legal instruments capable of integrating the agricultural dimension with the production of electricity.

The main solutions identified in both legal doctrine and practice include:

(i) the right of usufruct (Article 981 of the Italian Civil Code): which grants the holder the full enjoyment of the land and the right to collect its fruits, thereby ensuring the continuation of cultivation;

(ii) the loan for use agreement (Article 1803 of the Italian Civil Code): which secures the use of the land for agricultural purposes without transferring ownership, while maintaining flexibility in the allocation of rights; and

(iii) the rural land lease agreement (Articles 1628 et seq. of the Italian Civil Code and Law No. 203/1982): expressly designed to govern the management and cultivation of agricultural land and therefore particularly suited to contexts in which agricultural activity must be safeguarded.

Even in situations where both agricultural and energy activities are entrusted to a single special purpose vehicle (SPV), the entity must still be vested with the appropriate legal rights.

4.2 Flexible models of cooperation between agricultural and energy operators

The absence of codified provisions leaves room for flexible arrangements and case-specific solutions, often developed through contractual practice, administrative guidelines, and the gradual consolidation of sectoral best practices.

In general terms, as set forth by the Italian Guidelines, the following subjects are entitled to obtain authorisation for Agri-PV projects, identified as follows:

(i) **Agricultural enterprises**, whether individual or associated, which implement Agri-PV projects with the aim of reducing production costs through the utilisation of their own agricultural land; and

(ii) **Temporary associations of enterprises**, composed of energy sector operators together with one or more agricultural enterprises, which, by virtue of a specific agreement, make available their land for the construction of the Agri-PV projects.

In both scenarios, the regulatory framework requires that the agricultural activity will continue to be carried out, maintaining the centrality of farming as the qualifying element of such projects.

On the other hand, with reference to access to the incentives set forth by the Agrivoltaic Decree the related GSE operating rules, the framework of subjective eligibility requirements is set out in a binding and detailed manner. In particular, the following categories are entitled to apply for incentives:

(i) **Agricultural entrepreneurs**: this category includes agricultural entrepreneurs in the form of natural persons or companies, agricultural cooperatives, agricultural companies governed by Legislative Decree No. 99/2004, consortia composed of several entrepreneurs or agricultural companies, as well as cooperatives and their consortia engaged in the activities referred to in Article 2135 of the Civil Code. All these entities are expressly classified as "agricultural operators" for the purposes of the decree and are, as such, eligible for incentives; and

(ii) **Temporary associations of companies (ATI)**: these are also eligible provided that they include at least one of the above-mentioned agricultural operators. Where the ATI takes the form of a separate legal entity, compliance with the eligibility requirements is verified with reference to that entity. In any event, at least one member of the ATI must meet the subjective requirements set out in Article 4(1)(a) of the decree, and at least one member must qualify as a "producer" within the meaning of Appendix A to the GSE Operating Rules.

In light of the foregoing, it clearly emerges that the regulatory framework for Agri-PV is characterised by significant gaps and by the absence of a uniform and comprehensive set of provisions capable of governing all relevant profiles. As a result, while certain parameters are prescribed in a binding and detailed manner (notably with respect to access to incentives), other aspects are merely outlined through non-binding guidelines or left entirely to contractual and notarial practice. Accordingly, the definition of the most appropriate legal structure for each project cannot be resolved through the application of a single model. Rather, it necessarily requires a case-by-case assessment, tailored to the specific needs of the parties involved, to ensure both the continuity of agricultural activity and the bankability and long-term stability of the energy investment.

4.3 The development perspective

The lack of a sole model to adhere to and the need to implement the contractual relationship on a case-by-case basis, contributes to increase the uncertainty among the RES operators. Indeed, the partnership between energy operators and agricultural stakeholders is currently developing within a regulatory environment that, although politically and institutionally supportive of agrivoltaics, remains heavily influenced by agrarian legal structures designed for a different economic context, no longer suited to the multifunctional use of agricultural land enabled by agrivoltaic systems. Rather than promoting true contractual freedom, the system often requires parties to negotiate in derogation of rigid norms, creating legal uncertainty and operational risks. The challenge lies in introducing new contractual models specifically designed for agrivoltaics, capable of reconciling the need for flexible and modern agreements with compliance obligations related to agricultural qualification, land availability, and the respect of both the agronomic plan and the continuity of agricultural activity throughout the system's operational life. These models should ideally be officially recognized by competent authorities to ensure legal certainty and facilitate implementation. A constructive dialogue between the agricultural and energy sectors, supported by legal and technical expertise, could foster the evolution of contractual practices toward more modern standards, without compromising the autonomy of the parties.

4.4 Practical issue: transferability of Agri-PV projects under the Agrivoltaic Decree

A further issue concerns the admissibility of transferring Agri-PV projects or replacing the beneficiary operator after the award of incentives. This question has become increasingly relevant in practice, as several operators admitted to the Agrivoltaic Decree call for tenders, have raised doubts regarding the extent to which changes in project ownership or operator substitution may be lawfully carried out.

The GSE operating rules provide that any subjective or objective change occurring after the competitive procedure, upon entry into operation, or during the incentive period must be duly notified in accordance with the prescribed procedures. The same rules further specify that all eligibility requirements must continue to be met throughout the duration of the incentive scheme.

Neither the Agrivoltaic Decree nor the GSE operating rules, however, expressly regulate the admissibility of transfers of projects or changes in the beneficiary operator. As a result, there is no interpretative certainty on this issue. In this regulatory vacuum, it appears reasonable to consider, by analogy, the principles set out in the Legislative Decree No. 36/2023 (Public Procurement Code) regarding subjective changes.

Nonetheless, the actual compatibility of those principles with the specific features of PNRR measures and Agri-PV projects remains to be assessed.

Under public procurement law, Article 119 of Legislative Decree No. 36/2023 lays down the principle of the non-transferability of agreements, subject to the specific derogations provided in Article 120. These derogations allow a change of contractor in cases of corporate restructuring, insolvency, or succession *mortis causa*, provided that the incoming operator satisfies the original selection criteria, that no substantial amendments are made to the contract, and that no attempt at circumvention is evident. Administrative case law (Council of State, No. 1370/2013; No. 3819/2015; TAR Sicily, No. 2881/2019; Council of State, No. 6216/2019) has gone further, extending the principle to successful tenderers who had not yet signed a contract, to safeguard freedom of corporate reorganisation.

Two main principles emerge:

(i) **Principle of substantial continuity of the operator**: to avoid circumvention, the contracting authority must verify the legal basis for the proposed takeover, the subjective suitability of the incoming operator, and the continuing compliance of the outgoing operator with the initial requirements; and

(ii) **Limits on "additional" changes**: a distinct issue arises in respect of replacing members of a temporary association of companies (ATI). The new Public Contracts Code no longer treats such changes as automatically prohibited. They may be admissible provided that the conditions laid down in the legislation are satisfied (see Articles 68, 94, 95, 97(2), and 100), and that no alteration is made to the financial offer. In this regard, the Campania Regional Administrative Court, in its judgment No. 5211/2024, confirmed the admissibility of subjective changes within an ATI, provided that these served to ensure the consortium's operational capacity and did not introduce elements detrimental to transparency or competition.

5   THE MULTIDISCIPLINARY APPROACH

The potential positive impact of Agri-PV and its relevant proper installation can be better addressed by means of a joint professional approach. Associations between professionals and players in the energy, environment and agricultural sectors, in a common effort, can certainly support to define an appropriate policy frameworks and a common strategy for Agri-PV as well as to reach the targets of the European Green Deal.

With the concrete support of AIAS as well as of the researchers' approach, it is possible to reach an integration of Agri-PV into the landscape - that remains a significant barrier to their implementation - and to overcome the practical criticalities that RES operators and legal experts are daily facing.

In detail, energy-law experts, together with policymakers and researchers can play a key-role to explain to the renewable energy industry the concrete advantages deriving from the combination and synergy of agricultural activity and renewable energy production:

-   Energy-law experts play a crucial role in shaping and interpreting Agri-PV policy and legal framework, by helping to balance the interests of the agriculture and energy sectors. As noted above, energy-law experts can help reduce uncertainty and attract investment to the Agri-PV sector. Moreover, they can influence policy developments that support the broader objectives of the European Green Deal, such as climate neutrality by 2050.

- Technical experts and researchers have the responsibility to collaborate with institutions and other market participants by offering agronomic data and innovative solutions, in order to allow a sustainable transformation of the agricultural landscape. Indeed, it is not uncommon for public authorities responsible for protecting the landscape values to mistakenly focus on land consumption, without considering that agrivoltaic systems are inherently designed to preserve agricultural land use and implement appropriate mitigation measures. This achievement can be made possible through public-private partnerships, able to play a key-role in establishing necessary unified regulations.

- Developers' aim is to ensure the most competitive solutions, which do not raise energy costs for consumers and for the development of Agri-PV. The simplification of administrative regimes and grid connection procedures is necessary to achieve such renewables goals. From the development perspective, it is crucial to establish a clear regulatory framework that financially supports advanced, experimental agrivoltaics technologies, allowing them to mature and reach their full value and potential.

public parties.

Conversely, an excessively prescriptive approach would risk either degenerating into speculative exploitation of agricultural land, or, at the other extreme, paralysing the development of a sector which, by its very design, has the potential to contribute decisively to the twin objectives of ecological transition and rural development.

5 CONCLUDING REMARKS

The foregoing analysis demonstrates that the existing legal framework applicable to Agri-PV projects remains fragmented and, to a significant extent, undeveloped. While certain profiles are governed by binding provisions of positive law, others are merely outlined in soft-law instruments or are left to be structured through contractual autonomy and notarial practice.

In such a context, the simplified administrative procedures cannot clearly explain their concrete *favor* to Agri-PV development, as the single public bodies involved may act in a different way – basing on the different interpretation and application they may give to the legislative framework – and no uniform legal model can be regarded as dispositive or capable of universal application.

More broadly, the considerations set out in this paper support a general principle: the regulation of Agri-PV projects should be directed towards ensuring a genuine balance between the primacy of agricultural activity and the long-term sustainability of energy production.

Such balance is more effectively achieved through flexible and cooperative model legal structures than through rigid or exclusionary regulatory prescriptions. Indeed, notwithstanding the entry into force of several legal prescriptions, it is clear they do not sufficiently cover all the sub-fields connected to the agricultural sector. As experts of renewable energy sectors, we learnt that a pragmatic and tailor-made approach may fill the lack of a proper regulation and may be more capable to meet the needs of all the parties involved during the development phase as well as during the negotiation among private and

Road to ecological transition: the Italian perspective of the agrivoltaics development

RESEARCH PERSPECTIVE

The effective integration of agrivoltaic systems requires ongoing research to ensure a sustainable transformation of the landscape and demonstrate social acceptance. This calls for innovative regulatory and technical solutions that highlight their tangible value to the public. Such integration relies on a cohesive, transdisciplinary vision that combines diverse perspectives and shares experimental and technical results.

Alessandra Scognamiglio, Senior Researcher and Coordinator task force Sustainable Agrivoltaics at ENEA

ASSOCIATION PERSPECTIVE

Associations are crucial in advancing agrivoltaics by uniting institutions, trade associations and companies, supporting EU and State Members in shaping policy frameworks and a common strategy. This collaboration is essential to enhance regulations, align partnerships with the RES market, and advance the energy transition in line with European Green Deal objectives.

Alessandra Scognamiglio, President of AIAS

LEGAL PERSPECTIVE

Italy has introduced a dedicated regulation for agrivoltaic systems, recognizing their key role in the energy transition. Recent legal updates aim to accelerate their deployment, highlighting the synergy between renewable energy development and agricultural land use. This collaboration between RES developers, stakeholders and agricultural partners requires specific legal regulation through ad hoc contractual forms, designed to balance and integrate the distinct needs of both the renewable energy and agricultural sectors. In view of the PNRR and FER X incentives, it is essential that the contractual regulations set out a framework that will stand the test of time.

Celeste Mellone, Partner and Co-head of Regulatory at Green Horse Legal Advisory
Valeria Viti, Partner at PedersoliGattai
Giulia Guidetti, Senior Associate at Green Horse Legal Advisory
Lorenzo Massaro, Senior Associate at PedersoliGattai
Cesare Gatti, Associate at PedersoliGattai

DEVELOPMENT PERSPECTIVE

The partnership between energy operators and agricultural stakeholders is growing within a regulatory framework still shaped by outdated agrarian laws, unsuited to the multifunctional use of land enabled by agrivoltaics. A constructive dialogue, supported by legal and technical expertise, is essential to modernize contractual practices while preserving party autonomy and ensuring legal protection for both sides.

Fabio Salis, Regulatory and Public Affairs Manager at Iberdrola Renovables Italia

GREEN HORSE
Green Horse Advisory Website

PedersoliGattai
PerdersoliGattai Website

Iberdrola
Iberdrola Website

ENEA
Enea Website

AIAS
AIAS Website

POTENTIAL OF AGRIVOLTAICS IN THE EU UNDER DIFFERENT REGULATION SCENARIOS

Julien Van Overstraeten[2], Caroline Plaza[2], Philippe Macé[1], Elina Bosch[1], Mélodie de l'Épine[2]
[1]Becquerel Institute, Brussels (Belgium) [2]Becquerel Institute France, Lyon (France)
Rue Praetere 2, 1000 Brussels, Belgium. +32 493 451 720

ABSTRACT: The use of agricultural land for photovoltaic (PV) deployment has raised concerns, as rising installation rates intensify competition between food and energy production. To address this, several countries have introduced restrictions on PV use in agriculture. Agrivoltaics (AgriPV) offer a promising alternative by enabling the dual use of land for food cultivation and renewable electricity generation. Estimates of the technical potential vary widely: the Joint Research Centre of the European Commission calculated 944 GWp for 1% of the Utilized Agricultural Area (UAA) in the EU [1], while Danish researchers estimated up to 51 TWp if the entire UAA were used [2]. Unlike studies focused on maximum potential, this work evaluates a more restricted AgriPV potential, explicitly shaped by regulations designed to safeguard agricultural activity and food security. The analysis estimates a "minimal" potential by systematically excluding unsuitable land and applying regulatory constraints such as crop suitability, yield preservation, and ground coverage ratios. Even under the most stringent scenarios, the remaining potential remains significant, corresponding to 34% of the REPowerEU 2030 solar target. These results show that AgriPV can make a meaningful contribution to Europe's decarbonisation strategy without undermining agricultural production. *Keywords: Agrivoltaics, Technical potential, Regulatory constraints, Land use.*

1 INTRODUCTION

Photovoltaic installations on agricultural land have long been explored as a means to expand renewable energy production. Traditionally, such projects often replaced agricultural activities, but rising PV adoption has intensified competition for land, prompting some countries to impose restrictions. Agrivoltaics offers a promising alternative by enabling dual land use, combining food production with electricity generation. Beyond energy, AgriPV systems can protect crops and livestock from extreme weather while providing additional income for farmers.

Studies have estimated significant technical potential in Europe, with figures ranging from 51 TWp across the continent to 944 GWp if just 1% of agricultural land were utilized [1][2]. These figures highlight the transformative role agrivoltaics could play in achieving renewable energy targets while safeguarding food systems.

However, realizing this potential requires overcoming barriers such as technological adaptation for different crop types, alignment with agricultural practices, and the establishment of clear regulatory frameworks. Despite growing interest, concerns from farmers' organizations and the public highlight the need for robust governance to balance renewable energy goals with food security and responsible land use.

2. METHODOLOGICAL APPROACH

The assessment of the agrivoltaics market potential in this work follows a multi-step approach, divided into two main sections. The first section focuses on estimating the current technical potential for agrivoltaics, starting from the area in the European Union actively used for agricultural activities, known as the Utilized Agricultural Area. This excludes idle lands and wooded areas and represents the Gross Technical Potential. To refine this estimate and obtain a Realistic Technical Potential, several exclusions were applied, including protected agricultural and landscape areas, prohibitive terrains such as steep or flood-prone lands, and High Nature Value farmland important for biodiversity and traditional farming practices.

Then, economic considerations were incorporated to determine the Economic Technical Potential. Surfaces deemed unprofitable due to low PV yield or difficult synergy with crops were excluded, as were areas incompatible with agrivoltaic systems, such as energy crops or tree plantations, either due to physical constraints or intrinsic opposition to dual-use systems. Initially expressed in millions of hectares, these areas are later converted into potential installed capacity in GWp during the market potential analysis.

The second section evaluates the specific market potential through scenario-based modeling. Using the diffusion of innovations framework, an S-shaped curve is applied to project the annual Total Addressable Market (TAM) for agrivoltaics from 2024 to 2100, with the Economic Technical Potential defining the maximum achievable capacity by 2100.

To account for regulatory constraints and the need to maintain agricultural productivity, three scenarios were designed to estimate the Serviceable Addressable Market (SAM), reflecting variations in ground coverage limits, yield preservation, and other restrictions.

Table I: Summary of scenarios considered for the SAM assessment

	Loose regulation scenario	Medium regulation scenario	Strict regulation scenario
Prioritization of degraded soil	No	Yes	Yes
Selection of crops	No	No	Yes
Average density	0,60 MWp/ha	0,57 MWp/ha	0,54 MWp/ha

Although not considered here, a further step could define the Serviceable Obtainable Market (SOM) by integrating additional political, social, supply chain, and economic constraints, providing a more realistic projection of agrivoltaics deployment potential.

10.4229/EUPVSEC2025/5DV.3.32

3. RESULTS

3.1. Technical potential for AgriPV in Europe

The gross technical potential for agrivoltaics in Europe accounts for over 155 million ha. Through exclusion of land that is either protected, under high nature value farming recognition, or subject to adverse terrain conditions, a realistic technical potential of just under 78 million ha is calculated. Finally, taking into out areas subject to insufficient irradiation conditions or intrinsically incompatible with agrivoltaics, an economic technical potential of 76,6 million ha is obtained.

3.2. Specific market potential for AgriPV in Europe

The total addressable market, here taken as equivalent to the economic technical potential of 76,6 million of ha, represents a very significant surface area, which will likely not be entirely exploited by agrivoltaics. Instead, the serviceable addressable market (SAM) assessment provides a more realistic vision of the evolution of the area that could be exploited by agrivoltaics.

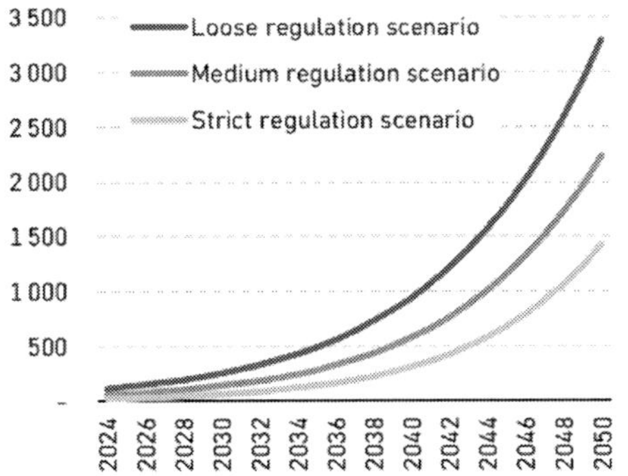

Figure 1: Cumulative serviceable addressable European agriPV market, in GWp

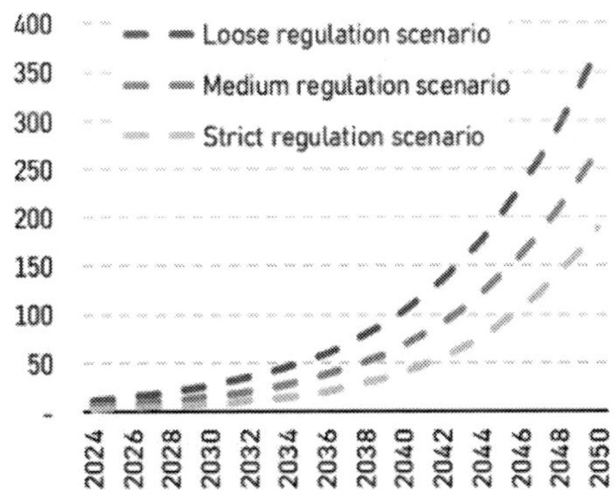

Figure 2: Annual serviceable addressable European agriPV market, in GWp

The serviceable addressable market assessment provides a realistic outlook on the potential deployment of agrivoltaics in Europe, taking into account regulatory constraints that safeguard agricultural activity and food security. Figure 1 and Figure 2 illustrate the evolution of cumulative and annual SAM up to 2050, expressed in GWp. While initial deployment progresses slowly, growth accelerates toward the middle of the century, positioning agrivoltaics as a key contributor to PV deployment in Europe, where competition for land limits the availability of large, non-agricultural sites for ground-mounted PV plants.

By 2050, the cumulative SAM reaches approximately 3,000 GWp under loose regulation, slightly above 2,000 GWp under medium regulation, and around 1,400 GWp under strict regulation. The corresponding annual SAM peaks at 377 GWp, 272 GWp, and 193 GWp, respectively. Despite the limitations inherent in the stricter scenario, agrivoltaics could still cover up to 34% of the EU's 2030 solar target of 750 GWDC (600 GWAC) under REPowerEU [3].

These scenarios highlight the decisive role of regulation in shaping AgriPV's development. While larger, high-density projects may accelerate progress toward PV targets, smaller-scale installations designed with strong synergies between energy generation and agricultural activity may provide a more sustainable pathway. The balance between these approaches will depend on the regulatory framework, which will ultimately determine how agrivoltaics can support both renewable energy expansion and the continuity of European agriculture.

Table II: Summary of serviceable addressable market (SAM) results for AgriPV in Europe [GWp]

Regulation scenario	2050		
	Loose	Medium	Strict
Cumulative	3289	2232	1424
Annual	377,3	272,1	193,1

4 CONCLUSIONS

Unlike studies focused on estimating maximum technical potential, this work evaluates a more restricted agrivoltaics potential, explicitly shaped by regulations aimed at preserving agricultural activity and safeguarding food security. Even under the most stringent regulatory scenarios, the remaining potential proves substantial, corresponding to 34% of the REPowerEU 2030 solar target and thus capable of covering a significant share of Europe's future energy demand. This highlights that agrivoltaics can make a meaningful contribution to decarbonization strategies without compromising agricultural production.

Nonetheless, regulatory uncertainty remains a central challenge for the sector. Overly strict land-use policies could unnecessarily constrain deployment and delay the achievement of renewable energy targets, while excessively loose frameworks risk encouraging "alibi agriculture," where the agricultural function becomes secondary to energy generation. Both extremes threaten the credibility and long-term sustainability of the concept.

To unlock agrivoltaics' full potential, coordinated policy support is required, along with transparent and robust regulatory frameworks that align energy and agricultural priorities. Furthermore, building awareness within markets and among stakeholders—farmers, energy developers, policymakers, and the public—will be critical to foster acceptance and encourage models that deliver both food and energy security. In this way, agrivoltaics can evolve from a niche concept into a cornerstone of Europe's sustainable energy transition.

5 REFERENCES

[1] A. Chatzipanagi, N. Taylor and A. Jaeger-Waldau, "Overview of the potential and challenges for Agri-Photovoltaics in the European Union," Publications Office of the European Union, Luxembourg, 2023.
[2] K. A. K. Niazi and M. Victoria, "Comparative analysis of photovoltaic configurations for agrivoltaic systems in Europe," Progress in Photovoltaics: Research and Applications, vol. 31, no. 11, pp. 1101-1113, 2023.
[3] B. Meban, "Landmark EU Solar Strategy: SolarPower Europe Response", SolarPowerEurope. www.solarpowereurope.org/press-releases/landmark-eu-solar-strategy-solar-power-europe-response. 2022.

6 ACKNOWLEDGMENT AND FUNDING

 The work described has received funding as part of the SEAMLESS-PV project from the European Union's Horizon Europe research and innovation program under grant agreement N° 101096126.

SMART ENERGY SYSTEM INTEGRATION OF PHOTOVOLTAIC:
FROM STRATEGIC AND RESEARCH INNOVATION AGENDA TO EU FUNDED PROJECTS

Grazia BARCHI[1], Maximilian SCHÖNAU[2], Pierre-Jean ALET[3], Venizelos EFTHYMIOU[4], Gofran CHOWDHURY[5], Marion PERRIN[6], Elham SHIRAZI[7], Ioannis (John) A. TSANAKAS[8]

[1] EURAC Research - Institute for Renewable Energy, Italy, grazia.barchi@eurac.edu
[2] smartblue AG / Coburg University of Applied Sciences, Dept. of Electrical Engineering and Computer Sciences, Germany, maximilian.schoenau@smartblue.de
[3] CSEM, Switzerland, pierre-jean.alet@csem.ch
[4] EPL Technology Frontiers Ltd, Cyprus, venizelos@epltechfront.com
[5] 3E, Belgium, gofran.chowdhury@3e.eu
[6] Energy Pool, France, marion.perrin@energy-pool.eu
[7] Faculty of Engineering Technology, University of Twente, Enschede, The Netherlands, e.shirazi@utwente.nl
[8] CEA-INES, France, venizelos@epltechfront.com

ABSTRACT: The EU has set an ambitious target to reach climate neutrality by 2050, with a rapidly rising share of PV and wind generation reshaping the energy system in terms of planning and operation. A high penetration of PV systems requires advanced monitoring and control systems and techniques, as well as technology that provides system stability and minimises congestion during peak production hours. In this context, Challenge 4 of the Strategic Research and Innovation Agenda (SRIA), developed within ETIP-PV, is dedicated to "Smart Energy System Integration of Photovoltaics for Large-Scale Deployment and High Penetration". Despite the Challenge identified six roadmaps, a systematic and scalable synthesis of the thematic evolution and strategic relevance of grid integration PV challenges, solutions, and evolutions remains limited in relation to EU-funded projects. This paper introduces an LLM-based methodology for analyzing a decade of EU-funded projects data, mapped to the Challeng 4 SRIA roadmap, and extracting indicators to reveal trends, dominant themes, and gaps. The framework provides a reproducible methodology to possibly guide research directions, funding priorities, and policy development.

Keywords: Photovoltaic, Smart Energy System, Digitalization, Large Language Model, Artificial Intelligence

1 INTRODUCTION

The cumulative installed solar photovoltaic (PV) capacity in the EU reached 338 GW in 2024, representing a significant increase from the 16 GW in 2009 when the Renewable Energy Directive was first introduced [1]. The European Solar Energy Strategy foresees 600 GW of PV deployment overall across European countries by 2030 [2]. The increase of PV is mainly due to lower production and installation costs, as well as the support of policy frameworks, where PV is becoming one of the technology drivers for the European energy transition.

In 2024, the International Energy Agency (IEA) reported that global investments in solar PV exceeded those for all other sources of electricity generation combined, highlighting the central role of PV in the ongoing energy transition [3].

The European Union's climate neutrality target by 2050 requires a rapid increase in the integration of renewable energy sources into the energy system, particularly wind and solar systems, which are expected to cover at least 50% of energy demand.

This transition brings significant challenges for grid integration in the energy system, as renewables are inherently variable and unpredictable. In particular, the system operation and planning procedure will evolve to properly address local voltage stability issues, regional congestion risks, and the complexities of cross-border power exchanges. Advanced solutions require real-time control, predictive monitoring, demand-side flexibility, and the deployment of new technologies, such as grid-forming inverters and energy storage systems, to ensure reliable and resilient grid performance as renewable energy sources become more dominant.

To overcome such present and future limitations as well as to increase PV deployment further and boost efficiency, the European Technology and Innovation Platform for Photovoltaics (ETIP-PV) has recently updated the Strategic Research and Innovation Agenda (SRIA) on PV [4] to identify, among other priorities, the five most crucial challenges that should be addressed in the coming years as priority, to establish reasonable targets for 2035. In this multifaceted scenario, Challenge 4 on "Smart Energy System Integration of Photovoltaics for Large-Scale Deployment and High Penetration" aims to enhance and develop seamless energy systems capable of better utilizing and optimizing the amount of available PV energy alongside other renewable energy sources, in order to meet the expectation of both users and stakeholders in terms of lower costs, higher remuneration and overall higher efficiency.

Over the past decade, numerous EU-funded projects have contributed to advancing PV innovation, integration, and sustainability through technical development, socio-economic impact, and policy alignment, forming a rich yet complex landscape of strategic efforts. Despite the volume and diversity of these projects, a systematic and scalable analysis of their thematic evolution and strategic relevance remains limited.

This paper introduces a methodology based on large language models (LLMs) to analyze and synthesize insights from ten years of EU project data on PV system topics related to the Challenge 4 SRIA (SRIA-Ch4) priorities. Considering the semantic abilities of LLMs, we aimed to extract key values and indicators that reveal trends, dominant themes, and contribution distribution within the SRIA-Ch4 areas. The approach enables us to capture a snapshot of project trends and identify relevant topics that may inform future research directions, funding priorities, and policy frameworks.

Our analysis contributes to the field of AI-assisted research synthesis and provides a replicable framework for strategic intelligence in energy innovation.

In this way, the findings are expected to support stakeholders, including researchers, policymakers, and industry actors, in navigating the evolving landscape of PV energy system integration with greater clarity and foresight.

2 METHODOLOGY

LLM models of OpenAI [5] were used to analyze EU PV project data related to the SRIA priorities. LLMs have shown promising results for conducting literature reviews, especially for screening smaller texts [6], [7]. OpenAI's models have also proven to have satisfactory accuracy when applied to problems within the photovoltaic domain [8], [9].

Before going into the detail of the methodology, we summarize in Table 1 the correspondence between the specific six roadmap in SRIA-Ch4 [4] and what we refer to as "roadmap topic".

For the specific meaning and objectives of each roadmap item, we refer readers to the SRIA-Ch4.

Table 1: Mapping of roadmaps identified in Challenge 4 of the SRIA and the selected and used roadmap topics

Roadmap SRIA-Ch4	Roadmap Topic
R1: More intelligence in distributed control	Distributed control intelligence
R2: Improved efficiencies by integration of PV-systems in DC-networks	PV integration in DC Networks
R3: Hybrid systems including demand flexibility (PV + storage + batteries + green hydrogen/fuel cells or gas turbines etc)	Hybrid RES Systems with Demand flexibility
R4: Aggregated energy and VPPs	Aggregation and Market participation
R5: Interoperability in communication and operation of RES smart grids	Interoperability in Smart Grids
R6: Digitalization of PV systems	Digitalization of PV systems

2.1 Using LLMs for the Analyzation of EU funded Projects

All projects funded by the EU under the Horizon framework program for research and innovation from 2014 to 2027, publicly available [10], [11] were downloaded, imported and analyzed by their project titles and objectives. The dataset consists of 52,848 research projects, most of which are unrelated to PV. Thus, the projects were preprocessed with a smaller system prompt and *GPT4o-mini* [12], to filter projects, that do not relate to the PV domain. This resulted in 474 projects that are relevant to the SRIA on PV.

A more detailed system prompt and *GPT5* [13] were employed to implement a second, stricter filter and a

deeper analysis. The model was instructed to assign a percentage w_{pt} indicating how much of the project p aligns with each of the roadmap topics t (including the category "other" to attribute the percentages that did not match the roadmap).

GPT5 was able to reliably return percentages that summed up to 1 across all topics. To avoid inconsistencies that smaller models may introduce (e.g., percentages not summing exactly to 1), we recommend first having the model assign each topic to a simple scale and, second, converting these scores to percentages through normalization of the simple scores.

The second filtering by *GPT5* resulted in 255 projects, with varying levels of alignment with the evaluated roadmaps.

The estimated relevance R_t of every topic was calculated by the average of these percentages over the number of projects n_p:

$$R_t = \frac{1}{n_p} \cdot \sum_p w_{pt} \qquad (1)$$

By multiplying the percentages by the project funding F_p, the funding for the strategic topics F_t was estimated:

$$F_t = \sum_p w_{pt} \cdot F_p \qquad (2)$$

The project's duration in every year Δt_{py} divided by the total project duration Δt_p was utilized, to get an estimation of the budget for every strategic roadmap topic of the SRIA-Ch4 over the last years F_{ty}:

$$F_{ty} = \sum_p w_{pt} \cdot F_p \cdot \frac{\Delta t_{py}}{\Delta t_p} \qquad (3)$$

Figure 1 illustrates the methodology's outline. The system prompts are in Appendix A1 and A2. As a user prompt, the project title and objective were given.

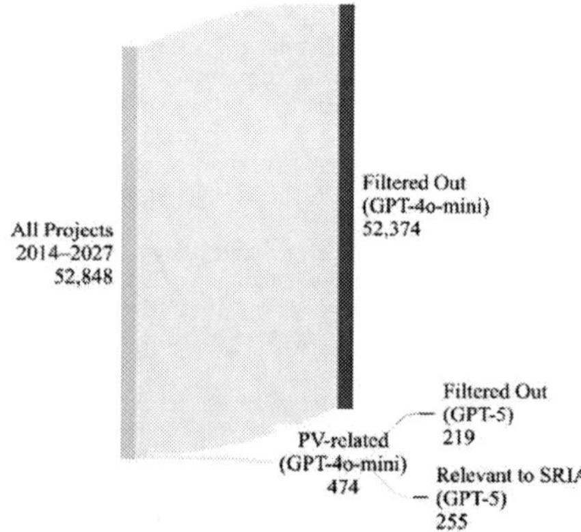

Figure 1: Outline of the project screening

This is not a rigorous quantitative method. It is a heuristic proxy constrained by the limited information contained in the project's objective and the subjectivity of topic taxonomies as well as the uncertainty inherent to the LLM-based classification. The results should therefore be read as indicative, comparative trends, useful for assessing the relative salience of topics across the portfolio, rather than as exact, auditable allocations at the level of individual projects.

2.2 Validation

The filtering of the *GPT4o-mini* model and the analysis of *GPT5* were manually labelled for a subset of 100 and 50 projects, respectively. For the validation of the filtering, the test dataset was randomly sampled of 50 predicted positives (projects that are part of the PV domain) and 50 predicted negatives (projects that do not relate to PV).

Coincidentally, the validation yielded 3 false positives and 3 false negatives. This proves that the filtering process is very reliable, with accuracy, precision, specificity, and recall of 94% each. None of the incorrectly classified samples had PV as their primary focus; misclassifications occurred only in borderline cases.

The share of the project attributable to the individual strategic topics returned by *GPT5* w_p were manually labelled for a test subset of 50 projects. Comparing *GPT5*'s outputs with these annotations yielded a mean absolute error of 9 percentage points and a root mean squared error of 15 percentage points on average over all categories. This indicates a significant discrepancy between the prediction and manual label, highlighting the subjective and qualitative nature of the labels. Thus, an evaluation strategy emphasizing agreement within relative ranking, rather than exact equality was adopted by calculating the spearman correlation [14]. With a spearman correlation of 50 % on average over all categories, the correlation of the ranking of the projects seems adequate for comparative analyses.

3 RESULTS ON EU-PROJECT DISTRIBUTION

Based on the methodology and analysis described in Section 2, we found that 255 projects were classified as relevant to the SRIA-Ch4 and the strategic roadmaps. Table 2 displays the difference between the estimated relevance of the topics, Eq (1), and the distribution, when it is scaled by the funding, Eq. (2). Larger differences between these values could indicate topics that were more prominent in the project summaries but had less funding on average. **Error! Reference source not found.** displays the funding share by strategic topic over time, Eq. (3). The values are normalized, and they are grouped by four periods, i.e. before 2019, 2020-2022, 2023-2025 and beyond 2025. It is interesting to see how the roadmap topics distribution changes from before 2019 till 2025.

Table 2: Comparison between the estimated relevance and the estimated funding share of strategic topics.

Strategic Topic	Estimated Relevance	Estimated Funding Share
Aggregation & Market Participation	19 %	21 %
Hybrid RES Systems with Demand Flexibility	17 %	21 %
Interoperability in Smart Grids	17 %	21 %
Digitalization of PV Systems	25 %	19 %
Distributed Control Intelligence	18 %	16 %
PV Integration in DC Networks	3 %	2 %

We can appreciate that in the first three bars, there is a higher distribution of funded projects in the topic of *Aggregation & Market Participation*. This is not surprising, as the topic is broad and covers not only projects more focused on PV but also energy systems and smart grids in general. Moving from left to right, we can notice no significant changes in the Hybrid RES and Distributed Control Intelligence topics, which on average remain almost the same, while the Digitalization of PV Systems and PV Integration in DC Networks show some variation. This trend is reasonable and aligns with, on one hand, the growing relevance of digitalization, especially with the advent of AI, and, on the other hand, the increase in distributed energy resources that naturally operate on DC. Along with PV, this drives the evolution of fully supplied DC networks.

Figure 3 shows the distribution of the normalized estimated relevance across roadmap topics. The first four topics resulted in similar slices. *Digitalization of PV Systems* seems to be a common topic, accounting for 25% of the share. *Aggregation & Market Participation*, *Hybrid RES Systems with Demand Flexibility*, *Interoperability in Smart Grids* and *Distributed Control Intelligence* accounted for roughly one-fifth each. The topic *Distributed Control Intelligence* was mentioned a bit less, with only

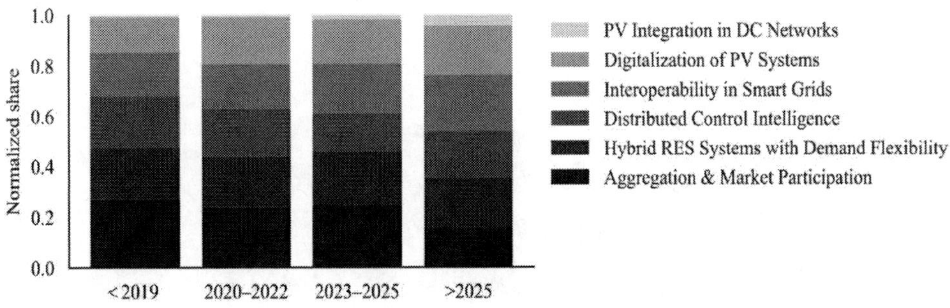

Figure 2: Estimated share of funded budget by strategic topic over time.

16 % percent. *PV Integration in DC Networks* represents only a small fraction.

This figure results complementary with respect to Figure 2. Indeed, if from one side we report the distribution based on the total budget allocated to the specific topics on the other side (Fig. 3) we report the normalized value based on the number of funded projects. The results do not change too much, but they are also not the same and this lead to the consideration that different budget has been allocated to different number of projects by suggesting that some of them require possible an higher investment due possible to different reasons: infrastructure requirements, starting technology readiness level, number of partners to be involved and so on.

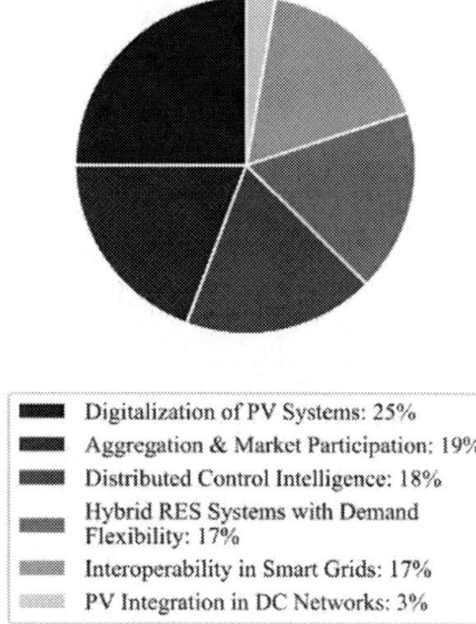

Figure 3: Estimated distribution of the projects alignment to the strategic topics.

Error! Reference source not found. displays the sum of the estimated funding of all strategic topics over time. The trajectory from 2018 to 2025 demonstrates an increase with a peak in 2024 at nearly €125 million. This upward trend reflects a period of intensified investment, potentially linked to strategic research initiatives or policy shifts. The slight decline projected for 2025 is mainly related to the fact that we have only a partial view based on the project funded by under the Horizon Europe in the first

phases, so limited to the ones reported in the public database from CORDIS. A general consideration that we can assess, but as more a qualitative than a quantitative comment is that while the annual installation of PV increased over 4-fold from 2018 to 2023 [15], the estimated funding into the strategic topics based on the proposed methodology seems to have increased only 2-fold in this timeframe.

4 QUERING PROJECTS FOR SPECIFIC TOPICS

LLMs can be used for topic-centric retrieval - i.e., to ask when a specific technique first appears in EU proposals and how it evolves thereafter. As an example, we queried the data for drone-based fault detection in PV modules. Using the prompt provided in Appendix A3, we acquired all projects related to drone-based monitoring, which were summarized by *GPT5* to:

EU support for drone-based PV inspection first appears in Horizon 2020 proposals in the mid-2010s. EASY PV (2016–2018) explicitly deployed RPAS to capture thermal imagery of PV plants, georeferenced with high-accuracy GNSS/RTK to pinpoint defective modules—marking the entry of drone thermography into EU-funded O&M workflows. In parallel, CDRONE (2016) explored an autonomous inspection-and-cleaning concept for large-scale solar, positioning aeronautical robotics as a lever to cut O&M costs. Together, these feasibility- and implementation-oriented projects show early EU interest focused on proving that aerial imaging could be made precise, safe, and economically relevant for utility PV.

Under Horizon Europe, the theme matures from proofs of concept to integrated asset-management toolchains. PROMISE (2022–2025) built a Malta-based reliability platform that includes satellite and drone vision for data collection and modeling, embedding UAV imagery within broader reliability science and capacity building. SOLARIS (2024–2028) goes further, specifying automated multi-spectral PV inspection using drones for early fault detection and linking these inspections to forecasting, preventive maintenance, and trading via an AI-driven asset-management suite. In short, drone inspection entered EU proposals in 2015–2016 with thermographic RPAS pilots and, by 2022–2024, evolved into multi-sensor, automated, and AI-integrated inspection pipelines at fleet scale.

Functionality-centric retrieval with LLMs enables the tracing of when concrete techniques first appear in the proposals and how they evolve. In future, this method can be developed further to yield reproducible evidence to inform about specific funding priorities.

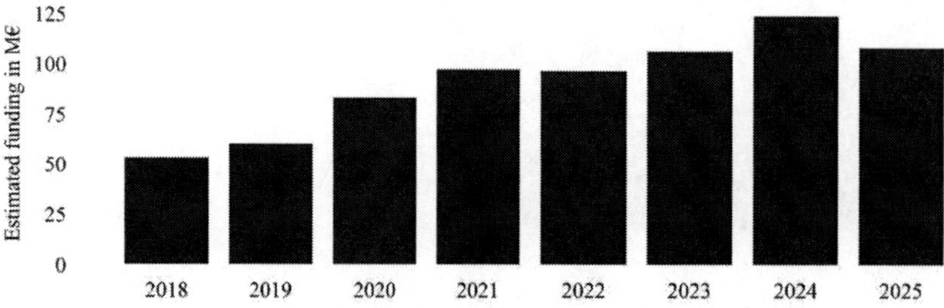

Figure 4: Estimated funding into all strategic topics over time.

5 CONCLUSIONS

A LLM-based pipeline to map Horizon 2020 and Horizon Europe programme to ETIP-PV's SRIA-ch4 was presented in this study. From 52,848 records, a two-stage process yielded 255 PV-relevant projects with graded alignments across the six roadmap topics. Validation shows LLMs are suited for high-volume triage and thematic synthesis.

To strengthen the analysis of EU fund allocation, rejected proposals (if made publicly available) could be included alongside funded ones in future works, enabling a comparative assessment that identifies the factors for funding success.

Subsequent work may also analyze the remaining 99 % of the funded projects more detailed. Especially the share of renewable energies related to so-called conventional energy projects of the EU could be of public interest.

In future, LLMs may be utilized to increase the transparency of bureaucratic processes. Future infrastructure enabled by LLMs could provide a queryable view of how EU funds are allocated.

ACKNOWLEDGEMENT

Special thanks to Sander Schubert and Joseph Jachmann for their support with this work.

REFERENCES

[1] A. Jaeger-Waldau, "PV Status Report 2010," JRC Publications Repository. Accessed: Sep. 12, 2025. [Online]. Available: https://publications.jrc.ec.europa.eu/repository/handle/JRC59708

[2] European Parliament, "EU Solar Energy Strategy | Legislative Train Schedule," European Parliament. Accessed: Sep. 16, 2025. [Online]. Available: https://www.europarl.europa.eu/legislative-train/package-repowereu-plan/file-eu-solar-strategy

[3] "Overview and key findings – World Energy Investment 2024 – Analysis," IEA. Accessed: Sep. 12, 2025. [Online]. Available: https://www.iea.org/reports/world-energy-investment-2024/overview-and-key-findings

[4] ETIP PV, "Strategic Research and Innovation Agenda on Photovoltaics, Update." Accessed: Sep. 16, 2025. [Online]. Available: https://media.etip-pv.eu/filer_public/f5/8b/f58b06d7-60fa-457a-8562-80eb71fa667c/etip_pv_-_sria_report_update-_august24.pdf

[5] "OpenAI Platform." Accessed: Feb. 06, 2025. [Online]. Available: https://platform.openai.com

[6] J.-L. Lieberum et al., "Large language models for conducting systematic reviews: on the rise, but not yet ready for use—a scoping review," Journal of Clinical Epidemiology, vol. 181, p. 111746, 2025, doi: https://doi.org/10.1016/j.jclinepi.2025.111746.

[7] M. Mostafapour, J. H. Fortier, K. Pacheco, H. Murray, and G. Garber, "Evaluating Literature Reviews Conducted by Humans Versus ChatGPT: Comparative Study," JMIR AI, vol. 3, p. e56537, Aug. 2024, doi: 10.2196/56537.

[8] M. Schönau et al., "Predicting the Shading of Photovoltaic Systems Using Machine Learning," PV-Symposium Proc, vol. 2, Aug. 2025, doi: 10.52825/pv-symposium.v2i.2636.

[9] M. Schönau et al., "String outages in photovoltaic plants," Renewable Energies, vol. 3, no. 1, Jan. 2025, doi: 10.1177/27533735251347879.

[10] Publications Office, "CORDIS - EU research projects under Horizon 2020 (2014-2020)." Publications Office of the European Union, 2015. doi: 10.2906/112117098108/12.

[11] Publications Office, "CORDIS - EU research projects under HORIZON EUROPE (2021-2027)." Publications Office, Jul. 25, 2022. doi: 10.2906/112117098108/20.

[12] "GPT-4o mini: advancing cost-efficient intelligence." Accessed: Aug. 20, 2025. [Online]. Available: https://openai.com/index/gpt-4o-mini-advancing-cost-efficient-intelligence/

[13] "Introducing GPT-5." Accessed: Aug. 20, 2025. [Online]. Available: https://openai.com/index/introducing-gpt-5/

[14] C. Spearman, "The Proof and Measurement of Association between Two Things," The American Journal of Psychology, vol. 15, no. 1, p. 72, Jan. 1904, doi: 10.2307/1412159.

[15] IEA, "Photovoltaic Power Systems Programme Task Updates 2024." Accessed: Aug. 27, 2025. [Online]. Available: https://iea-pvps.org/annual-reports/iea-pvps-task-updates-2024/

APPENDIX

A1 Prompt for the Filtering Process

Below the prompt that was provided to *gpt-4o-mini-2024-07-18* for the filtering of the research projects, using the models default configuration. Line breaks and white spaces were adapted to increase readability.

```
You are a senior research scientist working
for the European Commission at ETIP PV in
the working group Digital PV, Grid and
Storage.

TASK: Assess the alignment of the research
projects to the Strategic Research and
Innovation Agenda (SRIA).

Strategic Roadmap:
Distributed Control Intelligence,
PV Integration in DC Networks,
Hybrid RES Systems with Demand Flexibility,
Aggregation & Market Participation,
Interoperability in Smart Grids,
Digitalization of PV Systems

CRITICAL RULES:
- Return a JSON Object according to this
Schema:
{"type":"json_schema","json_schema":{"name"
:"SRIA_Alignment_Evaluation","schema":{"typ
e":"object","properties":{"Is_aligned":{"ty
pe":"boolean","description":"True if the
project     aligns     with     the
SRIA"}},"required":["Is_aligned"],"addition
alProperties":false},"strict":true}}

- Return False for projects that do not
relate to the PV domain.
- You will be penalized for incorrect
classifications or wrong JSON format.
```

A2 Prompt for the Evaluation Process

Below is the prompt that was provided to *gpt-5-2025-08-07* for the analysis of the filtered research projects, using the models default configuration:

```
You are a senior research scientist working
for the European Commission at ETIP PV in
the working group Digital PV, Grid and
Storage.

TASK: Assess the alignment of the research
projects to the Strategic Research and
Innovation Agenda (SRIA).

Decide based on the following criteria:

Technological Focus:
 Smart Inverters
 Grid-forming Inverters
 DC Networks / Microgrids
 Hybrid Systems (PV + Wind + Hydro + Storage)
 Virtual Power Plants (VPPs)
 Forecasting Tools
 Digital Twins
 Artificial Intelligence (AI) for PV.
 Edge AI & Big Data
 IoT in Energy Systems

Key Performance Indicators (KPIs):
 Forecasting Accuracy
 Grid Support Capabilities
 Energy Efficiency Gains
 LCOE (Levelized Cost of Energy) Reduction
 Interoperability Standards
 AI-based Predictive Maintenance

Enabling Technologies:
 Energy Storage (Batteries, Green Hydrogen)
 Vehicle-to-Grid (V2G)
 Smart Grids
 Cybersecurity for DER
 Sensor Integration
 Wireless Power Transmission

Core Themes:
 Smart Energy Systems
 Photovoltaics (PV)
 Energy System Integration
 Renewable Energy Sources (RES)
 Decarbonization
 Energy Transition
 Distributed Energy Resources (DER)

For each strategic roadmap in the SRIA for
the field Digital PV, Grid, and Storage,
evaluate the given project and assign a
percentage (0-100) indicating how much of
the project aligns with that specific
roadmap. Also include a value for <OTHER>,
which is the percentage of the project that
does not fit into any of the strategic
roadmap categories. The sum of all
percentages (including <OTHER>) must equal
exactly 100 %.

Strategic Roadmap:
Distributed Control Intelligence,
PV Integration in DC Networks,
Hybrid RES Systems with Demand Flexibility,
Aggregation & Market Participation,
Interoperability in Smart Grids,
Digitalization of PV Systems

CRITICAL RULES:
- Return a JSON Object according to this
Schema:
```


```
{"type":"json_schema","json_schema":{"name"
:"SRIA_Alignment_Evaluation","schema":{"typ
e":"object","properties":{"reasoning":{"typ
e":"string","description":"Short reasoning
for                                    the
percentages"},"alignment_scores":{"type":"o
bject","properties":{"Distributed  Control
Intelligence":{"type":"number"},"PV
Integration               in             DC
Networks":{"type":"number"},"Hybrid     RES
Systems              with            Demand
Flexibility":{"type":"number"},"Aggregation
&                                    Market
Participation":{"type":"number"},"Interoper
ability              in               Smart
Grids":{"type":"number"},"Digitalization of
PV
Systems":{"type":"number"},"<OTHER>":{"type
":"number"}},"additionalProperties":false,"
required":["Distributed            Control
Intelligence","PV     Integration     in DC
Networks", "Hybrid RES Systems with Demand
Flexibility",    "Aggregation   &    Market
Participation",  "Interoperability in Smart
Grids",        "Digitalization    of     PV
Systems","<OTHER>"]},"Is_aligned":{"type":"
boolean","description":"True if the project
aligns                                  with
SRIA"}},"required":["reasoning","alignment_
scores","Is_aligned"],"additionalProperties
":false},"strict":true}}
```


```
- Return zeros for projects that do not
relate to the PV domain.
- You will be penalized for incorrect
classifications or wrong JSON format.
```

A3 Prompt for Quering the Drone-Based Monitoring

Below is the prompt that was provided to *gpt-5-2025-08-07* for querying the filtered research projects for drone based-monitoring, using the models default configuration:

```
You are a senior research scientist working
for the European Commission at ETIP PV in
the working group Digital PV, Grid and
Storage.

TASK: Decide if the given project
contributes to drone-based PV fault
detection using heat signatures.

Return True, if the project mentions
drones/UAVs/UAS for PV inspection, if it
uses thermal / infrared imaging,
thermography, or heat signature analysis or
if it clearly enables
these.

CRITICAL RULES:
- Return a JSON Object according to this
Schema:
```


```
{       "type":      "json_schema",
"json_schema":        {          "name":
"Drone_Monitoring_Evaluation", "schema": {
"type":     "object",      "properties": {
"reasoning":      {      "type":  "string",
"description": "Short reasoning for the
decision",  },  "Is_aligned":  {   "type":
"boolean",  "description": "True  if  the
project contributes to drone-based PV fault
detection.", }, }, "required": ["reasoning",
"Is_aligned"],        "additionalProperties":
False, }, "strict": True, }, }
```


```
- You will be penalized for incorrect
classifications or wrong JSON format.
```

ETIP Photovoltaics

SMART ENERGY SYSTEM INTEGRATION OF PHOTOVOLTAIC: FROM STRATEGIC AND RESEARCH INNOVATION AGENDA TO EU FUNDED PROJECTS

Grazia BARCHI[1], Maximilian SCHÖNAU[2], Pierre-Jean ALET[3], Venizelos EFTHYMIOU[4], Gofran CHOWDHURY[5], Marion PERRIN[6], Elham SHIRAZI[7], Ioannis (John) A. TSANAKAS[8]

[1]EURAC Research - Institute for Renewable Energy, Italy; [2]smartblue AG / Coburg University of Applied Sciences, Dept. of Electrical Engineering and Computer Sciences, Germany; [3]CSEM, Switzerland; [4]EPL Technology Frontiers Ltd, Cyprus; [5]3E, Belgium; [6]Energy Pool, France; [7]Faculty of Engineering Technology, University of Twente, Enschede, The Netherlands; [8]CEA-INES, France

INTRODUCTION

- The ETIP-PV has recently updated its Strategic Research and Innovation Agenda (SRIA) to address the most crucial challenges for photovoltaic (PV) deployment and efficiency by 2035. Considering that the most of PV installation will be integrated into the energy system, Challenge 4 focuses on the **"Smart Energy System Integration of Photovoltaics for Large-Scale Deployment and High Penetration."**

- The aims of the paper are:
  - to present a methodology based on large language models (LLMs) to analyze and synthesize insights from almost ten years of funded EU project data on PV system topics related to Challenge 4 of the SRIA (SRIA-Ch4);
  - to extract key values and indicators that reveal trends, dominant themes in the selected EU funded project;
  - to support stakeholders in navigating the evolving PV energy system integration past, present and future trend.

Roadmap SRIA-Ch4	Roadmap Topic
R1: More intelligence in distributed control	Distributed control intelligence
R2: Improved efficiencies by integration of PV-systems in DC-networks	PV Integration in DC Networks
R3: Hybrid systems including demand flexibility (PV + storage + batteries + green hydrogen/fuel cells or gas turbines)	Hybrid RES Systems with Demand Flexibility
R4: Aggregated energy and VPPs	Aggregation and Market participation
R5: Interoperability in communication and operation of RES smart grids	Interoperability in Smart Grids
R6: Digitalization of PV systems	Digitalization of PV Systems

METHODOLOGY

- Scope & data: Objectives of 52,848 Horizon 2020 and Horizon Europe projects from 2014–2027.
- Two-stage screening:
  - Stage 1: GPT-4o-mini filters to PV domain → 474 candidates
  - Stage 2: GPT-5 assigns share of each project to 6 SRIA-Ch4 roadmap topics
- Result: 255 relevant projects with graded alignment across the 6 topics.
- Validation resulted in high accuracy of the filtering process, and acceptable accuracy for the topic shares for comparative analyses
- LLMs enables the tracing of when concrete techniques first appear in the proposals and how they evolve

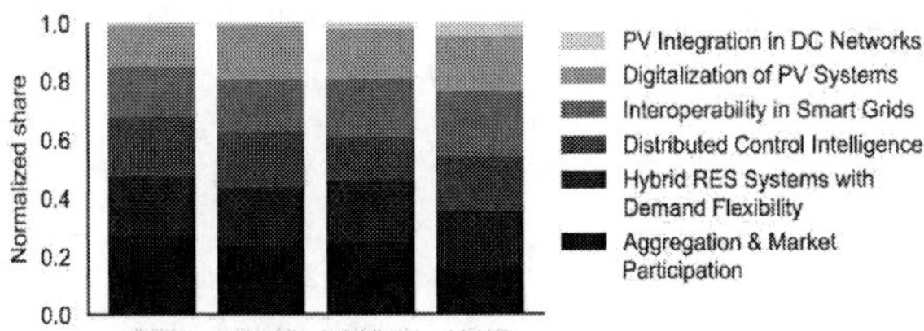

LLMs can increase the knowledge of EU funded project

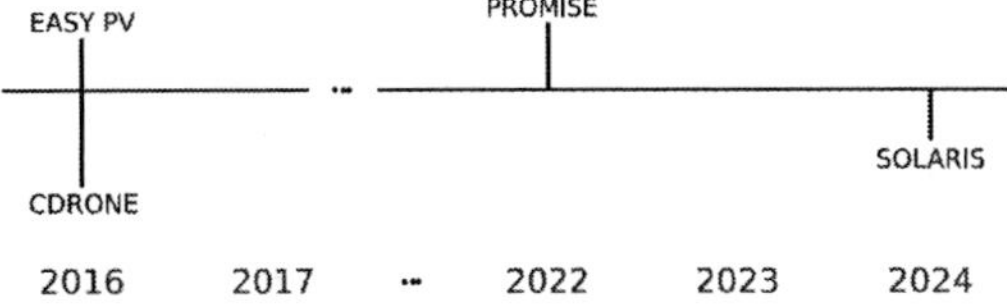

RESULTS ON EU FUNDED PROJECTS

- The barplot shows the funding share by strategic topic over time. The values are normalized, and moving from left to right we can appreciate that:

- higher distribution of the *Aggregation & Market Participation* topic in the past years;
- no significant changes in the *Hybrid RES* and *Distributed Control Intelligence* topics;
- *Digitalization of PV Systems* and *PV Integration in DC Networks* show increase demonstrating the up-to-date relevance of DC grid and AI in the near future.

- LLMs can be used for specific topic-centric retrieval - i.e., to ask when drone-based monitoring, was funded by the EU:

There were 4 projects related to drone-based monitoring:

- *EASY PV (2016–2018): Drone-based thermal imaging*
- *CDRONE (2016): Drone inspection-and-cleaning concept*
- *PROMISE (2022–2025): Integrating satellite and drone data into asset modeling*
- *SOLARIS (2024–2028): Automated multi-spectral drone inspections linked to AI-driven asset management*

Summary: An LLM-based methodology maps a decade of EU-funded PV projects to ETIP-PV's Strategic Research and Innovation Agenda, revealing trends, gaps, and possible funding priorities of the EU.

The European Technology and Innovation Platform for Photovoltaics — etip-pv.eu

FOSTERING COLLABORATION OF RESEARCH INFRASTRUCTURES AND STAKEHOLDERS IN EUROPE AND LATIN AMERICA TOWARDS CLIMATE-RESILIENT PV SYSTEMS: THE CACTUS PROJECT

Ioannis (John) A. Tsanakas[1*], Delfina Muñoz[1], Romain Couderc[1], Aitor Marzo[2], Asier Sanz Martinez[3], Atse Louwen[4], David Moser[4], Felipe Valencia[5], Nicole Torres Silva[5], Luis Alejandro Cardenas Garcia[6], Fernando Augusto Herrera Leon[6], Thu Nhi Tran Caliste[7], Mark R. Johnson[8], Sarah Essam T. Mohammed[9], Jose V. de Seoane[10]

[1] CEA, Liten, Univ. Grenoble Alpes, Campus INES, Le Bourget du Lac, France
[2] Universidad de Granada, Granada, Spain
[3] Tecnalia, Bilbao, Spain
[4] Eurac Research, Institute for Renewable Energy, Bolzano, Italy
5 ATAMOSTEC, Santiago, Chile
[6] Universidad Nacional de Colombia (UNAL), Bogota, Colombia
[7] European Synchrotron Radiation Facility (ESRF), Grenoble, France
[8] Institut Laue-Langevin (ILL), Grenoble, France
[9] EU SOLARIS, Almeria, Spain
[10] Becquerel Institute, Brussels, Belgium

*corresponding author : ioannis.tsanakas@cea.fr

ABSTRACT: The CACTUS project is an international initiative fostering collaboration between European (EU) and Latin American and Caribbean (LAC) research infrastructures (RIs) to enhance photovoltaic (PV) performance, reliability, and sustainability across diverse climatic conditions. Many high solar potential regions, such as LAC, lack dedicated research facilities for long-term PV performance evaluation, while European RIs require broader climate validation. CACTUS bridges this gap by integrating world-class RIs, expertise, and standardized methodologies for testing PV systems under real-world environmental stressors. The project employs a multidisciplinary approach that combines experimental field studies, advanced material characterization, and predictive modeling. Key areas of research include degradation mechanisms in extreme climates, harmonization of testing protocols, and development of predictive maintenance strategies. Leveraging state-of-the-art facilities such as ESFRI landmarks (ILL & ESRF) and EU-SOLARIS, CACTUS also explores novel PV materials and architectures, ensuring the transferability of research outcomes across global PV markets. Recent activities have focused on field studies in the Atacama Desert, where researchers are evaluating soiling measurement methodologies to assess dust accumulation and its impact on PV performance. Additionally, synchrotron-aided characterization techniques are being explored to analyze PV degradation mechanisms at the microscopic level. These early results provide promising insights into climate-specific PV behavior. The project's structured two-year implementation plan includes RI optimization, collaborative field studies, methodology standardization, and knowledge dissemination. By fostering international cooperation, CACTUS aims to deliver transformative advancements in climate-resilient solar energy deployment, enhancing durability, efficiency, and sustainability in the global PV sector.

Keywords: *PV systems; EU-LAC collaboration; research infrastructures; climate-specific PV O&M.*

1 INTRODUCTION: CONTEXT and AIM

The performance and long-term viability of photovoltaic (PV) technology are highly dependent on environmental conditions, yet current research and testing infrastructures are often limited in their ability to assess PV systems under diverse climatic stressors. Many regions with high solar potential, such as Latin America and the Caribbean (LAC), lack dedicated research facilities for long-term performance analysis. Conversely, European research infrastructures (RIs) have developed extensive methodologies but require broader climate validation. Addressing these gaps necessitates an international and interdisciplinary approach.

The CACTUS project emerges as a response to this need, fostering a bi-regional collaboration between Europe (EU) and LAC. The initiative brings together world-class RIs, scientific expertise, and technological capabilities to develop a sustainable ecosystem for PV research. This collaboration enables the exchange of methodologies, data, and best practices to improve the performance, reliability, and sustainability of PV technologies across different environmental conditions (Fig. 1). By building on existing RIs and establishing new synergies, CACTUS will provide tools to facilitate the deployment of solar energy in an efficient and climate-resilient manner.

The primary objective of CACTUS is to advance the scientific understanding of PV systems' long-term behavior in different climates by improving testing infrastructures and developing standardized methodologies. This effort is crucial for optimizing PV performance, enhancing system bankability, and ensuring widespread social acceptance of solar technologies.

10.4229/EUPVSEC2025/5DV.3.38

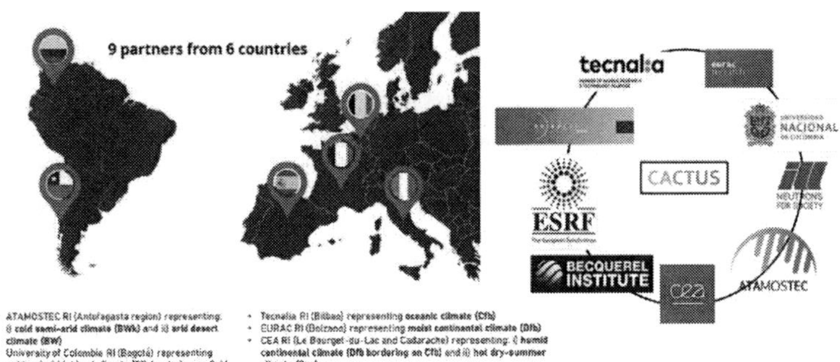

Figure 1: Geographic distribution of RIs involved in CACTUS and their respective climate zones per Köppen classification

2 APPROACH

CACTUS employs an integrative methodology combining experimental field studies, advanced material characterization, and predictive modeling. The project's six work packages (WPs) encompass a comprehensive approach, addressing RI enhancement, knowledge exchange, sustainability assessment, and policy integration (Fig. 2).

A core aspect of CACTUS is the development and enhancement of both indoor and outdoor RIs across diverse geographic locations. This enables the study of degradation mechanisms under real-world conditions such as extreme heat, high humidity, sand abrasion, and UV exposure. The project leverages world-class facilities, including ESFRI landmarks (ILL & ESRF) and EU-SOLARIS, alongside premier PV research institutions in both EU and LAC.

Beyond physical infrastructure, CACTUS aims to standardize testing protocols and data-sharing methodologies. The project will establish common frameworks for PV module degradation analysis, operational reliability assessment, and predictive maintenance strategies. This harmonization of methodologies across regions will provide robust, transferrable knowledge applicable to different PV markets. A significant scientific contribution of CACTUS lies in its exploration of novel PV materials and architectures. By characterizing performance in diverse climatic settings, the project will provide critical data to refine material selection for emerging PV technologies, such as tandem solar cells and bifacial modules. The

research outcomes will feed into industry standards and best practices for PV design and deployment. Additionally, CACTUS incorporates sustainability and circular economy principles by conducting comprehensive life-cycle assessments (LCA). These assessments will evaluate the environmental footprint of PV technologies throughout their operational lifespan, providing essential data for policymakers and stakeholders.

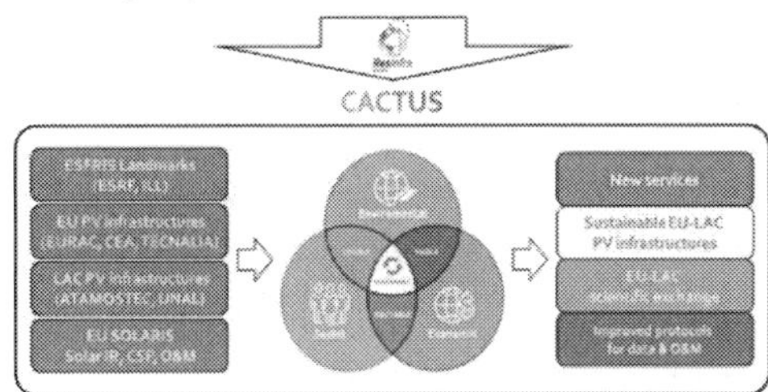

Figure 2: Conceptual framework of CACTUS, illustrating the interconnection between RIs, under the social-environmental-economic nexus for PV deployment.

The collaborative structure of CACTUS is pivotal to its innovation potential. By fostering exchanges between EU and LAC researchers, the project promotes skill development, knowledge transfer, and long-term partnerships. Workshops, training programs, and joint research campaigns will ensure the dissemination of best practices and accelerate innovation in PV performance optimization.

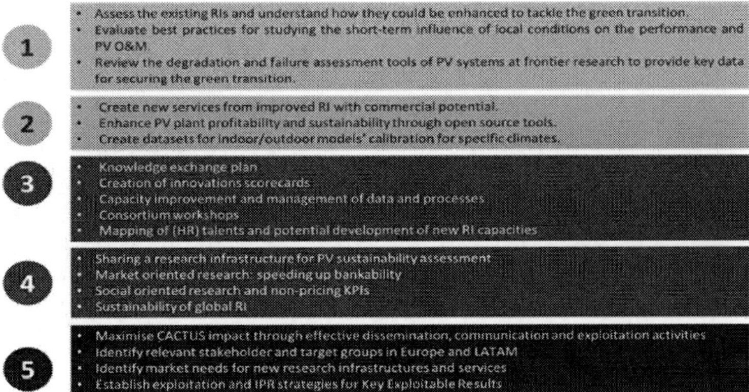

Figure 3: Outline of CACTUS activities.

10.4229/EUPVSEC2025/5DV.3.38
020546-002

3 MILESTONES and ONGOING WORK

CACTUS is expected to generate a wealth of collaborative scientific and technological outcomes towards climate-resilient PV, from design/component level to operational PV system scale (Fig. 4). One key outcome is the creation of a high-quality, long-term dataset on PV performance and degradation under real-world conditions. This dataset will serve as a foundation for developing more accurate reliability models, failure detection algorithms, and predictive maintenance strategies. Another critical result will be the establishment of guidelines, recommendations and best practices for testing, monitoring and maintenance of PV systems in diverse climatic stress profiles and different applications. These protocols will be shared both among the participating RIs and to interested PV stakeholders, facilitating greater alignment between EU and LAC research methodologies, improving the transferability of results across regions and setting the groundwork for future updates in existing (e.g. IEC) standards.

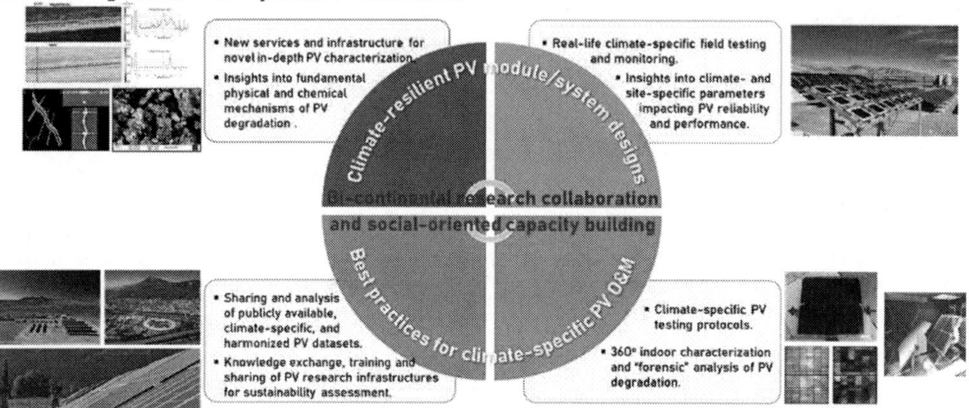

Figure 4: Ongoing collaborative research activities in CACTUS.

The implementation plan for CACTUS is structured over a two-year period, with key milestones including:

- Optimization and interconnection of RIs to facilitate high-quality PV performance monitoring.
- Execution of collaborative field studies and laboratory-based assessments to validate degradation models.
- Development and publication of standardized methodologies for climate-specific PV evaluation.
- Knowledge dissemination through international conferences, technical workshops, and training sessions.
- Delivery of policy recommendations based on sustainability assessments and techno-economic analyses.

By strengthening collaboration between research infrastructures in different climate zones, CACTUS is set to provide transformative insights that will enhance the durability, efficiency, and sustainability of PV systems.

Currently, there are two major activities carried out by CACTUS partners, the preliminary outcomes of which are summarized in Fig. 5 and 6. In Atacama desert, an activity led by ATAMOSTEC focuses on the intercomparison of soiling measurement methodologies, in order to:

- Evaluate and compare methodologies to measure dust accumulation and assess soiling losses on PV modules in the Atacama Desert.
- Validate soiling measurement methodologies using the advanced PSDA (Atacama Solar Platform) infrastructure.
- Generate results that can be extrapolated to other regions with similar climatic conditions.

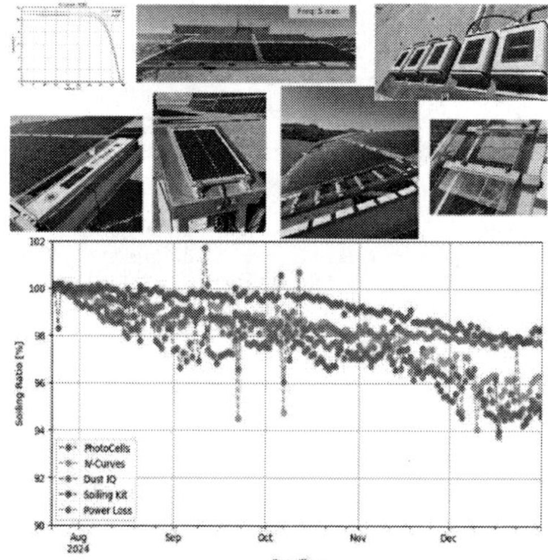

Figure 5: Overview of the employed infrastructure and preliminary results of the ongoing intercomparison of soiling measurement methodologies in Atacama Desert. The activity is led by ATAMOSTEC, involves all CACTUS partners' expertise and will carry on for at least 15 months, to shed light into seasonal, annual climate-specific effects.

Further, ESRF experts, along with CEA and ILL researchers are working on exploring and employing ESRF's unique Synchrotron-aided characterization techniques, as potential future services for advanced characterization and analysis of PV degradation mechanisms at microscopic scale. Results, so far, are very promising, suggesting that we can study in-depth not only the native state PV modules at solar cell and sub-cell level, but also to assess and distinguish degradation patterns over time, under the influence of different climatic profiles.

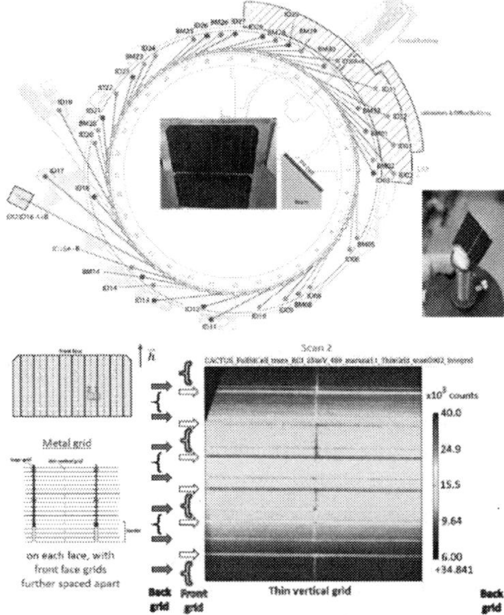

Figure 6: Overview of the employed infrastructure and preliminary results of the ongoing activity led by ESRF, for advanced characterization and analysis of PV degradation mechanisms at microscopic scale, employing ESRF's unique Synchrotron-aided testing methods.

The CACTUS project is strategically designed to bridge the critical gap between photovoltaic research advancements and industrial market requirements. A comprehensive stakeholder survey was conducted to align the project's objectives with practical needs, identifying paramount industry concerns such as long-term reliability across diverse climatic conditions, the accurate prediction of real-world performance, and establishing climate-specific bankability assurances. Prominent technical challenges include ultraviolet-induced degradation in desert environments, humidity-driven corrosion in tropical zones, and mechanical stress from snow and ice loading in alpine climates. To evaluate the project's capacity to address these needs, a systematic analysis of its research infrastructures was undertaken. A SWOT analysis of the project's testing capabilities (Fig. 7) confirmed the strategic strength of its geographically distributed facilities, which provide unparalleled environmental exposure. However, the analysis also revealed significant capability gaps within the project's scope, particularly in testing resilience to hail and high-wind impacts, a shortage of predictive maintenance tools, and the need for more affordable access mechanisms for small and medium-sized enterprises. In direct response to these industry-identified needs and infrastructural insights, the project has developed novel, climate-adaptive testing protocols.

Methodologies like the Desert Label and STROKE testing are already addressing market demand by providing more relevant and accelerated reliability assessments, thereby enabling manufacturers to develop more robust products and allowing investors to make better-informed financial decisions based on validated, climate-specific performance data.

Figure 7: Overview of the employed infrastructure and preliminary results of the ongoing activity led by ESRF, for advanced characterization and analysis of PV degradation mechanisms at microscopic scale, employing ESRF's unique Synchrotron-aided testing methods.

4 CONCLUSIONS - OUTLOOK

The CACTUS project has established a unique bi-regional collaboration between Europe and Latin America & the Caribbean, addressing one of the most pressing challenges in photovoltaic (PV) deployment: the lack of climate-representative infrastructures and standardized methodologies for long-term performance evaluation. By interconnecting world-class research facilities, harmonizing testing approaches, and fostering interdisciplinary knowledge exchange, CACTUS provides the foundation for advancing PV reliability studies across diverse climatic conditions. Early results from ongoing activities—such as the intercomparison of soiling methodologies in the Atacama Desert and synchrotron-aided degradation analysis at ESRF—demonstrate the project's capacity to generate high-quality data and innovative characterization methods, both of which are critical for bridging the gap between laboratory studies and field-relevant insights.

The project highlights that climate-specific stressors—including soiling, humidity-driven corrosion, UV degradation, and thermal cycling—require tailored testing and mitigation strategies. CACTUS directly responds to these needs by developing adaptive testing protocols, sustainability assessments, and techno-economic frameworks to ensure PV systems' durability, bankability, and social acceptance in different regions. Looking forward, key priorities include:

- expanding climate-tailored reliability assessments to encompass additional stress factors (e.g. hail, wind, and snow loads),
- integrating advanced predictive maintenance tools with real-time field data, and
- strengthening accessibility of testing infrastructures for industry stakeholders, particularly SMEs.

By aligning scientific research with market and policy needs, CACTUS not only advances the state-of-the-art in PV testing but also lays the groundwork for future updates of international standards and guidelines. Ultimately, the project is expected to deliver a lasting impact by enabling climate-resilient PV deployment, supporting the global energy transition with reliable, sustainable, and regionally adapted solar technologies.

ACKNOWLEDGEMENTS

This work has been carried out in the framework of the Horizon Europe CACTUS project. CACTUS project has received funding from the European Union's Horizon Europe research and innovation programme under grant agreement No. 101132182.

Fostering collaboration of research infrastructures and stakeholders in Europe and Latin America towards climate-resilient PV systems: the CACTUS project

Ioannis (John) A. Tsanakas[1], Delfina Muñoz[1], Romain Couderc[1], Aitor Marzo[2], Asier Sanz Martinez[3], Atse Louwen[4], David Moser[4], Felipe Valencia[5], Nicole Torres Silva[5], Luis Alejandro Cardenas Garcia[6], Fernando Augusto Herrera Leon[6], Thu Nhi Tran Caliste[7], Mark R. Johnson[8], Sarah Essam T. Mohammed[9], Jose V. de Seoane[10]

[1] CEA, Univ. Grenoble Alpes, Campus INES, Le Bourget-du-Lac, France; [2] Universidad de Granada, Granada, Spain; [3] Tecnalia, Bilbao, Spain; [4] Eurac Research, Instit. for Renewable Energy, Bolzano, Italy; [5] ATAMOSTEC, Santiago, Chile; [6] Universidad Nacional de Colombia, Bogota, Colombia; [7] European Synchrotron Radiation Facility, Grenoble, France; [8] Institut Laue-Langevin, Grenoble, France; [9] EU SOLARIS, Almeria, Spain; [10] Becquerel Institute, Brussels, Belgium

Project Coordinator and Corresponding Author: **Ioannis (John) A. Tsanakas** ioannis.tsanakas@cea.fr

Context

Solar photovoltaic (PV) technologies are expanding rapidly worldwide, but their long-term performance depends heavily on climatic conditions. Many regions with high solar potential (e.g., Latin America) lack dedicated testing facilities, while European infrastructures need broader climate validation.

CACTUS bridges this gap by fostering collaboration between European and Latin American research infrastructures (RIs) to develop reliable, bankable, and climate-resilient PV solutions.

Mission

The objectives/mission of CACTUS project are multifold:

- Build a **bi-regional ecosystem** of **complementary RIs** between EU & LAC.
- Develop **standardized testing protocols** for PV under **diverse climates**.
- Advance knowledge on **PV degradation mechanisms in extreme conditions**.
- Provide tools for industry, policymakers, and investors to **increase PV system bankability, sustainability, and acceptance**.
- Contribute to the green energy transition by ensuring PV reliability worldwide.

Research Infrastructures

CACTUS integrates unique infrastructures across diverse climates:

- Atacama Desert Solar Platform (Chile) – desert/high-irradiance testing.
- CEA-INES (France) – advanced climate chambers & accelerated stress tests.
- Universidad Nacional de Colombia – tropical climate outdoor monitoring.
- EURAC (Italy) – Alpine tests, electroluminescence, and PV-storage integration.
- TECNALIA (Spain) – smart grid & outdoor PV testing facilities.

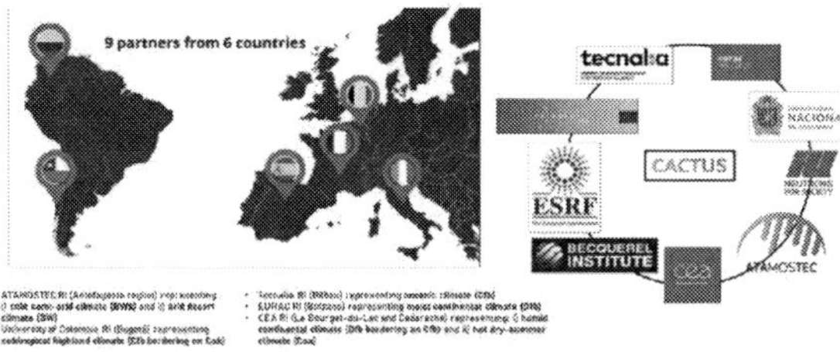

Example outcomes – Early insights

Climate-specific testing and reliability activities

- An ongoing 15+ month soiling measurement campaign in the Atacama Desert, led by ATAMOSTEC, is providing **the first intercomparison of soiling testing methodologies under extreme high-irradiance and low-humidity conditions**. This study aims to validate measurement techniques and quantify soiling losses, with **results applicable to other arid regions worldwide**.

- Preliminary synchrotron-aided analyses conducted by ESRF and ILL, in collaboration with CEA, are **revealing micro-scale degradation mechanisms in PV modules**. These high-resolution techniques offer unprecedented insights into material behavior under climatic stressors, enabling **deeper understanding of failure modes such as encapsulant degradation, corrosion, and cell-level defects**.

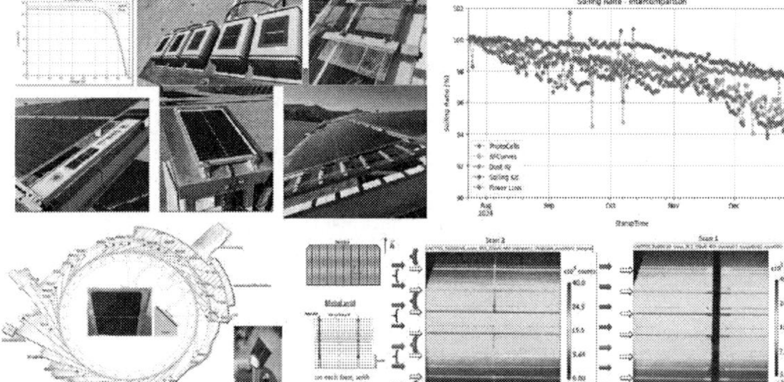

Strengths / Weaknesses / Opportunities / Threats

Bridging Research and Industry/Market Needs

- **Stakeholder Needs:** A CACTUS survey identified top concerns: reliability in diverse climates, real-world performance, and climate-specific bankability. Key issues include desert UV degradation, tropical humidity corrosion, and alpine snow mechanical stress.

- **Research Infrastructures:** A SWOT analysis confirmed the strength of CACTUS's distributed facilities but highlighted gaps in testing for hail/wind, predictive maintenance tools, and more affordable access for smaller players.

- **Novel Testing Protocols Development:** New climate-adaptive protocols like the Desert Label and STROKE testing are already addressing industry demand for more relevant and accelerated reliability assessments.

Impact and Outlook

- ☑ Providing guidelines and best practices for climate-specific PV testing and O&M.
- ☑ Supporting updates to international standards (IEC)
- ☑ .Strengthening EU–LAC scientific cooperation.
- ☑ Ensuring durable, efficient, and sustainable deployment of PV.

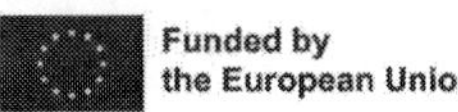

Funded by the European Union
This project has received funding from the European Union's Horizon Europe research and innovation programme under grant agreement Nr. 101132182.

PHOTOVOLTAIC SOLAR ENERGY INTEGRATION IN THE BASIC EDUCATION CURRICULA IN BRAZIL

Amanda Mendes Ferreira Gomes[1], Daniel Odilio dos Santos[1], Aline Cristiane Pan[2], Ricardo Rüther[1]
[1]Universidade Federal de Santa Catarina, Fotovoltaica/UFSC Laboratory, Florianópolis, Brazil
[2]Universidade Federal do Rio Grande do Sul, Engenharia de Gestão de Energia, Tramandaí, Brazil
E-mail: amandamendesfg@gmail.com, daniel.odilio@gmail.com, aline.pan@ufrgs.br, ricardo.ruther@ufsc.br

ABSTRACT: This study examines the integration of photovoltaic (PV) solar energy into Brazil's National Common Curricular Base (BNCC) to assess how early education can contribute to preparing future professionals for the renewable energy (RE) sector. With global PV capacity reaching record levels, the sector faces a growing demand for skilled workers in installation, maintenance, system design, and policy development. Education is a key driver to address this need, yet significant gaps persist in aligning school curricula with labor market demands. Using BNCC as a reference, the research analyzes competencies across the school levels. Findings reveal that PV-related content begins as early as the second year of elementary school with topics such as the Sun, light, heat, and recycling. In middle school, the curriculum expands to cover energy sources, thermal machines, the greenhouse effect, and electricity use. High school introduces more abstract competencies, including socio-environmental impacts, RE alternatives, and digital applications. However, advanced topics such as legislation, green hydrogen, and storage technologies remain absent. The study concludes that while the BNCC provides a valuable framework, curricular reforms are required to incorporate RE and practical applications. Finally, expanding PV education early supports the energy transition despite challenges.

Keywords: photovoltaic, education, school.

1 INTRODUCTION

In 2024, the power sector experienced an unprecedented expansion of renewable energy (RE) capacity, increasing by 18% with a record-breaking addition of 741 GW. Photovoltaic (PV) energy was the primary driver, contributing 602 GW, followed by wind energy, which contributed 117 GW. Other RE sources, whether for power, heat, or transport fuels, added only marginally to the global supply. This remarkable growth underscores the urgent need to address rising electricity demand, driven by population and economic growth, through continued investments in RE. In 2024, Global investment in RE amounted to $728 billion, representing an 8% increase compared to 2023. This pace of growth was significantly slower than in previous years, when investments expanded by 19% in 2023 and 23% in 2022. The primary factor behind this deceleration was the marked reduction in wind power financing [1]. As of August 2025, Brazil's installed PV capacity had surpassed 59 GW, constituting 23.5% of the country's electricity mix. This capacity is distributed between 70% distributed generation (DG) and 30% centralized generation, a different scenario from the rest of the world [2].

This growth in the RE market reinforces the pressing need for highly qualified professionals to respond to the sector's demands [1]. This trend has significantly impacted the PV energy sector, propelling its accelerated growth and driving an increasing demand for specialized expertise in installation, operation, maintenance, and system design. In response to this growing demand, educational institutions worldwide are integrating curricula centered on RE, with a particular focus on PV [3]. This involves comprehensively restructuring existing educational curricula, integrating novel technical courses, and providing students with theoretical knowledge and practical skills. This knowledge should be integrated into the foundational education of students from the earliest stages of their academic careers, ideally beginning in elementary school [4]. Despite this, studies have demonstrated that school curricula lack a significant focus on RE and Education for Sustainable Development (ESD), resulting in low levels of knowledge and awareness among students [5], [6], [7]. Furthermore, studies have revealed a

discrepancy between the number of courses available and industry demand [8]. This highlights a critical shortage of qualified professionals, particularly in developing countries, and a misalignment between educational curricula and the sector's specific needs [9], [10].

Brazil's recently proposed Basic Education (BE) curriculum introduces innovative concepts and pedagogical approaches, formally established through the National Common Curricular Base (BNCC, in Portuguese Base Nacional Comum Curricular) [11]. **Figure 1** shows the BE model in Brazil.

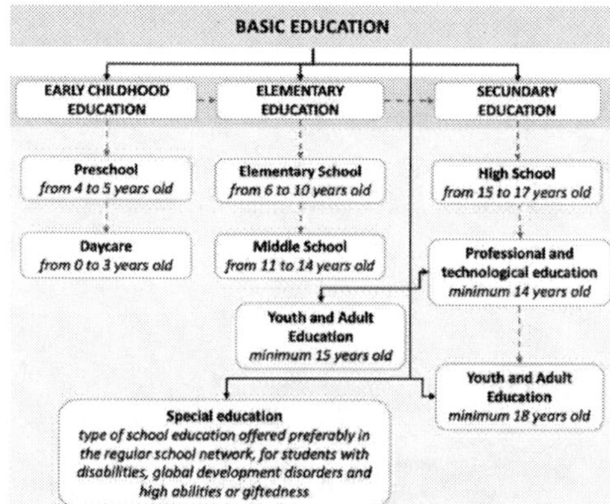

Figure 1. General diagram of the structure of Brazilian education and its divisions. Adapted from [12].

This document outlines the essential learnings to be addressed in Brazilian schools from Early Childhood Education to High School. BE encompasses general competencies and has three stages: early childhood, elementary and secondary education. It aims to ensure the right to learning and the full development of all students, promoting equality in the educational system, contributing to comprehensive education, and constructing a fairer, democratic, and inclusive society [11].

Considering this scenario, this study evaluates the implementation of the teaching of subjects and specific knowledge necessary for developing and stimulating professionals focused on PV energy in the future in basic education (elementary, middle, and high school education), using the BNCC as a basis. The innovation of this work is in the analysis of the curricula and evaluation of the training of elementary, middle, and high school students to ensure they are prepared to meet the challenges of the PV energy sector in the future. Additionally, it will examine the Brazilian government's primary initiatives to achieve this objective, which are closely related to the Sustainable Development Goals (SDGs) proposed for the 2030 Agenda, particularly quality education (SDG 4), gender equality (SDG 5), affordable and clean energy (SDG 7), decent work and economic growth (SDG 8), and climate action (SDG 13) [13].

2 PROFESSIONAL AND EDUCATIONAL SCENARIO IN BRAZIL AND THE WORLD

Globally, the solar PV sector is poised for significant job growth, with projections indicating the creation of up to 40 million energy sector jobs by 2050, including 18 million in RE - a threefold increase from current levels. The PV sector's growth catalyzes job creation, both directly within the industry (upstream) and indirectly in related fields such as manufacturing, construction, and logistics (downstream) [14]. The distribution of these jobs is expected to be as follows: 55% in Asia, 14% in Europe, and 13% in the Americas. In the European Union, employment is projected to reach 530,000 by 2026 and double by 2030, contingent on the efficacy of industrial strategies and workforce development. The PV energy sector in Brazil employs approximately 214,000 professionals, including both direct and indirect jobs, a figure propelled by large-scale projects and the expanding adoption of distributed generation (DG) systems [15]. Projections indicate that the number of jobs in this sector will reach 554,000 by 2030, 966,000 by 2034, and 1.4 million by 2038 [16].

Given this scenario, training new professionals has become an urgent priority. The education of professionals commences at an early stage in BE, preceding higher education. Environmental and RE education can shape individuals' perceptions of the world and influence how they treat and manage it. It serves as both a process and a tool to empower participation and learning across all age groups, particularly among young people, utilizing a bidirectional communication paradigm that flows from educators to learners and vice versa [17]. Integrating RE education into school curricula has been demonstrated to foster critical thinking skills and empower students to become environmentally conscious citizens capable of making informed decisions regarding energy consumption and conservation in their daily lives. This integration underscores the environmental issues and consequences of using non-RE sources [18]. The subject of energy, more specifically RE sources, is included in the educational curricula in several countries [19].

The BNCC advocates for a teaching model emphasizing student autonomy and an active, participatory process, including research, collaboration, and knowledge sharing. Students are encouraged to engage in investigative processes during the final years of elementary education and throughout high school. Consequently, the teaching of natural sciences aims to develop several key skills: observing the world and formulating questions, analyzing needs, identifying

problems, proposing hypotheses, developing explanations and models, and constructing evidence-based arguments. Furthermore, students must enhance their knowledge by gradually incorporating scientific principles. Studies highlight the importance of these skills in developing citizens who are capable of solving problems and making informed decisions [20].

Figure 2 illustrates the general competencies at the elementary and high education established by the BNCC.

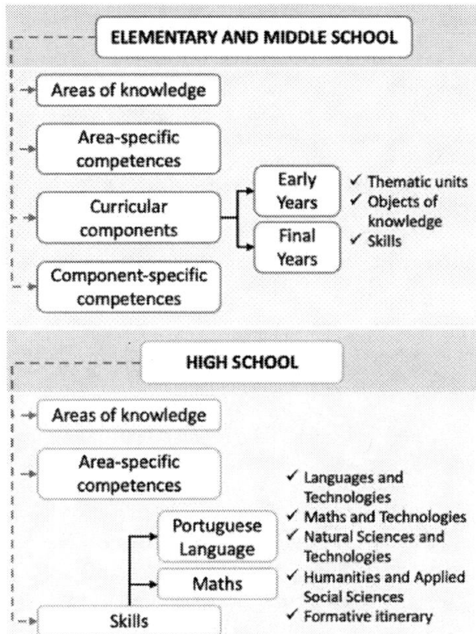

Figure 2. Diagram of the general competencies at the elementary and high school schools established by BNCC. Adapted from [21].

The elementary is organized into five areas of knowledge: Languages (Portuguese, Art, Physical Education, English – only for middle school), Maths, Natural Sciences, Human Sciences (Geography and History), and Religious Education. The sub-areas are designated as "component-specific competencies," which facilitate horizontal articulation between the areas, encompassing all curricular components and facilitating vertical articulation between the years. In contrast, high school education is structured into four areas of knowledge: Languages and Technologies (Portuguese language, Art, Physical Education, English language), Mathematics and Technologies, Natural Sciences and their Technologies (Biology, Physics and Chemistry), Human and Applied Social Sciences (History, Geography, Sociology and Philosophy). Furthermore, the recent amendments to the LDB, as a consequence of Law No. 13,415/2017, indicate a diversified and flexible model for high school education, including different formative itineraries [21]. Formative itineraries may be structured in several ways, focusing on one area of knowledge, technical and professional training, or mobilizing competencies and skills from different areas to create integrated itineraries [11].

Recent research emphasizes the necessity for educational institutions to implement curricula encompassing diverse topics, including PV, energy efficiency, and electric vehicles. Additionally, it should address broader issues such as energy, biodiversity, the environment, globalization, industrialization, and the impact of human beings on climate change [22]. These curricula should be integrated into the existing curricula and complemented by practical activities contributing to students' overall education and development. However, implementing such a plan poses several challenges, including the need for teacher training and the development of effective educational policies [23]. Furthermore, teachers need to be adequately equipped with the requisite knowledge and skills to effectively integrate these topics into their teaching [24].

3 MATERIALS AND METHODS

This study employs the BNCC as the foundation for a critical analysis of the subjects proposed for each year of primary and secondary education. It examines the subjects and their stated objectives, establishing direct connections with the knowledge and skills required of RE professionals, with particular emphasis on PV. **Figure 3** presents the materials and methods used in this article.

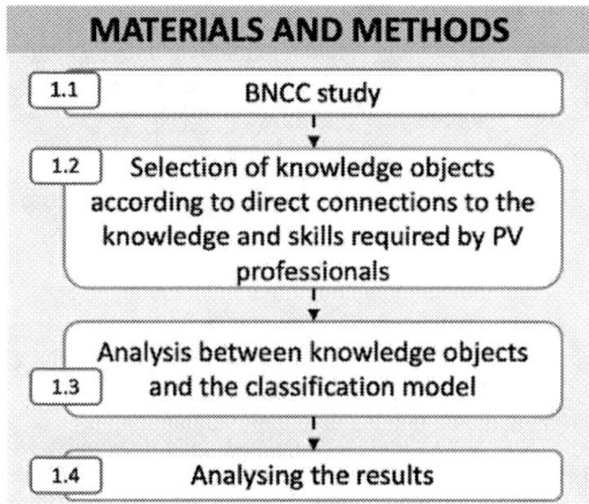

Figure 3. Materials and methods used in this article.

Table 1 illustrates the rationale for imparting the competencies and their interrelationships with PV energy. For each competency code, there are subjects associated with PV energy. The principal subjects of PV energy have been classified into seven categories: PV energy fundamentals and basic projects, Installation, O&M and commissioning, materials and chemical engineering, environmental impact, architectural integration, legislation, and additional topics. The PV sector may comprise a range of related areas, including sales, logistics, finance, accounting, law, and the infrastructure and health support sectors, which are not included in this work.

Table 1: Classification of the different areas of knowledge and competence

1 INDEX – SUBJECT	SPECIFIC SUBJECT	2 INDEX
1 – PV energy fundamentals and basic projects	PV energy fundamentals	1.1
	Optimizing the orientation of PV modules and using solar resources	1.2
	Calculating the site's PV energy potential	1.3
	Location planning for PV system installations	1.4
	Support for simulations and modelling	1.5
	Fundamentals of electricity and circuits	1.6
	Electrical equipment and components	1.7
2 – Installation, O&M and commissioning	Installation and O&M practices	2.1
	Training and certification of technicians	2.2
	Fault diagnosis	2.3
3 – Materials and chemical engineering	Development of PV materials	3.1
	Manufacturing processes	3.2
4 – Environmental impact	Life cycle assessment	4.1
	Impact on local ecosystems	4.2
	Reduction of carbon emissions	4.3
	Sustainability and recycling	4.4
5 – Architectural integration	Aesthetics and functionality	5.1
	Energy efficiency	5.2
6 – Legislation	Government incentives	6.1
	Safety regulations	6.2
	Energy market and tariffs	6.3
	R&D	6.4
7 – Adicional topics	BESS	7.1
	Electromobility	7.2
	Green hydrogen	7.3
	Fair energy transition	7.4

4 RESULTS AND DISCUSSIONS

Table 2 presents the knowledge objectives related to PV subjects in elementary and middle school curricula. The BNCC introduces the teaching of PV energy as early as the second year of elementary school science. For instance, one of the learning objectives is to compare the effects of solar radiation (heating and reflection) on various types of surfaces, such as water, sand, soil, dark, light, and metallic surfaces. The "Matter and energy" and "Earth and Universe" thematic unit of 8th-grade science presents specific topics related to energy sources and types, energy transformation, calculating electricity consumption, electrical circuits, and the conscious use of electricity. The units include EF08CI01, EF08CI02, EF08CI03, EF08CI04, EF08CI05, EF08CI06, EF08CI13, EF08CI15 and EF08CI16. For example, the code EF08CI01 focuses on identifying and classifying different sources (RE and non-RE) and types of energy used in homes, communities, or cities. The code EF08CI06 is specifically designed to discuss and evaluate electricity generation plants and their impacts.

Table 2: Knowledge objectives on PV-related subjects in elementary and middle school curricula

YEAR	THEMATIC UNITS	CODE - KNOWLEDGE OBJECTS

2° YEAR	Earth and Universe	EF02CI07 – The Sun moving in the sky EF02CI08 – The Sun as a source of light and heat
3° YEAR	Matter and energy	EF03CI02 – Effects of light on materials and Hearing and visual health
	Earth and Universe	EF03CI07 – Characteristics of the Earth EF03CI08 – Observing the sky EF03CI10 - Land uses
4° YEAR	Earth and Universe	EF04CI09 – Cardinal points
5° YEAR	Matter and energy	EF05CI01 – Physical properties of materials EF05CI05 – Recycling
	Earth and Universe	EF05CI11 – Earth's rotational movement
6° YEAR	Earth and Universe	EF06CI14 – Earth's shape, structure and movements
7° YEAR	Matter and energy	EF07CI05 – History of fuels and thermal machines
	Earth and Universe	EF07CI13 – Greenhouse effect EF07CI14 – Ozone layer
8° YEAR	Matter and energy	EF08CI01 – Sources and types of energy EF08CI02 – Energy transformation EF08CI03 – Classify residential electrical equipment EF08CI04 – Calculating electricity consumption EF08CI05 – Electrical circuits EF08CI06 – Conscious use of electricity
	Earth and Universe	EF08CI13/EF08CI15 – The Sun, Earth and Moon system EF08CI16 – Climate
9° YEAR	Matter and energy	EF09CI04 – The structure of matter EF09CI06 – Radiation and its applications

In high school, as show on **Table 3**, students are introduced to more abstract concepts, including non-technical aspects of RE and PV energies. The code EM13CNT309 of the Specific Competencies and Skills requires the analysis of socio-environmental, political, and economic issues related to the world's current dependence on non-RE resources. It also requires a discussion on the need to introduce alternative and new energy and materials technologies, including a comparison of different types of engines and production processes for new materials.

Table 3: Knowledge objectives on PV-related subjects in high school curricula

COMPETENCE	KNOWLEDGE OBJECTS
SPECIFIC COMPETENCE 1	EM13CNT101, EM13CNT103, EM13CNT106, and EM13CNT107 – Analyze natural phenomena and technological processes, based on the interactions and relationships between matter and energy, to propose individual and collective actions that improve production processes, minimize socio-environmental impacts and improve living conditions at local, regional and global levels.
SPECIFIC COMPETENCE 3	EM13CNT302, EM13CNT303, EM13CNT307, EM13CNT308, EM13CNT309, and EM13CNT310 – Investigate problem situations and evaluate applications of scientific and technological knowledge and their implications in the world, using procedures and languages specific to the natural sciences, to propose solutions that consider local, regional and/or global demands, and communicate their findings and conclusions to a variety of audiences, in a variety of contexts and through different media and Digital Information and Communication Technologies (TDIC).

4.1 Analyses of Basic Education Competencies

Table 4, **Table 5**, and **Table 6** present a detailed analysis of each competence, focusing on its application in the context of elementary, middle, and high schools, respectively. Each competence is assigned a code (base on **Table 1**) provides a detailed account of the codes pertinent to the competency analyses. A review of the competencies reveals numerous subjects already encompassed within the BNCC following its new revision. The syllabus includes a diverse range of technical subjects. Notably, the elementary school competencies covered are the initial ones, mainly within the first five indexes. The first four indexes are the subject of intensive study in the second year. From the 3° year onwards, there is an integration with elements related to the environment, such as conservation, life cycles, and recycling. The more advanced indexes, such as legislation and other areas of knowledge, have not yet been introduced to students.

Table 4: Analysis of competencies of elementary school

BNCC CODE	ANALYSIS OF COMPETENCIES
SCIENCES – 2° YEAR	
EF02CI07	1.1, 1.2, 1.4, 1.5, 1.6, 5.1
EF02CI08	1.1, 1.2, 1.5, 1.6, 4.1, 4.3 and 4.4
SCIENCES – 3° YEAR	
EF03CI02	1.1, 1.2, 1.5, 3.1, 5.1 and 5.2
EF03CI07	4.2, 4.3, 5.1, and 5.2
EF03CI08	1.1, 1.2, 1.3, 1.5 and 5.2
EF03CI10	1.1, 1.3, 1.4, 1.5, 2.1, 2.2, 4.2, 4.3, and 5.2
SCIENCES – 4° YEAR	
EF04CI09	1.1, 1.2, 1.3, 1.5, 1.6, 5.1, and 5.2
SCIENCES – 5° YEAR	
EF05CI01	1.1, 1.5, 1.6, 2.3, 3.1, 3.2, and 5.1
EF05CI05	2.1, 4.1, 4.2, 4.3, 4.4, 5.2, and 6.1
EF05CI11	1.1, 1.2, 1.3, 1.4, 1.5, 1.6, 5.1

As students progress through middle school, it becomes evident that the subjects are increasingly interconnected, both with one another and with the real world. The competencies encompass a greater degree of dialogue and critical thinking about various subjects, including thermal machines, RE in general, the ozone layer, and the environment. The suggestions for the competencies are continually developed through dialogue to propose solutions to the problems presented. The incorporation of the items in index 7 has yet to be openly discussed, yet they represent a significant number of the currently known solutions to the problems studied by the students. In 8º year, there are nine competencies related to the subject. Conversely, the 9º year is focused on material properties, an essential area for the development and improvement of one of the main elements of the PV system: the PV module.

Table 5: Analysis of competencies of middle school

CODE	ANALYSIS OF COMPETENCIES
SCIENCES – 6º YEAR	
EF06CI14	1.2, 1.3, 1.5, 1.6, 5.1, and 5.2
SCIENCES – 7º YEAR	
EF07CI05	4.1, 4.2, 4.3, 4.4, 6.1, 6.3, 7.2, and 7.3
EF07CI13	4.1, 4.2, 4.3, 4.4, 6.1, 6.3, 7.1, 7.2, and 7.3
EF07CI14	4.1, 4.2, 4.3, 4.4, 5.2, 6.1, 6.3, 7.1, 7.2, and 7.3
SCIENCES – 8º YEAR	
EF08CI01	1.1, 1.3, 4.1, 4.2, 4.3, 5.2, 6.1, 7.1, 7.2, and 7.3
EF08CI02	1.1, 1.6, 1.7, 2.1, 2.2, 2.3, and 5.2
EF08CI03	1.1, 1.6, 5.2, 6.1, 7.1, and 7.2
EF08CI04	1.1, 1.6, 5.2, 6.1, 7.1, and 7.2
EF08CI05	1.1, 4.3, 4.4, 5.2, 6.1, 6.3, 7.1, 7.2, and 7.3
EF08CI06	4.2, 4.3, 4.4, 6.1, 6.2, 6.3, 7.1, 7.2, and 7.3
EF08CI13	1.1, 1.2, 1.3, 1.5, 1.6, 5.1, and 5.2
EF08CI15	1.1, 1.2, 1.3, 1.5, 1.6, 2.1, 3.1, and 3.2
EF08CI16	4.1, 4.2, 4.3, 4.4, 5.1, 5.2, 6.1, 6.3, 7.1, 7.2, 7.3, and 7.4
SCIENCES – 9º YEAR	
EF09CI04	1.1, 1.3, 3.1, and 3.2
EF09CI06	1.1, 1.3, 3.1, and 3.2

Notably, the elementary school competencies covered are the initial ones, mainly within the first five indexes. The first four indexes are the subject of intensive study in the second year. From the 3º year onwards, there is an integration with elements related to the environment, such as conservation, life cycles, and recycling. The more advanced indexes, such as legislation and other areas of knowledge, have not yet been introduced to students.

Table 6: Analysis of competencies of high school

GENERAL COMPETENCIES OF HIGH SCHOOL NATURE SCIENCES AND THEIR TECHNOLOGIES IN HIGH SCHOOL: SPECIFIC COMPETENCES AND SKILLS	
CODE BNCC	**CODE**
SPECIFIC COMPETENCE 1	
EM13CNT101	1.1, 3.1, 3.2, 4.1, 4.2, 4.3, 4.4, 7.1, 7.2, 7.3, and 7.4
EM13CNT103	1.1, 1.3, 1.6, 4.2, 4.3, 5.2, and 6.1
EM13CNT106	1.1, 1.7, 4.1, 4.2, 4.3, 4.4, 5.2, 6.1, 6.2, 6.3, 7.1, 7.2, 7.3, and 7.4
EM13CNT107	1.1, 1.6, 2.1, 7.1, 7.2, and 7.3
SPECIFIC COMPETENCE 3	
EM13CNT302	6.1, 6.2, 6.3, and 6.4
EM13CNT303	6.1, 6.2, 6.3, and 6.4
EM13CNT307	3.1, 3.2, and 4.2
EM13CNT308	6.1 and 6.4
EM13CNT309	4.1, 4.2, 4.3, 4.4, 6.1, 6.2, 6.3, 6.4, 7.1, 7.2, and 7.3
EM13CNT310	4.2, 6.1, 6.3, and 6.4

At the high school level, the competencies become more comprehensive, encompassing a range of analytical, evaluative, interpretative, and investigative tasks. A more extensive analysis of applications and connections with the wider world is proposed, necessitating a deeper level of reflection and critical thinking than at the middle school level. Furthermore, the indications are linked to digital devices and applications.

5 CONCLUSIONS

The findings of this study reveal both gaps and opportunities that call for targeted strategies to better align the education sector with the current and future demands on PV market. In particular, they highlight structural shortcomings that limit the capacity of the existing system to prepare professionals adequately for this field.

A review of the relevant literature, combined with an analysis of government-proposed curricula, indicates that the current educational framework requires substantial improvement. Despite the BNCC's recommendations, many basic and technical education programs still fail to incorporate essential content related to PV energy. The omission of topics such as emerging technologies and practical applications restricts students' ability to acquire the knowledge and competencies necessary to pursue careers in the sector.

6 ACKNOWLEDGMENT

This work was conducted during a scholarship supported by the International Cooperation Program PROBRAL fostering a collaborative exchange between TH Köln-University of Applied Sciences and the Universidade Federal de Santa Catarina (UFSC). The partnership was financed by Capes – Brazilian Federal Agency for Support and Evaluation of Graduate Education within the Ministry of Education of Brazil and the German Academic Exchange Service (DAAD). A.M.F.G acknowledges CAPES (Coordenação de Aperfeiçoamento de Pessoal de Nível Superior) for a Ph.D scholarship. D.O.S acknowledges CNPq (Conselho Nacional de Desenvolvimento Científico e Tecnológico.) for a Ph.D scholarship.

7 REFERENCES
[1] REN21, "Renewables 2025 Global Status Report: Global overview," Paris, 2025.
[2] ABSOLAR, "Energia Solar Fotovoltaica no Brasil - Infográfico ABSOLAR," 2025. [Online]. Available: https://www.absolar.org.br/mercado/infografico/
[3] P. Jennings, "New directions in renewable energy education," *Renewable Energy*, vol. 34, no. 2, pp. 435–439, Feb. 2009, doi: 10.1016/j.renene.2008.05.005.
[4] P. Rillero, A. Koerner, A. K. Daragmeh, and K. Soykal, "Active Learning Methodologies in a Solar Power, Middle-Grade Curriculum for Palestinian Schools," *Int J Env Sci Ed*, vol. 16, no. 2, Feb. 2020, doi: 10.29333/ijese/7814.
[5] L. Agirreazkuenaga and P. M. Martinez, "Secondary students' perception, positioning and insight on education for sustainability," *International Research in Geographical and Environmental Education*, vol. 30, no. 3, pp. 218–237, Jul. 2021, doi: 10.1080/10382046.2021.1877952.
[6] E. Çakirlar Altuntaş and S. L. Turan, "Awareness of

secondary school students about renewable energy sources," *Renewable Energy*, vol. 116, pp. 741–748, Feb. 2018, doi: 10.1016/j.renene.2017.09.034.

[7] F. Hoque, R. M. Yasin, and K. Sopian, "Revisiting Education for Sustainable Development: Methods to Inspire Secondary School Students toward Renewable Energy," *Sustainability*, vol. 14, no. 14, p. 8296, Jul. 2022, doi: 10.3390/su14148296.

[8] L. R. do Nascimento, M. Braga, R. A. Campos, H. F. Naspolini, and R. Rüther, "Performance assessment of solar photovoltaic technologies under different climatic conditions in Brazil," *Renewable Energy*, vol. 146, pp. 1070–1082, Feb. 2020, doi: 10.1016/j.renene.2019.06.160.

[9] D. Kimuli, R. Nabaterega, N. Banadda, I. Kabenge, A. Ekwamu, and P. Nampala, "Advanced Education and Training Programs to Support Renewable Energy Investment in Africa," *International Journal of Education and Practice*, vol. 5, no. 1, pp. 8–15, 2017, doi: 10.18488/journal.61/2017.5.1/61.1.8.15.

[10] H. Lucas, S. Pinnington, and L. F. Cabeza, "Education and training gaps in the renewable energy sector," *Solar Energy*, vol. 173, pp. 449–455, Oct. 2018, doi: 10.1016/j.solener.2018.07.061.

[11] Brasil, "Base Nacional Comum Curricular: Educação é a base," MEC, Brasília, 2018.

[12] Brasil, "Conheça a história da educação brasileira." Accessed: Jul. 03, 2024. [Online]. Available: http://portal.mec.gov.br/pet/33771-institucional/83591-conheca-a-evolucao-da-educacao-brasileira

[13] UN, "Transformando Nosso Mundo: A Agenda 2030 para o Desenvolvimento Sustentável," 2015.

[14] A. F. Almarshoud and E. Adam, "A transition toward localizing the value chain of photovoltaic energy in Saudi Arabia," *Clean Techn Environ Policy*, vol. 23, no. 7, pp. 2049–2059, Sep. 2021, doi: 10.1007/s10098-021-02102-2.

[15] IRENA, "Renewable energy statistics 2024," International Renewable Energy Agency, Abu Dhabi, 2024.

[16] D. G. für I. Z. (GIZ) G. GIZ, "A mão de obra na cadeia produtiva do setor solar brasileiro," 2023.

[17] H. R. Hungerford and T. L. Volk, "Changing Learner Behavior Through Environmental Education," *The Journal of Environmental Education*, vol. 21, no. 3, pp. 8–21, Mar. 1990, doi: 10.1080/00958964.1990.10753743.

[18] M. K. A. Sulaiman, L. Halim, N. Mohamad Arsad, and R. Mohamad Yasin, "Exploring Challenges for Integrating Solar PV Technology in Secondary Schools' Education," in *Proceedings of the 2nd International Conference on Social Sciences, ICONESS 2023, 22-23 July 2023, Purwokerto, Central Java, Indonesia*, Purwokerto, Indonesia: EAI, 2023. doi: 10.4108/eai.22-7-2023.2335096.

[19] R. Corina, T. Ovidiu, A. Iulia, M. Cristina, and A. Ștefan, "A critical review of the photovoltaic effect teaching in high-school," *Rom. Rep. Phys.*, vol. 76, no. 1, pp. 901–901, Mar. 2024, doi: 10.59277/RomRepPhys.2024.76.901.

[20] A. R. Da Conceição and E. C. Fireman, "Controvérsias sociocientíficas e o ensino por investigação: uma estratégia didática para auxiliar no desenvolvimento de habilidades propostas pela Base Nacional Comum Curricular," *#Tear*, vol. 9, no. 2, Dec. 2020, doi: 10.35819/tear.v9.n2.a4308.

[21] Brasil, "Lei Nº 13.415, de 16 de Fevereiro de 2017," 2017.

[22] A. T. E. D. Oliveira, A. A. Sobreira, H. F. D. Costa, J. D. S. Ferreira, and C. A. S. Perez, "A energia solar fotovoltaica: transformação, evolução, aspectos ambientais e abordagens na sala de aula," *RSD*, vol. 11, no. 9, p. e25811932533, Jul. 2022, doi: 10.33448/rsd-v11i9.32533.

[23] L. F. A. Cordeiro and M. A. G. Fernandes, "Perspectivas da energia fotovoltaica na capacitação de professores para desenvolvimento de uma educação ambiental," *Environmental Scientiae*, vol. 3, no. 2, pp. 60–68, Jan. 2022, doi: 10.6008/CBPC2674-6492.2021.002.0006.

[24] M. F. Ferreira, M. A. V. Freitas, N. F. Da Silva, A. F. Da Silva, and L. R. L. D. Paz, "Insertion of Photovoltaic Solar Systems in Technological Education Institutions in Brazil: Teacher Perceptions Concerning Contributions towards Sustainable Development," *Sustainability*, vol. 12, no. 4, p. 1292, Feb. 2020, doi: 10.3390/su12041292.

PHOTOVOLTAIC DEVELOPMENT AND LANDSCAPE CONFLICTS IN TAIWAN: STATUS AND RESOLUTIONS

WANG TZU-YA, WANG CHIA-CHEN/
Industrial Technology Research Institute
DianaWang@itri.org.tw, molly.wang@itri.org.tw

ABSTRACT: The turbulent international situation in recent years has triggered a global fossil fuel supply crisis, leading to a rise in renewable energy; and solar photovoltaics (solar PV) accounts for over half of the current worldwide renewable energy production. Aiming to achieve its 2050 Net zero Emissions goals, Taiwan is actively promoting the development of solar PV and other renewable energy sources. Although solar PV causes fewer environmental issues than traditional power generation methods and related impact can usually be mitigated through proper measures, the public may still have reservations about the installations' impact on local landscapes, environment, and ecosystem since the solar panels are usually set up near living zones. This study complied relevant past literature and categorized them into impacts on the visual landscape, environment, and habitats for discussion.

Looking back on Taiwan's development of solar PV, there were several incidents in which the public expressed concerns related to landscape, environment, and ecosystem issues. There was much controversy and conflict surrounding the installation sites as well. This study looked at the three most controversial cases in Taiwan and realized the importance of communicating with the public. Taiwan has introduced the *Directions for the Landscape and Ecological Environment Assessment of Ground-Mounted Photovoltaic Systems* (設置地面型太陽光電設施景觀及生態環境審定原則) for the solar PV operators' reference to reduce the impact on landscape and environment when setting up solar power facilities and a lot of sites are designed as per *The Directions*. Yet we discovered that when compared with similar regulations or policy in other countries, Taiwan's *Directions* do not include guidelines and instructions on how to communicate with the locals as well as how the implementations can be adjusted according to local conditions. In the future, our government should review and refine these aspects to improve the overall domestic solar PV installation environment and reduce the pertinent impacts on landscape, environment, and ecosystems.

Keywords: Solar PV, Landscape, Renewable Energy Policy

1 INTRODUCTION

A global fossil fuel crisis has been set off by recent regional wars and the COVID-19 pandemic. This significantly affected the global supply chain and energy industry, highlighting the importance of renewable energy, especially solar PV[1]. As the pandemic gradually slowed down in 2023, the growth of worldwide solar PV cumulative capacity hit a record high of 1,552.3 GW. The annual new installed capacity increased by nearly 50% and solar PV development continues to take up a major role in the global renewable energy industry[2].

Located in East Asia and on the west side of the Pacific, Taiwan has an area of 35,980 m²[3] and is the 38th largest island in the world. About 70% of this island is mountain terrain. The average temperature is 23.5℃, the average global solar radiation (Rs) accumulates to 5,287.2 MJ/m² per year, and the average sunshine hours reach 1,732 days/year [4]. The population is around 23,278,642 people, Gross domestic product (GDP) is about USD 791.61 billion, and GDP per capita is approximately USD 34,050[5]. By the end of 2023, Taiwan's solar PV installed capacity reached 12.42GW[6].

As more countries respond to the 2050 net-zero declaration, Taiwan also announced our 2050 Net zero Emissions goals in 2021. The government later released *Taiwan's Pathway to Net zero Emissions in 2050 and Strategy Details*[7], *The 12 Key Strategies*[8], and *Net zero Emissions Pathway 2023-2026 Outline Plan*[9]. Renewable energy thus became a key player in Taiwan's transition to Net zero Emissions by 2050. In 2009, the Legislative Yuan adopted the Renewable Energy Development Act which serves as the basis for renewable energy development in Taiwan. The Act was amended in 2019 to optimize the regulatory environment for launching renewable energy policies and speed up the development of renewable energy. According to the Ministry of Economic Affairs (MOEA), the objectives for Taiwan's energy transition are to "promote green energy, increase natural gas, reduce coal-fired power, achieve nuclear-free". In the category of "promote green energy", the MOEA projects that by 2025, 20% of the total power generated should come from renewable energy sources [10], solar PV installed capacity should reach 20 GW, wind power at 5.6 GW, hydropower at 2 GW, and biomass energy at 800 MW. Taiwan launched a series of promotion plans since 2016 to gradually achieve the goal of 20% renewable energy[10] and set the target of 20 GW solar PV installation capacity in 2025.

Although renewable energy can strongly support the sustainable development of energy, the rapid increase of solar PV installed capacity has led to issues caused by inappropriate site selections or development projects that occur without sufficient planning beforehand. These incidents bring on conflicts between solar PV, landscape, and the environment, not only hindering the installation of solar PV in Taiwan, many countries are also facing similar issues[11], [12], [13]. Therefore, in addition to exploring the potential impacts of solar PV development on the landscape and environment in Taiwan, this study will also explain the *Directions for the Landscape and Ecological Environment Assessment of Ground-Mounted Photovoltaic Systems* which was released to solve the conflicts between solar PV and landscapes and explore how solar panels affect the surrounding ecological environment. What kind of countermeasures can Taiwan come up with? And what other regulations or examples abroad can be used as references?

10.4229/EUPVSEC2025/5DV.3.41
020549-001

2 THE POTENTIAL IMPACTS OF SOLAR PV DEVELOPMENT ON THE LANDSCAPE

Solar PV can reduce greenhouse gas emissions, reactivate degraded land, improve air and water quality, and strengthen the energy autonomy of a nation. It also contributes to sustainable development and therefore generally receives more support from the public[14]. It should be noted that renewable energy generation facilities still have some impact on the surrounding environment. While the impact caused by solar PV is usually lesser and may be minimized through appropriate mitigation measures[14], the setting of solar panels could still impact the surrounding landscape. In this study, a "landscape" is defined according to the European Landscape Convention: "The landscape is part of the land, as perceived by local people or visitors, which evolves through time as a result of being acted upon by natural forces and human beings[15]." In other words, the landscape is associated with the emotional relationship between people and the land. According to relative literature, types of impact on the landscape caused by solar panels can be categorized into Visual, Environmental, and Habitat impact.

2.1 Visual Impacts

Although society is very accepting of solar PV, the energy conversion efficiency of solar power is not as high as traditional power-generating methods and requires more land. Site selection often clashes with local land use and natural landscape [19], and the subjective visual impact is one of the main reasons why the public objects to setting up renewable energy equipment such as solar panel [19], [25]. The visual impact caused by solar panels mainly depends on subjective preferences, and these preferences may be affected by life experience, culture, age, and education level[19], [20], [26]. Past studies[20] usually use the term "Unity" to describe the degree of coherence and harmony of the visual elements and present the level of visual impact. However, it is difficult to quantify the visual impact caused by solar panels[14]. Many past research[14] [16], [17], [18], [20] pointed out that solar panels could cause visual impact on the surrounding landscape. Impact factors mentioned in most literature include visual aesthetics impact, color, fractality, and visibility.

2.1.1 Visual aesthetics impact

The impact of visual aesthetics is defined in literature as changes in landscapes caused by development, resulting in changes in our subjective and objective perceptions of the environment[16]. In other words, the landscape created by solar panels and the surrounding environment affects visual experience. If solar panels are set up in a natural environment, their visual impact increases; contrarily, if the solar panels are integrated into modern buildings, they may have a positive aesthetic impact[18]. Some studies[14] mentioned that California has established regulations that state large areas of land cannot be used as solar PV sites. The regulation takes the potential recreation value of the land into consideration as well as the possible visual impact and impacts on the ecosystem and habitats. However, the setup of solar panels can replace a portion of the mining industry and transform large highland forests into recreational areas. Therefore, even if solar panels have some impact on visual aesthetics, it also frees up visual landscapes[14].

There is a study[16] points out that visual impact is one of the main landscape impact factors to consider when installing solar PV sites. The objective indicators of visual aesthetic impact include visibility, color, and fractality[16], [21]. This paper went through related literature[18], [20], [22], [27] and summarized the objective indicators that affect visual aesthetics as follows:

2.1.1.1 Color

Literature[21] indicates that there is a contrasting relationship between the surface color of solar panels and the color of surrounding landscapes (e.g., vegetation, soil, sky, etc.). There is a research[20] also mentions that color is considered an important objective factor in the perception of aesthetics in many studies. The paper on the aesthetic impact of solar panels concludes that solar panels cause an aesthetic impact since they change the landscape. Furthermore, adjacent colors affect our perception of a particular color, and the color of the solar panels often does not blend in with the surrounding buildings or environments. Especially in rural areas, the color of the solar panels strongly stands out from the color scheme of the natural landscape, making it more likely to cause negative visual experiences[20]. Fernandez-Jimenez et al. also listed color as one of the indexes when selecting new site locations. They converted the colors of the planned installation area grid into variables and then standardized the variables so that the values of all grids are between 0 and 1. The numeral values of all grids under various conditions were then compared. Solar panels installed in grids with values closer to 0 would have less visual impact. If the value is 0, then observers onsite or pedestrians barely notice the solar PV equipment[27].

2.1.1.2 Fractality

Fractality refers to the overall profile of the solar panels[21]. Usually when designing the deployment of solar panels, the objective is to spread out to the largest area possible within the limited plot of land to maximize generation capacity and reduce installation costs[16]; yet the visual relationship between the solar panels and the surrounding landscape is often overlooked during the designing process, and the arrangement, layout, and shape of the panels may affect the visual experience of pedestrians and viewers. Measures to address this issue include employing Building-integrated photovoltaics (BIPV) and increasing patterns in the grid to further integrate the panels with the surrounding landscape as well as adjusting the space porosity within the module layout to complement the surrounding landscape. Major design parameters that affect the porosity are the azimuth angle, angle of inclination, and density. Flexible designing for solar PV landscapes formed by large areas of land use and landscape transformation can reduce the impact of large-scale ground-mounted solar PV systems on the landscape and increase ecosystem protection potential[16]. If we want to let the equipment blend in with the surrounding landscape, it may be necessary to cut down a certain degree of generation efficiency to allow better integration of the panels and the surrounding landscape[22].

2.1.1.3 Visibility

In the paper by Kapetanakis et al., impact caused by Visibility is considered the most important. The impact, or how obvious the facility is, depends on the total area covered by solar PV. When installing solar PV, either hide them around buildings or roads or set them up in a place where people can see them[18]. While operators are usually more inclined to hide the panels to avoid affecting the visual scene, it should be noted that when the visibility of solar PV is low, the public would have less of a positive impression of the facility. Thus, experts normally suggest integrating solar PV with buildings, a method that also increases the panels' installation capacity and shading properties. Furthermore, the correct site selection can also reduce the visual impact of large solar PV sites[18]. Relevant study[22] analyzed the proportion of solar PV facilities with visible by the edges and launched obscuring measures such as planting hedges or orchards around them. This reduces the visibility of solar PV facilities and increases the growing space for plants and animals. Some sites will set up observation decks for visitors and promote the deck as a local attraction to enhance the positive impression of solar PV[22].

2.1.2 Other factors

In addition to visual impacts, relevant literatures[16], [20], [28] also mention other visual influence factors caused by solar PV, including objective factors such as shape and size, density, contrast, and regularity. These are mainly controlled by the distance between solar panels and have a great impact in urban[20]. Integration, which is similar to Visibility, is divided into Non-integration, Partial Integration, and Integration in the research. The difference is that the term is usually used when discussing integration with buildings[20], [28]. There is also a study[16]that assess relevant landscape factors based on landscape sensitivity. The factors include terrain, patches, particles, and landscape characteristics. Highly intense, diverse, and unique terrains as well as complex, rugged, and irregular plots have higher landscape sensitivity and are more likely to see landscape conflicts at renewable energy installation sites[16].

2.2 Environmental Impact

Solar PV may also cause microclimate impact during the power generation process. We compiled the environmental impact factors frequently mentioned in relevant literature, namely temperature, glare, noise, electromagnetic fields, waste, and emissions, as follows:

2.2.1 Temperature

The principle of solar PV power generation is that the solar PV modules absorb solar radiation and then directly convert it into electricity[23]. Chiabrando et al. pointed out that the modules may reach 70°C during the power generation process, resulting in a temperature increase in the surrounding air[19] and may affect the soil carbon cycle[24] as well as plant productivity and organic mass decomposition rates. However, we can significantly reduce the module overheating problem by setting up ventilation equipment and thus avoid power generation efficiency decrease due to overheated module components. To summarize, the temperature of the modules may increase during power generation, but under normal weather conditions, this would only cause a slight effect on the surrounding microclimate[19].

2.2.2 Glare

Glare is a visual stimulus caused by uncontrolled brightness. Excessive light and reflected sunlight could cause short-term photophobia[27], yet it is still relatively difficult to eliminate the glare effects of solar PV [19], [20]. Currently, the negative glare effects caused by solar PV

can be mitigated by computer simulations or Anti-Reflection Coating (ARC) materials[20].

Yet past study[20] also mentions that while existing computer software can use the DEM (Digital Elevation Model) and GIS (Geographic Information System) to simulate glare in specific situations and predict the path and direction of reflected beams, there are still disparities between the simulations and the actual situations. Moreover, so far there is no literature that provides glare indexes for such special situations, nor are there any standard values for reference. Nevertheless, the simulation results can still be used as a reference during the designing stage to alleviate glare problems that may occur after the solar panels are set. There are also many types of ARC materials that are being developed, such as nanostructure materials with composites of silicon, silicon dioxide, titanium oxide, zirconium oxide, zinc oxide, cobalt oxide, stannic oxide, carbon, and GaN, as well as ARCs with metal ions that can reduce the glare effect on viewers[20].

2.2.3 Noise

According to previous studies[18], solar PV sites generate less noise than general building activities and diesel generator units[18], [29] as the lack of significant operating components and mechanical vibrations in the solar PV system allows it to operate quietly. The only sources of noise in these systems are the transformers and booster stations. Since solar panels mainly generate power during the day, any possible noise impact is usually limited to the daytime and causes less interference to the residents during nighttime or silent hours. Effective soundproofing and noise control measures are set up during construction to reduce potential noise impact on the locals. In summary, the operation process of solar PV is quiet. Noise mitigation measures should be implemented during construction to ensure the lowest impact on local communities[18].

2.2.4 Electromagnetic field

Currently, there are no study indicates that solar PV sites have higher electromagnetic waves, however, there may be higher electromagnetic waves during the transition from low to medium or high voltage during electricity transmission. As a result, some medium- and high-voltage cables are buried underground to reduce their magnetic field. The setup of the facilities should also comply with local standards to assure the public[17].

2.2.5 Waste and emissions

Solar PV generates less waste and emissions than traditional power generation methods. Greenhouse gas and $PM_{2.5}$ emissions, in particular, are significantly reduced[16], [29]. Notwithstanding, the production process of solar panels can still produce gas and may cause pollution if not handled properly.[19] Furthermore, the processing of decommissioned solar panels also requires special care. Panel materials such as metals, silicon, glass, and plastic may contaminate the soil if handled improperly[19]. There are also a study[18] mentions that if a solar panel catches fire during operation, certain chemicals could be released into and pollute the atmosphere. Hence, it is crucial to have emergency responding actions and disaster prevention measures in place for material storage, operations, and maintenance to avoid the negative effects of waste and emissions[18].

2.2.6 Other factors

Other environmental impacts solar PV may generate include soil erosion during construction and impact on water quality, historical landscapes, surface runoff, surface albedo, and surface roughness. As solar panels are static power generating facilities, most impacts occur during the manufacturing and construction phases, for example, wastewater produced during manufacturing. However, the severity of the impact still requires more supporting research[19], [29]. In terms of surface runoff effects, changes in land use and land cover or the panels installed on hill slopes could double or even triple soil penetration, runoff ratio, and evapotranspiration; thus, proper protection of water and land resources and the deployment of monitoring facilities are necessary during the construction of solar PV, especially when setting up facilities on hill slopes[14]. In general, the operation of solar panels does not have a significant impact on the environment.

2.3 Habitat Impacts

This section compiled the impacts of solar PV on the ecosystem that are discussed more frequently in previous literature. Topics covered include land occupation, land use and land cover effects, the impact on birds and wildlife, habitat fragmentation, and soil erosion.

2.3.1 Land occupation

Solar PV is a renewable energy power source that requires a large area of land. Although some solar panels are mounted on the roof and thus avoid the land use issue, the setup of other solar panels still needs land. If the site is set on degraded land, it can not only avoid additional land use or land cover changes but also support land activation in the area. It could even increase the supply of the local ecosystem, such as stabilizing soil and having carbon sequestration properties[30]. Research[16] has also shown that cutting down the required land area and increasing power density decreases not only land occupation but also the visual impact[16].

2.3.2 Land use and land cover

The installation of solar panels changes the land use and land cover of an area. Depending on the site selection, different types of land use and land cover create different degrees of impact. For example, a site located on arable land could disrupt the local agricultural production landscape and ecosystem. It could also destroy the rich soil and lead to conflicts with the locals who have an emotional connection with the land[18]. However, in terms of land use intensity, if a solar PV installation has a lifespan of 30 years, the land of each unit generation capacity does not change with time; but for mines that supply coal to coal-fired power plants, the surface soil would require decades to recover. Solar PV has the advantage that as the equipment lifespan increases, the land occupied per unit generation capacity gradually decreases[29]. Past studies[29] indicate that the land occupied by solar PV can recover more quickly and the land use intensity is significantly less than that of coal-fired power plants. The impact on local land use and land cover is also notably less[17], [29].

2.3.3 Birds risk and wildlife

Birds and wildlife are often crucial factors in the review for solar PV installation permits, yet studies on the correlations between this new technology and the surrounding ecosystem are relatively few. Since solar PV sites are usually encircled by fences that keep wildlife from entering, this could disrupt the hiding places, migratory routes, and food supply of local wildlife. In some overseas cases, operators even use herbicide to clean up the site area, which impacts wildlife habitats as well[29], [30].

A previous study in South Africa[31] looked at the abundance of invertebrate colonies in the solar PV site area, power supply area, and the surrounding ranch area. Results showed no significant differences, indicating solar PV facilities have little impact on invertebrate animal colonies[31]. Another study in the UK[32] also compared bird monitoring results of a solar PV site with control sites ranging from 6 to 280m away from the site. Findings indicated that the average number of bird species on the solar PV project site was 15.2 species, which is higher than the control areas (12.8 species). The site also had a higher total number of birds (averaging 47.8 birds). This concludes that the solar PV site has a higher bird diversity and their behavior onsite is not much different from other locations[32].

Some research[18] [29] suggests that customized studies and analyses of the surrounding wildlife and ecosystem should be conducted during the development phase and ecologically sensitive areas or natural reserves should be avoided to reduce the impact of solar PV installations on the surrounding environment[18] [29].Nevertheless, there are not many related studies and more research and confirmation will be needed to determine the impact of solar PV on birds and wildlife and subsequent countermeasures.

2.3.4 Habitat fragmentation

The installed solar panels could cause the vegetation beneath them to degrade or disappear, especially on farmland sites, the panels are more likely to affect the growth of local plants. The project site could also affect the local animal habitat as well as the growth pattern of flora and fauna[19]. Habitat loss and fragmentation are considered major threats to biodiversity, and the layout of solar PV facilities could affect the distribution of species and alter the biological corridor[19].

Nevertheless, studies[32] have shown that local biodiversity can be improved when solar PV sites implement site management measures. These measures include seeding various species at one location, limiting herbicide use, conducting protective grazing or mowing, and managing the edges of wildlife habitats. These actions expand the diversity of plants, especially wildflowers, and consequently boost the diversity of other species. The increasing number of butterflies and bees can pollinate and benefit the surrounding farmlands or orchards and give the neighboring landscape beautiful flowers[32], [33].

2.3.5 Soil erosion

Land preparation work for the solar PV project site includes removing existing vegetation, evening out the surface, and compacting the soil[17]. When farmlands or forests are converted for solar PV use, the soil penetration rate and evapotranspiration volume will be affected[29] and, without relevant protection measures, could lead to soil erosion and even increase the possibility of floods, especially for solar PV sites set on hill slopes.[17] Proactive monitoring and related research are necessary to protect local hydrology and soil resources[17], [29].

2.3.6 Other factors

The above-mentioned ecological effects aside, the installment of solar PV will change the use of land yet the impact on land modification and soil quality is milder and more neutral compared to conventional power generation systems. Actual impacts will require continuous observation through research.[29] In terms of soil quality impact mitigation measures, the study[18] proposes that the impact can be reduced by avoiding ecologically sensitive areas and restoring affected plants and animals around the project site. Changes in land use and land cover can also lead to the degradation of plants and loss of habitats, both of which affect the local ecosystem.[29] As described in 3.4, the setup of solar PV could cause some degree of habitat loss and fragmentation and thus disturb the migration or food foraging of certain species. As a result, the study also highlights the importance of habitat management and recommends avoiding sensitive areas when setting up the site, especially for large-scale sites[17], [18]. Nonetheless, the study[29] also suggests that more research is needed to observe and confirm the actual impact since solar PV show a lesser impact on ecosystems and habitat loss compared to conventional power generation methods. Furthermore, the construction process may cause surface disturbances. Although most of these effects are temporary, permanent damage could occur if appropriate mitigation measures are not taken. For that reason, an appropriate site selection should avoid ecologically sensitive areas and valuable historic and natural beauty areas to minimize impact[18].

3 CASES OF CONFLICT BETWEEN SOLAR PV INSTALLATIONS AND LANDSCAPE IN TAIWAN

As Taiwan begin to aggressively develop solar PV, the process generated many conflicts between the solar PV sites and local landscape, environment, and ecology. While the conflicts delayed the progress of related cases, they have also made the community more aware of these issues. This chapter will discuss the cases from the perspectives of visual, environmental, and ecological impacts.

3.1 Case of Visual Impact

According to past studies[14], [16], [17], [18], [20], the visual impacts caused by solar PV include visual conflicts and not blending in with the surrounding landscapes. The most controversial case of visual impact in Taiwan happened at a solar PV site in Pingtung in Southern Taiwan. This site is located on the slopes along Highway where leads to Kenting, a popular tourist destination. When the operators were setting up the solar panels, they removed the original vegetation on the slopes to prepare the land. Most of the removed plants were white popinac trees, which is a foreign species. Although the operators had conducted visual landscape simulation analysis before construction and continuously rolled out landscape engineering projects according to their development plan, the construction continued for over a year and the visitors going to and from Kenting filed complaints to the local government for this eyesore along the road. This action garnered much attention from the public. In this case, we see that solar PV sites set on the slopes of the roadside are more likely to conflict with the surrounding landscape as they are highly visible due to their location. This affects the travelers' visual aesthetics, causing a negative impression among the public and consequently toward solar PV.

3.2 Case of Environmental Impact

There are many studies[14], [17], [18] indicate that solar PV may cause issues such as light pollution and noise in the environment. Although no studies have clearly shown that solar PV are harmful to humans, the Taiwanese public is still skeptical about setting up solar panels. For example, during the construction phase of a solar PV site in Tainan City, the public severely protested because of concerns about the environment. This solar PV project site is situated close to a residential community, and during the construction period, residents have protested multiple times against the possible light pollution, low-frequency noise, and hot island effect. The local government later executed noise tests onsite after the construction was completed and found all to be within regulatory standards (maximum outside noise value at 53.6 dB), yet the public protested fiercely during the construction process. This project was eventually completed; however, we recommend that in the future, the operators, local government, and public should communicate better to minimize these conflicts and protect the rights of the public.

3.3 Case of Habitat Impact

Previous studies[14], [16], [17], [19] have shown that the impacts of solar PV on the ecological environment can destroy animal habitats and endanger certain species.[29], [30] However, operators are usually inclined to select a land area of a certain size for ground-mounted PV system setups due to setup cost and size. Taiwan has limited land and a dense population, and our flat plains are nearly fully developed. In recent years, local operators have turned to hill slopes or coastlines for solar panel setups. However Taiwan's unique geographic location has created a rich biodiversity and cultivated many indigenous species, and the slopes that are potential solar PV sites are the main living areas of endangered animals. A solar PV project site located on the slopes in Miaoli County is an example. Since the development area overlaps with the habitat of protected wildlife, the administration process review and operations have attracted much attention from environmental protection groups and the local public. This slope area is the habitat of endangered animals such as pangolins, crab-eating mongooses, and leopard cats, as a result, the operators invited ecologists to serve as advisors during the initial stage of development to reduce the impact on the ecosystem. The operators also promised to avoid highly sensitive zones, minimize construction areas, and carry out ecological compensation and thus received permission from the government[34]. To further protect the environment and ecosystem, the operators installed automatic cameras after the site started operations and even successfully captured images of wildlife including masked palm civets and leopard cats. Yet despite these measures, the Leopard Cat Association of Taiwan was still skeptical of the installation of this solar PV facility and pointed out that the biggest issue is site selection[35] as the facility is in an area where leopard cats frequent and the forest form of the area is intact. Even with ecological compensation measures afterward, it is still difficult to restore the functionality of the original habitat. The Association also suggested that local briefings should be held in areas with major ecological disputes and the operators should communicate clearly with residents to reduce the opposition[35].

4 HOW DOES TAIWAN RESOLVE THE

CONFLICTS BETWEEN SOLAR PV DEVELOPMENT AND LANDSCAPE?

Densely populated and with limited land resources, Taiwan only has a few suitable areas for renewable energy, and the power generation conversion efficiency of solar PV is relatively lower and requires larger areas of land[19]. Even though solar PV is a type of low-degree development, has multiple uses for the same piece of land, and the development process is strictly regulated by law, the public is still skeptical of solar PV in terms of visual, environmental, and habitat and landscape impacts. In response, Energy Administration, the MOEA, introduced the *Directions for the Landscape and Ecological Environment Assessment of Ground-Mounted Photovoltaic Systems*[36] for solar PV operators and relevant management agencies to use as a reference when designing the landscape and conducting reviews to decrease the impact solar PV setups could have on the surrounding landscape, habitats, and environments.

4.1 Newly established *Directions for the Landscape and Ecological Environment Assessment of Ground-Mounted Photovoltaic Systems*

To maintain the overall landscape of our country while promoting solar PV, the Energy Administration established the *Directions for the Landscape and Ecological Environment Assessment of Ground-Mounted Photovoltaic Systems* according to the resolution of the Ponds and Hydro Facilities Policies Environmental Evaluation meeting session called by the Executive Yuan on March 30, 2018. *The Directions* were announced on May 1, 2018, after the contents of the Directions were discussed in two cross-department expert meetings.

The Directions mainly targets large-scale ground-mounted solar PV sites (only those with a scale of 2 MW are regulated) to balance solar PV development and landscape and ecological environment protection. Furthermore, Class I environmentally sensitive areas are avoided according to the *Regulations for Examination Operations of Non-urban Development* (非都市土地開發審議作業規範). The overall content of *The Directions* mainly focuses on matters related to landscape and ecological aspects so that solar PV operators have guidelines for the initial stage of site selection and planning as well as the later construction and operation phases to reduce the impact of solar PV on the environment and landscape as much as possible.

For landscape's aspect, the content includes local contour lines should be taken into consideration when planning solar sites, panel module design should be adjusted accordingly to fit local characteristics, avoid elevated setups for cables, remove unnecessary lighting equipment, and maintain the original site landform.

For ecological aspect, since the establishment of the solar PV site could affect the surrounding ecological environment, operators are required by law to carry out suitable greening measures with indigenous species as the primary vegetation choice to avoid damaging the local indigenous ecosystem.

The construction and operation phases of solar PV are also regulated. During the construction phase, the site authorities can request the operator to conduct ecological surveys and implement environmental, safety, and health protection measures for planning and construction. After the facilities begin operations, regulations state that when maintaining the solar PV facilities, cleaning agents are prohibited to avoid polluting the water quality and ecological environment of the surrounding farmlands.

4.2 Revising the *Directions for the Landscape and Ecological Environment Assessment of Ground-Mounted Photovoltaic Systems*

The number of solar PV installations in Taiwan continues to grow annually as local sites rapidly expand, and the public's concerns about the noise, glare, and landscape ecology issues caused by solar PV have increased as well. To decrease the public's apprehension, the Energy Administration reviewed the appropriate distance between solar PV and settlements at the end of 2023 and revised *The Directions*. The Energy Administration commissioned a research team to launch tests at the solar PV sites. *The Directions* were decided based on the glare simulation and noise measurement reports as well as the conclusions of the discussion meetings attended by the Ministry of Agriculture, the Ministry of the Interior, the PVGSA, and the Taiwan Photovoltaic Industry Association on September 7 and October 17, 2023.

According to the results of the glare simulation, when the distance between the solar PV site and settlements exceeds 15 m, the glare impact on humans caused by solar panels is greatly reduced, and when paired with a hedge fence setup, the glare effect can be eliminated. To ensure that the glare caused by solar panels will not affect the settlements, the Administration took public opinions and the *Regulations for Examination Operations of Non-urban Development* into consideration and added *Article 6* in the revised version of *The Directions*. The new regulation mandates that ground-mounted solar PV installments that reach 2 MW should be set up in accordance with The Directions and comply with *Subsection 1* or *2* according to the installment model.

Article 6, Subparagraph 1 of *The Directions* regulates compound fishery and electricity symbiosis models. Fishery and electricity symbiosis models are usually large-scale installments and located close to farming villages and thus need to be regulated. Furthermore, according to *The Regulations for Examining the Application of Structuring Farming Facilities on Agricultural Land* (申請農業用地作農業設施容許使用審查辦法), solar PV facilities should not exceed 40% of the located farm-use land area. Since the installation has already reserved space for flexible retractions, there are only regulations on the adjunct boundary to settlements with over 50 households to avoid the solar PV landscape from affecting the residents.

Article 6, Subparagraph 2 regulates non-compound models. As non-compound models are usually large-scale setups that could easily cause land use conflicts with their neighbors, borders that are non-adjacent to settlements are also required to retract 15m and more or retract 10m and have hedge fences over 1.5m tall. Regarding the form of the hedge fences, fences irrelevant to agricultural operations are not allowed to be set up on farm-use land, therefore, the hedge fences should be installed with a transparent mesh without a fixed base to allow for other uses of the land in the future. In addition, the hedge fences are required to be set at least 5m from the site boundaries to reduce the visual pressure and protect the safety of road users as well as enhance overall landscape aesthetics. Indigenous climbing plants are preferred for the hedges to protect local biodiversity.

In addition to introducing *Subparagraph 1 and 2* to *The Directions* based on the glare simulation results,

Subparagraph 3 was also added based on the noise measurement results. Since the results show that the noise levels can only fall below the Class 2 standards stated in *The Noise Control Standards* when they are over 20m away from the unit substations, *Subparagraph 3* stipulated that the unit substation and converter, which are the main noise sources of solar PV sites, should be placed at 20m from settlements, and the noise measured around the site should be lower than the residential-use Class 2 daytime standard (57 dB). If the noise level exceeds the standard, soundproofing facilities must be added to avoid any noise disturbing the surrounding environment.

5   ANALYSIS AND DISCUSSION ON SOLAR PV AND LANDSCAPE CONFLICT COUNTERMEASURES

There are many solar PV developments in Taiwan have encountered landscape, ecological, and environmental conflicts, but these issues are not exclusive to Taiwan. Other countries are also experiencing many challenges in terms of balancing solar PV development and ecological environment protection. The International Union for Conservation of Nature and Natural Resource (IUCN) released the "Mitigating biodiversity impacts associated with solar and wind energy development: Guidelines for project developers" in February 2021[37] to help solar PV and wind power operators understand the potential risks these installations could have on the ecosystem, habitats, and communities. It also suggests a series of evaluation structures and methods which include four principles: Avoidance, Minimizations, Restoration, and Offset. For example, the sites should avoid sensitive zones, avoid construction during certain seasons or periods, and use as much surface soil and indigenous plants as possible to recover the ecosystem.

In addition to guidance from international organizations, countries have also formulated regulations or guidelines for solar PV and other renewable energy operators to reduce the impact on the surrounding ecological environment. For example, the city of Lingewaard[38] in the Netherlands launched a series of energy installation plans to achieve its 2050 net-zero goals and formulated relevant self-government ordinances as well. Solar energy parks were set up since roof-mounted solar panels could not satisfy the current energy demand. These sites not only increase renewable energy production volume but also prevent land fragmentation issues. If other farming areas wish to set up solar panels, the project must be proposed and widely supported by the locals, and approved sites are required to give back to the local community. The solar energy parks are also required to blend in with the existing landscape. The existing landscape elements, vegetation types, historical buildings, and openness of the space should all be taken into consideration. If we use the dike zone as an example, the facility and surrounding landscape are integrated by using indigenous plants to shape the riverbank, building windbreaks, setting up recreational routes, and planting natural herbs to beautify the sides of the ditches.

South Korea, like Taiwan, has many mountains and less plain areas, and thus many solar panels are installed on mountain slopes. To avoid slope disasters caused by solar PV setups, the sites must be evaluated and reviewed as many environment-related regulations. Moreover, different regions also have pertinent regulations to prevent setting solar PV sites too close to settlements or scenic areas. For example, Yeongju City introduced *The Standards for the Permission of Solar Power Generation Facilities Development* (발전시설의개발행위허가기준, Bal Jeon Si Seol Ui Gae Bal Haeng Wi Heo Ga Gi Jun)[39] which stipulates that solar PV sites should be 1,000m away from tourist areas, 500m away from communities with more than 10 households and roads, 300m away from communities with 5-10 households, and must not be installed in national cultural properties or protected scenic areas. Yet, to increase renewable energy setups, *The Site Selection Standards*, announced by the South Korean Ministry of Trade, Industry, and Energy Resources in February 2023, stated that the maximum isolation distance for solar PV facilities set in residential areas is 100m. If it is a residential area with more than 10 people, a briefing meeting needs to be held and the project can only go forward with the consent of two-thirds of the residents. There are also local incentives for relaxing or abolishing the isolation distance limit for renewable energy power generation facilities, such as weighted incentives for Korean renewable energy certificates.

Japan has *The Environmental Impact Assessment Act* (環境影響評価法) which included solar PV into the environmental assessment recognition criteria on March 5, 2019. It stipulates that a Class-1 business environmental assessment should be conducted if the site reaches more than 40 MW, and 30-40 MW sites should undergo a Class-2 business environmental assessment (whether the environmental assessment is required should be decided case by case). In addition, there are also *The Regulations on the Prevention of Sediment Disasters Act* (土砂災害警戒区域等における土砂災害防止対策の推進に関する法律, Dosya saigai keikai kuiki nado ni okeru dosya saigai bousi taisaku no suisin ni kan suru houritu) and *The Forest Act* (森林法, Sinrinhou) that restrict development in sediment disaster monitoring areas, steep slopes, and forests. Many local governments also have self-government ordinances to protect the surrounding landscape and ecological environments from being affected by solar PV developments. Examples include Hyōgo Prefecture's *Solar Power Generating Facilities and Local Environment Coordination Act* (太陽光発電施設等と地域環境との調和に関する条例, Taiyoukou hatuden sisetu nado to tiiki kankyou to no tyouwa ni kan suru zyourei)[40]. It listed out the factors that should be considered during the planning and setup stages, such as solar power generation facilities installed on sloped areas that are visible from main roads and urban areas must be located at sites with a 30-degree or lower angle of inclination. It also states that development areas of 5,000 m^2 should maintain good communications with stakeholders such as adjacent land owners or lessees, adjoining building owners and lessees, local neighborhood committee residents, and personnel designated by the mayor of the city/village; and the operators must submit their business plan to the local government at least 60 days before the construction commences. The Japanese Ministry of Environment introduced *The Guidance on the Solar Power Generation Environment* (太陽光発電の環境配慮ガイドライン, Taiyoukou hatuden no kankyou hairyo gaidorain) in 2020. *The Guidance* is a reference for operators setting up solar PV in regions that do not have specific regulations on landscape environments. According to the Guidance, during the designing phase, operators should consider the environmental impacts of the installation, including land stability, sewage discharge, noise, glare, dust and vibration caused by construction, landscape, wildlife and ecosystem, and the possibility of interacting with nature, to lessen the public's doubts.

Energy Administration, Ministry of Economic Affairs, R.O.C introduced the *Directions for the Landscape and Ecological Environment Assessment of Ground-Mounted Photovoltaic Systems* in 2018 to provide guidance on the protection of landscapes and ecosystems for large-scale sites and reduce the impact of solar PV development on surrounding areas. In 2023, The Principle was revised and protection provisions regarding hedge fences and the distance between solar PV sites and settlements were added. Compared with the relevant regulations and guidelines of other countries, Taiwan's Central Government is not only spearheading solar PV developments and setting pertinent administrative guidance but also has launched regulations and standards for different models with clear target groups and concrete numbers to protect the surrounding environment. Nevertheless, if we wish to decrease the public's concerns about solar PV installments, in future revisions of relevant regulations, legislative authorities could consider the suggestions from the Leopard Cat Association of Taiwan concerning the case on the Miaoli hillside site and the developments done in protected wildlife habitats as well as the importance of public communication as highlighted in the self-government ordinances in the Netherlands, South Korea, and Japan. The new regulations can also stipulate the proportion of people who consent to the matter. Furthermore, since *The Directions* are a guidance introduced by the Central Government and set for large-scale sites, regional governments should also set up their self-government ordinances or guidelines according to their respective landscape features and conditions. This can further protect the important natural resources of the area and make the public more accepting of solar PV.

6 CONCLUSION

As countries move towards their sustainable net zero goals, the importance of renewable energy is rising. Nonetheless, the public is still skeptical of the increasing solar PV installments and concerned about the landscape, environmental, and ecological impacts caused by the facilities owing to their proximity to cities, rural areas, and settlements. Visual impact issues can be effectively reduced with landscape visual and color analyses and additional hedge fences. In terms of environment, solar PV have a smaller impact on the environment compared to traditional power-generating facilities, and most of these impacts can be significantly lessened with measures such as deploying ventilation facilities, ARC, or sound-proofing devices. As for the land area requirement for solar PV installations, although some panels can be mounted on rooftops, some panels are still set on the ground, thus giving the impression that solar PV takes up a larger land area than traditional power generation facilities. However, traditional power generating facilities require large areas of land and the coal mine environments are difficult to restore. Ground-mounted solar PV systems are usually set on degraded land and consequently increase land use rate, and after a 20- to 30-year installation period, solar PV does not cause as much negative damage to the site land in terms of land use and occupation. If the solar PV site avoids sensitive areas during the planning stage and later deploys site management measures, research[32] shows that the bird diversity at the site is actually higher.

This demonstrates that with the proper protection measures and thoughtful site selection, solar PV can help protect vulnerable habitats[41].

Solar PV installations in Taiwan have generated much public concern regarding landscape, environment, and ecological aspects. We found that lack of communication with the locals is the main cause of their concern. *The Directions for the Landscape and Ecological Environment Assessment of Ground-Mounted Photovoltaic Systems* was introduced by the Taiwanese government to lessen the impact on landscape and ecological environment caused by solar PV facilities in Taiwan and serve as a reference for solar PV operators in the areas of landscape and ecological environment protection. Many sites have followed *The Directions*' guidance and designed setups that blend in with local landscape features while protecting the ecosystem. Examples include the Taixi Offshore Island Emerging Industrial Zone in Yunlin (**Figure 1**) and the solar PV site in Chiayi's salt field (**Figure 2**). Still, although Taiwan's central government has introduced clear administrative guidelines on the distance between the sites and residential buildings as well as the planning and design of the setups, when compared with the regulations in other countries, Taiwan still lacks regulations and guidelines for communication with the local public as well as the flexibility for adjustments according to regional characteristics. If we are to improve Taiwan's overall solar PV environment and achieve our renewable energy development goals of 2025, 2030, and 2050, we would work harder in these areas. Hopefully, the conflicts between solar PV and landscape, environment, and habitats can be reduced through relevant research.

Figure 1: Aerial view of the solar PV site at the Taixi Offshore Island Emerging Industrial Zone in Yunlin[42]

Figure 2: Aerial view of the solar PV site in a salt field in Chiayi[43]

7 REFERENCE

[1] H. H. Pourasl, R. V. Barenji, and V. M. Khojastehnezhad, "Solar energy status in the world: A comprehensive review," Energy Reports, vol. 10. Elsevier Ltd, pp. 3474–3493, Nov. 01, 2023. doi: 10.1016/j.egyr.2023.10.022.

[2] International Energy Agency, "Renewables 2023 — Analysis and forecast to 2028," Jan. 2024.

[3] Central Intelligence Agency, "Taiwan-Country Summary." Accessed: Feb. 06, 2024. [Online]. Available: https://www.cia.gov/the-world-factbook/countries/taiwan/summaries

[4] TAIWAN CENTRAL WEATHER BUREAU, "CLIMATOLOGICAL DATA ANNUAL REPORT PART I–SURFACE DATA," 2022.

[5] International Monetary Fund, "Taiwan Province of China Datasets." Accessed: Feb. 06, 2024. [Online]. Available: https://www.imf.org/external/datamapper/profile/TWN

[6] Bureau of Energy, "Renewable Energy Generation Capacity," energy statistics monthly report.

[7] National Development Council et al., "General Introduction on the Taiwan 2050 Net Zero Emission Pathway and Strategy," Mar. 2022.

[8] Ministry of Economic Affairs, "12 Key Strategies." Accessed: Feb. 16, 2024. [Online]. Available: https://www.ndc.gov.tw/Content_List.aspx?n=733396F6 48BE2845

[9] Environmental Protection Administration, Executive Yuan, "Net-Zero Emissions Pathway 2023-2026 Outline Plan," Jan. 2023.

[10] Ministry of Economic Affairs, Renewable Energy Development Act. Taiwan, 2019.

[11] R. Ioannidis and D. Koutsoyiannis, "A review of land use, visibility and public perception of renewable energy in the context of landscape impact," Appl Energy, vol. 276, Oct. 2020, doi: 10.1016/j.apenergy.2020.115367.

[12] J. Cousse, "Still in love with solar energy? Installation size, affect, and the social acceptance of renewable energy technologies," Renewable and Sustainable Energy Reviews, vol. 145, Jul. 2021, doi: 10.1016/j.rser.2021.111107.

[13] L. Späth, "Large-scale photovoltaics? Yes please, but not like this! Insights on different perspectives underlying the trade-off between land use and renewable electricity development," Energy Policy, vol. 122, pp. 429–437, Nov. 2018, doi: 10.1016/j.enpol.2018.07.029.

[14] D. Turney and V. Fthenakis, "Environmental impacts from the installation and operation of large-scale solar power plants," Renewable and Sustainable Energy Reviews, vol. 15, no. 6. Elsevier Ltd, pp. 3261–3270, 2011. doi: 10.1016/j.rser.2011.04.023.

[15] Council of Europe, Council of Europe Landscape Convention. European Treaty Series, 2004, pp. 2–3.

[16] A. Scognamiglio, "'Photovoltaic landscapes': Design and assessment. A critical review for a new transdisciplinary design vision," Renewable and Sustainable Energy Reviews, vol. 55. Elsevier Ltd, pp. 629–661, Mar. 01, 2016. doi: 10.1016/j.rser.2015.10.072.

[17] A. Dhar, M. A. Naeth, P. D. Jennings, and M. Gamal El-Din, "Perspectives on environmental impacts and a land reclamation strategy for solar and wind energy systems," Science of the Total Environment, vol. 718. Elsevier B.V., May 20, 2020. doi: 10.1016/j.scitotenv.2019.134602.

[18] T. Tsoutsos, N. Frantzeskaki, and V. Gekas, "Environmental impacts from the solar energy technologies," Energy Policy, vol. 33, no. 3, pp. 289–296, Feb. 2005, doi: 10.1016/S0301-4215(03)00241-6.

[19] R. Chiabrando, E. Fabrizio, and G. Garnero, "The territorial and landscape impacts of photovoltaic systems: Definition of impacts and assessment of the glare risk," Renewable and Sustainable Energy Reviews, vol. 13, no. 9. pp. 2441–2451, Dec. 2009. doi: 10.1016/j.rser.2009.06.008.

[20] N. Sánchez-Pantoja, R. Vidal, and M. C. Pastor, "Aesthetic impact of solar energy systems," Renewable and Sustainable Energy Reviews, vol. 98. Elsevier Ltd, pp. 227–238, Dec. 01, 2018. doi: 10.1016/j.rser.2018.09.021.

[21] I. A. Kapetanakis, D. Kolokotsa, and E. A. Maria, "Parametric analysis and assessment of the photovoltaics' landscape integration: Technical and legal aspects," Renew Energy, vol. 67, pp. 207–214, 2014, doi: 10.1016/j.renene.2013.11.043.

[22] D. Oudes and S. Stremke, "Next generation solar power plants? A comparative analysis of frontrunner solar landscapes in Europe," Renewable and Sustainable Energy Reviews, vol. 145, Jul. 2021, doi: 10.1016/j.rser.2021.111101.

[23] M. Zeman, "Introduction to photovoltaic solar energy," Delft University of Technology, vol. 2, no. 6, 2003.

[24] A. Armstrong, S. Waldron, J. Whitaker, and N. J. Ostle, "Wind farm and solar park effects on plant-soil carbon cycling: Uncertain impacts of changes in ground-level microclimate," Glob Chang Biol, vol. 20, no. 6, pp. 1699–1706, 2014, doi: 10.1111/gcb.12437.

[25] X. Pang, U. Mörtberg, and N. Brown, "Energy models from a strategic environmental assessment perspective in an EU context - What is missing concerning renewables?," Renewable and Sustainable Energy Reviews, vol. 33. pp. 353–362, May 2014. doi: 10.1016/j.rser.2014.02.005.

[26] V. Bertsch, M. Hall, C. Weinhardt, and W. Fichtner, "Public acceptance and preferences related to renewable energy and grid expansion policy: Empirical insights for Germany," Energy, vol. 114, pp. 465–477, Nov. 2016, doi: 10.1016/j.energy.2016.08.022.

[27] L. A. Fernandez-Jimenez et al., "Site selection for new PV power plants based on their observability," Renew Energy, vol. 78, pp. 7–15, Jun. 2015, doi: 10.1016/j.renene.2014.12.063.

[28] S. Naspetti, S. Mandolesi, and R. Zanoli, "Using visual Q sorting to determine the impact of photovoltaic applications on the landscape," Land use policy, vol. 57, pp. 564–573, Nov. 2016, doi: 10.1016/j.landusepol.2016.06.021.

[29] D. Turney and V. Fthenakis, "Environmental impacts from the installation and operation of large-scale solar power plants," Renewable and Sustainable Energy Reviews, vol. 15, no. 6. Elsevier Ltd, pp. 3261–3270, 2011. doi: 10.1016/j.rser.2011.04.023.

[30] R. R. Hernandez et al., "Environmental impacts of utility-scale solar energy," Renewable and Sustainable Energy Reviews, vol. 29. pp. 766–779, 2014. doi: 10.1016/j.rser.2013.08.041.

[31] C. Jeal, V. Perold, C. L. Seymour, S. Ralston-Paton, and P. G. Ryan, "Utility-scale solar energy facilities – Effects on invertebrates in an arid environment," J Arid Environ, vol. 168, pp. 1–8, Sep. 2019, doi: 10.1016/j.jaridenv.2019.05.008.

[32] B. Hannah Montag, D. Guy Parker, T. Clarkson, and H. Montag, THE EFFECTS OF SOLAR FARMS ON LOCAL BIODIVERSITY: A COMPARATIVE STUDY.

[33] H. Blaydes, S. Potts, D. Whyatt, and A. Armstrong, "On-site floral resources and surrounding landscape characteristics impact pollinator biodiversity on solar parks," in EGU General Assembly Conference Abstracts, 2022, pp. EGU22-2180.

[34]   Miaoli County Government, "Creating A Solar PV Site That Exists In Harmony With The Natural Environment, Miaoli County Government Hopes For 'Win-Win-Win' Solution For The Zhusen Solar Photovoltaic Site" Accessed: Mar. 18, 2024. [Online]. Available: https://www.miaoli.gov.tw/News_Content2.aspx?n=285&s=498443

[35]   Leopard Cat Association of Taiwan, "Why Is Zhusen Solar Photovoltaic Site So Important? The Association Supervisor Clarifies The Context Of The Disputes And Case." Accessed: Mar. 18, 2024. [Online]. Available: https://www.twlcat.org/2022/06/2613/

[36]   Bureau of Energy, MOEA, Principles for Landscape and Ecological Environment Assessments for Ground-mounted Solar Photovoltaic Facility Installation. Taiwan, 2023. Accessed: Feb. 19, 2024. [Online]. Available: https://www.moeaea.gov.tw/ECW/populace/Law/Content.aspx?menu_id=15558

[37]   L. van B. J. N. C. F. C. W. D. P. N. C. G. Bennun, "Mitigating biodiversity impacts associated with solar and wind energy development," Gland, Cambridge, 2021. Accessed: Jun. 27, 2024. [Online]. Available: https://portals.iucn.org/library/node/49283

[38]   Gemeenteblad van Lingewaard, "Beleidsregel van de gemeenteraad van de gemeente Lingewaard houdende regels omtrent Beleidskader zonne-energie," Lingewaard, Jan. 2020. Accessed: Jun. 25, 2024. [Online]. Available: https://zoek.officielebekendmakingen.nl/gmb-2020-14308.html#extrainformatie

[39]   여의도멋쟁이, "영주시 태양광 조례 - 발전시설의 개발행위 허가기준 [출처] 영주시 태양광 조례 - 발전시설의 개발행위 허가기준|작성자 여의도멋쟁이." Accessed: Jun. 27, 2024. [Online]. Available: https://blog.naver.com/PostView.naver?blogId=eovoice&logNo=222193682327&parentCategoryNo=&categoryNo=130&viewDate=&isShowPopularPosts=true&from=search

[40]   兵庫県庁, 太陽光発電施設等と地域環境との調和に関する条例. 日本, 2018. Accessed: Jun. 27, 2024. [Online]. Available: https://web.pref.hyogo.lg.jp/ks29/taiyoukoujourei.html

[41]   SEIA, "Climate, Conservation, Community: Moving the Land Use Conversation from Conflict to Solution." Accessed: Mar. 25, 2024. [Online]. Available: https://www.seia.org/blog/climate-conservation-community-moving-land-use-conversation-conflict-solution

[42]   Vena Energy, "Yunlin Emerging Power Plant." Accessed: Jun. 27, 2024. [Online]. Available: https://venaenergy.tw/project/e2/

[43]   Vena Energy, "Chiayi Yizhu Power Plant." Accessed: Jun. 27, 2024. [Online]. Available: https://venaenergy.tw/project/mingus/

Photovoltaic Development and Landscape Conflicts in Taiwan: Status and Resolutions

WANG, TZU-YA (DianaWang@itri.org.tw), WANG, CHIA-CHEN / Industrial Technology Research Institute (ITRI)

1 Introduction

1,1552.3GW — 2025 PV goals — Emissions goals

NET ZERO 2050

BUT IMPACT

Landscape — Environment — Habitat

Literature review — Identify the landscape-related issues solar PV installations may encounter.

Case study — The situation of solar PV and landscape conflicts with Taiwan's cases.

Solution analysis — With forming the *Directions for the Landscape and Ecological Environment Assessment of Ground-Mounted Photovoltaic Systems*.

2 The Potential Impacts of Solar PV on the Landscape

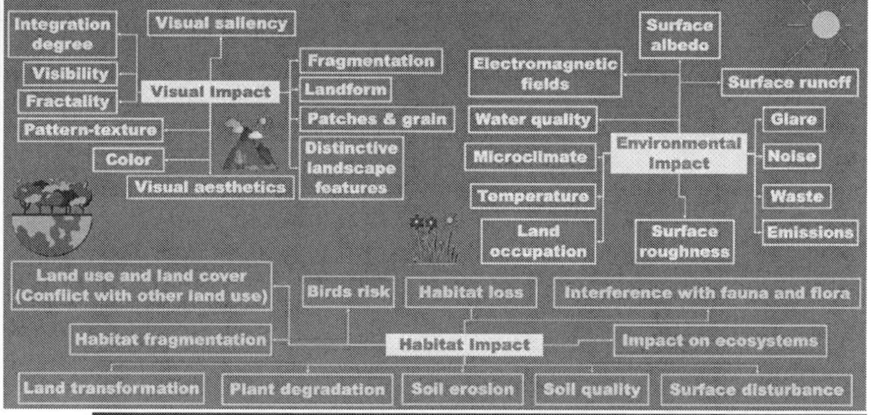

Visual Impact

Visual saliency — Integration degree — Visibility — Fractality — Pattern-texture — Color

Visual aesthetics

Fragmentation — Landform — Patches & grain — Distinctive landscape features

Environmental Impact

Surface albedo — Surface runoff — Electromagnetic fields — Water quality — Microclimate — Temperature — Glare — Noise — Waste — Emissions — Land occupation — Surface roughness

Land use and land cover (Conflict with other land use)

Habitat Impact

Birds risk — Habitat loss — Interference with fauna and flora — Habitat fragmentation — Impact on ecosystems — Land transformation — Plant degradation — Soil erosion — Soil quality — Surface disturbance

3 Cases of Conflict Between Solar PV and Landscape in Taiwan

A solar PV site in Pingtung

Case of Visual Impact

- The operators removed the original vegetation on the slopes to prepare the land.
- Located on the slopes along Highway leading to a popular tourist destination that affect the travelers' visual aesthetics.

(Source: https://sdgs.udn.com/sdgs/story/123880/7692490)

A solar PV site in Tainan

Case of Environmental Impact

- Close to a community, and residents protested against the possible light pollution, noise, and hot island effect.
- The noise tests onsite was within regulatory standards.
- Operators should communicate with the stakeholders better to minimize conflicts.

A solar PV site in Miaoli

Case of Habitat Impact

- With limited land and a dense population, recently, operators have turned to slopes.
- The area is the habitat of endangered animals such as leopard cats.
- An ecological association suggested that these areas should held local briefings.

(Source: https://conservation.forest.gov.tw/0002225)

4 How Does Taiwan Resolve the Conflicts Between Solar PV Development and Landscape?

Taiwan Ministry of Economic Affairs established *Directions for the Landscape and Ecological Environment Assessment of Ground-Mounted Photovoltaic Systems*

With cross-department expert meetings 2 times + Discussion meeting 1 time

May 1, 2018 announced

1. Targeting large-scale ground-mounted solar PV (2MW ↑).
2. Important regulations:
   1) Avoiding Class I environmentally sensitive areas.
   2) Considering local contour lines and maintaining the original site landform.
   3) Carrying out suitable greening with indigenous species as the primary.
   4) Requesting to conduct ecological surveys.
   5) Prohibiting cleaning agents.

With glare simulation + noise measurement + Discussion meetings 2 times

November 22, 2023 Revised

Continue to use the important previous version related to landscape and ecology.

Adding maintaining a certain distance between solar PV & buildings:

1) Fishery and electricity symbiosis models:
2) Non-compound models:

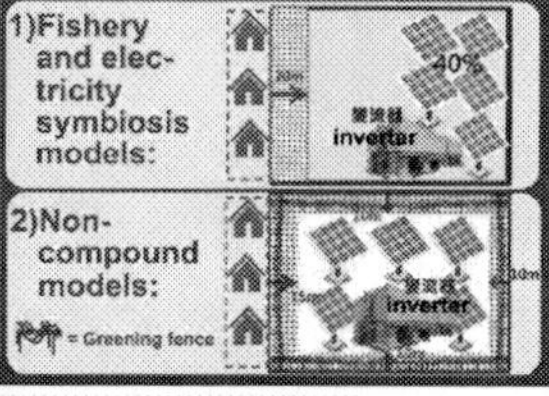

= Greening fence

glare simulation + noise measurement + Discussion meetings 3 times

March 31, 2025 Revised

Continue to use the previous version related to landscape and ecology, but not limited to 2 MW.

Modify the distance between solar PV & buildings:

1) 2ha ↑:
2) 2ha ↓:
3) Inverter:

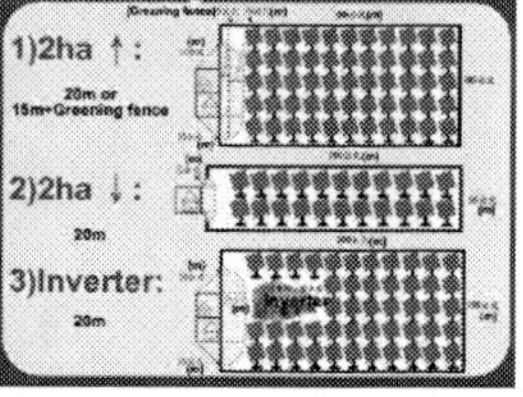

5 Discussion

Landscape conflict between solar PV cases in Taiwan, and overseas examples for reference.

Impact Category	Cases in Taiwan	Overseas examples for reference	Future suggestions
Visual	Site in Pingtung which is next to Highway	1. Lingewaard City, the Netherlands: take into account the existing landscape elements to integrate the facilities with the local landscape during the planning stage. And in farming areas must be supported by the locals. 2. Hyōgo Prefecture: Install the facility on the main road slope area, the slope angle must be less than 30°, and retained a percentage of green space.	1. Visual landscape simulation analysis should be carried out and pertinent response solutions should be proposed. 2. Communicate with the locals before development and obtain local government support.
Environment	Site in Tainan which is closed to a community	Refer to the self government ordinances of Japan and South Korea: It should be explained to the local public before development and the consent of residents should be obtained. 1. Hyōgo Prefecture, Japan: *Solar Power Generating Facilities and Local Environment Coordination Act* (太陽光発電施設等と地域環境との調和に関する条例) 2. Yeongju City, South Korea: The Standards for the Permission of Solar Power Generation Facilities Development (발전시설의개발행위허가기준)	1. Prior to planning, the operator, government, and residents need to communicate better. 2. Energy-related authorities should promote correct information related to solar photovoltaics more actively.
Habitat	Site in Miaoli which near the habitat of endangered animals	According to the *Guidance on the Solar Power Generation Environment* released (太陽光発電の環境配慮ガイドライン) by Japan's Ministry of Environment, the operator should learn more about the local habitat and wildlife lifestyle through literature studies, interviews, field surveys, and other methods before development.	1. Avoid Class 1 sensitive areas protected by law. 2. The operator should start ecological monitoring before development and carry out conservation work in the surrounding area.

Reference

1. D. Turney and V. Fthenakis, "Environmental impacts from the installation and operation of large-scale solar power plants," Renewable and Sustainable Energy Reviews, vol. 15, no. 6, Elsevier Ltd, pp. 3261–3270, 2011, doi: 10.1016/j.rser.2011.04.023.
2. Council of Europe, Council of Europe Landscape Convention, European Treaty Series, 2004, pp. 2–3.
3. A. Scognamiglio, "Photovoltaic landscapes': Design and assessment. A critical review for a new transdisciplinary design vision," Renewable and Sustainable Energy Reviews, vol. 55, Elsevier Ltd, pp. 629–661, Mar. 01, 2016, doi: 10.1016/j.rser.2015.10.072.
4. A. Dhar, M. A. Naeth, P. D. Jennings, and M. Gamal El-Din, "Perspectives on environmental impacts and a land reclamation strategy for solar and wind energy systems," Science of the Total Environment, vol. 718, Elsevier B.V., May 20, 2020, doi: 10.1016/j.scitotenv.2019.134602.
5. M. Tsoutsos, N. Frantzeskaki, and V. Gekas, "Environmental impacts from the solar energy technologies," Energy Policy, vol. 33, no. 3, pp. 289–296, Feb. 2005, doi: 10.1016/S0301-4215(03)00241-6.
6. R. Chiabrando, E. Fabrizio, and G. Garnero, "The territorial and landscape impacts of photovoltaic systems: Definition of impacts and assessment of the glare risk," Renewable and Sustainable Energy Reviews, vol. 13, no. 9, pp. 2441–3451, Dec. 2009, doi: 10.1016/j.rser.2009.06.008.
7. N. Sánchez-Pantoja, R. Vidal, and M. C. Pastor, "Aesthetic impact of solar energy systems," Renewable and Sustainable Energy Reviews, vol. 98, Elsevier Ltd, pp. 227–238, Dec. 01, 2018, doi: 10.1016/j.rser.2018.09.021.
8. I. A. Kapetanakis, D. Kolokotsa, and E. A. Maria, "Parametric analysis and assessment of the photovoltaics' landscape integration: Technical and legal aspects," Renew Energy, vol. 67, pp. 207–214, 2014, doi: 10.1016/j.renene.2013.11.043.
9. D. Oudes and S. Stremke, "Next generation solar power plants? A comparative analysis of integrative solar landscapes in Europe," Renewable and Sustainable Energy Reviews, vol. 145, Jul. 2021, doi: 10.1016/j.rser.2021.111101.
10. M. Zeman, "Introduction to photovoltaic solar energy," Delft University of Technology, vol. 2, no. 5, 2003.
11. A. Armstrong, S. Waldron, J. Whitaker, and N. J. Ostle, "Wind farm and solar park effects on plant-soil carbon cycling: Uncertain impacts of changes in ground-level microclimates," Glob Chang Biol, vol. 20, no. 6, pp. 1699–1706, 2014, doi: 10.1111/gcb.12437.
12. Gemeenteblad van Lingewaard, "Beleidsregel van de gemeenteraad van de gemeente Lingewaard houdende regels betrent Beleidskader zonne-energie," Lingewaard, Jan. 2020. Accessed: Jun. 25, 2024. [Online]. Available: https://zoek.officielebekendmakingen.nl/gmb-2020-15208.html#extrainformatie

Acknowledgments

The work was supported by the Energy Administration, Ministry of Economic Affairs, Taiwan, through financial funding as well as administrative and technical guidance.

6 Conclusion

Solar PV installation ↑

Visual Impact Solution → 1. landscape visual and color analyses 2. Adding hedge fences

Environmental Impact Solution → 1. Deploying ARC, ventilation, or sound-proofing devices 2. setting on degraded land and increase land use rate

Habitat Impact Solution → Avoiding sensitive areas and deploying site management measures an help protect vulnerable habitats.

Taiwan has Revised the *Directions for the Landscape and Ecological Environment Assessment of Ground-Mounted Photovoltaic Systems* → designing with local landscape and protecting the ecosystem & maintaining distance from buildings

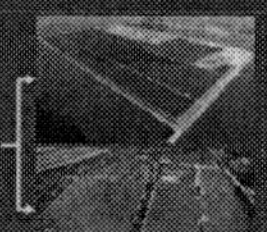

BREEZE PROJECT: ADVANCING PV IMPLEMENTATION IN BUILDING RENOVATIONS

Duygu Celik*[1], Johannes Stierstorfer[1], Claire Morin[2], Thomas Garabetian[2], Cristian Pozza[3], Francesco Babich[3], Akshit Gupta[3], Giobertti Raul Morantes Quintana[3], Laura Maturi[3], Ulrich Oberegger Filippi[3], Daniele Antonucci[3], Pawel Wargocki[4], Andrei Vladimir Litiu[5], Nicolandrea Calabrese[6], Giovanni Murano[6], Francesca Caffari[6], Jerzy Kwiatkowski[7], Katarzyna Rajkiewicz[7], Olivier Greslou[8], Dominique Caccavelli[8]

[1]WIP Renewable Energies, [2]Solar Power Europe, [3]EURAC Research, [4]Technical University of Denmark, [5]EPB Center, [6]ENEA - Italian National Agency for New Technologies, Energy and Sustainable Economic Development, [7]NAPE - National Energy Conservation Agency, [8]CSTB - Scientific and Technical Centre for Building

WIP Renewable Energies, Sylvenstein Strasse 2, Munich, Germany (*duygu.celik@wip-munich.de)

ABSTRACT

BREEZE (Building Renovation Efforts for Zero Emission Buildings) aims to accelerate the integration of solar photovoltaic (PV) systems into new and renovated buildings across EU Member States in line with the Energy Performance of Buildings Directive (EPBD). The project supports national implementation of the Solar Mandate by addressing key technical, financial, and regulatory barriers to large-scale PV deployment.

BREEZE focuses on the effective use of rooftop PV, building-integrated photovoltaics (BIPV), and balcony PV to improve building energy performance while maintaining architectural quality. By developing standardized tools and practical frameworks, the project promotes cost-effective PV integration in renovation projects and strengthens the link between energy efficiency and on-site renewable generation.

Pilot activities in Poland, Italy, and France will test PV deployment strategies under different building types, climates, and regulatory conditions, generating insights applicable across the EU. In parallel, BREEZE advances energy performance assessment methods to ensure compliance with EPBD targets and Indoor Environmental Quality (IEQ) standards.

Through capacity-building activities, policy guidance, and best practice development, the project equips policymakers, designers, and industry professionals with the knowledge and tools needed to support a coordinated, sustainable, and scalable approach to solar energy integration in Europe's building sector.

Keywords: Building Renovation, Energy Performance of Buildings Directive (EPBD), Building-Integrated Photovoltaics (BIPV), Solar Mandate

1 AIM AND APPROACH

BREEZE project aims to optimize the implementation of the Energy Performance of Buildings Directive (EPBD)[1] with a focus on supporting the Solar Mandate, which requires the integration of solar photovoltaic (PV) systems in new and renovated buildings across EU Member States (MSs). The project aims to identify, address, and overcome key technical, financial, and regulatory barriers that hinder the deployment of solar PV technologies in the building sector, thereby facilitating the large-scale integration of renewable energy solutions into Europe's building stock.

BREEZE follows a multi-phase, data-driven methodology designed to generate actionable results at both technical and policy level. The approach starts with identifying Member States' needs and challenges regarding Solar Mandate implementation, followed by the development of analytical frameworks, indicators, and best practices to assess PV potential and deployment scenarios. Pilot activities in Poland, France, and Italy will test these methodologies, while capacity-building and stakeholder engagement will ensure the long-term adoption of project outcomes.

Project's PV-specific objectives include supporting the Solar Mandate[2] implementation at national level and promoting the integration of PV and BIPV (Building Integrated Photovoltaics) into renovation projects. Through this, BREEZE will help Member States align renovation practices with EU sustainability goals by developing cost-optimal renovation scenarios and regulatory guidelines for effective PV adoption.

2 SCIENTIFIC INNOVATION AND RELEVANCE

The scientific innovation of BREEZE lies in its approach to quantify and contextualize the potential of solar PV integration within the broader framework of building energy performance. The project combines technical analysis, geographic data, and economic

---

[1] https://commission.europa.eu/news-and-media/news/focus-energy-efficiency-buildings-2020-02-17_en

[2] https://energy.ec.europa.eu/topics/energy-efficiency/energy-performance-buildings/energy-performance-buildings-directive/solar-energy-buildings_en

modelling to estimate the potential for solar deployment across different building types and European climates, offering policymakers a comprehensive understanding of how the Solar Mandate can be effectively implemented.

An important focus is the development of a data-driven decision-support framework that integrates solar PV potential into building performance assessment methodologies. This framework will include parameters such as local irradiation, building typology, grid connection, energy consumption patterns, and investment costs. By introducing key performance indicators (KPIs) for solar PV and BIPV integration, the framework aims to enable a transparent evaluation of energy, economic, and environmental benefits, tailored to national contexts. These insights will directly inform future policy development and investment strategies related to building decarbonization.

In parallel, BREEZE will place a strong emphasis on BIPV systems, which merge architectural functionality with on-site renewable generation. The project will assess BIPV's potential to improve energy self-sufficiency, reduce electricity demand, and contribute to long-term sustainability goals, while preserving aesthetic and structural integrity. The results will support the creation of performance benchmarks and deployment scenarios for BIPV systems that reflect different climatic, technical, and socio-economic conditions.

3 SOLAR PV DEPLOYMENT AND RENOVATION FRAMEWORK

Building on its base, BREEZE is developing a comprehensive framework for solar PV deployment within building renovation strategies, and linking technical potential, economic feasibility, and policy applicability. The framework aims to demonstrate how solar PV can be systematically integrated into building retrofit processes. This approach ultimately will help Member States and industry actors meet the goals of the Energy Performance of Buildings Directive (EPBD) while accelerating the shift toward a greener building stock.

At its core, this framework connects energy efficiency improvements with solar energy generation. BREEZE will produce detailed renovation case studies that explore PV integration under a wide range of conditions, including different building types (residential, commercial, and public), architectural forms, climatic zones, and energy consumption profiles. These studies will assess both traditional rooftop PV systems and building-integrated photovoltaic (BIPV) applications, as well as façade and balcony-mounted PV, providing a full picture of how solar technologies can be adapted to urban and rural contexts.

The renovation scenarios will consider future energy needs such as the electrification of transport and heating through electric vehicles (EVs) and heat pumps, recognizing the increasing role of self-consumption and demand-side management in modern buildings. Each scenario will be assessed in terms of cost-effectiveness, energy yield, grid interaction, and occupant comfort, using performance indicators consistent with EPBD requirements and Indoor Environmental Quality (IEQ) standards.

These case studies will not only quantify PV potential but will also provide guidance for decision-makers on how to identify cost-optimal renovation pathways. By combining energy performance simulations with local solar resource data and economic modeling, BREEZE will show how the integration of solar PV can lower energy demand, reduce operating costs, and improve building resilience. The results will feed directly into national and regional planning instruments, providing concrete evidence for policymakers and investors.

An important outcome of this work will be the development of best practice guidelines to help Member States implement the Solar Mandate at national level. These guidelines will include a combination of regulatory, technical, and procedural recommendations. Regulatory best practices will focus on adapting building codes and permitting rules to facilitate solar installations during renovation, ensuring that PV systems, including BIPV, are considered from the design phase. The guidance will also address technical standards, safety requirements, and architectural integration, helping to align innovation with practical implementation.

In addition, BREEZE will compile country specific best practices based on lessons from the project's pilot regions (Poland, Italy, and France) and other EU experiences that its project partners have. These examples will cover construction permits, grid connection procedures, and inter-agency coordination, offering real insights into how permitting and administrative processes can be simplified to support the broader uptake of solar technologies.

To support on-the-ground implementation, the framework will include practical reference materials for professionals, such as rooftop PV installation examples, user-friendly checklists, and design guidelines tailored for renovation projects. These resources are intended for a broad range of stakeholders such as installers, engineers, architects, and building owners, helping ensure safe, efficient, and compliant PV integration. Special attention will be given to BIPV applications, providing recommendations on component selection, mounting solutions, and maintenance practices that maintain both energy performance and visual quality.

By combining technical baseline with policy relevance, the PV deployment and renovation framework will serve as a bridge between high-level solar policy objectives and practical implementation at building level. It aims to make PV integration in renovation projects both achievable and scalable, equipping European Member States with the knowledge, methods, and examples needed to turn the Solar Mandate into real, visible progress across Europe's building sector.

4 EXPECTED IMPACTS

BREEZE will have a practical impact on how Member States plan and implement the Solar Mandate under the Energy Performance of Buildings Directive (EPBD). The project will provide clear tools, data, and guidelines to help national and local authorities integrate solar PV systems in both new constructions and renovation projects. These materials will demonstrate how combining energy efficiency measures with solar generation can reduce energy use, cut emissions, and improve the overall performance of buildings in a realistic and cost-effective way.

By analysing data from various building types, climates, and socio-economic contexts, BREEZE will give policymakers a comprehensive understanding of where and how solar PV can deliver the greatest benefits. This will support the preparation of national Solar Mandate implementation plans that reflect local conditions, such as sunlight availability, grid capacity, electricity prices, and the existing building stock, while ensuring consistency with EU energy and climate targets. The pilot projects in Poland, Italy, and France will play a key role in testing these methods under real conditions, producing lessons that can be transferred to other Member States.

Beyond the policy level, BREEZE will also help the construction and renovation sectors adopt solar technologies more informed. Through applied case studies, the project will illustrate how rooftop, façade, and building-integrated PV systems can enhance energy performance, increase self-consumption, and reduce pressure on electricity networks. The tools developed will assist architects, engineers, and building owners in selecting and designing PV systems that match their technical needs and financial possibilities.

5   LONG-TERM OUTLOOK AND CONCLUSIONS

In addition to its technical and analytical contributions, BREEZE places strong emphasis on training and knowledge sharing. The project will engage national authorities, local governments, and industry professionals through workshops, practical guides, and policy dialogues. These activities will ensure that the knowledge and experience gained within BREEZE can be distributed and applied well beyond the project's lifetime. By creating a shared understanding among regulators, installers, and designers, BREEZE will help bridge the gap between policy and on-the-ground implementation.

In the longer term, BREEZE aims to make solar energy integration a standard element of building renovation across Europe. The project's work on harmonized regulations, simplified permitting, and well-documented best practices will remove key barriers that currently slow down PV deployment. Its emphasis on cost-effective and scalable renovation solutions will help Member States meet their EPBD targets while reducing reliance on fossil fuels and improving building resilience.

Ultimately, BREEZE contributes to a more consistent approach to solar deployment in the European building stock. By linking technical knowledge with practical policy tools, it will support the creation of national strategies that are realistic, flexible, and aligned with EU objectives. In doing so, the project will not only increase the integration of solar PV systems but also help make Europe's buildings cleaner and more efficient for the energy transition towards a climate-neutral future.

6   ACKNOLWEDGEMENTS

This project is funded by the European Union, in the frame of LIFE Programme. Views and opinions expressed are however those of the authors only and do not necessarily reflect those of the European Union. Neither the European Union nor the granting authority can be held responsible for them.

INTEGRATING ENERGY POLICY INTO SPATIAL PLANNING FRAMEWORKS: A STUDY OF TAIWAN'S APPROACH

Tzu Han Hung
Industrial Technology Research Institute (ITRI)
14F.-1, No.248, Sec. 3, Nanjing E. Rd., Songshan Dist., Taipei City 105403, Taiwan, R.O.C.

ABSTRACT: Taiwan faces the dual challenges of limited land availability and the urgent need to transition to renewable energy in pursuit of its 2050 net-zero carbon emissions target. This study explores how Taiwan can effectively integrate energy policy—particularly solar power development—into its spatial planning system. Despite recent legal advances, such as the 2016 Spatial Planning Act and the subsequent National Spatial Plan (2018), existing mechanisms still fall short in resolving land use conflicts between energy infrastructure and other sectoral priorities. Current energy-related spatial plans often lack specific siting criteria or actionable implementation strategies, especially at the local level. To address this policy gap, the study reviews solar development governance models from four high-density countries—Japan, India, South Korea, and the Netherlands—each demonstrating successful integration of spatial and energy planning. Comparative insights reveal key strategies: Japan emphasizes community-driven implementation within a hierarchical planning system; India promotes state-level autonomy supported by central energy goals; South Korea demonstrates close policy alignment across planning levels; and the Netherlands exemplifies integration through a robust permitting and environmental planning system. The paper argues that Taiwan should establish a more effective framework that enables cross-sectoral coordination, clarifies site selection principles, strengthens local government participation, and encourages multifunctional land use such as agrivoltaics. It highlights the opportunity presented by Taiwan's upcoming revision of county and municipal spatial plans, as well as the development of the Solar Power Land Use White Paper, to embed spatial considerations more concretely into renewable energy strategies. Ultimately, the study concludes that a successful integration model must include clear spatial guidance, legal mechanisms for coordination, adaptive policy tools, and stakeholder engagement processes. These recommendations serve not only to improve Taiwan's internal planning coherence but also to contribute to global knowledge on renewable energy integration in densely populated, land-constrained contexts.
Keywords: Spatial Planning Integration, Renewable Energy Policy, Solar PV

1 INTRODUCTION

Taiwan, an island nation situated on the western edge of the Pacific Ocean, faces unique challenges in land resource management. Its territory of 36,197 square kilometers accommodates approximately 23 million people, resulting in a population density of 640 people per square kilometer. Beyond meeting residential needs, Taiwan must balance industrial development—particularly in the technology-intensive sector with major players such as TSMC and Vanguard International Semiconductor—while addressing food security, climate change adaptation, and disaster prevention concerns. Through the implementation of the Spatial Planning Act of 2016 and the subsequent approval of the National Spatial Plan (2018) [1] and 18 municipal/county spatial plans (2021), Taiwan has established a comprehensive spatial planning and management framework. This framework progressively integrates various sectoral development plans, including housing, commercial, agricultural, energy, water resources, and disaster management policies, coordinating them at the policy level to foster harmonious development with minimal conflicts.

In alignment with global net-zero carbon emissions initiatives, Taiwan enacted the Renewable Energy Development Act in 2009 and established subsequent subsidiary regulations to promote energy security and green economy objectives. Under this legislation, the Ministry of Economic Affairs (MOEA) set an ambitious target of 20GW solar power generation by 2025, initially planning for 3GW from rooftop installations and 17GW from ground-mounted systems [2]. Recent implementation assessments have led to adjusted targets of 8GW for rooftop installations and 12GW for ground-mounted

systems. These policy directives are being incorporated into the forthcoming White Paper on Land Use for Renewable Energy Development: Solar Power, which aims to integrate with national and local spatial plans to ensure comprehensive energy development considerations, establish appropriate site selection criteria and planning design principles, and mitigate intersectoral conflicts and coordination challenges with local development objectives.

The brief two-year period between the implementation of the Spatial Planning Act and the approval of the National Spatial Plan has limited the effective integration of various sectoral development proposals into spatial planning. The energy policy component of the National Spatial Plan, for instance, merely references the 2025 power generation targets without providing substantive guidance on development locations or suitable installation types. Moreover, it fails to grant local governments sufficient autonomy in implementation. The current National Spatial Plan also lacks effective mechanisms to resolve conflicts when locations designated by different sectoral policies overlap, particularly in establishing development priorities or facilitating composite development opportunities.

This paper examines countries that, like Taiwan, successfully manage solar power facility generation despite limited land resources and high population density, specifically focusing on Japan, India, South Korea, and the Netherlands. Through analysis of their spatial and sectoral planning systems, particularly examining how different levels of spatial planning interface with sectoral plans, this study aims to understand how these nations optimize solar power development within constrained territories. These insights will inform Taiwan's strategy to achieve its policy objectives while contributing to the global initiative toward 2050 net-zero carbon emissions.

2 SPATIAL PLANNING AND LAND USE CONTROL MEASURES FOR SOLAR ENERGY POLICY

2.1 Sectoral spatial plans in the spatial planning system

Taiwan's current spatial planning and land use control legislation is based on the Regional Planning Act. The planning and management framework follows a top-down hierarchy: National Spatial Development Strategy, Regional Plans, County/Municipal Comprehensive Development Plans, and Urban Plans. Although the National Spatial Development Strategy exists at the highest level, it lacks legal effectiveness and thus holds no substantive spatial planning and control authority. Consequently, within Taiwan's overall planning system, the Regional Plan serves as the highest-level statutory spatial plan, providing spatial planning guidance and control authority to municipalities and counties. Most sectoral plans—such as tourism development, technical industry introduction, and agricultural policy implementation—are generally implemented according to relevant control regulations after their policy plans receive Executive Yuan approval, rather than being integrated into spatial planning. This excludes town building plans, large-scale industrial park development, and urban plan expansion and renewal projects.

Following the Ministry of the Interior's announcement of the revised National Regional Plan on May 16, 2017, a "Regional Sectoral Plan" chapter was added to incorporate policy and plan contents approved by the Executive Yuan. However, this addition still lacks site selection principles and fails to identify development scopes, making it difficult for local governments to guide appropriate land use and balance conflicts between different sectoral policies.

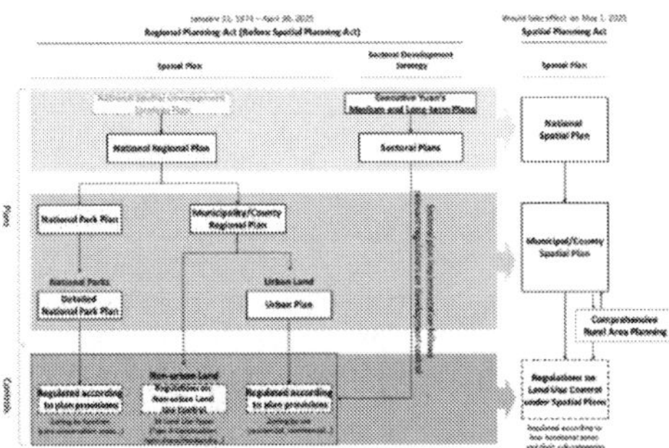

Figure 1: Spatial Planning System in Taiwan

In response to climate change and the needs for environmental conservation and cultural asset preservation, while promoting reasonable resource and industrial allocation and strengthening national land integration management mechanisms, Taiwan initiated a series of legal framework operations after enacting the Spatial Planning Act in 2016. This initiative aims to establish comprehensive legal management and a new national spatial planning system by May 2025. The system will encompass planning and management from mountains to oceans, urban to rural areas, and national parks to general development areas, integrating existing systems including national park plans, urban plans, and

various Executive Yuan-approved sectoral policy plans to construct a more comprehensive and balanced development framework.

Given the extensive planning scope and broad policy content, spatial planning will be implemented at three levels. First, the central government (Ministry of the Interior) announced and implemented the National Spatial Plan in 2018, establishing unified principles for designating land functional zones. Land classification is based on carrying capacity, conservation sensitivity, and disaster potential, while also presenting overall policy development goals. Following this national guidance, local governments develop county/municipal spatial plans, considering local conditions to fine-tune land functional zone designations and establish suitable development directions and specific implementation measures [3]. At the town, township, and district levels, comprehensive rural area planning is developed under county/municipal spatial plan guidance. This planning responds to local settlement conditions and development context, as well as local industry needs, to formulate future development visions and spatial configurations. These local-level plans, in turn, inform and may lead to adjustments in the county/municipal spatial plans and enable the development of distinctive land use control measures that reflect local conditions, thereby facilitating autonomous planning and governance.

To prevent conflicts between ministerial policies, Articles 9 and 10 of the Spatial Planning Act mandate that national and county/municipal spatial plans must integrate the policies, goals, current development status, future potential capacity, and locations of various sectors. Article 4 of the Spatial Planning Act Enforcement Rules specifies that sectoral spatial plans must include, at minimum, development strategies and locations for policy plans. According to the County/Municipal Spatial Plan Planning Manual published by the Ministry of the Interior, development strategies must address policy implementation issue analysis, response methods, and related public facility or construction planning. Development locations should consider plans and locations already approved by the Executive Yuan, central ministries, and local governments. These plans should provide supply-demand gap analysis and response measures for different sectoral policy items, including housing, industry, transportation, sewerage facilities, long-term care facilities, medical care, energy, water, and other important public facilities.[3]

As shown in Table I, sectoral plans in the National Spatial Plan can be categorized into four types:
(1) "Facility Construction Plans" - such as fishing port development, specific industrial park expansion plans, and railway underground projects in specific areas, which have clear development sites and scales, representing areas of active government investment and construction.
(2) "Development Guidance Areas" - plans that primarily involve government incentives and guidance for private enterprise investment, without clearly defined policy boundaries, requiring coordination with other laws, subsidies, or related supporting measures for implementation.
(3) "Legal and Operational Mechanism Revisions" and
(4) "Subsidy and Guidance Measures" - both categories represent government administrative planning with no spatial planning content.
This classification reveals that only the first category

of sectoral plans fully complies with the guidance of the Spatial Planning Act, its Enforcement Rules, and the Spatial Planning Manual by providing specific development scale and location details. The second type of sectoral plans, which guide industrial development, typically have development targets but lack specific site locations. With modifications, these could comply with relevant regulations. The third and fourth types of sectoral plans, having no spatial planning elements, cannot fulfill the regulatory requirements.

Table I: Classification of Public Facilities Plans in Taiwan's National Spatial Plan

Subsector	Responsible Authority	Plan Types			
		A	B	C	D
Sewerage	National Land Management Agency	✓		✓	✓
Environmental Protection	Ministry of Environment				✓
Long-term Care Facilities	Ministry of Health and Welfare (MOHW)			✓	✓
Medical Facilities	MOHW			✓	
Education	Ministry of Education			✓	✓
Energy	Bureau of Energy	✓	✓	✓	✓
Water	Water Resources Agency	✓			

Plan Types:
A: Facility Construction Plans
B: Development Guidance Areas
C: Legal and Operational Mechanism Revisions
D: Subsidy and Guidance Measures

Among the sectoral plans classified in the National Spatial Plan, only three sectors fall under the "Development Guidance Areas" type: manufacturing, mining and soil/stone extraction, and energy facilities. The manufacturing sector plan involves site inventory and supporting measure development based on the "White Paper on Industrial Land Use," which guides industries toward suitable locations. For mining and soil/stone extraction, the sector plan is based on the mineral resource distribution inventory conducted by the Bureau of Mines, Ministry of Economic Affairs. After local governments complete these sectoral plans identifying suitable mining locations, the land use controls in spatial planning will be adjusted to accommodate the development areas specified in the sectoral plans.

The energy facilities sector plan is more complex, encompassing multiple energy types including traditional nuclear, thermal, and hydroelectric power facilities, as well as various renewable energy sources. This diversity makes it challenging for the National Spatial Plan to designate specific development locations due to the varying requirements for site selection and planning across different energy types. For instance, some counties have implemented stricter land use control measures and developed energy conservation and alternative energy programs in response to existing nuclear and thermal power facilities within their jurisdictions. In terms of alternative energy development, counties are currently prioritizing solar and wind power deployment, working to identify potential development locations and installation types.

The solar power development guidance in the National Spatial Plan follows the "Two-Year Solar Power Promotion Plan" [2], prioritizing rooftop installations on public buildings, factories, agricultural facilities, and other structures. For ground-mounted solar power installations, the six counties and cities shown in Table II are located in Taiwan's southwestern region, which receives more sunlight than other areas and possesses more undeveloped and underutilized land. These areas include idle salt industry lands, severe land subsidence areas, water bodies, sealed landfills, and contaminated lands, which are designated as priority development areas. However, the spatial plan does not provide comprehensive location guidelines or planning design principles, limiting the sector plan's effectiveness in implementing spatial planning guidance functions.

The salt industry lands serve as an illustrative example. Taiwan's southwestern coast contains numerous areas previously designated for salt production, some of which are adjacent to settlements or near migratory bird habitats. Not all these areas are suitable for renewable energy facility development. However, due to the lack of clear guidance in the National Spatial Plan, there is no framework to guide developers toward suitable locations or formulate response strategies for local ecological and social issues.

As demonstrated by the ground-mounted solar development guidance in the counties shown in Table II, the absence of suitable location guidance and clear development directions in the National Spatial Plan has led to varying approaches among counties. Some jurisdictions, like Changhua County, cannot delineate locations suitable for solar power development. Other counties largely adhere to the areas specified in the National Spatial Plan, such as garbage landfills and contaminated lands, as designated areas for ground-mounted solar power installations.

Table II: Development Guidance for Ground-mounted Solar Power in Six Southwestern Counties' Spatial Plans

City / County	Designated Development Sites
Changhua County	1. Agriculturally unsuitable areas
	2. Aquavoltaic zones
Yunlin County	1. Agriculturally unsuitable areas
	2. Aquavoltaic zones
	3. Offshore industrial zones
Chiayi County	1. Coastal public salt industry lands
	2. Public landfills
	3. Agriculturally unsuitable areas
	4. Aquavoltaic zones
Tainan City	1. Salt industry lands
	2. Closed or rehabilitating landfills
	3. General lands (urban agricultural zones / non-urban lands)
	4. Agriculturally unsuitable areas
	5. Aquavoltaic zones
Kaohsiung City	1. Agriculturally unsuitable areas
	2. Aquavoltaic zones
Pingtung County	Revitalization of severe land subsidence areas

2.2 Functional Zones and Land Use Control Measures

Following the National Spatial Plan's guidance, marine and terrestrial areas are divided into different functional zones based on conservation, utilization, and management needs, as well as land use patterns and resource conditions. These zones include:

- National Conservation Areas (protecting terrestrial and marine ecological resources)
- Marine Resource Areas
- Agricultural Development Areas (focusing on maintaining agricultural, forestry, and fishery production)
- Urban-Rural Development Areas (for population concentration and diverse uses such as commercial and industrial activities)

Within these four functional zones, further detailed classifications are made based on environmental conditions and development carrying capacity. [4]

As shown in Figure 2, draft functional zone maps for six counties in southwestern Taiwan are currently under review pending approval. Analysis of the draft zoning results reveals four distinct zones:

(1) From Changhua County to northern Tainan City: This region shows concentrated agricultural production, with land primarily classified as Type 1 Agri. Development Areas. It emphasizes preserving agricultural production functions and maintaining food crop capabilities, mainly permitting uses related to agricultural production, processing, storage, and marketing.
(2) Eastern mountainous areas of the six counties: These are primarily designated as Type 1 and Type 2 National Conservation Areas, prioritizing ecological and natural resource conservation. In areas with steep slopes and environmentally sensitive resources, only public facilities or other essential life-supporting functions are permitted. In forest and hillside areas with lower environmental sensitivity, moderate flexibility in land use is permitted, such as tourism and recreation facilities. Areas on hillsides used for fruit trees, tea plantations, and other agricultural purposes are designated as Type 3 Agricultural Development Areas to support hillside agricultural development.
(3) Western coastal areas of Tainan City and Kaohsiung City: This region serves as the main population concentration area, with land designated as Type 1 Urban-Rural Development Areas to support urban functions and industrial-commercial development.
(4) Areas between urban areas and hillsides: These are designated as Type 2 Agricultural Development Areas, allowing diverse agricultural use and partial conversion to non-agricultural uses. [5], [6], [7], [8], [9], [10]

According to the draft Regulations for Land Use Controls in National Spatial Plans released for public review in late April 2024, land use controls will be implemented based on functional zone classifications and the development goals established in local governments' spatial plans. For example:

- In Agricultural Development Areas, aquavoltaic development is primarily regulated as "aquaculture facilities," with solar installations classified as auxiliary facilities and thus exempted from spatial planning authority approval.
- In Urban-Rural Development Areas, ground-mounted solar installations require written approval from spatial planning authorities to prevent adverse impacts on rural settlements.
- For developments exceeding certain scale thresholds, solar facilities must undergo public participation procedures, including public exhibitions and hearings, before obtaining approval from the spatial planning review committee.

Article 23 of the Spatial Planning Act authorizes local governments to establish their own control measures based on the local development context. These measures, specified in the Land Use Guidelines chapter of county/municipal spatial plans, take precedence once approved by the Ministry of the Interior.

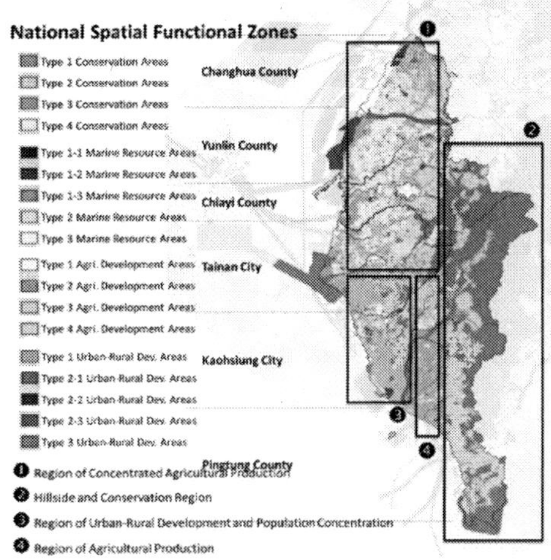

Figure 2: Draft Map of National Spatial Functional Zones for Six Counties in Southwestern Taiwan

3 SOLAR ENERGY DEVELOPMENT POLICY

3.1 Solar Energy Types and Distribution

In response to the global emphasis on energy conservation and renewable energy transition toward net-zero emissions, Taiwan has progressively developed relevant policies. The implementation of the Renewable Energy Development Act and its subsidiary regulations in 2009 aimed to achieve energy security, green economy, and environmental sustainability goals. To promote solar power development, the Executive Yuan approved the "Two-Year Solar Power Promotion Plan" in 2016, focusing on both rooftop and ground-mounted installations. The plan prioritizes rooftop installations sequentially on public buildings, factories, agricultural facilities, and other buildings, while targeting ground-mounted facilities in idle salt industry lands, Class 1 groundwater management zones where groundwater extraction for irrigation is not feasible, water bodies, and closed landfills. [2]

To expand solar power policy implementation, the Renewable Energy Development Act was partially amended in 2019, adopting the principle of "reduce coal, increase gas, phase out nuclear, expand green energy" as its long-term direction. The amendment stipulates that by 2025, renewable energy capacity should reach 29GW, with solar power accounting for 20GW, approximately 70% of the total renewable energy capacity. The Plan for Achieving 6.5GW Solar Power Target, released in the same year, emphasized three main pillars: requiring industrial park development projects to install solar power systems and major electricity users to fulfill environmental sustainability commitments as part of their corporate social responsibilities; establishing joint central-local government guidelines to expedite development review and dispute resolution; and promoting the integration of solar development with farming, animal husbandry, and aquaculture facilities, emphasizing multiple-use principles to address concerns about solar power encroaching on agricultural land.

Following these policy implementation principles, the current solar power development distribution in Taiwan is shown in Table III. Nearly 3,000 hectares of development area is located in Type 2 Agricultural Development Areas, designated for agricultural production and diversified development. Approximately 70% consists of green energy facilities integrated with agricultural operations, primarily focusing on aquavoltaic systems. The remaining 30% comprises ground-mounted solar power installations. Under future National Spatial Plan controls, only developments exceeding certain scale thresholds will granted with use permits.

Table III: Distribution of Solar Power Installations by National Spatial Functional Zone Classification in Taiwan

National Functional Zone & Zone Type		Area (Hectares)	Percentage of Total Area
National Conservation Area	Type 1	4.621	0.07%
	Type 2	40.255	0.61%
	Type 4	72.881	1.10%
Agricultural Development Area	Type 1	2,139.660	32.41%
	Type 2	2,984.546	45.21%
	Type 3	11.324	2.90%
	Type 4	0.060	0.00%
	Type 5	12.348	0.19%
Urban-Rural Development Area	Type 1	167.220	2.53%
	Type 2-1	53.366	0.81%
	Type 2-2	932.322	14.12%
	Type 2-3	3.545	0.05%
Total		6,602.148	100.00%

The second highest concentration of solar power development is in Type 1 Agricultural Development Areas, which encompass prime agricultural environments, including special agricultural areas designated under the Regional Plan Act and aquaculture production zones established by the Ministry of Agriculture. Our analysis indicates that approximately 30% of existing solar installation sites will be classified as Type 1 Agricultural Development Areas under the new system. Among these, around 75% are agricultural green energy facilities—solar power systems integrated with agricultural operations—which comply with agricultural land use controls under the new system, as they are categorized as agricultural facilities.

3.2 Taiwan Solar Energy Development White Paper

The Ministry of Economic Affairs initiated planning for the "White Paper on Land Use for Renewable Energy Development: Solar Power" in late 2022. Throughout 2023, the ministry conducted 47 expert and scholar interviews and organized five large-scale public engagement events. Through these activities, the ministry aimed to communicate energy policy visions while gathering stakeholder concerns and improvement suggestions to refine renewable energy land planning goals and development strategies.

The white paper establishes short-term goals of achieving 31GW installation capacity by 2030 and long-term goals of reaching 40-80GW cumulative solar power generation by 2050. The implementation framework consists of three main approaches:

(1) Establishing mutually beneficial partnerships between central and local governments, emphasizing central-level framework development to guide local autonomous planning.
(2) Scale-differentiated energy governance, developing site selection, development, and supervision measures for large-scale special zones, while providing subsidy and guidance measures for small-scale community-based autonomous energy development.
(3) Renewable energy development with local co-prosperity, proposing mechanisms for solar power development to benefit local neighborhood development and strengthen community participation.

The policy programs and implementation strategies are shown in Table IV. Based on their nature, the implementation measures fall into four categories: spatial planning, legal and operational mechanism construction, guidance or subsidy measures, and local support and compensation programs. Among these, legal regulations and local support are the primary policy promotion methods, with the Administration of Energy developing regulations for solar power site selection, development standards, design specifications, and public rights protection to implement energy and industrial development that can prosper alongside local communities.

Table IV: Policy Implementation Strategies in the White Paper on Land Use for Renewable Energy Development: Solar Power

Strategies	Implementation			
	A	B	C	D
Application Streamlining		✓		
Technical Standards		✓		
Subsidy Programs			✓	
Aquavoltaic Zones	✓			
Demonstration Zones	✓	✓		
Community Energy		✓		✓
Environmental Compensation	✓	✓		
Local Transparency				✓
Public Participation		✓		✓
Indigenous Rights		✓		✓
Local Service Stations				✓
Compensation Schemes			✓	✓
Local Authority Coordination		✓		
Implementation:				
A: Spatial Planning				
B: Legal & Mechanism Improvement				
C: Subsidy & Guidance				
D: Local Support & Compensation				

As shown in Table IV, the spatial planning category includes promoting aquavoltaic zones, establishing environmental compensation mechanisms and operation management regulations, and developing site selection principles for national demonstration zones. This category also emphasizes the construction of development review and operation management systems for large-scale projects. The mechanism prioritizes national and public lands and Taiwan Sugar Corporation's lands for large-scale developments while encouraging local autonomous development for small-scale projects. These smaller projects continue to focus on integrated PV installations combined with agriculture, along with community-based rooftop solar power systems.

Overall, while the white paper has established a comprehensive social communication framework and identified key action items, it has not yet specified implementation procedures for individual policies, evaluated program feasibility, or conducted spatial mapping. Furthermore, it does not fully meet the requirements for sectoral plans as specified in Articles 4 and 6 of the Spatial Planning Act Enforcement Rules, and additional research is needed to determine how to align these elements in the future.

4 METHODOLOGY

4.1 Review of Recent Studies

Recent academic research addressing both spatial planning and energy development has primarily focused on three areas: energy development strategies across different cities, integrated planning for spatial and energy systems, and the roles of central and local governments in multi-level governance. These studies provide valuable theoretical and practical insights for this research.

Asarpota and Nadin (2020) developed an assessment framework through a literature review and policy analysis to evaluate the relationship between energy planning and spatial planning in Hong Kong, Auckland, Oslo, and Vancouver. Their analysis compared transportation and accessibility, urban patterns, energy grid structure, and infrastructure systems including drainage and waste management. The study revealed that none of these cities had effectively incorporated nergy infrastructure planning and supply efficiency considerations into their spatial structure and urban patterns [11]. ⸳

In the same year, Stoeglehner examined the implementation of integrated spatial and energy planning in Austria's Styria province. Using quantitative analysis, the study evaluated the balance between renewable energy generation potential and CO2 emissions to identify areas both requiring and suitable for energy plan implementation. Through talent development and government subsidy programs, the province supported local governments in implementing these strategies. The results demonstrated Styria's successful implementation of integrated spatial and energy planning strategies, emphasizing the crucial role and responsibilities of local governments in the process [12].

Drawing on both literature review and case studies, Dobravec, Matak, Sakulin, and Krajačić (2021) examined the mechanisms and impacts of decentralized central-local governance in Austria's local government energy and climate policy implementation. Through interviews and policy analysis, they identified key challenges and opportunities facing local governments in policy development and implementation. Their findings indicated that while local governments have significant potential in energy and climate policy implementation, they require stronger coordination in decentralized governance, including increased funding, human resources, technical support, and improved vertical and horizontal communication [13].

De Laurentis and Pearson (2021) investigated how Italy and England adapted their policy planning to promote renewable energy, examining various government departments, governance methods, and infrastructure arrangements. Their comparative case study analyzed conditions in three Italian regions (Apulia, Tuscany, and Sardinia) and two UK autonomous territories (Wales and Scotland). Through interviews and literature analysis, they gathered policy formulation data and statistics from these regions to compare approaches and outcomes. Their research demonstrated that social structure, economic conditions, and infrastructure configuration significantly influence energy policy implementation in regional energy transitions [14].

4.2 Analytical Approach to Taiwan's Spatial-Energy Policy Integration

While recent research on spatial planning and energy policy provides valuable theoretical and practical insights, some aspects are not directly applicable to Taiwan's context. Most studies focus on countries with relatively mature energy development systems, whereas Taiwan faces the distinct challenge of enhancing renewable energy development within limited land area. Furthermore, Taiwan is currently transforming its spatial planning system. To achieve policy goals during this transition period and effectively integrate energy and spatial planning systems, it is essential to analyze policy planning mechanisms and hierarchical governance frameworks to identify a development path suitable for Taiwan.

This study will employ methods including literature review, comparative research, case study, and policy analysis. First, it will systematically collect and analyze relevant domestic and international literature to examine how different countries with similar land conditions manage their spatial planning policies, controls, and energy policy implementation and support measures. Second, by comparing Taiwan's approach with other countries' spatial planning and energy policies, it will identify applicable successful experiences and conduct an in-depth analysis of specific implementation cases to extract key feasible strategies and policy recommendations. Finally, applying these case studies to Taiwan's context, along with the integrated application of the aforementioned research methods, will enable this study to thoroughly analyze Taiwan's current challenges and opportunities. Through analyzing the relationship between spatial planning and energy policy, we will propose specific recommendations to strengthen coordination between these two policy systems and facilitate smooth policy implementation.

5 CASE STUDY AND DISCUSSION

Taiwan's 2018 National Spatial Plan lacks clear spatial guidance for solar power development, which has hindered local governments from identifying appropriate development areas and has led to conflicts in sectoral policy implementation. The energy authority should leverage the upcoming comprehensive five-year review of county/municipal spatial plans to address this issue. Before the finalization of spatial plan changes in 2028, they should translate the current White Paper on Land Use for Renewable Energy Development: Solar Power into concrete spatial terms, developing site selection principles and land use guidance that can be integrated into spatial plans. Concurrently, they should align with spatial planning authorities' timeline for comprehensive rural area planning, providing energy development recommendations to facilitate the systematic implementation of energy policy goals across different scales.

This study examines countries that, like Taiwan, have achieved higher solar power development capacity despite high population density, aiming to construct an appropriate spatial guidance framework. By analyzing how these countries integrate their spatial planning and energy policies, we can derive insights for Taiwan's improvement. The study focuses on four countries: Japan, India, South Korea, and the Netherlands, examining each country's spatial planning framework, energy sector planning system, and methods of integrating spatial planning with energy promotion policies.

5.1 Japan

Japan has a population density of approximately 333 people per square kilometer, ranking 27th globally. Despite its dense population and limited land resources, Japan's solar power development reached 78GW by 2022, ranking third worldwide. To understand its national spatial planning framework and methods of integrating spatial planning with energy policies, we analyze its national spatial planning system, central energy planning guidance, and local decentralized governance to identify lessons for improving Taiwan's integration of spatial and sectoral plans.

5.1.1 Spatial Planning Framework

Japan released its revised National Spatial Plan in July 2023 under the National Spatial Planning Act [15]. The plan addresses national challenges including accelerated population decline leading to local development crises, climate disaster risks, and changing international conditions. In response to these challenges, Japan established the vision of "National Spatial Strategy: Harnessing Regional Strengths for a New Era" and formulated comprehensive, long-term development directions.

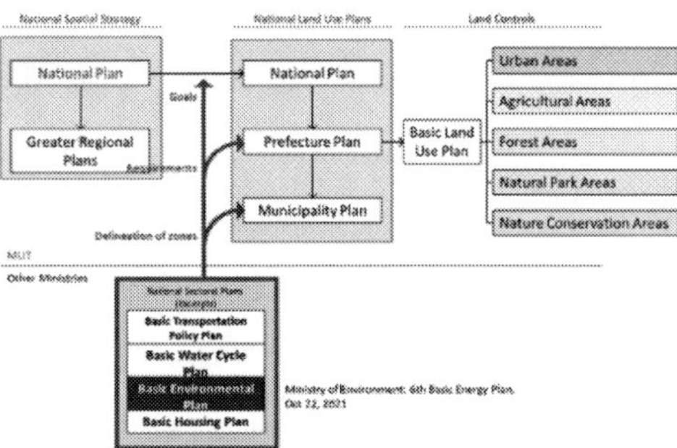

Figure 3: Japan's Spatial Planning System

As shown in Figure 3, Japan's spatial planning framework follows a hierarchical structure from planning to implementation control. At the central level, the Ministry of Land, Infrastructure, Transport and Tourism develops the National Spatial Strategy, dividing the country into eight major living spheres and collaborating with local governments to formulate eight greater regional plans with specific policy implementation goals. At the prefecture level, following national and regional development visions, local spatial strategies are developed. These strategies classify land into five categories based on location, environmental resources, and social, economic,

and cultural needs, establishing land use guidance principles for each category. At the municipality level, local authorities propose specific land use control measures based on prefecture guidance, implementing the spatial planning framework through substantive controls [15], [16], [17].

5.1.2 Energy Sector Planning

To achieve its 2050 carbon neutrality goal, Japan's Ministry of Economy, Trade and Industry approved the "6th Basic Energy Plan" in October 2021. This plan outlines future energy development directions, policy implementation methods, integration requirements with other plans, and measures to address energy supply-demand structure issues. For renewable energy promotion, the Basic Energy Plan emphasizes "communities" as the primary implementation unit, focusing on mutual prosperity between energy businesses and communities. It designates "Energy Development Promotion Zones" based on community needs to provide flexible land use control measures. Considering the Fukushima nuclear disaster and tsunami experiences, the plan integrates with the Basic Disaster Management Plan, positioning renewable energies as alternative energy sources during disasters to ensure stable energy supply during evacuation and disaster relief [18].

At the prefecture level, policy planning focuses on two main pillars: energy and disaster management, through the "Plan for Implementing Global Warming Countermeasures" and "Regional Disaster Management Plan" respectively. The former emphasizes both energy conservation and generation, addressing low-carbon materials, recycling and circular use, diverse energy resource development and investment, improved energy storage applications, and value-added directions for multi-functional developments. These include combining agriculture with renewable energy development and incorporating renewable energy into urban public facilities. The disaster management plans vary by region according to prevalent disaster types. For example, in areas prone to storms and floods, plans emphasize stable energy supply strategies during disasters, including coastal wind turbine utilization and solar power development in hillside rural areas, while focusing on connecting energy storage facilities with evacuation centers.

At the municipality level, implementation is the primary focus. For global warming countermeasures, municipalities establish specific subsidy requirements for residents and local businesses developing energy projects, while also inventorying public infrastructure and introducing new construction projects, such as solar-powered parking lots and expanded special zones for energy businesses. Disaster management plans focus on inventorying evacuation sites and examining overall energy use and storage to ensure effective utilization during disasters [19].

5.1.3 Spatial Planning and Energy Sector Integration

Central-level plans in Japan establish only future development directions and overall national goals. The spatial plans outline development visions for the country and its eight living spheres without specifying detailed plans or land controls. Similarly, energy and disaster management plans highlight future development visions, policy programs, and related regulations, explicitly designating municipalities as the main implementation bodies and empowering local governments to determine appropriate planning programs.

At the prefecture level, land use plans clearly establish land classifications and usage guidance for each category. Controls specified in energy plans and disaster management measures for different land categories are incorporated into land use plans, which establish permitted and conditional installation requirements. For example, land use plans specify that renewable energy promotion zones are designated for renewable energy development, and projects involving agricultural land must obtain land use conversion permits under the Cropland Act. At the municipality level, land use plans must clearly define land use controls and building management requirements for each land parcel. Reviews must be conducted to determine locations for future energy facilities and evacuation sites in disaster prevention plans, ensuring development plan feasibility and enabling contextual adjustments based on each village's development needs.

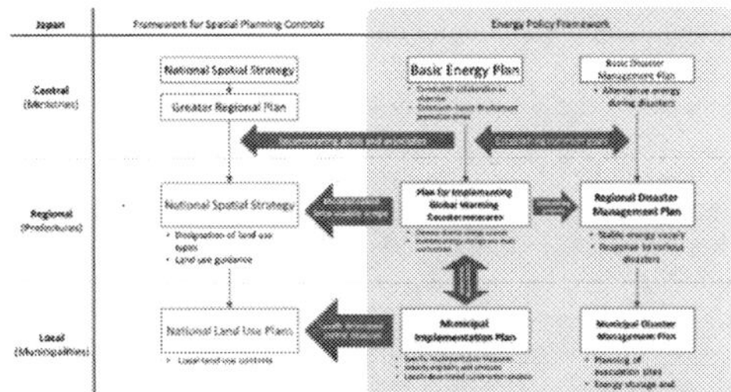

Figure 4: Japan's Spatial–Energy Policy Integration

5.2 India

India has a population density of approximately 431 people per square kilometer, ranking 26th globally. Despite its limited development space, India achieved a solar power installation capacity of 63.19GW by 2022, ranking fourth worldwide. This study analyzes India's comprehensive national plans and basic energy plans to examine its policy integration approaches and identify effective strategies for Taiwan's spatial and sectoral planning coordination.

5.2.1 Spatial Planning Framework

India, as a federal system, designates the National Land Use Planning Commission of the federal government to coordinate national land use planning and development strategies through comprehensive plans spanning decades. These plans, reviewed every five years, cover economics, finance, employment, education, agriculture, and other sectors. During the implementation of the 12th Five-Year Plan (2012-2017), the Indian federal government established the National Institution for Transforming India (NITI Aayog) to replace the commission in 2015. This restructuring transformed India's development strategies and governance methods, establishing a committee led by the Prime Minister with department heads as members to promote state cooperation and develop national development priorities collaboratively. The new institution focuses on providing consultation, conducting surveys, and offering guidance for collaboration, no longer drafting national five-year comprehensive plans but allowing state governments to formulate their own spatial planning approaches.

Currently, spatial planning in India is managed by state governments through Development Plans (DP), which are updated every 10 years. These plans encompass two main components: regulation formulation and developable area identification. The former includes detailed land use controls, building management rules, building design specifications, and urban design guidelines. The latter divides land into functional zones based on location and environmental sensitivity levels to balance orderly development and ecological protection. For areas where the government intends to introduce specific development, Special Plan Development zones (SPD zones) are designated to clearly identify areas requiring future attention.

Following the development plan visions proposed by state governments, cities within their jurisdiction are divided into multiple districts, with each district governed by specific Town Planning Schemes (TPS) established by municipal governments. For example, in Gujarat state, 33 cities have proposed town planning schemes for 222 districts. As of 2023, 80 schemes have received formal approval, while the remaining schemes are in the review and hearing stages. Each district's town planning scheme must clearly delineate road patterns, designate open spaces, and establish reasonable distribution of industry and public facilities. These plans must comply with their respective state government's development plan controls and enable developers to apply for required development permits, promoting orderly development of India's national space [20], [21].

5.2.2 Energy Sector Planning

India's energy sector planning began in 2008 with the National Action Plan on Climate Change (NAPCC) proposed by the Ministry of Environment, Forest and Climate Change. This plan launched several ambitious initiatives, including the Jawaharlal Nehru National Solar Mission (JNNSM) proposed in 2010 by the Ministry of New and Renewable Energy (MNRE). The mission initially aimed to achieve 20GW of solar power generation by 2022. Due to strong electricity demand across the country, particularly in off-grid areas, both rooftop and ground-mounted solar power zones achieved remarkable results. Consequently, in 2015, the mission target was revised to 100GW by 2022, allocating 40GW for rooftop installations and 60GW for medium and large-scale ground-mounted solar power zones. The mission also aimed to promote the widespread application of solar technology to reduce fossil fuel dependence and address global climate change challenges [22].

To implement the National Solar Mission, MNRE collaborates with two state-owned enterprises: the Indian Renewable Energy Development Agency Limited (IREDA) and the Solar Energy Corporation of India (SECI). IREDA manages renewable energy development financing and preferential loans, providing financial support for solar power development, while SECI focuses on solar power technology development and increasing its application scope, including constructing large-scale solar zones and promoting off-grid solar street lights in rural communities.

Considering the disparity between urban and rural development, with uneven distribution of off-grid and grid-connected areas and some rural communities lacking power resources, the National Solar Mission promotes both off-grid and grid-connected solar power facilities. Since 2014, off-grid solar power development has prioritized installing solar-powered street lights in areas with less than 50% grid coverage. Additionally, solar-powered lighting and irrigation pump facilities are installed in rural areas, along with home lighting systems and student study lamps for households still using coal, improving rural areas' quality of life and production conditions.

For grid-connected areas, solar power development is guided and promoted through various policy initiatives including:

- The Solar Park Scheme, which focuses on establishing large-scale ground-mounted solar power parks to increase generation through concentrated installation.
- The Viability Gap Funding Scheme (VGF Scheme), which provides federal government subsidies to reduce initial installation costs, attracting more small and medium enterprises to invest and participate.
- The Central Public Sector Undertakings (CPSU) Scheme, which encourages central public agencies to invest in solar power facility installation, expanding commercial applications and enhancing technology application diversity.
- The Canal Bank & Canal Top Scheme, which installs solar panels above waterways, conserving terrestrial land while increasing national solar power generation and enhancing its economic viability and market competitiveness [23].

The Solar Park Scheme exemplifies this approach. The federal government's MNRE coordinates with state governments to review and designate locations for large-scale park development projects, with state governments managing implementation details, including development scope, scale, and arrangement patterns. State governments also determine whether to collaborate with MNRE and SECI for bidding and developer selection, ensuring selected developers can access IREDA financing support. A unique feature of this scheme is "landowner shareholding," which invites original landowners to participate as investors. In a system similar to rights conversion in urban renewal, landowners can use their land as share capital. This approach contributes to the local economy while reducing community resistance to solar power facilities.

5.2.3 Spatial Planning and Energy Sector Integration

India's central-level spatial planning provides policy consultation and survey services without explicit control and planning guidance. Planning principles, legal regulations, and development goals are established at the state level, with implementation details delegated to individual cities. This ensures plans align with local conditions, visions, and development needs while enabling concrete implementation controls.

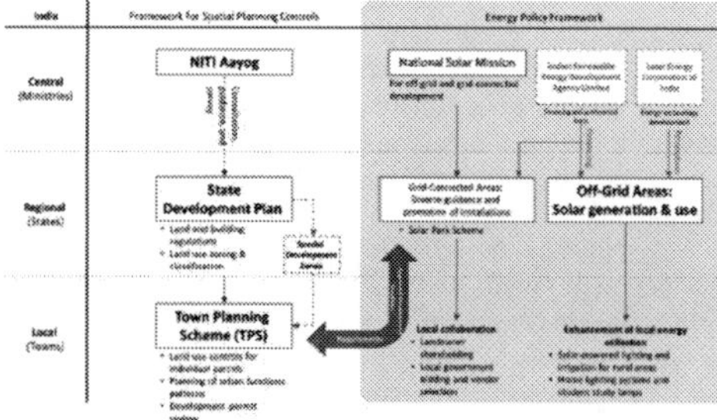

Figure 5: India's Spatial–Energy Policy Integration

In contrast, energy planning maintains clear policy

guidance and responsibility division at the central level. The National Solar Mission specifies future development goals and sub-plan scopes for both off-grid and grid-connected projects. While state governments propose specific implementation plans for various sub-plans, it is the city governments that review solar project applications to verify compliance with Town Planning Scheme (TPS) controls, thereby achieving integration between spatial planning and energy sectors.

5.3 South Korea

South Korea has a population density of approximately 516 people per square kilometer, ranking 20th globally. Despite limited development space, its solar power installation capacity reached 22GW by 2022, ranking eighth worldwide. This study analyzes South Korea's comprehensive national spatial plans and basic energy plans to examine its integration of spatial and energy policies, seeking insights for Taiwan's policy integration.

5.3.1 Spatial Planning Framework

South Korea's spatial planning framework is based on two regulations: the Framework Act on The National Land and the National Land Planning and Utilization Act. Under these laws, the central government, special autonomous cities, and provincial governments develop Comprehensive Plans, while city and county governments prepare City/County Management Plans and District Unit Planning. These plans propose specific development programs and implementation measures based on their respective Comprehensive Plans and land use control laws [24].

The Fifth National Comprehensive Plan (2020-2040), proposed by the South Korean central government in 2019, aims to address domestic population decline, which has necessitated adjustments to industrial transformation strategies, living needs, and sustainable development approaches. The plan places "people" at its core, establishing land development visions and proposing multiple development management strategies, including:

- Promoting distinctive and decentralized regional development.
- Strengthening cross-administrative district solidarity and cooperation.
- Revitalizing regional industrial innovation.
- Promoting culture and tourism.
- Building safe and livable environments.
- Constructing efficient infrastructure and smart national land management systems.

Regarding energy development, the plan proposes three major goals and policy strategies for local governments to implement in their spatial planning:

(1) Promote energy-saving green buildings and gradually strengthen requirements for zero-energy buildings.
(2) Enhance self-sufficiency capabilities in specific development zones, such as industrial parks and designated development areas, achieving the zones' energy generation and consumption goals through expanded energy storage facilities and distribution.
(3) Construct low-energy consumption urban patterns by integrating energy facilities, spatial distribution of urban activities, and transportation systems to transition toward energy-efficient urban spatial structures.

At the local government level, special autonomous

cities and provincial governments develop local development plans following the central government's comprehensive planning goals. For example, in the Fifth National Comprehensive Plan, Jeju Island is designated to develop with the vision of "Carbon Free Island Jeju." Subsequently, the Jeju Special Self-Governing Province government drafted the Third Jeju Free International City Comprehensive Plan (2022-2031) in 2022, providing detailed implementation strategies for this vision:

- Urban structure: Enhance smart management and information systems to strengthen smart infrastructure construction, creating comfortable and safe living environments.
- Industrial development: Create diverse development and multi-functional island living by introducing and developing agriculture, forestry, livestock, marine, tourism, and logistics industries, while upgrading industries and combining them with technology to enhance productivity and innovation.
- Tourism: Establish management regulations for natural landscape resources and improve international accessibility and community amenities and services to develop tourist potential.

These comprehensive plans, approved by autonomous cities and provincial governments, identify developable regions and authorize cities and counties within their jurisdiction to propose specific development locations, project procedures, and compliance requirements based on local conditions. For example, Seogwipo City within Jeju's jurisdiction developed its management plan following Jeju's Fifth Comprehensive Plan. The plan divides the city into five areas: residential, commercial, industrial, green, and special management areas. Different land use control measures are established for each category to ensure land use rationality and implementation of visions from the higher-level plan. Additionally, considering the higher-level plan's emphasis on tourism and its implications for livable environments, local quality of life, and culture, Seogwipo City's management plan requires public participation mechanisms for all development projects and coordinates with local residents on landscape requirements to balance urban development and environmental quality.

5.3.2 Energy Sector Planning

South Korea's current national energy policy follows the Third Basic Energy Plan developed by the Ministry of Trade, Industry and Energy (MOTIE) in 2019. This plan is reviewed and updated every five years to address the latest developments and challenges in the energy sector, and work has already begun on formulating the Fourth Basic Energy Plan. The Third Basic Energy Plan [25] aims to improve energy use efficiency and strengthen electricity demand management across industrial, transportation, and building sectors to rationalize energy pricing. To achieve these goals, the plan promotes electric vehicle adoption, energy storage system (ESS) installation, and development of both large-scale ground-mounted solar power zones and small-scale distributed generation facilities at the community level to increase energy industry flexibility and grid stability, while encouraging public participation in energy development to achieve overall green transformation of the energy structure.

To implement the Basic Energy Plan's goals, Korea Electric Power Corporation (KEPCO) drafted Korea's Tenth Basic Power Supply and Demand Plan in 2023, which was approved by MOTIE to establish timeline and phase goals for the next 15 years. The plan, reviewed every two years to adjust energy source proportions, aims to gradually reduce nuclear energy's share while increasing renewable energy power supply to meet future energy demands and respond more flexibly to climate change challenges.

Following guidance from the Basic Energy Plan and Basic Power Supply and Demand Plan, each special autonomous city and provincial government must develop its own "local energy plan." Currently, 17 local energy plans have been completed and are updated every five years, following the Basic Energy Plan's review frequency. For example, Jeju Island's local energy plan sets a development goal of achieving 1.5GW within five years and establishes three local development principles:

(1) Ensure local communities share in the economic benefits of renewable energy development.
(2) Integrate energy storage system (ESS) deployment with electric vehicle infrastructure and transportation networks.
(3) Improve public acceptance of solar power and other renewable energy projects through resident collaboration and engagement.

Through top-down guidance on energy infrastructure planning, with each special autonomous city and provincial government autonomously proposing suitable local implementation measures, South Korea is achieving a more sustainable, low-carbon, and democratic energy transition.

5.3.3 Spatial Planning and Energy Sector Integration

At the central government level, South Korea's spatial and energy plans present only overall national development goals and evaluable development directions. For example, spatial plans indicate goals of combining low-carbon energy with rural joint development, while energy basic plans respond by suggesting rural communities can achieve spatial planning goals through electric vehicle promotion, expanded energy storage facilities, or distributed small power plant installation.

At the special autonomous city and provincial government level, Jeju Island provides an illustrative example. Its comprehensive spatial planning coordinates electric vehicle infrastructure with transportation network planning, integrating energy storage facilities while inventorying urban road networks and related public facility distribution. The spatial plan establishes building controls and landscape regulations, authorizing local authorities for review while specifying review criteria. This approach constructs locally self-governed mechanisms to guide public-private partnerships, including subsidy mechanisms for businesses installing energy management facilities, methods for managing industrial energy demand, requirements for landscape and buffer distances, and regulations for solar power equipment in new buildings.

At the city and county level, governments propose specific implementation methods for higher-level plans according to each jurisdiction's management plan. Seogwipo City in Jeju Island demonstrates this through several approaches:

- Establishing site selection principles for energy facilities, identifying suitable locations for hybrid facilities and agricultural land eligible for conversion to energy facilities to delineate areas for future development.
- Developing landscape agreements with local residents

to ensure development projects align with local landscape planning.

- Evaluating key construction projects and industries desired by local communities, such as establishing an energy research base in the eastern area and a smart grid certification center to support local renewable energy development.
- Expanding its smart grid outward from the research base, integrating tourism hotspots to create green tourism routes, and gradually incorporating populated areas into the smart grid region.

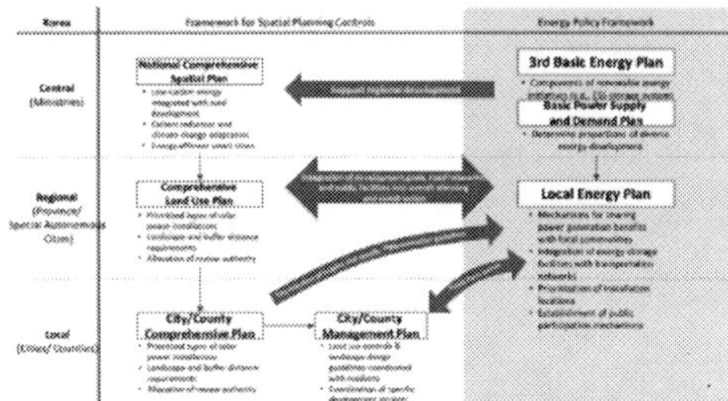

Figure 6: South Korea's Spatial–Energy Policy Integration

5.4 The Netherlands

The Netherlands has a population density of approximately 423 people per square kilometer, ranking 24th globally. Despite limited development space, its solar power installation capacity reached 18.85GW by 2022, ranking 13th worldwide. This study analyzes the Netherlands' comprehensive national plans and basic energy plans to examine its integration of spatial planning and energy policies to inform Taiwan's approach to policy integration.

5.4.1 Spatial Planning Framework

The Netherlands' spatial planning system has recently undergone major reform through the Environment and Planning Act (Omgevingswet), which was amended in 2023 and implemented on January 1, 2024. This amendment marks a shift from top-down central guidance toward collaborative planning between different levels of government. As many laws and supporting regulations are still being established, the regulatory transition period is expected to continue until 2030, when the new planning and control mechanism will be fully implemented.

Under the 2024 Environment and Planning Act, two central-level ministries—the Ministry of Infrastructure and Water Management and the Ministry of Interior and Kingdom Relations—collaborate with provincial governments to develop environmental visions (Omgevingsvisie), establishing long-term environmental management goals to guide sustainable development. For specific areas or cross-sectoral priorities, such as water resource conservation or air quality improvement zones, programs (Programma) are developed to establish implementation strategies and goals. Cities under Dutch provinces then develop their environmental plans (Omgevingsplan) based on national and provincial guidelines, detailing local building management, land use regulations, and urban design requirements.

This planning system enables all levels of government to establish detailed regulations and effectively control land development rights. This planning system establishes a hierarchy from broad environmental vision goals, through specific program actions, to detailed environmental plan requirements, ensuring consistency and effectiveness in spatial development and environmental management. All land use activities, including logging, building facade modifications, or solar panel installations on buildings and in courtyards, must follow environmental permit (Omgevingsvergunning) procedures and obtain approval from municipal governments. The permit system verifies whether proposed activities comply with environmental plans for specific areas, examining potential impacts on endangered species habitats, effects on birds and mammals, and compliance with building and landscape regulations. Municipal governments evaluate these impacts and issue time-limited environmental permits. For solar power facilities, environmental permits are typically valid for 15-20 years, depending on installation location and type. Upon expiration, compliance with updated regulations must be verified for renewal or extension. Through this system, the Netherlands achieves coordinated and efficient planning and development review while ensuring proper protection of natural and human environments.

5.4.2 Energy Sector Planning

The Netherlands' energy and climate policy framework has recently undergone comprehensive updates and consolidation to address global climate change challenges and promote national energy transition. Energy policy implementation is guided by two primary national agreements: the Energy Agreement (Energieakkoord) and the Climate Agreement (Klimaatakkoord). The former focuses on improving energy efficiency, increasing renewable energy adoption, and creating green economy employment opportunities, while the latter establishes specific goals and pathways for reducing greenhouse gas emissions. In 2023, the Ministry of Economic Affairs and Climate Policy developed the "National Energy System Plan" (Nationaal Plan Energiesysteem, NPE) based on these agreements to establish its energy development vision and long-term goals. This led to the National Regional Energy Strategy Program (Nationaal Programma Regionale Energiestrategie, NP RES), which guides regions in developing localized Regional Energy Strategy (RES) plans to achieve national energy and climate goals [27].

The National Energy System Plan (NPE) focuses on achieving energy transition while ensuring energy supply security and sustainability, promoting economic growth and technological innovation, and improving energy system flexibility and efficiency. It emphasizes cross-sector cooperation mechanisms, incorporating government, business, and civil society participation. By employing multiple communication channels to gain insights into diverse perspectives, it aims to build consensus and advance energy transition. The National Regional Energy Strategy Program (NP RES) coordinates regional energy strategy plans (RES) across the country, ensuring local actions align with national goals while encouraging regions to leverage their unique resources and conditions to develop renewable energy and improve energy efficiency.

Recognizing that addressing climate change and energy transition challenges requires more than individual local government action, Regional Energy Strategies (RES) connect provincial and municipal governments to effectively integrate local resources and address regional challenges, thereby enhancing energy efficiency and renewable energy expansion. Social equity and economic sustainability must be considered to ensure the transition neither creates social division nor places undue economic burden on specific groups. Each regional strategy undergoes updates every five years to reflect local circumstances, including technological advances, policy changes, and current development conditions, ensuring the strategies remain timely and context-appropriate.

5.4.3 Spatial Planning and Energy Sector Integration
The Netherlands' Environmental Vision (Omgevingsvisie) and National Regional Energy Strategy Program (NP RES) share aligned development goals of achieving sustainable energy transition and addressing climate change challenges while emphasizing cross-sector cooperation and local participation. The Netherlands' Environmental Vision (Omgevingsvisie) and National Regional Energy Strategy Program (NP RES) share aligned development goals of achieving sustainable energy transition and addressing climate change challenges while emphasizing cross-sector cooperation and local participation.

The National Regional Energy Strategy Program and local Regional Energy Strategies (RES) interface closely with local Environmental Plans (Omgevingsplan) regarding solar power development regulations. These strategy plans emphasize renewable energy, particularly solar power's role in the Dutch energy system, establishing development goals and implementation measures. Local Environmental Plans provide specific development regulations for solar power, including suitable locations, scale restrictions, design requirements, and ecological impact considerations. These regulations ensure solar power development meets both energy transition needs and maintains regional environmental quality, ecological conservation, and landscape character. Additionally, Environmental Plans highlight the importance of public participation, which it requires for larger-scale solar power developments to ensure broad social support and acceptance.

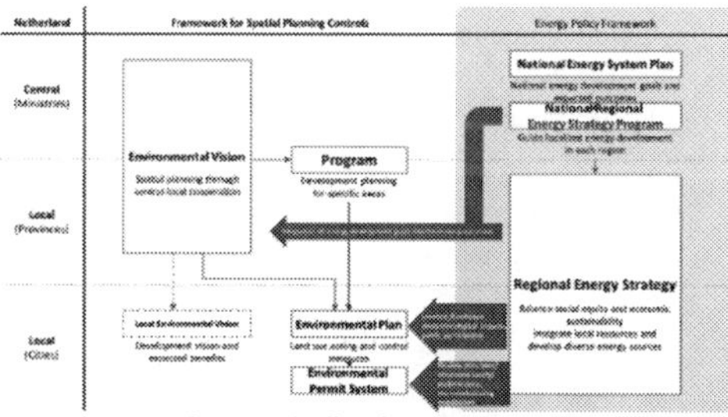

Figure 7: The Netherlands' Spatial–Energy Policy Integration

The Environmental Permit (Omgevingsvergunning) system provides crucial oversight during development, ensuring solar facilities comply with local Environmental Plan requirements. These permits govern the entire project lifecycle from construction through operation, maintenance, and eventual dismantling and site restoration, including safety standards for electrical and structural systems. Developers must conduct regular maintenance and monitoring to ensure long-term operational safety and efficiency while minimizing environmental impacts. The permits also stipulate dismantling and restoration requirements, ensuring sites can return to their original state or remain suitable for alternative uses, maintaining sustainable land use practices.

6   DISCUSSION

Taiwan faces challenges similar to those of Japan, India, South Korea, and the Netherlands, including limited spatial resources, high population density, and urgent needs to address climate change and energy transition. Analysis of these countries provides practical models for integrating spatial planning and energy policies that can inform Taiwan's national land and energy policy development.

Japan's spatial planning framework most closely resembles Taiwan's. Taiwan can learn from Japan's layered spatial governance and community-led model, particularly how community participation plays a key role in energy development plans. For Taiwan, this suggests that when advancing renewable energy policies, especially solar and wind power, efforts should focus on strengthening local government and community leadership and participation. This approach ensures energy development plans meet both national net-zero carbon emission goals and gain local support, while reflecting specific local development needs and conditions, making it more feasible to implement the policies.

Japan's spatial planning framework most closely resembles Taiwan's. Taiwan can learn from Japan's layered spatial governance and community-led model, particularly how community participation plays a key role in energy development plans. For Taiwan, this suggests that when advancing renewable energy policies, especially solar and wind power, efforts should focus on strengthening local government and community leadership and participation. This approach ensures energy development plans meet both national net-zero carbon emission goals and gain local support, while reflecting specific local development needs and conditions, making the policies more feasible to implement.

India's approach is distinctive in highlighting state governments' crucial role in spatial and energy planning within a federal system, particularly in their proactive promotion of solar power development and implementation of landowner shareholding, which helps reduce public resistance to solar power installations. India's planning and energy policy integration process suggests approaches for Taiwan to enhance local government autonomy and responsibility, encouraging regions to formulate and implement spatial planning and energy transition strategies based on their specific characteristics and conditions. Simultaneously, county/municipal governments should maintain consistency with national policy goals to ensure energy targets are effectively implemented.

South Korea's experience demonstrates close coordination between national comprehensive spatial planning and basic energy plans, particularly in improving energy efficiency and promoting renewable energy use, with both aspects responding to and aligning with each other at the planning stage. For Taiwan, this emphasizes that energy policy and spatial planning have the potential for further alignment, particularly in incorporating energy efficiency and renewable energy development goals into spatial planning. This alignment enables clear policy directions and related controls to be proposed during spatial plan formulation, promoting policy integration across land use, buildings, and industries.

The Netherlands offers a distinct approach, with nationally controlled land development rights and mandatory government environmental permits for all development projects. Through its Environment and Planning Act, the Netherlands establishes sustainable development as the foundation of national planning, emphasizing both public participation and local government responsibilities in plan formulation. In this system, central and provincial governments propose development goals and frameworks, while cities establish specific environmental plans including land use, landscape, and urban design requirements. At the development stage, the environmental permit system interfaces with energy sector plans, ensuring energy development complies with land regulations. Taiwan can learn from this approach that cross-departmental collaboration and public participation mechanisms during the planning stage can strengthen the harmony and inclusiveness of national and energy plans, reducing stakeholder concerns about and resistance to energy development.

7 CONCLUSION

In practice, Taiwan's spatial planning and energy policies often show inconsistencies, particularly in renewable energy policy implementation. Questions arise about whether sustainable development should prioritize land conservation and agricultural use, or whether energy transition should take precedence. Recent years have seen pronounced disputes between solar power development and spatial planning, primarily because solar power, as a relatively mature renewable energy technology domestically, is mostly installed in terrestrial areas. This easily provokes discussions about impacts on surrounding areas, including potential ecological effects, community landscape issues, and preservation of agricultural production environments. These conflicts indicate insufficient integration between spatial planning and energy policies, affecting both energy transition progress and the ability of central and local spatial plans to provide effective guidance, making it difficult to balance local development visions with centrally determined directions and capacity allocation.

Currently, Taiwan is working to integrate various sectoral plans—including housing, commercial, agricultural, energy, water resources, and disaster management policies—through the 2016 Spatial Planning Act, National Spatial Plan, and county/municipal spatial plans to create a harmonious development environment with minimal conflicts. However, these efforts require further strengthening, particularly in effectively integrating energy policies with spatial planning.

In this context, the publication of the White Paper on Land Use for Renewable Energy Development: Solar Power presents Taiwan with an opportunity to integrate energy planning with municipal and county spatial plans, which are scheduled for review and update in 2026. The White Paper systematically addresses energy and spatial plan integration issues by providing clear site selection principles and development guidance, ensuring energy development plans meet both national energy transition goals and local spatial planning needs. For example, while former salt production lands may be suitable for solar power development in principle, areas containing bird habitats and foraging zones should be excluded for environmental conservation and ecological preservation. Coastal windbreak forests should be protected to prevent impacts on inland microclimates. Depending on local conditions, developments must either maintain appropriate buffer distances from nearby communities to preserve rural landscapes, or establish close cooperation with adjacent settlements and contribute a portion of power industry revenue to local development. If this white paper effectively fulfills its integration function, Taiwan can promote consistency between spatial planning and energy policies during its energy transition while building a foundation for achieving its 2050 net-zero carbon emissions goal through robust planning and implementation.

Analysis of Japan, India, South Korea, and the Netherlands provides valuable insights for effectively integrating spatial planning and energy policies. These countries demonstrate the importance of layered governance at central and local levels, enhanced community participation channels and intensity, and cross-departmental collaboration in promoting spatial and energy integration. Notably, strengthening public participation and local government leadership facilitates smoother implementation of energy plans. Additionally, case studies show that domestic technological innovation can improve energy efficiency and diversify renewable energy installation options, enabling more choices in multi-functional solar power facilities. For example, semi-transparent solar modules can better integrate with agricultural facilities, while smaller modules can reduce building form restrictions. Beyond technology, establishing clear policy and planning goals remains crucial for achieving energy transition and sustainable development.

Integrating these key factors, Taiwan can pursue effective energy policy implementation through the following adjustments to policy support measures:

(1) Strengthen policy consistency and cross-departmental collaboration: Ensure effective integration between energy plans and spatial planning through establishing cross-departmental collaboration mechanisms, promoting information sharing and policy coordination across departments.

(2) Strengthen local government and community participation: Grant local governments greater decision-making authority in energy plan formulation and implementation, and encourage community engagement in energy plan discussion, planning, and execution to enhance acceptance and implementation effectiveness.

(3) Promote technological innovation and policy flexibility: Encourage technological innovation, particularly in improving energy efficiency and renewable energy utilization, while maintaining policy flexibility to respond to rapid changes in energy markets and climate conditions.

(4) Strengthen public participation and social acceptance: Enhance public understanding and support for energy policy and spatial planning integration through effective communication mechanisms, ensuring transparency and fairness in policy formulation and implementation.

Beyond these general policy adjustments, to effectively address Taiwan's challenges in integrating spatial planning and energy policies, the following regulatory principles should be incorporated into the White Paper on Land Use for Renewable Energy Development and spatial sector plans, drawing from international development strategies and key success factors. These should serve as central-level guidelines, while local spatial plans and township/district rural area comprehensive planning should lead implementation:

(1) The spatial plan for the energy sector, which guides local spatial plans, should highlight local development conditions and community needs: Municipal and county governments can adjust energy development strategies according to local conditions while complying with the total capacity goals and site selection principles established in the central-level spatial plan. This ensures flexibility and innovation in energy policy implementation. Furthermore, under Article 17 of the Spatial Planning Act, sectoral authorities may consult with spatial planning authorities of the same level during policy planning. When agencies face conflicts over site selection in spatial planning, they may coordinate through the Ministry of Interior. By utilizing public participation procedures specified in spatial plans and legally required project review processes, the government can successfully integrate policy implementation across different sectors.

(2) Propose site selection principles: Drawing from international experience, when promoting renewable energy, particularly the technologically mature solar and wind power, the balance between ecological protection and land use must be considered. Site selection should prioritize previously developed or less ecologically sensitive areas, actively promoting multi-functional facilities that integrate energy installations with existing buildings or agricultural operations to minimize environmental impacts.

(3) Establish comprehensive monitoring and evaluation mechanisms: Regularly review the progress and effectiveness of energy policy and spatial planning integration, and adjust policy strategies and supporting measures—including subsidies, penalties, and guidance—based on actual conditions. This ensures continued policy adaptability and effectiveness, enabling timely responses to technological progress, market changes, and evolving social needs.

In conclusion, as Taiwan faces the challenges of integrating spatial and energy systems in a new era, it should learn from international development processes and successful experiences, adopting systematic yet flexible strategies that allow for innovation. This requires continuous adjustment of policy directions, strengthening of institutional and regulatory frameworks, and promotion of active participation across social sectors to achieve harmonious development of spatial and energy systems, working together toward a greener and more sustainable future.

8 REFERENCE

[1] Ministry of the Interior, Taiwan. (2018). "National Spatial Plan."

[2] Ministry of Economic Affairs, Taiwan. (2017). "Two-Year Solar power Promotion Plan (revised version)".

[3] Ministry of the Interior. (2019), Taiwan. "Manual for Municipal and County Spatial planning".

[4] Ministry of the Interior, Taiwan. (2023). "Operational Manual for National Spatial Planning: Functional Zoning, Sub-classification, and Land Use Delineation".

[5] Yunlin County Government, Taiwan. (2021). "Yunlin County Spatial Plan".

[6] Kaohsiung City Government, Taiwan. (2021). "Kaohsiung City Spatial Plan".

[7] 2021. Tainan City Government, Taiwan. (2021). "Tainan City Spatial Plan".

[8] Chiayi County Government, Taiwan. (2021). "Chiayi County Spatial Plan".

[9] Changhua County Government, Taiwan. (2021). "Changhua County Spatial Plan".

[10] Pingtung County Government, Taiwan. (2021). "Pingtung County Spatial Plan".

[11] K. Asarpota and V. Nadin, "Energy Strategies, the Urban Dimension, and Spatial Planning," Energies (Basel), vol. 13, no. 14, 2020.

[12] G. Stoeglehner, "Integrated spatial and energy planning: a means to reach sustainable development goals," Evolutionary and Institutional Economics Review, vol. 17, no. 2, pp. 473–486, Jul. 2020, doi: 10.1007/s40844-020-00160-7.

[13] V. Dobravec, N. Matak, C. Sakulin, and G. Krajačić, "Multilevel governance energy planning and policy: a view on local energy initiatives," Energy Sustain Soc, vol. 11, no. 1, Dec. 2021, doi: 10.1186/s13705-020-00277-y.

[14] C. De Laurentis and P. J. G. Pearson, "Policy-relevant insights for regional renewable energy deployment," Energy Sustain Soc, vol. 11, no. 1, Dec. 2021, doi: 10.1186/s13705-021-00295-4.

[15] Ministry of Land, Infrastructure, Transport and Tourism, Japan. (2023). "National Spatial Strategy (National Plan)".

[16] Ministry of Land, Infrastructure, Transport and Tourism, Japan. (2023). "Sixth National Land Use Plan (National Plan)".

[17] Ministry of Land, Infrastructure, Transport and Tourism, Japan. (2016). "Greater Regional Plan for the Tohoku Region—From Earthquake Reconstruction to Independent Development".

[18] Ministry of Economy, Trade and Industry, Japan (2021). "Sixth Basic Energy Plan".

[19] Niigata City Government, Japan. (2023). "Niigata Citys' Regional Plan for National Resilience (revised)".

[20] G. of G. Urban Development and Urban Housing Department, Comprehensive General Development Control Regulations-2017. 2017.

[21] S. Ballaney, "Town Planning Mechanism in Gujarat, India," 2008.

[22] F. and C. C. Ministry of Environment, "National Action Plan on Climate Change (NAPCC)," 2021. [Online]. Available: https://dst.gov.in/climate-change-programme

[23] Ministry of New and Renewable Energy, "Off-grid and Decentralised Solar PV Applications Program Phase 3 Guidelines and Amendments," 2018.

[24] S. Choo, Spatial Planning System. Korea Research Institute for Human Settlements, 2013.

[25] l. and E. Ministry of Trade, "The 3rd Basic Energy Plan-A New Energy Paradigm for the Future," 2019.

[26] K. Changhoon, "Status and Evaluation of Regional Energy Plans - Centered on Guidelines," 2019.
[27] Ministry of Economic Affairs and Climate Policy. (2023). "National energy system plan. Netherlands".

Integrating Energy Policy into Spatial Planning Frameworks: A Study of Taiwan's Approach

Tzu Han Hung
Industrial Technology Research Institute

ABSTRACT

How can land-scarce regions balance development needs with ambitious renewable energy goals for a sustainable future?

Taiwan, an island of 36,197 km² with a population of 23 million and density of 640/km², faces competing demands for housing, high-tech industry, food security, climate adaptation, and disaster prevention. The 2016 Spatial Planning Act, the National Spatial Plan (2018), and 18 municipal plans (2021) established a framework to integrate sectoral policies, yet challenges remain. Energy policy, for example, sets a 20GW solar target by 2025 (revised to 8GW rooftop, 12GW ground-mounted) under the Renewable Energy Development Act (2009), but national planning offers limited spatial guidance, weak local autonomy, and insufficient mechanisms to coordinate overlapping land uses.

To address this gap, this article compares four land-constrained countries with higher solar deployment—**Japan, India, South Korea, and the Netherlands**. By analyzing how their spatial planning systems align with sectoral policies, it identifies governance and planning approaches that guide solar development within limited territory. The study aims to provide lessons for Taiwan to strengthen land—energy integration, resolve policy conflicts, and achieve its net-zero 2050 goals.

INTRODUCTION

Taiwan enacted the Spatial Planning Act in 2016, launching a new system to be fully applied by 2025. The framework operates at three levels: the National Spatial Plan (2018) sets broad zoning principles; municipal/county plans adapt them locally; and township plans reflect settlement and industry needs with community-based controls. While the law requires integration of sectoral policies, energy planning remains difficult, as diverse facility types—nuclear, thermal, hydro, and multiple renewables—make it hard to designate suitable zones or guide capacity.

For solar PV, the only clear rule is that composite systems combining agriculture or aquaculture with PV are widely permitted, resulting in most installations being placed in farmland, particularly fishpond-based aquavoltaics. Ground-mounted PV, by contrast, is mainly limited to already developed areas or low-value lands such as idle salt fields, subsidence zones, reclaimed landfills, and contaminated sites. This distribution reflects the current lack of precise spatial guidance and planning principles for renewable energy under the spatial planning system.

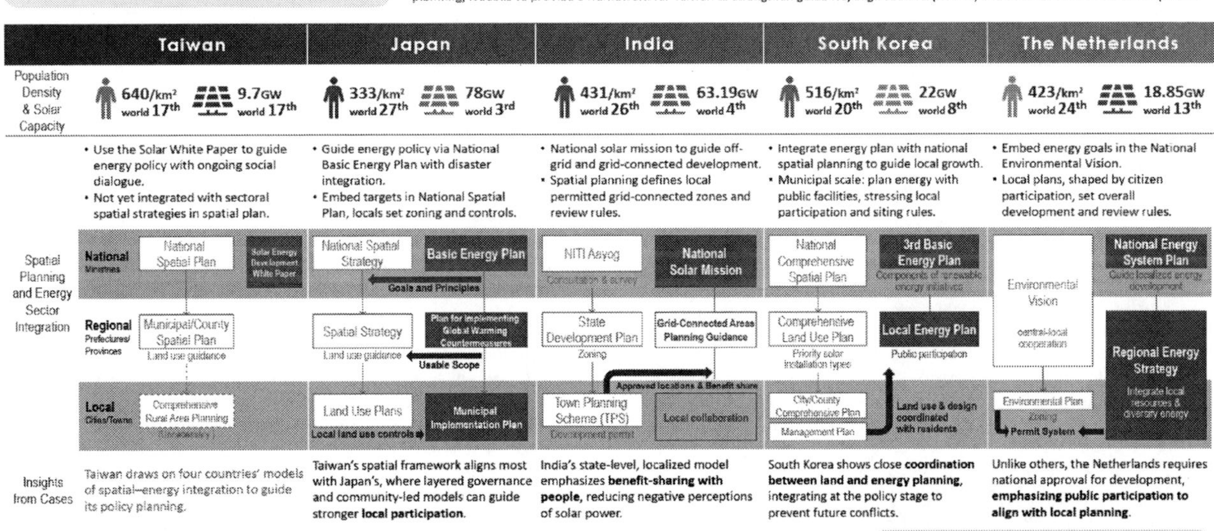

CASE STUDY & DISCUSSION

Taiwan's 2018 National Spatial Plan lacks clear solar siting guidance, limiting local governments and causing policy conflicts. The energy authority should use the 2028 spatial plan review to turn the Solar Land Use White Paper into concrete site selection and land use principles, aligning with rural planning to better implement energy goals. This study compares four land-scarce, high-density countries—Japan, India, South Korea, and the Netherlands—that achieved higher solar capacity. By analyzing how they integrate spatial and energy planning, it seeks to provide a framework for Taiwan to strengthen guidance, align sectoral policies, and advance renewable development.

	Taiwan	Japan	India	South Korea	The Netherlands
Population Density & Solar Capacity	640/km² world 17th — 9.7GW world 17th	333/km² world 27th — 78GW world 3rd	431/km² world 26th — 63.19GW world 4th	516/km² world 20th — 22GW world 8th	423/km² world 24th — 18.85GW world 13th
	• Use the Solar White Paper to guide energy policy with ongoing social dialogue. • Not yet integrated with sectoral spatial strategies in spatial plan.	• Guide energy policy via National Basic Energy Plan with disaster integration. • Embed targets in National Spatial Plan, locals set zoning and controls.	• National solar mission to guide off-grid and grid-connected development. • Spatial planning defines local permitted grid-connected zones and review rules.	• Integrate energy plan with national spatial planning to guide local growth. • Municipal scale: plan energy with public facilities, stressing local participation and siting rules.	• Embed energy goals in the National Environmental Vision. • Local plans, shaped by citizen participation, set overall development and review rules.
Spatial Planning and Energy Sector Integration	**National** (Ministries): National Spatial Plan; Solar Energy Development White Paper — **Regional** (Prefectures/Provinces): Municipal/County Spatial Plan (Land use guidance) — **Local** (Cities/Towns): Comprehensive Rural Area Planning	National Spatial Strategy → Basic Energy Plan (Goals and Principles); Spatial Strategy (Land use guidance) ← Plan for Implementing Global Warming Countermeasures (Usable Scope); Land Use Plans (Local land use controls) ← Municipal Implementation Plan	NITI Aayog (Consultation & survey) → National Solar Mission; State Development Plan (Zoning) — Grid-Connected Areas Planning Guidance (Approved locations & Benefit share); Town Planning Scheme (TPS) (Development permit) — Local collaboration	National Comprehensive Spatial Plan → 3rd Basic Energy Plan (Components of renewable energy initiatives); Comprehensive Land Use Plan (Priority solar installation types) → Local Energy Plan (Public participation); City/County Comprehensive Plan / Management Plan → Land use & design coordinated with residents	Environmental Vision (central-local cooperation) — National Energy System Plan (Guide localized energy development) → Regional Energy Strategy (Integrate local resources & diversify energy); Environmental Plan (Zoning) → Permit System
Insights from Cases	Taiwan draws on four countries' models of spatial—energy integration to guide its policy planning.	Taiwan's spatial framework aligns most with Japan's, where layered governance and community-led models can guide stronger **local participation**.	India's state-level, localized model emphasizes **benefit-sharing with people**, reducing negative perceptions of solar power.	South Korea shows close **coordination between land and energy planning**, integrating at the policy stage to prevent future conflicts.	Unlike others, the Netherlands requires national approval for development, **emphasizing public participation to align with local planning**.

CONCLUSION

To bridge Taiwan's land—energy planning gap, the White Paper and spatial plans should adopt other countries' strategies in the following principles:

1 Local spatial plans should align energy development with community needs and local characteristics.
- Localized, community-driven
- Social dialogue & coordination

2 Local plans should define siting principles for energy development.
- Landscape preservation
- Ecological sensitivity

3 Central—local governments should coordinate robust monitoring and evaluation mechanisms.

REFERENCES

■ Taiwan Government Reports. (2018–2023). National Spatial Plan; White Paper on Land Use for Renewable Energy Development: Solar Power; Municipal spatial plans; Approved project lists.
■ Japan (MLIT & METI). (2015, 2021). National Spatial Strategy; 6th Strategic Energy Plan.
■ India (GoI & MNRE). (2008, 2010). National Action Plan on Climate Change; Jawaharlal Nehru National Solar Mission.
■ South Korea (MOLIT, MOTIE & KEPCO). (2019–2020). 5th Comprehensive National Territorial Plan; 3rd National Energy Master Plan; 10th Basic Power Supply Plan.
■ Netherlands Government. (2019–2020). National Spatial Strategy (NOVI); National Energy and Climate Plan (NECP).

ACKNOWLEDGMENTS This work was supported by the Energy Administration, Ministry of Economic Affairs, Taiwan.

UTILIZATION OF SMALL-SCALE SOLAR POWER PRODUCTION IN FINNISH GRID-BALANCING MARKETS THROUGH A VIRTUAL POWER PLANT

Eino Kujansivu[1 2], Aleksi Ojala[1], Juho Ylipaino[2 3], Juha Koskela[2]
[1] Solarigo Systems Oy, Pirkkala, Finland
[2] Tampere University, Tampere, Finland
[3] Tampere University of Applied Sciences, Tampere, Finland
eino.kujansivu@solarigo.fi, aleksi.ojala@solarigo.fi, juho.ylipaino@tuni.fi, juha.j.koskela@tuni.fi

ABSTRACT: This study analyses the techno-economic feasibility of small-scale solar photovoltaic (PV) systems (<1 MWp) in Finnish reserve markets through a virtual power plant (VPP) framework. The focus of this study is on the Frequency Containment Reserve for Disturbances (FCR-D) down, which requires rapid response to over-frequency events. In this study, high-resolution production data from one PV portfolio is analysed together with 0.1-second frequency measurements to assess both technical suitability and revenue potential. The results show that aggregated small-scale solar PV systems can actively contribute to grid stability while offering notable financial benefits for solar producers. Compared to pure day-ahead trading, aggregated PV portfolios can offer reserve capacity and generate additional revenues of 5-10 % or 4-6 €/MWh during high output periods, with only marginal energy curtailment.
Keywords: Photovoltaic systems, virtual power plant, power system balancing, demand response, reserve markets

1 INTRODUCTION

The ongoing transition from traditional synchronous generators to renewable, inverter-based sources, such as solar PV, brings challenges to grid stability and power system operations [1]. Solar and wind power are characterized by variability, weather dependency, and a lack of inherent rotational inertia [1], [2]. These factors can contribute to power fluctuations and periods of overproduction during high-output periods increasing the need for fast-acting reserves and renewable energy curtailment [1]. In Finland, the demand for fast-acting, downward regulatory reserves, particularly FCR-D down, has increased rapidly in recent years [3].

As the share of distributed generation (DG), including solar PV, continues to grow, its role in supporting system stability becomes increasingly important [4]. Beyond supplying energy, DG units are expected to provide flexibility, balancing, and ancillary services, thereby complementing traditional large-scale generators in maintaining the reliability of the main grid [5].

By aggregation, distributed energy resources (DER) can actively participate in reserve markets thereby providing both transient and long-term grid services [2], [6]. Aggregation can be enabled through a virtual power plant (VPP) framework, where for example geographically distributed solar PV units can be pooled into a unified cloud-based resource [6]. This enables them to meet the needed minimum market entry constraints [6]. By participating in these markets, aggregated PV can contribute to grid balancing and reduce reliance on conventional flexibility sources. This in turn helps mitigate frequency deviations and supports the integration of higher shares of renewable energy sources (RES).

In addition to technical benefits, integrating into these markets also creates new revenue opportunities for DER owners. In Finland, the average electricity price has decreased each year since 2023, settling at a considerably lower level compared with the price peaks of 2022 [7]. Moreover, price fluctuations have intensified alongside growth in RES production. It has also been argued that the average electricity price in the Finnish day-ahead market will decrease significantly by 2030 as the share of RES increases [8].

For solar PV in particular, this implies lower attainable market values. Because solar PV generation is concentrated during specific hours of the day, additional capacity tends to coincide with existing production peaks. This oversupply lowers market prices during those hours, leading to the so-called cannibalization effect. It has been studied that adding 1 GW of solar capacity to the Finnish grid reduces attainable revenues from solar PV by around 5%, while 2 GW and 3 GW reduce them by approximately 8% and 12%, respectively [9].

As investments in RES are mostly driven by the return rate of the investment, which is largely determined by electricity market prices, these effects have major implications for project viability [8]. Even modest revenue reductions may prevent projects from reaching a final investment decision. This further underlines the importance of diversifying revenue streams, for instance through participation in reserve markets and/or long-term power purchase agreements.

This study focuses on analysing the potential FCR-D down revenues for small-scale solar PV aggregated in different portfolio configurations. The analysis is based on one real-world PV portfolio (VPP1) as well as scaled scenarios with multiplied installed capacities. The objective is to evaluate the extent to which aggregated PV can reliably contribute to FCR-D and how different portfolio sizes impact achievable revenues. By examining these scenarios, the study provides insights into the economic viability of pure PV-based participation in FCR-D. Participation in these markets offers a potential hedge against declining day-ahead revenues and market cannibalization, creating opportunities to stabilize long-term returns on investment.

The study provides new knowledge on techno-economic feasibility of aggregated small-scale PV systems in Finnish reserve markets. To the best of the authors' knowledge, there are no prior studies on the issue. The paper is structured as follows: section 2 describes the methodology and data , section 3 presents the main results, section 4 discusses their implications, and in the end section 5 concludes the paper.

2 METHODOLOGY

This study applies a quantitative approach to evaluate the revenue potential of aggregated small-scale PV systems in the Finnish FCR-D down market. The analysis focuses on the month of June 2025, chosen due to its high solar irradiance and peak PV production conditions in Finland. This period provides a representative case for assessing PV-based participation in reserve markets during times of maximum technical feasibility.

To maintain clarity, the analysis excludes acquisition and operational costs of the virtual power plant (VPP), such as platform management fees. All results are presented on a net-of-tax basis. Reported revenues therefore reflect only the relative improvement obtained from reserve markets in addition to day-ahead trading. It is further assumed that the portfolios participate in reserve markets in all hours where technical feasibility is met.

2.1 Data Collection

An existing PV portfolio was selected as the empirical data for the study. Portfolio VPP1 comprised 16 PV units owned by Solarigo Systems Oy, with a total installed power of 4.9 MWp / 4 MVA. Measured power data with 15-second and 1-hour resolution was obtained for the whole portfolio. To assess scalability, additional scenarios were created by scaling the measured power data of VPP1 by factors of 3 and 6 thus creating VPP2 (14.6 MWp / 12 MVA) and VPP3 (29.2 MWp / 24 MVA).

In addition, data from Fingrid (Finnish TSO) and ENTSO-E transparency platforms were used in the analysis [7], [10]. Fingrids data accounted for 0.1 second frequency data metered across different substations in Finland and FCR-D down hourly market prices. Finnish day-ahead prices were gathered from ENTSO-E.

2.2 Market Requirements

When participating in hourly FCR-D markets, each unit must define a maintained reserve power level, i.e. the minimum power that can be guaranteed for the entire bidding period [11]. For generation in down-regulation reserves, this corresponds to the lowest instantaneous active power within the hour. The maintained power must be equal to or greater than the offered bid to the market, since the full offered capacity may be activated in the worst-case scenario.

Due to the variability of solar PV, short cloud passages can significantly reduce intra-hour power, making the hourly minimum output often considerably lower than the hourly average. In this study, the hourly power offered to FCR-D was determined to be the VPPs lowest forecasted instantaneous power gathered from 15-second data $P_{min,h}$. Due to minimum market entry constraints, the $P_{min,h}$ needs to be equal or greater than 1 MW:

$$P_{min,h}(t) \geq 1MW$$

2.3 Calculation of Down-Regulated Energy

For FCR-D down, down-regulation is directly linked to frequency deviations above the normal operating band. When system frequency rises above 50.1 Hz, down-regulation begins, increasing linearly until full activation at 50.5 Hz [12]. To calculate the energy regulated during a one-second interval, a C_s coefficient was introduced. The coefficient accounts for full and minimal activation (50,5 Hz corresponds to $C_s = 1$, 50,1 Hz to $C_s = 0$) and is constrained to lie within the interval [0,1]. The coefficient

was defined as a normalized function of grid frequency f:

$$C_s(t_2) = \frac{f(t_2) - 50.1\,\text{Hz}}{50.5\,\text{Hz} - 50.1\,\text{Hz}}, \quad C_s(t_2) \in [0,1] \quad (1)$$

- $C_s = 1$: full activation at $f \geq 50.5$ Hz
- $C_s = 0$: minimal activation at $f \leq 50.1$ Hz
- $C_s \in [0,1]$: partial activation, linearly scaled between 50.1 and 50.5 Hz

To calculate the average activation level of down-regulation over one hour, the one-second coefficients are aggregated into an hourly coefficient C_h. This represents the mean share of offered capacity that was activated during hour t:

$$C_h(t) = \frac{1}{3600} \sum_{t_2=1}^{3600} C_s(t_2) \quad (2)$$

To calculate the amount of down-regulated energy during hour t, the hourly activation coefficient is multiplied by the offered minimum power:

$$E_{reg,h}(t) = C_h(t) \cdot P_{min,h}(t) \quad (3)$$

2.4 Calculation of Financial Revenues

To quantify the economic impact of FCR-D participation, three revenue streams were calculated: day-ahead market revenues, day-ahead losses caused by down-regulation, and FCR-D market revenues. These were combined to evaluate both absolute income levels and the relative improvement compared with pure day-ahead trading. The following equations define the main steps of the calculation.

To calculate the loss of day-ahead market revenue L_{DA} caused by down-regulation, the day-ahead price is multiplied by the curtailed energy during hour t:

$$L_{DA}(t) = A_{DA}(t) \cdot E_{req}(t) \quad (4)$$

To calculate the revenue R_{DA} from the day-ahead market during hour t, the average day-ahead price A_{DA} is multiplied by the produced energy E_{PV}:

$$R_{DA}(t) = A_{DA}(t) \cdot E_{PV}(t) \quad (5)$$

To calculate the revenue from participation in the FCR-D reserve market R_{RM}, the hourly FCR-D market price A_{RM} is multiplied by the offered minimum power $P_{min,h}$:

$$R_{RM}(t) = A_{RM}(t) \cdot P_{min,h}(t) \quad (6)$$

To compare the baseline revenue with the revenue including down-regulation, three measures are defined. The baseline revenue per unit of production was obtained by dividing the day-ahead revenue by the produced energy. The revenue including regulation per unit of production was calculated by subtracting the day-ahead revenue loss and adding the FCR-D revenue. Finally, the additional revenue share was determined by comparing the revenue including regulation to the baseline revenue.

3 RESULTS

This section presents the main findings of the study regarding both the technical activation behaviour of the

FCR-D down product and its economic implications for aggregated PV portfolios. The analysis focuses on two aspects: (3.1) the frequency deviations that determine when down-regulation is triggered, and (3.2) the resulting revenue effects for different portfolio sizes. By combining high-resolution frequency measurements with detailed PV production data, the results highlight how often activations occur, how much energy is curtailed, and what additional revenues can be obtained through market participation

3.1 Analysis of Frequency Deviations and Down Regulation

The month of June 2025 was analysed to capture high solar irradiance and frequent PV generation. Frequency deviations above 50.1 Hz occurred almost daily, although their total duration was relatively short. Over the observation period, the system frequency exceeded 50.1 Hz for 18,887 seconds (0.73% of all seconds). Despite the limited total duration, the number of individual exceedance events was high: on average 28.6 events occurred each day, with a mean duration of 22.5 seconds per event (Table I).

These findings indicate that although the total time over 50,1 Hz remains minimal, reserve activations take place relatively frequently. Consequently, the FCR-D down market represents a low-utilization but high-activation product.

Table I: Summary of findings from frequency analysis (June 2025).

Indicator	Result
Duration of frequency over 50,1 Hz (s)	18887 s
Duration of frequency over 50,1 Hz (%)	0.73%
Total amount of exceedance events	858
Average amount of daily exceedance events	28.6
Average duration of exceedance event	22.54 s

Figure I further illustrate that activations occurred almost daily throughout the month. This underlines the recurrent nature of frequency exceedances, even though their durations varied strongly from day to day. From the perspective of PV portfolios, this means that down-regulation events are a regular feature of system operation.

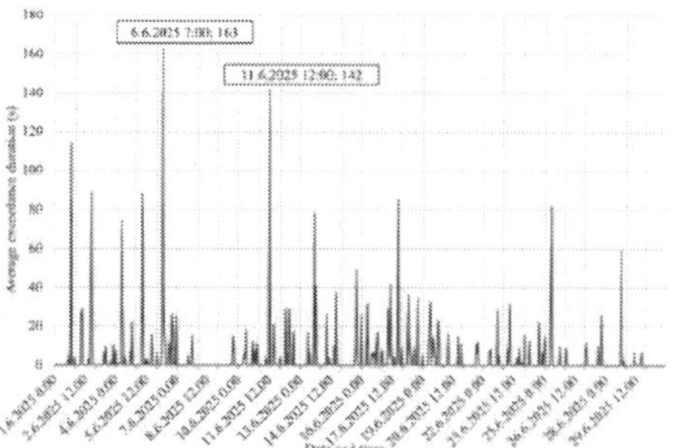

Figure I: Hourly average durations of individual frequency exceedance events above 50.1 Hz (June 2025).

Figure II illustrates the hourly distribution of PV generation (bars) and the total duration of frequency exceedances above 50.1 Hz (line) during June 2025. The results show that frequency deviations are not evenly distributed across the day. Instead, they tend to coincide with the midday hours when PV production is highest.

Interestingly, during the hours between 14:00 and 17:00, when PV output is near its maximum, the frequency exceedances are minimal. This suggests that system frequency stabilises during the very peak generation hours, while activation events cluster more strongly in the morning and late afternoon periods. For PV operators, this pattern implies that the highest production hours may be less exposed to down-regulation, further reducing the effective curtailment risk.

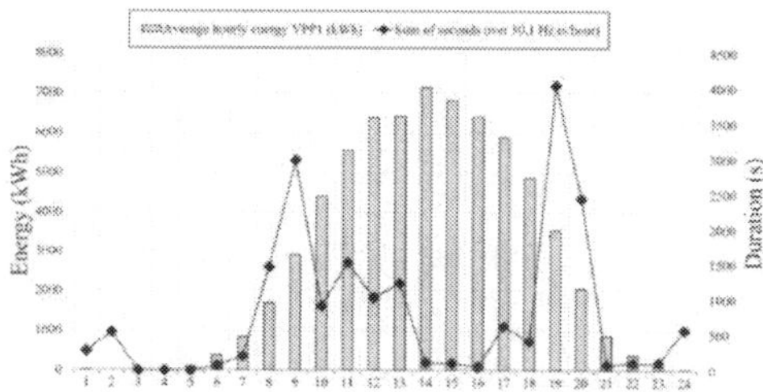

Figure II: Hourly averages of produced energy from VPP1 (bars) and total duration with grid frequency >50.1 Hz (brown line).

Figure III presents the hourly averages of down-regulated energy (bars, left axis) together with the activation coefficient C_h (line, right axis) for June 2025. The results demonstrate that down-regulated energy volumes remain very small, with noticeable curtailment occurring only during a few isolated hours. In these hours, PV production and the corresponding activation coefficient peaks, indicating that system frequency exceeded the 50.1 Hz threshold more persistently.

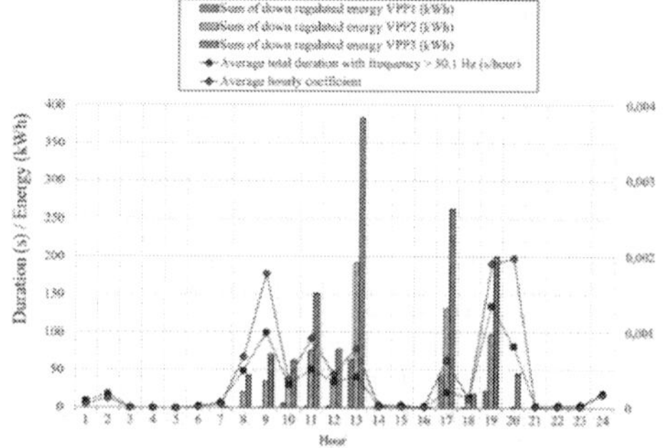

Figure III: Hourly sums of down-regulated energy (bars, left axis), average duration with grid frequency >50.1 Hz (blue line, left axis), and average hourly down regulation coefficient (green line, right axis).

3.2 Financial Implications

In the FCR-D down market, curtailed generation during activation events is not compensated. Consequently, energy losses must be accounted for in the revenue assessment. Table II illustrates, that across all portfolio sizes, curtailed energy represented less than

0.05% of total production, confirming that energy losses are economically insignificant.

At the same time, participation in the reserve market increased revenues by 5–10% during June 2025 compared with day-ahead trading alone. Larger portfolios benefited disproportionately, as they met the 1 MW minimum bidding requirement more consistently and could allocate a higher share of generation to the market.

Table II: Summary of Financial Implications from FCR-D Down Participation in all Scenarios (June 2025).

Indicator	VPP1	VPP2	VPP3
Power plant capacity (MVA)	4	12	24
Allocations:			
Total generation (MWh)	667.9	2003.8	4007.6
Energy offered to FCR-D market (MWh)	209.8	927.7	1982.7
Offered share to FCR-D market (%)	31.4	46.3	49.5
Down-regulated energy (MWh)	0.14	0.64	1.32
Share of down-regulated energy (%)	0.02	0.03	0.03
Gross revenues:			
Day-ahead revenue (€)	15 900	47 700	95 300
FCR-D revenue (€)	1 100	4 600	9 700
Day-ahead losses (€)	-11	-35	-71
Revenue efficiency:			
Day-ahead (€/MWh)	59.1	59.1	59.1
Total (€/MWh)	63.0	64.7	65.1
Revenue increase (%)	6.6	9.5	10.1

Figure IV further illustrates that the smaller portfolios failed to meet the 1 MW minimum bid requirement more often, lowering available revenues. Larger portfolios could allocate bids in lower production hours. Moreover, the hourly revenue pattern closely follows the typical solar production profile, with revenues peaking around midday and vanishing during night-time hours. This shows that the financial potential of FCR-D down participation is strongly coupled with the normal generation profile of PV.

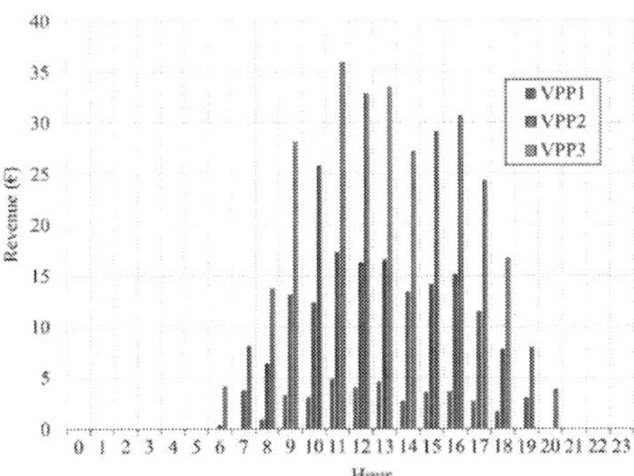

Figure IV: Hourly averages of additional gain (€) from FCR-D participation.

Figure V illustrates that revenues per offered capacity were largely similar across portfolios during active hours, indicating that the marginal value of each MWh in FCR-D down is independent of system size. The decisive factor is the ability to consistently cross the market entry threshold.

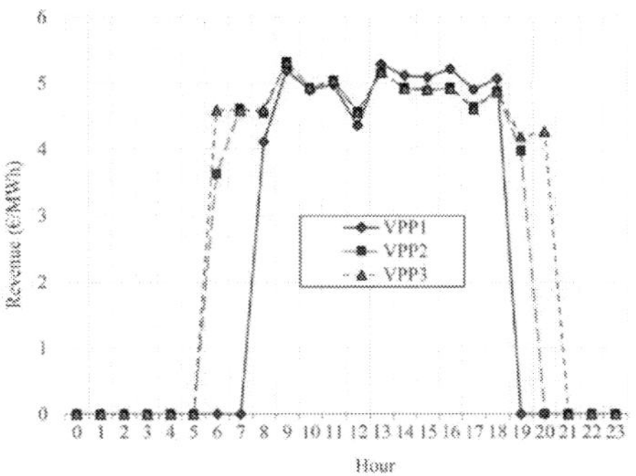

Figure V: Hourly averages of additional revenue (€/MWh) from FCR-D participation normalized to total capacity (lines, left axis).

4 DISCUSSION

This study assessed the techno-economic feasibility of aggregating small-scale PV portfolios for participation in the Finnish FCR-D down market. The findings indicate that while even modest portfolios can technically qualify, the economic benefits scale disproportionately with aggregated capacity. VPP1 (~5 MWp) generated only marginal additional revenues, whereas VPP3 (~30 MWp) achieved a significantly higher improvement in portfolio profitability. These results underline that aggregation is not only a prerequisite for market entry but also the key driver of economic viability.

From a technical perspective, down-regulation energy losses were found to be negligible compared with total PV production. However, activations occurred on average 29 times a day, which may place additional operational stress on components despite the small amount of curtailed energy.

Defining the available bidding capacity remains crucial for PV-only portfolios. The hourly minimum output often falls well below the hourly mean, requiring conservative bidding strategies to avoid non-compliance. High-resolution 15-second data revealed substantial intra-hour variability, underlining the need for accurate forecasting methods and robust VPP management. In practice, this could involve pyranometer-based irradiance forecasting.

It should also be emphasized that the analysis was limited to June 2025, representing conditions most favourable for PV-based reserve participation. The results therefore provide illustrative insights rather than annual averages. Extending the analysis to other months and seasonal regimes is essential for capturing the full potential. Furthermore, it should be emphasized that the revenues showcased in this study are not guaranteed in the long term. The total demand for FCR-D down is limited, and if the total reserve capacity offered increases substantially, clearing prices may decrease. This could lead to a cannibalization effect similar to that observed in electricity markets, where additional capacity reduces the market value of its own production. Therefore, while the present analysis demonstrates clear short-term benefits, the long-term revenues of PV participation in reserves will also depend on market development and the balance between supply and demand.

5 CONCLUSION

This study demonstrates that aggregated small-scale PV systems can provide both technical and economic value in the Finnish FCR-D down market. While individual units cannot meet the 1 MW entry requirement, aggregated portfolios are able to participate effectively. The results indicate that during peak production months, portfolio revenues can increase by 5–10% or 4-6 €/MWh compared with day-ahead trading alone, with curtailed energy losses remaining insignificant.

The findings therefore suggest that VPP-based aggregation offers a viable pathway for integrating distributed PV into reserve markets. Participation can provide an additional and stable revenue stream for PV owners, helping to mitigate the effects of declining day-ahead prices and market cannibalisation. At the same time, it supports the reliability of the Nordic power system by offering fast-acting reserves in periods of over frequency.

Overall, while small-scale PV alone cannot deliver balancing capacity, aggregated portfolios can contribute meaningfully to system flexibility. The results underline that market design enabling distributed resources to participate is crucial for both the profitability of future PV investments and the stability of the evolving energy system.

Future research should extend the temporal scope to cover different seasons and longer time frames in order to capture annual dynamics more accurately. Another important direction is to investigate hybrid VPP concepts that combine solar PV with battery energy storage systems, thereby increasing reliability and market participation hours. Moreover, while this paper concentrated on FCR-D down, other reserve products such as aFRR and mFRR represent promising markets for aggregated PV portfolios and deserve dedicated analysis.

6 DECLARATION OF GENERATIVE AI AND AI-ASSISTED TECHNOLOGIES IN THE WRITING PROCESS

During the preparation of this work the authors used ChatGPT-5 to improve readability and language. After using this tool, the authors reviewed and edited the content as needed and take full responsibility for the content of the publication.

7 REFERENCES

[1] N. Riaz, S. Repo, and A. Lindfors. "Evaluating the Self-Balancing Potential of Rooftop Photovoltaic Systems and its Impact on the Net Demand Profile," in *2023 IEEE PES Innovative Smart Grid Technologies Europe (ISGT EUROPE)*. IEEE, 2023, pp. 1-6. doi: 10.1109/ISGTEurope56742.2023. 10287534.

[2] R. Sharma and M. Karimi-Ghartemani, "Addressing Abrupt PV Disturbances, and Mitigating Net Load Profile's Ramp and Peak Demands, Using Distributed Storage Devices," in Energies, vol. 13, no. 5, p. 1024, Feb. 2020.

[3] Fingrid Oyj, "Reserve Market Day 2025," publication, 2025. Accessed Sept. 6, 2025. [Online]. Available:https://www.fingrid.fi/globalassets/doku mentit/en/electricity-market/reserves/reservimarkkinapaiva-2025-eng.pdf

[4] R. Nida, L. Peltonen, A. Hilden, S. Repo and P. Järventausta, "Frequency response of a microgrid under the influence of enhanced spatial and orientational smoothing of photovoltaic output." in IET Conference Proceedings CP823. Vol. 2023. No. 6. Stevenage, UK: The Institution of Engineering and Technology, 2023. pp. 3734-3738. doi: https://doi.org/10.1049/icp.2023.0738

[5] Fingrid Oyj, " Johtokatu – tiekartta vihreään sähköjärjestelmään," publication, 2017. Accessed Sept. 7, 2025. [Online]. Available: https://www.fingrid.fi/globalassets/dokumentit/fi/sa hkomarkkinat/kehityshankkeet/fingrid-tiekartta-vihreaan-sahkojarjestelmaan-2017-web.pdf

[6] V. Lopes, J. Alves, J. Teixeira, R. Faia, L. Gomes, Z. Vale and P. Salomé, "Enhancing Energy Systems Efficiency through Virtual Power Plants: considerations for the Portuguese case." *2024 IEEE 22nd Mediterranean Electrotechnical Conference (MELECON)*. IEEE, 2024, pp. 1072-1077. doi: 10.1109/MELECON56669.2024.10608732.

[7] ENTSO-E, Day-ahead prices, [Online]. Available: https://transparency.entsoe.eu/dashboard/show

[8] P. Hasanpori Divshali, N. Riaz, A. Kulmala and S. Repo, "Day-ahead electricity market estimation of finland in 2030," in *26th International Conference and Exhibition on Electricity Distribution, CIRED 2021: Online*. Institution of Engineering and Technology IET, 2021. pp 3075-3079. doi: https://doi.org/10.1049/icp.2021.2113

[9] A. Junkala, "The Impact of Cannibalization on Profitability of Utility Scale Solar Power in Finland," Aalto University publication, 2025. Available: https://aaltodoc.aalto.fi/server/api/core/bitstreams/ce ae462e-b502-4a49-a4b6-3a4a12e5e9db/content

[10] Fingrid Oyj, avoin data, [Online]. Available: https://data.fingrid.fi/

[11] Fingrid Oyj, "Liite 1: Ehdot ja edellytykset taajuuden vakautusreservin (FCR) toimittajalle." Accessed: Sept. 7, 2025. Available: https://www.fingrid.fi/sahkomarkkinat/reservit/reser vituotteet-ja-markkinoille-osallistuminen/fcr-taajuusohjattu-kaytto--ja-hairioreservi/

[12] Fingrid Oyj, "Liite 2 Taajuuden vakautusreservien (FCR) teknisten vaatimuksien todentaminen ja hyväksyttämisprosessi." Accessed: Sept. 7, 2025. Available: https://www.fingrid.fi/sahkomarkkinat/reservit/reser vituotteet-ja-markkinoille-osallistuminen/fcr-taajuusohjattu-kaytto--ja-hairioreservi/

SOLARIGO

Tampere University
Tampere University of Applied Sciences

Utilization of Small-Scale Solar Power Production in Finnish Grid-Balancing Markets Through a Virtual Power Plant

Eino Kujansivu[1,2], Aleksi Ojala[1], Juho Ylipaino[2,3] and Juha Koskela[2]

[1] Solarigo Systems Oy, Pirkkala, Finland
[2] Tampere University, Tampere, Finland
[3] Tampere University of Applied Sciences, Tampere, Finland

Introduction

The ongoing energy transition from traditional synchronous generators to renewable, inverter-based sources, such as photovoltaic (PV) systems, creates new challenges for grid stability and increases the need for balancing resources. One important solution is participation in reserve markets, where flexible assets help maintain system frequency. The Nordic Frequency Containment Reserve for Disturbances, down-regulation (FCR-D down) is a reserve product that activates when system frequency rises above 50.1 Hz. To participate, units must meet a minimum bid size of 1 MW, which small-scale PV systems cannot reach individually. Recent advances in aggregation through virtual power plants (VPPs) allow distributed PV systems to be combined into larger cloud-based units, enabling market access. This creates an opportunity for PV operators to gain additional revenues while contributing to grid stability. This study evaluates the potential revenues from FCR-D down in June 2025 (Finland) for small-scale solar PV combined in different aggregated system configurations. June was chosen as it represents high solar irradiance and strong PV production in Finland.

Methodology

Data and Scenarios

The analysis is based on measured solar PV production data and high-resolution system frequency records, combined with market price data. Three virtual power plants (VPP1–VPP3) are used as case studies, and together they represent aggregated systems of different sizes. This allows us to examine how aggregation level affects market eligibility and revenue potential.

Measured data:
PV production from VPP1, consisting of 16 small-scale systems (4.9 MWp / 4 MVA) with 15-second and 1-hour resolution for June 2025 (Finland).

Frequency data:
0.1-second resolution frequency measurements from substations across Finland from Fingrid. The data was averaged out to a one-second interval.

Market data:
Hourly FCR-D down prices from Fingrid and day-ahead prices from ENTSO-E.

Scaled aggregated scenarios:
Two larger virtual power plants created from the VPP1 dataset:
    VPP2 → 14.6 MWp / 12 MVA
    VPP3 → 29.2 MWp / 24 MVA

Market Requirements and Assumptions

- In hourly FCR-D markets, each unit must define a maintained reserve power level ($P_{min,h}$) i.e. the lowest active power that can be guaranteed during the bidding hour.

- To qualify for market entry, the maintained power must be at least 1 MW: $P_{min,h}(t) \geq 1MW$

- Activation is triggered when frequency rises above 50.1 Hz and increases linearly until full down-regulation at 50.5 Hz.

- The analysis excludes VPP purchase and operational costs (e.g., platform fees).

- All values are net-of-tax, and results reflect only the relative revenue increase compared to day-ahead markets.

- Participation is assumed in all hours that are technically feasible for the system.

Calculations

1. Regulation coefficient, C_s
To calculate the energy regulated during a one-second interval, a C_s coefficient was introduced. The coefficient was defined as a normalized function of grid frequency f:

$$C_s(t_2) = \frac{f(t_2) - 50.1\text{Hz}}{50.5\text{Hz} - 50.1\text{Hz}}, \quad C_s(t_2) \in [0,1]$$

- $C_s = 1$: full activation at $f \geq 50.5$ Hz
- $C_s = 0$: minimal activation at $f \leq 50.1$ Hz
- $C_s \in [0,1]$: partial activation, linearly scaled between 50.1 and 50.5 Hz

2. Hourly coefficient, C_h
To calculate the average activation level of down-regulation over one hour, the one-second coefficients are aggregated into an hourly coefficient C_h. This represents the mean share of offered capacity that was activated during hour t:

$$C_h(t) = \frac{1}{3600} \sum_{t_2=1}^{3600} C_s(t_2)$$

3. Down-regulated energy, E_{reg}
To calculate the amount of down-regulated energy during hour t, the hourly activation coefficient is multiplied by the offered minimum power:

$$E_{reg,h}(t) = C_h(t) \cdot P_{min,h}(t)$$

4. Day-ahead market revenue, R_{DA}
To calculate the revenue R_{DA} from the day-ahead market during hour t, the average day-ahead price A_{DA} is multiplied by the produced energy E_{PV}:

$$R_{DA}(t) = A_{DA}(t) \cdot E_{PV}(t)$$

5. Day-ahead revenue loss, L_{DA}
To calculate the loss of day-ahead market revenue L_{DA} caused by down-regulation, the day-ahead price is multiplied by the curtailed energy during hour t:

$$L_{DA}(t) = A_{DA}(t) \cdot E_{reg}(t)$$

6. FCR-D revenue, R_{RM}
To calculate the revenue from participation in the FCR-D reserve market R_{RM}, the hourly FCR-D market price A_{RM} is multiplied by the offered minimum power $P_{min,h}$:

$$R_{RM}(t) = A_{RM}(t) \cdot P_{min,h}(t)$$

7. Revenue comparison
To compare the baseline revenue with the revenue including down-regulation, three measures are defined. The baseline revenue per unit of production was obtained by dividing the day-ahead revenue by the produced energy. The revenue including regulation per unit of production was calculated by subtracting the day-ahead revenue loss and adding the FCR-D revenue. Finally, the additional revenue share was determined by comparing the revenue including regulation to the baseline revenue:

Key results

- Frequency deviations >50.1 Hz occurred only 0.73% of the time → confirms FCR-D down is low utilization product.

- Deviations happened almost daily (858 times in June, ~29 times/day), with an average duration of ~23 seconds.

- Larger aggregated systems (VPP2–VPP3) met the 1 MW requirement more often, enabling more hours of market eligibility.

- Down-regulated energy was minimal (0.02–0.03% of generation), even though frequency exceeded 50.1 Hz frequently.

- Additional revenues increased with aggregation: up to +10% compared to day-ahead trading alone.

Table 1 summarizes generation, revenues, and revenue efficiency for the three aggregated systems in June of 2025 (VPP1–VPP3)

Indicator	VPP1	VPP2	VPP3
Power plant capacity (MVA)	4 MVA	12 MVA	24 MVA
Allocations:			
Total generation (MWh)	667.9 MWh	2003.8 MWh	4007.6 MWh
Energy offered to FCR-D (MWh)	209.8 MWh	927.7 MWh	1982.7 MWh
Offered share to FCR-D (%)	31.4%	46.3%	49.5%
Down-regulated energy (MWh)	0.14 MWh	0.64 MWh	1.32 MWh
Share of down-regulated energy (%)	0.02%	0.03%	0.03%
Gross revenues:			
Day-ahead revenue (€)	15 900 €	47 700 €	95 300 €
FCR-D revenue (€)	1 100 €	4 600 €	9 700 €
Day-ahead losses (€)	-11 €	-35 €	-71 €
Revenue efficiency:			
Day-ahead (€/MWh)	59.1 €/MWh	59.1 €/MWh	59.1 €/MWh
Total (€/MWh)	63.0 €/MWh	64.7 €/MWh	65.1 €/MWh
Revenue increase (%)	6.6%	9.5%	10.1%

Discussion

- **Aggregation is essential:** Small PV systems cannot meet the 1 MW market entry limit alone. Larger aggregated systems enable more hours of FCR-D participation.

- **Economic benefits are moderate but positive:** In June, participation in FCR-D down increased revenues by 5–10% compared to day-ahead trading, while down-regulation losses stayed minimal.

- **Market saturation and cannibalization risks:** As more PV and other flexible capacity enters reserve markets, increased supply may reduce prices and erode long-term profitability.

- **Low activated energy eases integration with contracts:** Minimal down-regulation makes participation compatible with many solar PPAs and guarantee-of-origin frameworks without risking production guarantees.

- **Accurate forecasting and communication are critical:** Reliable high-resolution data is needed for conservative bidding. Pyranometers can improve irradiance forecasts, while local frequency measurements reduce communication needs.

Conclusions

- **PV participation in FCR-D down increases profitability:** Aggregation enables market entry and provides moderate but positive additional revenues.

- **FCR-D down is characterized by frequent but low-volume activations:** Although the total curtailed energy is minimal, activations are frequent and fast, which may stress equipment.

MARKET UPTAKE ROLE OF COLORED PV: A STAKEHOLDER-CENTRIC ANALYSIS OF FACILITATING AND RESTRAINING FORCES

Bilge Senturk*, Pinar Derin-Gure*,**, Gunes Kurtulus*
* ODTU GUNAM, Middle East Technical University Center for Solar Energy Research and Applications, Ankara, Türkiye
** METU, Middle East Technical University Departmant of Economics, Ankara, Türkiye
bilge.senturk@odtugunam.org, pderin@metu.edu.tr, gunes.kurtulus@odtugunam.org

ABSTRACT: This study examines the market uptake of colored photovoltaic (PV) technologies developed for building-integrated photovoltaics (BIPV), with the aim of elucidating the driving and restraining forces that shape their acceptance across diverse stakeholder groups. Semi-structured interviews were conducted, the qualitative data were thematically coded, and subsequently analyzed through force field analysis (FFA), thereby enabling a systematic comparison of facilitating and constraining dynamics. The findings indicate that restraining forces presently outweigh facilitating ones. Primary among the barriers are high upfront costs, protracted payback periods, and regulatory uncertainties. In contrast, architects' emphasis on aesthetic integration, the visibility afforded by public pilot projects, and the environmental benefits of adoption emerge as salient facilitating factors. Government incentives are revealed to play a dual role: acting as a powerful enabler when present, yet becoming a formidable barrier when absent. Overall, the results suggest that while structural and financial impediments continue to constrain short-term commercialization, the active involvement of architects, combined with targeted policy frameworks, financial incentives, and awareness-raising strategies, can recalibrate the balance in favor of facilitating forces. In the long term, colored PV may thus evolve beyond a technological novelty to become a transformative paradigm that fuses architectural aesthetics with sustainable energy transitions in the built environment.
Keywords: Building-integrated photovoltaics, Colored photovoltaics, Market uptake, Stakeholder analysis, Force-field analysis, Semi-structured interviews, Türkiye

1 INTRODUCTION

In the development of BIPV technology, the redesign of the building envelope as a multifunctional element has come to the forefront. Photovoltaic modules replace building components such as roofs, façades, skylights, and windows, thereby generating electricity while also providing additional benefits such as thermal insulation and daylight control. This multifunctionality enables the creation of a building material that, beyond its role as an energy technology, also supports architectural aesthetics and sustainability. However, it is emphasized that BIPV solutions still face constraints such as high initial costs and maintenance challenges; therefore, access to and widespread adoption of the technology largely depend on further cost reductions [1,2].

In recent years, colored PV applications, a prominent type of BIPV, have been developed particularly to enhance integration into dense urban fabrics and protected historical buildings. Colored PVs make it possible to camouflage photovoltaic cells with unique colors and patterns. Indeed, the ability to obtain various shades such as blue, green, yellow, and orange by altering the thickness of anti-reflective coatings, the application of semi-transparent and diverse color variations with thin-film, OPV, and DSSC-based modules, as well as the incorporation of distinctive patterns through digital printing, ceramic, or mineral coatings on the front glass surface, can be cited as examples of this technological diversity [3]. Market forecasts indicate that colored PVs are largely shaped by aesthetic compatibility and social acceptance. Conventional PVs (black and dark blue) create visual incompatibility in urban contexts and therefore face limited adoption, whereas colored solutions align with architectural aesthetics and are more widely accepted, particularly in public and office buildings [4,5]. Therefore, colored PV technologies gain value in the context of architectural integrity and acceptance, and it is suggested that the market will initially develop in prestigious public and commercial buildings and, over time, become standardized and widespread in the residential sector [6,7,8]. Although coloring processes lead to losses in electrical efficiency, their ability to preserve architectural integrity while enhancing market acceptance renders these solutions a strategic option in line with the nearly zero-energy building target.

The importance of stakeholder analysis in understanding market processes for innovative applications such as colored PV lies in revealing their societal functions beyond being merely technical innovations. In this respect, it is argued that technological performance should be assessed in conjunction with users' needs, aesthetic perceptions, cultural values, and institutional regulations [9]. Indeed, interviews conducted with different actors make visible the barriers and opportunities that standard individuals may not perceive, thereby overcoming preconceptions and contributing to the development of a more realistic roadmap for the market [10,11]. Therefore, interviews can be considered a key methodological tool in such research for understanding market acceptance dynamics, comprehensively assessing the barriers and opportunities related to the technology, and developing more feasible policy and design recommendations. Examining both the barriers limiting the diffusion of BIPV technologies and the driving dynamics aimed at overcoming them is an important step for market acceptance research. In this study, force field analysis, a managerial analysis tool [12] based on stakeholder interviews, will be applied to understand the adoption and architectural integration of the technology.

Stakeholder analysis research on colored PV solutions has found very limited coverage in the literature. In particular, field studies employing qualitative methods on color preferences and perceptions regarding the use of colored PV remain scarce. Among the prominent studies in the literature, Hille et al. [5], in their survey-based empirical research conducted with 408 homeowners in Switzerland, demonstrated that the color of the modules and the degree of integration with the building are decisive factors in user preferences. The same study also revealed that a large proportion of participants, despite higher costs, showed a tendency toward aesthetically compatible and colored PV solutions. In a more recent study [13] conducted in China, two different methods were employed. The first was an online survey supported with photographs, and the second consisted of face-to-face interviews in which colored modules were shown to participants. Through these methods, different building types and color compatibility scenarios were evaluated, and the results revealed that colored modules significantly enhance integration, particularly in urban areas and historical buildings.

Aqel [10], examining the application of colored PV in municipal buildings in Sweden, conducted interviews with 17 solar energy experts from different cities and revealed the decisive role of architects and municipalities in the dissemination of this technology. Similarly, in their study on the colored PV market in Denmark, Klysner et al. [11] clarified the barriers (e.g., efficiency loss, installation difficulties, lack of knowledge) and opportunities (e.g., aesthetic compatibility, biomimetic solutions) to the diffusion of colored panels through qualitative interviews with manufacturers, installers, building owners, municipal officials, and architects. In conclusion, the limited number of studies conducted on colored PV demonstrate that such technologies are shaped by cultural and perceptual dimensions such as aesthetic compatibility, architectural integrity, and user perception. Nevertheless, the fact that the literature has not yet been sufficiently examined through in-depth qualitative analyses clearly indicates the need for interdisciplinary research on this subject.

In this study, the stakeholder analysis to be conducted for colored PV technologies is expected to provide a significant scientific contribution by offering a unique framework for the integration of this innovative technology into current market dynamics and for enhancing its social acceptance. Understanding stakeholders' aesthetic expectations, levels of technological trust, and the opportunities and challenges they may encounter in the BIPV market reveals the critical factors influencing the widespread adoption of colored PVs. Finally, the analysis carried out within the scope of this study demonstrates that BIPV technologies can be associated with green business models in the context of Türkiye and contributes to the debates on green growth and sustainable development.

2 METHODOLOGY

2.1. Aim and Approach

For this purpose, information was first gathered from different stakeholders through semi-structured interviews based on themes appropriate for force field analysis, then coded into data, and finally analyzed using the force field method.

2.2 Semi-Structured Interviews

In line with the aim of the study, a total of 13 interviews were conducted. While most of the interviewees consisted of architects, all participants were experts/experienced in the field of solar energy technology (Table 1). In this way, it becomes possible to highlight the driving and restraining factors that need to be taken into account for the diffusion and development of the market.

Table 1. Stakeholder List

ID	Stakeholder Category	Sub-Category	Experience Duration (Years)
1	Public	Ministry of Energy and Natural Resources	10
2	Public	Ministry of Environment, Urbanization and Climate Change	19
3	Academia	Architecture	42
4	Academia	Architecture	25
5	Academia	Electric Electronical Engineer	20
6	Private	Architecture	38
7	Private	Architecture	23
8	Private	Architecture	21
9	Private	Glass Manufacturing	16
10	Private	Panel Manufacturing	8
11	Private	Panel Mounting/ Installing	12
12	NGO	Solar Energy Association	15
13	NGO	Solar Energy Association	16

During the final review of the coded data obtained from the interviews, 15 key factors (Figure 1) were identified under four main themes (aesthetic and social acceptance, policy and institutional framework, financial dynamics, and technical capacity), and the force field analysis method was applied to the driving and restraining factors.

2.3 Force Field Analysis: Comparison of Facilitating and Restraining Stakeholders

Force field analysis, developed by Kurt Lewin [14], systematically reveals the interaction of opposing forces that shape the adoption processes of innovative technologies. In the adoption of BIPV, the most common facilitating stakeholders are typically architects, contractors, governments, investors, and manufacturers [15,16,17,18], while the restraining stakeholders are generally identified as building owners and individual users [15,19].

The FFA process consists of four steps. First, each stakeholder's comments on the technology (for example, glass manufacturers' emphasis on technical requirements, architects' aesthetic concerns, and users' perceptions of comfort) were extracted as open codes. Second, these codes were then combined and transformed into higher-level themes (e.g., "Aesthetic and architectural integration," "Uncertainty in energy policies"). In the third stage, each factor was scored within a range of -5 to +5 according to its degree of importance and direction of influence (Figure 1). In other words, scoring was carried out by considering how frequently a factor was emphasized by stakeholders and to what extent it influenced their decisions [20]. A factor with a high total score is regarded as both a more critical determinant compared to others and one that needs to be addressed strategically. For instance, if "high costs and long payback periods" received one of the highest total scores, this should be understood as the strongest restraining force in the commercialization of colored PV. Finally, the interaction of the factors was interpreted in terms of how they were strengthened or weakened within the same context. The graphic design is based on Lewin's [14] classical force field model. On one side are the facilitating forces, and on the other side are the restraining forces. In the diagram (Figure 1), the length of the arrows or the total score of a factor visually reflects its relative importance. Thus, rather than direct causality between factors, the graphic illustrates the balance (which side is more dominant) and highlights which forces stand out.

3. RESULTS

The force field analysis conducted in this study comparatively reveals the driving and restraining forces shaping the diffusion of colored PV technologies in Türkiye.

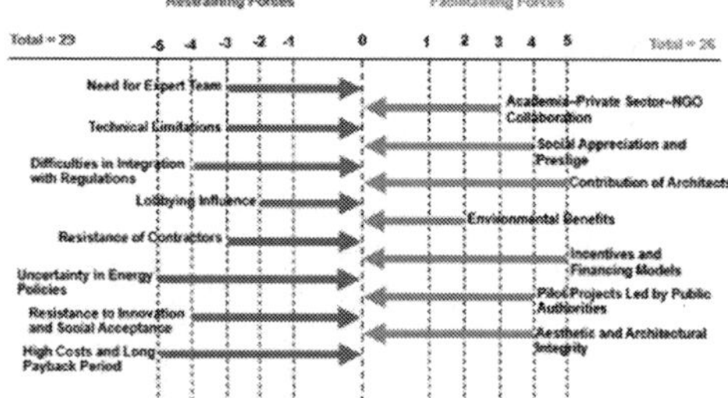

Figure 1. Force Field Diagram

The findings indicate that, at present, restraining forces are more dominant than facilitating dynamics, and therefore the potential for large-scale adoption remains limited in the short term. In particular, high initial costs and uncertainties regarding energy policies emerge as the most critical barriers. By contrast, architects' strong interest in aesthetic integration and the visibility that public demonstration projects can create are among the key facilitating factors. The analysis also points to the dual nature of certain forces. For instance, when public support exists through incentives and policy instruments, it functions as a strong driving dynamic, whereas in its absence it becomes a significant barrier. However, uncertainties in energy policies and difficulties in regulatory integration materialize this dual nature in favor of restraining forces.

Moreover, these forces are also seen to interact with one another. For instance, increasing public awareness of environmental benefits both weakens a restraining factor such as low acceptance levels and simultaneously becomes a supportive force for concerns over aesthetics and sustainability. Therefore, targeted policies, financial incentives, and awareness-raising strategies are of critical importance for shifting the balance.

4. CONCLUSION

In the diffusion of colored PV technology, both driving and significant restraining dynamics are observed to coexist. Beyond the need for incentives and appropriate financing models in the face of high costs, factors such as architects' interest in aesthetic integration, the active involvement of glass manufacturers in the process, and the visibility created by public pilot projects stand out as key elements facilitating the adoption of the technology. In addition, the alignment of colored PVs with sustainability policies and their potential to enhance building value provide a strong basis of legitimacy in terms of social

acceptance and prestige effects. Nevertheless, the lack of public incentives, difficulties in regulatory integration, and uncertainties in energy policies are among the main constraints hindering the widespread diffusion of the technology.

On the other hand, the continued dominance of restraining forces particularly high costs and long payback periods creates a lack of social acceptance at the user level, while raising public awareness and making applications that integrate with aesthetic values more visible can enhance acceptance. In this context, activating incentive mechanisms, developing creative financing models, and promoting experience sharing through exemplary projects in public buildings are of critical importance. In this way, the impact of restraining factors can be weakened, facilitating forces can become more visible, and ultimately the path can be opened for colored PV technology to become a more viable option in the context of Türkiye.

References

[1] Biyik, E., Araz, M., Hepbasli, A., Shahrestani, M., Yao, R., Shao, L., Essah, E., Oliveira, A. C., del Cano, T., Rice, E., Lechon, J. L.Andrade, L., Mendes, A. & Atlı, Y. B. (2017). A key review of building integrated photovoltaic (BIPV) systems. Engineering science and technology, an international journal, 20(3), 833-858.

[2] Lu, L., & Law, K. M. (2013). Overall energy performance of semi-transparent single-glazed photovoltaic (PV) window for a typical office in Hong Kong. Renewable energy, 49, 250-254.

[3] Eder, G., Peharz, G., Trattnig, R., Bonomo, P., Saretta, E., Frontini, F., Polo Lopez, C. S., Wilson, H. R., Eisenlohr, J., Chivelet, N. M.,Karlsson, S., Jakica, N. & Zanelli, A. (2019). Coloured bipv: Market, research and development. https://www.diva-portal.org/smash/get/diva2:1305998/FULLTEXT01.pdf

[4] Hardy, D., Kerrouche, A, Roaf, S. C. and Richards, B.S. (2013). Improving the aesthetics of photovoltaics through use of coloured encapsulants. In: PLEA2013 - 29th Conference, Sustainable Architecture for a Renewable Future, Munich, Germany, 10-12 September 2013, Munich, Germany.

[5] Hille, S. L., Curtius, H. C., & Wüstenhagen, R. (2018). Red is the new blue–The role of color, building integration and country-of-origin in homeowners'preferences for residential photovoltaics. Energy and Buildings, 162, 21-31.

[6] Lim, J.W., Kim, G., Shin, M., Yun, S.J. (2017). Colored a-Si: H transparent solar cells employing ultrathin transparent multi-layered electrodes. Sol. Energy Mater. Sol. Cells, 163, 164–169.

[7] Wang, M., Peng, J., Li, N., Yang, H., Wang, C., Li, X. & Lu, T. (2016) Comparison of energy performance between PV double skin facades and PV insulating glass units. Appl. Energy, 194, 148–160.

[8] Peharz, G., Berger, K., Kubicek, B., Aichinger, M., Grobbauer, M., Gratzer, J., Nemitz, W., Großschädl, B., Auer, C. & Prietl, C. (2017). Application of plasmonic coloring for making building integrated PV modules comprising of green solar cells. Renew. Energy, 109, 542–550.

[9] Müggenburg, H., Tillmans, A., Schweizer-Ries, P., Raabe, T., & Adelmann, P. (2012). Social acceptance of PicoPV systems as a means of rural electrification—A socio-technical case study in Ethiopia. Energy for Sustainable Development, 16(1), 90-97.

[10] Aqel, S. (2021). Application of Colored Solar Panels on Municipal Buildings in Sweden: The Multiple Benefits for an Innovative Renewable Society.

[11] Klysner, N. F., Lenau, T. A., & Lakhtakia, A. (2021, March). Building-integrated photo-voltaics: market challenges and bioinspired solutions. In Bioinspiration, Biomimetics, and Bioreplication XI 11586, pp. 32-47.

[12] Taleb, H. M., & Pitts, A. C. (2009). The potential to exploit use of building-integrated photovoltaics in countries of the Gulf Cooperation Council. Renewable Energy, 34(4), 1092-1099.

[13] Zhou, A., Thomaschke, R., Wessels, A., Glunz, S., Speck, T., & Kiesel, A. (2024). (Not) in my city: An explorative study on social acceptance of photovoltaic installations on buildings. Technology in Society, 79, 102725.

[14] Lewin K. (1951). Field Theory in Social Science. Harper Row, London.

[15] Curtius, H. C. (2018). The adoption of building-integrated photovoltaics: barriers and facilitators. Renewable Energy, 126, 783-790.

[16] Yap, A. B. K., Goh, K. C., Seow, T. W., & Goh, H. H. (2015, May). Stakeholder Roles in Building Integrated Photovoltaic (BIPV) Implementation. In InCIEC 2014: Proceedings of the International Civil and Infrastructure Engineering Conference 2014 (pp. 951-961). Singapore: Springer Singapore.

[17] Chang, R., Cao, Y., Lu, Y., & Shabunko, V. (2019). Should BIPV technologies be empowered by innovation policy mix to facilitate energy transitions?- Revealing stakeholders' different perspectives using Q methodology. Energy Policy, 129, 307-318.

[18] Tabakovic, M., Fechner, H., Van Sark, W., Louwen, A., Georghiou, G., Makrides, G., ... & Betz, S. (2017). Status and outlook for building integrated photovoltaics (BIPV) in relation to educational needs in the BIPV sector. Energy Procedia, 111, 993-999.

[19] Wu, J. H. (2023). A holistic exploration on the development of Innovation Ecosystems: A Dutch case study on Building Integrated PhotoVoltaics (Master Thesis). Eindhoven University of Technology.

[20] Pavloudakis, F., Spanidis, P. M., & Roumpos, C. (2023). Using force field analysis for examining and managing stakeholders' perceptions of mining projects. Materials Proceedings, 15(1), 5.

Rooftop PV on Apartment Buildings:
Business Models and Experiences

Christoph v. Friedeburg   cvfriede@cf-energy.eu   www.cf-energy.eu

CF ENERGY
Research-Consulting-Operation GmbH

Abstract   Apartment building roofs offer several GW of PV capacity. But business models must be **usable for laypeople, ideally without extensive hardware, and characterized by intuitive quantities.** Shown are case studies with real consumption data series.

Motivation   More than **77% of Germany's citizens live in cities** (1). Globally, 57% of the global population lived in cities in 2021 (2). Accordingly, substantial measures to curb carbon emissions must be continued in urban areas, which includes the energy sector. Clean energy deployment in proximity to consumption also mitigates the need for costly transmission grid upgrades.
In the city of Berlin, the **estimated PV potential is 6.5 – 10 GW.** About 75% of that is on the roofs of multi-family homes (3). Using the rough estimate of 1000 kWh/kWp for PV in Germany (4), 6.5 GW can yield **6.5 TWh of clean energy** from rooftops. 2024 saw an addition of 101 MWp of PV, and a new total of 381 MWp (5). In 2024, almost 60 % of Germany' s electric power generation was from clean power, with the rest still coming from fossil sources (6). **Tapping the rooftop potential is a critical step to reach climate targets.**

Situation and Approach   While single-family homes can use an easy self-consumption business model, and large buildings offer economies of scale, **smaller to medium apt. buildings** (2 - 50 units) are facing a difficult situation, with less roof space, and involving owners, tenants, and investors. In Berlin, Germany, on average each building has 2.6 apartments (7). Business models exist (8), but only 2022/23 has new legislation removed some key hurdles (9). Models must be **financially acceptable and usable for laypeople.** System owners must **maximise the self-consumption rate R_{SC}** to achieve acceptable economics, i.e. sell PV el. in-house for higher prices than they receive from feed-in tariffs; whereas the **autarky rate A** determines the savings for the end users who replace external electricity with cheaper solar. Studies recommend R_{SC} of 25-35% depending on system size and external electricity prices (e.g. 10,11). System capacities in relation to in-house consumption is of relevance.
Key quantities: Total electricity consumption in building=C; PV production W_T (inverter data); W_F fed to grid (meter data); self-consumption (in the building) $W_{SC}=W_T-W_F$; self-consumption rate $R_{SC}=W_{SC}/W_T$; $A=W_{SC}/C$

Case 1: Consumption in bldg systems

Framework: Apt. bldg owned by Owners Association (OA). System 8.8 kWp; no battery storage, no smart meters

Business model:
- OC members are system owners and el. consumers
- easy allocation of external el. purchase savings and FIT income acc. to OC member´s bldg. shares
- building system consumption (elevators, garage, lighting…)
- C = 6,15 MWh/a
- April ´23 – March ´24

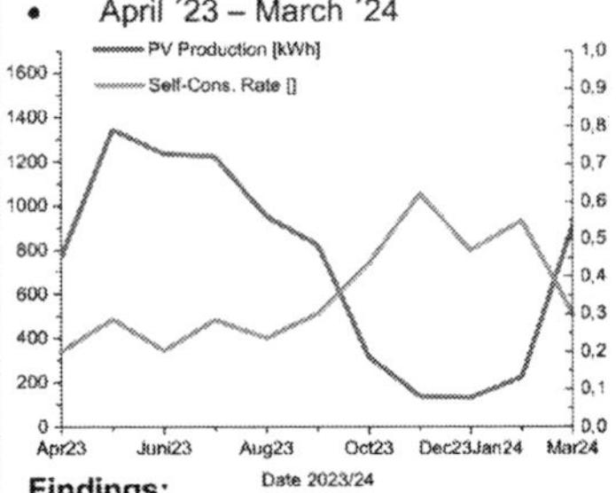

Findings:
- R_{SC}: annual avg. 29%
- A: annual avg. 36,3%
- low during spring/summer - more daytime excess PV electricity
- higher in winter, but much lower production figures during that period

Case 2: Case 1 upgrade, connection of bldg systems bus with EV charging stations in garage

Business model:
- like Case 1 + electricity sold by OA to charge pot. users (mostly OA members)
- C = 11213,1 MWh/a, thereof assumed C_{EV} 5 MWh for EV charging, rest C_B for bldg
- May´24-April´25

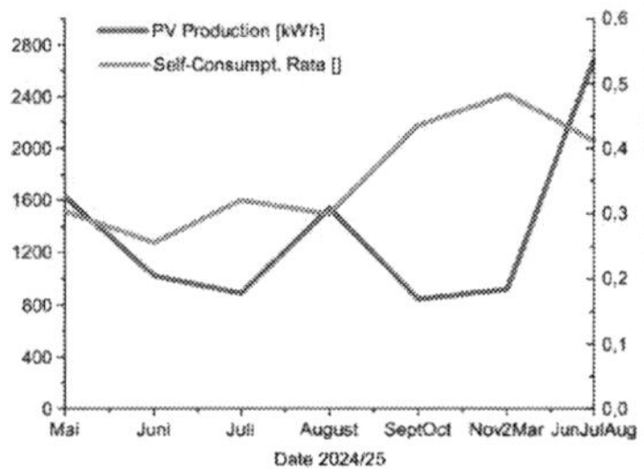

Findings:
- R_{SC}: annual avg. increased to 35%
- A: dropped to 21,3% based on C
- (A based on C_B raised to 38,9%)
- again lower in spring/summer
- Measure worked, but effect lower-than-hoped

Comparison of autarky rates in relation to PV production per consumption

Framework: Six apt. bldgs. with mixed owner and tenant occupancy. Systems between 8.8 and 99.8 kWp, no battery storage.

Business models:

P1, 2: see Cases 1, 2 (light blue, purple)

P3: (yellow) collective-net-metered system (no smart meters) operated by CF Energy, electricity sold to apts and for bldg. systems, data from launch April 24-Dec24. **A=0.49, R_{SC}=0.27**

P4-7: system operated by cooperative BuergerEnergie Berlin (12), electricity sales managed by energy provider EWS (13).

P4 (dark blue) el. used for bldg. systems only

P5,6,7 for bldg. systems and apts. Usage data for CY2024 courtesy of BEB, EWS

Shown is autarky rate A in relation to ratio W_T/C

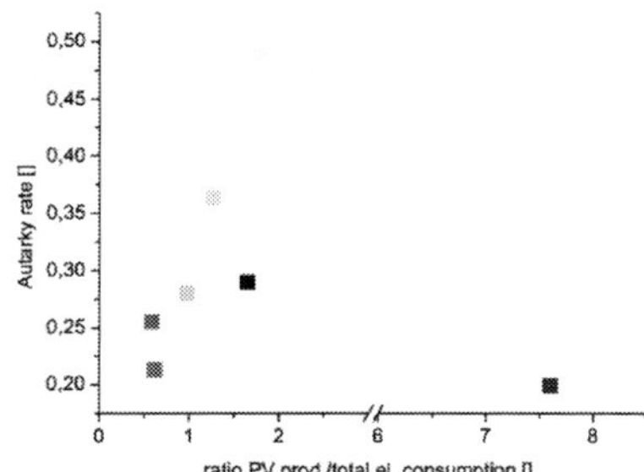

Findings:
- For projects considered, A up to 49% achievable w/o battery storage
- W_T/C ratios of 0.5-2 seem advisable from autarky rate viepoint

Conclusions Simple business models for small apt bldgs have been tested over different seasons or a full year. They have been shown in terms of self-consumption rates to be economically feasible, even without battery storage, smart meters or systematic demand-side management. Increasing the number of users increases profitability, demand-side management and battery storage offer further potential for profitability.

References   **(1)** Turulski (2023) Grad der Urbanisierung in Deutschland bis 2021, statista.com **(2)** Urban population set to increase by almost 700 million by 2030 (acc. 15/06/23), destatis.de **(3)** Bergner J. et al. (2019) Das Berliner Solarpotential, HTW Berlin **(4)** regional-photovoltaik.de and Global Solar Atlas (acc16092025) **(5)** SolarCity Berlin – monitoring report 2024 (2025) **(6)** PR Nr.091: Stromerzeugung 2024 (2025), Stat. Bundesamt **(7)** Gebäude- und Wohnungsbestand in Deutschland (2014), Statistische Ämter des Bundes und der Länder **(8)** e.g. Neue Geschäftsmodelle, Bundesverband Solarwirtschaft e.V., solarwirtschaft.de, acc15/06/23 **(9)** e.g. Das neue Erneuerbare-Energien-Gesetz 2023, Energieagentur Niedersachsen, acc.16/06/23 **(10)** D. Ritter et al. (2021) Wirtschaftlichkeit von Photovoltaik-Dachanlagen, Umweltbundesamt 2021 **(11)** Fina et al. (2018) Wirtschaftlichkeitsbewertung und Methoden zur optimalen Dimensionierung von PV-Anlagen und Speichersystemen in Mehrparteienhäusern, 15. Symp. Energieinnovation **(12)** BürgerEnergie Berlin www.buerger-energie-berlin.de **(13)** EWS www.ews-schoenau.de

5 DV.3.66 22.-26.9.2025

TECHNO-ECONOMIC MODELLING OF INDUSTRIAL-SCALE SINGLE-JUNCTION PEROVSKITE MODULE MANUFACTURING

Ian Kenchington, Anna Bargues, Philippe Macé, Melodie de l'Épine, Gaëtan Masson, Akhildev Pillai
Becquerel Institute
Rue Praetere 2, 1000 Brussels, Belgium. +32 493 451 720

ABSTRACT:
As the PV industry expands to meet Net-Zero targets, it is entering the multi-terawatt era. Perovskite solar cells (PSCs) are widely viewed as the next technological leap. Competitiveness in Europe requires assessing the economic viability of large-area, solvent-free manufacturing, not just efficiency. This study applies a bottom-up techno-economic model that integrates materials, utilities, labour, and equipment at each process step to estimate factory-gate costs of vacuum thermal evaporation-based perovskite, using a GW-scale baseline and sensitivity analysis.

Results show that vacuum thermal evaporation, while solvent-free, is the costliest deposition step owing to high CAPEX and significant material losses, indicating a need for yield-improvement and recovery strategies. Beyond deposition, structural layup steps (e.g., glass and framing) are major cost drivers, amplified by labour-intensive handling and logistics mark-ups linked to extra-EU imports. Frameless or lightweight foil designs could lower material expenditures, though trade-offs in handling and performance should be studied. Sensitivity results highlight the dominance of equipment depreciation, pointing to automation and scale-up as key levers.

Overall, the findings prioritise R&D on process efficiency, material utilisation, automation, and design innovation to support EU-based industrial deployment of PSCs.
Keywords: Perovskites, vacuum thermal evaporation, techno-economic model, manufacturing.

1. INTRODUCTION

The rapid expansion of PV highlights both the promise of perovskite solar cells and the need to industrialise them sustainably in Europe. While PSCs combine high efficiency with low-temperature, scalable processing, deployment is constrained by stability, yield, and manufacturability, and by Europe's reliance on imported PV value chains. In this study, manufacturing using solvent-free, evaporation-based production routes are studies for better compatibility with the EU's manufacturing goals.

This study, conducted within the framework of the VALHALLA project, quantifies the step-by-step factory-gate costs of PSCs. The objectives are to identify the main cost drivers (labour, depreciation, materials, and yield), and to assess their implications for life-cycle costs. The analysis seeks to inform design decisions, guide R&D priorities on yueld and material utilization, and support eco-design and future EU industrial deployment.

2. METHODOLOGICAL APPROACH

The study applies a bottom-up techno-economic model developed by Becquerel Institute. This model is modular in design; allocating equipment, materials, consumables, and utilities to finite 'steps' to enable an analysis on specific sections of the productive flow.

The productive steps have been set to depict the layup and manufacturing of perovskite based in vacuum thermal evaporation, as set within this study's scope.

The specific process flow is described below. For analysis purposes, all Laser steps are analysed as one:
1. Substrate cleaning and layup
2. TCO sputtering
3. Laser P1
4. HTL evaporation
5. Perovskite evaporation
6. Organic ETL evaporation
7. Inorganic ETL ALD
8. Laser P2
9. Rear-electrode evaporation
10. Laser P3
11. ALD encapsulation
12. Back layup
13. Framing

The data inputs used combine insights from the VALHALLA project, partner consultations on OPEX and scheduling, literature review, vendor information, and expert judgement. A GW-scale baseline is used, with a sensitivity analysis on consumable prices, process and location-based variables. Outputs include factory-gate cost breakdowns by step, and a prioritised set of levers for cost reduction.

For the simulation, a 1GW manufacturing line is simulated to run on a three 8-hour shift per day basis, 5 days a week. The line is set to run at 85% availability, 92% performance and 9% quality yield for an overall equipment efficiency of 77%. **Table I** describes other general investment and operational cost inputs.

3. RESULTS

3.1. Stack and processs overview

For material choice, this analysis focuses in one of the main stacks studied in the VALHALLA project. **Table II** describes all materials used in the stack for the studied module design, depicting their role and application process —sputter, evaporation, ALD, or layup for materials that do not require granular deposition. To enable the objective of solvent-free manufacturing, the absorber (FAMAPbI$_3$) is applied via vacuum thermal evaporation.

10.4229/EUPVSEC2025/5DV.3.67
020558-001

Table I: Main assumptions

Energy	
Electricity cost	0,10 €/kWh
Labour	
Operator	54,9 k€/FTE
Engineer	103,9 k€/FTE
CAPEX	
Equipment	109 M€
Total consumption	20,4 MW
Depreciation	5 years

Table II: Stack description and application process

Material	Process	Role in Stack
Glass 2mm	Layup	*Front Layer*
ITO	Sputter	*Fr. Electrode*
MeO-2PACz	Evaporation	*SAM HTL*
FAMAPbI3	Evaporation	*Perovskite*
C60	Evaporation	*Organic ETL*
SnO2	ALD	*Inorganic ETL*
Cu	Evaporation	*Back Electrode*
Al2O3	ALD	*Encapsulation*
EVA	Layup	*Rear Layer*
Polybutadine	Layup	*Rear Layer*
Glass 2mm	Layup	*Rear Layer*
Al frame	Layup	*Framing*

3.2. Process cost breakdown

The full costs for the studied stack is 17,5 €cents per Wp, where 13,7 €ct come from defined process steps. The remainder is attributed to costs not related to production, such as overheads, R&D and sales. **Figure 1** provides a breakdown of those costs by each productive step.

Materials covers all net material utilization at their respective step. Utilities consider electricity and water per machine step. Labour represents the cost of the operator requirements per process. Maintenance and equipment items are proportional to each step's CAPEX. Material losses are specific to each material and its application, deposition or layup.

From the coating steps, perovskite evaporation has the highest cost at 1,5 €ct/Wp (**Figure 1**), mainly driven by materials and yield losses. This is followed by bottom contact evaporation, placing all evaporation stages at a relatively expensive position compared with sputtering and ALD. At the boundaries of the process, front layup and framing stand out as major costs, the latter adding high labour intensity. A further look into the components of these steps may explain the main cost drivers.

Cost breakdown per step, in €ct/Wp

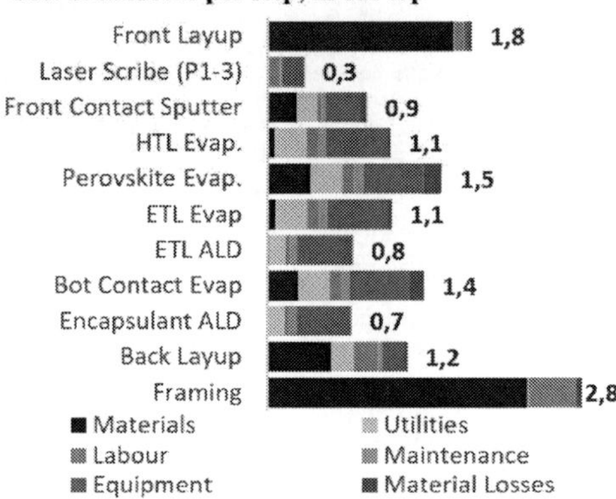

Figure 1: Manufacturing cost breakdown, per productive step

Net materials costs distribution

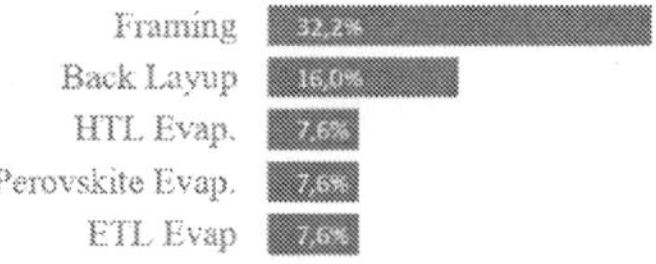

Figure 2: Top 5 net-material using steps, in € step materials/€ total materials

Regarding net materials distribution, framing stands as the most expensive, followed by front layup. Their costs are driven by bulky inputs with high logistics mark-ups, as they are normally procured from outside the EU.

Net labour costs distribution

Figure 3: Top 5 net labour using steps, in € step labour/€ total labour

Upon analysing labour requirements, the framing step again dominates, followed by back layup and evaporation steps, also requiring significant operator time. This is due to these steps' need for manual precision in assembly and coating.

Net losses distribution

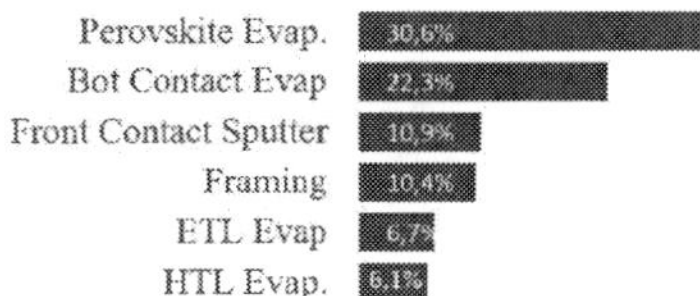

Figure 4: Top 6 net losses steps, in € step losses/€ total losses

On the net losses front, evaporation stands out as the steps concentrating the largest material losses with their low process yields, while front contact sputtering concentrates part of the inefficiencies.

Module cost sensitivity

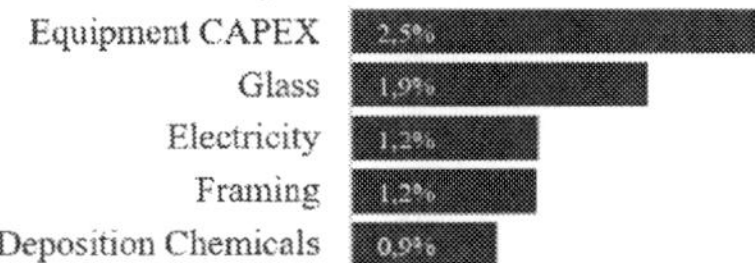

Figure 5: Sensitivity analysis results, in Total Costs variation from a 10% variation on each input

A sensitivity analysis is performed by varying by 10% several OPEX and CAPEX input variables; **Figure 5** displays the results from the top 5 most sensitive among such inputs.

The model is most sensitive to the equipment CAPEX, shifting costs by more than 2% upon a 10% variation. Glass follows closely, reflecting its heavy baseline share. Electricity and other consumables have smaller but still visible effects. These results underline the importance of equipment standardization for large scale manufacturing, and supply-chain optimization for reducing factory-gate costs.

4. CONCLUSIONS

As perovskite developments become increasingly promising regarding their performance and stability, a clear pathway towards mass manufacturing must be set. In this study, a bottom-up theoretical approach was taken to identify the main challenges that mature, GW-scale, solvent-free, and large-sized perovskite modules manufacturing, is set to present. Below are listed the main issues found.

Vacuum thermal evaporation:
EU-based perovskite manufacturing can perform as a solvent-free method under vacuum thermal evaporation, but it becomes the costliest deposition step due to its high CAPEX and significant material use.

Process efficiency and yield losses:
High material losses across all evaporation steps highlight the need for yield improvement and/or residue recovery strategies. Here, perovskite evaporation concentrates over almost a third (30,6%) of all lost materials, followed by copper losses (22,3%), also an evaporation step.

High costs on structural materials:
Framing and glass are major cost drivers, not related to deposition but to layup process steps. Their high reliance on manual processing increases costs and points towards the need for automation, but this is greatly amplified by logistics and import dependence as these must be sourced from ex-EU countries, facing high shipping and import duties.

Structure design alternatives:
Complementary to the above statement, design choices (frameless or lightweight foil structures) can reduce material costs by dropping glass or aluminium from the bill of materials altogether, but this may affect in-process handling or module performance.

Early CAPEX estimates:
Equipment weighs heavy on costs. Nonetheless, as there is little to no evidence of installed GW-capable facilities, some extrapolation was used to estimate the final CAPEX figures. Learning effects from large-scale deployment may reduce these costs over time.

5. ACKNOWLEDGEMENTS AND FUNDING

 The work described has received funding as part of the VALHALLA project from the European Union's Horizon Europe research and innovation program under grant agreement N° 101082176.

6. REFERENCES

[1]   J. Cordell, M. Woodhouse and E. Warren, "Technoeconomic analysis of perovskite/silicon tandem solar modules," *Joule*, 2025.

[2]   N. Chang, B. Newman and R. Egan, "Future cost projections for photovoltaic module manufacturing using a bottom-up cost and uncertainty model," *Solar Energy Materials and Solar Cells*, vol. 237, April 2022.

[3]   M. Dehghanimadvar, R. Egan and N. Chang, "Economic assessment of local solar module assembly in a global market," *Cell Reports Physical Science*, vol. 3, no. 2, 16 February 2022.

[4]   T. Abzieher, D. T. Moore, M. Roß, S. Albrecht, J. Silvia, H. Tan and e. a. Quentin Jeangros, "Vapor phase deposition of perovskite photovoltaics: short track to commercialization?," *Energy & Environmental Science*, vol. 17, pp. 1645-1663, 2024.

DECARBONIZING SOLAR PV: EVALUATING THE ROLE OF CRITICAL MINERAL SUPPLY CHAINS

Engin Deniz, Prof. Dr. Melih Soner Çeliktaş*
*Ege University, İzmir, Türkiye

The rapid growth of solar photovoltaics (PV) needed for global climate goals has intensified focus on the upstream critical mineral supply chains enabling this technology. This paper synthesizes recent findings on the greenhouse gas (GHG) emissions associated with key minerals used in PV systems – notably silicon, copper, lithium, and cobalt – and the strategies to decarbonize these supply chains. Life-cycle assessments and supply-chain analyses reveal that mining, processing, and refining of these minerals can contribute significantly to the embodied emissions of PV installations, with hotspots in energy-intensive stages like polysilicon refining, copper smelting, and battery metal production. Emissions vary widely by region depending on the energy mix and production practices, highlighting opportunities for supply chain optimization. We discuss mitigation options including renewable-powered mineral processing, electrification of mining equipment, energy efficiency, recycling, and alternative materials, alongside emerging policy frameworks (e.g. EU Critical Raw Materials Act, international due diligence regimes) aimed at aligning mineral supply chains with climate targets. The literature indicates that a combination of technological improvements and policy interventions could substantially reduce upstream emissions (by ~30–40% in many cases) and enhance supply security. Ensuring the sustainability of critical mineral supply chains is imperative for PV to deliver on its promise of truly clean energy.
Keywords: Solar PV; Critical minerals; Supply chain emissions; Life-cycle assessment; Decarbonization.

1   INTRODUCTION

Solar photovoltaic (PV) power is a cornerstone of global decarbonization, with deployment expected to quadruple by 2030 [1]. While PV generates electricity with negligible operational emissions, the upstream supply chains of critical minerals present significant sustainability challenges [2,3]. Modern PV systems rely on high-purity silicon for cells, copper and silver for conductive components, aluminum for frames, and, in storage applications, lithium, cobalt, and nickel. The production of these materials is energy intensive and generates substantial greenhouse gas (GHG) emissions [4,5]. Reducing embodied emissions is therefore essential to preserve PV's net climate benefits [1,2].

Beyond carbon impacts, extraction and processing raise environmental and social concerns. Over 70% of global cobalt originates in the Democratic Republic of Congo, where artisanal mining is associated with hazardous conditions and child labor [6]. Lithium brine extraction in Chile's Atacama Desert consumes about 90% of withdrawn water, stressing fragile ecosystems and indigenous livelihoods [7]. Polysilicon production in Xinjiang, which supplies nearly 45% of global output, relies on coal-based electricity and has been linked to forced labor [1,8]. These cases illustrate the risk of perpetuating environmental injustice in the pursuit of low-carbon energy. As Mulvaney (2024) argues, it is unjust to compromise public health and ecosystems in resource-producing regions to enable decarbonization elsewhere [9].

Together, these challenges highlight the need for a systematic assessment of how mineral supply chains affect PV's decarbonization potential. This paper evaluates the role of critical mineral supply chains in shaping the sustainability of PV by synthesizing evidence from life cycle assessments (LCAs), multi-regional input–output (MRIO) studies, and scenario analyses. It identifies major emission hotspots, compares regional and technological differences, and assesses mitigation strategies. This paper contributes by consolidating evidence across LCA, MRIO, and scenario studies into a unified framework. Unlike previous studies that focus on single minerals or stages, this approach provides a new comparative perspective across materials and regions, and identifies where interventions in supply chains have the highest leverage for decarbonization.

2   LITERATURE REVIEW AND METHODOLOGY

By integrating these strands of evidence, the analysis goes beyond individual case studies to provide a comparative assessment that links technical emission factors with policy and governance contexts. Evidence is drawn from life cycle assessments (LCAs), multi-regional input–output (MRIO) models, simulation studies, and institutional reports. Process-based LCAs provide cradle-to-gate emission factors for PV materials. Reported life-cycle intensities of PV electricity are typically 20–50 g CO_2/kWh, compared with more than 400 g CO_2/kWh for coal power [1,2]. Most emissions arise from upstream production of silicon, copper, aluminum, lithium, and cobalt [4,5].

MRIO and optimization models capture indirect emissions embedded in trade flows. Maeno et al. (2025) show that rerouting Japanese imports of iron and copper from coal-intensive suppliers to lower-carbon producers such as Canada could reduce embodied emissions by up to 40% [10]. Cui et al. (2025) demonstrate that reshoring or diversifying PV manufacturing significantly alters both carbon intensity and costs[2]. Simulation and material flow studies add insights on mineral demand and supply risks. Güz and Murakami (2025) emphasize the importance of integrating economic, environmental, and policy parameters when modelling flows of lithium, cobalt, nickel, and copper[11].

A few processes dominate embodied emissions. Polysilicon production accounts for 70–80% of module energy demand; coal-based production in Xinjiang emits roughly three times more CO_2 than production in Europe with hydro or nuclear power [1,2].
Copper refining and smelting are also energy intensive. Refining in Canada with hydropower results in far lower emissions than in Kazakhstan or Mongolia, where coal dominates [10]. Aluminum smelting shows similar contrasts, with coal-based production in China among the most carbon-intensive worldwide [1]. Lithium and cobalt refining add further emissions, especially in fossil-fuel-

based processes; spodumene roasting and brine conversion are energy demanding, and cobalt refining in China compounds the footprint [5,6,7].

2.1 Scope and Limitations

The review covers studies from 2000 to 2025, with scenarios extending to 2050. Minerals considered are silicon, copper, lithium, cobalt, and aluminum, with regional focus on China, the European Union, North America, Africa, and Latin America. The study synthesizes published analyses and institutional reports rather than generating new emission inventories. Limitations include incomplete disclosure of industrial data, variation in LCA methods, and uncertainty in MRIO assumptions. These are addressed by triangulating multiple sources and reporting ranges where possible.

3 RESULTS AND DISCUSSION

3.1 Emission Hotspots and Regional Variability

Embodied emissions in PV supply chains depend primarily on the energy intensity of refining and processing and the carbon profile of the electricity used. Fig. 1 summarizes upstream greenhouse gas (GHG) intensities for key minerals used in PV technologies, showing both average values and reported ranges.

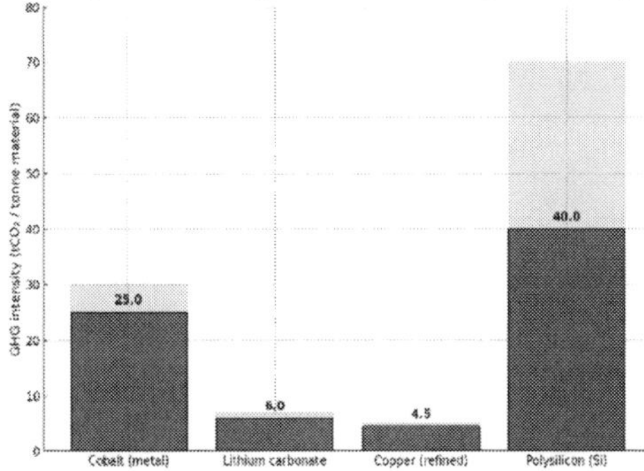

Figure 1: Upstream GHG emissions of key PV minerals (average and range). Data: IEA [1].

Beyond these averages, substantial regional and technological variability exists. Fig. 2 highlights this for polysilicon, lithium, and nickel. Polysilicon production dominates module manufacturing energy demand: coal-based production in Xinjiang emits nearly three times more CO_2 than hydropower- or nuclear-based production in Europe [1,2]. Comparable contrasts exist for copper and aluminum. Copper refined in Canada with hydropower has far lower emissions than copper from coal-dependent Kazakhstan or Mongolia [10]. Aluminum smelting in China, where coal dominates the power mix, remains among the most carbon-intensive globally [1]. Lithium and cobalt refining add further embodied emissions, as spodumene roasting, brine conversion, and cobalt processing are highly energy-intensive and often powered by fossil fuels [5,6,7].

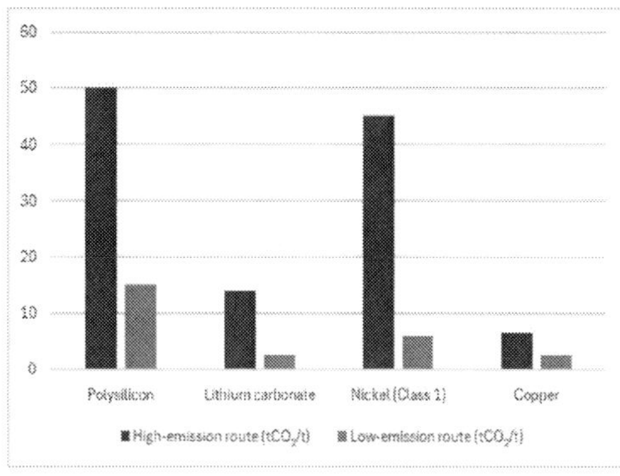

Figure 2: Regional and technological variability in emissions intensity of polysilicon, lithium, and nickel. Data: IEA [1], Maeno et al. [10].

3.2 Supply Chain Scenarios and Trade-Offs

Scenario-based analyses highlight how different supply chain configurations influence both emissions and system resilience. Localising PV manufacturing in Europe, where cleaner electricity mixes are available, yields modest but meaningful reductions in global supply chain emissions while supporting employment and reducing reliance on China [2]. Conversely, abrupt protectionist measures, such as eliminating imports from China without sufficient domestic capacity, may raise emissions as production shifts to coal-based regions. Evidence suggests that balanced diversification is the most effective approach: distributing production geographically to exploit low-carbon energy while maintaining open trade to preserve efficiency [10,3]. In parallel, technological advances have reduced the carbon intensity of PV production. Efficiency gains in wafer slicing, cell processing, and partial decarbonization of electricity halved module-level emission intensity between 2011 and 2021, although absolute emissions rose due to the rapid expansion of global production [1].

Geographic concentration of supply also introduces systemic risks. More than 80% of polysilicon and wafers are produced in China, linking global module availability to a single dominant supplier [1,2]. Over 70% of cobalt originates in the Democratic Republic of Congo, where governance challenges and artisanal mining raise both ethical and security concerns [6]. Lithium production in Chile's Atacama Desert is vulnerable to ecological limits and water scarcity [7]. The Global Critical Minerals Outlook projects that under current policies, supply from existing and announced projects may meet only 70% of copper demand and 60% of lithium demand by 2035 [3]. Addressing these risks requires investment in new, low-carbon mining and refining capacity, supported by streamlined permitting and robust environmental standards.

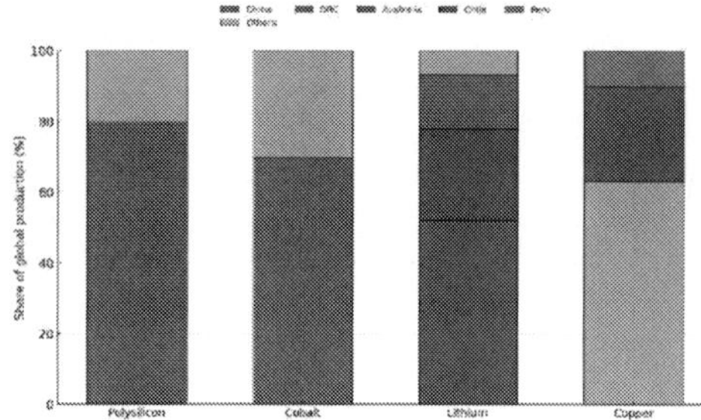

Figure 3: Geographic concentration of PV-critical mineral supply (polysilicon, cobalt, lithium, copper). Data: IEA [3], European Commission [15].

PV supply chain emissions and risks are determined by production geography, process energy sources, and market concentration. Cleaner electricity inputs, technological innovation, recycling, and diversification of suppliers can reduce embodied emissions while simultaneously strengthening resilience. These measures are essential for ensuring that the rapid scale-up of PV deployment proceeds in alignment with global climate targets.

3.3 Mitigation Strategies for Decarbonizing Mineral Supply Chains

Decarbonizing the mineral supply chains that underpin photovoltaic technologies requires a combination of technological, operational, and structural measures. The literature identifies three broad areas of intervention: the integration of clean energy and efficiency improvements in mining and refining, the reconfiguration of supply chains through low-carbon sourcing and recycling, and technological innovation in processes and materials.

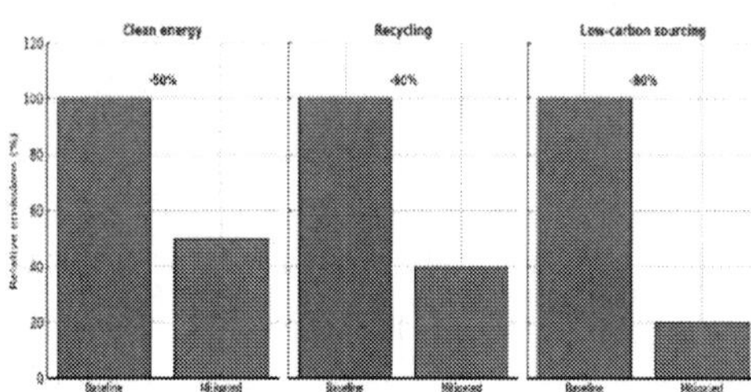

Figure 4: Mitigation strategies to decarbonize PV mineral supply chains (clean energy integration, recycling, low-carbon sourcing). Data: IEA [3], Islami et al. [5].

A principal pathway to reduce emissions is the replacement of fossil energy with renewable electricity in mining and refining. The deployment of on-site solar and wind systems, as well as the use of clean power for electro-refining and smelting, has already been adopted in a number of large-scale operations. These measures directly reduce Scope 1 and 2 emissions and can also lower operating costs in the long term, given the falling cost of renewable energy [1]. Complementary measures include the use of advanced grinding mills, heat recovery systems in smelters, and the application of digital optimization tools to improve energy efficiency. Increasingly, electrification of mining fleets is also being pursued, with

battery-electric and hydrogen-powered haul trucks offering the potential to eliminate diesel combustion if coupled with low-carbon electricity [5]. Taken together, renewable integration and efficiency improvements substantially reduce the baseline energy intensity of mineral production.

The geographical location and energy mix of mineral production are decisive factors in determining embodied emissions. Procuring materials such as aluminum and copper from regions powered by hydroelectric or nuclear energy, and avoiding imports from coal-intensive suppliers, can significantly lower supply chain emissions. Multi-regional input–output modelling suggests that such re-routing of imports could reduce embodied emissions by up to 40% for major importing economies [10]. Increasing transparency and traceability through certificates of origin and digital tracking systems supports this transition by enabling verification of carbon footprints [12]. In parallel, diversification strategies that expand domestic refining capacity or establish new supply partnerships in regions with cleaner energy mixes enhance both sustainability and security of supply.

Recycling represents another essential strategy for long-term decarbonization. Secondary production of metals such as aluminum and copper requires 70–90% less energy than primary extraction, and recycling of end-of-life photovoltaic modules and batteries can return significant quantities of silicon, silver, lithium, cobalt, and nickel to the supply chain. Projections suggest that by 2040 secondary materials could meet more than 20% of the cumulative demand for aluminum, copper, and silicon in the PV sector, and as much as 70% of silver demand, provided supportive policy frameworks are in place [3]. Although recycling technologies and collection systems are still developing, their future contribution to reducing emissions and resource pressures is expected to be substantial. Recent advances include environmentally benign methods such as subcritical water delamination [22] and enzymatic delamination [23], both of which demonstrate high recovery potential for crystalline silicon PV modules without the use of hazardous solvents.

Technological innovation also provides important opportunities to reduce emissions. Low-carbon process innovations such as the use of hydrogen in high-temperature metallurgy, the deployment of carbon capture and storage at refining plants, and the development of direct lithium extraction methods are being tested and could significantly reduce both energy consumption and process emissions [7]. At the same time, advances in photovoltaic and battery technologies are reducing dependence on the most emission-intensive or socially problematic minerals. In the PV sector, manufacturers are increasingly substituting silver with copper-based metallization, while in the battery sector the adoption of cobalt-free chemistries such as lithium iron phosphate reduces both emissions and supply risks associated with cobalt mining in the Democratic Republic of Congo. Emerging materials such as perovskite solar cells may further lower the energy and mineral intensity of PV production if stability and scalability challenges can be resolved.

These mitigation strategies are not mutually exclusive but complementary. The combination of clean energy integration, efficiency improvements, low-carbon sourcing, recycling, and innovation offers a realistic pathway to substantially reduce embodied emissions in photovoltaic supply chains while at the same time improving resilience and sustainability. Current modelling suggests that if implemented in parallel, these measures could reduce the carbon footprint of PV-related mineral production by one third to one half within the next two decades, compared to a continuation of current practices [1,2,10].

3.4 Policy implications and governance

Decarbonizing mineral supply chains for photovoltaics is not only a technical challenge but also a matter of governance. The achievement of global climate goals, including the 1.5 °C target of the Paris Agreement, depends on decarbonizing industrial supply chains in parallel with energy generation [13,14].

International accords such as the Paris Agreement [13] and the Glasgow Climate Pact [14] have expanded the focus of climate policy to include industrial emissions. Regional initiatives follow this trend. The European Union's Critical Raw Materials Act sets binding targets for domestic extraction (10%), processing (40%), and recycling (15%) of annual consumption, while requiring diversification of imports so that no more than 65% originates from a single country [15]. These provisions are coupled with strict environmental and social standards, effectively linking supply security with sustainability. Since exporters to Europe must comply with these requirements, the CRMA is expected to shape global production practices [3].

Responsible sourcing is increasingly codified in law. The EU Battery Regulation requires companies to calculate and disclose the carbon footprint of batteries and comply with OECD due diligence guidelines [12]. In the United States, enforcement actions restrict imports of polysilicon and related products linked to forced labor in Xinjiang, as documented in official labor investigations [8]. Traceability initiatives such as the Global Battery Alliance's Battery Passport are emerging to verify origin and sustainability metrics [17]. Trade measures are also evolving: the EU Carbon Border Adjustment Mechanism internalizes carbon costs for imports in energy-intensive sectors [18], while the Minerals Security Partnership coordinates cross-country investment in sustainable mining [19]. Incentives complement regulation: the U.S. Inflation Reduction Act provides tax credits for critical minerals processed domestically or in free-trade countries [20], and carbon pricing in Canada makes low-carbon metallurgy more competitive [21].

The policy landscape is developing rapidly, reflecting the recognition that mineral supply chains are central to the energy transition [3,17]. Concerns remain, however, that strict regulation could slow project development or raise costs, creating bottlenecks in mineral availability [3]. Policymakers therefore need to balance carrots and sticks: providing incentives for investment while enforcing sustainability standards. International coordination will be essential to avoid fragmentation or carbon leakage [10,2]. The emerging consensus is that critical minerals governance must integrate security and sustainability, ensuring that clean energy technologies are supported by clean and resilient supply chains [3, 15].

4 SUMMARY AND CONCLUSIONS

The decarbonization of solar PV must extend beyond electricity generation to the mineral supply chains that underpin the technology. Rising demand for silicon, copper, lithium, and cobalt could significantly increase upstream emissions if left unchecked, partially offsetting PV's climate benefits [1,2]. Scenario studies indicate that powering mining and refining with renewable energy, improving process efficiencies, and shifting to low-carbon suppliers can reduce embodied emissions by 30–40% in the near term [10,5]. In the longer run, scaling recycling of PV modules and batteries could meet a substantial share of demand, while material innovations such as low-silver cell designs or cobalt-free batteries further lessen dependence on high-impact inputs [3,6].

Achieving these gains requires stronger commitments from both industry and policymakers. Manufacturers can lead by disclosing upstream emissions and adopting Scope 3 reduction targets, while governments can align climate and resource policies through carbon pricing, recycling mandates, and critical minerals strategies [12,13]. Such measures move beyond incremental efficiency gains and address the systemic drivers of supply chain emissions. International cooperation on standards, transparency, and responsible mining practices will be essential to ensure security of supply without sacrificing environmental or social integrity.

Ultimately, reducing the upstream footprint of mineral supply chains is indispensable if PV is to remain one of the lowest-carbon energy sources. By combining clean energy inputs, circular material flows, and robust governance reforms, the PV industry can expand while enhancing resilience and equity. Only with sustainable and just supply chains can solar power fully deliver on its promise as the backbone of a net-zero future [3,2]. The novelty of this work lies in its integration of diverse methods into a coherent assessment of PV mineral supply chains. The synthesis offers new insights into priority areas for action, highlighting leverage points such as renewable-powered refining, diversified sourcing, and circular material flows. These results provide the PV community and policymakers with a consolidated framework for guiding sustainable supply chain strategies.

References

[1] International Energy Agency (IEA), Solar PV Global Supply Chains, Paris, 2022. Available at: https://www.iea.org/reports/solar-pv-global-supply-chains

[2] Cui, H. et al., Policy-driven transformation of global solar PV supply chains and resulting impacts, Nature Communications, Vol. 14, No. 61979, 2025. https://doi.org/10.1038/s41467-025-61979-5

[3] International Energy Agency (IEA), Global Critical Minerals Outlook 2025, Paris, 2025. Available at: https://www.iea.org/reports/global-critical-minerals-outlook-2025

[4] Ramírez-Márquez, C., Posadas-Paredes, T., and Ponce-Ortega, J. M., From Resource Abundance to Responsible Scarcity: Rethinking Natural Resource Utilization in the Age of Hyper-Consumption, Resources, Vol. 14, No. 8, p. 118, 2025. https://doi.org/10.3390/resources14080118

[5] Islami, M. S., Urmee, T., Lund, C., Bahri, P. A., and Anisuzzaman, M., Decarbonisation strategies for critical mineral supply chain: State-of-the-art in mining and refining industries, Renewable & Sustainable Energy Reviews, Vol. 218, 115811, 2025. https://doi.org/10.1016/j.rser.2025.115811

[6] Baumann-Pauly, D., Why cobalt mining in the DRC needs urgent attention, Council on Foreign Relations Blog, 2020. Available at: https://www.cfr.org/blog/why-cobalt-mining-drc-needs-urgent-attention

[7] Cambero, F., Lithium mining is slowly sinking Chile's Atacama salt flat, study shows, Reuters, 2024. Available at: https://www.reuters.com/sustainability/land-use-biodiversity/lithium-mining-is-slowly-sinking-chiles-atacama-salt-flat-study-shows-2024-08-22/

[8] U.S. Department of Labor (DOL), ILAB: Solar supply chain "forced labor" storyboard, Washington, DC, 2023. Available at: https://www.dol.gov/agencies/ilab/reports/child-labor/list-of-goods/supply-chains/solar

[9] Mulvaney, D., Embodied energy injustice and the political ecology of solar power, Energy Research & Social Science, Vol. 115, 103607, 2024. https://doi.org/10.1016/j.erss.2024.103607

[10] Maeno, T., Tokito, S., Yokoi, R., and Kagawa, S., Global supply chain restructuring for low-carbon procurement of minerals, Resources, Environment and Sustainability, Vol. 20, 100215, 2025. https://doi.org/10.1016/j.resenv.2025.100215

[11] Güz, Ş. and Murakami, S., A systematic literature review of simulation models for flows, markets, and sustainability of critical energy transition minerals, Resources, Conservation and Recycling Advances, Vol. 27, 200271, 2025. https://doi.org/10.1016/j.rcradv.2025.200271

[12] OECD, Responsible mineral supply chains, Paris, 2023. Available at: https://www.oecd.org/en/topics/sub-issues/due-diligence-guidance-for-responsible-business-conduct/responsible-mineral-supply-chains.html

[13] UNFCCC, Paris Agreement, Bonn, 2015. Available at: https://unfccc.int/process-and-meetings/the-paris-agreement

[14] UNFCCC, Glasgow Climate Pact, Bonn, 2021. Available at: https://unfccc.int/process-and-meetings/conferences/glasgow-climate-change-conference-october-november-2021/outcomes-of-the-glasgow-climate-change-conference

[15] European Commission, Critical Raw Materials Act, Brussels, 2023. Available at: https://single-market-economy.ec.europa.eu/sectors/raw-materials/areas-specific-interest/critical-raw-materials/critical-raw-materials-act_en

[16] European Parliament, Regulation (EU) 2023/1542 concerning batteries and waste batteries, Brussels, 2023.

[17] OECD, Global Battery Alliance: Battery Passport initiative, Paris, 2023. Available at: https://www.globalbattery.org/battery-passport/

[18] European Commission, Carbon Border Adjustment Mechanism (CBAM), Brussels, 2023. Available at: https://taxation-customs.ec.europa.eu/carbon-border-adjustment-mechanism_en

[19] U.S. Department of State, Minerals Security Partnership, Washington, DC, 2022. Available at: https://www.state.gov/minerals-security-partnership/

[20] U.S. Congress, Inflation Reduction Act, Washington, DC, 2022. Available at: https://www.congress.gov/bill/117th-congress/house-bill/5376

[21] Government of Canada, Carbon pricing framework, Ottawa, 2023. Available at: https://www.canada.ca/en/services/environment/weather/climatechange/climate-plan/carbon-pollution-pricing.html

[22] A. Birtürk, M.S. Çeliktaş, Subcritical water delamination: A promising path to efficient recycling of critical minerals, Journal of Cleaner Production, Vol. 469, 143147, 2024. https://doi.org/10.1016/j.jclepro.2024.143147

[23] S.C. Karagöz, T.K. Gündoğdu, H. Sarıaltın, M.S. Çeliktaş, A novel enzymatic delamination method for sustainable recycling of crystalline silicon photovoltaic (c-Si PV) modules, Separation and Purification Technology 361 (2025) 131373. https://doi.org/10.1016/j.seppur.2024.131373

DECARBONIZING SOLAR PV: EVALUATING THE ROLE OF CRITICAL MINERAL SUPPLY CHAINS

Engin Deniz, Prof. Dr. Melih Soner Çeliktaş*

*Ege University, İzmir, Türkiye

INTRODUCTION

Solar PV is central to global decarbonization, with capacity expected to quadruple by 2030. While PV electricity is nearly emission-free in operation, upstream supply chains of critical minerals present significant sustainability challenges. High-purity silicon, copper, lithium, and cobalt are energy-intensive to mine and refine, generating substantial greenhouse gas emissions that risk offsetting PV's climate benefits. Regional practices also raise environmental and social concerns, from child labor in cobalt mining to water stress in lithium brine extraction and coal-based polysilicon production in Xinjiang. Addressing these upstream impacts is essential for PV to remain a truly sustainable technology.

METHODOLOGY

This study synthesizes findings from life cycle assessments (LCA), multi-regional input–output (MRIO) models, simulation studies, and institutional reports. LCAs quantify cradle-to-gate emission factors for PV-critical minerals, while MRIO captures indirect emissions embodied in international trade flows. Simulation and material flow models are used to explore future demand and supply risks, while scenario analysis evaluates the effects of decarbonization measures such as renewable-powered refining, electrification of mining fleets, and recycling. This mixed-methods approach enables identification of emission hotspots, comparison of regional and technological differences, and assessment of mitigation strategies under alternative supply chain futures, with results reported as ranges to reflect uncertainty.

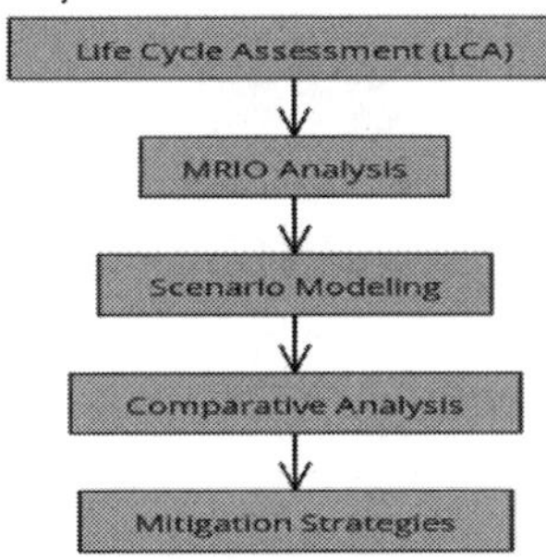

Figure 1: Analytical framework (LCA + MRIO + scenarios ⟶ comparative analysis ⟶ mitigation)

RESULTS

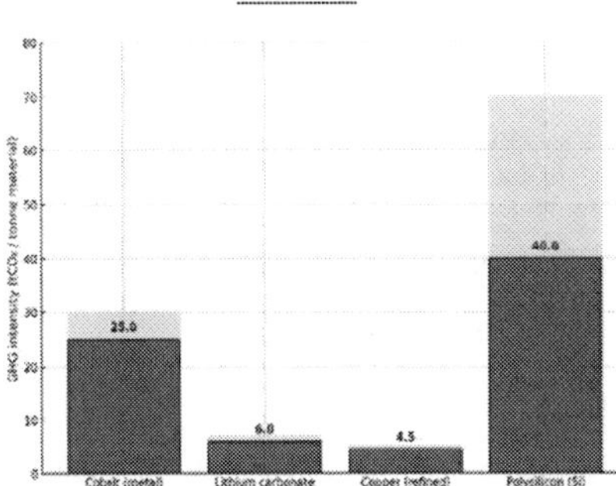

Figure 2: Upstream GHG intensity of key PV minerals (average + range). Data: IEA [1]

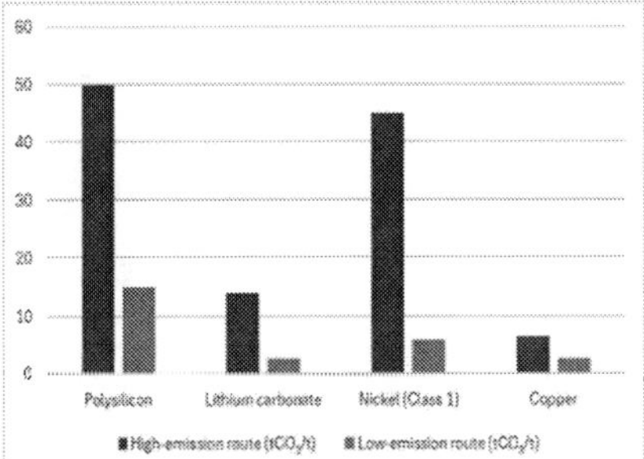

Figure 3: Regional variability in emissions intensity for polysilicon, lithium, nickel. Data: IEA [2].

RESULTS CONT.

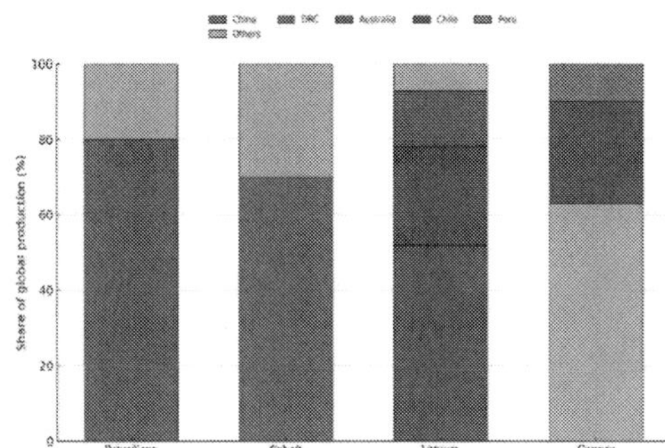

Figure 4: Geographic concentration of PV-critical mineral supply. Data: IEA [2].

MITIGATION STRATEGIES

- Renewable-powered refining can cut emissions by ~50%.
- Recycling reduces energy use by 70–90%.
- Electrified mining fleets eliminate diesel combustion.
- Substitution and material efficiency ease pressure on critical minerals.

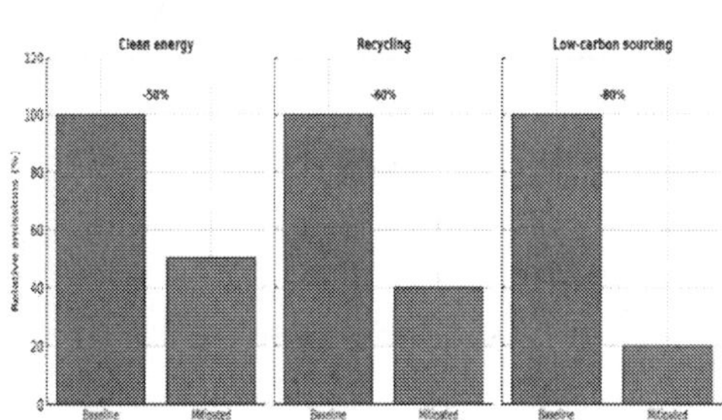

Figure 5: Mitigation strategies for upstream decarbonization (clean energy, recycling, low-carbon sourcing). Sources: IEA [2]

POLICY IMPLICATIONS

- EU Critical Raw Materials Act (CRMA): requires that at least 40% of strategic mineral processing capacity be located in the EU by 2030.
- Paris Agreement: links the decarbonization of mineral supply chains to global climate targets, reinforcing the need to cut upstream emissions.
- EU Carbon Border Adjustment Mechanism (CBAM): will place a carbon price on imported materials, increasing the competitiveness of low-emission supply routes.

CONCLUSIONS

- Critical minerals are major emission hotspots in the solar PV supply chain.
- Mitigation strategies can reduce embodied emissions by 30–40%, particularly through renewable-powered refining and recycling.
- Combining policy, technology, and recycling is essential to build resilient and low-carbon supply chains for solar PV.

REFERENCES

[1] International Energy Agency (IEA). Solar PV Global Supply Chains. Paris: IEA, 2022.

[2] International Energy Agency (IEA). Global Critical Minerals Outlook 2025. Paris: IEA, 2025.

[3] Cui, H. et al. Nature Communications, 2025 — analysis of PV supply-chain decarbonization and regional shifts.

[4] European Commission. Proposal for a Regulation on Critical Raw Materials (CRMA), COM(2023) 160 final, 2023.

[5] United Nations (UNFCCC). Paris Agreement, 2015.

A FINANCIAL MODEL FOR THE DEPLOYMENT OF KOREAN FARM-BASED PHOTOVOLTAIC SYSTEM

*Hye-mi Hwang, Seok-whan Ko , Woo-gyun Shin, Young Chul Ju, Jin-Seok Lee
Renewable Energy System Laboratory, Korea Institute of Energy Research, Rep. of Korea
presenting author (hyemi@kier.re.kr)

Abstract

With the increasing emphasis on the importance of photovoltaic (PV) deployment for achieving carbon neutrality by 2050, the expansion of PV systems in rural areas is expected to grow in Korea. As rural households in Korea represent economically vulnerable regions due to declining agricultural income caused by an aging population, the deployment of farm-based photovoltaic systems is expected to generate additional non-agricultural income (from solar power generation), thereby contributing to increased household income. However, current government-supported rural PV programs often require substantial upfront investment from participants, limiting access for many farming households.

To address this limitation, this study proposes a project financing model aimed at revitalizing rural PV deployment, based on a previously developed lightweight rooftop photovoltaic system. The proposed model is designed to enable broad participation among farmers while ensuring economic feasibility. This study establishes standardized deployment units for farm-based photovoltaic systems applicable to individual farmhouses, storage facilities, and livestock barns. A rental-based structure is proposed to ensure revenue generation for each deployment unit based on system capacity. Furthermore, the proposed financial model is applied to these standardized units to analyze its economic feasibility from both the farmers' and project developers' perspectives.

Rural Solar PV Financing Model Design

▓ Target characteristics

- Aging workforce
- Capital shortage from income decline
- Farmland/forest-based site

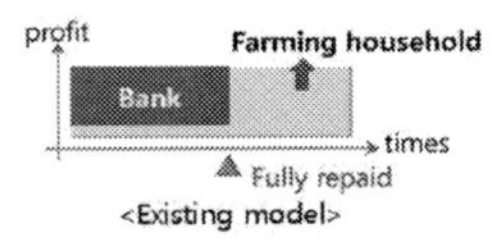

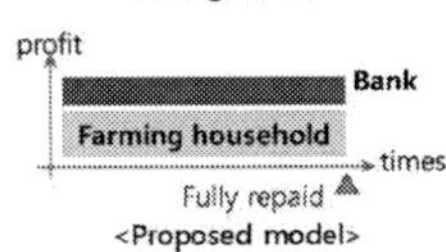

▓ Financing structure

- Social economy organization- based model
- PV equipment rental → short maturity profile
- Easy to recycle & re-use facilities

▓ Standard PV installation unit

- Set rental units : 3 kW, 9 kW
- Considering marginal cost changes & farm size
- Stable marginal cost at 100kW; reduced under 100kW
- 99 kW standard unit finalized (subsidized unit 30kW)

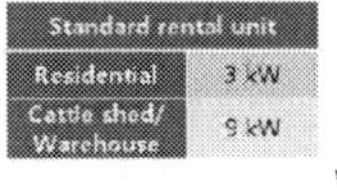

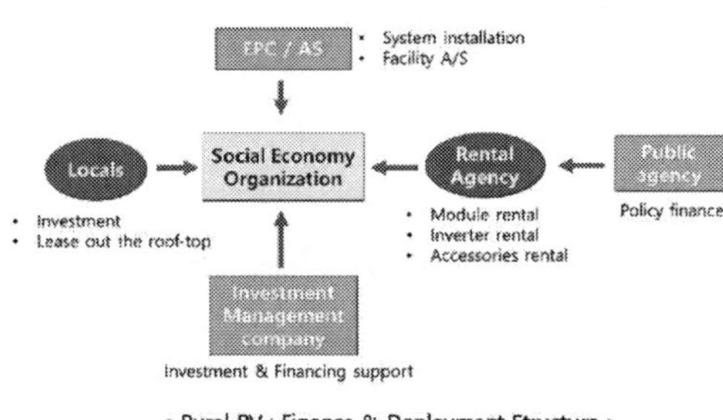

Financial Model Economic Analysis

▓ Return Analysis for Rental Providers

- Rental agency deploys PV to 20% of Farms (99kW/30kW)
- **Full Net Income Distribution : Equity IRR 3.29%**
- Case : 20-Year Rental
- 50% Leverage (3% interest, 20-year Amortization) : Equity IRR 4.23%

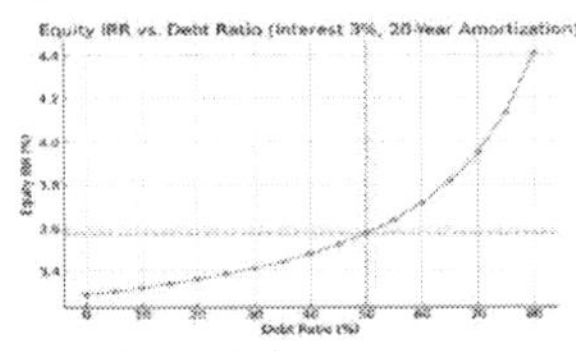

▓ Key Risk Analysis

- Key Risk
  : Rental termination, unpaid rental fees, Equipment failure
- If 5% of rentals are terminated after 1year
  → IRR drops by 0.4%
- Managing cost risks
  (1) cost-related risks reflected in rental fees
  (2) covered by insurance

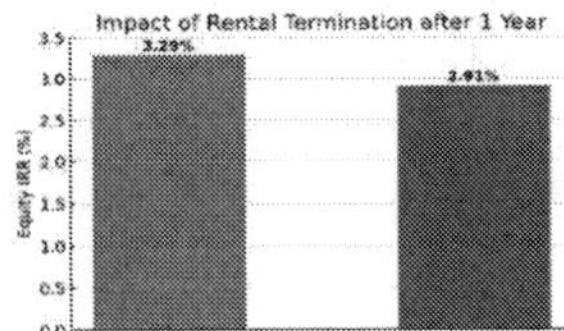

▓ Economic Analysis of Rural PV Financing Model

- Assumption
  : Capacity Factor 14%, REC+SMP 135 KRW/kWh
- Economic Feasibility Secured for 99kW/30kW

Item	Standard (99kW)	subsidized (30kW)
NPV	KRW 25.6 million	KRW 51.6 million
IRR	16.7%	9.3%
Pay back period	6 years	8 years
B/C	1.4	1.6

▓ Sensitivity Analysis of Rural PV Model

- 0.5% Increase in Capacity Factor → 2~ 3% Increase in IRR
- 5 KRW Increase in Electricity sales price → 2~3% Increase in IRR

C.F(%)	14.5	15	15.5	16	16.5
IRR(%)	16.5	19.1	21.6	24	26.4
NPV (KRW billion)	23.9	30.3	36.7	43.1	49.4
PBP(year)	5	4	4	4	3

Conclusions

- **Development of Deployment Model and Profit Structure** for Farmer-Led Rural PV Dissemination → Proposal of **Social Economy** Enterprise and Rental Operator Structure
- **Customized Deployment Framework** reflecting target regions and farm household characteristics, with **risk analysis-basid rental fee setting and operation plan**
- **Economic feasibility achievable** for both rental operators and social enterproses **without goverment support** under the proposed model

PHOTOVOLTAIC ENERGY PRODUCTION IN TWO UNIVERSITY CAMPUSES: A COMPARATIVE STUDY

Aarón Ortiz-Peña,[1] Mahamadou Abdou-Tankari[2], Andrés Honrubia-Escribano[1], Emilio Gómez-Lázaro[1]
[1]Renewable Energy Research Institute, and Department of Electrical, Electronic, Automatic and Communications Engineering, ETSII-AB, University of Castilla-La Mancha (UCLM) Albacete, Spain
Aaron.ortiz@uclm.es Andres.honrubia@uclm.es Emilio.gomez@uclm.es
[2]CERTES Laboratory, University Paris-Est Creteil (UPEC), 94010 Creteil, France
Mahamadou.abdou-tankari@u-pec.fr

ABSTRACT: The transition to renewable energy is vital to reduce dependence on fossil fuels and curb greenhouse gas emissions. Universities, as energy-intensive institutions with diverse activities, offer a particularly suitable context for photovoltaic system deployment. This study evaluates two operational PV installations at the University of Castilla-La Mancha, located on the Albacete and Toledo campuses, using hourly monitoring data from October 2024 to February 2025. At Albacete, all electricity produced was consumed, as demand consistently exceeded generation, with demand peaks of 2 MWh compared with maximum PV output of 400 kWh. In Toledo, demand surpassed 800 kWh, while PV generation reached 200 kWh. Average demand coverage was 8.2% in Toledo and 7.9% in Albacete, shaped by consumption profiles and the limitations of zero-injection systems. Generation patterns revealed broader, more centred curves at Albacete due to dual module orientations, while Toledo showed a skewed profile from west-facing modules. Economically, savings amounted to 26,600 € at Albacete and 14,600 € at Toledo, with results confirming that both PV generation and electricity prices determine financial benefits. Overall, the study demonstrates the capacity of PV systems in universities to lower electricity costs and grid dependence, while stressing the importance of analyses based on real operational data.
Keywords: Electricity demand coverage, solar pv systems in buildings, public buildings, real monitoring data

1 INTRODUCTION

The growing demand for renewable energy stems from both the need to reduce dependence on non-renewable sources and the urgency to mitigate their environmental impact [1]. Electricity generation from fossil fuels remains associated with high CO_2 emissions, in contrast with European energy efficiency plans that set ambitious targets for reducing greenhouse gas emissions by 2050 [2]. This energy transition is further conditioned by the increasing demand for electricity [3], as well as the sharp rise in energy prices in recent years, particularly following the war in Ukraine [4]. This context has reinforced the importance of reducing consumption from the external distribution grid, especially in the building sector, which accounts for around 40% of electricity demand and approximately 35% of CO_2 emissions [5].

Within this sector, universities represent a distinct group of large-scale buildings with high energy consumption, due to the wide variety of activities they host, ranging from teaching and administrative management to research, the latter being the most energy-intensive [6]. Added to this are significant cooling requirements during warmer periods, which further highlight the need for efficiency measures and renewable energy systems. However, such strategies are often not prioritised in these institutions, as energy costs are not directly borne by users [7]. Among the renewable technologies implemented in university environments, solar photovoltaic (PV) energy is the most widespread, as it can exploit available surfaces such as rooftops, façades and car parks without interfering with daily activities [8]. Numerous studies have assessed its feasibility through simulation-based approaches, analysing demand coverage and payback periods in universities across different countries [9–11]. Although some works report experiences of real-world installations [12,13], the majority of analyses remain based on estimated radiation and generation data, without incorporating measured values.

The literature review therefore reveals several limitations: a predominance of feasibility assessments over evaluations based on real operational data, a scarcity of comparative studies between installations under similar conditions, and a lack of detailed analyses considering aspects such as seasonal variability, performance across different types of days, or the influence of system design. These gaps justify the need for research that rigorously compares PV systems in real operation, in order to provide more accurate and useful results for future implementations. The literature review highlights several limitations. The gaps identified in the research are:

- Predominance of simulation studies over real operational data.
- Lack of comparative analyses between PV systems with measured data.
- Limited focus on system design and architectural integration.
- Efficiency often assessed with simulated rather than measured indicators.
- Seasonal variability and daily load patterns rarely addressed.

The objectives of this study are:

- Compare two PV installations at UCLM (Toledo and Albacete).
- Analyse operational performance using real data.
- Identify maximum generation values and demand coverage.
- Evaluate economic savings from solar PV generation.

2 CASE STUDY

The University of Castilla-La Mancha (UCLM) is a public higher education institution in Spain, with campuses spread across several cities, including Albacete and Toledo. This study focuses on these two campuses due to their contrasting architectural and climatic characteristics.

The Albacete campus (38.99° N, 1.86° W) is a modern, purpose-built site in the south-east of the city, hosting faculties such as Industrial Engineering, Medicine, and Computer Science. Its contemporary infrastructure, laboratories, and well-planned layout make it representative of university buildings in a continental Mediterranean climate. In contrast, the Toledo campus (39.86° N, 4.03° W), located along the River Tagus, occupies a refurbished historical site combining 19th-century industrial structures with modern educational buildings. It hosts faculties including Architecture, Environmental Sciences, and Humanities, providing a unique setting to examine energy efficiency in heritage and mixed-use university buildings.

In 2024, both campuses implemented solar PV systems to reduce reliance on the external grid and lower electricity costs, building on earlier measures taken in 2022 in response to rising energy prices [14]. The Albacete PV installation has a total capacity of 637.42 kWp, comprising 1,099 modules rated at 580 Wp, mainly distributed across the rooftops of biomedical sciences buildings. The Toledo campus installed a 339.35 kWp system with 617 modules rated at 550 Wp, spread over several rooftops across the campus.

The climatic differences between the locations are also notable: Toledo lies in climate zone C4, with mild winters and hot summers, whereas Albacete is classified as D3, with colder winters and moderately severe summers. These contrasts provide a valuable context for comparing the performance of PV systems under different environmental and architectural conditions.

Figure 1. Albacete University Campus.

Figure 2. Toledo University Campus.

3 METHODOLOGY

3.1 General methodology

This study presents a detailed analysis of the hourly energy generation in both campuses under investigation, alongside the total electrical energy demand. To this end, during the study period, which spans from October 2024 to February 2025, data were monitored on an hourly basis. Subsequently, the data were processed and analysed using the Matlab [14] software to identify null values or any values that did not correspond to reality. Following this procedure, the various results were obtained. Figure 3 illustrates the methodology applied in this study, encompassing data monitoring, preprocessing, and analysis.

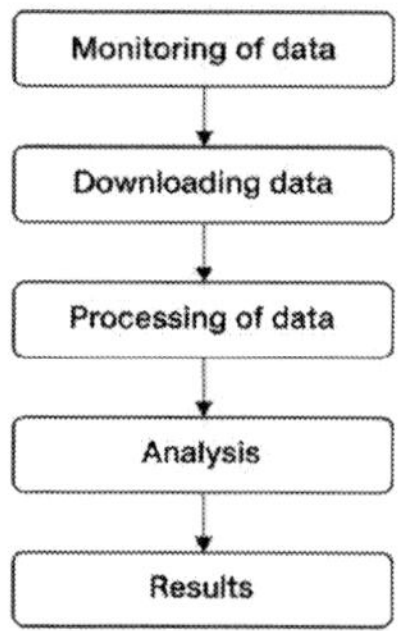

Figure 3. Applied methodology.

3.2 Equations

For this study, several equations were employed to analyse energy generation and consumption. A key indicator is the PV demand coverage, calculated as follows, Equation 1:

$$D.\,coverage\ (\%) = \frac{E_{PV}\ (kWh)}{Total\ consumption\ (kWh)} * 100 \qquad (1)$$

Where E_{PV} represents the energy generated by the solar PV system during the considered period, compared to the total campus consumption.

Another important parameter is the average solar PV generation, which allows for defining hourly generation patterns, Equation 2:

$$E_{mean} = \frac{\sum_{i=1}^{d} E_{ch}\ (kWh)}{d} \qquad (2)$$

Where E_{mean} is the energy generated in a specific hour and ddd is the number of days considered for the average. The monthly economic savings from solar PV generation are estimated using, Equation 3:

$$Monthly\ savings\ (€) = EF_m * EP_m \qquad (3)$$

Where EF_m is the energy generated in the month and EP_m is the average electricity price during that period.

4 RESULTS

This section presents the various results obtained from the data analysis. At the Albacete campus, all the energy generated is consumed, as the electricity demand exceeds generation, with recorded demand values reaching up to 2

MWh, while PV generation peaks at around 400 kWh. At the Toledo campus, electricity demand exceeds 800 kWh, compared with a generation of approximately 200 kWh. Figure 4 illustrates the monthly solar PV generation for both campuses under study. It can be observed that the highest consumption for both campuses occurs in February. Although the installed capacity at the Albacete campus is 1.9 times greater than that of Toledo, generation in Albacete during this month was 2.2 times higher than in Toledo, owing to climatic conditions. The increase in electricity consumption in February may be attributed to several factors, such as weather conditions or greater use of the facilities.

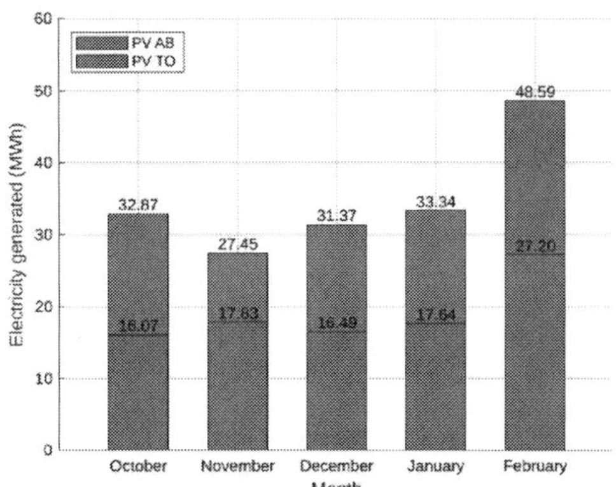
Figure 4. Monthly energy generated.

Figure 5 illustrates the daily demand coverage achieved by both generation systems, calculated on the basis of Equation 1. For the Toledo campus, demand coverage values range from 1% to 17%, while for the Albacete campus they vary between 2% and 15%. The fact that Albacete can reach higher daily coverage values is primarily due to its greater overall electricity demand. Nevertheless, it should also be noted that the effective coverage at this campus is constrained by the presence of zero-injection systems, which prevent surplus electricity from being fed into other parts of the network. As a result, the level of demand coverage is not solely indicative of higher PV generation; rather, it is strongly influenced by the interaction between generation and the specific consumption profile of each campus. In total terms, the average demand coverage during the study period was 8.2% for Toledo and 7.9% for Albacete, highlighting the relatively balanced performance of both systems despite their differences in size and configuration.

Figure 6 presents the average generation profiles for the two campuses under study. At Albacete, the maximum peak occurs between 12:00 and 13:00 hours, with values reaching approximately 200 kWh. In contrast, the Toledo installation records its maximum peak slightly later, at 13:00 hours, with generation approaching 120 kWh. When comparing the shapes of the generation curves, it becomes evident that the Albacete installation produces electricity over a broader time range than Toledo. This wider curve is the result of the system's design, which incorporates PV modules with both positive and negative azimuths, allowing it to capture solar radiation across different orientations and providing a more balanced, centred profile. Conversely, the curve for the Toledo installation shows a pronounced rightward skew. This asymmetry is

explained by the fact that most of its modules have a positive azimuth, oriented between south and west, which leads to higher generation levels when the sun shifts towards the western horizon in the afternoon.

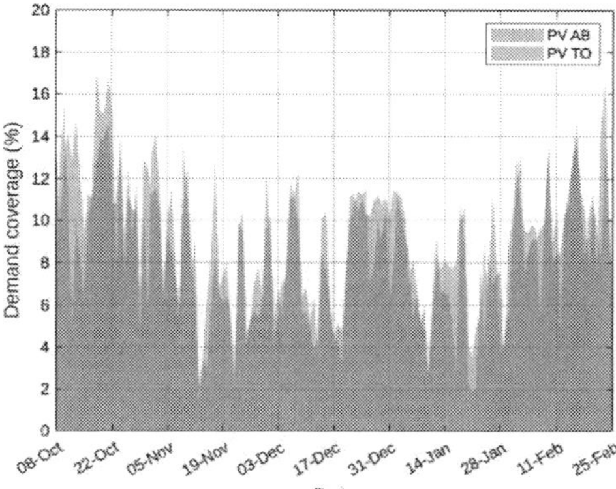
Figure 5. Daily demand coverage.

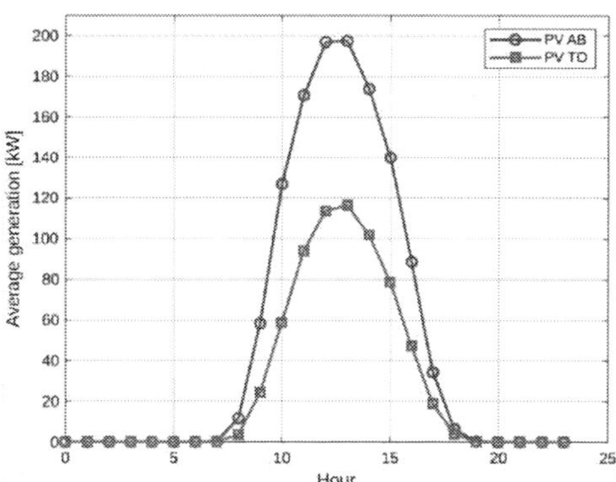
Figure 6. Average generation profile.

Solar PV generation leads to a reduction in the electricity bill, as it decreases the demand for power from the external grid. Figure 7 presents the monthly savings achieved through renewable generation, alongside the average hourly electricity price. The latter is calculated on the basis of the final hourly tariff applied to the university, which is derived from the market price plus additional coefficients that increase the final value above the wholesale market rate. When comparing these savings with Figure 4, which displays total monthly generation, it becomes evident that the month with the highest generation does not necessarily correspond to the month with the greatest financial savings. For instance, in December and January, both campuses generated significant amounts of renewable electricity; however, savings were higher in December. This is explained by the higher electricity price in December, 0.18 €/kWh, compared with January 0.15 €/kWh. Thus, the price of electricity is a determining factor in identifying which months yield the greatest reductions in the electricity bill. The month with the largest savings is February, which also corresponds to the highest level of generation. In this case, the amount of electricity generated was sufficiently high to offset the relatively lower price of 0.15 €/kWh. This confirms that financial savings depend on a dual effect: both the volume of electricity generated and the prevailing electricity price. In total, during the study period, the Albacete campus achieved savings of approximately 26,600 €, while the Toledo campus recorded savings of about 14,600 €.

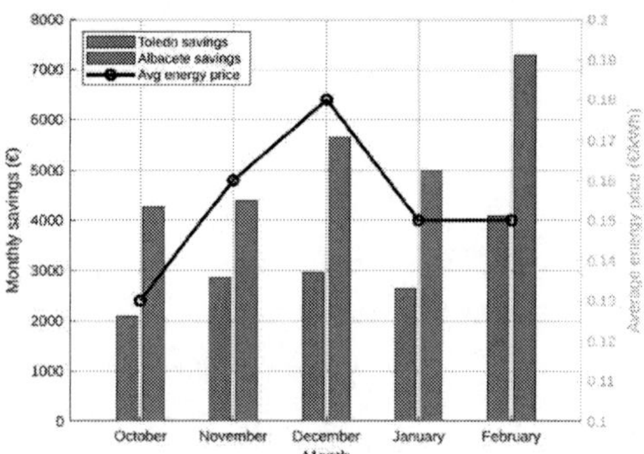

Figure 7. Monthly savings per solar PV generation.

5 CONCLUSIONS

This study compared two PV installations at the Albacete and Toledo campuses of the University of Castilla-La Mancha using real operational data. Both systems reduced demand from the external grid, with performance influenced by system design, consumption patterns and climatic conditions. At Albacete, all generated electricity was consumed, as demand exceeded PV output. Its installed capacity is 1.9 times greater than Toledo's, and generation in peak months was up to 2.2 times higher. Its wider, balanced generation curve, due to modules with both positive and negative azimuths, contrasted with Toledo's narrower, right-skewed profile caused by west-oriented modules. Average demand coverage reached 8.2% at Toledo and 7.9% at Albacete, shaped not only by generation but also by consumption levels and zero-injection system constraints. Thus, demand coverage is not solely an indicator of PV output.

Economically, savings depended on both generation and electricity prices. Although generation peaked in January, higher tariffs in December led to greater savings that month, while February achieved the largest overall savings due to much higher output despite lower prices. Over the study period, Albacete saved about 26,600 € and Toledo 14,600 €.

Overall, solar PV systems in universities show significant potential to cut costs and reduce reliance on the grid, while this work highlights the value of real operational data for accurate evaluation and planning of future installations.

6 ACKNOWLEDGMENT

This research was partially funded by the State Research Agency (Agencia Estatal de Investigación, AEI); by the European Regional Development Fund (Fondo Europeo de Desarrollo Regional, FEDER) through project PID2021-126082OB-C21; and by the Council of Communities of Castilla- La Mancha (Junta de Comunidades de Castilla-La Mancha, JCCM) through project SBPLY/23/180225/000226.

7 REFERENCES

[1] Yu, C., Moslehpour, M., Tran, T. K., Trung, L. M., Ou, J. P., & Tien, N. H. (2023). Impact of non-renewable energy and natural resources on economic recovery: Empirical evidence from selected developing economies. *Resources policy, 80*, 103221.

[2] Colmenar-Santos, A., Muñoz-Gómez, A. M., Rosales-Asensio, E., & López-Rey, Á. (2019). Electric vehicle charging strategy to support renewable energy sources in Europe 2050 low-carbon scenario. *Energy, 183*, 61-74.

[3] Karipoğlu, F., & Denizli, O. (2025). Towards renewable energy islands in Türkiye: Potential and challenges. *Renewable and Sustainable Energy Reviews, 211*, 115324.

[4] Kaur, C., Siddiki, J., & Singh, P. (2024). The asymmetric impact of input prices, the Russia-Ukraine war and domestic policy changes on wholesale electricity prices in India: A quantile autoregressive distributed lag analysis. *Energy Economics, 132*, 107428.

[5] Pérez-Lombard, L., Ortiz, J., & Pout, C. (2008). A review on buildings energy consumption information. Energy and buildings, 40(3), 394-398.

[6] Ortiz-Peña, A., Honrubia-Escribano, A., Gallego-Giner, I., Galán, Á., & Gómez-Lázaro, E. (2025). Analysis and impact of electrical energy consumption in the academic sector. A case study of the university of Castilla-La Mancha. *Energy Conversion and Management: X*, 100894.

[7] de Souza Silva, J. L., de Melo, K. B., dos Santos, K. V., Sakô, E. Y., da Silva, M. K., Moreira, H. S., ... & Villalva, M. G. (2022). Case study of photovoltaic power plants in a model of sustainable university in Brazil. *Renewable Energy, 196*, 247-260.

[8] Hasapis, D., Savvakis, N., Tsoutsos, T., Kalaitzakis, K., Psychis, S., & Nikolaidis, N. P. (2017). Design of large scale prosuming in Universities: The solar energy vision of the TUC campus. *Energy and Buildings, 141*, 39-55.

[9] Kalkan, N., Bercin, K., Cangul, O., Morales, M. G., Saleem, M. M. K. M., Marji, I., ... & Tsigkogianni, E. (2011). A renewable energy solution for Highfield Campus of University of Southampton. *Renewable and sustainable energy reviews, 15*(6), 2940-2959.

[10] Hasapis, D., Savvakis, N., Tsoutsos, T., Kalaitzakis, K., Psychis, S., & Nikolaidis, N. P. (2017). Design of large scale prosuming in Universities: The solar energy vision of the TUC campus. *Energy and Buildings, 141*, 39-55.

[11] Ahmed, A., Nadeem, T. B., Naqvi, A. A., Siddiqui, M. A., Khan, M. H., Zahid, M. S. B., & Ammar, S. M. (2022). Investigation of PV utilizability on university buildings: A case study of Karachi, Pakistan. *Renewable Energy, 195*, 238-251.

[12] Allouhi, A., Saadani, R., Kousksou, T., Saidur, R., Jamil, A., & Rahmoune, M. (2016). Grid-connected PV systems installed on institutional buildings: Technology comparison, energy

analysis and economic performance. *Energy and Buildings, 130,* 188-201.

[13] Obeng, M., Gyamfi, S., Derkyi, N. S., Kabobah, A. T., & Peprah, F. (2020). Technical and economic feasibility of a 50 MW grid-connected solar PV at UENR Nsoatre Campus. *Journal of Cleaner Production, 247,* 119159.

[14] MathWorks. (2024). *MATLAB (Version R2024b) [Computer software].* Natick, MA: The MathWorks, Inc. https://www.mathworks.com.

DRIVING GLOBAL LEADERSHIP IN THE SOLAR PV MODULE VALUE CHAIN: THE ROLE OF EARLY ADOPTION AND IMPLEMENTATION OF IEC STANDARDS

Deepti[1], Saurabh Kumar[2], Sushma Sharma[1], Gaurav Kumar[3]
[1]Faculty of Management and Commerce, SRM University, Delhi-NCR, Sonepat, Haryana, India
[2]PTB Braunshweig, Germany
[3]MERI College of Engineering and Technology, Bahadurgarh, Haryana, India

ABSTRACT: This paper will explore the relationship between early adoption of IEC standards, their implementation and a country's leadership in the solar PV module value chain. It will analyse economic and geo-economic trends in PV module manufacturing, the role of standards adoption and implementation in driving innovation and reliability, and how this correlates with cost reductions and production growth in these countries. The study will highlight countries that have demonstrated consistent adoption and implementation of IEC standards, their manufacturing output, and the impact on global competitiveness in the solar PV industry. The research will delve into the role of conformity assessment bodies like testing and calibration laboratories in Germany, China, India and Vietnam. These bodies play a pivotal role in implementation of standards, contributing to product quality, safety, and performance consistency. The study will examine how these technical frameworks support the solar PV ecosystem by fostering trust in components and systems, enabling seamless integration into global supply chains, and enhancing the credibility of manufacturers in the global market.
Keywords: Photovoltaic (PV), IEC Standards, Adoption vs. Implementation, Exports, Quality Infrastructure

1 INTRODUCTION

Photovoltaic technologies have given new means of providing electrical energy to the Global economy. The narrative of solar PV industry is shifting even beyond so called unending energy source available from the Sun. Factors like absence of continuous transportation like for conventional fuels, allure of lesser carbon emissions, phasing out of old coal-based plants are incentivising countries to push for development of domestic solar PV industry. For the development of solar PV industry, both supply-push policies and demand-pull policies are being tried by the authorities. [1] [2] Policies like production linked incentives and even local content requirement to attract local production for domestic demand are also being tried. [3] Rather than looking in silos, the impact of economic or market policies or focus on R&D activities, this paper has attempted approach to look at the solar PV industry trade outcomes of past few decades in selected countries and correlate them with quality infrastructure of these same countries with technical specifications acceptable at the Global level.

Standards formulated at the International Electrotechnical Commission (IEC) level are considered the most accepted technical norms at the Global level. Its membership is open to all the countries and participation activities are coordinated through their national standards body serving the role of national committee to the IEC. Other international standardisation organisations like ISO, ITU, Codex are also formulating standards in other different areas of the economy. Within the electrotechnical sector as well, there exists various areas of standardisation for which the structure of organising works into different technical committees (or even sub-committee or working groups) exists. Member countries can opt for participating or observer membership in their interest areas.

In this work, the role of both adoption and implementation of IEC standards on the export competitiveness for solar PV module value chain will be analysed. For the implementation aspects, the role of metrology and conformity assessment bodies are also studied in the context of establishing leadership in the solar PV module sector. Four countries, namely Germany, China, India and Vietnam, have been studied where policymakers are maintaining continuity in terms of policies for promotion of the solar PV industry.

2 METHODOLOGIES

2.1 Adoption of standards

The technical committee TC 82 at the level of IEC is formulating international standards in the area of solar PV technologies. Some of the major IEC Standards in this field are IEC 61215 (earlier 61646), IEC 61730, IEC TS 62804, IEC 62716, IEC TS 63342, IEC 60904 series, IEC 62446. Adoption of these standards at the national level through stakeholder consultation may serve as the first step to create awareness and push for their implementation. Aspects like test methods for design qualification and type approval, construction requirements, measurement of potential-induced degradation-delamination, ammonia corrosion resistance, light induced degradation at elevated temperatures are covered in these documents. Even though solar PV technologies are evolving rapidly and direct one-to-one specifications for latest technologies may not be addressed, some horizontal baseline criteria for evaluating outcomes still exist. A simpler evolution chart of solar PV technologies starting from monocrystalline to perovskite and tandem is given at Figure 1. More detailed mapping of different technologies since 1976 along with efficiency is also being maintained by NREL. [4] [5] For the innovation, patent filing statistics analysed in various studies reveals that after 2000; inventors from USA, Germany and China are among the leaders. However, after 2005, surge in new solar PV patent families from China was observed followed with subsequent rise in new solar PV patent families from Germany. But within a span of few years, these new patent numbers from USA and Germany decreased and China took the leadership position in the new solar PV patenting. [6]

1960s	1980s	2000s	2020s

Figure 1: Solar PV technologies over the years

If we look at national level standardisation efforts, all the four countries taken in this study have technical committees comprising national level stakeholders. In Germany (DE) it is DKE/K 373 [7], in China (CN) it is SAC/TC 90 [8], in India (IN) it is BIS/ETD 28 [9] and in Vietnam (VN) it is TCVN/TC/E8 [10]. Except Vietnam, the other three countries are also represented as participating members in the work of IEC TC 82 with the right to vote and involved in formulation, review and revision of standards. [11] Standards formulated at the level of IEC TC 82 are getting adopted as national standards by the national level technical committees in all the four countries. The information comparing year of publication of important IEC Standards in the area of solar PV with year of adoption in these countries is given at Table I gathered from the official website of those organisations.

As can be seen from the Table I, Germany is regularly adopting IEC standards in the area of solar PV as national standards. This adoption is also more often earlier as compared to other countries. India is also adopting these standards and delay gaps seen during the 1990s, 2000s are gradually decreasing. The same adoption process is comparatively very less in China. In the case of Vietnam it is even lesser prior to 2020.

2.2   Export of Commodities

Trade flow measurements among national economies happen on the basis of HSN codes which are presently harmonised till 6 digits level. HSN 854140 was in operation till 2021 with description as Photosensitive semiconductor devices, incl. PV cells whether or not assembled in modules or made up into panels; light emitting diodes (excluding PV generators). Afterwards, four distinct categorisation was done bringing out clearer demarcation by codes HSN 854142 meant for PV cells not assembled in modules or made up into panels and HSN 854143 meant for PV cells assembled in modules or made up into panels.

From the ITC trade map data [12], it is observed that under HSN 854140 in terms of US Dollars, in 2003 Germany had exports of 0.8 billion, China 0.3 billion, India 46 million and Vietnam just 3 thousand. In 2023, these amount values combined with HSN 854142 and 854143 changed to 0.5 billion for Germany, 1.5 billion for India, 8 billion for Vietnam and 43 billion for China. Year 2003 was a pivotal year which marked the beginning of rising patent filings, increased production and exports.

Table I: Adoption of IEC standards for solar PV in Germany, China, India and Vietnam

Sr No	IEC Standards/ Documents	Adoption year			
		DE	CN	IN	VN
1	61215-1:2016	2017	N/A	2019	2017
2	61215-1:2021	2022	N/A	2023	N/A
3	61215-1-1:2016	2018	N/A	2019	2017
4	61215-1-1:2021	2022	N/A	2023	2025
5	61215-1-2:2016	2017	N/A	2019	2020
6	61215-1-2:2021	2023	N/A	2023	N/A
7	61215-1-3:2016	2017	N/A	2019	2020
8	61215-1-3:2021	2023	N/A	2023	N/A
9	61215-1-4:2016	2017	N/A	2019	2020
10	61215-1-4:2021	2023	N/A	2023	N/A
11	61215-2:2016	2019	N/A	2019	2017
12	61215-2:2021	2022	N/A	2023	N/A
13	61646:1996	1998	2002	N/A	N/A
14	61646:2008	2009	N/A	2014	2015
15	61730-1:2004	2007	2006	2010	N/A
16	61730-1:2016	2018	N/A	2019	2018
17	61730-1:2023	N/A	N/A	2025	N/A
18	61730-2:2004	2007	N/A	2010	N/A
19	61730-2:2016	2018	N/A	2019	2018
20	61730-2:2023	N/A	N/A	2025	N/A
21	TS 62804-1:2015	2017	N/A	2019	N/A
22	TS 62804-1:2025	N/A	N/A	N/A	N/A
23	TS 62804-1-1: 2020	N/A	N/A	N/A	N/A
24	TS 62804-2:2022	N/A	N/A	N/A	N/A
25	62716:2013	2014	2023	2018	N/A
26	TS 63342:2022	N/A	N/A	N/A	N/A
27	60904-1:1987	1995	1996	1989	N/A
28	60904-1:2006	2007	N/A	2010	2020
29	60904-1:2020	2023	N/A	2024	N/A
30	60904-1-1:2017	2018	N/A	2020	2020
31	TS 60904-1-2: 2019	2022	N/A	2020	N/A
32	TS 60904-1-2: 2024	N/A	N/A	N/A	N/A
33	60904-2:1989	1995	1996	1993	N/A
34	60904-2:2007	2008	N/A	2013	N/A
35	60904-2:2015	2015	N/A	2018	2020
36	60904-2:2023	2024	N/A	2025	N/A
37	60904-3:1989	1995	1996	1998	N/A
38	60904-3:2008	2009	N/A	2013	N/A
39	60904-3:2016	2017	N/A	2018	N/A
40	60904-3:2019	2020	N/A	2020	2020
41	60904-4:2009	2010	N/A	2014	N/A
42	60904-4:2019	2021	N/A	2024	2020
43	60904-5:1993	1996	1997	2010	N/A
44	60904-5:2011	2011	N/A	2014	2020
45	60904-7:1995	N/A	N/A	N/A	N/A
46	60904-7:1998	1998	2006	N/A	N/A
47	60904-7:2008	2009	N/A	2013	N/A
48	60904-7:2019	2021	N/A	2023	2020
49	60904-8:1995	N/A	N/A	N/A	N/A
50	60904-8:1998	1998	2002	2010	N/A
51	60904-8:2014	2015	N/A	2018	2020
52	60904-8-1:2017	2018	2020	2020	2020
53	60904-9:1995	N/A	2006	N/A	N/A
54	60904-9:2007	2008	N/A	2010	2020
55	60904-9:2020	2024	N/A	2023	N/A
56	60904-10:1998	1998	2012	N/A	N/A
57	60904-10:2009	2010	N/A	2014	2020
58	60904-10:2020	2022	N/A	2023	N/A
59	60904-13:2018	2019	N/A	2020	N/A
60	TR 60904-14: 2020	N/A	N/A	2023	N/A
61	62446-1:2016	2016	N/A	N/A	2017
62	62446-2:2020	2021	N/A	2023	N/A
63	62446-3:2017	2018	N/A	2020	N/A
64	TS 63126:2020	2022	2024	2023	N/A

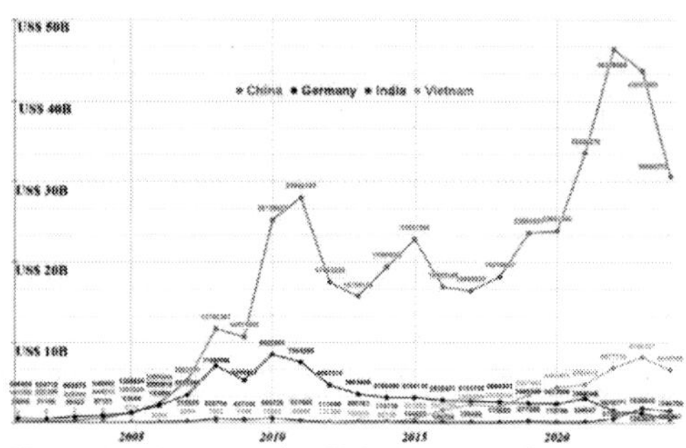

Figure 2: Exports under HSN 854140 (after 2021 - 854142 and 854143) from 2001 to 2024

2.3 Quality infrastructure for implementation

Implementation of technical specifications in any economy starts from the basic foundation of metrology providing traceable, consistent measurement services through a downstream network upto conformity assessment services like testing and certification bodies, which often runs via accreditation bodies.

Germany had the basic foundation of metrology services for the solar PV sector in its economy much earlier starting in 1986. [13] [14] China started these metrology services in its economy in 2006. [15] In India, the primary cell calibration facility has been established in 2024. [16] whereas Vietnam doesn't have any such service provider in its own domestic economy and relies on collaboration with other economies. [17]

In the downstream network of quality infrastructure services, data related to IAF and ILAC based certifications and reports is not publicly available. Another alternative multilateral mechanism in place, i.e. the IECEE conformity assessment system run by IEC itself is utilised to arrive at a measurable outcome of downstream services emanating from the quality infrastructure setup. Present figures of IECEE recognised certification bodies (NCBs) and test laboratories (CBTLs) in the solar PV sector as well as number of standards in the recognition scope are given in Table II. [18]

Table II: Number of IECEE recognised multilateral arrangement NCBs and CBTLs

	NCBs (Number of standards including year versions)	CBTLs (Number of Standards including year versions)
DE	5 (120)	5 (57)
CN	2 (28)	30 (398)
IN	0	6 (73)
VN	0	0

Going one step further, the number of IECEE certificates issued to factory locations in these four countries were also looked into to get perspective on implementation of Standards. Statistics of year wise such certificates issued are given in Figure 3.

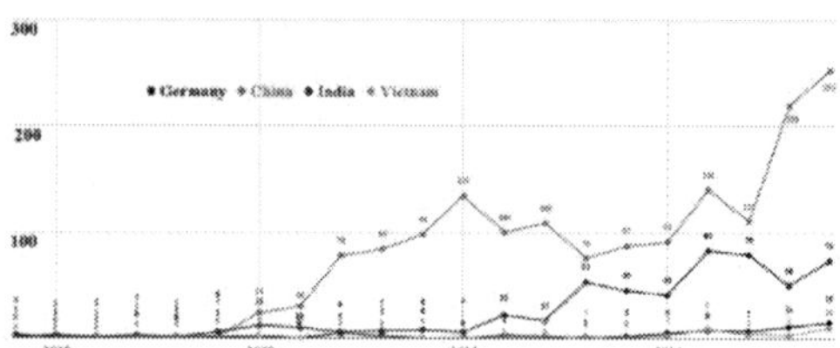

Figure 3: IECEE certificates issued to factory locations from 2004 to 2024

3 RESULTS

Information obtained from the methodologies, competitiveness in the Global market for potential future leadership in the solar PV sector was analysed.

3.1 Role of early adoption

Notional adoption of IEC standards giving them the status of national standards is found to have no positive correlation with competitiveness in the Global market. China and Vietnam have much larger scale of exports even without formal adoption of IEC standards at their respective national committee level.

3.2 Role of implementation

At the time when solar PV sector exports were insignificant, Germany had the basic foundation of metrology services in its economy. This may explain its better export competitiveness at the nascent stage in early 2000s. Later on, China started metrology services at the national level at the right time when the solar PV sector saw an initial spurt in 2006. Downstream services of multilateral certification saw rise in 2010 after exports started rising in 2008. In India, the exports growth has remained subdued despite the faster response in adoption of Standards after 2010s and scalability potential due to rising domestic demand. This may be explained by a combination of absence of metrology services in its economy as well as absence of multilateral certification bodies with local presence. In Vietnam, exports started rising in 2016 followed by an increase in issued certifications after 2019. Though not leading the exports, Vietnam has surpassed both India and Germany by a large margin despite the absence of both metrology services and multilateral recognised certification bodies in its country.

4 ADDITIONAL FACTORS

4.1 The results from the role of adoption and implementation of IEC standards are unable to be uniformly applied in all four countries. Additional policy factors by these countries may also be playing a part in these outcomes impacting each other.

4.2 Both supply-side push and demand-side pulls also need a deeper look with possible intertwining outcome results. In Europe, policies initiated in 2008 and 2009 could have aided in driving up exports from other countries while the domestic industry might not have been in a position to scale up to the level of pulls created from the demand-side. [19]

4.3   Starting from 2016, In India as well, similar demand-side pull policies were seen into effect which was also supplemented with supply-side pushes like local content requirements and production linked incentives. [20] However, the export competitiveness has not seen the results as compared to Vietnam despite a comparatively higher number of IECEE certificates issued to factories. The study combining more external factors with verifiable data still remains an opportunity for the future.

5   CONCLUSIONS

5.1   There emerges two models when it comes to standards for consideration of policymakers in making their decisions. One is the VIKAS model, where one actively pursues Validation of Knowledge to Advance Standards. It can be Indigenous knowledge and one shouldn't hesitate even if it's international knowledge. Countries are seen achieving competitiveness with direct use of IEC standards by their industries. Another is the GHULAM model, where Growth remains Hindered Under Loaned Adopted Manak/Standards. Notional adoption just conferring the national status without active implementation serves no purpose in driving competitiveness of the industry.

5.2   Quality of preparedness in terms of basic foundation of quality infrastructure in terms of metrology also emerges as a key aspect for seizing any demand-side pulls seen in the Global market. This basic foundation also needs to be built with downstream conformity assessment bodies providing services to the industry with multilateral acceptance.

6   ACKNOWLEDGMENTS

This research has been supported with sponsorship by the Physikalisch-Technische Bundesanstalt (PTB), International Cooperation Division, Germany.

7   REFERENCES

[1]   Daoyuan Wen *et al.*, "Development of solar photovoltaic industry and market in China, Germany, Japan and the United States of America using incentive policies", *Energy Exploration & Exploitation*, Volume 39, Issue 5, December 2020, doi:10.1177/0144598720979256

[2]   Alejandro Nuñez-Jimenez *et al.*, "Beyond innovation and deployment: Modeling the impact of technology-push and demand-pull policies in Germany's solar policy mix", *Research Policy*, Volume 51, Issue 10, December 2022, doi: 10.1016/j.respol.2022.104585

[3]   Narendra Shiradkar *et al.*, "Recent developments in solar manufacturing in India", *Solar Compass*, Volume 1, May 2022, 100009, doi: 10.1016/j.solcom.2022.100009

[4]   National Renewable Energy Laboratory, Best research-cell efficiency Chart, Washington, DC, NREL, [Online] Accessed: 01 September 2025

[5]   Zhenguo Li *et al.*, "Prospects of Photovoltaic Technology", *Engineering*, Volume 21, February 2024, doi: 10.1016/j.eng.2022.07.008

[6]   Pia Andres, "Adapting to Competition: Solar PV Innovation in Europe and the Impact of the 'China Shock'", *Environmental & Resource Economics*, Volume 87, Issue 12, October 2024, doi: 10.1007/s10640-024-00904-8

[7]   DKE/K 373, Accessed: 01 September 2025 [Online]   https://www.din.de/en/getting-involved/standards-committees/dke/publications

[8]   SAC/TC 90, Accessed: 01 September 2025 [Online] https://std.samr.gov.cn/search/orgDetailView?data_id=CFF3396241D07764E05397BE0A0A1558

[9]   BIS/ETD 28, Accessed: 01 September 2025 [Online] https://www.services.bis.gov.in/php/BIS_2.0/dgdashboard/Published_Standards

[10] TCVN/TC/E8, Accessed: 01 September 2025 [Online] http://tracuu.tcvn.vn/sdomain/front/tieu-chuan-viet-nam

[11] IEC/TC 92, Accessed: 01 September 2025 [Online] https://www.iec.ch/dyn/www/f?p=103:29:206618903840223::::FSP_ORG_ID,FSP_LANG_ID:1276,25

[12] ITC Trade Map, Accessed: 01 September 2025 [Online] https://www.trademap.org/

[13] J. Metzdorf *et al.*, "Absolute indoor calibration of large area solar cells", *5th European Symposium on Photovoltaic Generators in Space*, Proceeding Pages 397-401, November 1986

[14] S. Winter et al., "Primary Reference Cell Calibration at the PTB based on an improved DSR facility", *16th European Photovoltaic Solar Energy Conference*, March 2000, doi: 10.4324/9781315074405

[15] Institute of Electrical Engineering, Chinese Academy of Sciences, Accessed: 01 September 2025   [Online] http://english.iee.cas.cn/ns/es/201404/t20140422_119823.html

[16] Prathap Pathi *et al.*, "India's PV Quality Infrastructure Boost for Calibrating Solar Cells", *Akshay Urja*, Volume 15, Issue 3, April 2025

[17] Wolff Carl *et al.*, "The global dimension of the energy transition", *tm - Technisches Messen*, Volume 92, Pages 413-423, August 2025, doi: 10.1515/teme-2025-0041.

[18] IECEE certificates, Accessed: 01 September 2025 [Online] https://certificates.iecee.org/#/search

[19] Ole Langniß *et al.*, "Advanced mechanisms for the promotion of renewable energy—Models for the future evolution of the German Renewable Energy Act", *Energy Policy*, Volume 37, Issue 4, April 2009, doi: 10.1016/j.enpol.2008.11.007

[20] Malti Goel, "Solar rooftop in India: Policies, challenges and outlook", *Green Energy & Environment*, Volume 1, Issue 2, July 2016 doi: 10.1016/j.gee.2016.08.003

This presentation was selected by the Sc. Committee of the EU PVSEC 2025 for submission of a full paper to one of the EU PVSEC's collaborating peer-reviewed journals.

SOCIAL HOUSING AND ENERGY COMMUNITIES: BALANCING AFFORDABILITY AND PROFITABILITY IN MULTI-APARTMENT BUILDINGS.

Elina Bosch1, Caroline Plaza2, Melodie De L'Epine2, Gaëtan Masson1
1 Becquerel Institute, Brussels, Belgium;
2 Becquerel Institute France, Lyon, France

ABSTRACT: Energy poverty remains a major challenge in the European Union, disproportionately affecting residents of social housing. At the same time, declining photovoltaic (PV) costs and new EU legislation on renewable energy communities create opportunities for energy sharing schemes that can reduce bills and improve access to clean energy. Yet, translating this potential into practice is particularly complex in multi-apartment social housing. This paper identifies and categorises the barriers to PV-based energy sharing in this context, drawing on a literature review and empirical evidence from three demonstration sites of the ProLight project in Spain, Portugal, and Italy. The analysis highlights the central role of fair benefit allocation and scope definition, the constraints of limited roof space, and the challenges of high tenant turnover, arrears risk, and low administrative literacy. In addition, fragmented decision rights, split incentives, and procurement and state-aid rules create further institutional hurdles. The findings underline that energy sharing can only succeed when accompanied by tailored business models, trusted intermediaries, and supportive regulatory frameworks. Coupling energy sharing with refurbishment strategies, subsidies, and co-creation processes can enhance both fairness and feasibility, positioning social housing as a critical driver of an inclusive energy transition.
Keywords: solar photovoltaics, energy sharing, business models, social housing, energy poverty

1 INTRODUCTION

Energy poverty remains a persistent challenge across the European Union (EU). Estimates from the Joint Research Centre (JRC) suggest that between 8% and 16% of the EU population can be classified as energy poor, with the precise figure depending on the methodology used [1]. The issue is complex and multi-dimensional: it can manifest as low absolute energy expenditure, a disproportionately high share of household income spent on energy, inability to maintain adequate indoor warmth, or arrears on utility bills. While only a small fraction of EU citizens meet all these conditions simultaneously, almost 40% of households are energy poor according to at least one indicator.

At the same time, photovoltaic (PV) technology has become increasingly affordable, creating new opportunities to expand access to clean energy [2]. The EU has also introduced a supportive regulatory framework through the Clean Energy for All Europeans package, which includes Article 2 of the Electricity Directive (EU) 2019/944 and Article 22 of the Renewable Energy Directive (RED II). These legislative measures laid the foundation for and promote the establishment of joint self-consumption schemes, citizen energy communities (CECs) and renewable energy communities (RECs), allowing households, businesses, and public organisations to share locally generated electricity Importantly, the RED II explicitly requires Member States to ensure that participation in renewable energy communities is open to all consumers, including low-income and vulnerable households [3].

The integration of PV within energy-sharing schemes is therefore increasingly recognised as a promising strategy to alleviate energy poverty. Evidence suggests that households are willing to engage: for example, one recent study reported that 91.3% of respondents (in two Italian social housing neighbourhoods) would be willing to invest in or request shared PV systems from their landlords [4]. Such initiatives can improve access to affordable, sustainable electricity, reducing both costs and vulnerability for disadvantaged groups.

However, translating this potential into practice is far from straightforward. Multiple barriers—technical, social, regulatory, administrative, governance, and financial—continue to hinder the development and scaling of energy sharing initiatives. Against this backdrop, this study explores social housing and energy communities, focusing on how to balance affordability and profitability in multi-apartment buildings, with the aim of identifying viable pathways to address energy poverty while ensuring long-term sustainability.

2 METHODS

2.1 Approach to barrier identification and categorization

Our analysis aims at developing a clearer understanding of the barriers specific to social housing in the context of energy sharing schemes.

To this end, we conduct a literature review of academic papers and policy reports that explicitly address this topic, as well as publications presenting relevant case studies.

In parallel, we draw on empirical insights from the demonstration districts of the ProLight project, which provide practical evidence on how energy-sharing schemes are being implemented in multi-apartment social housing.

Identified barriers are contextualised in relation to the specific features of social housing, including the socio-economic profile of residents, governance and ownership structures, and the prevalence of energy poverty. For each barrier, it is further indicated whether it is most relevant during the setup phase, the operational phase, or across both stages of implementation.

2.2 ProLight demonstration sites

In the frame of the ProLight project, there are three demonstration sites which are related to social housing and energy sharing schemes. These demonstration sites are at different stage of energy-sharing scheme implementation (running phase, setting-up phase, feasibility assessment phase).

First, the Guernica TEK demonstration site in Spain which is a running energy community based on 200 solar panels located on the local San Fidel school. Electricity is shared with 150 homes, shops and public buildings.

10.4229/EUPVSEC2025/5EO.1.1
020564-001

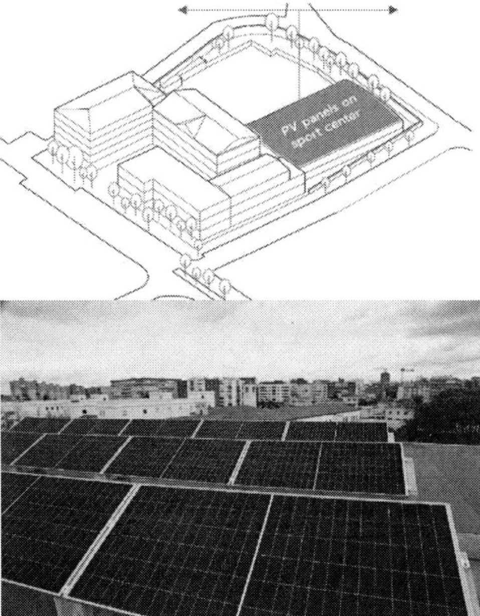

Figure 1: Gernika-San Fidel TEK (ProLight Spanish demonstration site)

Second, the Matosinhos demonstration site in Portugal where an energy sharing scheme is being set up in a recently refurbished social housing multi-apartment building. The energy sharing scheme will be based on a 200 kWp solar photovoltaic system located on the roof. Electricity will be shared with the residents as well as with a few local shops located on the ground floor of the building.

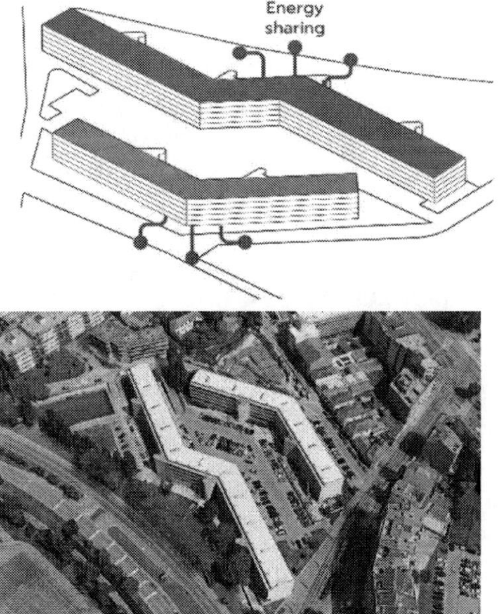

Figure 2: Matosinhos (ProLight Portuguese demonstration site)

Third, the Urbana New Living demonstration site in Italy. The establishment of an energy community is being considered in this recently refurbished social housing multi-apartment building. The building currently has a rooftop PV installation but which only covers the common electricity loads (corridors, elevators, …).

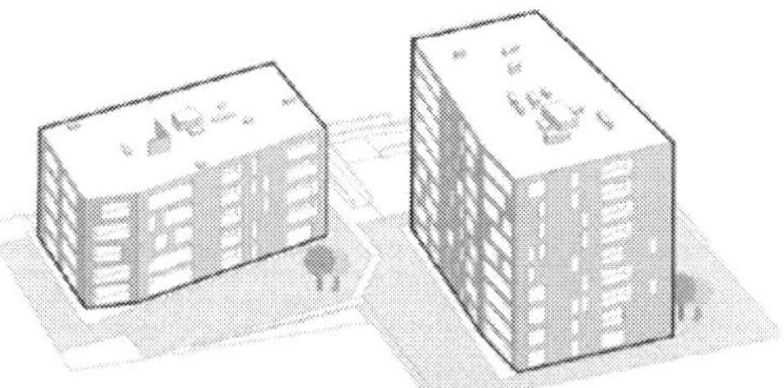

Figure 3: Urbana New Living (ProLight Italian demonstration site)

2.2 Recommendations for model definition

For the different identified challenges, recommendations with regards to model definition are provided. In particular, model definition recommendations resonate with Business Model Canvas components such as cost structure, ownership, benefit and revenue distribution, …. The Business Model Canvas was selected because it is a widely used and flexible tool that facilitates the structured analysis of value creation, stakeholder roles, and financial flows, making it particularly suitable for innovations at the intersection of technology, governance, and social objectives.

3 BARRIERS AND RECOMMENDATIONS WITH REGARDS TO MODEL DEFINITION

3.1 Barriers related to (PV-based) energy sharing scheme

Benefit allocation design (most relevant in setup phase): Establishing fair distribution keys is a central issue. While this applies broadly, the need for equitable allocation mechanisms is heightened in social housing, where affordability constraints mean that even small imbalances can have strong distributional consequences [4]. As seen in the examples of demonstration sites in ProLight, a certain diversity of socio-economic profiles as well as energy consumption profiles can be observed in a social housing building. In the Italian demonstration site, the social housing includes around half of 'affordable rents", around 15% of "social rent", the rest being sold units. In the Portuguese demonstration sites, the ground-floor of the social housing building, includes a few shops which can contribute positively to the overall energy sharing scheme profitability through the presence of complementary consumption patterns, but needs to be an attention point to avoid concentrating the energy saving benefits on a few profiles only.

Energy-sharing scope selection (most relevant in setup phase): Whether on-site produced electricity should cover only the common load (corridors, elevators, …) or also extend to the individual housing units' consumption directly shapes both fairness and feasibility. Indeed cost minimization and self-consumption maximization goals may conflict. For example, with a common load scope, the savings for each self-consumed kWh will typically be higher with savings on most electricity price components including taxes and network fees. On the contrary, if the scope extends to individual unit's load, each self-consumed kWh will allow savings on the commodity component of electricity price and in some case partially on network fees with taxes still being applicable.

Allocation and billing complexity (relevant in both setup and operational phase): Complex metering arrangements and the use of algorithms to manage sharing keys create higher onboarding and follow-up needs in social housing compared to private dwellings [4] [5] [6]. The example of the energy community demonstration site in Spain in ProLight has shown how the presence of an external private utility can play a key role in facilitating administrative, legal and financial procedures.

3.2 Barriers related to multi-apartment setting

Physical constraints (most relevant in setup phase): The limited roof surface relative to the number of dwellings restricts the scale of PV that can be installed. This is a general challenge in multi-apartment buildings, but in social housing the higher dwelling density exacerbates the limitation [6].

3.3 Barriers related to socio-economic setting

CAPEX and access to finance (most relevant in setup phase): Access to upfront investment is often more difficult in social housing, where both providers and tenants face tighter financial constraints and limited borrowing capacity [9] [10].

Tenant rotation and arrears risk (most relevant in operational phase): High participant turnover and the risk of non-payment are more salient in social housing than in private housing, directly affecting revenue stability and long-term viability [13]. This is particularly relevant for private social housing units, where the economic benefit of implementing an energy sharing scheme may not be immediately obvious to the owner. However, by lowering tenants' energy bills, such schemes can reduce the risk of rent arrears and thereby improve payment stability.

Awareness, trust, and administrative literacy (relevant in both setup and operational phase): Language barriers and low energy literacy levels increase onboarding and communication challenges in social housing, requiring additional support measures throughout the lifecycle of the project [1] [2] [3]. The example of the Italian demonstration site in ProLight project has shown that the presence of a local intermediary (i.e. a local social manager) is essential to build trust and enhances outreach activities towards local citizens. In general, across all demonstration site in ProLight, the implementation of energy sharing schemes (or other energy saving measures) are systematically accompanied with end-user information sharing, engagement and co-creation activities which can take various forms of communication and dissemination action such as workshops, door-to-door communication, …

3.4 Barriers related to social housing setting.

Fragmented decision rights (most relevant in setup phase): Multiple actors—housing companies, facility managers, tenant committees—hold decision-making power. This fragmentation often delays or complicates project development [7] [8].

Split-incentive / landlord–tenant dilemma (most relevant in setup phase): This barrier is especially acute in social housing because the social housing sector remains fundamentally tenant-based [11]. While mass giveaways (UK, Ireland, Romania, …) did significantly shift housing into owner-occupancy, those practices have been mostly phased out. Moreover, regulated rent regimes typically prevent the recovery of capital expenditures through tenants' energy bills, decoupling investment incentives from user benefits [8].

Procurement and state-aid constraints (most relevant in setup phase): In publicly owned or managed housing, strict procurement rules and state-aid considerations create additional delays and limit flexibility. These rules are designed to ensure transparency and fairness, but in practice they can create lengthy administrative processes and restrict the ability to experiment with innovative financing models. In particular, they can make it more difficult to mobilise alternative sources of support, such as sponsorships or donations, which could otherwise help reduce upfront investment needs [7].

3.5 Barriers related to energy poverty context

Reliance on pre-existing energy efficiency measures (most relevant in setup phase): Energy sharing typically becomes viable only after refurbishment or retrofitting, as inefficient building envelopes undermine both the economic case and comfort outcomes. This dependency is especially relevant in social housing, where building stock is often older and poorly insulated [14] [15].

Challenges in benefit quantification (most relevant in operational phase): If analysis focuses only on monetary savings, the true social benefits are underestimated. In social housing, affordability constraints often lead to energy under-consumption (e.g. not heating), meaning that savings appear low despite major improvements in comfort and well-being [1].

4   CONCLUSIONS

This study has shown that while photovoltaic-based energy sharing holds significant potential to alleviate energy poverty in social housing, its implementation faces a complex set of interrelated barriers. These range from technical and physical constraints, such as limited roof space and metering complexity, to socio-economic and institutional challenges, including limited investment capacity, tenant turnover, arrears risk, and fragmented decision rights. Importantly, the social housing context amplifies these challenges: affordability constraints heighten the distributional consequences of benefit allocation, administrative literacy gaps demand stronger engagement and support measures, and strict procurement and state-aid rules limit flexibility in financing.

Despite these obstacles, the analysis of the ProLight demonstration sites illustrates that energy sharing in social housing can be made viable when barriers are explicitly addressed in the design of business models. Careful definition of benefit allocation keys and scope, transparent billing arrangements, and the involvement of trusted intermediaries are essential for building trust and ensuring equity. Likewise, coupling energy sharing with refurbishment strategies, mobilising targeted subsidies and grants, and fostering cooperative governance arrangements can enhance both feasibility and long-term sustainability.

A better understanding of the barriers is also critical for shaping replication strategies, ensuring that lessons from the ProLight demonstration sites can be transferred to other contexts. Already at this stage, many insights have been gained regarding both technical and social aspects, while within a year, by the end of the project, more quantitative evidence will become available. These forthcoming results will further inform business model orientations, supporting the definition of viable pathways to scale up PV-based energy sharing in social housing.

Overall, PV-based energy sharing should not be viewed as a stand-alone solution but rather as part of a broader strategy to reduce energy poverty in multi-apartment buildings. By embedding such schemes within supportive regulatory frameworks and ensuring that social and economic safeguards are prioritised, they can deliver not only economic savings but also improved comfort, well-being, and social cohesion. In this way, social housing can become a key driver of an inclusive and just energy transition in Europe.

5 REFERENCES

[1] S. a. D. I. MAIER, «Who is "energy poor" in the EU,» 2024.

[2] IEA PVPS Task 1, «Trends in PV Applications 2024,» 2024.

[3] European Parliament and the Council , «Directive (EU) 2018/2001 of the European Parliament and of the Council of 11 December 2018 on the promotion of the use of energy from renewable sources,» 2024.

[4] L. Marchi, L. Felicioni, F. Sabatini et L. Errante, «Exploring Energy Literacy in Italian Social Housing: A Survey of Inhabitants Preparing the Ground for Climate Transition,» Sustainability , vol. 15, 2023.

[5] M. R. P. S. M. A. A. L. B. F. M. Federico Gianaroli, «Development of dynamic sharing keys: Algorithms supporting management of renewable energy community and collective self consumption,» Energy and Buildings, vol. 311, 2024.

[6] I. a. E. E. A. D.-G. f. E. F. B. L.-E. K. M. C. e. a. European Climate, «Report on energy sharing,» Publications Office of the European Union, 2025.

[7] V. M. G. P. M. M. D. Casalicchio, «Renewable Energy Communities: Business Models of Multi-family Housing Buildings,» Smart and Sustainable Planning for Cities and Regions, p. 261–276, 23 March 2021.

[8] M. K. E. N. F. S. R. M. Fritz Braeuer, «Optimal system design for energy communities in multi-family buildings: the case of the German Tenant Electricity Law,,» Applied Energy, vol. 305, 2022.

[9] J. a. D. Q. Arnould, «Energy communities in the EU: Opportunities and barriers to financing,» Amsterdam, 2022.

[10] J. a. D. Q. Arnould, « Energy Communities in the EU: Fulfilling consumer rights and protections,» Amsterdam, 2022.

[11] G. S. H. P. D. F. F. C. A. D. V. N. C. C. M.-B. I. a. U. A. Koukoufikis, «Energy Communities and Energy Poverty,» Publications Office of the European Union, Luxembourg, 2023.

[12] Housing Europe, «Alleviating energy poverty in social and privately-owned homes from 2020 until today,» [En ligne]. Available: https://www.housingeurope.eu/alleviating-energy-poverty-in-social-and-privately-owned-homes-from-2020-until-today/. [Accès le September 2025].

[13] F. G. R. Hanke, «The struggle of energy communities to enhance energy justice: insights from 113 German cases,» Energ Sustain Soc, vol. 13, n° %116, 2023.

[14] L. Marchi, L. Felicioni, F. Sabatini et L. Errante, «Exploring Energy Literacy in Italian Social Housing: A Survey of Inhabitants Preparing the Ground for Climate Transition,» Sustainability , vol. 15, 2023.

[15] E. F. I. S. T. D. A. Y. J. B. G. A. L. R. B. O.-S. S. P. B. M. A. B. Directorate-General for Energy, «Study on mapping of regulatory frameworks and barriers for individual and collective renewables self-consumption in EU Member States,» Publications Office of the European Union, 2024.

[16] B. R. A. R. Aravind Poshnath, «Adoption of Renewable Energy Systems in common properties of multi-owned buildings: Introduction of 'Energy Entitlement',» Energy Policy, vol. 174, 2023.

[17] OECD, «Social Housing: A Key Part of Past and Future Housing Policy,» 2020.

[18] L. B. P. E. M. Častellazzi, «Overcoming the split incentive barrier in the building sectors: unlocking the energy efficiency potential in the rental & multifamily sectors,» Publications Office of the European Union, Luxembourg, 2017.

[19] P. McManamon, «Toward Building Energy Reduction Through Solar Energy Systems Retrofit Options: An Equest Model,» Journal of Applied Engineering Sciences, 2018.

[20] U. Madushika, T. Ramachandra, G. Karunasena et Udakara, «Energy Retrofitting Technologies of Buildings: A Review-Based Assessment,» Energies, 2023.

6 ACKNOWLEDGMENT AND FUNDING

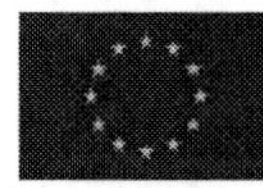 The work described has received funding as part of the PROLIGHT project from the European Union's Horizon Europe research and innovation program under grant agreement N° 101079902.

STUDY FOR AN AGRIVOLTAIC BASED RURAL
ENERGY COMMUNITY IN ALENTEJO PORTUGAL

José A. Silva[1], Joana Correia[1], Sara Pereira[1], Vasco Cabecinha[2], Dorivaldo Duarte[1], Henrique Fava[1], João Barroso[1],
Mauro Raposo[1], Luís Fialho[3], Afonso Cavaco[1], Pedro Horta[1]
[1]Renewable Energies Chair, Universidade de Évora, Polo da Mitra, Edifício Ário Lobo de Azevedo, 7000-083
Nossa Senhora de Tourega, Portugal
[2] Faculdade de Ciências e Tecnologia, Universidade Nova de Lisboa, 2829-516 Caparica, Portugal
[3]Eurac Research-Institute for Renewable Energy, 39100 Bolzano, Italy

ABSTRACT: We present a study for the creation of a rural renewable energy community (REC) based on an agrivoltaic
(or AgriPV) plant in the Portuguese region of Alentejo. The REC includes an AgriPV power plant with two different
configurations, overhead and interspatial with a total capacity of 175 kW, located at the university campus in Nossa
Senhora de Tourega. The community encloses the university campus and the neighbouring village of Valverde. The
daily energy production profiles of two AgriPV plant configurations are analysed, for a winter and a summer day. These
profiles are compared with the consumption profiles of the university campus, and an average household in Évora, and
the strategies to maximize the energy community self-consumption are discussed. The main difficulties and advantages
of managing agricultural activities and selling agricultural products in the energy community are also examined.
Keywords: agrivoltaics, sensors, monitoring, microclimate, soil

1   INTRODUCTION

In recent years, the installation of PV capacity has
been growing steadily, reaching 597 GW in 2024 [1]. This
growth has been particularly steep in Portugal, where the
installed capacity increased 5-fold in four years, reaching
5.7 GW last year [2]. The main driver for this growth has
been the deployment of large-scale photovoltaic power
plants, the spread of which is triggering protests from
various local stakeholders, raising issues as land-use
competition and landscape impact.

Recently, agrivoltaics has emerged as an effective
strategy to tackle these issues by proposing the integration
of energy and agriculture production in the same area, thus
mitigating the competition for land use, and lessening the
impacts on the landscape when compared to conventional
PV plants.

Renewable Energy Communities (RECs) are local
groups of citizens, companies and public authorities that
cooperate in production, management and consumption of
energy. RECs are a way to empower citizens and promote
engagement in renewable energy projects and allow them
to access lower electricity prices. The European Union
introduced the concept of renewable energy communities
in the Clean Energy for all Europeans, and considers REC
as way to enable citizen driven actions that can boost
energy decarbonization [3].

The expected increase in the installation of AgriPV
systems will promote distributed electricity production in
rural areas, where frequently electric grid access is limited.
Integrating agrivoltaic systems in RECs appears as an
interesting solution to use efficiently the PV energy
produced, and foster REC in rural areas, promoting
decarbonization and sustainable development in these
environments.

Moreover, energy poverty remains a challenge in
Portugal, with 15.7% of the population in 2024 reporting
that they could not afford to keep their home adequately
warm, levels that rise above 30% among those at risk of
poverty [4]. This situation is particularly significant in
Alentejo region due to low incomes, ageing population,
and extreme summer heat [5]. So, the development of
RECs in Alentejo can have a significant impact on the
population's living standard. Furthermore, due to the high
solar potential available in the region, as well as its large
agricultural area, AgriPV is particularly promising.

In this article, we present a study for the creation of a
REC coupling the campus from Universidade de Évora
with the neighbouring village of Valverde, considering an
AgriPV plant as the main source of renewable energy.

2   METHODS

Our study started by analysing the consumption
profiles of the Universidade de Évora's campus, Pólo da
Mitra, and of the village of Valverde. Next, the energy
production profiles for the agrivoltaic plant, to be installed
on the university's campus, were estimated using the
PVsyst 8.0.13 software [6], and compared with the
consumption profiles. Strategies for increasing energy
self-consumption in the community are then discussed.

Finally, the integration of agricultural activities in the
REC, as well as distributing agricultural products among
the REC's members, is discussed.

2.1 Valverde Renewable Energy Community

Valverde is a small village in Évora municipality, with
approximately 150 inhabitants and an area of 0.132 km2.
The university campus, *Pólo da Mitra*, is located at a
distance of approximate 1 km, making viable, according to
Portuguese legislation, the creation of a renewable energy
community between these two sites [7].

In Figure 1 a map a of the Renewable Energy
Community analysed is presented.

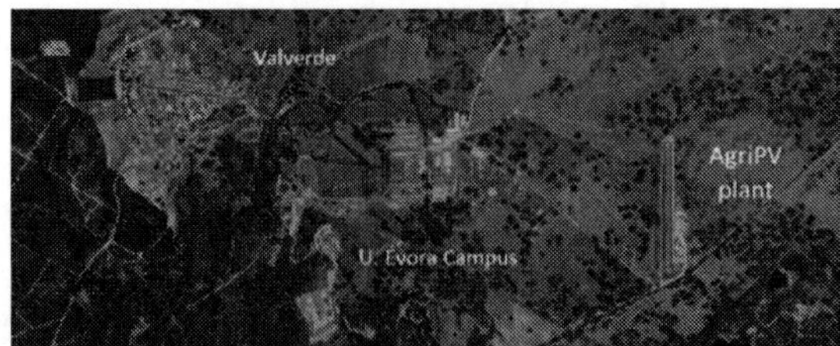

Figure 1: Valverde Renewable Energy Community [8].

2.1 Energy load profiles

Valverde Village

The rural community of Valverde is mainly composed
of households and a few small businesses (i.e., restaurants

and cafés). So, the energy demand for this community is mainly determined households' consumption. To determine the average daily energy consumption profile for a Valverde household, it was assumed that this profile is similar to consumption profile obtained by Gouveia et al for the municipality of Évora in 2014 [9]. The daily energy consumption profiles of a household in Évora, for a winter day, a summer day and the annual average are shown in Figure 2.

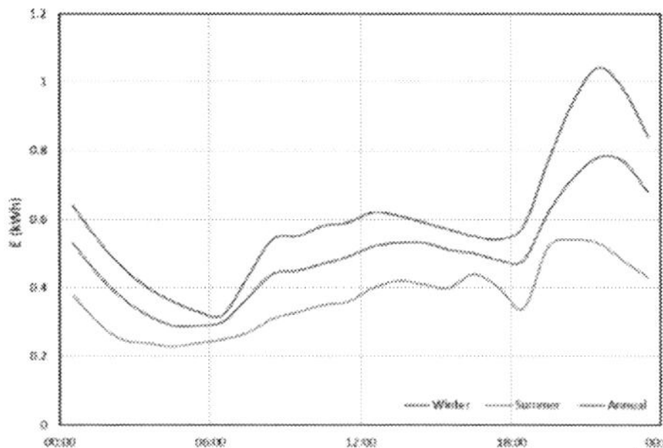

Figure 2: Average daily energy load profile for Évora municipality (adapted from [9])

It can be observed that in all three cases, the peak of energy demand occurs after 18:00, and this peak in winter is approximately twice as high as the summer peak. A second consumption peak can be observed during the morning, and similarly to the evening, the morning peak is also twice as high in winter as in summer.

<u>Pólo da Mitra university campus</u>
The university campus is composed of three main buildings that account for most of the energy load, two dedicated to education and research activities, and one Veterinary Hospital. There also some infrastructures that support research and education with smaller energy loads. In Figure 3, the daily energy loads of the university campus, for a day in summer and a day in winter in 2023 are presented.

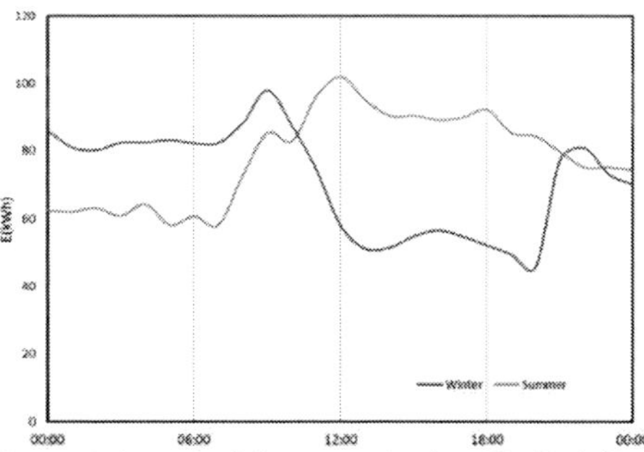

Figure 3: Average daily energy load profile for Pólo da Mitra university campus.

It can be observed that the load profiles are very distinct between winter, where the highest consumption is observed during morning and evening, and summer, where the highest load is observed during the afternoon, suggesting that climatization is the most significant energy consumption in the campus. Nonetheless, the maximum daily consumption for both days is similar (~100 kWh).

Also, as expected, unlike the energy load for households. The daily energy load profile of the university is mostly concentrated in sunny hours, thus more aligned with the typical production of PV.

2.2 Agrivoltaic power plant
The agrivoltaic system considered in this study includes two different configurations, one overhead and one interspatial. The characteristics of the two configurations considered are the following:

Overhead system:
- Bifacial monocrystalline silicon modules
- Capacity: 70.8 kWp
- Orientation: North-South, 30° or (-45°,45°)
- Height from the ground: 4 m
- Interrow distance: 4.5 m
- Ground coverage ratio: 35%
- Area: 1200 m^2 + control area
- Type of crops: Intensive

Interspatial system:
- Bifacial monocrystalline silicon module
- Capacity: 103.8 kWp
- Orientation: North-South; 90°
- Height from the ground: 0.5 m
- Modules/row: 2 × 22
- Interrow distance: 8 m
- Area for agricultural use: ~ 90%
- Area: 1700 m^2 + control area
- Type of crops: Extensive

The energy production of these agrivoltaic systems was estimated by performing computer simulations with PVsyst [6]. In the case of the overhead configuration, two scenarios were considered: one with a fixed tilt angle θ=30°, which is approximately the optimal angle for the site, and another considering a tracking path between -45° and 45°.

3   RESULTS AND DISCUSSION

3.1 AgriPV energy production

<u>Overhead configuration</u>
The specific energy production obtained for the two overhead AgriPV systems were the following:

Overhead system (θ=30°): 1412 kWh/(kWp·year)

Overhead system (-45 °<θ<=45°): 1748 kWh/(kWp·year)

As expected, the system with sun tracking has a significantly higher energy production, with a relative gain of 24% compared to the fixed one. However, it must be mentioned that, in an agrivoltaic system, the sun tracker path often needs to consider the radiation needs of the plants, rather than just maximising the energy yield [10].

In figures 4 and 5 are presented the energy production annual profiles for the overhead configuration, respectively fixed and with tracking.

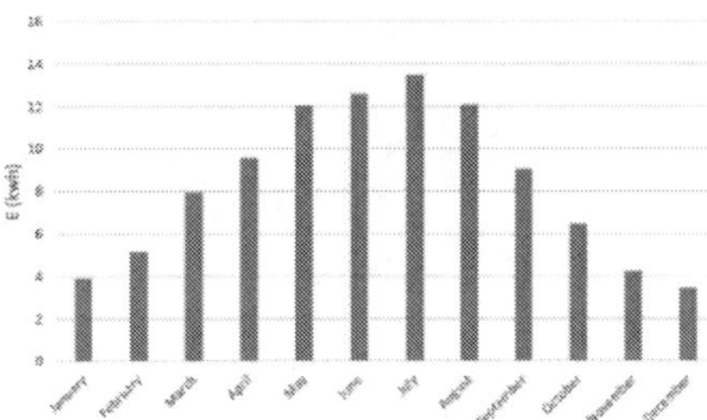

Figure 4: Annual energy production profile for the AgriPV plant with overhead configuration, θ=30°.

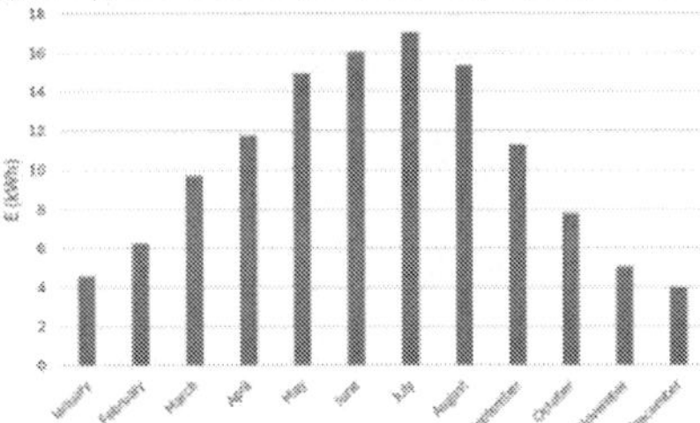

Figure 5: Annual energy production profile for the AgriPV plant with overhead configuration, -45° < θ < 45.

It can be observed that despite the significant difference in energy yield, the two AgriPV systems have similar annual energy production profiles, with a significantly higher energy production in summer than in winter. In fact, for the fixed system, the ratio between the maximum monthly production attained in July and the minimum monthly production attained in December is 3.9, while for the overhead system with tracking, it is 4.3.

In figures 6 and 7, the daily energy production profiles for the overhead AgriPV system with a fixed axis for a winter and a summer day are presented.

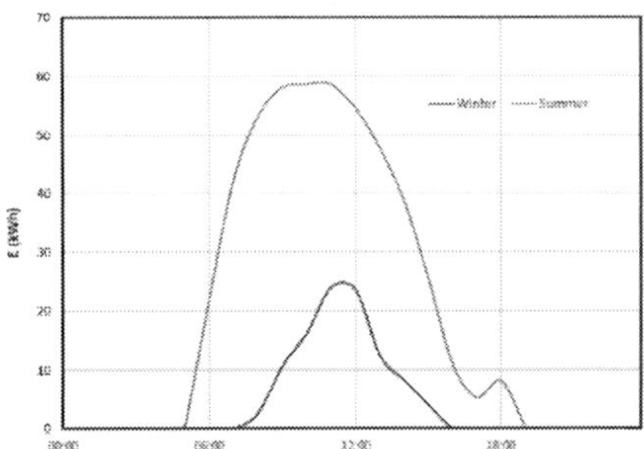

Figure 6: Daily energy production profile for winter and summer, for the AgriPV plant with overhead configuration, θ=30°.

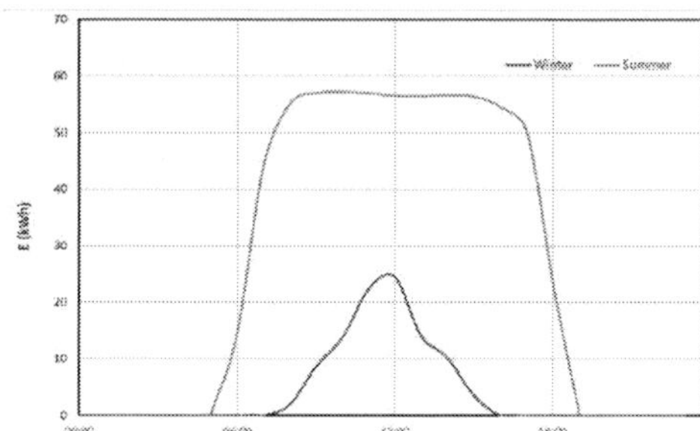

Figure 7: Daily energy production profile for winter and summer, for the AgriPV plant with overhead configuration, -45° < θ < 45.

It can be observed that, as expected, both the production peak and production hours are lower in the winter than in summer. Nevertheless, for the tracker system, a large production plateau is observed in the summer daily profile, contributing to the higher summer energy production of this system when compared to the fixed one.

<u>Interspatial configuration</u>

The specific energy production obtained for the AgriPV interspatial system was 673 kWh/(kWp·year), which is approximately half of the value obtained for the overhead fixed system. This feature is mainly due to the non-optimal tilt angle (40%) and near shading (20%) due to the trees that surround the installation site.

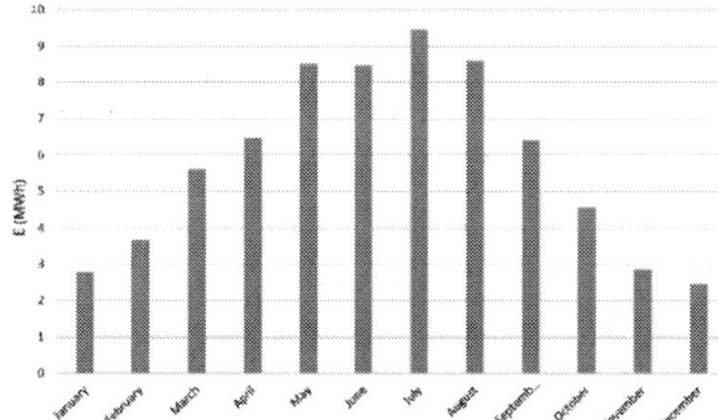

Figure 8: Annual energy production profile for the AgriPV plant with interspatial configuration.

Similar to what was observed for the two overhead systems analysed, there is a significant imbalance between summer and winter energy production for the AgriPV interspatial system (Figure 8). For this system, the ratio between the maximum monthly production, attained in July, and the minimum reached in December was 3.9.

In Figure 9 the daily energy production profile for the interspatial AgriPV plant for summer and winter is presented.

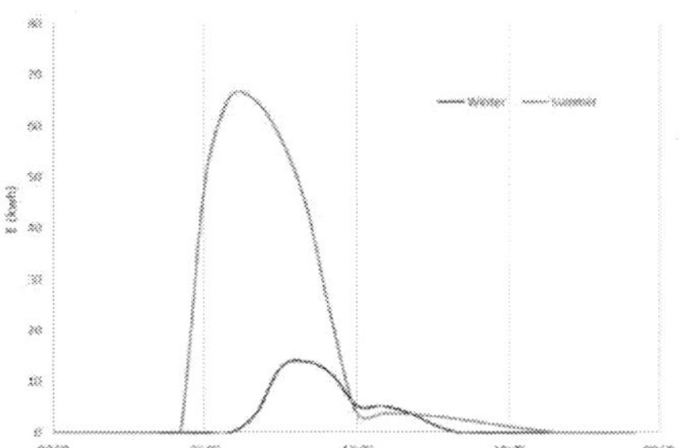

Figure 9: Daily energy production profile for winter and summer, for the AgriPV plant with interspatial configuration.

It can be observed that for both winter and summer, the daily energy production profile has a peak in the morning. Moreover, it can be observed that the near-shading of the surrounding trees impacts production in the afternoon. This effect is particularly significant in the summer.

3.2 Comparison energy load with energy production

When comparing the AgriPV plant energy production profiles, both daily and annual, it can be concluded that the production of the AgriPV does not fit well with the average energy demand for a typical Évora household. In fact, the energy production for the three AgriPV systems is significantly higher in summer, while the energy consumption is higher in winter. Also, the daily energy load peaks in the evening, when the production from the AgriPV systems is very low or zero. Still, the AgriPV production can supply the households' morning energy needs. Moreover, to maximise self-consumption of the AgriPV plant and improve the economic viability of the renewable energy community, the AgriPV plant installed power should consider the summer consumption.

3.3 Integrating agricultural activities in RECs

The successful integration of an AgriPV project in a renewable energy community strongly depends on the existence of a compromise between maximising energy and agricultural production. This must start with a clear definition of the main objectives of the renewable energy community by its members. Next, making a choice of compatible crops and plant configurations is crucial. Moreover, frequently the radiation needs of the crops require that the PV systems are not in the optimal position for energy production, thus limiting the energy yield of the AgriPV system.

In terms of the community organisation, the agricultural activities can either be developed in a cooperative way by the REC members (i.e., small farmers) or by farming enterprises. In any case, the REC members should have the possibility to access to the agricultural products at a lower price.

4   CONCLUSIONS

AgriPV and RECs are two innovative concepts that already play a key role in boosting PV deployment and energy decarbonization. The joint use of the two concepts has great synergistic potential.

Ensuring energy self-consumption within the REC can help to make AgriPV projects viable and boost PV energy production locally.

Besides electricity production and distribution, RECs members must have the possibility to participate in agricultural production and have access to food goods at reduced prices.

To improve the profitability of the agrivoltaic plant and the economic success of the REC, the sizing of the plant must be made, with the view of maximising the energy self-consumption rate, so in the case of the Valverde renewable energy, based on summer consumption

REC members must plan together the design and operation plan of the AgriPV plant to achieve their common goals.

5   ACKNOWLEDGEMENTS

This research was supported by the Alliance for the Energy Transition (56) co-financed by the European Union through the Recovery and Resilience Plan (PRR).

6   REFERENCES

[1] SolarPower Europe, "Global Market Outlook for Solar Power 2025-2029," 2025.

[2] Direção Geral de Energia e Geologia (DGEG), "Estatísticas rápidas das renováveis - junho de 2025".

[3] Directorate General for Energy - European Commission, "Clean Energy for all Europeans Package," 2019.

[4] Instituto Nacional de Estatítica (INE), "Press Release World Energy Efficiency Day," 2025. [Online]. Available: https://www.ine.pt/ngt_server/attachfileu.jsp?look_parent Boui=715631147&att_display=n&att_download=y.

[5] S. Peralta, B. P. Carvalho, J. Fanha and M. Fonseca, "Portugal, Balanço Social 2024. Nova School of Business and Economics,," 2025.

[6] PVsyst 8.0.13 Photovoltaic Software, Webgenève., [Online]. Available: https://www.pvsyst.com/.

[7] Diário da Républica (Portugal), vol. 10/22, pp. 3-185, 14 01 2022.

[8] Adapted from Google Earth, [Online]. Available: https://earth.google.com/.

[9] J. P. Gouveia, J. Seixas and A. Mestre, "Daily electricity consumption profiles from smart meters - Proxies of behavior for space heating and cooling," Energy, vol. 141, pp. 108-122, 2017.

[10] D. Fumey et al., "Dynamic agrivoltaics, climate protection for grapevine driven by artificial intelligence," in Proceedings 22nd GiESCO International Meeting, 2023.

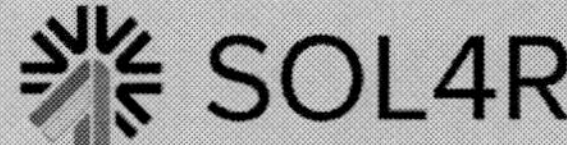

Study for an agrivoltaic based rural energy community in Alentejo Portugal

J. A. Silva[1], J. Correia[1], S. Pereira[1], V. Cabecinha[2], D. Duarte[1], H. Fava[1], J. Barroso[1], M. Raposo[1], L. Fialho[3], A. Cavaco[1], P. Horta[1]

[1] Solar4R, Universidade de Évora, Portugal
[2] Faculdade de Ciências e Tecnologia, Universidade Nova de Lisboa, Portugal
[3] Eurac Research - Institute for Renewable Energy, Italy

Outline

- Motivation & context
- Case study: Valverde AgriPV-REC
  - Compare energy production and load profiles
  - Maximize self-consumption in the REC
  - Integrating agricultural activities in RECs
- Conclusions & Future work

Motivation & context

UNIVERSIDADE DE ÉVORA

AgriPV & RECs

- RECs can address the problem of limited grid access in rural areas.
- AgriPV plants can boost the deployment of PV capacity and the creation of RECs in rural areas
- REC members can have a role in the energy and agricultural production, and access electricity and food at reduced prices

Source: Enel Green Power

Case study: Valverde AgriPV-REC

Location: Évora, Portugal

Case study: Valverde AgriPV-REC

AgriPV plant - Overhead system

- Bifacial c-Si modules; 70.8 kWp
- North-South, 30° or (-45°, 45°)
- Height from the ground: 4 m
- Interrow distance: 4.5 m
- Ground coverage ratio: 35%
- Intensive crops (ex: lettuce, potatoes)
- Area: 1200 m²

Source: AgriSolar Clearinghouse

Case study: Valverde AgriPV-REC

AgriPV plant - Interspatial system

- Bifacial c-Si modules; 103.8 kWp
- North-South; 90°
- Height from the ground: 0.5 m
- Modules/row: 2 × 22
- Interrow distance: 8 m
- Area for agricultural use: ~ 90%
- Extensive crops: (Ex: forage cereals)
- Total area: 1700 m^2

Source: Next2Sun

Case study: Valverde AgriPV-REC

UNIVERSIDADE DE ÉVORA

Energy production – Overhead system, N-S

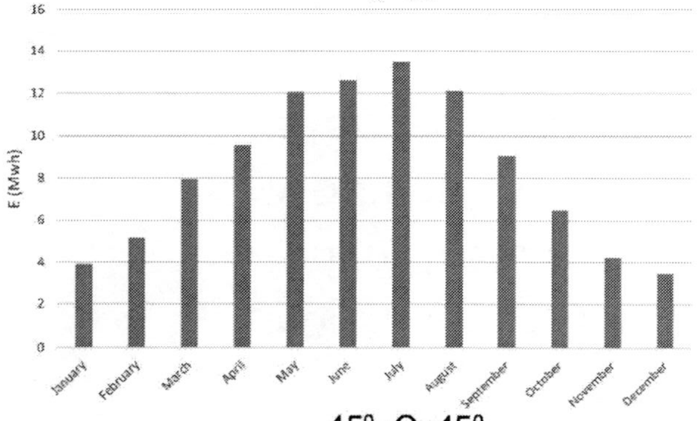

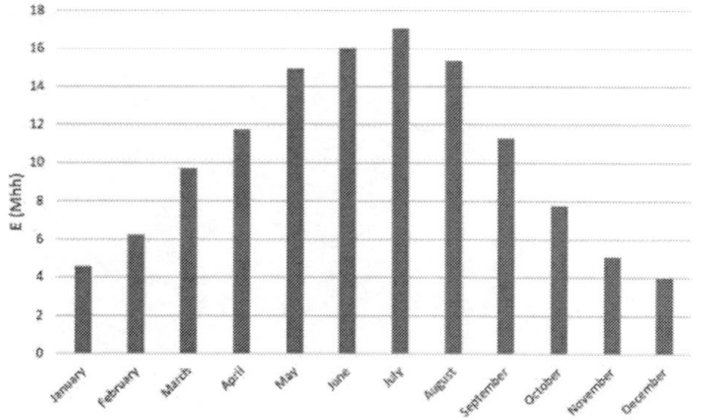

Annual profile

- Significant diferences between summer and winter production:
  - θ=30º: $Month_{max}/Month_{min} = 3.9$
  - -45º<θ<45º $Month_{max}/Month_{min} = 4.3$

Case study: Valverde AgriPV-REC

Energy production – Overhead system, N-S

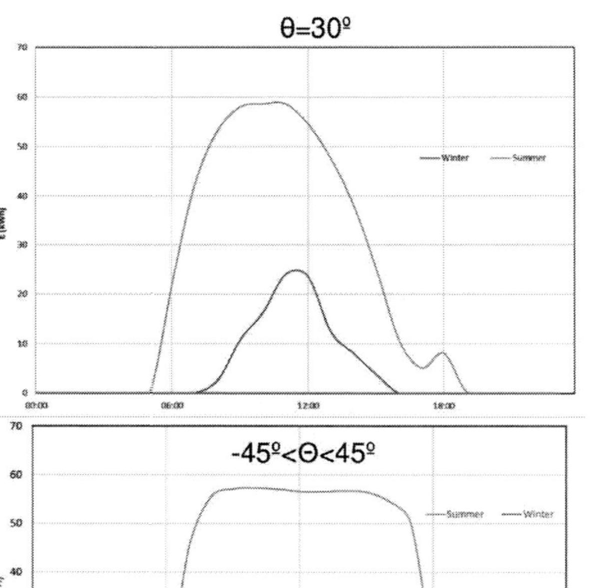

Annual profile

- Significant diferences between summer and winter production:
  - θ=30º: $Month_{max}/Month_{min}$ = 3.9
  - -45º<θ<45º $Month_{max}/Month_{min}$ = 4.3

Daily profile

- Large production plateau in summer for system with tracking
- Specific production:
  - θ=30º: 1412 kWh/kWp
  - -45º<θ<45º: 1748 kWh/kWp **+ 24%**

→ But sometimes tracking mode most be adapted to the crops needs

Case study: Valverde AgriPV-REC

Energy production – Interspatial system, N-S 90°

<u>Annual profile</u>
- $Month_{max}/Month_{min} = 3.9$

<u>Daily profile</u>
- Production peaks in the morning both in summer and winter
- Specific production:
  - 673 kWh/kWp ~ ½ Overhead system fixed
- Significant losses due to the tilt angle (~40%) and near shadings (~20%)

Case study: Valverde AgriPV-REC

Energy load profiles

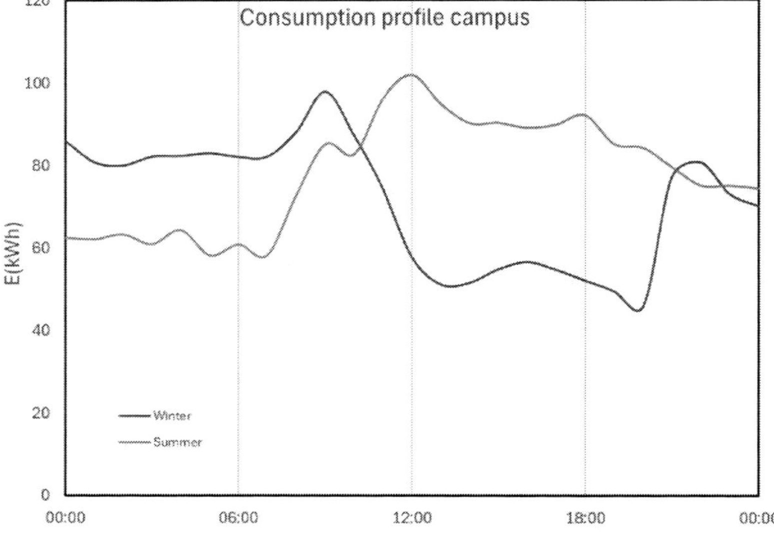

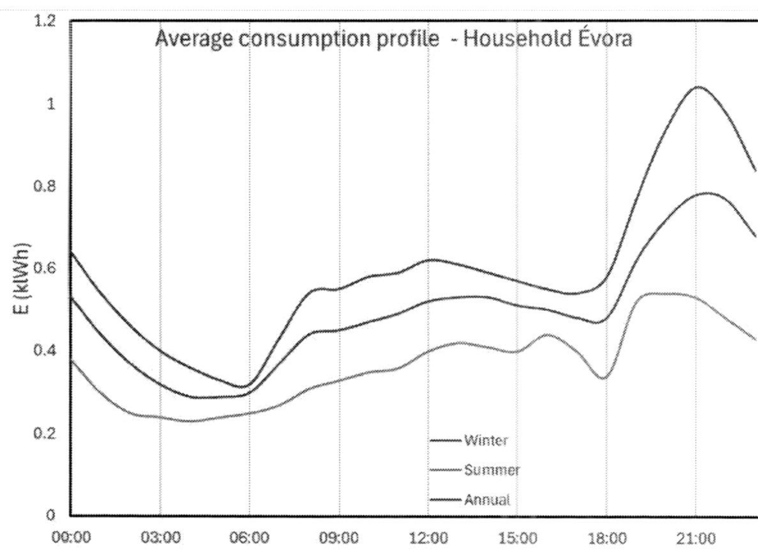

- Largest consumption after 18:00
- Winter peak ~ 2× summer peak
- AgriPV production can adapt to morning consumption

- Very distinct winter and summer consumption profiles
- Similar consumption maximum in winter and summer
- Can partially complement household consumption

Source: J. P. Goveia et al., Energy 141 (2017) 108 - 122

Case study: Valverde AgriPV-REC

Compatibility between energy supply and demand

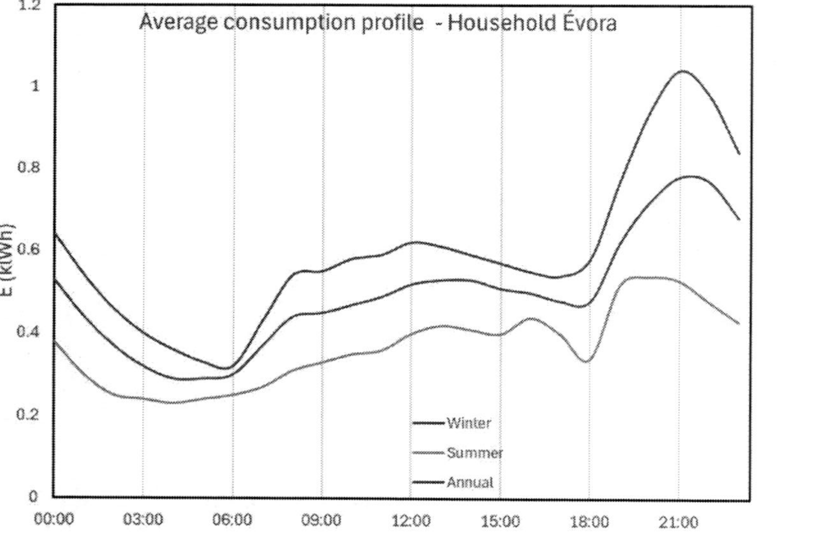

- The AgriPV plant energy production profiles (daily and annual) do not fit well the average energy demand for a typical Évora's household
- PV production can supply the morning energy needs (morning peak)
- To maximize self-consumption PV installed power should take in account summer consumption

Source: J. P. Goveia et al., Energy 141 (2017) 108 - 122

Case study: Valverde AgriPV-REC

Agricultural production

- In an AgriPV project, there must be a compromise between maximizing energy and agricultural production
  - → Not always easy!
- The choice of compatible crops and plant configurations is crucial
- Agricultural activities can either be developed in a cooperative way by the REC members or by farming enterprises.
- In any case, REC members should have access to the agricultural products at lower a price

Conclusions

- AgriPV and RECs will play a key role in energy decarbonization. The joint use of the two concepts has great synergistic potential.
- Ensuring energy self-consumption within the REC improves viability of AgriPV projects and boosts PV energy production locally
- Besides electricity production and distribution, RECs members can participate in crops growing and access food at reduced prices
- AgriPV plants must be planned to maximize the self-consumption rate → based on summer consumption
- REC members must plan together the design and operation plan of the AgriPV plant to achieve their common goals

Future work

- The AgriPV plant will allow for the identification of the best options in terms of crops, PV layouts, and tracking modes.
- Engage local farmers and populations in our AgriPV project namely by involving them in the choice of crops and agriculture practices
- Support the creation of future AgriPV-REC promoted by citizens, farmers associations, companies and local authorities

Also at this conference:

4DV.1.15 S. Pereira et al., Review of Sensor Technologies for Monitoring Agrivoltaic Systems

4DV.1.25 J. dos Santos et al., Agrivoltaic – Study of potential in Portugal

UNIVERSIDADE
DE ÉVORA

SOL4R

Thank you !

jose.silva@uevora.pt

CHALLENGES AND LESSONS LEARNED IN THE IMPLEMENTATION OF A REGIONAL-SCALE PV ENERGY COMMUNITY IN SPAIN

L. M. Carrasco, R. H. Almeida, Kiane Alves e Silva, L. Narvarte
Instituto de Energía Solar, Universidad Politécnica de Madrid
luismiguel.carrasco@upm.es

ABSTRACT: This article presents the experience accumulated over two and a half years in the design, creation, and implementation of a large-scale regional renewable energy community in a rural area covering 2,500 km² in northern Spain. The implementation of this energy community has faced numerous barriers and challenges, including those stemming from rural depopulation and aging, legal limitations in the establishment of energy communities, technological innovation, and financing issues. The main barriers encountered and the lessons learned by this experience are listed and described, grouped into five categories, with the aim of sharing them to contribute to the creation of a new paradigm in the implementation of bottom-up initiatives with real local impact.
Keywords: Energy Community, Lessons Learned, PV self-consumption

1 INTRODUCTION

The European Commission launched in 2022 the REPowerEU [1] plan to responde to the hardships and global energy market disruption caused by Russia's invasion of Ukraine. The plan aims both to end the EU's dependence on Russian fossil fuels, and tackling the climate crisis through energy savings, diversification of energy supplies, and accelerated roll-out of renewable energy to replace fossil fuels in homes, industry and power generation.

One of the REPowerEU's proposals for achieving its objectives was the development of energy communities (EC). The aim was to establish at least one energy community in each municipality with a population of over 10,000 by 2025 [2]. This would mean that, by this year, around 90,000 energy communities should have been established across Europe. There is no updated information about the number of ECs in Europe, but this figure was set at 9,000 in early 2024 [3] [4], which is far from the goal set out in the plan.

While there is much that could be speculated about the causes of this gap, all the evidence suggests that the lack of a paradigm for implementing CEs is hindering the development of these initiatives [5]. The difficulty in creating such communities, whether renewable [6] or citizen-based [7] as defined by European Directives, lies in the absence of well-established, well-tested and widely accepted EC models, as already evidenced by some authors [8] [9] [10].

Since 2022, a new experience of innovative EC has been developed in Spain, creating a large-scale Renewable Energy Community (REC) in the Calatayud County (Aragon region), with the support of the LIFE European Commission programme [11], which aims to bring a new approach to facilitate the emergence and growth of citizen-led energy community projects throughout Europe.

This article discusses the creation of this REC and the challenges it faced to become an instrument of social innovation that contributes to solving local social needs in depopulated rural regions. The document analyses the lessons learned during the implementation of this REC over a period of two and a half years, from technical, economic, legal, administrative and organisational perspectives. The aim of this work is to contribute to the establishment of a future paradigm for the expansion of RECs throughout Europe.

2 A LARGE-SCALE REGIONAL RENEWABLE ENERGY COMMUNITY

2.1 Goals of the REC.

Comunidad de Energías Renovables de la Comarca de Calatayud (CERCA) [12], as was named this REC, was created in a bottom-up approach to tackle the social challenges of a depopulated rural area of around 2,500 km² in the north of Spain. This region is composed of 67 municipalities and a total population of around 36,000 people. The population of the area has shrunk by almost 60% over the past 80 years. This has resulted in an ageing population who are concerned about the future of their villages. In fact, depopulated rural areas are, in general, characterized by:
- Low population density,
- Migration process to cities,
- Ageing population,
- Lack of basic services (education, health, communications, etc.),
- Poor organizational structures to implement local initiatives.

CERCA was created with the aim of contributing to the fight against the phenomenon of depopulation and its consequences. The innovative character of the regional REC compared to other possible solutions, such as the creation of multiple local RECs in the various villages of the region, lies in the fact that, for this initiative to have a real local impact, it must maximise the economic, environmental and social benefits for its members.

Therefore, the benefits of creating a single regional-scale REC instead of multiple local RECs are:
- It creates "community" since the REC joints regional actors for a common purpose.
- It maximizes regional impact. A regional REC has the capacity to reach all the municipalities in the area, including those too small to establish their own local REC.
- Resource optimization. Centralized management consolidates expertise across technical, economic, fiscal, and administrative processes in renewable project deployment.
- Economies of scale. Centralized procurement of PV components and installation services results in more competitive prices than if the projects were implemented independently.

CERCA was established with the goal of integrating 5,000 people (around 13.5% of the total population) and

75 businesses and industries in the region into the energy community. Initially, CERCA's activity focuses on developing of photovoltaic self-consumption projects, which are financed by the users (prosumers) themselves. In order to maximise the impact of this PV energy in the area, CERCA has been set up as an electricity retailer, compensating for the lack of regulation surrounding energy communities in Spain. This enables CERCA to monetise the surplus electricity fed into the grid, as well as supply, aggregate and store energy.

Figure 1: 116 kWp PV generator in Maluenda, installed on the roof of a winery, supplying energy for the winery itself and 23 homes in the municipality

2.2 Achievements of CERCA.

As of August 2025, CERCA had 150 members and had developed 18 projects in 15 villages in the region (one of which is shown in Figure 1). These projects had a total nominal PV power of 825 kWp and directly benefited more than 500 people. The users themselves financed these projects entirely, amounting to €760,000. They will recover 21% VAT and 40% subsidy from the IDAE's IMPLEMENTA programme [13]. Additionally, CERCA supplies electricity to 180 consumption points with a total supply power of 850 kW.

3 CHALLENGES, BARRIERS AND LESSONS LEARNED

To implement the regional REC, CERCA developed from the outset a methodology based on fostering engagement, awareness, and skills within the region, with the aim of overcoming the challenges inherent in introducing such an innovative model in a decentralized, depopulated, and aging rural environment. In addition to this challenge, CERCA has had to overcome several other obstacles, including the absence of REC regulation in Spain, administrative barriers to the legalisation and activation of PV self-consumption systems, the lack of established technical criteria for designing such systems, and the shortage of technical qualifications in the region.

The main barriers and challenges overcome by CERCA are detailed below, along with the lessons learned. These are categorised as follows: organisational, financial, technical, legal and administrative.

3.1 Organizational aspects

Don't start from scratch, make a clear proposal. When CERCA started the process of creating a REC, one of the main roles of the local promoter group was to establish a clear proposal of the type of REC that they wanted to convey to the targeted residents, associations, businesses, companies and town councils.

There are many possibilities for RECs, and one of them must be chosen. They can be small (on a village scale) or large (on a regional scale); with little citizen participation or, on the contrary, trying to promote it; limited to PV self-consumption or with the ambition to offer all the services that the European Directive grants to RECs; and they can be cooperatives, foundations, associations, private companies, etc. It must also have a spirit that motivates the creation of the REC. This spirit is what drives the promoter group and must be passed on to potential participants. A spirit that is rooted in the need it seeks to address.

The CERCA promoter group suffered from a reality in the Calatayud region that is common to other regions of rural Spain: the lack of a future for its villages caused by population decline and, in general, institutional neglect. The motivation for building a REC was so that its villages could have a future. And this is the spirit of CERCA: a REC whose impact is to contribute to the future of the villages of the Calatayud region and reverse the trend toward depopulation.

- **LESSON 1:** Difficulty in developing bottom-up initiatives when starting from scratch. If the promoter group does not establish a clear REC proposal, the discussion on said proposal will be transferred to the potential participants, generating noise, producing confusion and delaying the process with endless discussions. This discussion should take place within the promoter group. If there are differing sensitivities within this group, they should be resolved before going out to plant the idea.

A structure based exclusively on volunteers is the main threat to the sustainability of a REC. While the REC's promoter group must be composed of local citizens mobilized around a clearly perceived need, the management and operation phase of the REC cannot rely solely on volunteer work. The scale of the REC, the technical complexity of managing PV systems, and the responsibility for managing relatively large volumes of micro-investments require a professional and well-compensated structure to sustain and provide the REC with the necessary stability.

- **LESSON 2:** The misidentification of real participation processes with volunteerism causes serious problems in the medium term. By definition, volunteers have limited time and capacity. They have an important role to play, namely, maintaining the spirit that gave birth to the REC and maintaining it throughout its existence. But they often resist coexisting with a professional structure that is necessary when the REC enters its phase of maturity, consolidation, and growth. Achieving this transition to coexistence between volunteers and professionals is a challenge for the sustainability of the REC.

Communicating the REC proposal established by the promoter group among residents, associations, businesses, companies and town councils takes much longer than initially imagined. It requires interviews with mayors prior to the multiple visits to each village. The initial visits serve only to introduce the idea. The idea is discussed by the interlocutors in the villages, and questions arise, necessitating revisits.

This process, which seeks real participation through the appropriation of the idea by the final recipients, is long, requires a lot of time in the territory and a lot of dedication from a specialized team.

- **LESSON 3**: The seeding phase takes much longer than initially imagined. A REC that aspires to truly engage its members must build awareness and commitment by spreading the word, spreading the REC spirit, and explaining the proposal in detail. This isn't done from a remote office; it requires numerous visits and a significant amount of time spent on the ground. This requires forming a professional local team to execute these actions and ensure a constant presence in the area. The financial means must be secured to maintain this local team for a longer period than previously planned.

Real participation of residents requires the involvement of municipal representatives. CERCA's experience of developing projects in Calatayud's villages has shown that citizens' trust can only be gained if their mayor's trust is first secured. Cooperation between mayors and council secretaries is mandatory for developing community projects in small villages.

Contrary to popular belief, politics has a greater influence in rural areas than in urban ones. If the mayor is not consulted when a project is initiated in a village, they will resist it and become an obstacle. Therefore, it is essential to obtain the mayor's approval before visiting a village to raise awareness, but this is not easy due to their workload, lack of resources, and the large number of invitations they receive to events. Consequently, invitations from the REC get lost among the many other messages they receive.

The CERCA experience shows that after a year of visiting the villages with no apparent results, the turning point came with a call from the Calatayud Region government itself to all its mayors and town secretaries for three workshops in which the mayors were explained the design and the economic impact that CERCA could have on their town councils and their residents, all the legal aspects were explained to the secretaries and the technical aspects were explained to the town council technicians. The call was a success; all the mayors were familiar with the CERCA project thanks to the hard work of the previous year, and the support of the Calatayud Region government gave them the confidence to join the project. After the workshops, the mayors and secretaries addressed the CERCA representatives, saying, "Come and introduce CERCA to my neighbours!".

- **LESSON 4**: Need of institutional support, mainly from Municipalities. In rural environments, real participation of residents in a REC requires the involvement of mayors.
- **LESSON 5**: In order to publicise the REC, it is necessary to have the collaboration of the supra-local institution that brings together all the municipalities in the region, so that it can convene them. This will encourage the mayors to attend and ensure high trust.

Lack of skills in depopulated rural areas. The region has been found to have a general lack of knowledge about energy and how the electricity sector works. This is not just a feature of rural societies; it also occurs in urban ones. There is also a notable lack of digitalisation among the population in the Calatayud region, which makes it difficult to sign contracts online, disseminate information through digital media or implement PV production monitoring systems.

- **LESSON 6**: Training in general technical aspects related to energy, as well as finding creative solutions to the lack of digitalisation in rural areas, must be prioritised.

3.2 Financial aspects

Grants do not respect the timeframes needed for real participation. CERCA has benefited from the IMPLEMENTA programme, a public aid scheme run by Spanish government through the IDAE agency and designed to subsidise PV installations within the RECs. Thanks to the appeal of subsidies when it comes to making investment decisions, this aid has accelerated the implementation of projects. However, the programme's implementation period was only 14 months, a timeframe incompatible with the participatory processes required by any initiative aiming for real citizen participation, which require a longer timescale.

Furthermore, CERCA has exploited the collective nature of RECs by aggregating demand through collective PV self-consumption. This has enabled installation costs to be reduced by up to 50%. For instance, while an individual 3 kWp PV system might cost around €1,500/kWp, that cost can drop to approximately €700/kWp in a jointly managed 60 kWp facility. This allows for more efficient use of public money in the form of subsidies, limiting it to its catalytic effect: taking as an example, the IMPLEMENTA programme subsidy, 40% of this reduced cost, would amount to around €280/kWp, just 18.7% of the individual system cost.

- **LESSON 7**: Public grants are a lever to promote RECs among the population, but the deadlines established by these grants do not match with the time needed for the awareness and engagement of the people for a real participation.
- **LESSON 8**: The ideal PV configuration is to group participants through collective self-consumption systems to achieve economies of scale and to increase the power to raise community awareness. Aggregation effect not only reduce costs but to use efficiently public funding as a catalyst mechanism.

Need of appropriate financial schemes. Even with a 40% grant and a 21% VAT refund on the remaining cost, these public supports were only accessible after project execution. Because CERCA was a newly created entity, banks were unwilling to finance neither the grant nor the VAT. Citizens had to front 100% of the investment and wait over two years for reimbursement, with no interest. This up-front burden effectively excluded low-income households from participating and reduced the participation in general. However, this experience also demonstrated the willingness of a large portion of the citizens of the Calatayud region to invest in private equity.

- **LESSON 9**: Innovative financing schemes are needed to reduce the financial risks of RECs while supporting them in project development.

Real participation in a REC, which translates into micro-investments, requires a significant amount of time spent in the territory. The creation and financing of collective projects by citizens both require a constant presence in the territory. Participatory activities involving engagement, awareness and skills, the organisation of collective initiatives and their continuous monitoring, as well as the region's lack of digitalisation, mean it is essential to be close to citizens. This situation requires personnel with highly specialised communication and interpersonal skills to be present in villages at weekends and public holidays – when villages are most populated –, building bonds of trust.

- **LESSON 10**: Projects financed by capital contributions from the users themselves requires a very strong presence in the territory and social skills.

3.3 Technical aspects.

Sizing PV systems for self-consumption. CERCA has sized PV systems with a self-consumption rate of at least 0.5, based on each user's historical consumption. However, users have different priorities and have generally requested more PV power than our calculations have suggested.

- **LESSON 11**: Sizing tools that enable to make decisions based on various criteria, not just technical or economic one, are needed.

Assuring quality in self-consumption PV systems. The profitability of micro-investments in PV systems depends on their continued performance for at least 25 years. This is only achieved if both the components and the system are of very high quality. The quality of PV systems is not a question of price but of ensuring good quality components and good practices in the installation phase.

It is widely known that this is achieved through the application of rigorous technical specifications and quality control testing to ensure compliance. However, these technical specifications are very rarely included in the contract with the installer, especially if the PV systems are relatively small.

- **LESSON 12**: To ensure the quality and lifetime of PV systems for at least 25 years, a set of technical specifications must be included in installation contracts and installers must be required to comply with them.

Maximise the local impact of renewable energy generation projects. PV surpluses are becoming increasingly cheaper on the electricity market because Spain's electricity production supply is saturated during peak hours. This causes electricity prices to fall below zero, resulting in the so-called 'duck curve', as shown in Figure 2. In order to reverse this situation and maximise the local impact of energy generated by RECs, it is necessary to implement storage systems and demand management strategies that enable generation to be matched with demand.

- **LESSON 13**: There is a need of advance management systems to balance generation and consumption in RECs integrating energy storage systems and demand management strategies.

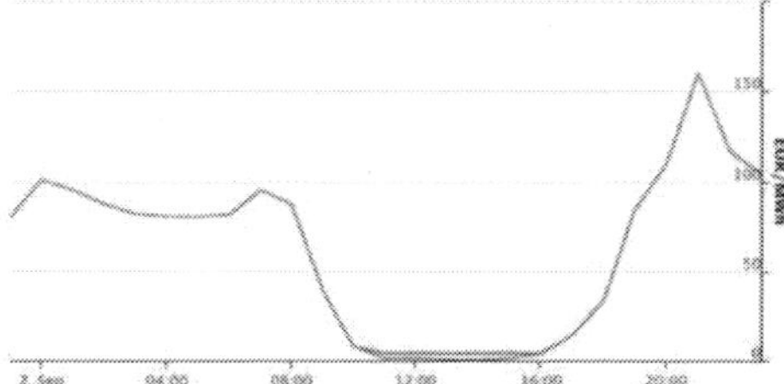

Figure 2: "Duck curve" that shows the evolution of the market price of electricity (€/MWh) in Spain and Portugal on 2 September 2025. At midday, the price is almost €0 (*source: OMIE* [14]).

Involving local installers as a driver for the project. CERCA's ambition is to collaborate with the region's communities to secure their future. This requires boosting regional economic activity, including that of local electricians and SMEs. To maximise local impact, CERCA involves local installers in the installation of its PV systems. These installers can also become REC representatives, which would benefit both themselves and REC. Local installers are trusted by some local councils, for whom they provide maintenance services.

- **LESSON 14**: Local engineers and PV installers must be involved in the REC projects and benefit from training in technical specifications and other issues. They can become representatives of the REC by proposing new projects that will benefit themselves and the energy community.

3.4 Legal aspects

Need of a REC's regulation adapted to rural communities. As a REC, CERCA's objectives are to provide its members with economic, environmental and social benefits through the production, consumption, trading, aggregation and storage of energy. However, Spain still has no regulations that permit RECs to carry out all these activities.

- **LESSON 15**: The failure to transpose the European directive into Spanish law prevents a REC from carrying out the activities envisaged in the EU legislation. No proper management of surpluses can be achieved within the self-consumption law. RECs must become electricity retailers to this end.

Self-consumption optimization. Collective PV self-consumption in Spain is carried out by assigning static distribution coefficients to consumers, regulated by law in Royal Decree 244/2019 [15]. This static distribution causes that some of the generated energy is fed into the grid instead of being used by other prosumers, preventing that energy from having a local impact throughout the year.

- **LESSON 16**: National regulation should be updated to allow for the implementation of dynamic distribution coefficients in collective PV self-consumption. This measure would maximize self-consumption rates in collective initiatives, increasing the local impact of RECs.

3.5 Administrative aspects

The development of collective PV self-consumption projects is a complex process due to the numerous requirements and regulations set by different competent bodies that must be met, as well as the interaction of a wide variety of actors involved in commissioning a self-consumption facility. This process involves everything from the initial design to the final activation of self-consumption by the utility and the effective application in the prosumer's electricity bill. However, the phase involving activation with the utility company takes the longest. This activation procedure has the following phases:

1. Having a connection point to the electricity distribution grid. If this does not exist, it will be necessary to request an electricity supply access point. This procedure can take up to a year.
2. Obtaining access and connection permits. The experience in Aragon with the electricity utility

operating in the region is that this procedure takes a few weeks unless the utility requires in its connection conditions the reinforcement of the distribution grid. In this case, the procedure can take many months and can be very costly.

3. Signing the technical access contract with the distributor. For this procedure, the utility has a maximum legal deadline of 5 months.
4. Obtaining approval from the utility after inspection of the connection to the electricity distribution grid. The time between the request for an inspection and the inspector's visit to the installation varies greatly and can take more than 1 month. In addition, we have found inconsistencies in the internal technical criteria of the utility, which makes these times much longer.
5. Activation of self-consumption with the electricity retailer. This procedure, which is carried out between the electricity retailer and the electricity company, has a very variable execution time, which can be up to 2 months.

Based on its experience with the 18 installations carried out to date, CERCA estimates that the average total activation time for self-consumption is approximately 12 months. This situation has been confirmed by other authors [16] and discourages project participants, as well as having a very negative impact on the return on investment for prosumers. Prosumers see their installations idle for months, without access to the economic and environmental benefits to which they have contributed.

- **LESSON 17**: The lead times for obtaining permits and legalising shared self-consumption systems are very long, several months or even a year in some cases. Simplified procedures with shorter response times are needed.

4 ABOUT THE STANDARIZATION OF LARGE-SCALE RECs IN RURAL AREAS

The previous barriers encountered and lessons learned raise the question of whether a standard could be formulated for the implementation of these energy communities. To answer this question, we must consider the maturity degree of these initiatives, bearing in mind that they are complex, since they involve technical, social, economic and legal aspects, among others.

Apart from the aforementioned problem of the war in Ukraine and the resulting difficulties in Europe's energy supply, the world is in the midst of an energy paradigm crisis due two main reasons. The first is the combination of climate change and the depletion of fossil fuels. Secondly, the emergence and falling cost of electricity generation technologies that do not require centralisation for efficient production (i.e. renewable energies) has opened the door to distributed electricity generation, as opposed to the old model of centralised production involving large thermal, nuclear and hydroelectric power stations.

The emergence of these renewable technologies has made it possible to propose a new, decentralised paradigm in which electricity can be produced where it is consumed using renewable technology.

Within this paradigm, various models are being developed, including distributed PV systems for self-consumption, large-scale PV plants, wind farms with or without integrated storage, and renewable energy communities. There are also different promotional and management models: some are government- or traditional electricity company-led (top-down), while others are led by civil society initiatives (bottom-up). The energy transition process promoted by Europe is an example of this alternative, top-down paradigm. The REC is one of the main examples of an energy transition designed in bottom-up way.

We are therefore still in the early stages of the emergence of multiple energy models, none of which have become established, nor has a new stable paradigm yet been formed. In this scenario, the only option is to share attractive experiences that contribute to the establishment of a prevailing model.

For this reason, we do not consider the lessons learned presented in this document to be universal. Therefore, they may not be applicable in other regions of Europe. The realities and challenges faced by rural communities vary widely, and what works in one place may not work in another.

These lessons do not represent a standard model that can be replicated with guaranteed success. Our aim is to share our experience of designing, establishing and implementing the large-scale regional renewable energy community of Calatayud, including the positive aspects and, above all, the things that should be avoided. We share this experience with the intention and responsibility of contributing to the development of a model for the new paradigm.

5 CONCLUSIONS

This document outlines the main barriers encountered and sets out 16 key lessons learned during the two-and-a-half-year design, creation and implementation process of the Calatayud Region's Regional Renewable Energy Community (CERCA).

These experiences have been categorised as organisational, financial, technical, legal and administrative, and the barriers encountered and lessons learned in each case have been defined.

The aim of this document is to share these lessons and thereby contribute to the creation of the model for the new REC paradigm.

6 ACKNOWLEDGEMENTS

This work has been possible thanks to the Project Joining Actors for LOcal development of New large-scale regional energy communities (LIFE21-CET-ENERCOM-JALON), under grant agreement 101076395. Funded by the European Union. Views and opinions expressed are, however, those of the author(s) only and do not necessarily reflect those of the European Union or CINEA. Neither the European Union nor the granting authority can be held responsible for them.

7 REFERENCES

[1] E. Commission., «REPowerEU: Joint European action for more affordable, secure and sustainable energy,» 2022.

[2] E. Comission, «https://ec.europa.eu/commission/presscorner/detail/en/ip_22_3131,» 18 May 2022. [On line]. Available: https://ec.europa.eu/commission/presscorner/detail/en/ip_22_3131. [Last access: 20 June 2025].

[3] L. Arfini, «EU now has 9,000+ "energy communities": smart, decentralised, flexible generation and consumption,» 13 November 2023. [On line]. Available: https://energypost.eu/eu-now-has-9000-energy-communities-smart-decentralised-flexible-generation-and-consumption/. [Last access: 20 June 2025].

[4] I. D. Region, «Recent Survey Highlights Potential of Energy Communities in the EU,» 2024.

[5] E. Commission, «Barriers and drivers report. 2024, Energy Communities Repository.».

[6] «Directive (EU) 2018/2001 on the promotion of the use of energy from renewable sources, as amended by Directive (EU) 2023/2413,» 2023. [On line]. Available: http://data.europa.eu/eli/dir/2018/2001/oj. [Last access: 20 June 2025].

[7] «Directive (EU) 2023/2413 of the European Parliament and of the Council of 18 October 2023 amending Directive (EU) 2018/2001 as regards the promotion of energy from renewable sources,» 2023. [On line]. Available: http://data.europa.eu/eli/dir/2023/2413/oj. [Last access: 20 June 2025].

[8] L. Gruber, U. Bachhiesl y S. Wogrin, «The current state of research on energy communities,» *Elektrotech. Inftech.*, n° 138, p. 515–524, 2021.

[9] M. Koltunov, S. Pezzutto, A. Bisello, G. Lettner, A. Hiesl, W. van Sark, A. Louwen y E. Wilczynski, «Mapping of Energy Communities in Europe: Status Quo and Review of Existing Classifications,» *Sustainability,* n° 15, 2023.

[10] L. Peeters, L. F. López y C. Trompoukis, «Addressing the gaps in understanding and assessing energy communities,» *Energy Research & Social Science,* vol. 127, 2025.

[11] «LIFE21-CET-ENERCOM-JALON,» 2022. [On line]. Available: https://ec.europa.eu/info/funding-tenders/opportunities/portal/screen/opportunities/projects-details/43252405/101076395/LIFE2027.

[12] CERCA, «cercaenergia.com,» [On line]. Available: https://cercaenergia.com/. [Last access: September 2025].

[13] Instituto para La Diversificación y Ahorro de la Energía (IDAE), *Programa de Incentivos a proyectos piloto singulares de comunidades energéticas (Programa CE Implementa)*, Orden TED/1446/2021, de 22 de diciembre de 2021 del Ministerio para la Transición Ecológica y el Reto Demográfico.

[14] OMIE, «Operador de mercado eléctrico,» [On line]. Available: https://www.omie.es/. [Last access: 02 09 2025].

[15] Ministerio para la Transición Ecológica, *Real Decreto 244/2019, de 5 de abril, por el que se regulan las condiciones administrativas, técnicas y económicas del autoconsumo de energía eléctrica.,* 2019, p. 35674 to 35719.

[16] Greenpeace España (colaboration with Alianza por el Autoconsumo), «Autoconsumo en España, diagnóstico, retos y propuestas,» 2023.

Systems transition theory

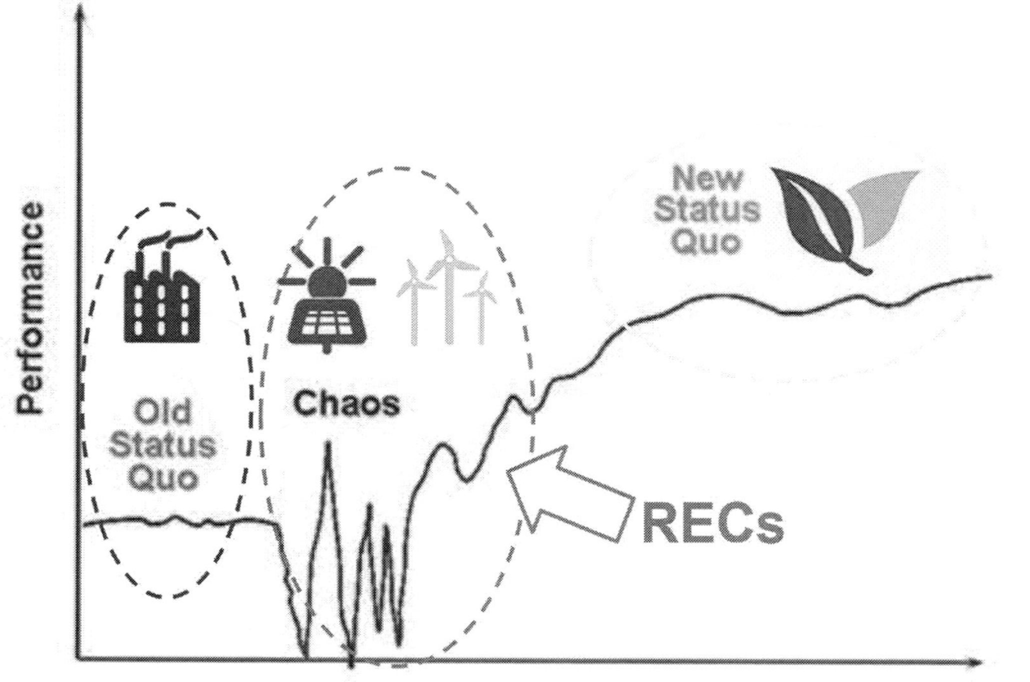

1

CHALLENGES AND LESSONS LEARNED IN THE IMPLEMENTATION OF A REGIONAL-SCALE PV ENERGY COMMUNITY IN SPAIN

L. M. Carrasco, R. H. Almeida, Kiane Alves e Silva, L. Narvarte

Instituto de Energía Solar, Universidad Politécnica de Madrid, Madrid (SPAIN)

020568-002

Introduction

INSTITUTO DE ENERGÍA SOLAR

LARGE-SCALE REGIONAL RENEWABLE ENERGY COMMUNITY

1. Objectives: **TO COMBAT RURAL DEPOPULATION AND CONTRIBUTE TO THE ENERGY TRANSITION.**

2. Legal entity: **COOPERATIVE**

3. Members: **INDIVIDUALS, LOCAL COUNCILS, ASSOCIATIONS and COMPANIES.**

4. Activity: **PRODUCING, CONSUMING and MANAGING ELECTRICITY from RENEWABLE SOURCES**

5. Funding:

   - **MEMBERS' CONTRIBUTIONS**

   - **SUBSIDIES**

020568-003

3

Introduction

INSTITUTO DE ENERGÍA SOLAR

METHODOLOGY

- AWARNESS, ENGAGEMENT and SKILLS CAMPAIGN
- PARTICIPATION MODELS
- WORKSHOPS FOR REGIONAL KEY ACTORS
- LOCAL INSTALLERS
- PV QUALITY SPECIFICATIONS
- 1st PHASE FUNDING:
  - 40% PUBLIC GRANT
  - 60% PARTICIPANTS' EQUITY
  - TRANSPARENCY

4

Introduction

INSTITUTO DE ENERGÍA SOLAR

ACHIEVEMENTS

- **150 members**
- **18 projects** in **15 villages (825 kWp)**
- **500 beneficiaries**
- **€760,000** invested by participants.

5

Barriers and lessons learned

1. Organizational
2. Financial
3. Technical
4. Legal
5. Administrative

Barriers and lessons learned

1. Organizational aspects

LESSON 1

Difficulty in developing bottom-up initiatives when starting from scratch. Don't start from scratch.

LESSON 2

The scale of the REC requires technical skills and responsible management. A structure based exclusively on volunteers is a threat to the sustainability of a REC.

LESSON 3

The seeding phase takes much longer than initially imagined. Communicating the REC proposal in the region requires a lot of time in the territory.

LESSON 4

Citizens' trust can only be gained if their mayor's trust is first secured. Need of institutional support, mainly from Municipalities.

POLITÉCNICA

7

Barriers and lessons learned

INSTITUTO DE ENERGÍA SOLAR

1. Organizational aspects

LESSON 5

Difficulties when trying to contact the mayors. Need of collaboration of the supra-local institution that unites all the municipalities in the region.

LESSON 6

Lack of skills on energy and poor digital culture. Training in these areas is necessary.

POLITÉCNICA

Barriers and lessons learned

2. Financial aspects

LESSON 7

Grants do not respect the timeframes needed for real participation.

LESSON 8

Grouping participants together through collective self-consumption systems creates economies of scale and increases the ability to raise community awareness.

LESSON 9

Innovative financing schemes are needed to reduce the financial risks of RECs while supporting them in project development.

LESSON 10

The creation and financing of collective projects by citizens both require a constant presence in the territory.

Barriers and lessons learned

3. Technical aspects

LESSON 11

Sizing tools for PV systems that enable to make decisions based on various criteria, not just technical or economic one, are needed.

LESSON 12

Technical specifications must be included in installation contracts and installers must be required to comply with them.

LESSON 13

To achieve real local impact, shared energy must be increased integrating energy storage systems and demand management strategies.

LESSON 14

Local installers must be involved in the REC projects and benefit from training in technical specifications.

Barriers and lessons learned

4. Legal aspects

LESSON 15

No proper management of energy surpluses can be achieved within the current Spanish self-consumption law. RECs must become electricity retailers to this end.

LESSON 16

National regulation should be updated to allow for the implementation of dynamic distribution coefficients in collective PV self-consumption.

5. Administrative aspects

LESSON 17

Lead times for obtaining permits and activating collective self-consumption systems are very long. Simplified procedures with shorter response times are required.

POLITÉCNICA

11

Conclusion

This new knowledge aims to contribute to the establishment of the new paradigm in the setting up of RECs.

Conclusions

https://jalon-ce.eu/

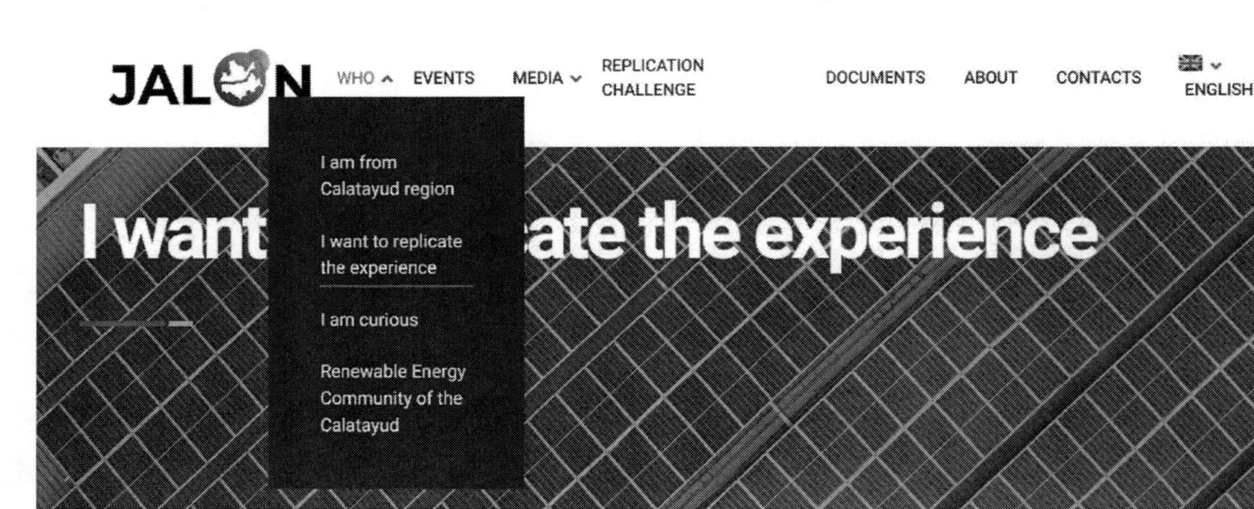

Guide Regional Energy Community Standard Model

Thank you for your attention

Dr. Luis Miguel Carrasco

luismiguel.carrasco@upm.es

Happy to take your questions

**Funded by
the European Union**

Funded by the European Union. Views and opinions expressed are however those of the author(s) only and do not necessarily reflect those of the European Union or CINEA. Neither the European Union nor the granting authority can be held responsible for them.

POLITÉCNICA

020568-014

KONSOLE WORKSHOP: A MODEL FOR RENEWABLE ENERGY EDUCATION AND CAREER DEVELOPMENT

Jayaprasad Arumughan, Monika Sarkadi, Radovan Kopecek, Florian Buchholz, Kristian Peter
International Solar Energy research Center, Rudolf-Diesel Strasse 15, D-78467 Konstanz, Germany.
konsole@isc-konstanz.de

ABSTRACT: KonSoLe (German: *Konstanzer Solare Lernwerkstatt*, translated as *Constance Solar Student Workshop*) at the International Solar Energy Research Center (ISC) Konstanz was developed to provide school students and young learners with a structured introduction to solar photovoltaic (PV) technology and sustainability. The program integrates short theory sessions, age-specific practical activities such as assembling simple solar devices or mini-modules, guided laboratory tours, and interactive exercises on energy consumption and climate impact. This blended approach allows participants to link scientific concepts with hands-on experience while fostering awareness of renewable energy in the context of social and ecological sustainability. Workshop evaluation combined short quizzes on theoretical and laboratory content with structured questionnaires administered immediately after the sessions. Responses were recorded anonymously using Likert scales and supplemented by open-ended feedback. The outcomes show consistently high levels of engagement, with over 85% of participants reporting increased knowledge and nearly 70% highlighting the practical module fabrication as a key learning element. Interest in renewable energy as a study and career field was reinforced, and more than half of respondents indicated that they could imagine pursuing a technical career path. Viewed through selected dimensions of Social Cognitive Career Theory (SCCT), the results suggest that the workshop strengthened self-efficacy, shaped positive career outcome expectations, and stimulated interest development. Younger participants in particular expressed openness to renewable energy careers, while older learners with established vocational orientations responded more variably. Across groups, social impact and innovation were cited as main perceived benefits, although limited job opportunities were identified as a concern. Overall, KonSoLe demonstrates the potential of practice-oriented interventions to enhance knowledge transfer and encourage sustainability-focused career intentions.
Keywords: Solar photovoltaic technology, Education for Sustainable Development (ESD), PV- career orientation, Social Cognitive Career Theory (SCCT)

1 INTRODUCTION

The transition to renewable energy depends not only on technological innovation but also on building a skilled and inclusive workforce. While engineering and policy measures aim to reduce greenhouse-gas emissions, social dimensions such as distributional fairness and meaningful participation determine whether energy transitions are equitable and effective. At the same time, energy poverty (the lack of reliable access to electricity in many rural areas of the Global South) highlights the need for actionable, locally adapted solutions. Decentralized photovoltaic systems frequently offer faster, more cost-effective, and context-sensitive routes to electrification than centralized grid expansion, and they can generate direct social benefits for education, health and livelihoods.

Education and capacity building are therefore central to ensuring that decentralized solar technologies are adopted in ways that are both technically sound and socially just. The International Solar Energy Research Center (ISC) Konstanz, founded in 2005, has developed a range of academic and professional training activities to bridge research, industry and public engagement. In 2017, the International Solar Energy Research Center (ISC) Konstanz launched the *Konstanzer Solare Lernwerkstatt* (KonSoLe, translated as *Constance Solar Student Workshop*), an outreach program that combines short lectures, hands-on module fabrication, laboratory visits, and group work to introduce students and local citizens to photovoltaic technology, sustainability, and renewable-energy careers. The feedback from the program indicates high engagement and effective knowledge transfer, and points to both opportunities and gaps in career guidance.

This paper examines the KonSoLe workshop as a practical model for renewable-energy education and career development. Using Social Cognitive Career Theory (SCCT) as an analytical frame, we assess how hands-on learning, role modelling by professionals, and reflective activities influence self-efficacy, outcome expectations and interest in PV careers. The paper presents participant feedback, interprets these findings in light of SCCT, and discusses implications for scaling similar educational programs and for policy makers seeking to strengthen workforce pipelines for the energy transition [1,2,3].

2 THE WORKSHOP PROGRAM

2.1 Program Structure

The KonSoLe workshop is a unique blend of Science, Technology, Engineering, and Mathematics (STEM) education and Education for sustainable Development (ESD). STEM education is an approach to learning and teaching the core subjects of STEM by integrating them and applying them to real-world problems. Its goal is to develop students' critical thinking, problem-solving, and creative skills, preparing them for future careers in a technology-driven world.

On the other hand, ESD is an educational approach that empowers individuals to take informed, responsible actions for a sustainable future. It integrates knowledge, skills, values, and attitudes related to environmental integrity, economic viability, and social justice into all forms of education. ESD also promotes competencies like critical thinking and collaborative decision-making to address global challenges such as climate change, inequality, and resource depletion.

The workshops are delivered in two parallel streams tailored to age and school grade: one for students through grade 7 (up to 13 years) and the other for students from grade 8 onward (14+ years). Each workshop begins with a concise, 30 minute theoretical introduction to solar energy covering basic photovoltaic principles with emphasis on crystalline-silicon technology, typical domestic applications such as rooftop and balcony systems, the role of balance of system (BOS) components, and the contribution of solar power to carbon-neutral goals. Participants learn the operation of a solar cell, key BOS elements, and the climate relevance of decentralized PV systems.

The theory block is followed by an age-appropriate practical session. Younger students construct simple, safe solar devices that demonstrate immediate cause–effect (for example, a small solar fan assembled from an upcycled glass bottle). Older students assemble mini solar modules from industry-standard components: soldering cells into strings, laminating a prototype module, and configuring outputs for USB charging. Materials provided for module fabrication include crystalline silicon cells, tabbing wire, EVA sheets, back-sheets and glass plates. Soldering and assembly are carried out by participants under instructor supervision, and the finished modules are taken home.

Figure 1: Students participating in the hands-on session

As appropriate for participant level, assembled modules are characterized using IV-curve measurements and imaging techniques such as electroluminescence (EL) and photoluminescence (PL) to introduce basic testing and quality concepts. Modules may be paired with a DC–DC converter or small storage device to provide stable USB power for practical demonstrations, including smartphone charging.

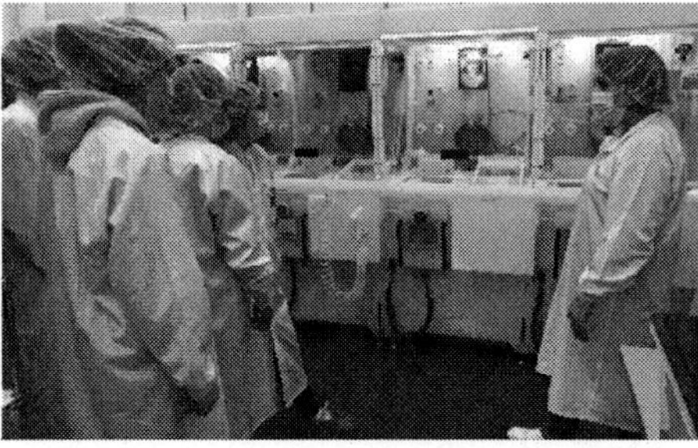

Figure 2: Participants visiting the solar cell fabrication cleanroom.

All participants undertake a laboratory visit to observe cell and module processing and to see key characterization equipment (for example, IV tracers and EL imaging) in operation, and to view the institute's operational PV installations. Prior to the lab tour participants receive brief safety instructions; cleanroom entry requires protective coats and gloves (figure 2). Cleanroom access is limited to six participants at a time, so larger groups rotate in subgroups.

The third segment is devoted to interactive ESD-Methods (Education for Sustainable Development, also known as Global Education) and is aimed to place PV technology in a social-ecological frame. This perspective has proved to be an effective incentive for students with less affinity for technical subjects. The methods used are include an illustrated presentation with interactive exercises: a game analyzing the distribution of the Earth's population compared to the distribution of energy consumption, leading to an overall insight on Earth overload, energy poverty and the outstanding climate (in)justice. These concepts are discussed in the group and the role of PV as one important solution for these global challenges is highlighted. Students are encouraged to inspect their own lifestyles through a CO_2-footprint calculation, connecting local choices to global impacts. Depending on the age – they are encouraged to explore their handprint potential for more transformative action: one of these being a future career in the field of renewable energies. The typical workshop group consists of 12–16 students.

Figure 3: Interactive session on sustainability

The workshop concludes with a structured feedback questionnaire assessing engagement, perceived knowledge gain and career interest. Participants receive brief wrap-up materials, certificates and take-home items as appropriate, for example a solar propeller or a USB module charger fabricated by the participants.

3 EVALUATION APPROACH AND FEEDBACK INSTRUMENTS

3.1 Evaluation Methods

To evaluate the success and participant involvement in the KonSoLe workshops, we administered a short structured questionnaire at the end of the workshop. Responses were collected anonymously on a five-point Likert scale (1 = strongly disagree to 5 = strongly agree), without personal identifiers. For analysis, responses were grouped into three categories: *fully agree*, *agree*, and *not agree*. The questionnaire covered multiple dimensions, including program engagement, perceived knowledge gain, prior knowledge of solar energy, interest in further study, ease of completing the practical task (e.g., assembling a solar propeller or mini-module), technical career aspirations, concern about climate change, and willingness to contribute to a sustainable future. Open-ended fields invited participants to provide additional comments and suggestions.

3.2 Evaluation Outcomes

The feedback indicates exceptionally high levels of engagement and knowledge transfer. Specifically, 88.7% fully agreed that the program was engaging, and 87.5% fully agreed that they gained new knowledge. In contrast, the statement "New to Topic" garnered only 30.4% full agreement, with 32.4% not agreeing, which implies that many participants already had some familiarity with the subject matter. Interest in solar and renewable energy was robust (45.7% fully agree and 41.1% agree), and the practical, hands-on component, solar module fabrication, was well received (69.4% fully agree). Regarding career interests, 54.5% fully agreed on the potential for a technical career, although 21.7% did not agree, indicating an opportunity for enhanced career guidance. Additionally, concerns about climate change (68.7% fully agree) and commitment to sustainability (71.4% fully agree) were prominent. Overall, these preliminary results demonstrate that the KonSoLe workshop effectively engages participants, imparts valuable knowledge, and fosters a strong commitment to sustainability, while also highlighting areas for further refinement in addressing varied levels of prior knowledge and career guidance.

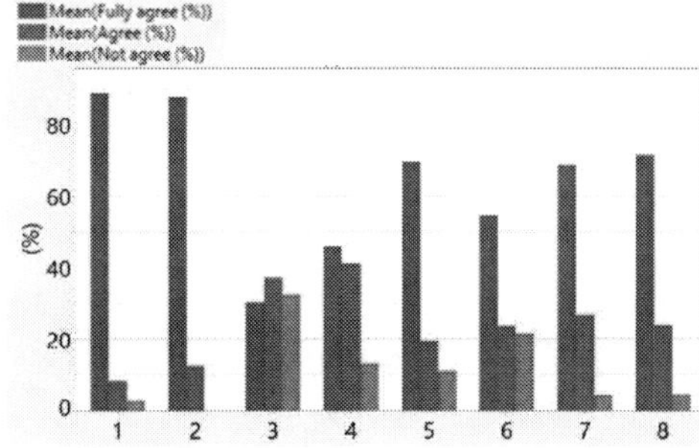

Figure 4: Student engagement and learning outcomes in renewable energy from the KonSoLe Workshop. The graph summarizes responses to eight statements: 1) The program was very engaging, 2) I gained substantial new knowledge, 3) I am already familiar with the topic, 4) I would like to learn more about solar or renewable energy, 5) I could build the solar module with ease, 6) I could imagine pursuing a technical career, 7) I am concerned about climate change and its ecological and social impacts, and 8) I am committed to promoting a sustainable future.

3.3 Evaluation of the Results Using SCCT

Viewed through the lens of SCCT, our evaluation highlights several relevant dimensions, even though the study does not probe the theory in depth. The questionnaire items were designed to address key career-related aspects: confidence in skills and knowledge (self-efficacy), expected benefits of a career in renewable energy (outcome expectations), interest in further learning, career intentions, and external influences such as school, policy, and perceived job market conditions.

Participants reported increased confidence in their skills and knowledge. Responses regarding outcome expectations revealed that a majority considered a career in renewable energy to be rewarding, with particular emphasis on social impact and technological innovation. Most participants indicated that their interest in renewable energy increased after the workshop, with hands-on activities and teamwork identified as the most engaging components. Many expressed that they could envision pursuing a career in the renewable energy sector. Younger students appeared more open to this possibility, whereas participants from vocational training backgrounds showed mixed responses, as many already had firmly defined career goals. A large share expressed interest in further training, internships, or mentorship opportunities in renewable energy. The most frequently cited challenge was the perception of limited job opportunities. Follow-up feedback, collected indirectly through schoolteachers, suggested that several former participants had already chosen career paths within the renewable energy sector; however, due to data protection regulations, systematic tracking was not possible, and such responses were obtained only on a voluntary basis.

4. SUMMARY

This paper presents the design, implementation, and evaluation of the KonSoLe workshop, an educational program aimed at introducing young learners to solar photovoltaic (PV) technology and renewable energy careers. The workshop combines lectures, laboratory visits, and hands-on activities, giving participants both theoretical understanding and practical experience. Many students who attended the KonSoLe workshop later returned to ISC for their bachelor's or master's theses, and a few went on to join ISC as engineers or scientists. To assess its impact, two evaluation tools were employed: a structured feedback questionnaire developed by the project team and an additional survey based on selected principles of SCCT.

The results show consistently high levels of engagement, increased knowledge, and strong interest in renewable energy. Participants reported greater confidence in their skills (self-efficacy), positive expectations about career opportunities, and motivation to explore further learning and training. While younger students were particularly open to renewable energy careers, participants with existing vocational training showed more mixed responses, highlighting the importance of targeted career guidance at an early age. Social impact and innovation were perceived as the most rewarding aspects of the sector, although limited job opportunities were cited as a challenge.

Overall, the findings demonstrate that the KonSoLe workshop effectively combines education with career orientation, fostering knowledge, motivation, and commitment to sustainability. The approach highlights the potential of hands-on, practice-oriented learning formats to inspire the next generation of renewable energy professionals.

Future development of the KonSoLe workshop should place stronger emphasis on career guidance by linking participants to study pathways, apprenticeships, and local job opportunities in the renewable sector. Expanding follow-up opportunities such as mentoring or internships, while tailoring activities to different knowledge levels, will help sustain motivation and ensure long-term impact.

With careful scaling and ongoing evaluation, KonSoLe can serve as a replicable model for renewable energy education that not only builds knowledge but also guides students toward meaningful career pathways.

4.1 References

[1] Bandura, A. 1986. Social foundations of Thought and Action: A social Congnitive Theory. Engelwood Cliffs, NJ: Prentice-Hall.
[2] Lent, R. W., Brown, S. D., & Hackett, G. (1994). Toward a unifying social cognitive theory of career and academic interest, choice, and performance. Journal of Vocational Behavior,*45*(1),79–122. https://doi.org/10.1006/jvbe.1994.1027
[3] Lent, R. W., Brown, S. D., & Hackett, G. (2000). Contextual supports and barriers to career choice: A social cognitive analysis. *Journal of Counseling Psychology,* *47*(1), 36–49. https://doi.org/10.1037/0022-0167.47.1.36

10.4229/EUPVSEC2025/5EO.1.5
020569-004

A SNAPSHOT OF GLOBAL PV MARKETS – 2024

Gaëtan Masson[1], Melodie de l'Epine[2], Arnulf Jäger Waldau[3],
Izumi Kaizuka[4], Amelia Oller Westerberg[5], Jose Donoso[6]
[1] IEA PVPS Task 1, Brussels, Belgium; [2] IEA PVPS Task 1, Lyon, France;
[3] European Commission JRC, Ispra, Italy; [4] RTS Corporation, Tokyo, Japan;
[5] Becquerel Sweden, Knivsta, Sweden; [6] UNEF, Madrid, Spain

ABSTRACT: The objective of this paper is to propose a reliable and accurate perspective on key markets and policies related to PV development in 2024 and previously. It aims at offering a clear analysis of how PV markets have developed in 2024, with updated numbers, along with an analysis of the policies behind the development. In this paper are displayed and analyzed survey results for the calendar year 2024 concerning PV markets and policies, as well as other key issues. An increasing number of national markets experienced notable growth in 2024 with impacts on policy development. Figures show that over 601 GW of PV systems have been installed in the world last year. Consequently, cumulative capacity crossed the 2.3 TW mark in 2024.

Keywords: Photovoltaic (PV), Market, IEA PVPS

1 INTRODUCTION

This Trends paper gives information on the development of PV power applications in the PVPS member and non-member countries and is largely based on the information provided by IEA PVPS countries in addition to Becquerel Sweden and the European Union through its European Commission. The report includes information on national market developments at the end of the former year, in this case, 2024. The International Energy Agency – Photovoltaic Power System Programme (IEA PVPS)'s Task 1 is responsible for strategy and outreach within the IEA PVPS program. This includes policy, market and industry analysis. A key deliverable of Task 1 is the annual Snapshot of Global PV Markets publication, together with the annual flagship report Trends in PV Application.

The objective of the series of annual Snapshot and Trends reports — which have been published since 1992 (Trends) [1] and 2013 (Snapshot) [2] — is to present and interpret developments in both the PV systems and components being used in the PV power systems market and the changing applications for these products within that market. These trends are analyzed in the context of the business, policy and non-technical environment in the reporting countries.

2 THE GLOBAL PV INSTALLED CAPACITY

This paper presents the latest survey results for the calendar year 2024 concerning PV markets and policies, as well as other key issues. An increasing number of national markets experienced notable growth in 2024, and that impacted policy choices. The capacity figures given are nominal DC peak power (Wp) under standard test conditions (i.e. 1 000 W irradiance, air mass 1.5 light spectrum and 25 °C device temperature) for consistency reasons. As not all countries report DC peak power (Wp) for solar PV systems, instead reporting AC power, these capacity figures are converted to Wp DC.

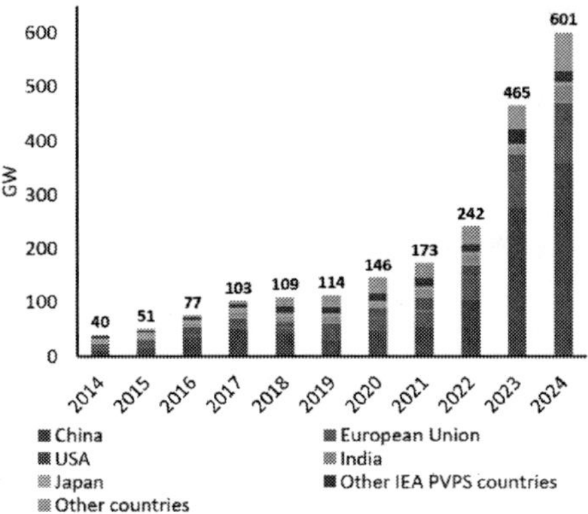

Figure 1: Evolution of annual PV installations (GW-DC)

While the final figures for 2024 could slightly continue to be refined in the future, nearly final figures show that around 601 GW of PV systems have been installed in the world last year. Some important trends observed are as follows.

The global PV market grew to around 601 GW in 2024, compared to around 465 GW in 2023. This represents a year-on-year growth of approximately 30%.

Asia scored the first place again in 2024 with China (357 GW[1]) and India (32 GW) leading the way. With around 47 GW deployed this year, the market in USA grew nearly 35%, after an already high 2023 (35 GW).

The market in EU grew significantly to around 66 GW. The top countries are Germany with (17 GW) and Spain with (8.7 GW) installed in 2024, followed by Italy (6.7 GW), France (6 GW) and Poland (4.2 GW).

---

[1] China's National Energy Administration (NEA) publishes in AC and Becquerel Institute applies a conversion ratio from AC to DC. A range of values is often provided to account for uncertainty in AC/DC conversion ratios, with regards to new utility scale capacity in China, where the minimal annual volume considers official China reporting and the maximal annual volume considers a further 42 GW that *could* have been installed considering the uncertainty surrounding official conversion ratios from AC to DC of Utility scale systems. If no range is specified, compiled data refers to the **higher** totals with Official China reporting values.

Preliminary numbers show that installations in the Middle East and Africa regions amounted to around 8.7 GW last year.

Fast development was observed once again in Latin America, with around 14.3 GW installed in Brazil, and 2.1 GW in Chile.

Drivers for PV development include record-breaking competitiveness levels and development of distributed PV.

Annual installed capacity largely surpassed the 500 GW threshold reached for the first time in 2024, while total cumulative installed capacity in the world reached at least 2.3 TW.

3 MARKET DEVELOPMENT

In 2024, the PV market saw an important growth for the fifth year in a row after 2019's limited growth. Globally, the trend is upwards by exceeding the 601 GW annual installed capacity as expressed in Fig. 1.

Asia remains the leader of the global PV market. Next to China (357 GW), India and Japan remain a relevant presence in the global market with respectively 32 GW and 5.6 GW installed.

In other parts of Asia, the market observed steady growth in Thailand (3 GW) and decrease in South Korea (2.5 GW). Pakistan showed a massive increase with 18 GW installed in the last year. Australia installed 5.3 GW in 2024, a highest level since 2021.

In the Americas, the USA market grew from the previous year by approximately 35% (47 GW), on the other hand Brazil installed at least 14.3 GW in 2024 (it maintained the growth rate of the previous year, and cumulative capacity reached 52 GW). PV installations in Chile almost doubled in 2024 reaching a cumulative installed capacity of 11.3 GW while installations in Mexico were at a higher level (2.1 GW) compared to 2023. The market in Canada remained at a low level in 2024 with 321 MW installed compared to the record level seen in 2021 (2.0 GW).

In the European Union, Germany has gained back the leading position with nearly 17 GW installed in this period, surpassing Spain. In 2024, Spain (8.7 GW), Italy (6.7 GW), France (6 GW) and Poland (4.2 GW) can be mentioned as leading countries as well. The Netherlands added over 3.4 GW and Greece 2.6 GW while seven, countries added more than 1 GW namely Austria, Portugal, Hungary, and Ireland.

New development occurred in Africa (Egypt, South Africa) and in the Middle East (UAE, Saudi Arabia) which led to GW-scale cumulative installation levels: 8.7 GW in South Africa, 7.6 GW in the UAE, 4.7 GW in Egypt, and 6.6 GW in Saudi Arabia, for instance. Israel installed 0.9 GW in 2024.

In 2024, thirty-six countries passed the GW mark concerning annual installed PV capacity. Fifty-eight countries reached at least 1 GW cumulatively in 2024. China alone represented 1.1 TW. Germany, which used to lead the rankings for years, lost its leading position in 2015 and now ranks fourth (100 GW). The USA are second (225 GW) and India is third (124 GW). With close to 398 GW of total capacity, Europe is now significantly behind Asia, leading with at least 1.4 TW, with much more to come in the coming years.

4 GRID-CONNECTED CENTRALIZED AND DISTRIBUTED

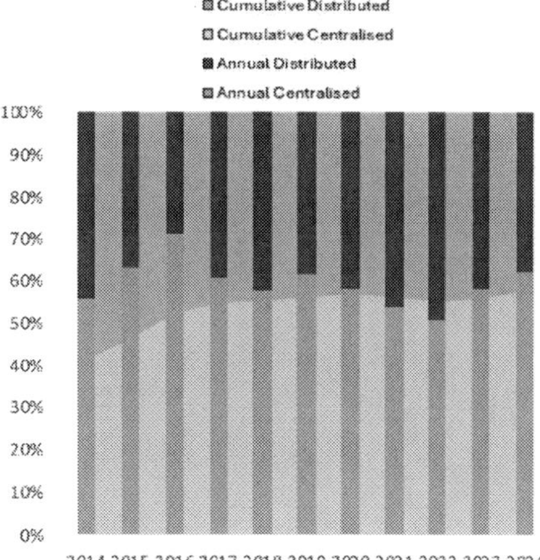

Figure 2: Segmentation of PV installation 2014-2024

Regarding the share of distributed and centralized installations at the global level, the trend has changed several times over the years.

Before 2013, most new PV installations were distributed systems, i.e. mainly installed on rooftops.

However, in more recent years, the market has seen a strong development of grid connected centralized installations. This changing trend is because centralized PV has evolved faster in terms of cost, and most of the major PV development in emerging PV markets are coming from utility-scale PV. The success of utility-scale installations is attributed to the fact that installation time and cost per Wp are lower than for distributed PV plants.

In the last years, tenders have driven PV development and continued to be granted in many countries in the world with extremely competitive prices, well below 20 USD/MWh in the sunniest places. One of the key trends of 2024 is the further development of utility-scale plants without financial incentives. Such development is mostly independent of policy decisions, which makes its potential virtually unlimited.

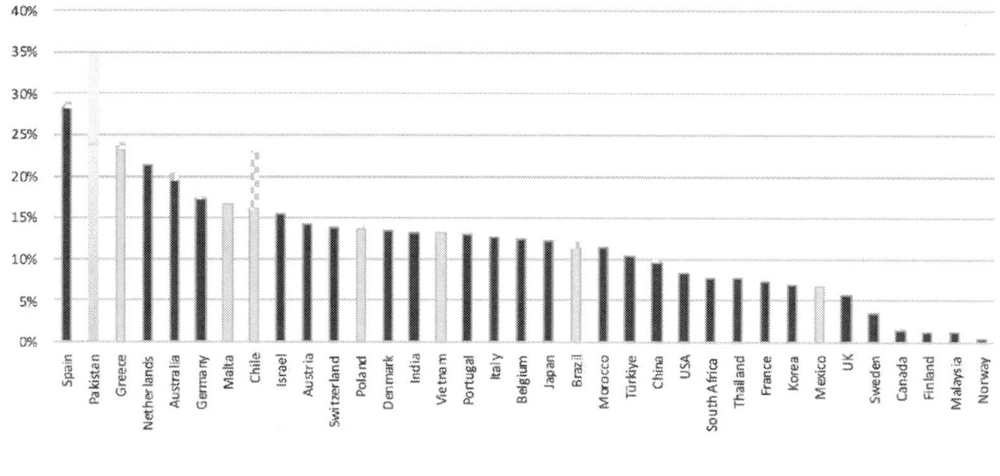

Figure 3: National PV penetration in % of the final electricity demand based on 2024 capacities.

Note: the electricity production from PV per country in this report is an estimate of what the minimal theoretical production should be the following year, when all the PV systems installed at the end of the year have generated electricity for one year. For this reason, the PV penetration rates here are an estimate and are likely to differ from official PV production and penetration numbers in many countries - they should be considered as indicative, providing a reliable estimation for comparison between countries and do not replace official data.

Distributed PV market share, after suffering from a small decline in 2019, has gradually increased, reaching an even higher level in 2024 than in 2017.

The market has also continued to diversify in 2024. While floating PV (FPV) adds to utility-scale, BIPV complements BAPV in the built environment, although it remains a niche. Other emerging segments such as agricultural PV (APV) or PV integrated in vehicles (VIPV) are showing the potential for further diversification of PV components, but their current levels of development remain limited. Dual use of land and surfaces is an option deeply investigated around the world.

At the local level, the region with the highest share of grid-connected centralized installations was Europe until 2011 which was holding 80% of the utility-scale system installed globally. Starting from 2012, American and Asian countries share started to grow and by the end of 2013 Asia became the main region for utility-scale projects.

5 ELECTRICITY PRODUCTION

The electricity production from PV per country as shown in Fig. 3 estimates what the PV production could be, based on the cumulative PV capacity at the end of 2024 (close to optimum siting, orientation and average weather conditions). These numbers, which are not based on actual measurements, should therefore be considered as indicative, aiming at comparing different situations in different countries rather than official data. In several countries, the PV contribution to the final electricity demand has passed the 5% mark with Spain in the first place with more than 25%. Greece and Pakistan tie at second with nearly 23%, and Netherlands, Chile, Australia and Germany follow. In total, PV contribution amounts to more than 8% of the electricity demand in the world.

6 CONCLUSIONS

This brief overview of the situation of the PV market and its deployment shows that in 2024 the annual PV market reached at least 601 GW worldwide and the cumulative installed capacity represented over 2.3 TW. The global PV market is, more than ever, dominated by a few leading countries even if many new PV markets are developing on all continents, at different paces. Although, slowed by supply chain issues and regulation changes in some countries, solar PV has continued its relentless progression overall in 2024. Production capacities have significantly increased in 2024, in particular, upstream (polysilicon and wafer). China remains the main manufacturing hub worldwide, by far. Larger wafers and larger modules continue their dominance on the market, with 182 mm and 210 mm wafers established as the new standards, and 166 mm disappearing.

7 REFERENCES

[1] IEA PVPS, TRENDS 2024 In Photovoltaic application, https://iea-pvps.org/trends_reports/trends/
[2] IEA PVPS, 2024 Snapshot of Global PV Markets, https://iea-pvps.org/snapshot-reports/snapshot-2023

This presentation was selected by the Sc. Committee of the EU PVSEC 2025 for submission of a full paper to one of the EU PVSEC's collaborating peer-reviewed journals.

EXPLORING THE REVENUE POTENTIAL OF PHOTOVOLTAIC SYSTEMS PARTICIPATING IN FREQUENCY CONTAINMENT RESERVE

Emil Petkovski, Theo Bosma, Marcel Eijgelaar, Ravi Singh
Group Research and Development, DNV
Utrechtseweg 310, 6812 AR Arnhem, The Netherlands
emil.petkovski@dnv.com

ABSTRACT: This paper investigates the financial prospects of photovoltaic (PV) systems without battery storage providing frequency containment reserve (FCR) services by operating with a dedicated active power reserve. Using operational data from a 49.5 MWp PV system in the Netherlands the potential revenue from FCR provision was compared against earnings in the day-ahead (DA) electricity market, over the period of January 1st to October 31st 2024. The analysis indicated that in 136 out of 304 days, average FCR prices exceeded DA market prices, during the 12:00–16:00 interval, relevant for PV systems. Moreover, actively providing FCR services would have been possible and profitable on 71 of these days, generating an additional revenue of €53,661, corresponding to an 11.34% increase compared to selling energy exclusively on the DA market for those days. Overall, incorporating FCR into the operational strategy resulted in a revenue boost of approximately 2.87% over the entire 10-month study period. These findings highlight the potential economic benefits for PV systems without battery storage actively participating in frequency regulation.
Keywords: photovoltaics, frequency containment reserve, ancillary services, power reserve, solar power

1 INTRODUCTION

The total cumulative installed photovoltaic (PV) system capacity at the end of 2024 is estimated at 2.25 TW, of which 602 GW were added in the last year alone [1]. This rapid expansion confirms that solar power will remain central in addressing global energy demand while reducing greenhouse gas emissions. However, as PV integration accelerates, updated grid regulations increasingly impose additional requirements on these systems, such as frequency driven active power curtailment. This can be achieved using traditional hill-climbing methods such as the Perturb and Observe (P&O) by imposing an upper limit for the produced power, so that further maximum power point (MPP) tracking is disabled once this point is reached. Moreover, there are multiple constant power generation (CPG) strategies which also enable reduced power operation, without providing the knowledge of the MPP and the available power reserve at any given moment [2, 3].

Still, achieving full participation in frequency regulation of PV systems without costly battery storage, would require maintaining a dedicated active power reserve to be used during underfrequency events. Multiple flexible power point (FPP) tracking algorithms have been presented in literature to achieve this goal. [4, 5] are based on curve fitting techniques, while in [6, 7] neural network have been trained to perform an estimation of the maximum power and require as input the measurement of solar radiation and PV cell temperature. [8, 9] present an FPP tracking algorithm based on a single diode model, requiring only the measurement of PV cell temperature. Such model-based algorithms must be periodically updated to reflect PV aging and other degradation factors. [10] presents an update strategy by switching to the P&O algorithm in intervals when the system is targeting maximum power production.

Practical demonstrations also exist. For instance, in [11] the National Renewable Energy Laboratory (NREL) demonstrated that a 300 MW PV plant, equipped with an advanced power plant controller (PPC), can provide multiple frequency response functions by maintaining a 30 MW active power reserve. This was achieved by having one of the 80 inverters comprising the PV plant perform MPP while the others operate at a reduced power point.

Finally, [12] shows that storage-less PV systems equipped with strategy agnostic FPP trackers can reliably provide frequency containment reserve (FCR) and automatic frequency restoration reserve services, by combining dynamic modeling with a statistical assessment of forecast errors to meet stringent transmission system operator (TSO) availability requirements.

Nonetheless, it is important to highlight that there is currently no FPP tracking algorithm implemented on a commercially available solar converter or PPC. The reason is twofold. Firstly, FPP trackers are more complicated from a technical point of view than existing CPG strategies which enable simple power curtailment. Secondly, if a PV system is operating with an active power reserve, then by definition it is sacrificing potential revenue. Solar inverter manufacturers will prioritize the development of FPP trackers if there are specific grid requirements mandating full PV participation in frequency regulation, or if there are economic benefits for PV systems doing so.

[13] demonstrated that integrating PV systems into primary frequency regulation can significantly lower the operating costs of power systems. The work also showed that by having PV participate in ancillary services the power system can accommodate more PV energy, which should in turn improve PV profitability, however this improvement is not quantified.

The following paper investigates the potential for revenue of PV systems operating with an active power reserve to provide FCR services in the Netherlands. The aim and approach of this research are presented in section 2. In section 3, multiple constraints are defined to ensure that the PV system complies with the requirements of the FCR service. The results and conclusions are presented in sections 4 and 5, respectively.

2 AIM AND APPROACH

This research has investigated the economic viability of PV systems operating with an active power reserve to provide FCR services in the Netherlands. To that end, the

10.4229/EUPVSEC2025/5EO.3.2
020571-001

potential revenue of a PV system on the DA market was compared to that of the FCR market.

The DA and FCR market prices for the Netherlands were sourced from the transparency platform of the European Network of Transmission System Operators for Electricity (ENTSO-e) for the interval from January 1st until October 31st 2024. Moreover, the field data of a PV system in the Netherlands with an installed DC capacity of 49.45 MWp and AC capacity of 35.6 MW at point of connection was utilized.

The FCR market prices were quoted with a unit of [€/MW/ISP] where ISP stands for Imbalance Settlement period and lasts for 15 minutes. Therefore, the values were multiplied by 4 to reflect the revenue earned per MW for 1 hour [€/MW/h]. In contrast, the DA market prices are expressed directly with the unit of [€/MWh].

Currently, the FCR market is operated jointly by the Austrian, Belgian, Czech, Danish, Dutch, French, German, Slovenian, and Swiss TSOs. Bidding opens seven days before delivery (D-7 at 11:00 CET), with closure on the day before delivery (D-1 at 08:00 CET). Once the bids of all TSOs are collected, they are sent to a common optimization algorithm [14]. The market stipulates a minimum bid of 1 MW, with the same resolution [15].

Activation of FCR begins as soon as possible but no later than 2 seconds after a frequency deviation; and rises at least linearly. The activation speed is 30 s for the full allocated volume. These requirements could be easily met by PV or any converter-based resource, owing to their fast dynamic response. The FCR market is organized in six 4-hour blocks throughout a 24-hour interval. The block of interest for PV systems would be from 12:00 to 16:00 hours, therefore it is the only time block considered in this analysis.

The starting assumption of this research was that in the intervals of the day when there is abundant production of PV power, the price of electricity on the DA market will be very low (even negative). Moreover, the value of FCR in the same intervals should be relatively high because the share of electricity production of traditional sources would be low, and PV systems do not provide FCR.

Figure 1 presents the DA and FCR prices in the Netherlands in the interval of 12 to 16 o'clock for every day from January 1st until October 31st. It can be observed that the electricity price drops in the spring and summer months. Moreover, the figure shows that in the same

months the price of FCR is generally higher. Note that, for better visualization, the y-axis of Figure 1 is limited to a lower value of -25, however there are multiple days for which the DA market price is far lower than this value.

Once the average DA and FCR market prices were compared over this 10-month interval it was identified that for 136 out of 304 days the average prices of FCR are higher, for the 4-hour interval of interest. The next step is to assess the actual PV production during these periods, in order to determine the amount of active power the system could maintain in reserve, for FCR participation.

3 CONSTRAINTS

Since FCR is defined as a symmetric service, any participating PV system must be capable of both increasing and decreasing its output by the nominated power reserve (P_R). Hence, the **first power constraint** is that the value of the selected power reserve must be smaller or equal to half of the maximum available power (P_{MAP}) that the PV system can sustain throughout the selected 4-hour interval, as expressed in Equation 1.

$$P_{MAP} - 2 \cdot P_R \geq 0 \qquad (1)$$

Modern PV systems in the Netherlands commonly use string or multistring inverters. Therefore, by selectively disconnecting strings, the output power of the systems can be adjusted in steps of a few kilowatts. Nonetheless, in order to implement power as a function of frequency droop control, a more continuous change of the output power would be required which can be achieved using the aforementioned FPP trackers. These trackers cannot accurately operate at very low irradiation (less than 100 W/m²) due to the changes in the I-V characteristic of the PV modules. Therefore, a **second power constraint** has been added that the P_{MAP} of the PV system must be higher than 6 MW, This roughly construes to an irradiation of 120 W/m², considering that the installed power of the PV system is 49.45 MW.

The **third power constraint** is that the reserve bids must be submitted in multiples of 1 MW. For example, if P_{MAP} is 21 MW for a certain 4-hour interval, according to the first condition, the amount of power kept in reserve can be 10.5 MW, however the third condition will limit P_R to

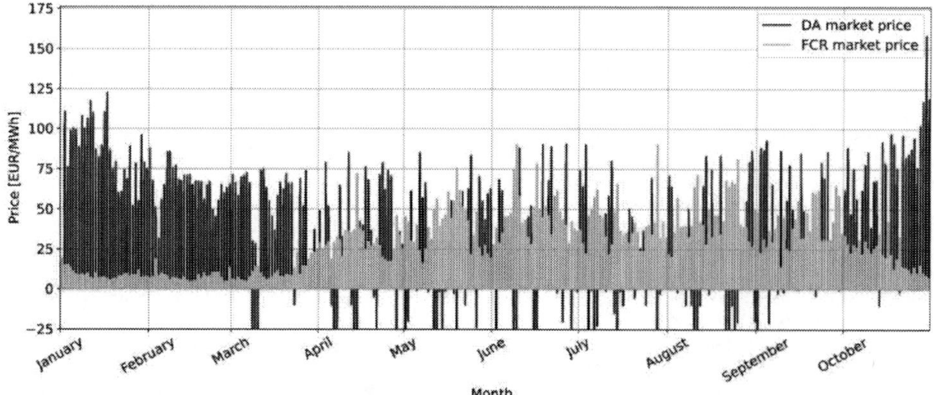

Figure 1: DA and FCR market price in the Netherlands in the interval of 12:00 to 16:00 hours for every day from 1st of January until 31st of October

10 MW.

A PV system without battery storage will opt to maintain an active power reserve only if in the selected 4-hour block the average price per MW of the FCR service (FCR_p) is higher than the DA market price (DA_p) per MWh (Equation 2). Moreover, when the DA market prices are negative, a modern PV system is capable of curtailing its production down to zero. However, a PV system providing FCR would have to operate with the selected power reserve, in order to maintain the symmetrical provision requirement of FCR. This means that during negative DA prices the average price of FCR must be higher than the negative value of the DA market price, for that 4-hour interval.

$$FCR_p > DA_p, \ if \ DA_p \geq 0 \qquad (2)$$
$$FCR_p > -DA_p, \qquad if \ DA_p < 0$$

Therefore, a price constraint is formed dictating that the average value of the FCR price during the 4-hour interval of interest must be higher than the absolute value of the DA price, as shown in Equation 3.

$$FCR_p > |DA_p| \qquad (3)$$

Only days which meet this price constraint and the 3 aforementioned power constraints have been considered in this research.

4   RESULTS

For the purpose of this study, it is assumed that the PV system has perfect foresight of the DA and FCR market prices, as well as a perfect forecast of its power production. The goal is to evaluate whether the total revenue made in a year can be increased by participating in the FCR and DA markets as opposed to just participating in the DA market.

In the first case, it is considered that the PV system earns revenue solely by participating in the DA market ($DA_{revenue}$). This revenue is calculated as the sum of the product of the available PV production ($P_{available}$) and the day ahead prices, calculated for every minute of PV data. It is equal to zero when the DA price is negative because the PV system would cease production, as shown in Equation 4.

$$DA_{revenue} = \sum DA_p \cdot P_{available} , \ if \ DA_p \geq 0 \quad (4)$$
$$DA_{revenue} = 0, \qquad if \ DA_p < 0$$

In the second case, it is considered that the PV system utilizes its reserve in the interval of 12 to 16 o'clock to earn a revenue providing FCR ($FCR_{revenue}$), equal to the sum of the product of FCR price and P_R, as shown in Equation 5. Of course, during negative DA market prices this will result in a loss (FCR_{cost}). The net revenue (FCR_{net}) is their difference.

$$FCR_{revenue} = \sum FCR_p \cdot P_R$$
$$FCR_{cost} = \sum DA_p \cdot P_R , \ if \ DA_p < 0 \qquad (5)$$
$$FCR_{net} = FCR_{revenue} - FCR_{cost}$$

At the same time, the system continues to participate on the DA market with the remaining power which is $P_{available}$ minus P_R. This results in a reduced revenue on the DA market ($DA_{reduced}$). For all hours outside the 4 hour interval $DA_{reduced}$ is equal to $DA_{revenue}$, as shown in Equation 6.

$$DA_{reduced} = \sum DA_p \cdot (P_{available} - P_R), \ if \ DA_p \geq 0$$
$$DA_{reduced} = 0, \ if \ DA_p < 0 \qquad (6)$$

The overall increase of revenue (RI) of the PV system is calculated according to Equation 7.

$$RI = FCR_{net} + DA_{reduced} - DA_{revenue} \qquad (7)$$

Figure 2 shows the minute and minimum hourly production of the PV system on April 12th 2024. For this day, the maximum production available throughout the 4-hour interval is 18.668 MW, therefore P_R = 9 MW.

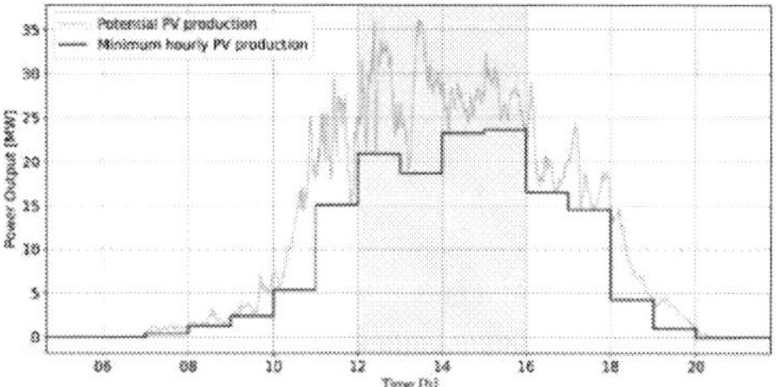

Figure 2: Comparison of minute and minimum hourly PV production values for April 12th 2024

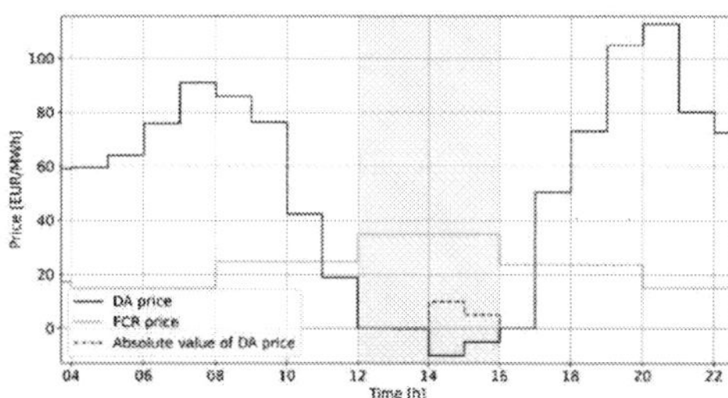

Figure 3: Comparison of the DA market electricity price, its absolute value and the price of FCR for April 12th 2024

The results for the day are shown in Table I. Notably, $DA_{reduced}$ is equal to $DA_{revenue}$ because the DA prices during the 12:00 to 16:00 hours are zero or negative, as shown in Figure 3, which means a PV system would be curtailed if it was not providing FCR. The revenue earned on the FCR market is equal to €1,251. However, by participating in FCR the PV system must produce the 9 MW of P_R also during the period of 14:00 to 16:00 hours, in which the price of electricity on the DA market is negative, thus incurring an FCR_{cost} of €136. Therefore, the revenue for this day has been increased by €1,115, which is a 32,6 % increase with respect to simply participating in the DA market.

Table I: Economic outlook for April 12th 2024

Metric	Value [€]
$DA_{revenue}$	3,420.6
$DA_{reduced}$	3,420.6
$FCR_{revenue}$	1,251.4
FCR_{cost}	-136.4
FCR_{net}	1,115
RI	1,115

The same analysis has been performed over the entire period from January 1st to October 31st 2024 and the results are presented in Table II.

When the power and price constraints are considered, 71 days have been identified in which providing FCR would be profitable for the PV system. The revenue for the 71 days has been increased by €53,661 which is an increase of 11.34%. Equally interesting is that the PV system only sacrificed a revenue of €12,005 on the DA market to earn €65,666 on the FCR market. Therefore, the main conclusion is that it is financially justified for PV systems to participate in FCR in certain intervals, however opportunities might be limited, since only 71 days met the necessary criteria. When multiplying the available PV production by the DA market prices for the entire observed 10-month interval it was calculated that the total revenue of the PV system for this period equals €1,869,207. Relative to this figure, the revenue increase for the PV system participating in FCR is equal to 2.87%. Nevertheless, there could be even more favorable conditions for FCR participation in countries with many more clear and sunny days than the Netherlands. Furthermore, if the FCR service is redefined in 1-hour instead of 4-hour time slots, there would be more hours in a year in which it would be favorable for PV to participate.

Table II: Economic outlook for the entire observed 10-month period

Metric	Value [€]
$DA_{revenue}$	473,377
$DA_{reduced}$	461,372
$FCR_{revenue}$	77,659
FCR_{cost}	-11,993
FCR_{net}	65,666
RI	53,661

This analysis, however, has relied on the assumption of perfect day-ahead forecasting of PV production, which enables the precise estimation of the active power that can be reserved. However, the irradiance falling on a PV system can rapidly change due to the passage of a dense cloud, resulting in a proportionally large change in the output power. In reality, forecasting PV production one day in advance is accurate in estimating energy production over longer, hourly periods, but cannot exactly predict the timing of such dips in production, nor their severity.

This limited accuracy is acceptable for the DA electricity market, however the FCR service demands the highest degree of confidence that the allocated capacity will be available throughout the selected time interval.

The extended version of this paper will address this limitation by considering 1 Hz irradiance and PV panel data from three locations in the Netherlands. The goal is to show how aggregating PV production at different locations can reduce the variability of the combined power output and increase the amount of power reserve that can be reliably provided for FCR.

5 CONCLUSION

This research assessed the economic viability of PV systems operating with an active power reserve to provide FCR services in the Netherlands. The analysis used minute-resolution production data from a 49.45 MWp PV plant and FCR and DA market prices covering the period from January 1st to October 31st, 2024.

It was found that on 136 out of 304 days, the average FCR prices exceeded DA prices during the 12:00–16:00 interval, which is particularly relevant for PV systems. Based on the PV production data, 71 days were identified where providing FCR would have been profitable. During these intervals, the PV system could have earned an additional €53,661, representing an 11.34% increase compared to supplying its energy solely to the DA market on those days. This additional revenue stream corresponds to an overall increase of 2.87% in total DA market earnings over the 10-month period. Equally interesting is that the PV system sacrificed only €12,005 on the DA market to earn €65,666 from FCR participation. Therefore, the results indicate that it is financially justified for PV systems to participate in FCR provision, albeit opportunities might be limited, since only 71 days met the necessary criteria. Finally, regions with higher solar irradiance and more sunny days then the Netherlands should offer even more favorable conditions. Redefining FCR provision from 4-hour to 1-hour time blocks would also increase the number of profitable hours in a year, for PV systems.

6 REFERENCES

[1] "Renewables 2025 Global status report: Global Overview", Available online: https://www.ren21.net/wp-content/uploads/2019/05/25-1395_GO_2025_Full_Report_13opt.pdf

[2] A. Sangwongwanich, Y. Yang, F. Blaabjerg and H. Wang, "Benchmarking of constant power generation strategies for single-phase grid-connected Photovoltaic systems," 2016 IEEE Applied Power Electronics Conference and Exposition (APEC), Long Beach, CA, USA, 2016, pp. 370-377, doi: 10.1109/APEC.2016.7467899.

[3] H. D. Tafti et al., "Extended Functionalities of Photovoltaic Systems With Flexible Power Point Tracking: Recent Advances," in IEEE Transactions on Power Electronics, vol. 35, no. 9, pp. 9342-9356, Sept. 2020, doi: 10.1109/TPEL.2020.2970447.

[4] E. I. Batzelis, G. E. Kampitsis and S. A. Papathanassiou, "Power Reserves Control for PV Systems With Real-Time MPP Estimation via Curve Fitting," in IEEE Transactions on Sustainable Energy, vol. 8, no. 3, pp. 1269-1280, July 2017, doi: 10.1109/TSTE.2017.2674693.

[5] E. I. Batzelis, S. A. Papathanassiou and B. C. Pal, "PV System Control to Provide Active Power Reserves Under Partial Shading Conditions," in IEEE Transactions on Power Electronics, vol. 33, no. 11, pp. 9163-9175, Nov. 2018, doi: 10.1109/TPEL.2018.2823426.

[6] J. M. Gomez and P. K. Shanmugam, "Flexible power point tracking using a neural network for power reserve control in a Grid-Connected PV system,"

Energies, vol. 15, no. 21, p. 8234, Nov. 2022, doi: 10.3390/en15218234.

[7] P. Verma, T. Kaur, and R. Kaur, "Power control strategy of an integrated PV system for active power reserve under dynamic operating conditions," Sustainable Energy Technologies and Assessments, vol. 45, p. 101066, Feb. 2021, doi: 10.1016/j.seta.2021.101066.

[8] L. Cristaldi, M. Faifer, C. Laurano, R. Ottoboni, E. Petkovski and S. Toscani, "Power Generation Control Algorithm for the Participation of Photovoltaic Panels in Network Stability," in IEEE Transactions on Instrumentation and Measurement, vol. 72, pp. 1-9, 2023, Art no. 9000809, doi: 10.1109/TIM.2023.3238745

[9] L. Cristaldi, M. Faifer, C. Laurano, E. Petkovski, F. Ponci, I. Sowa et al, "Model-Based algorithm for flexible power point tracking for photovoltaic participation in primary frequency regulation," Energies, vol. 17, no. 9, p. 2049, Apr. 2024, doi: 10.3390/en17092049.

[10] L. Cristaldi, M. Faifer, C. Laurano, E. Petkovski, S. Toscani and R. Ottoboni, "Parameters Update Strategy for Model-Based MPPT for PV Systems," 2024 IEEE International Instrumentation and Measurement Technology Conference (I2MTC), Glasgow, United Kingdom, 2024, pp. 1-5, doi: 10.1109/I2MTC60896.2024.10560743.

[11] C. Loutan, P. Klauer, S. Chowdhury, S. Hall, M. Morjaria, V. Chadliev et al., "Demonstration of essential reliability services by a 300-MW solar photovoltaic power plant," Mar. 2017. doi: 10.2172/1349211.

[12] C. Konstantinopoulos, I. Avramiotis-Falireas, S. Bolognani, D. Groß, A. Chacko and G. Hug, "Reliability assessment of PV units in primary and secondary frequency control ancillary services," 2019 16th International Conference on the European Energy Market (EEM), Ljubljana, Slovenia, 2019, pp. 1-6, doi: 10.1109/EEM.2019.8916279.

[13] X. Fang, J. Tan, H. Yuan, S. Yin and J. Wang, "Providing Ancillary Services with Photovoltaic Generation in Multi- Timescale Grid Operation," 2020 52nd North American Power Symposium (NAPS), Tempe, AZ, USA, 2021, pp. 1-5, doi: 10.1109/NAPS50074.2021.9449700.

[14] ENTSO-E, "Frequency Containment Reserves (FCR)," Network Codes – Electricity Balancing. [Online]. Available: https://www.entsoe.eu/network_codes/eb/fcr/. [Accessed: Jul. 31, 2025].

[15] TenneT TSO B.V., "FCR Manual for BSPs: Requirements and Procedures for Supply of FCR," Version 3.3, SOP-SYS FCR HB, Arnhem, The Netherlands, Mar. 17, 2022. [Online]. Available:https://netztransparenz.tennet.eu/fileadmin/ user_upload/SO_NL/Handboek_FCR_voor_BSPs_-_EN_version.pdf [Accessed: Jul. 4, 2025].

WHEN TRUST MATTERS

Exploring the Revenue Potential of Photovoltaic Systems Participating in Frequency Containment Reserve

Emil Petkovski, Theo Bosma, Marcel Eijgelaar and Ravi Singh
emil.petkovski@dnv.com

26 September 2025

020572-001

Introduction

- As the integration of PV systems accelerates, updated grid regulations increasingly impose additional requirements on these systems, such as active power curtailment during overfrequency events

- However, full participation of PV systems without battery storage in frequency regulation will require operating with an active power reserve

- Various flexible power point (FPP) tracking algorithms that enable such operation have been presented in literature. However, commercially available solutions are lacking due to technical and economic challenges

DNV

Introduction

- As the integration of PV systems accelerates, updated grid regulations increasingly impose additional requirements on these systems, such as active power curtailment during overfrequency events

- However, full participation of PV systems without battery storage in frequency regulation will require operating with an active power reserve

- Various flexible power point (FPP) tracking algorithms that enable such operation have been presented in literature. However, commercially available solutions are lacking due to technical and economic challenges

- Solar inverter manufacturers will prioritize the development of FPP trackers if there are specific grid requirements mandating full PV participation in frequency regulation, or if there are economic benefits for PV systems doing so

- **This research has investigated the economic viability of PV systems operating with an active power reserve to provide frequency containment reserve (FCR) services in the Netherlands**

Introduction II

- The potential revenue of a PV system participating on the day ahead (DA) and FCR markets was compared

- The DA and FCR market prices were downloaded for the Netherlands in the interval of January 1st to October 31st, 2024, from the ENTSO-e website

- The FCR service in the Netherlands is organized in 6 four-hour blocks throughout a 24-hour interval. The block of interest for PV systems, considered in this analysis, is **from 12 to 16 hours**

- The production data of a PV system in the Netherlands with an installed DC capacity of 49.5 MWp and an AC capacity of 35.6 MW at the point of connection was utilized

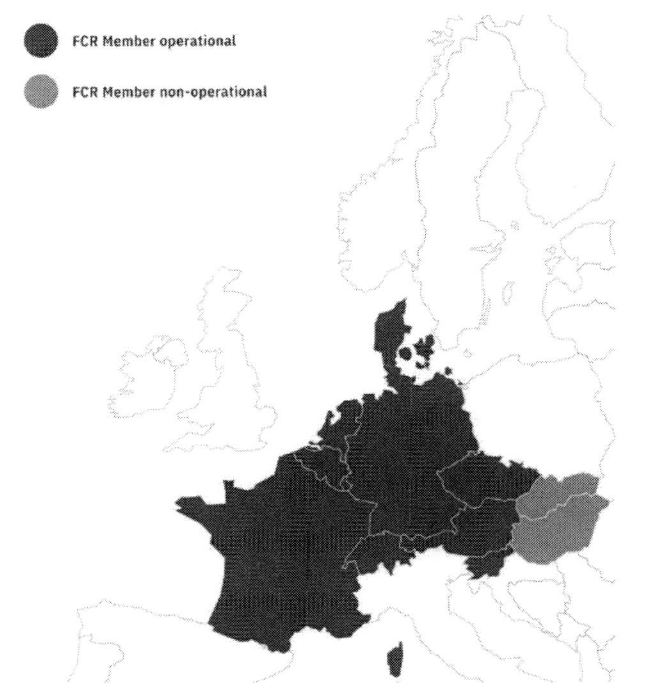

EU PVSEC

DNV

020572-004

Initial assumption

- In periods of the day when there is abundant PV production, the price of electricity on the DA market will be very low (even negative). However, the price of FCR in the same intervals would be relatively high because the share of electricity production by traditional sources would be low, and PV systems do not provide FCR

- Once the average DA and FCR prices were compared over the 4-hour interval it was identified that for **136 out of 305 days the FCR prices are higher**

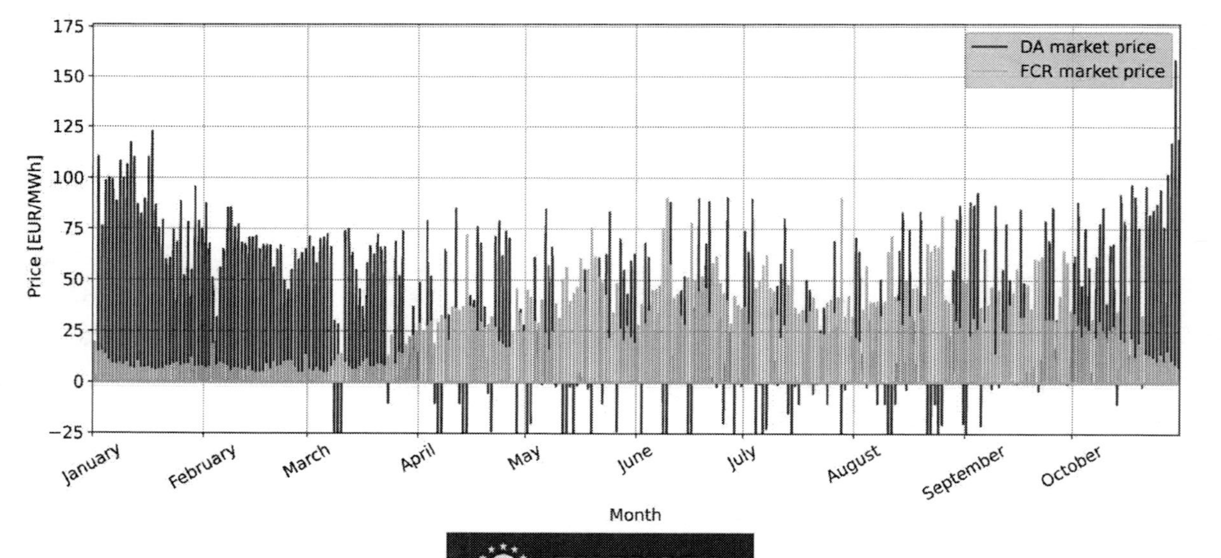

EU PVSEC

DNV

020572-005

Initial assumption II

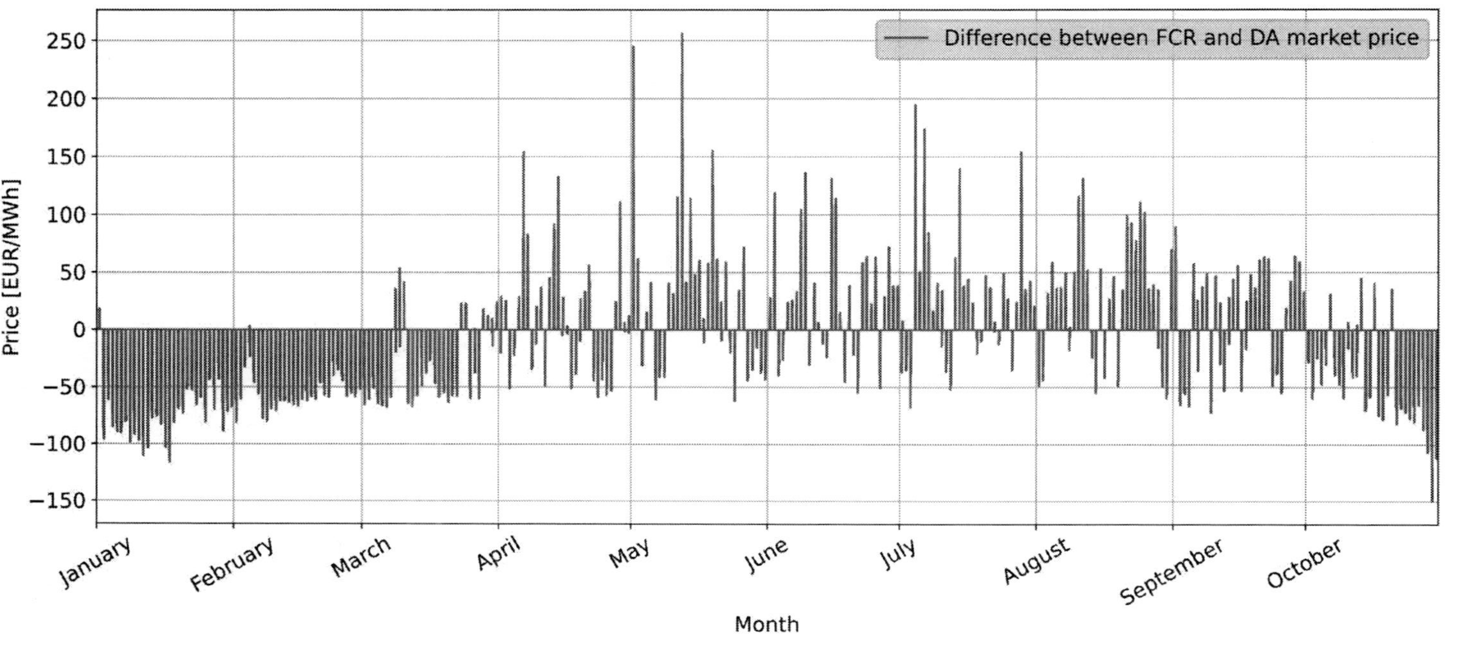

DNV

020572-006

Economic Metrics

- It is assumed that the **PV system has perfect foresight of the DA and FCR market prices, and perfect forecast of its power production**

- **The goal is to show whether the total revenue made in a year can be increased by participating in the FCR and DA market as opposed to just participating in the DA market**

- In the first case, it is considered that the PV system earns revenue solely by participating in the DA market ($DA_{revenue}$)

- This revenue is calculated as the sum of the product of the available PV production ($P_{available}$) and the day ahead prices (DA_p), calculated for every minute of PV data

$$DA_{revenue} = \sum DA_p \cdot P_{available}, \qquad if\ DA_p \geq 0$$

$$DA_{revenue} = 0, \qquad if\ DA_p < 0$$

020572-007

Economic Metrics II

- In the second case, it is considered that the PV system utilizes its reserve in the interval of 12 to 16 hours to earn a revenue providing FCR (FCR$_{revenue}$), equal to the sum of the product of FCR price (FC$_p$) and P$_R$. Of course, during negative DA market prices this will result in a loss (FCR$_{cost}$)

$$FCR_{revenue} = \sum FCR_p \cdot P_R$$

$$FCR_{cost} = \sum DA_p \cdot P_R, \quad if\ DA_p < 0$$

$$FCR_{net} = FCR_{revenue} - FCR_{cost}$$

- Moreover, the system still participates in the DA market with the remaining power which is P$_{available}$ minus P$_R$. This will result in a reduced revenue on the DA market (DA$_{reduced}$)

$$DA_{reduced} = \sum DA_p \cdot (P_{available} - P_R), \quad if\ DA_p \geq 0$$

$$DA_{reduced} = 0, \quad if\ DA_p < 0$$

- The overall increase of revenue (RI) of the PV system is calculated as:

$$RI = FCR_{net} + DA_{reduced} - DA_{revenue}$$

Results: 12 April 2024

- The figure on the left shows the minute and minimum hourly production of the PV system on 12 April 2024. The maximum available production throughout the 4-hour interval is **18.7 MW**, therefore $P_R = 9\ MW$

- The figure on the right shows the electricity price on the DA and FCR markets

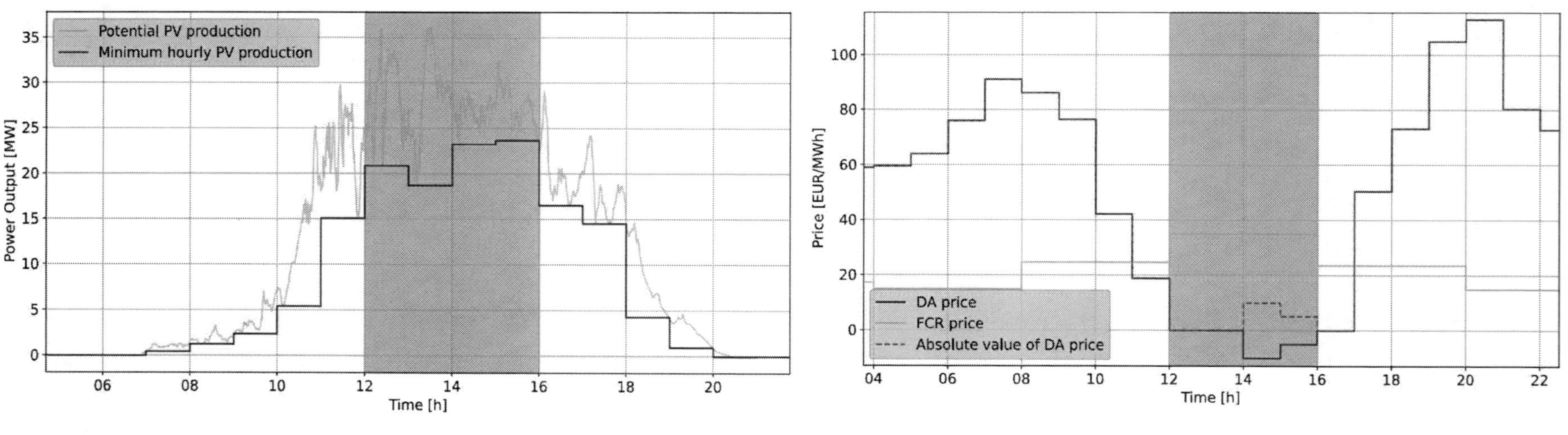

020572-009

Results II: 12 April 2024

- Notably, $DA_{reduced}$ is equal to $DA_{revenue}$ because the DA prices during the 12 to 16 hours are zero or negative which means a PV system would be curtailed if it wasn't providing FCR

- The revenue for this day has been increased by **1,115 EUR, or 32,6%**

Time interval	12.04.2024
$DA_{revenue}$ [EUR]	3,420.6
$DA_{reduced}$ [EUR]	3,420.6
$FCR_{revenue}$ [EUR]	1,251.4
FCR_{cost} [EUR]	-136.4
FCR_{net} [EUR]	1,115
RI [EUR]	1,115

020572-010

Results: 10-month analysis

- The analysis has been performed on the entire period from 1 January to 31 October 2024. When the power and price constraints are taken into account, **71 days have been identified** in which providing FCR would be profitable for the PV system

- The **revenue for the 71 days has been increased by 53,661 EUR which is an increase of 11.34%.** Therefore, it is financially justified for PV systems to participate in FCR in certain intervals, but opportunities might be limited

- The total revenue made by the PV system on the DA market over the 10-month interval equals 1,869,207 EUR. Relative to this figure, the **revenue increase for the PV system participating in FCR is equal to 2.87%**

Time interval	01.01.2024 – 31.10.2024
$DA_{revenue}$ [EUR]	473,377
$DA_{reduced}$ [EUR]	461,372
$FCR_{revenue}$ [EUR]	77,659
FCR_{cost} [EUR]	-11,993
FCR_{net} [EUR]	65,666
RI [EUR]	53,661

DNV

Conclusion & extended analysis

- It was financially justified for the analyzed PV system to provide FCR for 71 out of the 305 considered days

- The revenue for those days has been increased by 53,661 EUR which is an increase of 11.34%, or 2.87 % when compared to the total revenue earned on the DA market during the 10-month period

- Results could be much better for countries with more sunny days in a year and more stable irradiance profiles than the Netherlands

- Redefining FCR provision from 4-hour to 1-hour time blocks would also increase the number of profitable hours in a year, for PV systems

- The extended paper considered 1 Hz resolution irradiance and PV panel temperature data from three locations in the Netherlands. The results demonstrated the potential of spatial aggregation to enhance the reliability of PV systems in providing FCR services, enabling a portfolio of PV plants to participate more frequently and offer a higher guaranteed power reserve

Thank you for your attention!

emil.petkovski@dnv.com

020572-013

Appendix

EU PVSEC

DNV

020572-014

Constraints

- The **first power constraint** is that the value of the selected power reserve must be smaller or equal to half of the maximum available power (P_{MAP}) sustained throughout the 4-hour interval

$$P_{MAP} - 2 \cdot P_R \geq 0$$

- The **second power constraint** dictates that the P_{MAP} of the PV system must be higher than 6 MW, which roughly construes to an irradiance of 120 W/m^2

$$P_{MAP} \geq 6\ MW$$

- The **third power constraint** is that the power reserve must be traded in blocks of 1 MW

Constraints II

- **A price constraint** is introduced, dictating that the average value of the FCR price during the 4-hour interval of interest must be higher than the absolute value of the DA price

$$FCR\ price > DA\ price, \qquad if\ DA\ price \geq 0$$
$$FCR\ price > -(DA\ price), \qquad if\ DA\ price < 0$$

Which can be more coherently summarized as:

$$FCR\ price > |DA\ price|$$

- **Only days which meet all these constraints have been considered in the analysis!**

DNV

020572-016

Results: 3 August 2024

- The figure on the left shows the minute and minimum hourly production of the PV system on 3 August 2024. The maximum available production throughout the 4-hour interval is **13.2 MW**, therefore $\mathbf{P_R = 6\ MW}$

- The figure on the right shows the electricity price on the DA and FCR markets

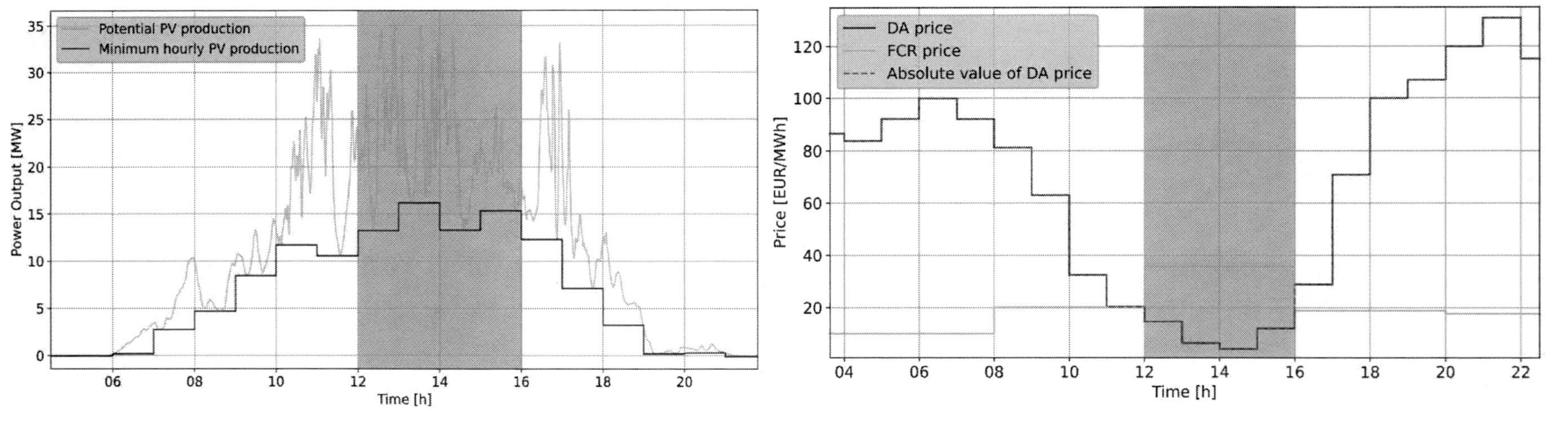

020572-017

Results II: 3 August 2024

- Notably, $DA_{reduced}$ is lower than $DA_{revenue}$ because the DA prices are higher than zero. Of course, the DA price is still lower than the FCR price, otherwise the day wouldn't be of interest

- The revenue for this day has been increased **by 628.4 EUR, or 10,27%**

Time interval	03.08.2024
$DA_{revenue}$ [EUR]	6,121.3
$DA_{reduced}$ [EUR]	5,898.2
$FCR_{revenue}$ [EUR]	851.5
FCR_{cost} [EUR]	0
FCR_{net} [EUR]	851.5
RI [EUR]	628.4

DNV

Results: 10-month interval & Pmax > 8 MW

- When the new power constraint is considered, **56 days have been identified** in which providing FCR would be profitable for the PV system.

- The **revenue for the 56 days has been increased by 48,587 EUR which is an increase of 12%.**

- Relative to the 1,869,207 EUR figure, the **revenue increase for the PV system participating in FCR is equal to 2.6%**.

Time interval	01.01.2024 – 31.10.2024
$DA_{revenue}$ [EUR]	405,038
$DA_{reduced}$ [EUR]	394,457
$FCR_{revenue}$ [EUR]	70,205
FCR_{cost} [EUR]	-11,036
FCR_{net} [EUR]	59,169
RI [EUR]	**48,587**

DNV

020572-019

REVENUES AT RISK AND MITIGATION STRATEGIES FOR SOLAR PV PLANTS IN TIMES OF NEGATIVE ELECTRICITY PRICES

Philippe Macé[1], Elina Bosch[1], Caroline Plaza[2], David Moser[3] Gaëtan Masson[1]
[1]Becquerel Institute
[2]Becquerel Institute France
[3]Becquerel Institute Italia
p.mace@becquerelinstitute.org

ABSTRACT: The European PV market is entering a new phase as negative electricity prices increasingly overlap with midday solar generation, shifting market risk back to producers. With subsidy-free business models and corporate PPAs expanding while traditional support schemes contract, project revenues and financing conditions are becoming more constrained. Mitigation strategies can help manage these challenges, though their effectiveness varies. Options such as revenue-oriented system design and PV–storage integration can reduce exposure to low or negative prices, but they typically involve cost trade-offs and uncertain returns, often requiring multiple revenue streams to ensure profitability. Beyond enhancing competitiveness, these measures are becoming critical for project feasibility. By supporting financing, securing grid access, and strengthening debt service resilience, they can determine whether PV projects are viable at all. As European electricity markets evolve, the capacity to implement effective mitigation strategies will be central to sustaining the growth and resilience of solar deployment.
Keywords: solar PV, negative prices, mitigation strategies, competitiveness, risk

1 INTRODUCTION

In many European countries, an increasing occurrence of very low and negative prices on electricity markets has been observed in recent years. In 2024, the number of negative day-ahead price hours reached 4838, which marked a 98% year-on-year growth. Researchers have shown that it is correlated with the increasing penetration of renewable energy, such as wind and solar photovoltaics. This correlation implies that the occurrence of low and negative prices typically happens in times of high PV production (in comparison to electricity demand level) [1] [2] [3] [4] [5].

At the same time, PV producers face higher market exposure.

In the case of unsubsidized photovoltaic (PV), projects depend partially or totally on wholesale market revenues (merchant or PPA-backed assets). Such projects are common in countries with little to no guaranteed remuneration schemes, (e.g., Spain, Belgium) but also in other countries where such schemes are in place as with increased competitiveness of solar PV and the higher electricity prices on the European market in 2022 / early 2023 PV developers have been encouraged to investigate unsubsidized options. In February 2024, 40% of utility-scale PV additions in Germany were unsubsidized (outside of the national EEG scheme) with business models predominantly based on Power Purchase Agreements but also on merchant PV [7]. In France, as per a report published in November 2024 by the energy regulation commission, close to 20% of the PV electricity generation came from unsubsidized PV [5].

Higher market exposure is also observed for subsidized PV as policy markers are increasingly shifting the risk to producers. In Great Britain, since the fourth Contract for Difference (CfD) Allocation Round (AR) which opened at the end of 2021, the CfD contracts foresee that no payment is issued in case of negative day-ahead price [10]. In France, under the feed-in premium ("complément de rémunération"), PV producer do not receive any remuneration during periods of negative prices, but, beyond a certain threshold of annual negative price hours, they will receive a specific "negative price

premium" provided they stopped all production (and injection) during these hours. [5] In Germany, since 2016, if negative prices occur for a period longer than 6 consecutive hours, no market premium is paid during the negative price episode. However, the feed-in premium contract duration is extended by the number of hours during which the market premium was lost. Recent regulatory change in early 2025 reduced the negative price episode duration as of which no market premium is received 1 hour in 2027 [11]. These examples show that there is a common trend to reshape support mechanisms conditions to optimize the allocation of public funding and reduce the burden of negative prices in order to incentivize PV producers to adapt and react upon electricity market signals.

These two parallel trends of increasing occurrence of negative prices and increasing exposure of PV producers to electricity market trends impact profitability at different PV project steps. During project development and planning, this renders revenue modelling more complex and increases uncertainty. Before construction and installation, this deteriorates financing conditions with some banks reluctant or not willing to finance merchant PV projects and less attractive gearing ratio being imposed (from 70:30 to 50:50). Eventually during the operation phase of PV project, this puts revenues at risk. In Belgium the solar capture rate has decreased from 92% in 2023 to 56% in 2024 [4].

This study aims at quantifying this impact and investigating different mitigation strategies.

2 METHODS

2.1 Input data

Hourly PV production was obtained from PVGIS. Capital and operational expenditures (CAPEX and OPEX) were derived from industry watch reports and targeted surveys. Hourly day-ahead electricity prices were generated through a prospective scenario-based approach, explicitly exploring different trajectories to capture the uncertainty surrounding long-term trends in negative prices over the next 20–30 years. While negative prices are expected to act as corrective market signals, leading to gradual self-balancing, the timing and pace of this adjustment remain highly uncertain. Finally, project revenues were computed by matching hourly PV production with hourly electricity prices on a one-to-one basis.

2.3 Output

Main profitability indicators are used such as the Net Present Value Equity (NPVe), the Internal Return Rate Equity (IRRe) as well as the Debt Service Coverage Ratio allowing to measure availability of cash flows to cover debt obligations.

3 PROFITS AT RISK

3.1 Quantification of the profitability at risk

Under the assumed assumptions found in Table I, it can be seen in Figure 1A, 1B and 1C, how the decreasing solar capture rate under a merchant PV business model combined with deteriorated conditions (gearing ratios shifting towards lower shares of debt) lead to deteriorated profitability indicators such as NPV equity and IRR equity. With a 65% solar capture rate and the least attractive gearing ratio the break-even of the project is almost not reached under the considered assumptions.

Table I: Key assumptions for the profitability at risk assessment

Yield [kWh/kWp]	1171 (South Germany)
CAPEX [€/Wp]	0.54
OPEX [€/kWp]	19
Lifetime [years]	30
Degradation rates	1%/0.4%
Installed capacity [MW]	10
Interest rate	4%
Cost of equity	10%
Share of debt	50%-70%
Business model	Merchant

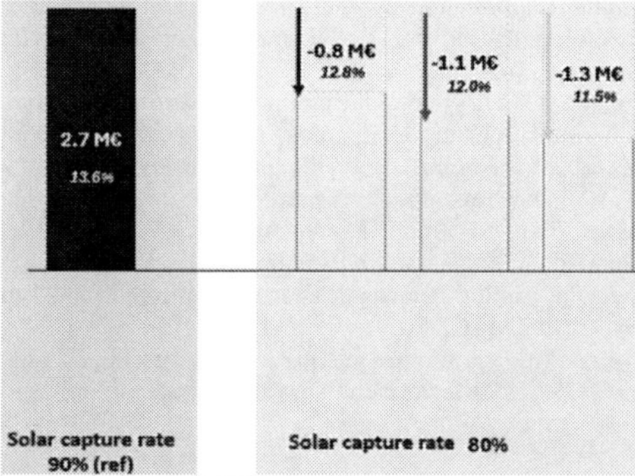

Figure 1A: Profitability at risk with a 80% capture rate under different gearing ratio assumptions (dark blue 70:30, medium blue 60:40, light blue 50:50).

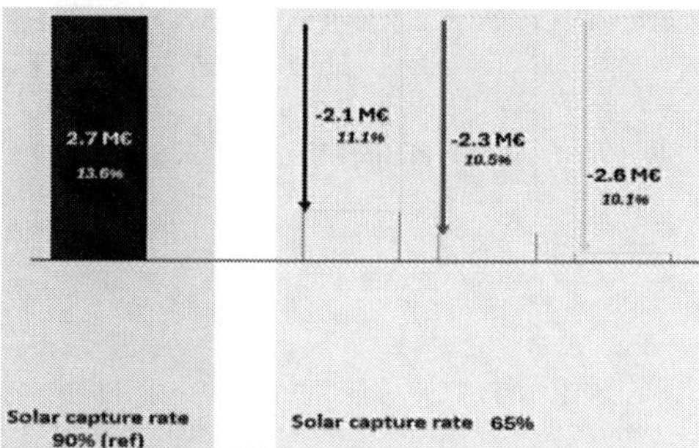

Figure 1B: Profitability at risk with a 65% capture rate under different gearing ratio assumptions (dark blue 70:30, medium blue 60:40, light blue 50:50).

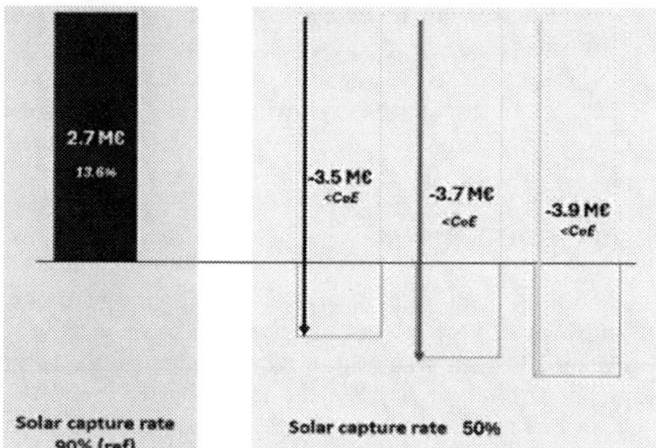

Figure 1C: Profitability at risk with a 50% capture rate under different gearing ratio assumptions (dark blue 70:30, medium blue 60:40, light blue 50:50).

4 MITIGATION STRATEGIES RESULTS

The investigated mitigation strategies include (a) alternative PV designs as well as (b) the addition of battery storage.

3.2 Alternative PV designs

3.2.1 Comparison based on lifetime based profitability indicators.

The considered alternative designs which are compared to a conventional south-oriented and optimally tilted ground-mounted PV (S_O) are (i) a Vertical PV system oriented East and West (V_EW), (ii) a ground-mounted PV plant mixing East- and West-oriented, tilted PV panels with a 50° tilt (EW_50°) and (iii) a ground-mounted PV plant with a one-axis tracker (sun-tracking strategy) (Trac.). These different PV designs are characterised by differences in terms of CAPEX, OPEX, yield, and weighted average selling price (WASP) as shown in Table II.

Table II: Key assumptions for the different considered PV designs

	S_O	V_EW | EW_50° | Trac.
Yield [kWh/kWp]	1171	1174 | 935 | 1324
CAPEX [€/Wp]	0.54	0.61 | 0.53 | 0.58
OPEX [€/kWp]	19	20.4 | 18.5 | 20
WASP* [€/MWh]	55.6	65.9 | 59.4 | 62.8
Lifetime [years]		30
Degradation rates		1%/0.4%
Installed capacity [MW]		10
Interest rate		4%
Cost of equity		10%
Share of debt		60%

** Calculated with 2024-2025 German Day-Ahead Prices*

As shown in Figure 2, under the considered assumptions, alternative design (i) shows an interest in terms of NPV improvement compared to the South Optimal reference starting with 5 to 10 years of negative prices. It requires 10 to 15 years of negative prices to reach a NPV higher by 10% or more compared to the reference South Optimal system.

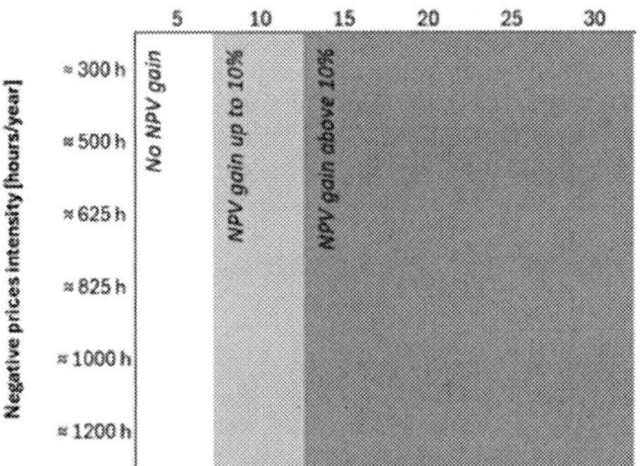

Figure 2: NPV comparison between the South Optimal and the vertical East-West PV design.

As shown in Figure 3, under the considered assumptions, for alternative design (ii) the lower yield is never compensated by the higher average selling price and lower CAPEX/OPEX.

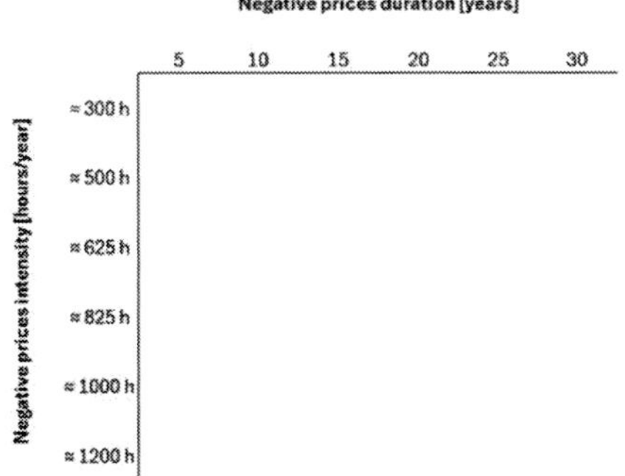

Figure 3: NPV comparison between the South Optimal and the tilted East-West PV design.

As shown in Figure 4, under the considered assumptions, for alternative design (iii) there is a clear

advantage of the presence of the tracker as the additional costs are compensated by the additional production and higher average selling price. When looking whether the additional costs are compensated by the higher average selling price only (i.e., not taking into account the higer yeild from the sun tracking), there is an interest in terms of NPV improvement compared to the South Optimal reference starting with 5 to 10 years of moderately frequent (300h-900h per year) negative prices. It requires either higher frequency of negative prices (<900h per year) or longer periods of negative prices (10 to 15 years) to reach a NPV higher by 10% or more compared to the reference South Optimal system.

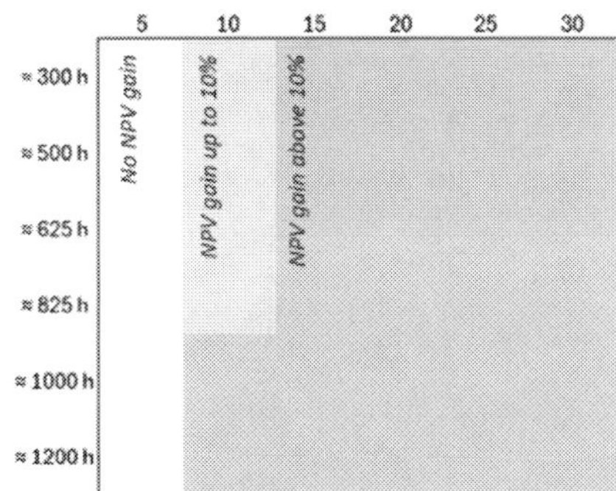

Figure 4: NPV comparison between the South Optimal and the PV system with one-axis tracker.

It can be added that whether similar results would be obtained in other countries would have to be investigated under country specific conditions. Although it is expected that the alternative designs would lead similar advantages in terms of weighted average selling price, some national conditions such as the irradiation conditions or the electricity prices patterns would influence results.

3.2.2 Comparison based on monthly indicators

In markets with negative prices, projects can face monthly cash gaps that certain indicators, including annual financial metrics, can hide but which are critical to consider as it can have an impact on the project's robustness with regards to solvency.

Focusing on the vertical East-West alternative design, when looking at a monthly time scale, the advantages can be also be appreciated in terms of average monthly value from generated electricity (Figure 5), monthly cash flow available for Debt Service (Figure 6) and Debt Service Coverage Ratio (Figure 7). Looking at this later indicator, it can be seen how selecting a vertical East-West alternative design can be an efficient mitigation strategy for the PV project to withstand periods of stress, by safeguarding monthly debt service coverage ratios (DSCR).

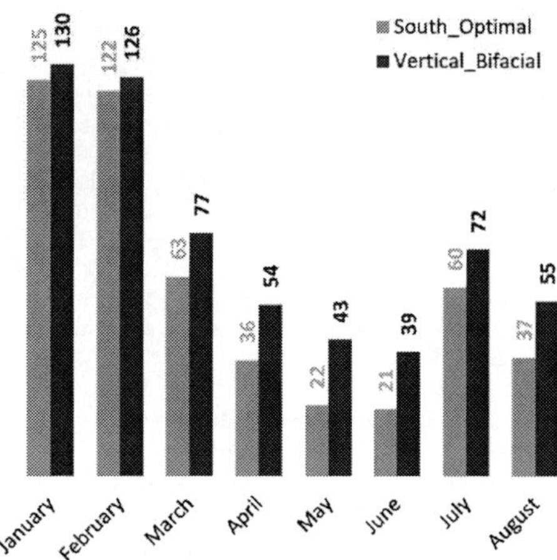

Figure 5: Average monthly value from generated electricity in €/MWh (based on 2025 Day-Ahead prices)

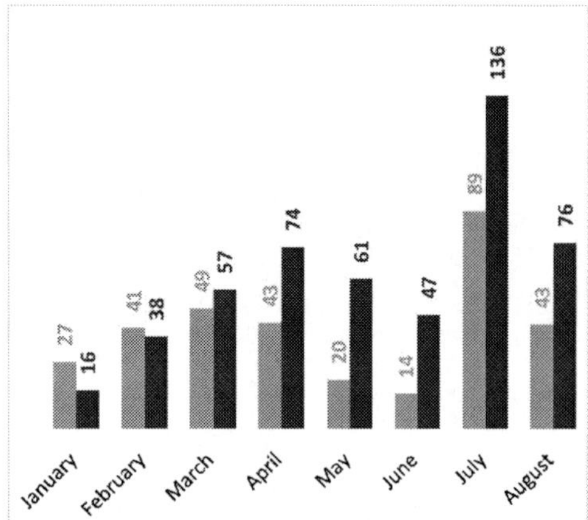

Figure 6: Monthly Cash Flow Available for Debt Service in thousand euros (based on 2025 Day-Ahead prices)

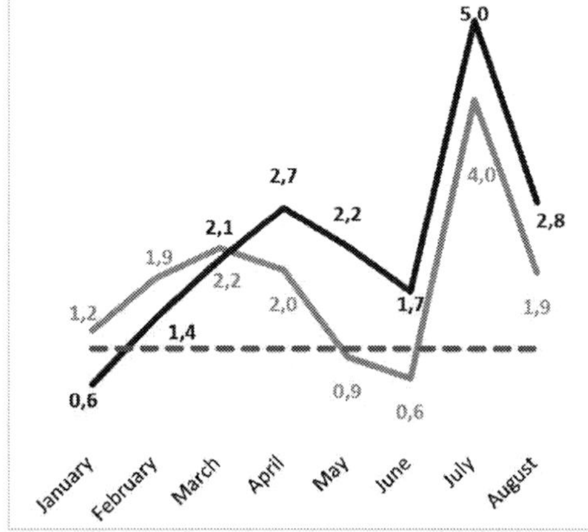

Figure 7: Debt Service Coverage Ratio (DSCR) (the red dotted line corresponds to the threshold of DSCR=1)

3.2.3 Addition of storage

The second studied mitigation strategy is the addition of a storage system. The main techno-economic assumptions can be found in Table III.

Table III: Key assumptions for the addition of storage mitigation strategy

Yield [kWh/kWp]	1171 (South Germany)
CAPEX PV [€/Wp]	0.54
CAPEX BESS [€/kWh]	350
OPEX PV [€/kWp]	19
OPEX BESS [€/kWh.yr]	5.25
Lifetime [years]	15
Degradation rates	1%/0.4%
Installed capacity PV [MW]	10
Installed capacity BESS [MWh]	14
Interest rate	4%
Cost of equity	10%
Share of debt	60%
Business model PV	Merchant (+ charging the battery)
Business model BESS	Arbitrage (charging from PV)

As shown in Figure 8, the addition of a storage system shifts part of the production to higher-value hours. This allows to increase the average selling price of produced PV electricity from 56 €/MWh in the South Optimal case without storage to 79 €/MWh. Specifically, the electricity which is produced by the PV system, then stored, then injected into the grid has an average weighted value of 125 €/MWh.

Nevertheless, for the considered business model, where the battery system's revenue are solely based on arbitrage using PV electricity only, the additional revenues do not compensate the additional costs, worsening the business case overall. For the addition of storage to be a relevant mitigation strategy for PV against negative prices, it is important to unlock higher revenue for the battery. For example, the arbitrage model can be either extended by also allowing charging from the grid (while giving priority to charging from the PV system) or decoupled by only charging from the grid to fully leverage the occurrence of negative prices. Moreover, revenue stacking by capturing revenues from grid services also contributes to consolidate the battery system business case. Eventually, for this mitigation strategy as well, having sufficient long and pronounced (i.e., high price spreads) negative prices episodes, remains an important prerequisite for the profitability of BESS which based at least part of their revenues from arbitrage business models.

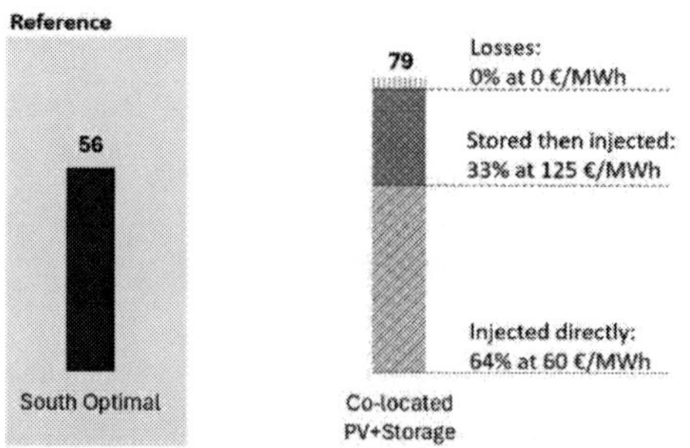

Figure 8: Weighted average electricity valuation in €/MWh (based on 2024-2025 Day-Ahead prices)

5 CONCLUSIONS

The European PV market is undergoing rapid transformation as market conditions evolve. Rising occurrences of negative electricity prices increasingly coincide with midday solar output, shifting market risk back to producers in an environment where subsidy-free business models, merchant PV, and corporate PPAs are expanding, while traditional support schemes are tightening. These dynamics directly affect project profitability through reduced revenues and more restrictive financing conditions, requiring careful consideration of mitigation strategies.

A range of measures exists, though their efficiency varies widely. Adjustments in PV system design can improve revenue resilience by prioritizing value capture over maximum generation, albeit at the cost of higher investment or operational expenses and potential reductions in annual output—an approach that only proves beneficial if negative price trends persist. Similarly, pairing PV with storage enables producers to shift electricity to higher-priced hours and thus raise its value. However, the economics of battery storage remain challenging, as investment costs are not always offset by arbitrage revenues alone, necessitating stacked revenue streams to secure profitability.

Importantly, these mitigation measures can play a decisive role beyond enhancing competitiveness. By enabling access to financing, securing grid connection, or improving solvency and debt serviceability, they can determine whether projects are viable at all. As such, the capacity to integrate effective mitigation strategies is becoming a critical factor not only for profitability but also for the feasibility and resilience of PV deployment in Europe's changing market landscape.

6 REFERENCES

[1] Market Observatory for Energy of the European Commission, «Quarterly report on European electricity markets,» 2024.

[2] Brian Publicover, «Europe posts record negative power prices for 2024 as renewables rise,» PV Magazine, 21 January 2025.

[3] Bundesnetzagentur, «Bundesnetzagentur veröffentlicht Daten zum Strommarkt 2024,» 3 January 2025. [En ligne].

[4] CREG, «Étude sur l'impact de l'intégration des énergies renouvelables sur le fonctionnement des marchés de l'électricité à court terme,» 2024.

[5] CRE, «Analyse de la CRE sur le phénomène de prix de l'électricité négatifs et recommandations relatives aux dispositifs de soutien aux énergies renouvelables,» 2024.

[6] S. Enkhardt, «https://www.pv-magazine.de/2024/03/21/photovoltaik-anlagen-ohne-eeg-foerderungen-machen-im-februar-40-prozent-des-zubaus-aus/,» PV Magazine Deutschland, 21 March 2024.

[7] Renewable Exchange, «Negative Prices in 2024: Is the Sun Setting On the CfD?,» 16 January 2025. [En ligne]. Available: https://renewable.exchange/blog/negative-prices-in-2024-is-the-sun-setting-on-the-cfd/.

[8] FFE, «Negative Strompreise – Wie viele Anlagen erneuerbarer Energien fahren durch?,» 21 October 2024. [En ligne]. Available: https://www.ffe.de/veroeffentlichungen/negative-strompreise-wie-viele-anlagen-erneuerbarer-energien-fahren-durch/.

This presentation was selected by the Sc. Committee of the EU PVSEC 2025 for submission of a full paper to one of the EU PVSEC's collaborating peer-reviewed journals.

A COMMODITY TODAY, INCOMPATIBLE TOMORROW: THE PARADOX OF PV?

Bert Herteleer[1], Gernot Oreski[2], Silvana Ovaitt[3], Ulrike Jahn[4],
Ralph Gottschalg[4], Ian Marius Peters[5], Gabriele Friesen[1], Mauro Caccivio[1]
[1]SUPSI, Switzerland, [2]PCCL, Austria, [3] NREL, USA [4] Fraunhofer CSP, Germany [5] HI ERN, Germany
bert.herteleer@supsi.ch

ABSTRACT: Since the year 2000, the PV industry has seen a thousand-fold increase in deployments to over 2 TW by 2024, while module prices have dropped more than 98%. During this time, the perception has grown of PV modules as commodities. However, when PV modules have to be replaced beyond available spares, owners are confronted with the challenge that modules compatible with the existing modules and mounting systems are not available at scale. When PV modules must be sourced on the market, the second paradox of PV emerges: module warranties have lengthened and strengthened, while variations in the bill of materials have increased, yet testing durations and scopes have not scaled accordingly. The findings underscore the urgent need for industry-wide standardisation, increased transparency and trust-but-verify mentality, extended qualification protocols, and strategies to mitigate the operational and economic risks associated with PV module obsolescence.

Keywords: reliability, technological evolution, module testing for lifetime, material qualification, transparency, repowering

1   Introduction

The PV industry and PV modules have experienced spectacular growth and cost declines over the past decades, with deployments growing a thousand-fold from 1-2 GWp in 2000 to over 2 TWp by 2024, with costs dropping 98% over the same time, thanks to widespread learning and innovation, and economies of scale, and translating lab champion cells to production lines in 2.5 to 3 years [1]. Particularly in the past decade, the rate of technology change and innovation within the PV module industry has accelerated, moving from 1.6 m^2 and ~300 Wp Al-BSF mono-facial modules to 2-3 m^2 500-700 Wp PERC/TOPCon/HJT bifacial modules [1].

The intense competition and cost pressures have seen Original Equipment Manufacturers (OEMs) pre-qualifying suppliers, allowing OEMs to host reverse auctions to reduce costs, as well as use functionally "identical" materials from different suppliers, whose formulations often vary from each other. Consequently, variations in the Bill of Materials (BOM) such as differences in adhesives, encapsulants, and backsheets, are possible within one series of modules, even with "live" BOM updates during production [2], or documented in utility-scale PV farms [3], leading to different degradation and failure modes within the same PV systems.

At some point during the technical lifetime of a PV power plant, modules must be replaced due to a variety of reasons. These can include Extreme Weather Events (EWEs) such as hurricanes or snow events [4], to floods [5], hail and lightning [6], poor O&M practices or poor siting [7], and module failures (quality and reliability), including aggressive degradation [8]. While still nascent, repowering of PV systems is starting, where PV systems may see modules replaced (reskinning) all the way to deep re-engineering of the full power plant, with causes ranging from technical to economical [9].

Depending on the spare parts management strategy established in the development phase, spare modules will be readily available, or the CAPEX-saving reduction in spares sees the need to procure modules on the market. Given the rapid technological development, it is then impossible to procure replacement modules at scale whose physical and electrical characteristics are directly compatible with the existing Balance-of-System (BOS).

Even new, more efficient PV modules obtained **for free** would still carry a significant cost for a farm, as much of the engineering, design and installation work would have to be repeated, to accommodate the modules with different characteristics and match these with the mounting equipment and inverters in use. Thus, the **commodity-incompatibility paradox of PV modules**: these are treated price-wise as a commodity, yet the need for PV modules to be compatible physically and electrically to ensure long-term reliable and safe operation with maximum possible yield makes them outdated shortly after they are installed.

This paper aims to shed light on the implications of these practices, including the challenges posed by accelerated material innovation, the lack of long-term reliability data, and the systemic obstacles to effective lifecycle management.

2   Background and historical overview

Between 1954 and 1985, the PV industry experimented widely with various designs, cell technologies, encapsulants, and front cover solutions [10]. The USA-funded Block Buys I-V between 1975 and 1985 stimulated the industry to address weak points while providing the guaranteed revenue needed for the manufacturing of the modules. In this period, most manufacturers converged on a common design: strings of series-connected crystalline silicon solar cells integrated into a multilayer encapsulant composite and supported by a robust frame. This architecture proved durable in the field and has remained largely unchanged since, with minor tweaks over time.

The Block Buys also had a fundamental impact on testing and qualification methodologies, developed by the Jet Propulsion Laboratory (JPL). These tests informed subsequent IEC 61215 qualification tests, particularly the accelerated test designs that inform current Module Qualification Test (MQT) protocols [11] of IEC 61215 and IEC TS 63397. Already in 2009, Osterwald and McMahon identified an important issue that has not yet been resolved until today:

"A serious flaw with identifying a test report as a certification is that the product quality requirements normally enforced by an outside agency are missing. A manufacturer is free to make changes to a module, such as changing the supplier of the encapsulation material, and still claim that the module is "certified." It is not difficult to imagine scenarios in which such manufacturing changes could adversely affect the lifetime of a PV module." [11]

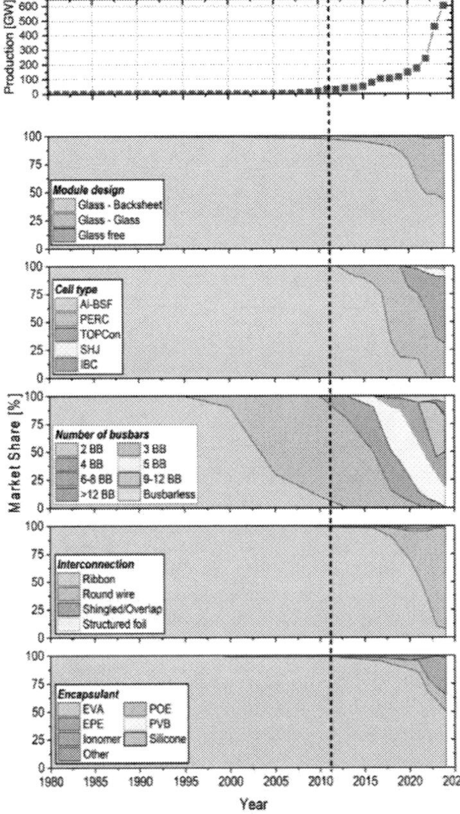

Figure 1: Yearly PV module production and market shares for different module designs and Bill of Materials between 1980 and 2024. Data compiled from IEA PVPS Snapshot Reports, ITRPV Reports, Fraunhofer ISE PV Reports, and verified against annual reports of top module manufacturers.

Similarly, PV module manufacturers were known to overstate their nominal power by 6-7%, which, when combined with Light Induced Degradation (LID) of ~3%, resulted in real-life performance of -10% versus nameplate in 2005 [10]. Figure 1 shows the evolution of commercially successful c-Si PV modules and key BOM components over time. (By definition, this therefore excludes experimentation and small batches by manufacturers that did not achieve lasting success.) These charts were reconstructed by combining data reported in the literature with interpolation to fill in missing years. This analysis focuses on crystalline silicon PV cell architectures (Al-BSF, PERC, TOPCon, SHJ, IBC), module design variants (glass–glass, glass–backsheet, lightweight glass-free), encapsulant materials,

interconnect types (round wire, ribbon), and busbar configurations.

The historical analysis of photovoltaic (PV) production and shipments between 1980 and 2024 reveals a clear inflection point in the industrial growth trajectory. From 1980 through 2000, global PV production expanded slowly from 0.01 GWp to 0.3 GWp per year, with cumulative shipments below 2 GWp, reflecting a niche market supported mainly by off-grid systems and early demonstration projects. During the subsequent decade (2001–2010), growth accelerated under the influence of feed-in tariff policies in Europe and Japan, raising annual production to 20 GWp and cumulative shipments to approximately 41 GWp by 2010. The true industrial turning point occurred in the period 2010–2012, when annual production exceeded 20 GWp and cumulative shipments crossed the 100 GWp threshold, marking the transition from early market expansion to large-scale industrialization. This inflection coincides with the entry and rapid rise of Chinese manufacturing and steep cost reductions, as steps of the strategy to establish PV as a mainstream energy technology.

Figure 2 illustrates the exponential growth of PV installations worldwide over the past 25 years, achieving a thousand-fold increase from 2 GWp in 2000 to 2.2 TWp in 2024, while experiencing similarly spectacular cost declines of 98% or more, with spot prices for Tier-1 c-Si modules reaching 0.1 $/W in 2024. Even the period 2010-2024 saw cost declines of 90% or more in $/W terms for PV modules.

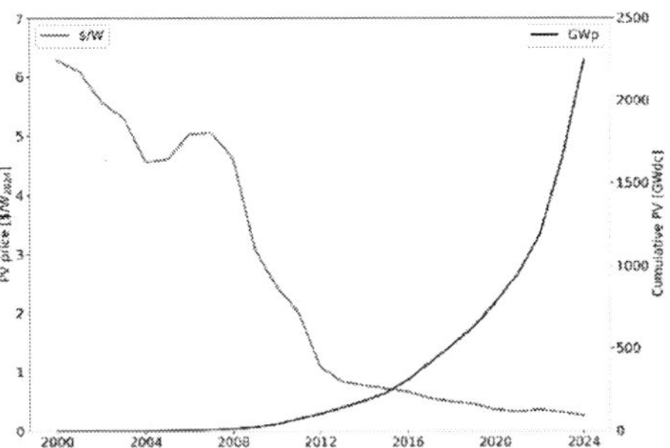

Figure 2: Cumulative worldwide deployments 2000-2024, with module prices in 2024 $/W. Price data from [12], installation data from [13].

From Figure 1 and Figure 2, together with the rapid increase of maximum commercially available module power between 2018 (~350 Wp) and 2022 (~650 Wp) documented by [1], the **first paradox of PV** becomes evident: PV modules are treated price-wise as a commodity, yet the need for PV modules to be compatible physically and electrically to ensure long-term reliable and safe operation with maximum possible yield makes them outdated as soon as they are installed.

The consequences of this paradox are manyfold, with most of the risk residing with asset owners. To further lower costs, PV systems typically are highly optimised for the chosen PV module and inverter combination, together with the mounting solution (fixed or single-axis tracking). This combination drives system design, including string lengths, and the length and width of arrays, as well as inter-row distances. Asset owners usually have between 0.1% and 3% of modules as spares, with 0.5% the most prevalent, to use for expected and reasonable module failures. If, for whatever reason more than the available spare modules need to be replaced within the technical lifetime of the power plant, the asset owner and the O&M provider are confronted with a serious challenge: finding compatible spares, with the same or very similar BOM *at scale* is next to impossible, once more than two years have passed, as module manufacturers continuously implement technology and process changes to their production lines. A PV module failure is defined here as the most stringent combination of an effect or issue that poses a safety risk, or that the power output of the module(s) is so low due to performance loss that reliable operation of the solar plant is not possible. For the latter, this means that the current and/or voltage of the modules has declined enough that inverters are unable to operate within their designed DC input range, or unable to meet grid performance standard requirements.

Industry experience compiled by IEA PVPS Task 13 shows that many early-life failure modes take at least one to three years to be identified from their first deployment at scale, while (slightly) slower yet important degradation modes such as PID can be reported by year 3 and 4 of operation [14]. Even in moderate climates, module failures by year 10-12 of operation have also damaged inverters due to repeated insulation resistance issues [15]. In times of exponential deployment, 2-5 years equates to 50-70% of worldwide cumulative installations, with currently more than 1.4 TWp less than 5 years old.

When comparing the PV industry to other industries, some challenges and peculiarities can be identified. The PV industry's rapid technological evolution and cost-reduction efforts have prioritized innovation over long-term material qualification, where new module designs, e.g., "big floppy modules" [16] are put on the market and deployed faster than they can be tested by independent third parties. Compounding this issue, the PV industry operates in large-scale yet unique production batches (100 MW to 5 GWp), with rapid iteration and technological advancement [1] ensuring that specific module designs and configurations are not replicated.

Using cumulative doublings from reaching 1 GWp cumulative installations since the year 2000 as an indicator for maturity, an outside look of the industry would yield the black dotted curve of Figure 3. The (semi-) viable moment for each technology can then be indicated, while the "birth" of the technology occurs when 1 GWp/y of installations is reached. An outside view of the industry misses the contributions of the different technologies over time, where until 2012, there was only Al-BSF being produced and sold at GW-scale. From 2012 onwards, PERC rapidly gained market share due to its efficiency and cost benefits. The growth of TOPCon has been nothing short of spectacular, with cumulative deployments surpassing Al-BSF in 4 to 5 years. By contrast, back contact (IBC) and heterojunction (HJT) technologies have scaled slower than PERC and TOPCon, due to more complex processing steps, higher production quality requirements and commensurate manufacturing costs.

A key benefit for the industry has been that technology and manufacturing learnings are transferable for c-Si technologies, and that many of the cell technologies share common processes and machines, whereby transitioning from lab to fab could happen within 1-3 years [1]. Nevertheless, this still required enormous investments over the past years, with top Chinese manufacturers building ingot, cell, wafer and module fabs at 5 GW to 25 GW scales, repeating this effort over multiple years. These high investments to scale rapidly while defending or gaining market share during intense price wars have affected the financial stability of many manufacturers, with the Chinese government taking steps to reduce overcapacity [17].

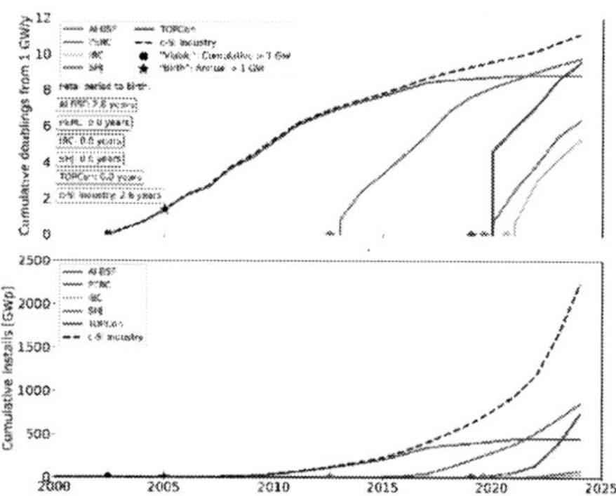

Figure 3: Worldwide cumulative doublings by c-Si cell technology and cumulative GWp deployments.

The actions of the leading Chinese manufacturers regarding changes to module warranty durations, both for workmanship (10 to 25 years, depending on the company) and STC power loss over time (from -0.5%/year to -0.3%/y, from 25 years to 30 years or more), suggest that they are confident that these new module technologies are better made, and will suffer lower degradation rates compared to previous generations. While module manufacturers have increased automation and with-it improved quality control of the manufacturing process, design and material choices such as variations in encapsulant recipes, or glass thickness and treatments, still represent potential avenues for unknown, or faster-than-expected failure modes. Recent examples with glass-glass modules have seen spontaneous glass breakage occur [16], while BOM variations such as different EVA recipes of modules within utility-scale farms result in different degradation modes and speeds [18].

The very rapid growth of new cell technologies in the past decade, combined with the introduction of larger module sizes and variations in BOM components, thus leave the industry with potential risks, where the impact can be in the multi-GW range. Compared to the mature 20+ years of Al-BSF learning and deployment period to reach ~0.45 TW, PERC and TOPCon are TW-scale toddlers, where long-term (10 years or more) outdoor reliability data is non-existent. Already, new failure modes such as UV-induced degradation (UVID) have emerged for PERC and TOPCon, with the manufacturing process also appearing to play a role, more than only the cell technology [19].

3 Main challenges

3.1 Module warranties

PV module manufacturers typically provide limited warranties on their products:

- A workmanship warranty, covering manufacturing defects. These are currently in the range of 10-15 years, with some manufacturers offering 25 years.
- An STC power warranty, often called a degradation warranty. Here, the power output of PV modules is guaranteed for 25 to 30 years, with guaranteed end-of-warranty values ranging between 87% and 80%, expressed as an initial power loss of 1% to 3% in the first year, and subsequent 0.3% to 0.5% power loss per year.

Most module manufacturers appear to use the reliability and failure model of Vázquez and Rey-Stolle [20], where they assume that 1% of modules will fail over the warranty period. They have three parameters to optimise for power warranties: the duration of the warranty, the guaranteed power or equivalent annual degradation rate, and the associated percentage of modules that will fail over the warranty period. For this, they typically set aside 1% of PV module revenues as liabilities on their balance sheet when modules are sold and use warranty claims data and forecasting models to determine which portion of the liability will be used in the current year, and the remainder for future years. As module costs have dropped significantly over the years, current practice for warranty liability budgeting is to use the average price of PV modules over the past two years. Hence, while PV module shipments by the leading manufacturers have shown an exponential trend, the monetary impact on their balance sheet has been much less severe.

Some manufacturers self-insure for module warranties and carry this liability on their balance sheet, whereas others take out insurance against warranty claims. Importantly, standard warranty documents from manufacturers mention that they decide on the solution, if a warranty claim is valid:

- Replacement modules, to make up for the power underperformance;
- A cash equivalent using current spot prices; or,
- Repairing PV modules.

Replacement modules are provided by the manufacturer from available modules, and therefore provide zero guarantee to owners that replacement modules will be compatible (physically and electrically) with the purchased PV modules.

The exponential decline in PV module prices while sales have grown exponentially (Figure 2) has been a boon for module manufacturers, as the monetary liability has declined with module prices. Conversely, all PV systems built during this period of exponential cost declines have owners who stand to lose much, if the performance is (much) less than expected during the warranty period, and particularly if the useful lifespan is shortened.

3.2 Tests of PV modules

A major challenge accompanying the accelerated innovation cycles in PV module technology is the mismatch between the pace of material and design changes and the long service lifetimes expected from PV systems. While the introduction of novel materials and components has enabled cost reductions and performance gains,

modules are now being deployed at the gigawatt scale without sufficient long-term reliability data, particularly from outdoor field testing [21]. This has led to the emergence of unexpected failure modes only a few years after deployment, including potential-induced degradation (PID) [22], backsheet chalking and cracking [23], light- and elevated-temperature-induced degradation (LeTID) [24], ultraviolet-induced degradation (UVID) [25], cell corrosion [26] and low-stress glass fracture. Many of these issues were not detected by the standardized single stress accelerated tests commonly applied at the time, highlighting the need for more representative qualification protocols.

Consequently, new accelerated testing approaches increasingly employ combinations or sequences of stressors that better capture real-world conditions and enable earlier identification of degradation modes linked to new module materials and architectures [21].

A further complication is the lack of transparency in the bill of materials (BOM). Externally, modules may appear identical, yet employ different encapsulants, backsheets, or other polymeric components, with variations not only across manufacturers but also within product lines over time. Polymers are particularly problematic, as their performance depends strongly on stabilizer and additive formulations, which are often proprietary and subject to change. Additives also govern material interactions, which are key drivers of degradation. For example, polyamide (PA)-based backsheets exhibit markedly different cracking behaviour depending on the type of EVA encapsulant employed [27]. Such interactions make it difficult to predict module reliability based on individual component properties alone [28].

The consequences of this variability are already evident at the system level. Field studies have documented cases where modules installed in the same PV park but with different BOMs showed divergent degradation pathways, resulting in heterogeneous degradation patterns and performance losses across the site. In more severe cases material incompatibilities have led to insulation issues followed by inverter shutdowns, which were triggered by the unexpected module behaviour [29].

3.3 Repowering and replacement challenges

The decision to repower or replace comes after either a specific fault or underproduction has been identified in the system (reliability-driven repowering), or economic gains are desired and have been evaluated by a technical team. A main consideration upon doing the feasibility evaluation of repowering, is the availability of spare parts and compatibility dilemmas.

As a first step to determining if repowering is needed, whether for reliability or economic reasons, requires knowledge of the health of the system. This can be assessed by perceived underperformance in the SCADA daily data production. After removing simple yet common causes like offline inverters, stuck trackers, and soiling, if the degradation of the system is pervasive it might signal to a bigger underperformance issue. Ground-teams might be sent to identify some of these issues and do visual inspections of the array, with thermal imaging a second easily accessible technique. In cases where the reason of power loss is not clear, third parties and consultants are often involved, and beyond data and visual inspection they might involve drone-aerial inspections. Electrical measurements by qualified electricians in the inverter as well as module level can also detect any ground faults, or specific module underperformance. If power loss is due to a couple outlier modules or a section, owners might opt for replacement or repair of that section by either using the spares, or purchasing similar modules in the resale market.

The format of PV modules (width and size) has changed considerably over the last decade, posing physical challenges to adapt the racking solution to the new module type. Furthermore, the change in area and efficiency mean power output and voltages will also vary, and might not match the rest of the strings or inverter requirements. Inversely, inverters' end of life, whether planned or premature, can kick into gear repowering and replacement decisions, as new inverters have also changed from 600 V to 1000 V and even now 1500 V input requirements, with very few legacy options available. DC-DC optimizers can offer partial relief from this re-engineering challenge, albeit at relatively high cost, and recent findings indicating that their use at scale may be less of panacea than expected [30].

For PV systems impacted by Extreme Weather Events (EWEs), repowering options become highly situation-specific, as the nature of the damage can vary, from a portion of the system (e.g., a tornado cutting through a wind farm, or hail damage), to wholescale damage due to flooding, hurricanes, or typhoons [7]. Nevertheless, on the technical side, in-depth analyses are typically required, which may have to extend beyond the path of visible damage, for example by doing on-site electroluminescence (EL) [31] or photoluminescence (PL) inspections.

If the asset owner, together with the insurer, deems the asset worthy of being restored to its pre-damaged state, the question then arises as to how this can be achieved. In practice, severely damaged modules or inverter sections will be restored with new PV modules, as physically and electrically compatible modules are unavailable at scale: the first paradox of PV rearing its head again.

4 Reliability and testing

When comparing the PV industry to other industries, some challenges and peculiarities can be identified. The PV industry's rapid technological evolution and cost-reduction efforts have prioritized innovation over long-term material qualification, where new cell technologies (e.g. high efficiency solar cell technologies like TOPCon or SHJ) or new module designs are put on the market and deployed faster than they can be tested by independent third parties. Consequently, unanticipated failure modes such as spontaneous glass fracture and UV-induced degradation (UVID) cell degradation have emerged.

The lack of standardisation for PV modules contrasts sharply with other industries, where spare parts with consistent specifications remain available for years or decades.

Hence, the **second paradox of PV** emerges: Increased warranty durations, more product and BOM variations, while testing is reduced in time and cost. This interacts directly with the first paradox of PV, as the low margins for PV module manufacturers and the commodity-like perception decrease the appetite for more stringent product qualification tests by manufacturers, or product quality testing and verification by customers and wholesale distributors.

5 Solutions and recommendations

5.1 Transparency

Even though the PV industry and its stakeholders have more data and more transparency than other industries, significant improvements can still be made.

While manufacturers are loath to lose their competitive advantage by sharing the ingredients to their winning recipe, the lack of information on the BOMs impacts knowledge generation on the link between materials and degradation and failure modes.

As annual PV module deployments have risen sixfold to 600 GWp since 2017-2018, the speed and duration of accelerated tests has not shortened, nor have research groups and companies specialised in reliability testing of PV modules scaled accordingly. Furthermore, the need for in-depth data and insights on material-specific and multi-material interactions has grown.

Improved and faster information flows between manufacturers, laboratories and research groups, and field data from commercially deployed systems are needed. Multiple possible solutions are possible that satisfy the competing needs and requirements of manufacturers and asset owners. These can range from dual reporting of module failures, once to the module manufacturer for warranty claims and information, and on the other to a trusted third party, whether this is the government of a country, or a multi-country institute or organisation.

5.2 Reliability

With PV moving firmly into the TW era, its importance to the safe and reliable operation of electrical grids grows too. In the short term, the performance of newly deployed PV systems is likely going to be as expected; the risk to asset owners, investors, and electrical grids may materialise much later. For long-term investors such as pension funds, the longevity and performance of the asset is crucial: they stand to lose most if the lifetime of the asset is years shorter than expected. The larger challenge is with investors with much shorter investment horizons: a PV farm may change hands multiple times over its lifetime. One of the technical challenges for the due diligence phase for the soon-to-be owner is the estimation of Remaining Useful Life (RUL), which requires a deep understanding of PV system performance and degradation, combined with the use of historical performance data and the judicious use of additional tests, such as drone-based IR, EL or PL. Here, non-destructive testing methods that can detect the BOM of PV modules may generate valuable complementary information for the RUL model of the power plant, which then informs the financial model.

This still requires fundamental science to be done, where weathering of materials is tested in outdoor conditions as well as accelerated tests. Acceleration factors for module qualification testing from IEC 61215 have been based on practical considerations, cost, and time. However, practical evidence from the industry shows that tests from IEC 61215 are deemed to not be stringent enough, with testing companies advertising 2 times or 3 times IEC [61215] as being a better indicator of module reliability.

Here, the development of physics and chemistry-based acceleration factors is still a much-needed work in progress, which can be informed by approaches used in the car and roofing material industries.

5.3 Maturity and financial viability

Whether module manufacturers are prudent in extending warranty durations and guaranteeing higher rated performance over the warranty duration is yet to be seen. Module warranty claims may be much higher in the future than historical rates: not necessarily because the product is fundamentally different, rather that improved metrology of PV systems combined with machine learning or AI permit under-performance to be more rapidly and accurately determined. For module manufacturers operating for years on razor-thin or even negative margins, even a small change in warranty claims rates can have devastating impacts. The Chinese government, together with module manufacturers have been expressing concern over the consequences of the price wars on the viability of the PV module value chain [17], yet the potential impact of warranty claims is not yet publicly mentioned.

5.4 Increased standardisation

Increasing standardisation of shapes and sizes of PV modules has been a bottom-up process, driven by manufacturers aiming to optimise for volume usage within shipping containers [32]. Consortia of the largest module manufacturers have been created, with the aim of adhering to the same physical dimensions [33]. Compared to the rapid changes in physical dimensions in the past decade [1], this evolution marks as a respite for industry stakeholders. The risk that arises from further standardisation is that it continues the cycle of the first paradox of PV: more (physical) standardisation allows modules to be more easily interchangeable and replaceable, further supporting the view of modules as commodities. Moreover, if sizes do stabilise for the coming years or even decades, the advent of AI and robotics has the potential to reduce labour costs for installation, O&M, as well as removal or replacement. Surprisingly, *more* commoditisation of PV *whilst* remaining standardised may prove to be a possible way out of the first paradox of PV. Nevertheless, module reliability is a key factor for the survival of the industry and investors.

6   Conclusions

Despite the outside or whole-of-industry view that PV modules are a commodity, a deeper look shows that modules are not interchangeable between brands, nor are modules replaceable one-for-one with newer designs. This first paradox of PV is strongly linked to the second paradox of PV, where module warranties have become longer and more stringent, yet testing has not adapted accordingly. In practice, PV modules are obsolete within a few years of installation, with spares at scale unavailable. The potential risks for asset owners are large, as any event over the system lifetime where module damages or failures exceeds the available spare stock of modules leads to costly or sub-optimal solutions, such as partial or rolling repowering of the power plant. In such cases, financial returns can suffer a strong hit.

While sophisticated investors and stakeholders perform detailed due diligence on PV system suppliers, their view is still constrained to the tests they perform, while others such as rooftop PV system owners, purchase a product with the hope of good performance. Solutions such as a Production or Performance (quality) Border Adjustment Mechanism with mandatory testing with public-facing results, or similar forms of public data sharing can further drive manufacturers to ensure quality and reliability of products, and help maintain trust in PV as a durable cornerstone technology for a low-emissions economy. Here, "trust but verify" is a motto that must be applied widely, with the benefit that increased testing and transparency can root out unreliable products, manufacturers and suppliers. While the potential for PV to scale to TW-level installations per year exists, this rests on the need for PV systems and their components to be reliable for decades, while being exposed to the elements and potentially stronger storms.

One surprising (partial) way out of the PV as a commodity paradox is to lean in even more, by standardising and freezing module dimensions. This would allow modules to be more easily replaceable when inevitable failures occur. Addressing the second paradox of PV with increased warranty durations and more stringent terms while testing has not adapted accordingly will be a challenge that must be addressed head-on. The key to the survival of manufacturers, investors and customers alike though, is that module reliability and quality can be maintained, more transparency and testing implemented, while scaling further and potentially decreasing even more in price.

ACKNOWLEDGEMENTS
This paper was done within the IEA PVPS Task 13.

This report is supported by the Swiss Federal Office of Energy (SFOE) under the contract no. SI/502398-01.
The work in IEA PVPS Task 13 is supported by the Austrian Research Agency (FFG) under contract no. FO999908094.
This work is supported by the German Federal Ministry for Economic Affairs and Energy (BMWE) under contract no. 03EE1120B.
This work was authored [in part] by the National Renewable Energy Laboratory for the U.S. Department of Energy (DOE) under Contract No. DE-AC36-08GO28308. Funding provided by the U.S. Department of Energy's Office of Energy Efficiency and Renewable Energy (EERE) under Solar Energy Technologies Office (SETO) Agreement 52184. The views expressed in the article do not necessarily represent the views of the DOE or the U.S. Government. The U.S. Government retains and the publisher, by accepting the article for publication, acknowledges that the U.S. Government retains a nonexclusive, paid-up, irrevocable, worldwide license to publish or reproduce the published form of this work, or allow others to do so, for U.S. Government purposes.

REFERENCES

[1]   Y. Chen, D. Chen, P. P. Altermatt, S. Zhang, L. Wang, X. Zhang, J. Xu, Z. eng, H. Shen and P. J. Verlinden, "Technology evolution of the photovoltaic industry: Learning from history and recent progress," *Prog Photovolt Res Appl.*, vol. 31, no. 12, pp. 1194-1204, 2023.

[2] R. J. Gómez, E. Jiménez, D. Sanz, C. Sandoval, J. Cuaresma, J. C. Vázquez, S. Rodríguez-Conde, H. Silva and V. Parra, "Bifacial Modules for Large Scale PV Plants: Lessons Learned and Current Limitations from a Factory/Manufacturing Inspection Outlook," in *EU PVSEC*, 2020.

[3] C. Buerhop-Lutz, O. Stroyuk, T. Pickel, T. Winkler, J. Haugh and I. M. Peters, "PV modules and their backsheets - A case study of a Multi-MW PV power station," *Solar Energy Materials and Solar Cells*, vol. 231, p. 111295, 2021.

[4] N. D. Jackson and T. Gunda, "Evaluation of extreme weather impacts on utility-scale photovoltaic plant performance in the United States," *Applied Energy*, vol. 302, p. 117508, 2021.

[5] "Reliability and safety issues observed in flood affected PV power plants and strategies to mitigate the damage in future," in *46th IEEE PVSC*, 2019.

[6] D. C. Jordan, K. Perry, R. White and C. Deline, "Extreme Weather and PV Performance," *IEEE Journal of Photovoltaics*, vol. 13, no. 6, pp. 830-835, 2023.

[7] U. Jahn, B. Herteleer, C. Tjengdrawira, I. Tsanakas, M. Richter, G. Dickeson and A. Astigarraga, "Guidelines for Operation and Maintenance of Photovoltaic Power Plants in Different Climates," IEA PVPS, 2022.

[8] M. Köntges, S. Kurtz, C. Packard, U. Jahn, K. A. Berger, K. Kato, T. Friesen and H. Liu, "Review of Failures of Photovoltaic Modules," IEA PVPS, 2014.

[9] S. Ovaitt, H. Mirletz, B. Mirletz and M. Prilliman, "Repowering PV Systems Demystified: Terms, Motives, Economics and Impacts," in *53rd IEEE PVSC*, 2025.

[10] M. A. Green, "Silicon Photovoltaic Modules: A Brief History of the First 50 Years," *Prog. Photovolt: Res. Appl.*, vol. 13, pp. 447-455, 2005.

[11] C. R. Osterwald and T. J. McMahon, "History of accelerated and qualification testing of terrestrial photovoltaic modules: A literature review," *Prog. Photovolt: Res. Appl.*, vol. 17, pp. 11-33, 2009.

[12] IRENA (2025); Nemet (2009); Farmer and Lafond (2016), ""Solar photovoltaic module price" [dataset]," 2025.

[13] G. Masson, A. Van Rechem, M. de l'Epine and A. Jäger-Waldau, "Snapshot of Global PV Markets 2025," April 2025. [Online]. Available: https://iea-pvps.org/snapshot-reports/snapshot-2025/. [Accessed 25 Aug 2025].

[14] M. Köntges, G. Oreski, U. Jahn, M. Herz, P. Hacke and K.-A. Weiss, "Assessment of Photovoltaic Module Failures in the Field," IEA PVPS Task 13, 2017.

[15] M. Libra, D. Mrázek, I. Tyukhov, L. Severová, V. Poulek, J. Mach, T. Šubrt, V. Beránek, R. Svoboda and J. Sedláček, "Reduced real lifetime of PV panels – Economic consequences," *Solar Energy*, vol. 259, pp. 229-234, 2023.

[16] E. C. Palmiotti, M. Springer, J. Zuboy, T. J. Silverman, J. L. Braid, D. C. Jordan, S. Rabade and T. M. Barnes, "Growing Panes: Investigating the PV Technology Trends Behind Frequent Early Failures in Modern Glass–Glass Modules," *IEEE Journal of Photovoltaics*, vol. 15, no. 2, pp. 297-308, 2025.

[17] "China moves to curb solar overcapacity, stabilize pricing," PV Magazine, 7 July 2025. [Online]. Available: https://www.pv-magazine.com/2025/07/07/china-moves-to-curb-solar-overcapacity-stabilize-pricing/. [Accessed 19 September 2025].

[18] C. Buerhop, O. Stroyuk, O. Mashkov, A. Barabash, J. Hauch and I. Peters, "Polymer encapsulation impact on potential-induced degradation in PV modules revealed by a multi-modal field study," *Solar Energy Materials and Solar Cells*, vol. 277, p. 113111, 2024.

[19] F. Thome, P. Meßmer, S. Mack, E. Schnabel, F. Schindler, W. Kwapil and M. Schubert, "UV-Induced Degradation of Industrial PERC, TOPCon, and HJT Solar Cells: The Next Big Reliability Challenge?," *Solar RRL*, vol. 8, no. 23, p. 2400628, 2024.

[20] "Photovoltaic Module Reliability Model Based on Field Degradation Studies," *Prog. Photovolt: Res. Appl.*, vol. 16, no. 5, pp. 419-433, 2008.

[21] G. Oreski, J. S. Stein, G. C. Eder, K. Berger, L. Bruckman, R. French, J. Vedde and K.-A. Weiß, "Motivation, benefits, and challenges for new photovoltaic material & module developments," *Progress in Energy*, vol. 4, no. 3, p. 032003, 2022.

[22] V. Naumann, D. Lausch, S. Großer, M. Werner, S. Swatek, C. Hagendorf and J. Bagdahn, "Microstructural Analysis of Crystal Defects Leading to Potential-Induced Degradation (PID) of Si Solar Cells," *Energy Procedia*, vol. 33, pp. 76-83, 2013.

[23] Moffitt, S. L., S. Uličná, S.-S. Jhang, P.-C. Pan, M. Owen-Bellini, P. Hacke, M. D. Kempe, J. Tracy, K. R. Choudhury, L. T. Schelhas and X. Gu, "PVDF-based backsheet cracking: Mapping in situ phase evolution by X-ray scattering," *Solar Energy Materials and Solar Cells*, vol. 282, p. 113355, 2025.

[24] "New insights on LeTID/BO-LID in p-type mono-crystalline silicon," *Solar Energy Materials and Solar Cells*, vol. 226, p. 111085, 2021.

[25] M. U. Khan, C. Sen, M. Pollard, T. Huang, M. Gao, R. Lv, Y. Yu, X. Wu, H. Wang, X. Wang and B. Hoex, "UV-induced degradation in TOPCon solar cells: Hydrogen dynamics and impact of UV wavelength," *Solar Energy Materials and Solar Cells*, vol. 294, p. 113895, 2026.

[26] C. Sen, H. Wang, M. U. Khan, J. Fu, X. Wu, X. Wang and B. Hoex, "Buyer aware: Three new failure modes in TOPCon modules absent from PERC technology," *Solar Energy Materials and Solar Cells*, vol. 272, p. 112877, 2024.

[27] R. Heidrich, M. Lüdemann, A. Mordvinkin and R. Gottschalg, "Diffusion of UV Additives in Ethylene-Vinyl Acetate Copolymer Encapsulants and the Impact on Polymer Reliability," *EEE Journal of Photovoltaics*, vol. 14, no. 1, pp. 131-139, 2024.

[28] G. C. Eder, Y. Voronko, G. Oreski, Mühleisen, M. Knausz, A. Omazic, A. Rainer, C. Hirschl and H. Sonnleitner, "Error analysis of aged modules with cracked polyamide backsheets," *Solar Energy Materials and Solar Cells*, vol. 203, p. 110194, 2019.

[29] C. Buerhop-Lutz, T. Pickel, O. Stroyuk, J. Hauch and I. M. Peters, "Insulation resistance in relation to distribution of backsheet types in strings and inverters," *Solar Energy Materials and Solar Cells*, vol. 246, p. 111913, 2022.

[30] C. Bucher, J. Wandel and D. Joss, "Life Expectancy of PV Inverters and Optimizers in Residential PV Systems," in *WCPEC-8*, Milan, 2022.

[31] W. Hobbs, "Storms and Other Events: Experiences with Cell Cracks," in *PV Reliability Workshop*, Lakewood, 2020.

[32] Trina Solar, "The Trina Solar Vertex Module White Paper," May 2020. [Online]. Available: https://solar-media.s3.amazonaws.com/assets/DIGITAL%20S ERIES%202020/SSFDigital20/Vertex%20by%20 Trina%20Solar/Vertex%20White%20Paper.pdf. [Accessed 24 September 2025].

[33] Trina Solar, "Trina Solar partners with five other PV manufacturers to launch 700W+ Photovoltaic Open Innovation Ecological Alliance," December 2023. [Online]. Available: https://www.trinasolar.com/eu-en/resources/newsroom/eu-trina-solar-partners-five-other-pv-manufacturers-launch-700w-photovoltaic-open. [Accessed 24 September 2025].

[34] H. Inano, Y. Akemoto and K. Asakura, "Impact of silicon and other contaminants on the melting process in photovoltaic glass recycling," *Journal of Non-Crystalline Solids*, vol. 666, p. 123724, October 2025.

RENEWABLE ENERGY COMMUNITIES AND CITIZEN PARTICIPATION IN TECHNOLOGICAL AND SOCIAL INNOVATIONS

Cristina Sanz-Cuadrado, Kiane Alves e Silva, Luis Narvarte, Ana B. Cristóbal
Instituto de Energía Solar, Universidad Politécnica de Madrid
C/Alan Turing s/n, 28031 Madrid, Spain
cristina.sanzc@upm.es; kiane.asilva@alumnos.upm.es; luis.narvarte@upm.es; anabelen.cristobal@upm.es

ABSTRACT: Citizen engagement represents a crucial concern in innovation processes. Reaching high commitment and active levels for participatory actions is still challenging. This research seeks to illustrate the crucial role citizens have played in fostering both technological and social innovations within the low-carbon energy sector, particularly in the photovoltaic sector by analyzing the levels of participation defined by Arnstein's classification. To achieve this objective, this work examines real-world experiences that exemplify effective citizen engagement in innovation processes. Firstly, a comprehensive overview of the role citizens played in deploying technical innovations in the energy sector is described. It illustrates how these innovations have been enhanced through collaboration with citizens or have emerged directly from their involvement, combining original material with a thorough bibliographic review. Additionally, the paper delves into the levels of engagement observed in Energy Communities (ECs), one of the most significant social innovations. By exploring and analyzing 34 ECs, it becomes evident that the transition from passive to active citizen-led innovations remains a challenge. However, some inspirational examples are shown. By positioning citizens as vital agents of change, this exploration underscores their importance in the transition to sustainable energy systems and aims to inspire others to follow the described cases.
Keywords: technological innovation, social innovation, photovoltaic, citizen participation, energy communities

1 INTRODUCTION

To respond to the challenges of the climate change, innovation is one of the key responses, especially in the development of solutions to mitigate its impacts. Traditionally, innovation has been driven by a "triple helix" model [1], [2], consisting of the collaboration between industry, government, and academia. However, in the last decade, the role of citizens has been recognized as crucial in innovation ecosystems [3], [4], [5], [6], [7], [8], [9], [10] particularly in addressing the climate change [11], [12], [13]. With this new paradigm, known as the "quadruple helix" model, innovation move beyond centered innovations to citizen-centered processes, acknowledging citizens as both end-users and integral members of democratic systems. Such a responsible approach to development involves navigating Arnstein's Ladder of Citizen Participation [15].

Social acceptance of renewable energy is a key factor in the deployment of renewable energy technologies [15], [16], [17]. Since the introduction of its concept in 2006 [18], it has been studied in the energy transition planning, reporting the role of citizens as end-users in the literature [19], [20], [21].

However, the lack of meaningful citizen participation, where the highest levels of Arnstein's ladder, is observed in many initiatives that often adopt a paternalistic approach or a tokenistic strategy. Chilvers et al. [22] analyzed 257 public engagement initiatives in low-carbon energy revealing that most citizen participation efforts remain confined to the lower rungs of Arnstein's Ladder and are often institutionally driven rather than citizen-led. This underscores the gap in achieving deeper and transformative engagement.

The definition of social innovation in the energy transition came in 2018. It addresses the social and community well-being in innovations related to the low-carbon transition [23]. In this regard, the literature points to a growing trend developing mechanisms that empower citizens to co-design the energy transition and design citizen-driven business models [24], [25], [26].

In relation to this trend towards social innovations in the energy transition, the concept of energy communities (ECs) [27], [28] has also emerged as an innovative approach that involves citizens in the reconfiguration of energy systems [29] [28]. These collective initiatives represent citizen-driven energy actions to advance the energy transition [30], [31]. However, the idea of communities of energy [32] has existed for decades, empowering citizens as drivers of change and allowing them to take an active role in innovation in several ways. The novelty of the concept of ECs resides in its capacity to undertake a range of activities and its role in promoting real social impact by encouraging active and meaningful citizen participation.

Through this work, we aim to honor the anonymous contributions of countless citizens who have played a pivotal role in advancing science and technology, especially in the photovoltaic (PV) sector. By bringing to light stories that may have been overlooked, we seek to inspire the PV scientific and technological community to adopt diverse participatory methodologies to their own technical innovations' deployment. At the same time, we want to highlight a paradox: even in social innovations closely tied to this field, such as the fancy ECs, the urgency to capitalize on opportunities often overshadows the very essence of community involvement. Ironically, this leads to the promotion of so-called social innovations with minimal genuine community participation.

The paper is organized as follows, firstly, the state-of-the-art section reviews two cases where citizen participation was instrumental in driving technological innovation process in the PV sector during the last decades of the 20th century.

After this brief review, the paper explores the development of ECs, one of the most dynamic social innovation processes in the European energy sector. This section will examine the level of engagement of participants in those innovative initiatives aligning with Arnstein's levels of engagement. This is addressed through a comprehensive literature review, where we identified 34 ECs across Europe.

10.4229/EUPVSEC2025/5EP.1.5

2 STATE-OF-THE-ART

In 1986, researchers developed projects utilizing Solar Home Systems (SHSs) [33] in Sierra del Segura, Spain. SHSs are one of the earliest examples of direct collaboration between citizens and researchers in the development of PV innovations. In this project, the value of the researcher-citizen partnerships is highlighted. This experience continued into the early 1990s in countries such as Algeria, Bolivia, Mexico, and Sri Lanka [34] [35], [36], [37] [38], [39]. Through innovative citizen science methodologies developed by researchers, they successfully established self-consumption standards for rural electrification tailored to different family typologies. This approach ensured "social acceptability" by focusing on practical solutions that resonated with local communities. Interestingly, even residents with little or no literacy participated actively by recording their household energy use through meters installed by the research team.

After the success of SHSs, the advantages of collaboration between researchers and end-users became evident in the deployment of PV water pumping systems, largely due to their decentralized nature. In 2002, the involvement of more than 1,300 household from two regions of Morocco resulted in the participation of 20,000 people in the recording of their daily water consumption habits [40]. These collaborations were essential to tailor the water pumps to local needs. Researchers developed and implemented a methodology [41] for introducing technological innovations in social groups, drawing on General Systems Theory [42] and the concepts of "hardware," "software," and "orgware". In this framework, the perceived needs of end-users play a crucial role, as evidenced by findings reported 12 years after the systems were installed [43].

A standout example of public involvement in PV research is the "Counting the Sun" program [44], which represents one of the first citizen science projects in this area. This project collaborated with the Dutch Public Authorities and engaged 5,000 household with PV installations. It consisted of an awareness campaign on domestic PV systems performance. Participants provided data in a citizen science initiative. Some challenges were faced since the accuracy of the citizen science data is a critical issue [45].

The potential collaboration of engaging citizens within the PV sector is recognized in GRECO project [46]. Participants collaborated in the identification and access to some of the oldest PV installations worldwide to develop studies on the aging and repair of PV modules.

Another successful project is MASLOWATEN [47] which demonstrated the cooperation of farmers and irrigation communities with researchers to create different mechanisms for PV irrigation demonstrators [48]. This example shows the implication of farmers in the design process that led to the creation of ad-hoc technical solutions.

Some other examples of citizen collaboration with researchers can be found in the literature.

3 ENERGY COMMUNITIES

Moving from technical innovations to social innovations this research aims to analyze current citizen participation in ECs, one of the latest mechanisms of social innovations that has recently gained greater notoriety and interest. According to the European Federation of Citizen Energy Cooperatives, there are currently 1,900 European energy cooperatives and around 1,250,000 citizens participating [30]. Furthermore, the European Commission estimated that by 2030 EC will hold 17% of wind and 21% of solar capacity [49].

3.1 Methodology

Although citizen participation is the hallmark of ECs, how citizens organize and take action within these communities can vary significantly and should be categorized into distinct types. A literature review of 34 ECs was conducted using Harzing's Publish or Perish application that includes Google Scholar and Scopus databases. Three search axes have been included in relation to the topic, the application and the scope. The keywords used for the research were: citizen science, social motivation, energy community, renewable energy, lessons learned, case study and state of the art.

After the bibliographic research, the ECs were categorized on three parameters. (a) Community membership (residential households, commercial businesses, industrial facilities, municipal entities, or specific groups based on geographical locations, such as islands). (b) Energy power range: Range 1 (0-500 kW), Range 2 (501-1,000 kW), Range 3 (1,001-10,000 kW), Range 4 (10,001-100,000 kW), and Range 5 (>100,001 kW). (c) Business model: Group 1 (neighborhood associations), Group 2 (municipal initiatives), Group 3 (regional cooperatives), and Group 4 (national and international cooperatives).

Each group has been analyzed according to these categorizations focusing on citizen participation level. This analysis aims to identify the categories in which participants demonstrate the highest levels of engagement and to understand the mechanisms that drive this involvement. The level of citizen participation has been adapted from Arnstein's theory to align with the explanations presented in the GRECO Practical Guide on Open Science [50], which categorizes engagement into six levels, from direct participation in the decision-making and operational processes of the EC, to limited engagement where information flows primarily from the community to its members and complete absence of citizen participation or engagement efforts. Fig. 1 summaries and illustrates the six levels defined in the GRECO.

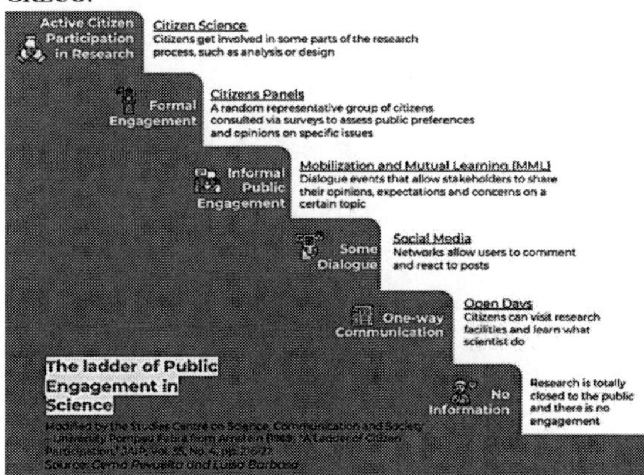

Figure 1: The ladder of Public Engagement in Science defined in GRECO [50].

3.2 Results

Regarding the 34 ECs analyzed and classified following the GRECO Practical Guide on Open Science, 32.4% of the cases achieve the highest level of citizen participation: Active Citizen Involvement (Fig. 2).

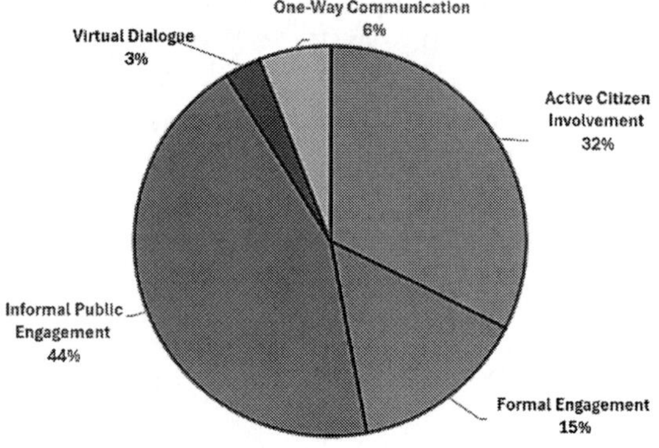

Figure 2: Distribution of citizen participation across the 34 ECs analyzed.

In the following, those ECs that reach the highest level of engagement (Active Citizen Involvement) are analyzed according to the three parameters that have been defined previously: community membership, range power and business model.

In terms of community membership, 36.4% of actively participating ECs are island-based projects, followed by 27.3% of residential ECs (Fig. 3).

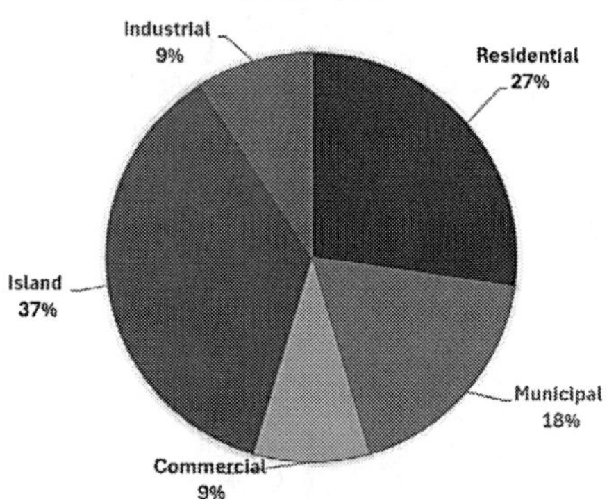

Figure 3: Distribution of ECs regarding community membership classification (Active Citizen Involvement)

Regarding the power range (Fig. 4), most of the ECs with active participation have power ranges below 500kW, corresponding to Group 1 (54.5%). In addition, it is observed that none of the ECs with installed power above 100,000kW have Active Citizen Involvement.

Finally, the predominant business model in the ECs with active participation corresponds to neighborhood associations (63.6%), which are included in Group 1 (see Fig. 5). As it was observed in the case of range power,

national and international cooperatives do not reach the highest levels of citizen participation.

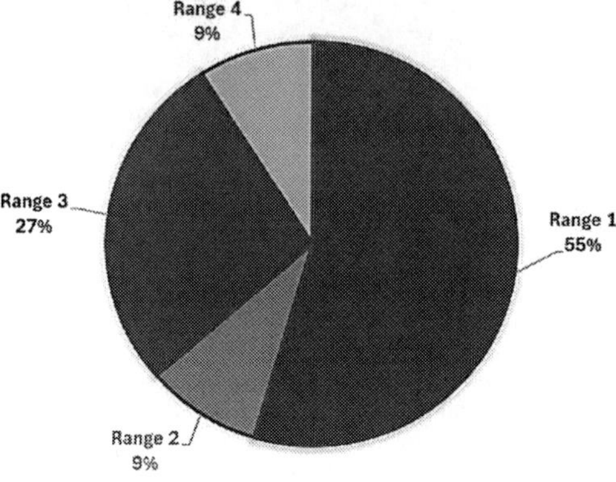

Figure 4: Distribution of ECs regarding range power classification (Active Citizen Involvement)

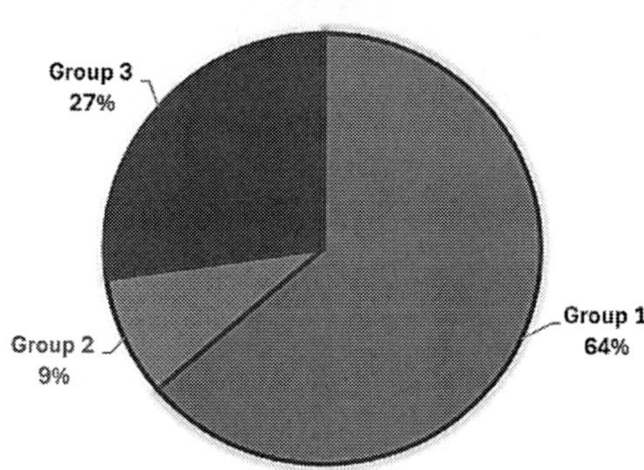

Figure 5: Distribution of ECs regarding business model classification (Active Citizen Involvement)

4 CONCLUSIONS

4.1 Key lessons learned

This study demonstrates how citizens can move beyond traditional surveys and opinion polls—while still acknowledging their complementary role—toward fostering responsible innovations that better meet societal needs. Public engagement plays a key role in achieving meaningful citizen collaboration in driving technical and social innovations.

In this regard, some key lessons can be drawn from our research.

- Researchers must maintain direct involvement to build trust and foster meaningful collaboration.
- Researchers must develop activities aligned within a framework of real, sustained partnership.

- Researchers must carefully design their activities, considering factors such as methodology, language barriers, and ways to measure participant satisfaction.
- Researchers must ensure compliance with relevant legislation and ethical guidelines, particularly when handling personal data.
- Researchers must address the challenge posed by citizen science activities, especially regarding the accuracy and reliability of data collected by non-expert participants.

4.2 Participation in Energy Communities

Social innovations, such as ECs, effectively promote citizen engagement by aligning technical solutions with social needs. Our analysis underscores the importance of smaller initiatives (neighborhood and municipal projects), which enable participation in a more personal way. This aligns with some successful examples such as CERCA in Spain [51] and the Feldheim community in Germany [52]. Small-scale initiatives prioritize social needs than economic benefits, providing a wide sense of belonging to the community.

In contrast, national and international ECs demonstrated to be more impersonal, and participation is often driven to obtain economic profits.

To conclude, these collective community-driven EC definitively pave the way for citizen science in a broad sense. ECs redefine citizens' traditional roles as mere end-users by transforming them into local micro-investors—through mechanisms such as loans or participation accounts.

ACKNOWLEDGEMENT

This project has received funding from the European Union's Horizon 2020 research and innovation programme under grant agreement No 101036418.

5   REFERENCES

[1] H. Etzkowitz, "Innovation in Innovation: The Triple Helix of University-Industry-Government Relations," *http://dx.doi.org/10.1177/05390184030423002*, vol. 42, no. 3, pp. 293–337, Sep. 2003, doi: 10.1177/05390184030423002.

[2] H. Etzkowitz and L. Leydesdorff, "The dynamics of innovation: from National Systems and 'Mode 2' to a Triple Helix of university–industry–government relations," *Res Policy*, vol. 29, no. 2, pp. 109–123, Feb. 2000, doi: 10.1016/S0048-7333(99)00055-4.

[3] "Why researchers should resolve to engage in 2017," *Nature*, vol. 541, no. 7635, pp. 5–5, Jan. 2017, doi: 10.1038/541005a.

[4] European Commission and D.-G. for R. and Innovation, *Re-finding industry – Defining innovation*. Publications Office, 2018. doi: doi/10.2777/927953.

[5] P. O. of the E. Union, "Outreach to newcomers and societal engagement in industrial technologies : reports of the Horizon 2020 Advisory Group on nanotechnologies, advanced materials, biotechnology, and advanced manufacturing and processing (NMBP).," Dec. 2018, doi: 10.2777/810639.

[6] European Commission, *LAB – FAB – APP — Investing in the European future we want*. Publications Office, 2017. doi: doi/10.2777/477357.

[7] C. Vélot, "Scientists and Civil Society Must Move Together toward a New Science," *Front Public Health*, vol. 4, May 2016, doi: 10.3389/fpubh.2016.00096.

[8] E. Pain, "To be a responsible researcher, reach out and listen," *Science (1979)*, Jan. 2017, doi: 10.1126/science.caredit.a1700006.

[9] B. K. Sovacool, "What are we doing here? Analyzing fifteen years of energy scholarship and proposing a social science research agenda," *Energy Res Soc Sci*, vol. 1, pp. 1–29, Mar. 2014, doi: 10.1016/j.erss.2014.02.003.

[10] European Commission, "Open innovation, open science, open to the world – A vision for Europe," Publications Office, 2015. doi: doi/10.2777/061652.

[11] EUROPEAN COMMISSION, "COM(2016)763 - Accelerating Clean Energy Innovation - EU monitor," Brussels. Accessed: Jul. 11, 2024. [Online]. Available: https://www.eumonitor.eu/9353000/1/j9vvik7m1c3gyxp/vk9u7wddoazh

[12] World Energy Council, "World Energy Scenarios- Composing energy futures to 2050," 2013, Accessed: Jul. 11, 2024. [Online]. Available: https://www.worldenergy.org/assets/downloads/World-Energy-Scenarios_Composing-energy-futures-to-2050_Full-report1.pdf

[13] Y. Cabannes, "Contributions of Participatory Budgeting to climate change adaptation and mitigation. Current local practices around the world & lessons from the field," 2020.

[14] S. R. Arnstein, "A Ladder Of Citizen Participation," *J Am Inst Plann*, vol. 35, no. 4, pp. 216–224, 1969, doi: 10.1080/01944366908977225.

[15] B. K. Sovacool and P. Lakshmi Ratan, "Conceptualizing the acceptance of wind and solar electricity," *Renewable and Sustainable Energy Reviews*, vol. 16, no. 7, pp. 5268–5279, Sep. 2012, doi: 10.1016/j.rser.2012.04.048.

[16] P. Zhai and E. D. Williams, "Analyzing consumer acceptance of photovoltaics (PV) using fuzzy logic model," *Renew Energy*, vol. 41, pp. 350–357, May 2012, doi: 10.1016/j.renene.2011.11.041.

[17] K. Buhr and V. Wibeck, "Communication approaches for carbon capture and storage: Underlying assumptions of limited versus extensive public engagement," *Energy Res Soc Sci*, vol. 3, pp. 5–12, Sep. 2014, doi: 10.1016/j.erss.2014.05.004.

[18] R. Wüstenhagen, M. Wolsink, and M. J. Bürer, "Social acceptance of renewable energy innovation: An introduction to the concept," *Energy Policy*, vol. 35, no. 5, pp. 2683–2691, May 2007, doi: 10.1016/j.enpol.2006.12.001.

[19] T. Sharpton, T. Lawrence, and M. Hall, "Drivers and barriers to public acceptance of future energy sources and grid expansion in the United States,"

Renewable and Sustainable Energy Reviews, vol. 126, p. 109826, Jul. 2020, doi: 10.1016/j.rser.2020.109826.

[20] M. Sarrica, S. Brondi, P. Cottone, and B. M. Mazzara, "One, no one, one hundred thousand energy transitions in Europe: The quest for a cultural approach," *Energy Res Soc Sci*, vol. 13, pp. 1–14, Mar. 2016, doi: 10.1016/j.erss.2015.12.019.

[21] B. K. Sovacool, "Rejecting renewables: The socio-technical impediments to renewable electricity in the United States," *Energy Policy*, vol. 37, no. 11, pp. 4500–4513, Nov. 2009, doi: 10.1016/j.enpol.2009.05.073.

[22] J. Chilvers, R. Bellamy, H. Pallett, and T. Hargreaves, "A systemic approach to mapping participation with low-carbon energy transitions," *Nature Energy 2021 6:3*, vol. 6, no. 3, pp. 250–259, Mar. 2021, doi: 10.1038/s41560-020-00762-w.

[23] T. Hoppe and G. De Vries, "Social Innovation and the Energy Transition," *Sustainability*, vol. 11, no. 1, p. 141, Dec. 2018, doi: 10.3390/su11010141.

[24] T. Höfer and R. Madlener, "A participatory stakeholder process for evaluating sustainable energy transition scenarios," *Energy Policy*, vol. 139, p. 111277, Apr. 2020, doi: 10.1016/j.enpol.2020.111277.

[25] B. Lennon, N. P. Dunphy, and E. Sanvicente, "Community acceptability and the energy transition: a citizens' perspective," *Energy Sustain Soc*, vol. 9, no. 1, p. 35, Dec. 2019, doi: 10.1186/s13705-019-0218-z.

[26] A. Ambrose, "Walking with Energy: Challenging energy invisibility and connecting citizens with energy futures through participatory research," *Futures*, vol. 117, p. 102528, Mar. 2020, doi: 10.1016/j.futures.2020.102528.

[27] European Union, *DIRECTIVES DIRECTIVE (EU) 2018/2001 OF THE EUROPEAN PARLIAMENT AND OF THE COUNCIL of 11 December 2018 on the promotion of the use of energy from renewable sources (recast) (Text with EEA relevance)*. 2018. Accessed: Jan. 29, 2024. [Online]. Available: https://eur-lex.europa.eu/legal-content/EN/TXT/PDF/?uri=CELEX:32018L2001

[28] M. European Union, "Directive (EU) 2019/944 of the European Parliament and of the Council of 5 June 2019 on common rules for the internal market for electricity and amending Directive 2012/27/EU," *Off. J. Eur. Union*, vol. 158, pp. 125–199, 2019.

[29] E. Commission and D.-G. for Energy, *Clean energy for all Europeans*. Publications Office, 2019. doi: https://data.europa.eu/doi/10.2833/9937.

[30] "REScoop." Accessed: Oct. 06, 2023. [Online]. Available: https://www.rescoop.eu/

[31] European Comission, "Energy communities." Accessed: Oct. 09, 2023. [Online]. Available: https://energy.ec.europa.eu/topics/markets-and-consumers/energy-communities_en

[32] E. Atutxa, I. Zubero, and I. Calvo-Sotomayor, "Scalability of Low Carbon Energy Communities in Spain: An Empiric Approach from the Renewed Commons Paradigm," *Energies 2020, Vol. 13, Page 5045*, vol. 13, no. 19, p. 5045, Sep. 2020, doi: 10.3390/EN13195045.

[33] E. Lorenzo, A. Krezinger, and M. Montero, "Consumo en Viviendas Rurales Fotovoltaicas Españolas," *Mundo Electrónico* , vol. 168, pp. 109–115, 1986.

[34] J. Aguilera and E. Lorenzo, "PV rural electrification in the Bolivian altiplane," in *1st World Renewable Energy Congress* , 1989, pp. 241–245.

[35] B. Yaici, S. Labd, and E. Lorenzo, "PV Electrification of a Village in a hot-arid area of Algeria," in *Proceedings 10th European Photovoltaic Solar Energy Conference and Exhibition*, Lisbon, 1991, pp. 1105–1106.

[36] J. M. Huacuz and J. Agredano, "Beyond the grid: photovoltaic electrification in rural Mexico," *Progress in Photovoltaics: Research and Applications*, vol. 6, no. 5, pp. 379–395, Sep. 1998, doi: 10.1002/(SICI)1099-159X(1998090)6:5<379::AID-PIP238>3.0.CO;2-Z.

[37] J. M. Huacuz and A. M. Martínez, "Renewable energy rural electrification: Sustainability aspects of the Mexican programme in practice," *Nat Resour Forum*, vol. 19, no. 3, pp. 223–231, Aug. 1995, doi: 10.1111/j.1477-8947.1995.tb00612.x.

[38] L. Gunaratne, "Solar Photovoltaics in Sri Lanka: a Short History," *Progress in Photovoltaics: Research and Applications* , vol. 2, pp. 307–316, 1994.

[39] L. Gunaratne, "Using the principles of marketing for commercial dissemination of solar PV in Sri Lanka," . *Energy for Sustainable Development* , vol. 2, no. 4, pp. 41–45, 1995.

[40] L. Navarte, E. Lorenzo, and M. Aandam, "Patrones de consumo de agua en sistemas rurales de bombeo fotovoltaico," *Era Solar*, vol. 109, pp. 20–29, 2002.

[41] L. Navarte, E. Lonrezo, and M. Aandam, "Lessons from a PV Pumping Programme in South Morocco," *Prog. Photovolt: Res. Appl.*, vol. 13, pp. 261–270, 2005.

[42] E. Rogers, *Diffusion of Innovations*. The Free Press, 1983.

[43] L. Navarte and E. Lorenzo, "Sustainability of PV water pumping programmes: 12-years of successful experience," *Prog. Photovolt: Res. Appl*, vol. 18, pp. 291–298, 2010.

[44] W. G. J. H. M. van Sark *et al.*, "'Counting the Sun' – a Dutch Public Awareness Campaign on PV Performance," in *29th European Photovoltaic Solar Energy Conference and Exhibition*, 2014, pp. 4161–4164. doi: 10.4229/EUPVSEC20142014-7AV.6.72.

[45] O. Tsafarakis *et al.*, "Three years experience in a Dutch public awareness campaign on photovoltaic system performance," *IET Renewable Power Generation*, vol. 11, no. 10, pp. 1229–1233, Aug. 2017, doi: 10.1049/iet-rpg.2016.1037.

[46] "GRECO- Putting Open Science into action in an engineering project - Greco Project." Accessed: Oct. 29, 2024. [Online]. Available: https://www.greco-project.eu/

[47] "MASLOWATEN: Market uptake of an innovative irrigation Solution based on low water-energy consumption," European Project 640771. Accessed: Jul. 11, 2024. [Online]. Available: https://cordis.europa.eu/project/id/640771

[48] R. H. Almeida *et al.*, "Development and Test of Solutions to Enlarge the Power of PV Irrigation and Application to a 140 kW PV-Diesel Representative Case," *Energies 2018, Vol. 11, Page 3538*, vol. 11, no. 12, p. 3538, Dec. 2018, doi: 10.3390/EN11123538.

[49] European Commission; Directorate-General for Energy, *COMMISSION STAFF WORKING DOCUMENT IMPACT ASSESSMENT Accompanying the document Proposal for a Directive of the European Parliament and of the Council on the promotion of the use of energy from renewable sources (recast).* 2016.

[50] L. Barbosa, E. Albiñana, C. Cañizo, A. Cristóbal, and G. Revuelta, "Practical guide on Open Science for researchers," 2021, doi: 10.5281/zenodo.3968115.

[51] "CERCA Energia | Comunidad de Energías Renovables de la Comarca de Calatayud." Accessed: May 05, 2025. [Online]. Available: https://cercaenergia.com/

[52] J. Young and M. Brans, "Analysis of factors affecting a shift in a local energy system towards 100% renewable energy community," *J Clean Prod*, vol. 169, pp. 117–124, Dec. 2017, doi: 10.1016/J.JCLEPRO.2017.08.023.

42nd European Photovoltaic Solar Energy Conference and Exhibition

Renewable Energy Communities and Citizen Participation in Technological and Social Innovations

Cristina Sanz-Cuadrado*, Kiane Alves e Silva, Luis Narvarte, Ana B. Cristóbal

Instituto de Energía Solar, Universidad Politécnica de Madrid, Madrid (SPAIN)

INSTITUTO
DE ENERGÍA
SOLAR

Image generated by Artificial Intelligence using Canva's AI Image Generator

POLITÉCNICA

42nd European Photovoltaic Solar Energy Conference and Exhibition (EUPVSEC 2025), Bilbao – 22nd – 26th September 2025

Innovation: classic model vs. responsible paradigm

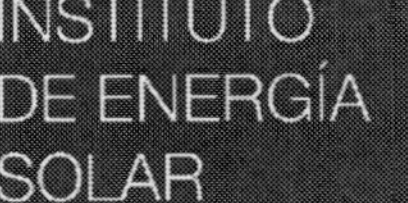

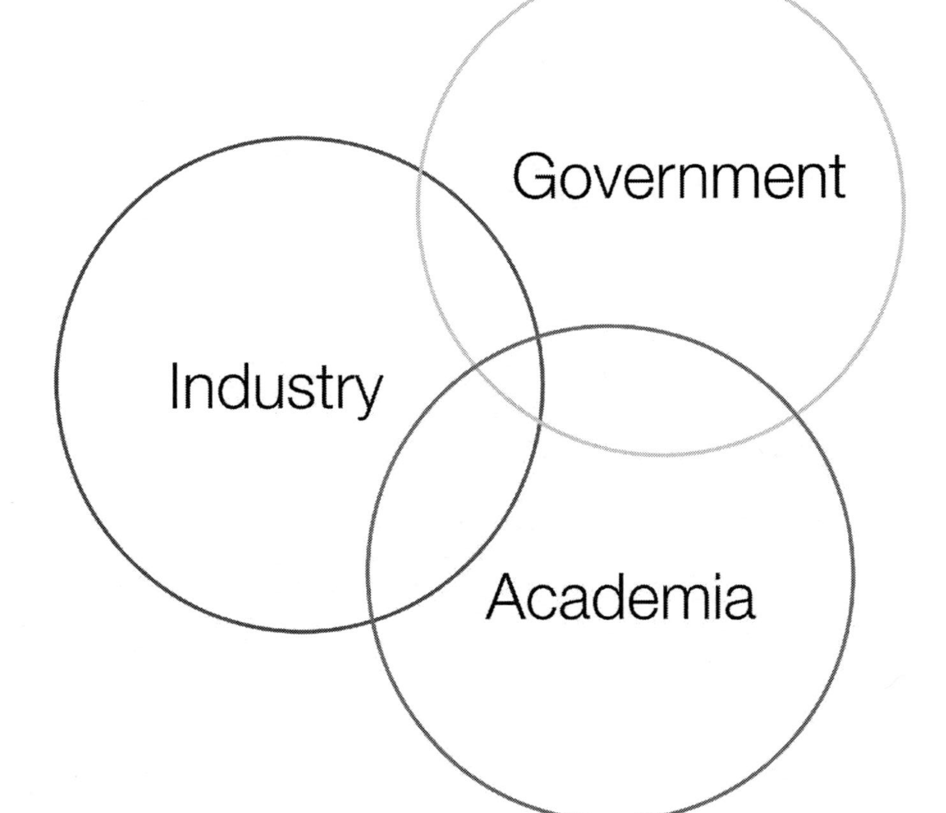

Innovation: classic model vs. responsible paradigm

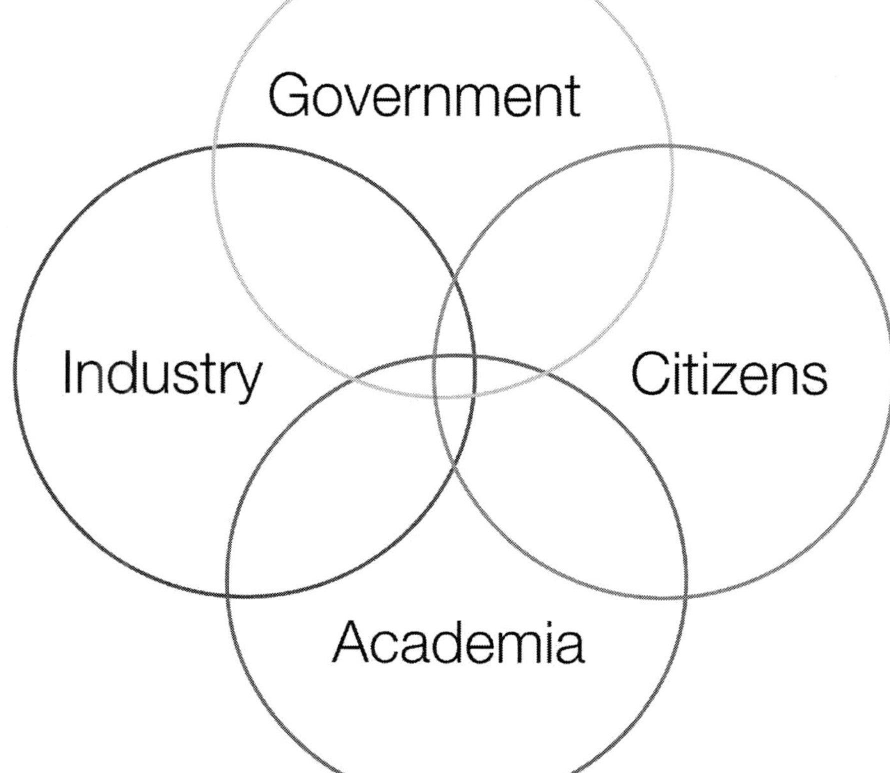

Objectives

- To unveil initiatives where citizens play a decisive role in driving technological and social innovations within the low-carbon energy sector

- Review several cases where citizen participation has been instrumental in technological innovation processes

- Energy Communities: Are ECs mechanisms for authentic citizen-led initiatives, or are they merely repurposing citizens as passive consumers under a new guise?

POLITÉCNICA

Solar Home Systems

- Rural electrification in the 1980s

- Sierra del Segura (Andalusia, Spain)

- Replication: Bolivia, Brazil, Mexico, Algeria, Sri Lanka…

- Citizen participation:

  - Listening to the real needs of citizens

  - Definition of a standard for technical specifications for SHSs based on the needs

  - Citizen science: coping the "symbols" of the counter due to illiteracy

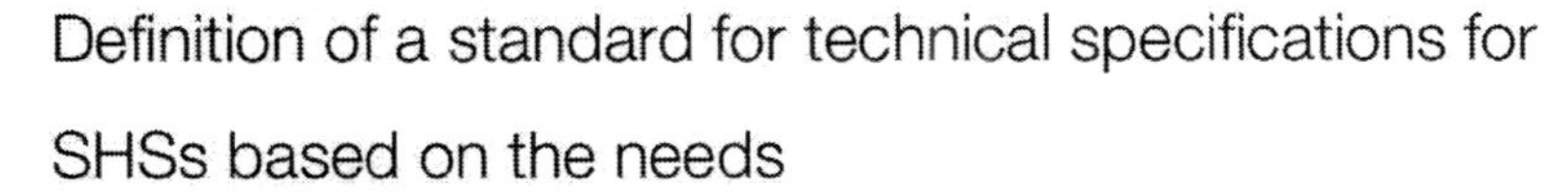
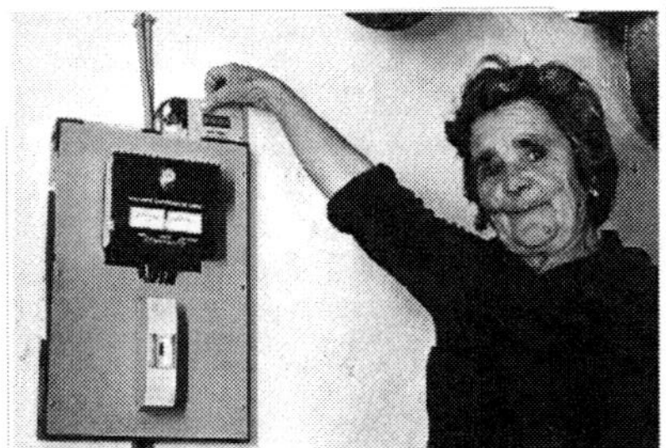

Figure 1. Details of the data recorded by the villagers in 1985 and the pre-addressed envelope to where they sent the data sheets. (Woman picture taken from [54])

Solar Home Systems

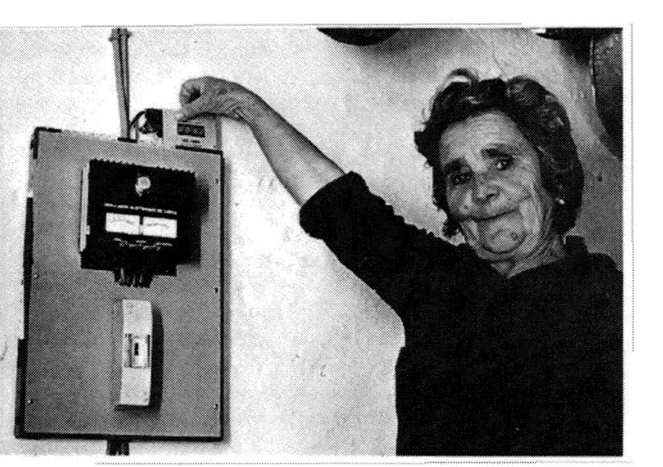

Universidad Politécnica de Madrid
Instituto de Energía Solar

VIVIENDA Nº 6 (Huerta) Sr. Agustina		
FECHA	HORA	LECTURA
1-11-85	10	0002
2-11-85	10	0007
3-11-85	5	0019
4-11-85	3	0002
5-11-85	6	0041
6-11-85	4	0050
7-11-85	3	0051
8-11-85	6	0071
9-11-85	7	0004
10-11-85	6	0094
11-11-85	7	0099
12-11-85	12	0114
13-11-85	6	0129
14-11-85	6	0139
15-11-85	6	0135

Solar Home Systems

INSTITUTO DE ENERGÍA SOLAR

5 11 85	6	0041
6 11 85	H	0050
7 11-85	3	0051
8 11 85	6	0071
9 11 85	7	0004
D 10 11 85	6	0094
11 11 85	7	0099.
12 -11-85	11	0114

PV water pumping systems

- 2002 – Morocco

- 1,300 households -> 20,000 people participating

- Replication: Algeria, Tunisia

- Methodology: according to users needs -> Citizen collaborations were essential for tailoring the water pumps to local needs

- Technological innovations: minimizing the level of innovation to be accepted by users

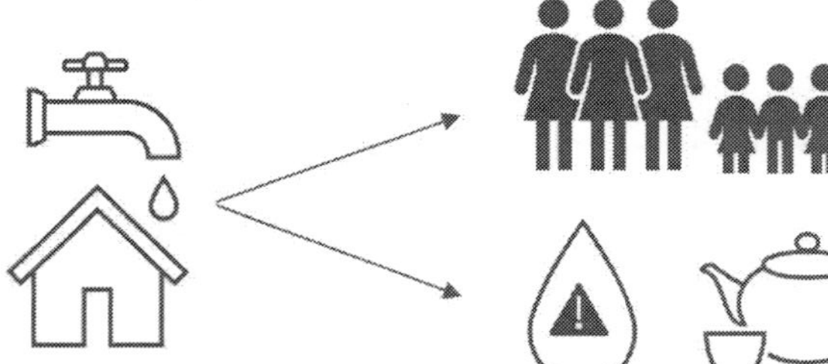

Figure 7. a) Register of water meter figures in each house; b) sketch of the total daily consumption in Iferd [95]); c) register and sketch of the monthly pumped water volume in Iferd

Energy Communities

- Collective participation in the energy system

- Idea of communities of energy: existed for decades

  – Empowering citizens as drivers of change

- Analysis of 34 Energy Communities across Europe

- Parameters of classification:

  – Community membership

  – Energy power range

  – Business model

  – Public Engagement in Science (GRECO)

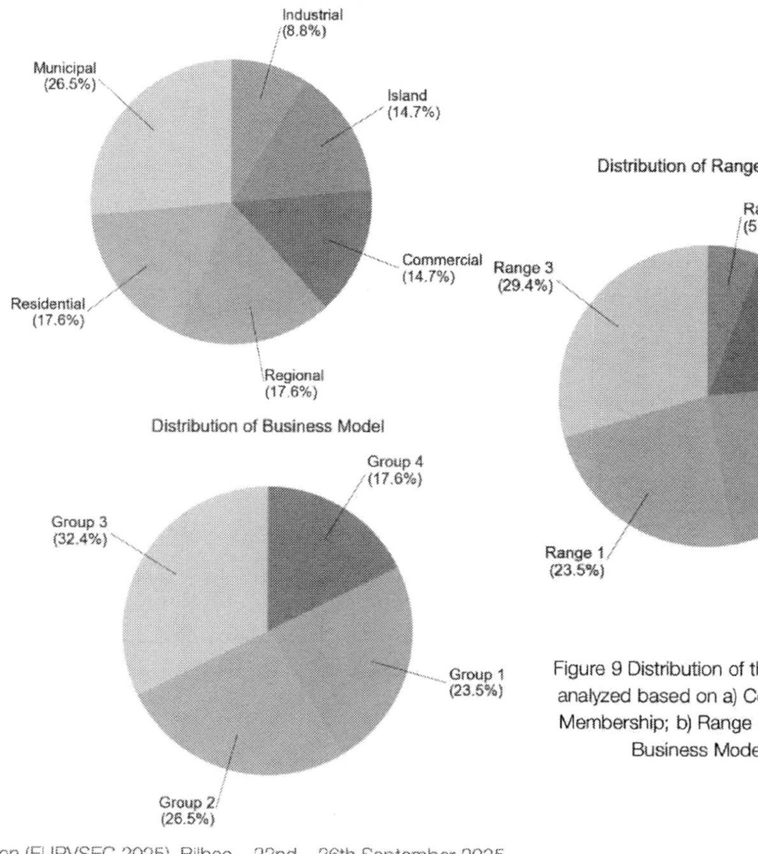

Figure 9 Distribution of the 34 ECs analyzed based on a) Community Membership; b) Range Power; c) Business Model

POLITÉCNICA

Energy Communities

INSTITUTO DE ENERGÍA SOLAR

- Classification based on the ladder of Public Engagement in Science (GRECO)

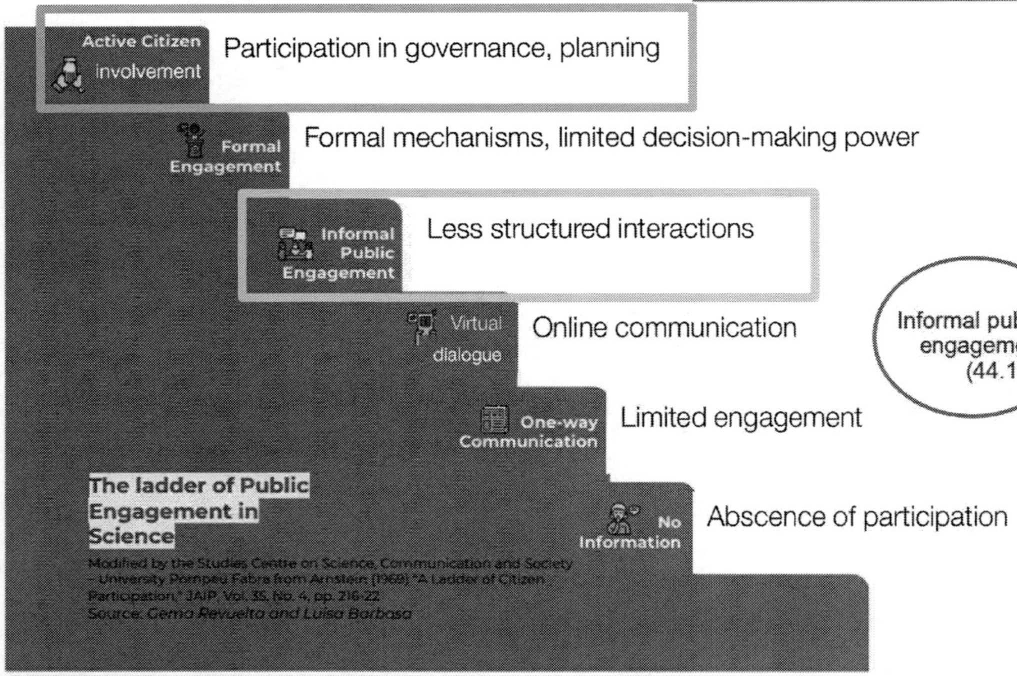

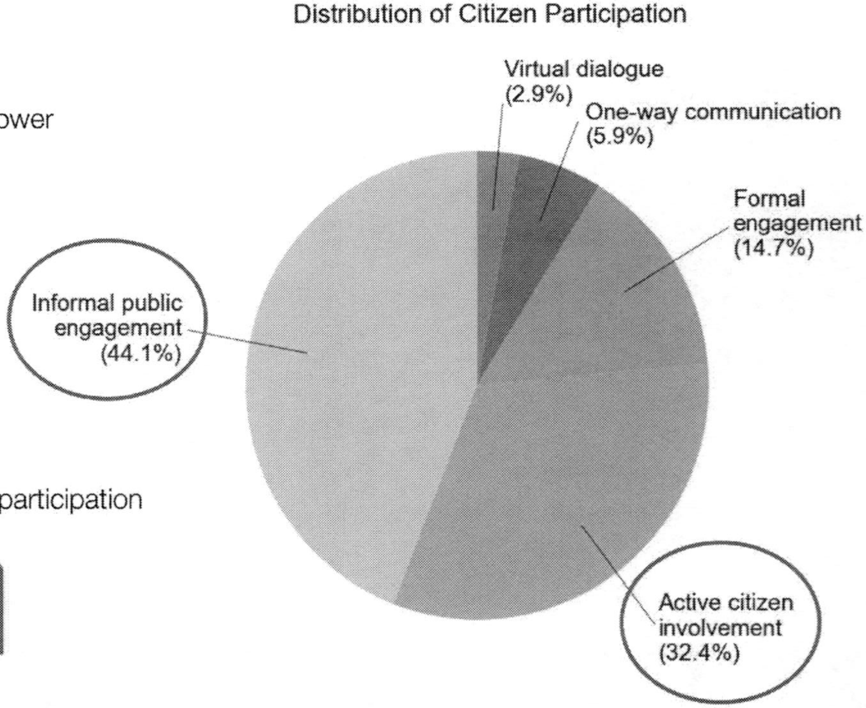

Figure 8 Distribution of Citizen Participation in the ECs analyzed

POLITÉCNICA

Energy Communities – Active citizen involvement

- Community membership

  - residential households

  - commercial businesses

  - industrial facilities

  - municipal entities

  - specific groups based on geographical locations

  (island-based or regional).

Distribution of Community Membership (Active Citizen Involvement)

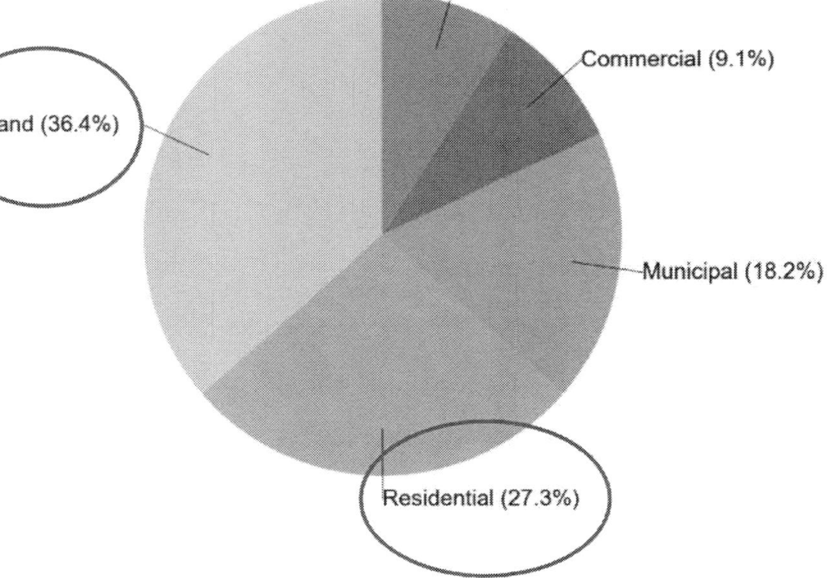

Figure 10 Distribution of the category "Community Membership" in those initiatives that achieved Active Citizen Involvement level

Energy Communities – Active citizen involvement

- Energy power range

  - Range 1: 0-500 kW

  - Range 2: 501-1,000 kW

  - Range 3: 1,001-10,000 kW

  - Range 4: 10,001-100,000 kW

  - Range 5: > 100,001 kW

Distribution of Range Power (Active Citizen Involvement)

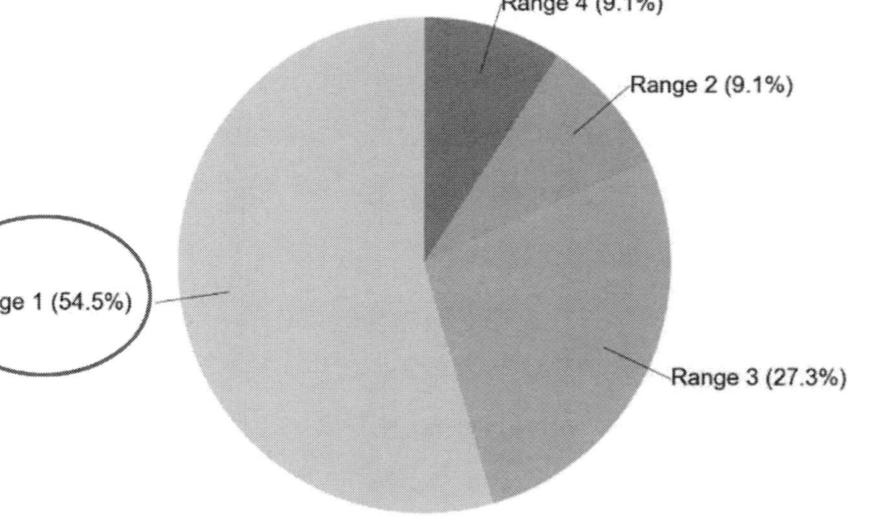

Figure 11 Distribution of the category "Range Power" in those initiatives that achieved Active Citizen Involvement level.

INSTITUTO
DE ENERGÍA
SOLAR

Energy Communities – Active citizen involvement

- Business model

  - Group 1 - neighborhood associations

  - Group 2 - municipal initiatives

  - Group 3 - regional cooperatives

  - Group 4 - national and international
    cooperatives

Distribution of Business Model (Active Citizen Involvement)

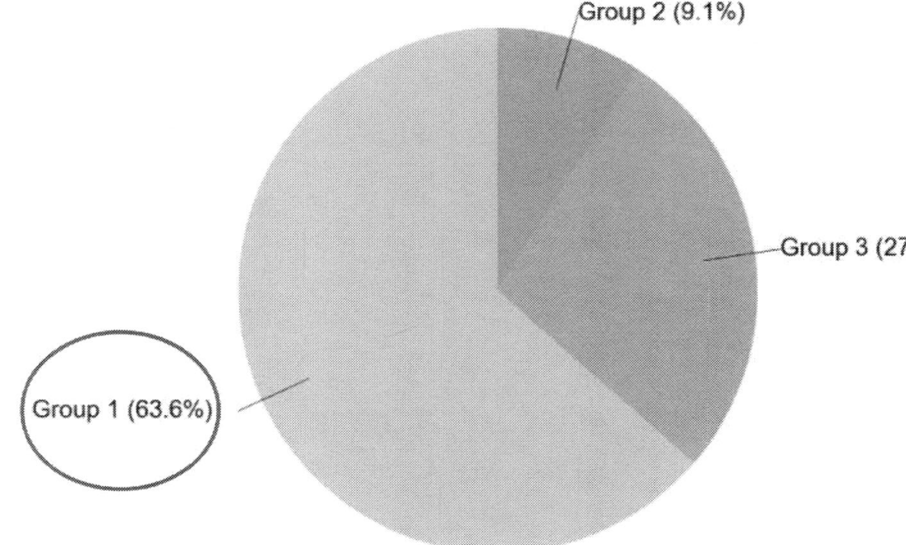

Figure 12 Distribution of the category "Business Model" in those
initiatives that achieved Active Citizen Involvement level

POLITÉCNICA

14

020576-014

Energy Communities – Active citizen involvement

- Observations
  - Residential households
  - Small systems (<500 kW)
  - Neighborhood associations

- Conclusions

  - **Redefinition of citizens' traditional roles** as mere participants and self-consumers.

  - Drivers: not simply providing cheap energy but also **to foster the social value** behind it

  - Models **to pave the way for citizen science** in a broad sense

020576-015

Key lessons learned

1. **Maintaining direct involvement** in the process:

   - to build trust and foster meaningful collaboration

2. **Collaboration** activities:

   - real, sustained partnership framework

3. **Planning** is a critical aspect:

   - design, methodology, language barriers, ways to measure participant satisfaction

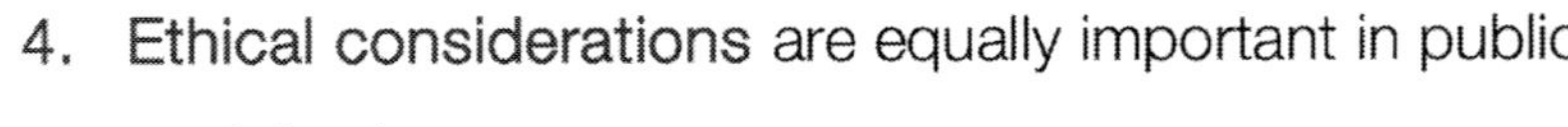

4. **Ethical considerations** are equally important in public participation:

   - relevant legislation and ethical guidelines, particularly when handling personal data

5. **Critical challenge** of citizen science activities:

   - regarding the accuracy and reliability of data collected by non-expert participants

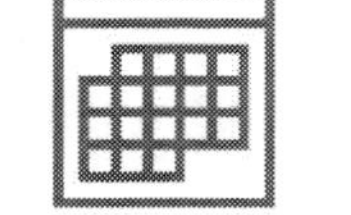
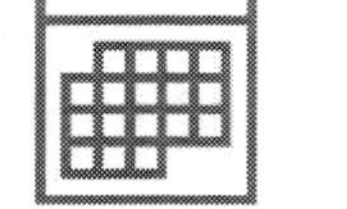

020576-016

We can continue to deliver tools, or we can finally start listening to those who hold the instruction manual

The **FUTURE** isn't a puzzle to be solved alone: it's a story to be written **TOGETHER**.

Image generated by Artificial Intelligence using Canva's AI Image Generator

INSTITUTO DE ENERGÍA SOLAR

Cristina Sanz-Cuadrado   cristina.sanzc@upm.es

Thank you for your attention

Happy to take your questions

We gratefully acknowledge the support of these institutions:

For more information, read our paper: "Citizen Engagement for Social and Technological Innovation in Sustainable Energy Systems" in Advanced Energy and Sustainability Research

POLITÉCNICA

INSTITUTO
DE ENERGÍA
SOLAR
Innovation in photovoltaics since 1979

EU PVSEC

22 — 26
September

BEC
Bilbao Exhibition Centre

Bilbao
Spain

EU
PVSEC
2025

42nd European
Photovoltaic Solar Energy
Conference and Exhibition

Conference Highlights

Robert Kenny

European Commission Joint Research Centre

EU PVSEC Technical Programme Chair

EU PVSEC
FACTS & FIGURES | Presentations
EU PVSEC
2025
EU PVSEC Programme -
Distribution of
Presentations per Type
CONFERENCE PLENARIES & ORALS
349
CONFERENCE VISUALS
562
OPENING & CLOSING
6
1000+
PRESENTATIONS
4
PANEL DISCUSSIONS WITH
29
PANELISTS
PARALLEL EVENTS
110
INDUSTRY SUMMIT
44
030001-004

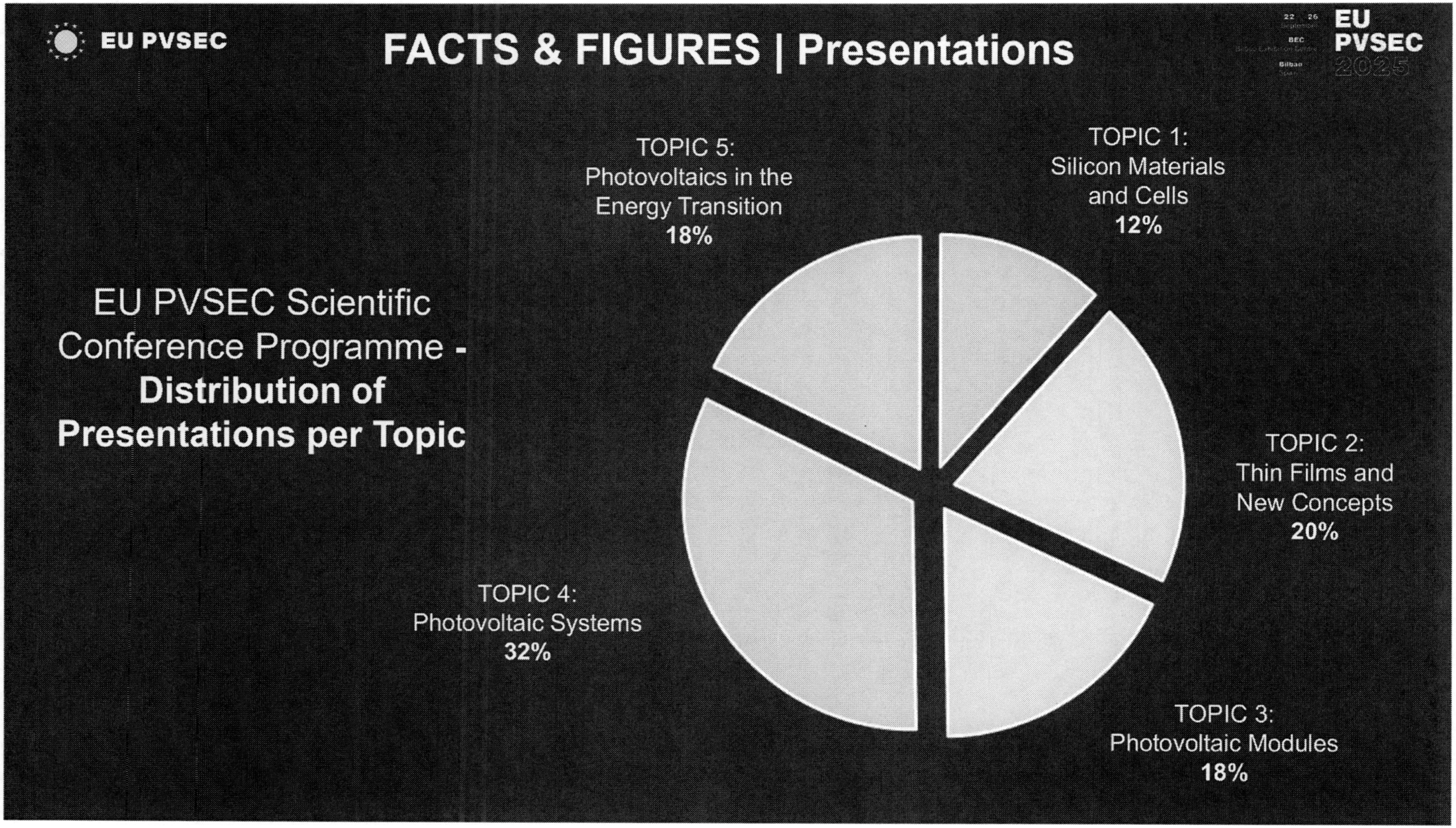

EU PVSEC
FACTS & FIGURES | Presentations
EU PVSEC 2025
EU PVSEC Scientific Conference Programme - Distribution of Presentations per Topic
TOPIC 5:
Photovoltaics in the Energy Transition
18%
TOPIC 1:
Silicon Materials and Cells
12%
TOPIC 2:
Thin Films and New Concepts
20%
TOPIC 4:
Photovoltaic Systems
32%
TOPIC 3:
Photovoltaic Modules
18%
030001-005

FACTS & FIGURES | Participants

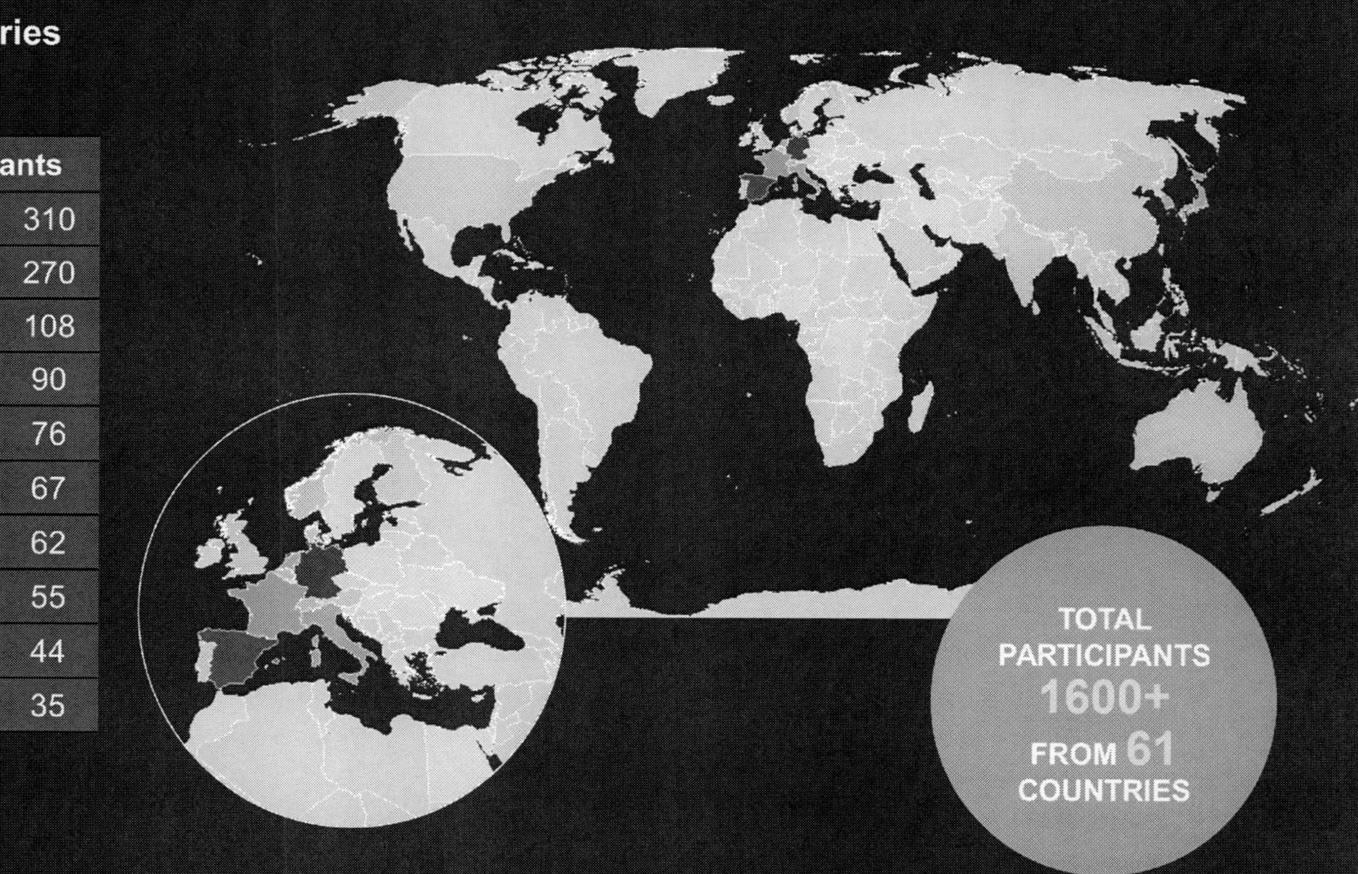

No	Country	Participants
1	Germany	310
2	Spain	270
3	France	108
4	Italy	90
5	The Netherlands	76
6	South Korea	67
7	Switzerland	62
8	Japan	55
9	Belgium	44
10	Norway	35

OPENING
Monday, 22 Sept. 2025
Plenary Session "PV Everywhere"
Welcome Messages
Key Note Speech "The Dual Face of Global Solar Growth"
Becquerel Prize Ceremony
Moderated Panel Discussion "Solar in Turbulent Times: Global Dynamics and the Way Forward"
Jon DE GREGORIO
Gaëtan MASSON
Carlos DEL CAÑIZO
Torsten BRAMMER

EU PVSEC
PANEL DISCUSSIONS
EU PVSEC 2025

BO.13 Reliability and Bankability in PV
"The rapid developments of PV technology require increased attention to be paid to reliability testing."

CO.7 Challenges and Opportunities of PV up to 2030
"PV Technology is already reliable and cost effective, and even though improvements are welcome, key blockages are storage and grid strengthening. AI and robotics are essential to meet the scale of developments needed."

DO.13 Scalability and Manufacturability Prospects in Europe for New Technologies
"The prospects for reaching the 30GW target for PV module manufacturing in Europe were discussed and policy measures proposed."

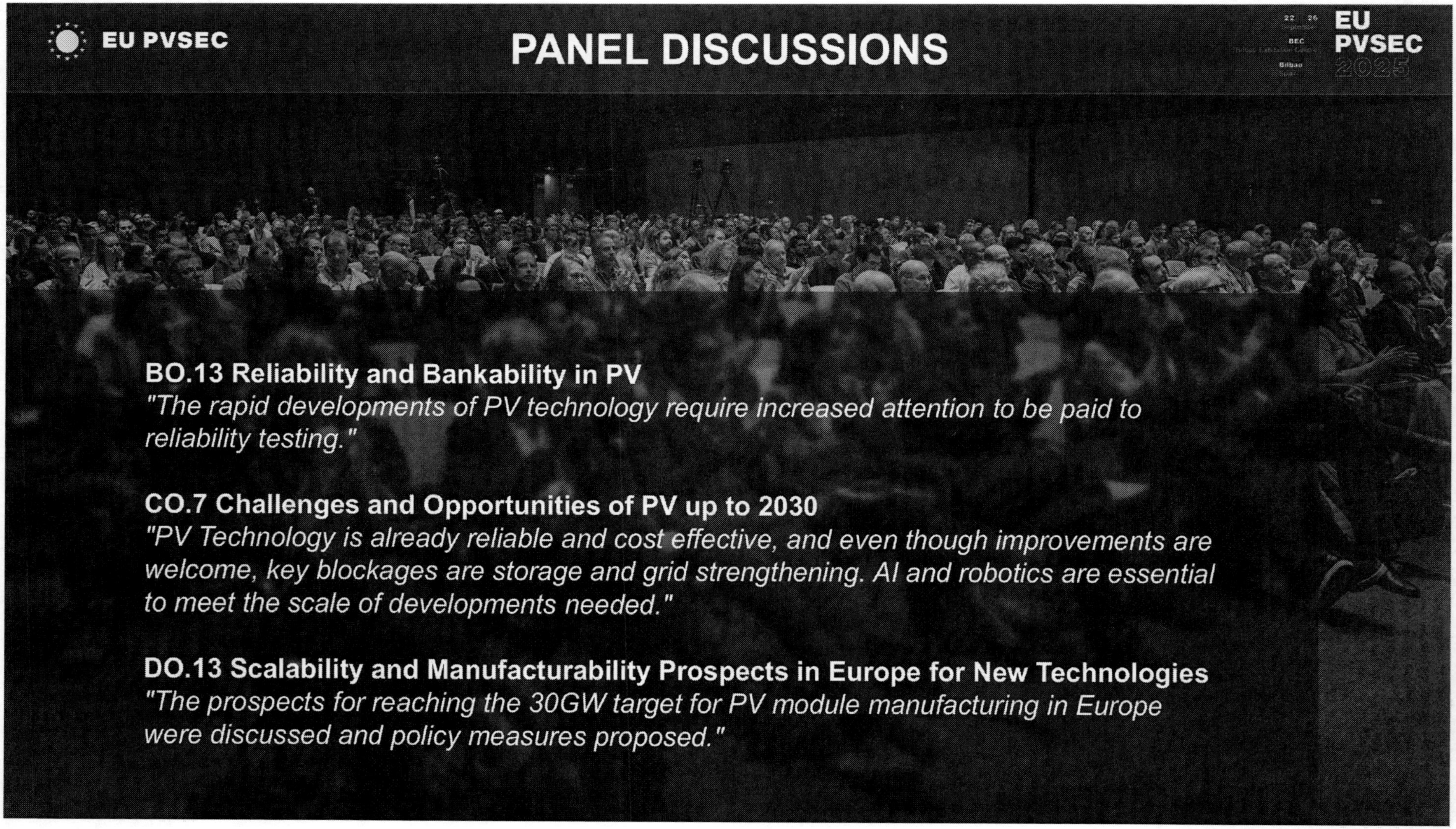

030001-008

CONFERENCE

Cross-cutting themes emerged throughout the programme, showcasing how solar technologies can be applied everywhere, from traditional to emerging fields.

- Sustainability and circularity remain central, with research focused on reducing material use, such as replacing silver with copper, and advancing end-of-life management of modules.

- Ensuring long-term stability and predictable energy yield is equally essential, with studies of degradation mechanisms such as UVID carried out.

- The role of AI across the PV value chain is rapidly expanding, from design to operations and maintenance, including drone applications.

EU PVSEC
EU PVSEC 2025
CONFERENCE

TOPIC 1:
SILICON
MATERIALS
AND CELLS

Enhancements in IV measurement procedures

- Michael Rauer, Fraunhofer ISE: 1AO.4.5 *Universal Contacting Approaches for the Characterization of Solar Cells*
- Shuai Nie, UNSW: 1AO.4.6 *Contact-Free J-V: a Simple Technique for Universal State-of-the-Art Solar Cells*

Replacement of critical by sustainable materials:

- Reduced Ag consumpion e.g. by replacing by Cu (plating)
- In-free SHJ solar cells and Pero-Si tandems

CONFERENCE

TOPIC 1: SILICON MATERIALS AND CELLS

Great advance in understanding of UV induced degradation and Hydrogen related degradation

- Excellent PLENARY by Bram Hoex (presenting for Muhammad Umair Khan), UNSW: 1CP.3.5 *Understanding the Root Cause of UV-Induced Degradation in TOPCon and PERC Solar Cells*

Further high quality orals:

- Christina Hollemann, ISFH: 1AO.4.2 *Mitigating UV-Induced Degradation: Impact of PECVD and PEALD AlOx Layers Deposited in a Tube-Type Direct Plasma-Enhanced Chemical Vapor Deposition System*
- Hugo Lajoie, CEA: 1AO.4.3 *New Insights on UV-Induced Degradation of SHJ Solar Cells*
- Byungsul Min, ISFH: 1BO.3.6 *UV Stable Passivation Stack with Plasma-Enhanced Atomic Layer Deposition of Aluminum Oxide from an Industrial Tube-Type Direct Plasma-Enhanced Chemical Vapor Deposition System*
- Wolfram Kwapil, Fraunhofer ISE: 1AO.5.6 *Impact of Illumination on Solar Cell Properties: Insights into Atomic Hydrogen Release*

CONFERENCE

Advances in TOPCon and SHJ technology → Pushing the Limits of Performance

- Fantastic keynote lecture (PLENARY) on heterojunction solar cells by Dr. Guangtao Yang, Trina: 1CP.1.1 *Silicon Surface and Interface Study for >27% Efficient SHJ Solar Cell*
  - Deep insight into technological aspects eg. influence of rear side polishing on cell performance
  - Very high efficiencies for both-sides contacted HJT > 27%
  - Issues with CAPEX, sustainibility (Ag, In)
  - Pero-Si tandem cells on large area and modules

Late News Presentation on 27.8% efficient back contact silicon solar cells by Hua Wu, Longhi: 1DO.9.1 *Hybrid Interdigitated Back Contact Silicon Solar Cells with Superior Efficiency*

Late News Presentation as TOPCon for Bottom Solar Cells in Pero-Si Tandem devices by Jana Polzin-Isabelle Polzin, Fraunhofer ISE: 1DO.9.3 *Silicon Solar Cells – From High Efficiency Single-junction to Bottom Cells in Two-Terminal Perovskite-Silicon Tandem Devices*

Further high quality orals:

- Hua Wu, Longhi: 1DO.9.1 *Hybrid Interdigitated Back Contact Silicon Solar Cells with Superior Efficiency*
- Daming Chen, Trina: 1AO.5.1 *Large Area i-TOPCon Solar Cells with 25.9% Record Efficiency*
- Maysa Sarsour, UNSW: 1AO.6.1 *Evaluating Silicon Heterojunction Solar Cell Stability under Industrial Illuminated Hydrogenation Conditions*

Bottom cell optimization for Pero-Si tandems

A lot of focus on the long-term stability improvement and upscaling of tandem devices based on a variety of materials (hence not only pero-Si).

Many companies (e.g. Hanwha Q-cells, Oxford PV, Microquanta Seminconductor, Jinko Solar, Longi, etc. non-exhaustive list) presented impressive results on industrial size single-junction pero modules and pero-based tandem modules. A highlight here was the plenary talk from Hanwha Q-cells showing a record large area (M10) pilot-scale Pk/Si tandem cell of 28.6% efficiency.

TOPIC 2:
THIN FILMS
AND NEW
CONCEPTS

In the field of pero-Si tandems, there is clearly more focus on improving the stability of the tandem devices than before with many contributions doing in-depth investigations into the different degradation mechanisms that can occur in pero-Si tandems.

In this respect, 2DO9.5 presented a consensus statement about reliability testing of perovskite-based tandems that is endorsed by specialists worldwide from both industry and research and presents a kind of minimum that should be done in terms of testing and reporting concerning the stability and lifetime of perovskite-based tandem devices.

More and more advanced characterization methods for perovskite and perovskite - silicon tandem solar cells are being used, hyperspectral imaging methods identify non-uniformities by layer for processing development.

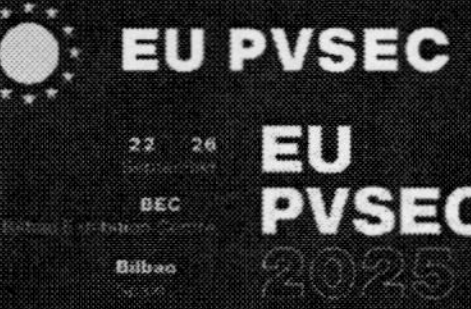

CONFERENCE

Another clear trend is that pero-TOPCon cells are nearing the same record efficiencies as pero-Heterojunction cells. A highlight talk here was the certified 34.22% efficiency perovskite/ topcon tandem solar cell(1cm2) by Jinko Solar 2CO2.1

Another highlight was the 30.5% triple junction pero/pero/silicon cell by EPFL (2CO2.3)

In the field of perovskite single junction devices, 2DO.7.3 showed perovskite devices with remarkable reliability, withstanding 4 years of outdoor exposure. The degradation mechanism is attributed to the diurnal behaviour, also verified and replicated with indoor experiments.

2AO3.6 investigated experimental degradation and recovery of perovskite solar cells, improving the comprehension of instability's dynamics, to extend the lifetime of devices.

In the field of compound semiconductors, there were many presentations on alternative materials for perovskite in tandems. In this way, first monolithic (AgCu)(InGa)Se2 on Si tandem cells were demonstrated as well as 16.1% semitransparent Ag doped Cu(InGa)S2 sulfide top cells.

An exciting highlight in this field was 2BO8.2 in which UPC Barcelona achieved 18% efficiency under indoor lighting for kesterite solar cells with alkali doping

CONFERENCE

TOPIC 3: PHOTOVOLTAIC MODULES

"Reliable packaging to Maximize the energy yield from high efficiency cells"

big theme: Optimizing module materials and packaging for long lifetime and predictable energy yield from high efficiency cells. The industry and research community are moving quickly to assess and improve reliability.

- Understanding, accelerated testing, and mitigating UV-ID in n-type cells and modules
- How do you develop accelerated tests for constantly changing BOMs - new encapsulants, new metallization, thinner glass, and high efficiency cells

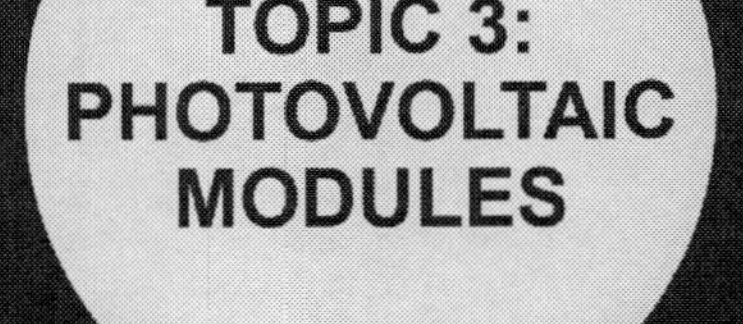

CONFERENCE

TOPIC 3: PHOTOVOLTAIC MODULES

- Degradation and metastability in packaged perovskite tandems - understanding energy yield and realistic degradation rates

- Characterization out of the lab and into the field and factory - accurate outdoor performance, online quality control measurements for encapsulant cross linking

- Reducing silver content and metallization temperatures - reliability of low temperature and low silver metallization

- Developing glass qualification requirements to minimize breakage

CONFERENCE

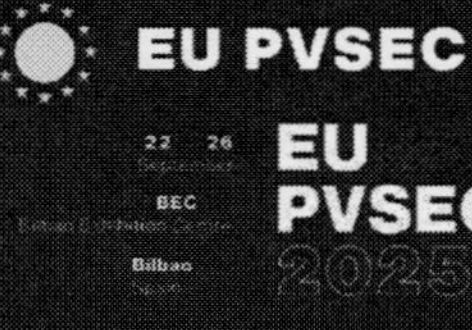

Advances in O&M of PV systems

(4CV.1) focuses on fault detection, cleaning optimization, soiling (and snow 4CO.8), UAV for autonomous monitoring and digital twin.

Data driven and AI based O&M (4CO.9) including a medicine-like workflow in Autonomous multi-AI agent system for health monitoring: a fully automated O&M pipeline with field robotics (4CO.9.4 D. Moser, EURAC)

PV Everywhere from space to agricultural applications like integration in vineyards (Mo, Opening plenary) and many other **integrated options** as we have seen throughout the week. On Thursday (4DO.4) agriPV, noise barriers and floating integrated systems. AgriPV technologies (4DO.2), BIPV

PV needs solar energy. **Solar resource and forecasting** (Mo, 4AO.7-9 & Tu 4BV.3). Shortly IEA PVPS T16 will publish minute irradiance data, some including GT over 220 stations worldwide with. Same format and quality controlled. (*Worldwide solar radiation measurement database with quality-control added value*, Anne Forstinger CSP Services, 4AO.7.1)

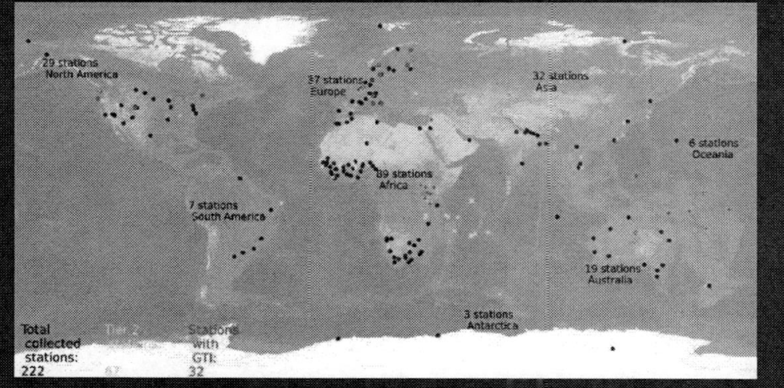

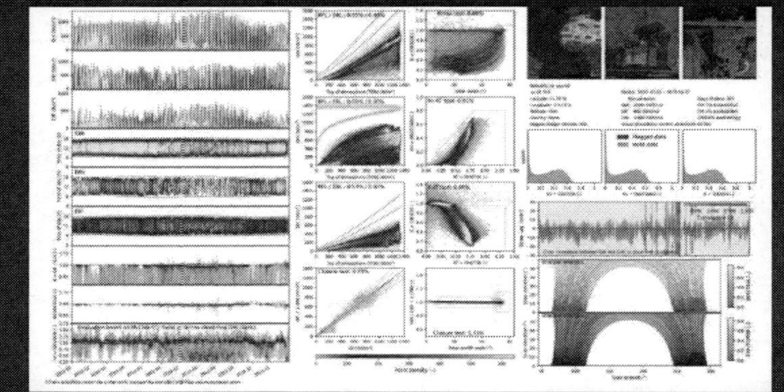

(4BV.3). Poster winner 4BV.3.12 *Advancing Very Short-Term Solar Irradiance Forecasting in Africa: A Low-Cost Sky Imaging and Machine Learning-Based Approach*, implications for PV deployment and grid integration (Martin Ansong, KIT). Runner-up 4BV.3.25 *Evaluating the Suitability of Köppen-Geiger Climate Classifications for Photovoltaic Systems: Micro-climate Analysis and Risk Assessment Maps*, with worldwide distribution of humidity related risk assessment for PV performance (Pavan Kumar Panda, Anhalt University of Applied Sciences).

Integrated PV

BIPV (4BO.16) examples of coloured modules (which was main topic of the poster session along with fire concerns of BIPV, 4BV.4), lightweight solutions (4BO.5) and modelling partial shading effects 4BO.17.1, *Modelling partial shading at the cell level on PV modules,* Jean-Paul Calin, ENSTA) and 4BO.17.3, *Comparing the energy yield and degradation rates of smart PV modules compared to conventional PV system designs in shaded urban scenario's,* Youri Blom, TU DELF.

AgriPV 4DO.2 the room was fully packed showing the interest in the topic. 5 talks were on new ways of sharing light (2 spectral splitting before the PV conversion, 2 semitransparent PV modules both c-Si and CdTe, 1 on downshifting encapsulate) + 1 new AgrivPV like application with Algae instead of crops.

4DO.4 also included AgriPV and **Others types of integration like noise barriers and floating.** In addition to performance other aspects like (*Hydrological and ecological effects on floating PV,* Konstantin Ilgen, FHO ISe) have been highlighted this week

4DO4.2

BOS and tracking systems (4DO.1) focused on backtracking strategies and terrains with complex topography.

4DO.1.4

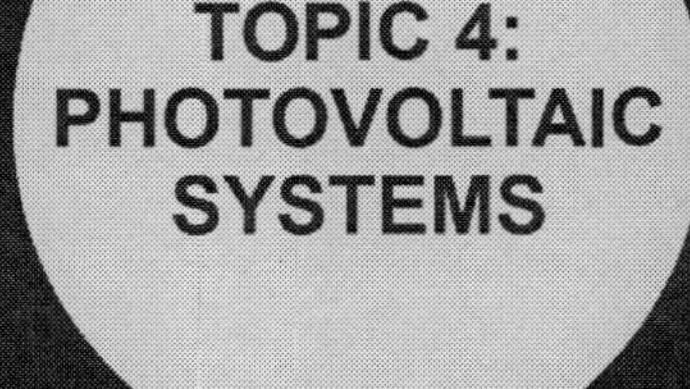

CONFERENCE

Reliability of PV systems

Several presentations focused long-term monitored degradation, failure modes and degradation modes identification techniques (non-destructive, aerial images, AI-based)

4BO.6.1 *Three decades, three climates: insights and lessons on PV reliability.* Good BOM offer very high reliability in power production, with 30-35 years old modules showing 0.24% degradation rate per year.

4BO.6.3 *Non-destructive detection of water ingress in solar modules using NIR spectroscopy* (Oleksandr Mashkow HI ERN) proved near-infrared absorption (NIRA) technique to detect water ingress in modules in the field, which correlated with the module degradation.

4BO.7.2 *Robust PV performance loss rate calculation for high latitudes* (Lauri Karttunen, Meteo Inst Helsinki) and 4BO.7. 3 *Detailed analysis of degradation rates of operating PV assets in tropical climate conditions* (Xioaqi Xu, Seris Singapore) Performance loss rates reported for high latitudes and tropics based on solid data sets. PLR in the tropics -1.4%/year

4DO.3.6 PV system design and assessment highlighted how inverter safety issues are extremely important and how more research about inverter safety and reliability is needed.

CONFERENCE

Main topics of interest :

- Flexibility

- Artificial intelligence

- EoL management

CONFERENCE

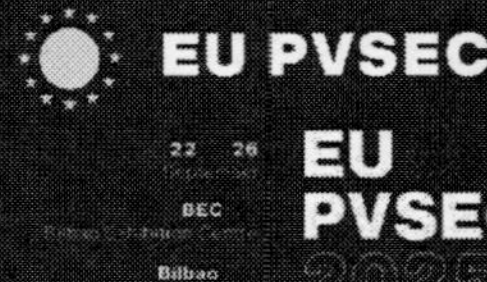

5.1 Grid Integration and Flexibility Enablers (2 sessions)

- Smoothing effect related to different orientations of PV systems in a given area allows 10 to 15% additional hosting capacity of the distribution grid compared to the conservative calculation that consists in summing the AC power. Such accurate calculation enabled by high resolution large area images and LIDAR and induces therefore very low costs.

5.2 Sustainability of PV (4 sessions)

- New inventories LCI and LCA for emerging technologies even though lack of data for perovskites, LCA showing a way for low environmental Impacts with technology improvement and localisation. / Technological improvements will contribute to the reduction of environmental Impact / Grid Efficiency has an Impact on the environmental Footprint.

- Manufacturing optimization / Reuse & recycling: results from the perspective of economic performance – would it convince manufacturer to consider it if economic benefit ?

- EoL Management /recycling -> emerging field attracting lots of activities / mainly EU projects (EVERPV / ICARUS / QASAR) – highlight on polymer, interesting question came up and to be debated for the next decade: is it worth it to consider polymer (EVA/ backsheet) recycling ?

- Major progress in methodology and indicators to assess sustainable design & circularity and improve transparency recyclability index, technical recyclability, digital passport)

CONFERENCE

TOPIC 5: PHOTOVOLTAICS IN THE ENERGY TRANSITION

5.3 Scenarios for Renewables, Policy, Global Challenges (1 session)

- wide scope of contributions on the way to massive, medium- to long-term PV deployment -> should not be taken for granted despite positive projections since there can be limiting factors such as public acceptance / regulatory restrictions and effect of climate change

5.4 Costs, Economics, Finance and Markets (1 session)

- Annual installed capacity over 400 GWp / total cumulative installed capacity worldwide over 2.1 TWp / Clear mismatch between PV module installations rate worldwide and PV module production rate leading to bunch of inventories and drastically reduced prices.

5.6 Societal Challenges; Citizens' Participation, Awareness (1 session)

- data and analysis in gender aspects are emerging in PV! (poster session) + Highlight on innovation in education! On example that targets students & skilled workers -> mobile Lab for advanced experimental training PV-related to bring skills and characterization tools everywhere.

PARALLEL
EVENTS
Collaborat* Network
Diversity
Prejudice
Justificat*
Change
Needs — Profile Match
Avoid Blind Spots
Job Loss?
Integration
Lack of Attractiveness
Resilience (People & Company)
Creativity
Different Communicat*
Internal Friction
More Efforts

- Perovskite Innovation Roundtable: Driving EU Leadership in Perovskite Innovation
- Women in PV presents: Leading with Inclusion – Embracing the 6 Traits of Inclusive Leadership
- Unlocking the Potential of Integrated Photovoltaic Systems - European R&D Approach
- Why Do PV Plants Perform Lower than Expected? (Estimating losses by backtracking algorithms in undulating terrain & Analysis of the loss chain and identification of deviations from initial expectations)
- PV Made in the EU: How Do Companies Die and How Can They Thrive?

22 — 26 September
BEC
Bilbao Exhibition Centre
Bilbao — Spain
EU PVSEC 2025
42nd European Photovoltaic Solar Energy Conference and Exhibition
EXHIBITION FORUM
INDUSTRY SUMMIT
The road to a sustainable future

Industry Summit Opening (session I)

Session Title: Solar PV production in Europe - the way forward

Moderators: Begoña Molinete, Walburga Hemetsberger

Key Takeaway:

This session discussed the state of play of European manufacturing projects and whether there is enough European support. It was clear that political support is further lacking – only 3 Member States have developed schemes to support European manufacturing. While the Net Zero Industry Act is helpful to diversify supplies, it will not particularly support European manufacturing.

All panellists agreed that apart from further policy support (financing, derisking) collaboration is the way forward.

Session II

Session Title: International corporations in the light of changing geopolitics
Moderators: Radovan Kopecek, Puzant Baliozian

Key takeaway:
EU machine builders are still supporting mostly Indian but also US and EU projects with their technology and expertise. The major arguments for choosing EU tech are quality, training, support and low OPEX.

Session III

Session Title: PV Systems: How do we get the produced electricity in Europe into the grid?
Moderators: Catarina Augusto, Peter Fath

Key Takeaway:
Hybrid PV + storage systems (co-located or distributed) are essential for integrating PV into electricity grids. Storage adds flexibility and stabilizes the grid, making it a cornerstone of resilient energy systems; while the technology is mature, scalable and bankable revenue models remain the key gap for widespread deployment.

LIST OF EXHIBITORS
(in alphabetical order)

Company name	Country
2nd Cycle FlexCo	Austria
9-Tech	Italy
Avalon ST / Pasan	Switzerland
BASQUENERGY Cluster	Spain
Becquerel Institute	Belgium
ECOPROGETTI	Italy
EKIENERGY	Spain
ESMC Pavilion	Belgium
Eternal Sun I WAVELABS	The Netherlands
EU PVSEC Startup Pavilion	
European Commission JRC	Italy
exateq	Germany
FLUXiM AG	Switzerland
G2V Optics	Canada
GALEA	Spain
halm elektronik	Germany
HighLine Technology	Germany
IEA PVPS	
Innovations in Optics, Inc.	United States of America
ISC Konstanz	Germany
LAB14	Germany
MBJ Solutions	Germany
Mondragon Assembly	Spain
Nagase Chemtex America	United States of America
NEO Messtechnik Holding	Austria
ODTÜ GÜNAM	Türkiye
Phoenixolar	China
PSE Instruments	Germany
PVsyst	Switzerland
RCT Future	Germany
RCT Solutions	Germany
RENA	Germany
ReNewPV-CA21148 / 5GSOLAR	Estonia
SALD B.V.	The Netherlands

SCIPRIOS	Germany
SEMILAB	Hungary
SINGULUS TECHNOLOGIES	Germany
Sinton Instruments	United States of America
SOLAR MATERIALS	Germany
SolarNL	The Netherlands
Soli Tek R&D	Lithuania
TAMURA ELSOLD	Germany
TECNALIA	Spain
The Netherlands Pavilion	The Netherlands
TNO	The Netherlands
University of the Basque Country	Spain
Vector Energy	Spain
VON ARDENNE	Germany
WCPEC-9	South Korea
WIP Renewable Energies	Germany
ZSW	Germany

We thank the EU PVSEC 2025 Sponsors

Platinum

Gold

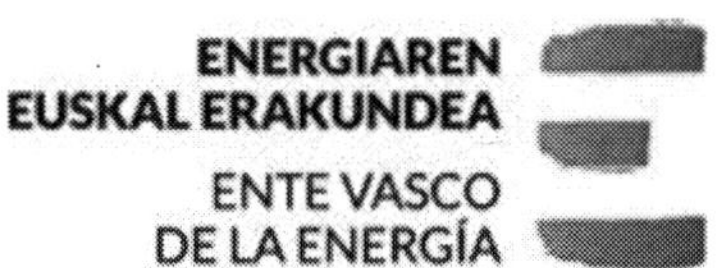

Silver

Bronze

AUTHORS OF EU PVSEC 2025 PROCEEDINGS PAPERS

A. dos Reis Benatto, Gisele
DTU, Roskilde, Denmark
020028, 020037, 020039, 020191, 020265, 020376, 020477

Aaltonen, Lauri
Tampere University, Tampere, Finland
020537

Abad Alcaraz, Verónica
University of Almería, La Cañada de San Urbano, Spain
020336

Abbott, Malcolm D.
PV Lighthouse, Coledale, Australia
020396

Abbotto, Alessandro
University of Milano-Bicocca, Milan, Italy
020077

Abdallah, Amir A.
QEERI, Doha, Qatar
020146, 020166

Abdel Nour, Christine
EDF R&D, Moret Loing Orvanne, France
020188

Abdelrahim, Mohamed
QEERI, Doha, Qatar
020166

Abdou-Tankari, Mahamadou
Paris-East Créteil University, Créteil, France
020562

Abrego, Gillen
ALLOTARRA, Allo, Spain
020392

Acciarri, Maurizio
University of Milano-Bicocca, Milan, Italy
020087

Acevedo Devoto, M. Ignacia
ISC Konstanz, Konstanz, Germany
020220

Achenbach, Jannik
University of Applied Science Cologne, Cologne, Germany
020522

Acinas, Victor
Applied Materials, Dublin, Ireland
020019

Adachi, Satoru
NIED, Shinjo, Japan
020436

Aden, Samira
HZB, Berlin, Germany
020513

Adinolfi Borea, Riccardo
University of Bologna, Bologna, Italy
020314

Adnan Hameed, Mohammed
Martin-Luther-University Halle-Wittenberg, Halle, Germany
020156

Adothu, Baloji
DEWA, Dubai, United Arab Emirates
020229

Aghaei, Mohammadreza
NTNU, Aalesund, Norway
020335, 020356

Aghaei, Mohammadreza
NTNU, Ålesund, Norway
020374, 020375

Aghamohammadi, Amirhossain   020356
Amirkabir University of Technology, Tehran, Iran

Aguirre, Aranzazu   020064
Hasselt Unversity, Genk, Belgium

Ahmadi, Mehdi   020066
CNR-IMM, Catania, Italy

Aiello, Andrea   020255
ACCA Software, Cosenza, Italy

Aimé, Jérémie   020217, 020311
CEA / INES, Le Bourget-du-Lac, France

Aissa, Brahim   020042, 020075, 020108, 020109, 020146,
QEERI, Doha, Qatar   020147

Aizpurua, Jon   020139
Tecnalia, Donostia - San Sebastián, Spain

Akbayrak, Serdar   020020
Necmettin Erbakan University, Konya, Türkiye

Akram, M. Waqar   020164
Hohai University, Changzhou, China

Al Katrib, Mirella   020116
IPVF, Palaiseau, France

Alam, Habeel   020394
Lancaster University, Lancaster, United Kingdom

Alberts, Vivian   020229
DEWA, Dubai, United Arab Emirates

Albuquerque, Daniel P.   020464
Centre for New Energy Technologies, Sacavém, Portugal

Alet, Pierre-Jean   020238, 020544
CSEM, Neuchâtel, Switzerland

Alexandris, Nikos   020210
European Commission JRC, Ispra, Italy

Alfieri, Felice   020497
Viegand Maagøe, Copenhagen, Denmark

Ali, Adnan   020147
QEERI, Doha, Qatar

Allen, Vince   020048
SunDrive Solar, Kurnell, Australia

Alloji, Esma   020020
Necmettin Erbakan University, Konya, Türkiye

Almeida Silva, José   020565
University of Évora, Évora, Portugal

Almuneau, Guilhem   020074
LAAS-CNRS, Toulouse, France

Alonso, Ricardo   020197, 020198, 020353, 020358
TECNALIA, Derio, Spain

Alonso-Montesinos, Joaquín   020100
University of Almeria, Almeria, Spain

Alonso-Montesinos, Joaquín   020336
University of Almería, La Cañada de San Urbano, Spain

Álvarez Hervás, José Domingo   020336
University of Almería, La Cañada de San Urbano, Spain

Alvarez, José   020040, 020058
CNRS, Gif-sur-Yvette, France

Álvarez, Marta   020300
CENER, Sarriguren, Spain

Álvarez-Pérez, Guillem   020062
IPVF, Palaiseau, France

Alvaro Høye, Ingar   020443
Solkraft Sør, Øyslebø, Norway

Alves e Silva, Kiane   020439, 020535, 020567, 020575
UPM, Madrid, Spain

Amaro e Silva, Rodrigo   020490
University of Lisbon, Lisbon, Portugal

Amatriain, Irati   020392
CENER, Sarriguren, Spain

Anamiati, Gaetana   020448, 020481
GreenPowerMonitor a DNV company, Barcelona, Spain

Anaya, Julian   020191, 020205
University of Valladolid, Valladolid, Spain

Ancillao, Andrea   020079
Polytechnic University of Turin, Turin, Italy

Anderlini, Alessandro   020155
Coveme, Gorizia, Italy

Andersen, Nanna L.   020250
DTU, Roskilde, Denmark

Andersen, Nanna Lysgaard   020306
DTU, Roskilde, Denmark

Andrade-Arvizu, Jacob   020094
IREC, Barcelona, Spain

Andreozzi, Federico   020494
University of Rome Tor Vergata, Rome, Italy

Anefnaf, Ikram   020093
University of Verona, Verona, Italy

Ansong, Martin   020272
KIT, Eggenstein-Leopoldshafen, Germany

Antognini, Luca   020196
PVsyst, Geneva, Switzerland

Antoine, C.   020508
IMDEA Nanoscience Institute, Madrid, Spain

Antón, Ignacio   020209, 020246, 020257, 020453, 020459
UPM, Madrid, Spain

Antonucci, Daniele   020551
Eurac Research, Bolzano, Italy

Apostoleris, Harry   020487
EPRI, Dubai, United Arab Emirates

Arakawa, Hayato   020436
NIED, Shinjo, Japan

Aranguren, Gerardo   020289, 020353
UPV/EHU, Bilbao, Spain

Arbaretaz, Sebastien   020317
CEA INES, Le Bourget-du-Lac, France

Ardissone, Bastien J. J.   020396
PV Lighthouse, Coledale, Australia

Arduino, Daniele   020079
Polytechnic University of Turin, Turin, Italy

Ariolli, Daniela Maria Godinho   020325
BayWa r.e, Rome, Italy

Ariza Camacho, Maria Jesus   020100
University of Almeria, Almería, Spain

Armstrong, Alona   020394
Lancaster University, Lancaster, United Kingdom

Arribat, Mathieu   020074
LAAS-CNRS, Toulouse, France

Arrizabalaga, Igor   020139
Tecnalia, Donostia - San Sebastián, Spain

Artegiani, Elisa   020057, 020089, 020093
University of Verona, Verona, Italy

Arumughan, Jayaprasad   020569
ISC Konstanz, Konstanz, Germany

Asaa, Shu-Ngwa   020393
imo-imomec, Genk, Belgium

Ascencio-Vásquez, Julián   020371
Univers, Courbevoie, France

Askins, Steve   020209, 020257
UPM, Madrid, Spain

Assaid, El Mahdi   020171
University of Chouaib Doukkali, El Jadida, Morocco

Aste, Niccolò   020249
Polytechnic University of Milan, Milan, Italy

Astigarraga, Alexander   020226
Eurac Research, Bolzano, Italy

Athienitis, Andreas   020248
Concordia University, Montreal, Canada

Aurrekoetxea, Olaia   020302
TECNALIA, Saint Sebastian, Spain

Awadallah, Carlos   020536
Wattkraft, Madrid, Spain

Azkona, Nekane   020055, 020097, 020153, 020287
UPV/EHU, Bilbao, Spain

Azzopardi, Brian   020318, 020334, 020520
FIR, Birkirkara, Malta

Azzopardi, Carmel   020334
FIR, Birkirkara, Malta

Babich, Francesco   020551
Eurac Research, Bolzano, Italy

Babics, Maxime   020217
CEA / INES, Le Bourget-du-Lac, France

Babin, Markus   020249, 020250, 020306, 020477
DTU, Roskilde, Denmark

Bachour, Dunia A.   020275, 020278
QEERI, Doha, Qatar

Bachour, Dunia   020291
QEERI, Doha, Qatar

Baderiya, Naman   020390
MARIN, Wageningen, The Netherlands

Badosa Franch, Jordi   020214
Polytechnic Institute of Paris, Palaiseau, France

Baeck, Pieter-Jan   020511
Flemish Institute for Technological Research (VITO), Genk,
Belgium

Bai, Jianbo   020164
Hohai University, Changzhou, China

Bailache, Simon   020303
CSTB, Marne-la-Vallée, France

Bakhtiari, Afshin   020121
AESOLAR, Koenigsbrunn, Germany

Balafoutis, Athanasios T.   020464
CERTH, Athens, Greece

Bald, Juan   020514
AZTI, PASAIA, Spain

Baldacchino, Alex J.   020065
UNSW, Sydney, Australia

Baležentienė, Skirmantė   020380
The Applied Research Institute for Prospective
Technologies, Vilnius, Lithuania

Baležentis, Algirdas   020380
The Applied Research Institute for Prospective
Technologies, Vilnius, Lithuania

Ballif, Christophe   020467
CSEM, Neuchâtel, Switzerland

Ballif, Christophe   020251
EPFL, Neuchâtel, Switzerland

Bandaru, Narendra   020039, 020043, 020104
Aarhus University, Aarhus, Denmark

Bang, Ole	020043
Technical University of Denmark, Copenhagen, Denmark

Barakel, Damien	020188
Toulon University, Marseille, France

Baraket, Mira	020039
ATLANT 3D, Taastrup, Denmark

Baranek, Philippe	020060
EDF R&D, Palaiseau, France

Barchi, Grazia	020485, 020489, 020544
Eurac Research, Bolzano, Italy

Bardizza, Giorgio	020181
TÜV Rheinland Italia, Milan, Italy

Bardizza, Giorgio	020208
TÜV Rheinland Solar, Cologne, Germany

Bardizza, Giorgio	020144
TÜV Rheinland, Cologne, Germany

Barguès, Anna	020505
Becquerel Institute France, Lyon, France

Barguès, Anna	020558
Becquerel Institute, Brussels, Belgium

Barnscheidt, Verena	020063, 020114
ISFH, Emmerthal, Germany

Barretta, Chiara	020325
PCCL, Leoben, Austria

Barrionuevo, Bruno	020464
CERTH, Athens, Greece

Barroso, João	020565
University of Évora, Évora, Portugal

Barrou, Alexis	020467
CSEM, Neuchâtel, Switzerland

Barrutia, Laura	020446, 020536
UPM, Madrid, Spain

Barth, Vincent	020134
CEA / INES, Le Bourget-du-Lac, France

Barth, Vincent	020019
CEA, Le Bourget-du-Lac, France

Barth, Vincent	020226
CEA/ INES, Le Bourget-du-Lac, France

Bartholomäus, Martin	020346
DTU, Roskilde, Denmark

Bartolo, Brian	020334
FIR, Birkirkara, Malta

Basta, Beata	020068
Roltec, Poznań, Poland

Basta, Marek	020068
Roltec, Poznań, Poland

Battisti, Kurt   020255
A-Null Development, Vienna, Austria

Bauhuis, Gerard   020067
Radboud University, Nijmegen, The Netherlands

Baumann, Kerstin   020470
bifa Umweltinstitut, Augsburg, Germany

Baumann, Sara   020063
ISFH, Emmerthal, Germany

Baumann, Ulrike   020006
ISFH, Emmerthal, Germany

Baur, Carsten   020246
European Space Agency, Noordwijk, The Netherlands

Beaucarne, Guy   020384
Dow Silicones Belgium, Seneffe, Belgium

Becker, Carl   020331
DLR, Almería, Spain

Behrensdorff Poulsen, Peter   020037
DTU, Lyngby, Denmark

Beinert, Andreas J.   020123
Fraunhofer ISE, Freiburg, Germany

Bejat, Timea   020225, 020500
CEA, Le Bourget-du-Lac, France

Belawadi, Aditya Girish   020231
Fraunhofer ISE, Freiburg, Germany

Belferkous, Brahim Anis   020325
PCCL, Leoben, Austria

Bellmann, Martin   020495, 020510
SINTEF, Trondheim, Norway

Bellvert, Eduard   020139
Tecnalia, Donostia - San Sebastián, Spain

Beltran-Condori, Sonia   020129, 020417
University of Antofagasta, Antofagasta, Chile

Belzunce, María Jesús   020514
AZTI, PASAIA, Spain

Bendix, Peter   020388
Next2Sun Technology, Dillingen, Germany

Bengoechea, Jaione   020181, 020300
CENER, Sarriguren, Spain

Bermudez Benito, Veronica   020146
QEERI, Doha, Qatar

Bermudez-Garcia, Anderson   020246
Thales Alenia Space, Cannes, France

Berrian, Djaber   020492
Belectric, Kolitzheim, Germany

Berson, Solenn   020134
CEA / INES, Le Bourget-du-Lac, France

Besson, Pierre   020373
INES, Le Bourget-du-Lac, France

Betak, Juraj   020241
Solargis, Bratislava, Slovakia

Bettucci, Ottavia   020077
University of Milano-Bicocca, Milan, Italy

Bhardwaj, Shashank   020515
TU Delft, Delft, The Netherlands

Bhatnagar, Shrey   020367
Nextracker, Fremont, United States of America

Biard, Yves   020303
SemperStyl, Eragny, France

Bieber, Lisa-Marie   020195
Fraunhofer ISE, Freiburg, Germany

Bilitu, Eddie   020393
Hasselt University, Hasselt, Belgium

Binani, Ashish   020225
TNO, Petten, The Netherlands

Binetti, Simona   020093
University of Milano Bicocca, Milan, Italy

Binetti, Simona   020087
University of Milano-Bicocca, Milan, Italy

Blakesley, James   020293
National Physical Laboratory, Teddington, United Kingdom

Blanc, Philippe   020291
MINES Paris, Nice, France

Blanco Aguiar, Adrián   020243
ieco.io, Vigo, Spain

Blieske, Ulf   020141
University of Applied Science Cologne, Cologne, Germany

Blieske, Ulf   020140
University of Applied Sciences Cologne, Cologne, Germany

Blstak Catlosova, Katarina   020274
Solargis, Bratislava, Slovakia

Blum, Niklas   020235, 020237, 020239
DLR, Almería, Spain

Boccardi, Roberto   020039
DTU, Copenhagen, Denmark

Boccardi, Roberto   020037
DTU, Lyngby, Denmark

Boccardi, Roberto   020028
DTU, Roskilde, Denmark

Boddaert, Simon   020302, 020303
CSTB, Marne-la-Vallée, France

Bokalič, Matevž   020047, 020319
University of Ljubljana, Ljubljana, Slovenia

Bolink, Henk J.   020226
University of Valencia, Paterna, Spain

Bonal, Victor   020085
UAM, Madrid, Spain

Bonnet, Martin   020141
University of Applied Science Cologne, Cologne, Germany

Bonnet-Eymard, Bénédicte   020251
CSEM, Neuchâtel, Switzerland

Borgers, Tom   020225
IMEC, Genk, Belgium

Borgna, Luciano   020369
BFH, Burgdorf, Switzerland

Borie, Benjamin   020039
ATLANT 3D, Taastrup, Denmark

Borowski, Peter   020307
Avancis, Munich, Germany

Borriello, Aniello   020378
ENEA, Portici, Italy

Borzi, Giovanni   020019
Enginsoft, Padua, Italy

Bosch, Elina   020252, 020543, 020564, 020573
Becquerel Institute, Brussels, Belgium

Bosma, Theo   020571
DNV, Arnhem, The Netherlands

Bothe, Karsten   020236
ISFH, Emmerthal, Germany

Bou-Nassif, Liliane   020338
CETHIL, Villeurbanne, France

Bouchier, Daniel   020058
CNRS, Palaiseau, France

Bouguerra, Sara   020156, 020294, 020389, 020393
imec, Genk, Belgium

Bourdin, Vincent   020406
CNRS, Paris, France

Bourgeois, Antoine   020102
SERIS, Singapore, Singapore

Bovesecchi, Gianluigi   020494
University of Rome Tor Vergata, Rome, Italy

Brabec, Christoph J.   020117
HI ERN, Erlangen, Germany

Bradford, David Roy   020077
Newcastle University, Newcastle upon Tyne, United
Kingdom

Brailovsky, Peter Henri   020475
Fraunhofer ISE, Freiburg, Germany

Braña, Alejandro F.   020508
Autonomous University of Madrid, Madrid, Spain

Brandstätter, Andreas 020227
Lenzing Plastics, Lenzing, Austria

Braun, Christian 020457
Luxembourg Institute of Science and Technology, Esch-sur-
Alzette, Luxembourg

Brecl, Kristijan 020269, 020319
University of Ljubljana, Ljubljana, Slovenia

Bredemeier, Dennis 020240
Leibniz University Hannover, Hannover, Germany

Breitenbücher, Marian 020225
Highline Technologies, Freiburg, Germany

Brendel, Rolf 020006, 020008, 020236, 020240, 020260,
ISFH, Emmerthal, Germany 020482

Brendstrup Møller, Clara Bolette 020028
DTU, Roskilde, Denmark

Bretzel, Tamara 020195
Fraunhofer ISE, Freiburg, Germany

Breyer, Christian 020479
LUT University, Lappeenranta, Finland

Brito, Miguel 020457
University of Lisbon, Lisbon, Portugal

Brivio, Elisabetta 020462
RSE, Milan, Italy

Brockmann, Lukas 020063
ISFH, Emmerthal, Germany

Brodnicke, Linda 020296
ETH, Zurich, Switzerland

Brueckner, Emanuel 020063
ISFH, Emmerthal, Germany

Bründlinger, Roland 020369
AIT, Vienna, Austria

Brun, Gonzalo 020414, 020517
ENDEF, Zaragoza, Spain

Bruno, Maddalena 020452
Fraunhofer ISE, Freiburg, Germany

Buceta, Alicia 020300
CENER, Sarriguren, Spain

Bucher, Christof 020179, 020322, 020359, 020369, 020386
BFH, Burgdorf, Switzerland

Buchholz, Florian 020035, 020225, 020569
ISC Konstanz, Konstanz, Germany

Buchmann, Johanna 020309
Berlin University of Applied Sciences, Berlin, Germany

Buck, Thomas 020033
ISC Konstanz, Konstanz, Germany

Buckland, Daniel   020119, 020218
Henkel, Düsseldorf, Germany

Buddana, Viswa Harinath   020482
DLR, Oldenburg, Germany

Bühlmann, Gian-Luca   020385
ZHAW, Winterthur, Switzerland

Buerhop, Claudia   020149, 020150, 020377
HI ERN, Erlangen, Germany

Buerhop-Lutz, Claudia   020185, 020230
HI ERN, Erlangen, Germany

Burgers, Antonius R.   020405
TNO, Petten, The Netherlands

Burri, Matthias   020179
BFH, Burgdorf, Switzerland

Busto, Chiara   020521
Eni, Novara, Italy

Butrichi, Fabio   020087
University of Milano-Bicocca, Milan, Italy

Butt, Nauman   020394
Lahore University of Management Sciences, Lahore,
Pakistan

C. Tavares, Fabiele   020090
Federal University of Rio de Janeiro, Duque de Caxias,
Brazil

Cabal, Raphael   020034
University Grenoble Alpes, Le Bourget-du-Lac, France

Caballero, Luis Jaime   020501, 020508
UPM, Madrid, Spain

Caballero, Raquel   020094
CSIC, Madrid, Spain

Caballero, Raquel   020085
IO-CSIC, Madrid, Spain

Cabecinha, Vasco   020565
Nova University Lisbon, Lisbon, Portugal

Cabello, Fatima   020085
IO-CSIC, Madrid, Spain

Caçapietra Pires da Silva, Lucas Teixeira   020025
PUCRS, Porto Alegre, Brazil

Caccavelli, Dominique   020551
CSTB, Bussy-Saint Georges, France

Caccivio, Mauro   020204, 020574
SUPSI, Mendrisio, Switzerland

Caffari, Francesca   020551
ENEA, Ispra, Italy

Calabrese, Nicolandrea   020551
ENEA, Ispra, Italy

Calin, Jean-Paul   020251
ENSTA Paris, Palaiseau, France

Çalışkan Arslan, Meriç   020006, 020135
Kalyon PV, Ankara, Türkiye

Caluori, Philip   020455
Virtual Vehicle, Graz, Austria

Camara, Assa   020274
Solargis, Bratislava, Slovakia

Cambarau, Werther   020139
Tecnalia, Donostia-San Sebastián, Spain

Campana, Pietro Elia   020381
Mälardalen University, Västerås, Sweden

Campos Guzman, Laura   020331
DLR, Almería, Spain

Cancro, Carmine   020378
ENEA, Naples, Italy

Canesse, Auriane   020196
PVsyst, Geneva, Switzerland

Cañizo, Carlos   020097
IES-UPM, Madrid, Spain

Cano, Francisco J.   020139
Tecnalia, Donostia - San Sebastián, Spain

Cano, Lucía   020127
ENDEF, Zaragoza, Spain

Cánovas, Enrique   020508
IMDEA Nanoscience Institute, Madrid, Spain

Cao, Han   020263
SERIS, Singapore, Singapore

Capitaine, Anna   020116
IPVF, Palaiseau, France

Cappelle, Jan   020329, 020351
KU Leuven, Ghent, Belgium

Capron, Guillaume   020217
CEA / INES, Le Bourget-du-Lac, France

Carballo López, José Antonio   020336
University of Almería, La Cañada de San Urbano, Spain

Cardenas, Luis Alejandro   020339, 020546
National University of Colombia, Bogotá, Colombia

Carmo, Paulo   020304, 020420
University of Évora, Évora, Portugal

Carrasco, Luis Miguel   020439, 020535, 020567
UPM, Madrid, Spain

Carrillo Mejía, Luis   020279
District University of Bogotá, Bogotá, Colombia

Carrillo, Rafael E.   020238
CSEM, Neuchâtel, Switzerland

Carroy, Perrine   020226
CEA/ INES, Le Bourget-du-Lac, France

Carstens, Justus   020003
ISC Konstanz, Konstanz, Germany

Cartenì, Fabrizio   020378
University of Naples Federico II, Naples, Italy

Casappa, Michele   020087
National Research Council, Parma, Italy

Casasola Paesa, Marta   020389
Hasselt University, Diepenbeek, Belgium

Castilla Nieto, María del Mar   020336
University of Almería, La Cañada de San Urbano, Spain

Castillo Patton, Daniel Jason   020326
Enertis Applus+, Madrid, Spain

Castro, Luis Guilherme   020530
Casa dos Ventos, Fortaleza, Brazil

Castro, Rui   020464
University of Lisbon, Lisbon, Portugal

Castro-Gallardo, Fernando   020417, 020422
University of Antofagasta, Antofagasta, Chile

Cavaco, Afonso   020304, 020565
University of Évora, Évora, Portugal

Cebecauer, Tomas   020274
Solargis, Bratislava, Slovakia

Çekerek, Gamze   020006
Kalyon PV, Ankara, Türkiye

Celik, Duygu   020551
WIP Renewable Energies, Munich, Germany

Çeliktaş, Melih Soner   020559
Ege University, İzmir, Türkiye

Centazzo, Massimo   020006
EnPV, Karlsruhe, Germany

Centeno Brito, Miguel   020421, 020490
University of Lisbon, Lisbon, Portugal

Cereceda, Eneko   020055, 020097, 020153, 020287
UPV/EHU, Bilbao, Spain

Ceretti, Mattia   020204
SUPSI, Mendrisio, Switzerland

Cesar, I.   020405
TNO, Petten, The Netherlands

Ceuppens, Ignas   020302
BUILD`UP, Aarschot, Belgium

Chatterji, Nithin   020071
SVNIT, Surat, India

Chen, Daniel   020048
SunDrive Solar, Kurnell, Australia

Chen, Syh-Homg 020161
ITRI, Hsinchu, Taiwan

Chen, Xiang 020111
Hohai University, Changzhou, China

Cheung, Kak Pong 020313
Kiel University of Applied Sciences, Kiel, Germany

Chhapia, Gaurang 020492
Belectric, Kolitzheim, Germany

Chiba, Takahiro 020436
Hokkaido University of Science, Sapporo, Japan

Chichignoud, Guy 020495
13Institut Polytechnique De Grenoble, Grenoble, France

Chicote, Beatriz 020289
Mondragon University, Arrasate-Mondragon, Spain

Chiesa, Matteo 020487
Khalifa University, Abu Dhabi, United Arab Emirates

Chini de Freitas, Felipe 020023
PUCRS, Porto Alegre, Brazil

Cho, Yunae 020045
KIER, Daejeon, South Korea

Choi, Kwan Bum 020102
SERIS, Singapore, Singapore

Chouder, Aissa 020301
University of M'sila, M'sila, Algeria

Chowdhury, Gofran 020276, 020544
3E, Brussels, Belgium

Christ, Anja 020063
ISFH, Emmerthal, Germany

Chrkavy, Daniel 020262
Solargis, Bratislava, Slovakia

Chueh, Wei-Lo 020021
TSEC, Hsinchu, Taiwan

Ciesla, Alison 020065
UNSW, Sydney, Australia

Cirimele, Vincenzo 020314
University of Bologna, Bologna, Italy

Clausing, Roland 020063, 020114
ISFH, Emmerthal, Germany

Clochard, Laurent 020031
Nines Photovoltaics, Dublin, Germany

Clochard, Laurent 020007
Nines Photovoltaics, Dublin, Ireland

Clyncke, Jan 020472, 020513
PV CYCLE, Brussels, Belgium

Coşkun, Özlem 020006, 020027, 020225
Kalyon PV, Ankara, Türkiye

Colberts, Fallon   020389
Zuyd University, Heerlen, The Netherlands

Colin, Hervé   020217, 020262
CEA / INES, Le Bourget-du-Lac, France

Collin, Stéphane   020074
C2N, Palaiseau, France

Colwell, Jack   020048
SunDrive Solar, Kurnell, Australia

Comak, Mertcan   020003
ISC Konstanz, Konstanz, Germany

Connolly, James Patrick   020058, 020060
CNRS, Gif-sur-Yvette, France

Cordeiro, Diogo   020464
EDP, Lisbon, Portugal

Cornago, Iñaki   020392
CENER, Sarriguren, Spain

Cornaro, Cristina   020494
University of Rome Tor Vergata, Rome, Italy

Correa, Guillermo   020412
Gonvarri MS R&D, Corvera - Asturias, Spain

Correia, Joana   020565
University of Évora, Évora, Portugal

Couderc, Romain   020217, 020311, 020546
CEA / INES, Le Bourget-du-Lac, France

Coutel, John   020244
SOLAÏS, Valbonne, France

Cowan, Don   020230
Kiwa PI Berlin, Hudson, United States of America

Cox, Joel D.   020250
SDU Climate Cluster, Odense, Denmark

Cox, Joel D   020306
SDU Climate Cluster, Odense, Denmark

Coz, Pier Luigi   020246
European Space Agency, Noordwijk, The Netherlands

Crespo, Carolina   020490
University of Lisbon, Lisbon, Portugal

Cristiane Pan, Aline   020548
UFRGS, Tramandaí, Brazil

Cristóbal, Ana Belén   020491, 020535, 020575
UPM, Madrid, Spain

Crozier McCleland, Jacqueline   020185, 020344
Nelson Mandela University, Port Elizabeth, South Africa

Cuadra, Juan Manuel   020318
CENER, Sarigurren, Spain

Cui, Jindan   020320, 020525
Tokyo University of Science, Tokyo, Japan

Culot, Dominique							020384
Dow Silicones Belgium, Seneffe, Belgium

Curon, Jonathan							020384
Dow Silicones Belgium, Seneffe, Belgium

Cusenza, Maria Anna						020466
RSE, Milan, Italy

D. Pinto, Luciana						020090
Federal University of Rio de Janeiro, Rio de Janeiro, Brazil

Daenen, Michael						020156, 020389, 020393
imec, Genk, Belgium

Dagla, Anastasia						020276
3E, Brussels, Belgium

Dahle, Arne							020225, 020495
Norsun, Oslo, Norway

Dahlioui, Dounia						020443
University of Agder, Grimstad, Norway

Dalibor, Thomas						020307
Avancis, Munich, Germany

Dalla Maria, Enrico						020485
Eurac Research, Bolzano, Italy

Dalla Torre, Francesco						020010
Applied Materials, Treviso, Italy

Dalmazzone, Didier						020251
ENSTA Paris, Palaiseau, France

Damon, Keanu							020382
7SecondSolar, Cape Town, South Africa

Danelli, Andrea						020462, 020466
RSE, Milan, Italy

Darsene Dimd, Berhane						020270
SINTEF, Trondheim, Norway

Das, Gourab							020005, 020222, 020463
RCT Solutions, Konstanz, Germany

Dasilva-Villanueva, Nerea					020014, 020501, 020508
UPM, Madrid, Spain

Daßler, David							020313
Fraunhofer CSP, Halle, Germany

Daßler, David							020355
Fraunhofer IMWS, Halle, Germany

Daume, Darwin							020361
pvnode, Rosenheim, Germany

Davidsen, Rasmus Schmidt					020028, 020039, 020043
Aarhus University, Aarhus, Denmark

De Almeida, Laura						020074
LAAS-CNRS, Toulouse, France

De Biasio, Martin   020504
Silicon Austria Labs, Villach, Austria

De Blasi, Mariam   020378
Enel Green Power, Pisa, Italy

de Graaf, Gertjan J.   020405
TNO, Petten, The Netherlands

de Groot, Koen M.   020405
TNO, Petten, The Netherlands

De Gruijter, Alvaro   020254
Eurac Research, Bolzano, Italy

de Jong, Minne M.   020169, 020425
TNO, Eindhoven, The Netherlands

De Jong, Richard   020156, 020294, 020389
imec, Genk, Belgium

de l'Epine, Mélodie   020252, 020505, 020543, 020564
Becquerel Institute France, Lyon, France

de l'Epine, Melodie   020225, 020334, 020520, 020558
Becquerel Institute, Brussels, Belgium

de l'Epine, Melodie   020570
IEA PVPS Task 1, Lyon, France

de la Casa Higueras, Juan   020269
University of Jaén, Jaén, Spain

de la Viuda, Eva   020205
University of Valladolid, Valladolid, Spain

de Meatza, Iratxe   020495
CIDETEC, San Sebastián, Spain

De Rose, Angela   020123
Fraunhofer ISE, Freiburg, Germany

De Rose, Jonas   020010
Fraunhofer ISE, Freiburg, Germany

Debastiani Benato, Betina   020019
AMIRES, Prague, Czech Republic

Deepti,   020563
SRM University, Sonipat, India

Del Campo, Valeria   020311
Federico Santa María Technical University, Valparaiso,
Chile

del Cañizo, Carlos   020014, 020501, 020507, 020508
UPM, Madrid, Spain

Del Pero, Claudio   020249
Polytechnic University of Milan, Milan, Italy

Del Pozo, Alberto   020197, 020198
TECNALIA, Derio, Spain

del Prado Santamaria, Rodrigo   020191, 020376
DTU, Roskilde, Denmark

del Ser, Javier   020358
UPV/EHU, Bilbao, Spain

Delgado-Sanchez, Jose Maria   020089
University of Seville, Seville, Spain

Delli Veneri, Paola   020378
ENEA, Naples, Italy

Denafas, Julius   020225, 020353
Solitek, Vilnius, Lithuania

Deniz, Engin   020559
Ege University, İzmir, Türkiye

Denke, Sebastian   020236
ISFH, Emmerthal, Germany

Dentz, Laurie   020058
CNRS, Palaiseau, France

Derin Gure, Pinar   020513, 020521, 020556
ODTU GUNAM, Ankara, Türkiye

Derj, Anyssa   020116
IPVF, Palaiseau, France

Dessì, Alessio   020077
CNR-ICCOM, Sesto Fiorentino, Italy

Devenson, Jan   020157
Center for Physical Sciences and Technology (FTMC),
Vilnius, Lithuania

Dhimish, Mahmoud   020346, 020376
DTU, Roskilde, Denmark

Di Matteo, Alfredo   020010
Enel Green Power, Catania, Italy

Diab, Mohanad   020203
Eurac Research, Bolzano, Italy

Diano, Marcello   020378
M2M Engineering, Naples, Italy

Diaz, Roberto   020300
Notio Association, Toledo, Spain

Díaz, Sara   020365, 020366
CENER, Sarriguren, Spain

Dietrich, Andreas   020355
DiSUN Deutsche Solarservice, Werder, Germany

Díez Alcántara, Eduardo   020501
UCM, Madrid, Spain

Díez, Eduardo   020508
UCM, Madrid, Spain

Dimd, Berhane Darsene   020495, 020510
SINTEF, Trondheim, Norway

Ding, Kaining   020233
FZJ, Jülich, Germany

Ding, Kung   020111
Hohai University, Changzhou, China

Dittmann, Sebastian   020318
Anhalt University of Applied Sciences, Köthen, Germany

Dittrich, Arne
ISFH, Emmerthal, Germany

020240

Dizier, Antoine
INES, Le Bourget-du-Lac, France

020373

Djeukeu, Ivanol Jaurece
halm elektronik, Frankfurt am Main, Germany

020050

Dobreva, Petja
University of Namibia, Windhoek, Namibia

020193

Dörenkämper, Maarten
TNO, Eindhoven, The Netherlands

020169

Dörn, Markus
A-Null Development, Vienna, Austria

020255

Doi, Minh Thong
CEA INES, Le Bourget-du-Lac, France

020317

Domínguez, César
UPM, Madrid, Spain

020209, 020246, 020257

Donadello, Alessandro
Edyna, Bolzano, Italy

020485, 020489

Donėlienė, Jolanta
Applied Research Institute for Prospective Technologies,
Vilnius, Lithuania

020157

Donoso, José
UNEF, Madrid, Spain

020570

Doppler, Christian
Virtual Vehicle, Graz, Austria

020455

dos Reis, Givaldo
University of São Paulo, São Paulo, Brazil

020348

dos Santos, Jeremias
University of Évora, Évora, Portugal

020409

Doucet, Jean-Baptiste
LAAS-CNRS, Toulouse, France

020074

Dovesi, Roberto
Academy of Sciences of Turin, Torino, Italy

020060

Driesse, Anton
PV Performance Labs, Freiburg, Germany

020211, 020293, 020452

Duarte, Dorivaldo
University of Evora, Évora, Portugal

020418, 020565

Dubois, Sebastien
University Grenoble Alpes, Le Bourget-du-Lac, France

020034

Dubravskij, Piotr
Applied Research Institute for Prospective Technologies,
Vilnius, Lithuania

020157

Dubravskij, Piotr
Modern E-Technologies, Vilnius, Lithuania

020380

Duerinckx, Filip
Hasselt Unversity, Genk, Belgium

020064, 020225

Düz, Cansel
Kalyon PV, Ankara, Türkiye
020135

Dullweber, Thorsten
ISFH, Emmerthal, Germany
020006, 020007, 020008, 020225

Dunlop, Ewan D.
European Commission JRC, Ispra, Italy
020173, 020210, 020213

Dupon, Olivier
imec, Genk, Belgium
020294

Dupuis, Julien
EDF R&D, Moret Loing Orvanne, France
020188

Dutykh, Denys
Khalifa University, Abu Dhabi, United Arab Emirates
020338

Duzellier, Sophie
University of Toulouse, Toulouse, France
020073

Dypvik Sødahl, Elin
IFE, Kjeller, Norway
020340

Ebert, Matthias
Fraunhofer CSP, Halle, Germany
020426

Ebert, Matthias
Fraunhofer IMWS, Halle, Germany
020355

Ebner, Rita
AIT, Vienna, Austria
020318, 020334, 020521

Echeverria, Oihane
Tecnalia, Donostia - San Sebastián, Spain
020139

Eder, Gabriele C.
OFI, Vienna, Austria
020160, 020162, 020249, 020500, 020504

Eelma, Tonis
IBS, Tartu, Estonia
020302

Efthymiou, Venizelos
EPL Technology Frontiers, Dhali, Cyprus
020544

Egan, Renate
UNSW, Sydney, Australia
020048

Egido, Miguel-Ángel
UPM, Madrid, Spain
020407

Eidtmann, Maximilian
ZHAW, Winterthur, Switzerland
020385

Eijgelaar, Marcel
DNV, Arnhem, The Netherlands
020571

Eikelboom, Erik
Futurasun, Citadella, Italy
020225

Einhaus, Roland
ZSW, Stuttgart, Germany
020312

Eisenacher, Matthias
University of Applied Science Cologne, Cologne, Germany
020141

Eiternick, Stefan   020004, 020052
Fraunhofer CSP, Halle (Saale), Germany

Ekins-Daukes, Nicholas J.   020065
UNSW, Sydney, Australia

El Ainaoui, Khadija   020171
Green Energy Park, Benguerir, Morocco

El mrabet, Yasmine   020171
Green Energy Park, Benguerir, Morocco

Elgaili, Mohamed   020166
QEERI, Doha, Qatar

Elhamaoui, Said   020171
Green Energy Park, Benguerir, Morocco

Ellis, Hanna   020213
European Commission JRC, Ispra, Italy

Engelen, Tine   020389
Hasselt University, Diepenbeek, Belgium

Erber, Alexander   020386
BFH, Burgdorf, Switzerland

Eryılmaz, Hande   020521
ODTÜ-GÜNAM, Ankara, Türkiye

Escudero, Ana   020414
IaSol, Zaragoza, Spain

Esmailifar, Seyyed Majid   020335, 020356, 020374, 020375
Amirkabir University of Technology, Tehran, Iran

Espinosa, Nieves   020497, 020506
University of Murcia, Murcia, Spain

Essam T. Mohammed, Sarah   020546
EU SOLARIS, Almeria, Spain

Esteras, Miguel   020358
TECNALIA, Derio, Spain

Eyhorn, Steffen   020369
Fraunhofer ISE, Freiburg, Germany

Fabel, Yann   020235, 020237, 020239
DLR, Almería, Spain

Fabris, Francesca   020225
Futurasun, Citadella, Italy

Faes, Antonin   020251
CSEM, Neuchâtel, Switzerland

Falangas, Alexandros   020210
TRASIS International, Brussels, Belgium

Fang, Xue   020525
Tokyo University of Science, Tokyo, Japan

Fano, Vanesa   020055, 020097, 020153, 020287
UPV/EHU, Bilbao, Spain

Farhat, Mohammad   020428
Australian University, Kuwait City, Kuwait

Farina, Andrea   020066
CNR-IFN, Milan, Italy

Farrias-Basulto, Guillermo   020101
HZB, Berlin, Germany

Fath, Moritz   020463
RCT Solutions, Konstanz, Germany

Fath, Peter   020005, 020463
RCT Solutions, Konstanz, Germany

Fava, Henrique   020565
University of Évora, Évora, Portugal

Feichtner, Markus   020255
Sonnenkraft Energie, St. Veit/Glan, Austria

Feichtner, Markus   020160
Sonnenkraft Energy, St. Veit/Glan, Austria

Feldbacher, Sonja   020136, 020500
PCCL, Leoben, Austria

Feldhof, Anne Maren   020522
University of Applied Science Cologne, Cologne, Germany

Fernandes, Cláudia   020464
Centre for New Energy Technologies, Sacavém, Portugal

Fernández Solas, Álvaro   020331
DLR, Almería, Spain

Ferrando, Jorge   020226
University of Valencia, Paterna, Spain

Ferreira, Catarina G.   020250
SDU Climate Cluster, Odense, Denmark

Ferreira, Catarina   020306
SDU Climate Cluster, Odense, Denmark

Ferrero, Sergio   020079
Polytechnic University of Turin, Turin, Italy

Feuerherdt, Niels   020309
Berlin University of Applied Sciences, Berlin, Germany

Fialho, Luis   020203, 020254, 020261, 020304, 020403,
Eurac Research, Bolzano, Italy   020409, 020418, 020420, 020565

Figueroa, Andrés   020339
National University of Colombia, Bogotá, Colombia

Fischer, Stefan   020495
SGL Carbon, Meitingen, Germany

Fleischanderl, Martin   020136
voestalpine Stahl, Linz, Austria

Fleury, Perine   020513, 020521
Biosphere Solar, Delft, The Netherlands

Flouchi, Imane   020171
Green Energy Park, Benguerir, Morocco

Fodor, Nikoletta   020521
SolarPower Europe, Brussels, Belgium

Fontani, Daniela   020066
CNR-INO, Florence, Italy

Forster, Jacob   020135
Fraunhofer ISE, Freiburg, Germany

Forstinger, Anne   020331
CSP Services, Cologne, Germany

Franch, Jordi Badosa   020406
Ecole Polytechnique, Palaiseau, France

Franchi, Daniele   020077
CNR-ICCOM, Sesto Fiorentino, Italy

Franquet, Erwin   020259, 020428
Côte d'Azur University, Nice, France

Frasson, Nicola   020019
Applied Materials, San Biagio di Callalta, Italy

Freer, Solomon   020396
PV Lighthouse, Coledale, Australia

Freitag, Marina   020077
Newcastle University, Newcastle upon Tyne, United
Kingdom

Freund, Timo   020312
EnBW, Karlsruhe, Germany

Friansyah, Rizal   020376
DTU, Roskilde, Denmark

Friesen, Gabi   020160, 020249, 020574
SUPSI, Mendrisio, Switzerland

Friesen, Thomas   020249
Megasol Energie, Deitingen, Switzerland

Fritz Muñoz, Benjamín   020099
UPV, Valencia, Spain

Froebel, Jens   020121, 020142, 020192, 020223
Fraunhofer CSP, Halle, Germany

Frontini, Francesco   020249, 020253
SUPSI, Mendrisio, Switzerland

Fuentealba-Vidal, Edward   020129, 020311, 020342, 020417, 020422
University of Antofagasta, Antofagasta, Chile

Füreder-Kitzmüller, Friedrich   020136
voestalpine Stahl, Linz, Austria

Fuertes Marrón, David   020014, 020501, 020507, 020508
UPM, Madrid, Spain

Fuertes, David   020097
IES-UPM, Madrid, Spain

Furnari, Alessandro   020010
Enel Green Power, Catania, Italy

Fuß, Michael   020206
MBJ Solutions, Ahrensburg, Germany

Gabor, Andrew M.   020166
BrightSpot Automation, Boulder, United States of America

Gaete, Martin   020311
University of Antofagasta, Antofagasta, Chile

Gafert, Michael   020369
AIT, Vienna, Austria

Gageot, Tristan   020040
CEA / INES, Le Bourget-du-Lac, France

Gainza, Eusebio   020392
ALLOTARRA, Allo, Spain

Galarza, Alejandra   020461
IPVF, Palaiseau, France

Galbiati, Giuseppe   020119, 020218
Henkel, Düsseldorf, Germany

Galdikas, Algirdas   020157
Applied Research Institute for Prospective Technologies,
Vilnius, Lithuania

Galiana, Beatriz   020085
Charles III University of Madrid, Madrid, Spain

Galiazzo, Marco   020019
Applied Materials, San Biagio di Callalta, Italy

Gall, Stefan   020101
HZB, Berlin, Germany

Gallmetzer, Sandra   020261, 020509
Eurac Research, Bolzano, Italy

Galparsoro, Ibon   020514
AZTI, PASAIA, Spain

Gamarra, Ana Rosa   020502
CIEMAT, Madrid, Spain

Ganter, Alissa   020296
ETH, Zurich, Switzerland

Gaona García, Elvis Eduardo   020279
District University of Bogotá, Bogotá, Colombia

Garabetian, Thomas   020551
SolarPower Europe, Brussels, Belgium

García Campos, Enrique   020336
University of Almería, La Cañada de San Urbano, Spain

García, Fernando   020326
UC3M, Madrid, Spain

García, Sonia   020139
Tecnalia, Donostia - San Sebastián, Spain

García-Cañas, Alejandro   020257
IMDEA Nanoscience, Madrid, Spain

García-Salinas, María José   020100
University of Almeria, Almería, Spain

Garcia-Sanchez, Almudena   020246, 020257
UPM, Madrid, Spain

Garg, Vivek   020069, 020071, 020081
SVNIT, Surat, India

Garraín, Daniel   020502
CIEMAT, Madrid, Spain

Gasse, Hugues   020073
University of Toulouse, Toulouse, France

Gassner, Anika   020160, 020162, 020500, 020504
OFI, Vienna, Austria

Gatti, Cesare   020541
PedersoliGattai, Milan, Italy

Gattu, Apoorva   020003
ISC Konstanz, Konstanz, Germany

Gautier, Damien   020505
Becquerel Institute, Brussels, Belgium

Gauvin, Xavier   020302
Bouygues Construction, Saint-Quentin-en-Yvelines, France

Ge, Hua   020249
Concordia University, Montreal, Canada

Gebhardt, Paul   020195
Fraunhofer ISE, Freiburg, Germany

Geerligs, L. J.   020030
TNO, Petten, The Netherlands

Gehrlein, Janek   020522
University of Applied Science Cologne, Cologne, Germany

Geier, Jutta   020234
PCCL, Leoben, Austria

Geml, Fabian   020031
University of Konstanz, Constance, Germany

Genovese, Maria   020378
Enel Green Power, Pisa, Italy

Georghiou, George E.   020534
University of Cyprus, Nicosia, Cyprus

Germani, Simone   020302
CEI, Milan, Italy

Getsiou, Maria   020181
Directorate General for Research and Innovation, Brussels,
Belgium

Geymayer, Lukas   020136
voestalpine Stahl, Linz, Austria

Ghahremani, Amirreza   020335, 020374
Amirkabir University of Technology, Tehran, Iran

Ghennioui, Abdellatif   020171
Green Energy Park, Benguerir, Morocco

Ghosh, Saptak   020519
CSTEP, Bengaluru, India

Girardi, Pierpaolo   020462, 020466
RSE, Milan, Italy

Giroux-Julien, Stephanie   020338
CNRS, Villeurbanne, France

Gissler, Antoine   020060
EDF R&D, Palaiseau, France

Göckeritz, Robert   020119
Fraunhofer CSP, Halle, Germany

Gohil, Hardik   020222
RCT Solutions, Konstanz, Germany

Gomes de Venuto, Vitor   020025
PUCRS, Porto Alegre, Brazil

Gomez Trillos, Juan Camilo   020482
DLR, Oldenburg, Germany

Gomez-Lazaro, Emilio   020562
University of Castilla-La Mancha, Albacete, Spain

Gonnella, Gabriella   020249, 020254
Eurac research, Bolzano, Italy

González Pérez, Sara   020151
ULL, San Cristóbal de La Laguna, Spain

González Rodríguez, Brais   020243
University of Vigo, Vigo, Spain

González, Miguel Ángel   020205
University of Valladolid, Valladolid, Spain

González-Díaz, Benjamín   020151
ULL, San Cristóbal de La Laguna, Spain

Goraya, Baljeet Singh   020475
Fraunhofer ISE, Freiburg, Germany

Gordillo, Gerardo   020110
National University of Colombia, Bogotá, Colombia

Gordon, Ivan   020521
imec, Genk, Belgium

Gottschalg, Ralph   020158
Anhalt University of Applied Sciences, Köthen, Germany

Gottschalg, Ralph   020056, 020201, 020229, 020233, 020284,
Fraunhofer CSP, Halle, Germany   020574

Govaerts, Jonathan   020019
imec, Genk, Belgium

Gracia Amillo, Ana María   020211
CENER, Pamplona, Spain

Gracia Amillo, Ana María   020318
CENER, Sarigurren, Spain

Gracia Amillo, Ana María   020181, 020365, 020366, 020497
CENER, Sarriguren, Spain

Gregory, Geoffrey   020006
EnPV, Karlsruhe, Germany

Greslou, Olivier   020551
CSTB, Bussy-Saint Georges, France

Grommes, Eva-Maria   020522, 020523
University of Applied Science Cologne, Cologne, Germany

Grosser, Stephan   020119, 020142, 020218
Fraunhofer CSP, Halle, Germany

Grünsteidl, Stefan   020307
Avancis, Munich, Germany

Gruginskie, Natasha   020067
Radboud University, Nijmegen, The Netherlands

Guedea, Isabel   020127, 020517
ENDEF, Zaragoza, Spain

Gülsoy, Eren Cihan   020521
METU, Ankara, Türkiye

Gümüs Çiftci, Burcu   020027
Kalyon PV, Ankara, Türkiye

Guerra, Gerardo   020448, 020481
GreenPowerMonitor a DNV company, Barcelona, Spain

Guidetti, Giulia   020541
Green Horse Advisory, Milan, Italy

Guillemoles, Jean François   020062
IPVF, Palaiseau, France

Guillevin, Nicolas   020225
TNO, Petten, The Netherlands

Gunbas, Gorkem   020113
ODTÜ-GÜNAM, Ankara, Türkiye

Gupta, Akshit   020551
Eurac Research, Bolzano, Italy

Gutierrez, Jose Ruben   020055, 020097, 020153, 020287
UPV/EHU, Bilbao, Spain

Gutjahr, Astrid   020030
TNO, Petten, The Netherlands

Haaland, Petry Kristine Nøttum   020476
NTNU, Trondheim, Norway

Haase, Felix   020063
ISFH, Emmerthal, Germany

Hadiwidjaja, Stella   020102
SERIS, Singapore, Singapore

Hadjipanayi, Maria   020064
University of Cyprus, Nicosia, Cyprus

Haedrich, Ingrid   020195, 020231
Fraunhofer ISE, Freiburg, Germany

Hämmer, Matthias   020470
bifa Umweltinstitut, Augsburg, Germany

Hafidi, Elias 020511
Inflights BV, Brussels, Belgium

Hagemann, Elizabeth M. 020416
Nelson Mandela University, Port Elizabeth, South Africa

Hallais, Géraldine 020058
CNRS, Palaiseau, France

Halle, Lasse 020359
BFH, Burgdorf, Switzerland

Hallensleben, Carina 020220
TAMURA-ELSOLD, Ilsenburg, Germany

Halm, Andreas 020218, 020220, 020221
ISC Konstanz, Konstanz, Germany

Halme, Janne 020249
Aalto University, Espoo, Finland

Hamada, Toshiyuki 020190
Osaka Electro-Communication University, Osaka, Japan

Hammer, Annette 020239
DLR, Oldenburg, Germany

Hamouda, Frederic 020058
CNRS, Palaiseau, France

Hanifi, Hamed 020121, 020125, 020137, 020223
AESOLAR, Koenigsbrunn, Germany

Hansen, Per-Anders 020017, 020503
Institute for Energy Technology, Kjeller, Norway

Harit, Amit Kumar 020064
Hasselt Unversity, Genk, Belgium

Harrison, Samuel 020225
CEA, Le Bourget-du-Lac, France

Hashem, Ahmad 020056, 020201
Anhalt University of Applied Sciences, Köthen, Germany

Hategan, Sergiu Mihai 020283
West University of Timisoara, Timisoara, Romania

Hauch, Jens 020117, 020149, 020150
HI ERN, Erlangen, Germany

Hauer, Martin 020255
Bartenbach, Vienna, Austria

Haverkamp, Helge 020008
centrotherm international, Blaubeuren, Germany

Hee Lee, Sang 020045
KIER, Daejeon, South Korea

Heidrich, Robert 020233
Fraunhofer CSP, Halle, Germany

Heikkinen, Kyösti 020423
VTT Technical Research Centre of Finland, Oulu, Finland

Heiser, Moritz 020230
Kiwa PI Berlin, Berlin, Germany

Helbig, Matthias ISC Konstanz, Konstanz, Germany	020220
Helten, David CSP Services, Cologne, Germany	020331
Hennig, Carsten saferay holding, Berlin, Germany	020313, 020355
Hennig, Patrick Kiel University of Applied Sciences, Kiel, Germany	020313
Heras, Jesús Wattkraft, Madrid, Spain	020536
Hermle, Martin Fraunhofer ISE, Freiburg, Germany	020475
Hernández Mora, Johann Alexander District University of Bogotá, Bogotá, Colombia	020279, 020441
Hernández, Jaime J. IMDEA Nanoscience, Madrid, Spain	020257
Hernández, Johann Francisco José de Caldas District University, Bogota, Colombia	020526
Herodotou, Panayiotis University of Cyprus, Nicosia, Cyprus	020534
Herrera Leon, Fernando Augusto National University of Colombia, Bogotá, Colombia	020339, 020546
Herrero, Leire Tecnalia, Donostia - San Sebastián, Spain	020139
Herrero, Rebeca UPM, Madrid, Spain	020209, 020453, 020459
Herrmann, Werner TÜV Rheinland Solar, Cologne, Germany	020208
Herteleer, Bert KU Leuven, Ghent, Belgium	020329, 020351
Herteleer, Bert SUPSI, Mendrisio, Switzerland	020574
Hessler-Wyser, Aïcha EPFL, Neuchâtel, Switzerland	020251
Heydari, Azim Eurac Research, Bolzano, Italy	020485
Hinken, David ISFH, Emmerthal, Germany	020236
Hladys, Bertrand CEA, Grenoble, France	020010
Hoex, Bram UNSW, Sydney, Australia	020065
Hofer, Leo BFH, Burgdorf, Switzerland	020322
Hoffmann, Erik EnPV, Karlsruhe, Germany	020006

Hogan Almeida, Rita   020535, 020567
UPM, Madrid, Spain

Hollemann, Christina   020008
ISFH, Emmerthal, Germany

Holovský, Jakub   020107
Czech Technical University, Prague, Czech Republic

Honrubia-Escribano, Andrés   020562
University of Castilla-La Mancha, Albacete, Spain

Hopp, Tobias   020384
Sunman Energy, Frankfurt, Germany

Horn, Jonas   020050
halm elektronik, Frankfurt am Main, Germany

Horta, Pedro   020304, 020403, 020409, 020418, 020420,
University of Évora, Évora, Portugal   020565

Hosatte, Mikaël   020068
SEGTON Advanced Technology, Versailles, France

Hoß, Jan   020004, 020035
ISC Konstanz, Konstanz, Germany

Hossain, Mohammad Istiaque   020042, 020075, 020108, 020109, 020146,
QEERI, Doha, Qatar   020147

Hou, Yi   020102
SERIS, Singapore, Singapore

Hsiao, Pei-Chieh   020048
UNSW, Sydney, Australia

Hsieh, Cho Fan   020083, 020161, 020163
ITRI, Hsinchu, Taiwan

Hu, Shuaifeng   020226
University of Oxford, Oxford, United Kingdom

Huang, Chris   020048
SunDrive Solar, Kurnell, Australia

Huang, Gan   020272
KIT, Eggenstein-Leopoldshafen, Germany

Huang, Lu-Jan   020425
TNO, Leiden, The Netherlands

Huang, Tzu-Yen   020096
National Synchrotron Radiation Research Center, Hsinchu,
Taiwan

Hügi, Matthias   020322
BFH, Burgdorf, Switzerland

Huemer, Martin   020227
University of Linz, Linz, Austria

Huerta, Hugo E.   020286, 020400
TUAS, Turku, Finland

Hüttl, Bernd   020361
Coburg University of Applied Sciences, Coburg, Germany

Hulik Jansova, Marketa Solargis, Bratislava, Slovakia	020274
Hung, Tzu Han ITRI, Taipei City, Taiwan	020552
Hutterer-Tik, Thomas Watt Analytics, Vienna, Austria	020347
Hwang, Hye-Mi KIER, Daejeon, South Korea	020324, 020357, 020561
Iglesias, Unai Tecnalia, Donostia - San Sebastián, Spain	020139
Ikeda, Kazuaki AIST, Koriyama, Japan	020436
Infante, Paulo University of Évora, Évora, Portugal	020420
Isabella, Olindo TU Delft, Delft, The Netherlands	020515
Ishikawa, Ryousuke Tokyo City University, Setagaya, Japan	020106, 020115
Iwaszko, Victorien ROSI Solar, Saint-Martin-d'Hères, France	020495
Izquierdo-Roca, Victor IREC, Barcelona, Spain	020094
J. N. Soares, Guillermo Federal University of Rio de Janeiro, Duque de Caxias, Brazil	020090
Jacob, Julieu METABUILD, Berlin, Germany	020302
Jacobs, Ayesha Zutari, Cape Town, South Africa	020382
Jaeckel, Bengt Fraunhofer CSP, Halle, Germany	020056, 020119, 020121, 020140, 020142, 020175, 020192, 020201, 020223, 020229
Jäger Waldau, Arnulf European Commission, Rome, Italy	020570
Jäger, Philip ISFH, Emmerthal, Germany	020006
Jäggi, Adrian BFH, Burgdorf, Switzerland	020179
Järventausta, Pertti Tampere University, Tampere, Finland	020445
Jaffré, Alexandre CNRS, Gif-sur-Yvette, France	020058
Jahn, Ulrike Fraunhofer CSP, Halle, Germany	020521, 020574

Jahn, Ulrike   020355
Fraunhofer IMWS, Halle, Germany

Jahreis, Sophia   020142, 020192
Fraunhofer CSP, Halle, Germany

Jakomin, Roberto   020090
Federal University of Rio de Janeiro, Duque de Caxias,
Brazil

Jakubik, Martin   020274
Solargis, Bratislava, Slovakia

Jakuza, Paola   020089
University of Padova, Padova, Italy

Jalkh, Judy   020455
Virtual Vehicle, Graz, Austria

Jandl, Ralf   020204
FFHS, Zurich, Switzerland

Jankovec, Marko   020197
University of Ljubljana, Ljubljana, Slovenia

Jaworczak, Kamil   020402
Technology Innovation Institute, Abu Dhabi, United Arab
Emirates

Jensen, Adam R.   020267
DTU, Kongens Lyngby, Denmark

Jeong, Jungi   020323
K-water, Daejeon, South Korea

Jeong, Kyung Taek   020045
KIER, Daejeon, South Korea

Jeong, Minsoo   020045
KIER, Daejeon, South Korea

Jeronimo, Pedro   020010
CEA, Grenoble, France

Jiang, Zonghan   020158, 020201
Anhalt University of Applied Sciences, Köthen, Germany

Jimenez, Maria   020302
Onyx Solar, Avila, Spain

Jimeno, Juan Carlos   020055, 020097, 020153, 020287, 020289,
UPV/EHU, Bilbao, Spain   020353

Jo, Hyunsik   020323
K-water, Daejeon, South Korea

Job, Enzo   020231
Fraunhofer ISE, Freiburg, Germany

Johnson, Mark Robert   020546
Institut Laue-Langevin (ILL), Grenoble, France

Joo, Dongmyoung   020449
KETI, Wonmi-gu, South Korea

Jooss, Wolfgang   020005, 020222, 020463
RCT Solutions, Konstanz, Germany

Joseph, Daniel Christopher   020123
Fraunhofer ISE, Freiburg, Germany

Joshi, Deepak   020069, 020081
SVNIT, Surat, India

Joss, David   020359, 020369, 020386
BFH, Burgdorf, Switzerland

Jouini, Anis   020034
ECM Technologies, Grenoble, France

Jouttijärvi, Sami   020286, 020298, 020398
University of Turku, Turku, Finland

Joziak, Roman   020230
Kiwa PI Berlin, Berlin, Germany

Ju, Young-Chul   020324, 020357, 020561
KIER, Daejeon, South Korea

Jugo, Josu   020437
UPV/EHU, Leioa, Spain

Junge, Sebastian   020008, 020482
ISFH, Emmerthal, Germany

Kaaya, Ismail   020156, 020294, 020389, 020393
imec, Genk, Belgium

Kähler, Jan-Dirk   020482
Centrotherm International, Blaubeuren, Germany

Kahraman, Mert   020027
Kalyon PV, Ankara, Türkiye

Kainz, Konrad   020430
AIT, Vienna, Austria

Kaiser, Martin   020215
Fraunhofer ISE, Freiburg, Germany

Kaizuka, Izumi   020570
RTS Corporation, Tokyo, Japan

Kajari-Schröder, Sarah   020063
ISFH, Emmerthal, Germany

Kallioharju, Kari   020444, 020445
TUAS, Tampere, Finland

Kalliojärvi, Heidi   020194
Tampere University, Tampere, Finland

Kalshetty, Mahesh   020519
CSTEP, Bengaluru, India

Kaltenbach, Thomas   020195
Fraunhofer ISE, Freiburg, Germany

Kamphues, Joshua   020031
University of Konstanz, Constance, Germany

Kandiyoti-Eskenazi, Selin   020467
CSEM, Neuchâtel, Switzerland

Kang, Min Gu   020045
KIER, Daejeon, South Korea

Kapetanovic, Viktor   020367
Nextracker, Fremont, United States of America

Karhu, Juha   020286
Finnish Meteorological Institute, Helsinki, Finland

Kari, Thøger   020191, 020376
DTU, Roskilde, Denmark

Karimy, Hedayatullah   020052
Fraunhofer CSP, Halle (Saale), Germany

Karttunen, Lauri   020298, 020398
University of Turku, Turku, Finland

Kasper, Ruth   020167, 020232
University of Applied Sciences Cologne, Cologne, Germany

Katouli, Tannaz   020195
Fraunhofer ISE, Freiburg, Germany

Kaufmann, Kai   020355
DENKweit, Halle, Germany

Kawabata, Rudy   020092
PUC-Rio, Rio de Janeiro, Brazil

Kemp, Linda   020390
MARIN, Wageningen, The Netherlands

Kenchington, Ian   020225, 020474, 020558
Becquerel Institute, Brussels, Belgium

Kenny, Robert   020210
European Commission JRC, Ispra, Italy

Khan, Abeer Ali   020513
First Solar, Mainz, Germany

Khosravi, Arash   020381
Mälardalen University, Västerås, Sweden

Kikkert, Benjamin W. J.   020405
TNO, Petten, The Netherlands

Kilickaya, Seda   020020
ODTÜ-GÜNAM, Ankara, Türkiye

Kim, Jin-Hong   020449
KETI, Wonmi-gu, South Korea

Kim, Jun-Tae   020249
Kongju National University, Chungnam, South Korea

Kim, Kihwan   020112
KIER, Daejeon, South Korea

Kim, Seok Won   020449
KETI, Wonmi-gu, South Korea

Kim, Yong-Jin   020045
KIER, Daejeon, South Korea

Kinge, Sachin   020117
Toyota Motors Europe, Brussels, Belgium

Kolahi, Mohammad   020356, 020375
University of Isfahan, Isfahan, Iran

Konagai, Makoto   020106, 020115
Tokyo City University, Setagaya, Japan

Kono, Toru   020484
Hitachi, Kokubunji, Japan

Konu, Christopher Bruce   020132
HTW Berlin, Berlin, Germany

Kopecek, Radovan   020569
ISC Konstanz, Konstanz, Germany

Kopp, Nils   020220
TAMURA-ELSOLD, Ilsenburg, Germany

Korkmaz Arslan, Melisa   020020
ODTÜ-GÜNAM, Ankara, Türkiye

Korpås, Magnus   020476
NTNU, Trondheim, Norway

Kortetmäki, Aki   020444, 020445
TUAS, Tampere, Finland

Koskela, Juha   020444, 020445, 020554
Tampere University, Tampere, Finland

Kossen, Eric J.   020030
TNO, Petten, The Netherlands

Kowalski, Julia   020237
RWTH, Aachen, Germany

Kräling, Ulli   020215
Fraunhofer ISE, Freiburg, Germany

Kraft, Thomas M.   020423
VTT Technical Research Centre of Finland, Oulu, Finland

Krainer, Diana Maria   020430
AIT, Vienna, Austria

Krasilnikov, Inga   020379
Tel Aviv University, Tel Aviv, Israel

Krever Lopes, Bruno   020023
PUCRS, Porto Alegre, Brazil

Kribus, Abraham   020379
Tel Aviv University, Tel Aviv, Israel

Krishnan, Sasikumar   020361
Coburg University of Applied Sciences, Coburg, Germany

Kroon, Jan   020225
TNO, Petten, The Netherlands

Kuan, Ta-Ming   020021, 020053
TSEC, Hsinchu, Taiwan

Kubicek, Bernhard   020281, 020318, 020334, 020347, 020430
AIT, Vienna, Austria

Kucuk, E. Busra   020030
TNO, Petten, The Netherlands

Kuczyńska-Łażewska, Anna   020498, 020499
Gdansk University of Technology, Gdansk, Poland

Kühne, Philip   020240
Leibniz University Hannover, Hannover, Germany

Kuhrmann, Bernd   020206
MBJ Solutions, Ahrensburg, Germany

Kujansivu, Eino   020554
Solarigo Systems, Pirkkala, Finland

Kumar, Gaurav   020563
MERI College of Engineering and Technology, Bahadurgarh, India

Kumar, Sagarika   020402
Technology Innovation Institute, Abu Dhabi, United Arab Emirates

Kumar, Saurabh   020563
PTB, Braunshweig, Germany

Kuo, Cheng-Wen   020021, 020053
TSEC, Hsinchu, Taiwan

Kurtulus, Gunes   020556
ODTU GUNAM, Ankara, Türkiye

Kuruganti, Vaibhav V.   020033
ISC Konstanz, Konstanz, Germany

Kurz, Hannes   020136
voestalpine Stahl, Linz, Austria

Kusch, Alexander   020361
Coburg University of Applied Sciences, Coburg, Germany

Kuzhagaliyeva, Nursulu   020402
Technology Innovation Institute, Abu Dhabi, United Arab Emirates

Kuznicki, Zbigniew T.   020013, 020068
SEGTON Advanced Technology, Versailles, France

Kwiatkowski, Jerzy   020551
NAPE, Warsaw, Poland

Kyranaki, Nikoleta   020156
Hasselt University, Genk, Belgium

Kyranaki, Nikoleta   020393
Hasselt University, Hasselt, Belgium

Kyranaki, Nikoleta   020294
imec, Genk, Belgium

Kyratsi, Theodora   020495
University of Cyprus, Nicosia, Cyprus

L. Andersen, Nanna   020477
DTU, Roskilde, Denmark

L. Souza, Patrícia   020090
Federal University of Rio de Janeiro, Rio de Janeiro, Brazil

Lachowicz, Agata   020039
CSEM, Neuchâtel, Switzerland

Lahr, Simon   020388
Next2Sun Technology, Dillingen, Germany

Lahr, Simon   020411
Next2Sun, Dillingen, Germany

Lajunen, Antti   020400
University of Helsinki, Helsinki, Finland

Lambertz, Andreas   020233
FZJ, Jülich, Germany

Lamblot, Hervé   020302
Sunstyle, Paris, France

Lamghari, Fouad   020402
Fujairah Research Centre, Fujairah, United Arab Emirates

Lamminaho, Jani   020250, 020306
SDU Climate Cluster, Odense, Denmark

Landaas, Christian   020495
Northern Silicon, Meråker, Norway

Landberg, Lars   020448
DNV Denmark, Hellerup, Denmark

Landberg, Lars   020481
DNV Denmark, Hellerup, Spain

Landes, Dieter   020361
Coburg University of Applied Sciences, Coburg, Germany

Landová, Lucie   020107
Czech Technical University, Prague, Czech Republic

Lansade, David   020073
University of Toulouse, Toulouse, France

Lappalainen, Kari   020194, 020528, 020537
Tampere University, Tampere, Finland

Lara, Yolanda   020127, 020414, 020517
ENDEF, Zaragoza, Spain

Larionova, Yevgeniya   020006, 020007, 020225
ISFH, Emmerthal, Germany

Låstad, Jonas   020011
NTNU, Trondheim, Norway

Laurens-Berge, Clarisse   020034
University Grenoble Alpes, Le Bourget-du-Lac, France

Laurikėnas, Paulius   020353
Solitek, Vilnius, Lithuania

Lauwaert, Johan   020064
Ghent University, Ghent, Belgium

Lazaro-Castrillon, Luna   020085
IO-CSIC, Madrid, Spain

Le Bossenec, Hugo   020116
IPVF, Palaiseau, France

Le Brun, Anton   020096
Australian Nuclear Science and Technology Organisation,
Lucas Heights, Australia

Lechón, Yolanda   020502
CIEMAT, Madrid, Spain

Ledesma, Javier R.   020337
UPM, Madrid, Spain

Ledesma, Javier   020446
UPM, Madrid, Spain

Lee, Chun-Wei   020021
TSEC, Hsinchu, Taiwan

Lee, Hyunju   020046
Meiji University, Kanagawa, Japan

Lee, Jieun   020323
K-water, Daejeon, South Korea

Lee, Jin-Seok   020324, 020357, 020561
KIER, Daejeon, South Korea

Legarrea, Aritz   020365
CENER, Sarriguren, Spain

Lelievre, Jean-Francois   020373
INES, Le Bourget-du-Lac, France

Lelong, Benoit   020373
Cythelia Energy, La Motte-Servolex, France

Leloux, Jonathan   020262
LuciSun, Villers-la-Ville, Belgium

Lenain, Philippe   020495
benkei, Lyon, France

Lennon, Alison   020048
UNSW, Sydney, Australia

Lenz, Markus   020226
School of Life Sciences FHNW, Muttenz, Switzerland

Lenzmann, Frank   020019
TNO Energy Transition, Petten, The Netherlands

Leone, Sander   020405
Novar, Rotterdam, The Netherlands

Leonforte, Fabrizio   020249
Polytechnic University of Milan, Milan, Italy

Leopold, Ulrich   020457
Luxembourg Institute of Science and Technology, Esch-sur-
Alzette, Luxembourg

Levrat, Jacques   020251, 020467
CSEM, Neuchâtel, Switzerland

Levtchenko, Alexandra   020116
IPVF, Palaiseau, France

Lewandowski, Simon   020073
University of Toulouse, Toulouse, France

Leza, Baurin   020412
Gonvarri MS R&D, Corvera - Asturias, Spain

Lezaca, Jorge   020239
DLR, Oldenburg, Germany

Li, Xinyang   020222
RCT Solutions, Konstanz, Germany

Li, Yung-Chih   020021
TSEC, Hsinchu, Taiwan

Li, Yuxuan   020001
East China University of Science and Technology,
Shanghai, China

Libal, Joris   020218, 020474
ISC Konstanz, Konstanz, Germany

Lichtenberger, Janine   020430
AIT, Vienna, Austria

Lițiu, Andrei Vladimir   020551
EPB Center, Rotterdam, The Netherlands

Lin, Shih-Chieh   020021
TSEC, Hsinchu, Taiwan

Lindahl, Johan   020486, 020532
Becquerel Sweden, Knivsta, Sweden

Linder, Johannes   020492
Belectric, Kolitzheim, Germany

Lindfors, Anders   020286
Finnish Meteorological Institute, Helsinki, Finland

Lindig, Sascha   020371
Univers, Courbevoie, France

Linke, Jonathan   020004, 020035, 020225
ISC Konstanz, Konstanz, Germany

Linß, Volker   020033
VON ARDENNE, Dresden, Germany

Lipovšek, Benjamin   020047
University of Ljubljana, Ljubljana, Slovenia

Lippke, Benjamin   020180, 020230
Kiwa PI Berlin, Berlin, Germany

List-Kratochvil, Emil   020101
HZB, Berlin, Germany

Litrico, Grazia   020010
Enel Green Power, Catania, Italy

Liu, Cui   020001
East China University of Science and Technology,
Shanghai, China

Liu, Dongyang   020063
ISFH, Emmerthal, Germany

Liu, Han-Chang   020350
ITRI, Tainan, Taiwan

Liu, Huiping   020495
GRÄNGES, Finspång, Sweden

Liu, Mengdi   020144, 020208
TÜV Rheinland, Shanghai, China

Liu, Yung-Tsung   020053, 020083
ITRI, Hsinchu, Taiwan

Livera, Andreas   020534
University of Cyprus, Nicosia, Cyprus

Lizin, Sebastien   020513, 020521
UHasselt, Hasselt, Belgium

Llarena, María Elena   020151
ITER, Granadilla de Abona, Spain

Loeckenhoff, Ruediger F.   020416
AZUR SPACE Solar Power, Heilbronn, Germany

Löhning, Martha   020063
ISFH, Emmerthal, Germany

Löhr, Johannes   020063, 020114
ISFH, Emmerthal, Germany

Lokhat, Ismaël   020262
Cythelia Energy, La Motte-Servolex, France

Lokhat, Ismael   020373
Trace Software, Saint-Romain-de-Colbosc, France

Lombardo, Salvatore   020066
CNR-IMM, Catania, Italy

Long, Yean-San   020053, 020083
ITRI, Hsinchu, Taiwan

Longo, Giulia   020099
UPV, Valencia, Spain

Lopes Gomes, Carlos Javier   020432, 020434
Sunveon, Madrid, Spain

Lopes, Ana Patrícia   020464
University of Lisbon, Lisbon, Portugal

López Cuéllar, Juan Manuel   020501
UCM, Madrid, Spain

López Dalmau, Daniel   020432, 020434
Sunveon, Madrid, Spain

López, Nuria   020451
DTU, Roskilde, Denmark

Lorenz, Dieter   020206
MBJ Solutions, Ahrensburg, Germany

Lorenzo Pigueiras, Eduardo   020363
UPM, Madrid, Spain

Lorenzo, Celena   020337, 020536
UPM, Madrid, Spain

Lorenzo, Eduardo   020439, 020446
UPM, Madrid, Spain

Maiz, Alexander   020437
UPV/EHU, Vitoria-Gasteiz, Spain

Majak, Martyna   020068
Roltec, Poznań, Poland

Makrides, George   020534
University of Cyprus, Nicosia, Cyprus

Malarkannan, Lavanya   020210
National Physical Laboratory, Teddington, United Kingdom

Malcorps, Philippe   020276
3E, Brussels, Belgium

Malik, Stephanie   020313
Fraunhofer CSP, Halle, Germany

Malik, Stephanie   020355
Fraunhofer IMWS, Halle, Germany

Maliutina, Kristina   020141
University of Applied Science Cologne, Cologne, Germany

Malo, Javier   020209
UPM, Madrid, Spain

Mancini, Simone   020425
TNO, Eindhoven, The Netherlands

Mandiola, Gotzon   020514
AZTI, PASAIA, Spain

Manganiello, Patrizio   020389
Hasselt University, Diepenbeek, Belgium

Manganiello, Patrizio   020294
imec, Genk, Belgium

Manito, Alex   020348
University of São Paulo, São Paulo, Brazil

Manochehrian, Rasoul   020539
Frankfurt University of Applied Sciences, Frankfurt am
Main, Germany

Manzolini, Giampaolo   020261
Polytechnic University of Milan, Milan, Italy

Maqsood, Ayman   020101
HZB, Berlin, Germany

Marangis, Demetris   020534
University of Cyprus, Nicosia, Cyprus

Marcos-Castro, Ana   020297
CIEMAT, Madrid, Spain

Marechal, Philippe   020217
CEA / INES, Le Bourget-du-Lac, France

Marí Soucase, Bernabé   020099
UPV, Valencia, Spain

Markert, Jochen   020231
Fraunhofer ISE, Freiburg, Germany

Marquardt, Cornelia   020063
ISFH, Emmerthal, Germany

Marteau, Baptiste   020034
ECM Technologies, Grenoble, France

Martín Rueda, Javier   020535
UPM, Madrid, Spain

Martín, Francisco José   020459
UPM, Madrid, Spain

Martín, Francisco   020209
UPM, Madrid, Spain

Martín-Chivelet, Nuria   020297
CIEMAT, Madrid, Spain

Martín-Rueda, Javier   020337, 020363
UPM, Madrid, Spain

Martínez González, Mario   020326
Enertis Applus+, Madrid, Spain

Martinez, Juan Ignacio   020252
Becquerel Institute Spain, San Sebastian, Spain

Martinez, Oscar   020191, 020205
University of Valladolid, Valladolid, Spain

Martínez-Barbeito, María   020243
ieco.io, Vigo, Spain

Maruyama, Rodrigo P.   020154, 020348
University of São Paulo, São Paulo, Brazil

Marzo, Aitor   020311, 020546
University of Granada, Granada, Spain

Mashkov, Oleksandr   020149, 020150, 020377
HI ERN, Erlangen, Germany

Massaro, Lorenzo   020541
PedersoliGattai, Milan, Italy

Masson, Gaëtan   020474, 020558, 020564, 020573
Becquerel Institute, Brussels, Belgium

Masson, Gaëtan   020570
IEA PVPS Task 1, Brussels, Belgium

Mateos, Yeray   020055, 020153
UPV/EHU, Bilbao, Spain

Maturi, Laura   020249, 020254, 020551
Eurac Research, Bolzano, Italy

Mayer-Ullmann, Philipp   020430
AIT, Vienna, Austria

Mazzoleni, Stefano   020378
University of Naples Federico II, Naples, Italy

McIntosh, Keith R.   020396
PV Lighthouse, Coledale, Australia

McNab, Shona   020065
UNSW, Sydney, Australia

Meereboer, Martijn   020225
Energyra, Westknollendam, The Netherlands

Meier, Rico   020132
HTW Berlin, Berlin, Germany

Meixner, Michael   020050
halm elektronik, Frankfurt am Main, Germany

Mekhaldi, Bouchra   020406
Ecole Polytechnique, Palaiseau, France

Melges de Andrade, Adnei   020154
University of São Paulo, São Paulo, Brazil

Melino, Francesco   020314
University of Bologna, Bologna, Italy

Mellone, Celeste   020541
Green Horse Advisory, Rome, Italy

Menard, Lionel   020291
MINES Paris, Nice, France

Mencaraglia, Denis   020058
CNRS, Gif-sur-Yvette, France

Menchaca, Iratxe   020514
AZTI, PASAIA, Spain

Mendes Ferreira Gomes, Amanda   020548
UFSC, Florianopolis, Brazil

Mendikoa, Iñigo   020514
Tecnalia, BRTA, Derio, Spain

Meneghini, Matteo   020089
University of Padova, Padova, Italy

Ménézo, Christophe   020317
LOCIE, Le Bourget-du-Lac, France

Menghini, Mariela   020508
IMDEA Nanoscience Institute, Madrid, Spain

Mercade Ruiz, Pau   020448, 020481
GreenPowerMonitor a DNV company, Barcelona, Spain

Merino, Amanda   020040
CEA / INES, Le Bourget-du-Lac, France

Merino, José Manuel   020085
UAM, Madrid, Spain

Mermoud, André   020196
PVsyst, Geneva, Switzerland

Merodio, Pablo   020337
UPM, Madrid, Spain

Mertens, Jan   020389
imec, Genk, Belgium

Mertens, Verena   020006, 020008
ISFH, Emmerthal, Germany

Meßmer, Marius   020031
Fraunhofer ISE, Freiburg, Germany

Messmer, Tobias   020218, 020221, 020225
ISC Konstanz, Konstanz, Germany

Messner, Christian   020369
AIT, Vienna, Austria

Mettner, Larissa   020063, 020114
ISFH, Emmerthal, Germany

Meusel, Manuel   020052
Fraunhofer CSP, Halle (Saale), Germany

Meyer, Kevin   020260
ISFH, Emmerthal, Germany

Meza, Carlos   020318, 020334, 020426, 020520
Anhalt University of Applied Sciences, Köthen, Germany

Mezzasalma, Frédéric   020217
CEA / INES, Le Bourget-du-Lac, France

Micha, Daniel   020092
CEFET/RJ, Petrópolis, Brazil

Michael, Poland   020193
Nelson Mandela University, Port Elizabeth, South Africa

Miclea, Paul-Tiberiu   020233
Fraunhofer CSP, Halle, Germany

Midtgård, Ole-Morten   020476
NTNU, Trondheim, Norway

Miettunen, Kati   020286, 020298, 020398
University of Turku, Turku, Finland

Migan-Dubois, Anne   020406
CNRS, Gif-sur-Yvette, France

Mignonac, Alexandre   020217
CEA / INES, Le Bourget-du-Lac, France

Mignonac, Alexandre   020334
CEA, Cadarache, France

Mignonac, Alexandre   020318
CEA, Saint-Paul-Lez-Durance, France

Miguel Laborda, María   020414
IaSol, Zaragoza, Spain

Mihailetchi, Valentin Dan   020033
ISC Konstanz, Konstanz, Germany

Mihailetchi, Valentin   020225
ISC Konstanz, Konstanz, Germany

Mihaylov, Blago   020210
European Commission JRC, Ispra, Italy

Milani, Emanuele   020495
Marelli Europe, Venaria Reala, Italy

Milesi, Frédéric   020068
CEA, Grenoble, France

Min, Byungsul   020008, 020482
ISFH, Emmerthal, Germany

Mirandona López, Haritz   020432, 020434
Sunveon, Madrid, Spain

Miró-Llorente, Marta   020094
IREC, Barcelona, Spain

Misra, Prashant   020429
NISE, Gurugram, India

Miszczuk, Andrzej   020068
Roltec, Poznań, Poland

Mittag, Max   020137
Fraunhofer ISE, Freiburg, Germany

Mittal, Ankit   020318
AIT, Vienna, Austria

Mittelman, Gur   020379
Afeka Tel-Aviv Academic College of Engineering, Tel
Aviv, Israel

Mizushima, Io   020028
IPU P/S, Virum, Denmark

Mizushima, Io   020037
IPU, Virum, Denmark

Mngomezulu, Ndumiso   020344
PVinsight, Port Elizabeth, South Africa

Mo, Alvin   020065
UNSW, Sydney, Australia

Mockeviciute-Azzopardi, Austeja   020334
FIR, Birkirkara, Malta

Moe Nygård, Magnus   020340
IFE, Kjeller, Norway

Moehlecke, Adriano   020023, 020025
PUCRS, Porto Alegre, Brazil

Mohammadi, Mohammad Hossein   020037, 020104
Aarhus University, Aarhus, Denmark

Mollier, Stéphane   020262
CEA / INES, Le Bourget-du-Lac, France

Moltke, Asbjørn   020043
Technical University of Denmark, Copenhagen, Denmark

Mondaca-Cuevas, Gino   020422
University of Antofagasta, Antofagasta, Chile

Monokroussos, Christos   020181
TÜV Rheinland Shanghai, Shanghai, China

Monokroussos, Christos   020144, 020208
TÜV Rheinland, Shanghai, China

Monteiro Martins, Filipa   020317
Galp Energia, Lisbon, Portugal

Montes, Carlos   020151
ITER, Granadilla de Abona, Spain

Montoya, Josefa   020311
University of Antofagasta, Antofagasta, Chile

Morabito, Floriana   020066
CNR-IFN, Milan, Italy

Moradi Sizkouhi, Amirmohammad   020356, 020375
Concordia University, Montreal, Canada

Moradi Zavie Kord, Soroush   020400
University of Helsinki, Helsinki, Finland

Morales, Sergio   020491
UPM, Madrid, Spain

Morantes Quintana, Giobertti Raul   020551
Eurac Research, Bolzano, Italy

Mordvinkin, Anton   020233
Fraunhofer CSP, Halle, Germany

Moreda, Guillermo P.   020407
UPM, Madrid, Spain

Morin, Claire   020551
SolarPower Europe, Brussels, Belgium

Morisset, Audrey   020068
CSEM, Neuchâtel, Switzerland

Morlier, Arnaud   020156
Hasselt University, Genk, Belgium

Morlier, Arnaud   020294, 020389
imec, Genk, Belgium

Mortazavifar, Leila   020056, 020158, 020201, 020284
Anhalt University of Applied Sciences, Köthen, Germany

Moruno, Ricardo   020209, 020453
UPM, Madrid, Spain

Mosel, Frank   020015
PVA TePla, Wettenberg, Germany

Moser, David   020573
Becquerel Institute Italy, Trento, Italy

Moser, David   020316
Becquerel Institute, Bolzano, Italy

Moser, David   020254
Bequerel Institute, Trento, Italy

Moser, David   020203, 020226, 020261, 020325, 020485,
Eurac Research, Bolzano, Italy   020489, 020546

Mouhoubi, Felicia   020134
CEA / INES, Le Bourget-du-Lac, France

Müllejans, Harald   020208, 020213
European Commission JRC, Ispra, Italy

Müller, Alexander   020119
Fraunhofer CSP, Halle, Germany

Müller, Larissa   020523
University of Applied Sciences Cologne, Cologne, Germany

Mugica, Maikel   020139
Tecnalia, Donostia - San Sebastián, Spain

Mujovi, Fahradin   020251
CSEM, Neuchâtel, Switzerland

Mukherjee, Srijani   020338
CEA / INES, Le Bourget-du-Lac, France

Mukhtar, Mariyam   020057
University of Verona, Verona, Italy

Mulder, Peter   020067
Radboud University, Nijmegen, The Netherlands

Muller, Matthew   020314
NREL, Denver, United States of America

Munkhammar, Joakim   020532
Uppsala University, Uppsala, Sweden

Muñoz Cerón, Emilio   020269
University of Jaén, Jaén, Spain

Muñoz, Delfina   020040, 020311, 020546
CEA / INES, Le Bourget-du-Lac, France

Muñoz, Delfina   020521
CEA, Le Bourget-du-Lac, France

Muñoz, Delfina   020226
CEA/ INES, Le Bourget-du-Lac, France

Muñoz, Ildefonso   020365, 020366, 020392
CENER, Sarriguren, Spain

Muñoz, Jesús Ángel   020508
UCM, Madrid, Spain

Muñoz-García, Miguel-Ángel   020407
UPM, Madrid, Spain

Murano, Giovanni   020551
ENEA, Ispra, Italy

Murillo, Asier   020497
CENER, Sarriguren, Spain

Musembi, Robinson J.   020272
University of Nairobi, Nairobi, Kenya

Nabipouor, Mohammad   020426
Anhalt University of Applied Sciences, Köthen, Germany

Nagel, Henning   020475
Fraunhofer ISE, Freiburg, Germany

Nakamura, Kyotaro   020046
Toyota Technological Institute, Nagoya, Japan

Nanno, Ikuo   020190
Nanno Energy Research Center, Yamaguchi, Japan

Nargelienė, Viktorija   020157
Center for Physical Sciences and Technology (FTMC),
Vilnius, Lithuania

Narsi Patel, Hitarth   020069
SVNIT, Surat, India

Narvarte, Luis   020337, 020446, 020491, 020535, 020536,
UPM, Madrid, Spain   020567, 020575

Nascimento, Lucas   020377
Solar Energy Research Laboratory Fotovoltaica/ UFSC,
Florianópolis, Brazil

Nasebandt, Lasse   020063
ISFH, Emmerthal, Germany

Nasser, Hisham   020226
ODTÜ-GÜNAM, Ankara, Türkiye

Naveiro, José Manuel   020414
ENDEF, Zaragoza, Spain

Nazififard, Mohammad   020259, 020428
Côte d'Azur University, Nice, France

Nejim, Ahmed   020058
SILVACO, St. Ives, United Kingdom

Nel, Paul   020382
7SecondSolar, Cape Town, South Africa

Nelson, Jenny   020394
Imperial College London, London, United Kingdom

Neuba, Adam   020114
Paderborn University, Paderborn, Germany

Neuber, Viola   020031
Fraunhofer ISE, Freiburg, Germany

Neuhaus, Holger   020123, 020140
Fraunhofer ISE, Freiburg, Germany

Neumaier, Lukas   020504
Silicon Austria Labs, Villach, Austria

Neussl, Vassilissa   020318, 020430
AIT, Vienna, Austria

Neykova, Neda   020107
Czech Technical University, Prague, Czech Republic

Nezhad, Mahyar   020230
Kiwa PI Berlin, Hudson, United States of America

Nguyen, Viet Xuan   020008
centrotherm international, Blaubeuren, Germany

Nicolet-dit-Félix, Kléber   020251
EPFL, Neuchâtel, Switzerland

Nicot-Senneville, Zoltan   020102
SERIS, Singapore, Singapore

Nielsen, Michael P.   020065
UNSW, Sydney, Australia

Nissen, Hauke   020313
Wattmanufactur, Galmsbüll, Germany

Nitsche, Tobias   020119, 020218
Henkel, Düsseldorf, Germany

Nobre, André M.   020263
PV Doctor, Singapore, Singapore

Noels, Serge   020472
PV CYCLE, Brussels, Belgium

Noh, Yong-Su   020449
KETI, Wonmi-gu, South Korea

Nold, Sebastian   020461
Fraunhofer ISE, Freiburg, France

Nold, Sebastian   020475
Fraunhofer ISE, Freiburg, Germany

Nordboe, Eirik   020495
Fiven Norge, Lillesand, Norway

Norde Santos, Fernanda   020331
DLR, Almería, Spain

Nouri, Bijan   020235, 020237, 020239
DLR, Almería, Spain

Nova, David   020339
National University of Colombia, Bogotá, Colombia

Núñez, Rubén   020209, 020453
UPM, Madrid, Spain

Núñez-Osorio, Alessia   020100
University of Almeria, Almeria, Spain

Nurmesjärvi, Antti   020423
VTT Technical Research Centre of Finland, Oulu, Finland

Nussbaumer, Hartmut   020385
ZHAW, Winterthur, Switzerland

Nyang'onda, Thomas N.   020272
University of Nairobi, Nairobi, Kenya

Obeidavi, Sahereh   020361
Coburg University of Applied Sciences, Coburg, Germany

Oberbeck, Lars   020461
TotalEnergies OneTech, Paris, France

Oberegger Filippi, Ulrich   020551
Eurac Research, Bolzano, Italy

Ocaña, Luis Manuel   020151
ITER, Granadilla de Abona, Spain

Ockert, Ajka   020312
EnBW, Karlsruhe, Germany

Odilio dos Santos, Daniel   020548
UFSC, Florianopolis, Brazil

Öhgren, Gustav   020532
Becquerel Sweden, Knivsta, Sweden

Öttl, Christian   020347
Watt Analytics, Vienna, Austria

Öz, Aksel Kaan   020135
Fraunhofer ISE, Freiburg, Germany

Özden, Talat   020226
ODTÜ-GÜNAM, Ankara, Türkiye

Özkalay, Ebrar   020160, 020204
SUPSI, Mendrisio, Switzerland

Ogura, Atsushi   020046
Meiji University, Kanagawa, Japan

Ohdaira, Keisuke   020131
JAIST, Ishikawa, Japan

Ohshita, Yoshio   020046
Toyota Technological Institute, Nagoya, Japan

Ojala, Aleksi   020554
Solarigo Systems, Pirkkala, Finland

Okawa, Hayato   020115
Tokyo City University, Setagaya, Japan

Okel, Lars A. G.   020030
TNO, Petten, The Netherlands

Oksanen, Jani   020067
Aalto University, Espoo, Finland

Oliosi, Michele   020196
PVsyst, Geneva, Switzerland

Olivares, Douglas   020311
University of Antofagasta, Antofagasta, Chile

Olivares, Gregorio   020365, 020366, 020392
CENER, Sarriguren, Spain

Oliveira Santos, João Victor   020188
EDF R&D, Moret Loing Orvanne, France

Oliveira, Helena   020420
University of Évora, Évora, Portugal

Oller Westerberg, Amelia   020570
Becquerel Sweden, Knivsta, Sweden

Ollo, Olatz   020139
Tecnalia, Donostia - San Sebastián, Spain

Oozeki, Takashi   020436, 020525
AIST, Koriyama, Japan

Opatovsky, Martin   020241, 020262
Solargis, Bratislava, Slovakia

Oreski, Gernot   020136, 020234, 020325, 020500, 020574
PCCL, Leoben, Austria

Ortega, Eneko   020055, 020153, 020287, 020353
UPV/EHU, Bilbao, Spain

Ortega, Eneko   020289, 020437
UPV/EHU, Leioa, Spain

Ortega, Pascal   020214
University of French Polynesia, Faa'a, French Polynesia

Ortiz-Pena, Aaron   020562
University of Castilla-La Mancha, Albacete, Spain

Ory, Daniel   020188
EDF R&D, Palaiseau, France

Ory, Daniel   020116
EDF, Palaiseau, France

Osman, Alaa   020006
ISFH, Emmerthal, Germany

Osuna, Jose Antonio   020358
MAGTEL, Córdoba, Spain

Osvald, Oliver   020274
Solargis, Bratislava, Slovakia

Otaegi, Aloña   020055, 020097, 020153, 020287
UPV/EHU, Bilbao, Spain

Otnes, Gaute   020169
Institute for Energy Technology, Kjeller, Norway

Otto, Nicolas   020101
HTW, Berlin, Germany

Otto, William   020390
MARIN, Wageningen, The Netherlands

Ou, Chao-Wei   020350
National Chin-Yi University of Technology, Taichung,
Taiwan

Ovaitt, Silvana   020314
NREL, Denver, United States of America

Ovaitt, Silvana   020574
NREL, Golden, United States of America

Oviedo Hernandez, Guillermo   020325
BayWa r.e, Rome, Italy

Ozer, Shay   020379
Agricultural Research Organization, Rishon LeZion, Israel

P. Pires, Maurício   020090
Federal University of Rio de Janeiro, Rio de Janeiro, Brazil

Pabiou, Herve   020338
CETHIL, Villeurbanne, France

Pabst, Elena   020312
ZSW, Stuttgart, Germany

Paiva, Lúcio   020530
Casa dos Ventos, Fortaleza, Brazil

Palais, Olivier   020188
Toulon University, Marseille, France

Palitzsch, Wolfram   020225, 020495
LuxChemTech, Freiberg, Germany

Palomino, Laura   020491, 020535
UPM, Madrid, Spain

Pamir Aly, Shahzada   020229
DEWA, Dubai, United Arab Emirates

Pamula, Bindu   020069
SVNIT, Surat, India

Panda, Pavan Kumar 020284
Anhalt University of Applied Sciences, Köthen, Germany

Pandar, Matthias 020229
Fraunhofer CSP, Halle, Germany

Pander, Matthias 020121, 020142, 020175, 020192, 020218,
Fraunhofer CSP, Halle, Germany 020223, 020232

Panduri, Fabio 020322
BFH, Burgdorf, Switzerland

Pantoja, Jaime 020526
Francisco José de Caldas District University, Bogota,
Colombia

Papantoni, Veatriki 020482
DLR, Oldenburg, Germany

Paraficz, Danuta 020204
FFHS, Zurich, Switzerland

Paraskeva, Vasiliki 020064
University of Cyprus, Nicosia, Cyprus

Pardo, Eduardo 020414
Tecnova, Almeira, Spain

Parfeniukas, Karolis 020039
ATLANT 3D, Taastrup, Denmark

Parion, Jonathan 020064
Hasselt Unversity, Genk, Belgium

Park, Hyeonwook 020112
KENTECH, Naju-Si, South Korea

Parmar, Richa 020429
NISE, Gurugram, India

Parra, Johan 020406
Ecole Polytechnique, Palaiseau, France

Parra, Johan 020214
Polytechnic Institute of Paris, Palaiseau, France

Parrilla, Carlos G. 020402
Fujairah Research Centre, Fujairah, United Arab Emirates

Pascual Gallego, Valero 020407
UPM, Madrid, Spain

Pasquier, Mathis 020451
DTU, Roskilde, Denmark

Passaro, Marcello 020513
Sunzest Solar, Rotterdam, The Netherlands

Patel, Dharm 020355
Fraunhofer IMWS, Halle, Germany

Paul, Ananta 020250, 020306
SDU Climate Cluster, Odense, Denmark

Paulescu, Marius 020283
West University of Timisoara, Timisoara, Romania

Paviet-Salomon, Bertrand   020068, 020467
CSEM, Neuchâtel, Switzerland

Payno, David   020085, 020094
UAM, Madrid, Spain

Pearce, Pheobe   020065
UNSW, Sydney, Australia

Peche, René   020468, 020495
bifa Umweltinstitut, Augsburg, Germany

Pehlivanli, Ezgi   020521
METU, Ankara, Türkiye

Peibst, Robby   020006, 020063, 020114
ISFH, Emmerthal, Germany

Pelfort Ojer, Marta   020241
Solargis, Bratislava, Slovakia

Pelland, Sophie   020211
Natural Resources Canada, Varennes, Canada

Pelle, Martina   020249, 020254
Eurac Research, Bolzano, Italy

Peña-Bermudez, Julian   020110
University of the Caribbean, Santo Domingo, Dominican
Republic

Peng, Cheng-Yu   020350
National Chin-Yi University of Technology, Taichung,
Taiwan

Pera, David   020457
Luxembourg Institute of Science and Technology, Esch-sur-
Alzette, Luxembourg

Perani, Martina   020204
FFHS, Zurich, Switzerland

Peraticos, Elias   020064
University of Cyprus, Nicosia, Cyprus

Pereda, Ainhoa   020198, 020358
TECNALIA, Derio, Spain

Pereira Fialho, Luis Andre   020509
Eurac Research, Bolzano, Italy

Pereira, Sara   020403, 020418, 020565
University of Évora, Évora, Portugal

Pérez García, Manuel   020336
University of Almería, La Cañada de San Urbano, Spain

Pérez, Ernesto   020339
National University of Colombia, Bogotá, Colombia

Pérez, Jairo   020412
Gonvarri AgroTech, Corvera - Asturias, Spain

Pérez, Jorge   020412
Gonvarri AgroTech, Corvera - Asturias, Spain

Pérez, Luis   020412
Gonvarri MS R&D, Corvera - Asturias, Spain

Perez, Richard University at Albany, Albany, United States of America	020494
Perez-Astudillo, Daniel QEERI, Doha, Qatar	020275, 020278, 020291
Pérez-García, Manuel University of Almeria, Almería, Spain	020100
Pérez-Rodríguez, Alejandro IREC, Barcelona, Spain	020085, 020094
Pernas, Tomás Gonvarri AgroTech, Corvera - Asturias, Spain	020412
Pernau, Thomas centrotherm international, Blaubeuren, Germany	020008
Perrin, Marion Energy Pool, Le Bourget-du-Lac, France	020544
Pervan, Nikolina PCCL, Leoben, Austria	020136, 020234
Peter Amalathas, Amalraj University of Jaffna, Jaffna, Sri Lanka	020107
Peter, Kristian ISC Konstanz, Konstanz, Germany	020569
Peters, Ian Marius Forschungszentrum Jülich, Erlangen, Germany	020230, 020263
Peters, Ian Marius HI ERN, Erlangen, Germany	020149, 020150, 020377, 020574
Petersons, Karlis Stensborg, Roskilde, Denmark	020250, 020306
Petkovski, Emil DNV, Arnhem, The Netherlands	020571
Petzschmann, Jonas ZSW, Stuttgart, Germany	020312
Pfau, Jan Hendrik Leibniz University Hannover, Hannover, Germany	020240
Pfeiffer, Oliver University of Applied Science Cologne, Cologne, Germany	020141
Pfeiffer, Oliver University of Applied Sciences Cologne, Cologne, Germany	020140
Philipp, Daniel Fraunhofer ISE, Freiburg, Germany	020215, 020231
Pierro, Marco Eurac Research, Bolzano, Italy	020489, 020494
Pieters, Bart E. FZJ, Jülich, Germany	020180
Pieterse, Marco Chemconserve, Bussum, The Netherlands	020495
Pietralunga, Silvia Maria CNR-IFN, Milan, Italy	020066

Pietsch, Veith 020331
Aquila Capital, Hamburg, Germany

Pilat, Eric 020311
CEA / INES, Le Bourget-du-Lac, France

Pilat, Eric 020317
CEA INES, Le Bourget-du-Lac, France

Pillai, Akhildev 020558
Becquerel Institute, Brussels, Belgium

Pinheiro, Philippe 020457
Luxembourg Institute of Science and Technology, Esch-sur-
Alzette, Luxembourg

Pinho Almeida, Marcelo 020348
University of São Paulo, São Paulo, Brazil

Pinto, Cristina Leyre 020497
CENER, Sarriguren, Spain

Pinto, Luciana 020092
UFRJ, Rio de Janeiro, Brazil

Pitaval, Sébastien 020244
SOLAÏS, Valbonne, France

Pitz-Paal, Robert 020237, 020331
DLR, Cologne, Germany

Plakhotnyuk, Maksym 020039
ATLANT 3D, Taastrup, Denmark

Platero Gaona, Carlos A. 020332
UPM, Madrid, Spain

Plaza, Caroline 020543, 020564, 020573
Becquerel Institute France, Lyon, France

Polacchi, Cristina 020509, 020513
Eurac Research, Bolzano, Italy

Polo, Jaime 020300
CENER, Sarriguren, Spain

Polo, Jesús 020297
CIEMAT, Madrid, Spain

Polverini, Davide 020181
Directorate General for Internal Market, Industry,
Entrepreneurship and SMEs, Brussels, Belgium

Polverini, Davide 020497
European Comission, Brussels, Belgium

Pongthanacharoenkul, Nattapark 020230
Kiwa PI Berlin, Berlin, Germany

Poortmans, Jef 020064
Hasselt Unversity, Genk, Belgium

Popescu, Lacramioara 020068
ISC Konstanz, Konstanz, Germany

Pospischil, Maximilian 020225
Highline Technologies, Freiburg, Germany

Poulsen, Peter B.   020039
DTU, Copenhagen, Denmark

Poulsen, Peter B.   020250, 020265, 020267, 020376, 020451
DTU, Roskilde, Denmark

Poulsen, Peter Behrensdorff   020028, 020306, 020346
DTU, Roskilde, Denmark

Pourshafi, Pouya   020121, 020125, 020137
AESOLAR, Koenigsbrunn, Germany

Pozza, Cristian   020551
Eurac Research, Bolzano, Italy

Prakash, Jai   020429
NISE, Gurugram, India

Prando, Davide   020485, 020489
Edyna, Bolzano, Italy

Prasad, Manjunath   020225
ISC Konstanz, Konstanz, Germany

Pravettoni, Mauro   020402
Technology Innovation Institute, Abu Dhabi, United Arab
Emirates

Preis, Pirmin   020003
ISC Konstanz, Konstanz, Germany

Preu, Ralf   020475
Fraunhofer ISE, Freiburg, Germany

Preuschoff, Jonas   020101
HTW, Berlin, Germany

Protti, Alexander Aguilar   020140
Fraunhofer ISE, Freiburg, Germany

Protti, Alexander   020137
Fraunhofer ISE, Freiburg, Germany

Provost, Marion   020116
IPVF, Palaiseau, France

Puel, Jean Baptiste   020062
IPVF, Palaiseau, France

Puertas López, Antonio Manuel   020100
University of Almeria, Almeria, Spain

Puttock, Claire   020367
Nextracker, Fremont, United States of America

Queste, Samuel   020068
Marie and Louis Pasteur University, Besançon, France

Quiroz, Mónica   020328
Qualifying Photovoltaics, Madrid, Spain

R. Ledesma, Javier   020363
UPM, Madrid, Spain

Raval, Mehul   020005, 020222, 020463
RCT Solutions, Konstanz, Germany

Razanajao, Aina   020244
SOLAÏS, Valbonne, France

Razi, Umair   020085
IREC, Barcelona, Spain

Recart, Federico   020097
UPV/EHU, Bilbao, Spain

Redondo Cuevas, Marta   020332
UPM, Madrid, Spain

Redondo, Juan Manuel   020209
UPM, Madrid, Spain

Rehan, Muhammad   020112
KIER, Daejeon, South Korea

Rehman, Anees ur   020111, 020164
Hohai University, Changzhou, China

Reichart, Hannah   020167, 020232
University of Applied Sciences Cologne, Cologne, Germany

Reichel, Christian   020123, 020137, 020140
Fraunhofer ISE, Freiburg, Germany

Reichle, Julian   020005, 020222, 020463
RCT Solutions, Konstanz, Germany

Reinders, Angele   020253
TU Eindhoven, Eindhoven, The Netherlands

Reindl, Thomas   020263
SERIS, Singapore, Singapore

Reis, Luiz Filipe   020530
Casa dos Ventos, Fortaleza, Brazil

Rémondeau, Paul   020251
EPFL, Neuchâtel, Switzerland

Renard, Charles   020058
CNRS, Palaiseau, France

Rende, Fedele   020255
ACCA Software, Cosenza, Italy

Rennhofer, Marcus   020180, 020281, 020318, 020334, 020347,
AIT, Vienna, Austria   020430

Rentsch, Jochen   020475
Fraunhofer ISE, Freiburg, Germany

Rerat, Michel   020060
IPREM, Pau, France

Reshef, Liad   020379
Agricultural Research Organization, Rishon LeZion, Israel

Revol, Inès   020074
LAAS-CNRS, Toulouse, France

Reyal, Jean-Pierre   020303
SemperStyl, Eragny, France

Riaño, Sandra   020197, 020358
TECNALIA, Derio, Spain

Richards, Bryce S.   020272
KIT, Karlsruhe, Germany

Riechelman, Stefan   020181
PTB, Braunschweig, Germany

Riechelmann, Stefan   020177, 020199, 020211
PTB, Braunschweig, Germany

Riedel-Lyngskær, Nicholas   020451
DTU, Roskilde, Denmark

Rienäcker, Michael   020063
ISFH, Emmerthal, Germany

Rindert, Sören   020230
Kiwa PI Berlin, Berlin, Germany

Ríos Moral, Lucía   020501
UCM, Madrid, Spain

Ríos-Ledesma, Felipe   020446
UPM, Madrid, Spain

Ripke, Melanie   020006
ISFH, Emmerthal, Germany

Riva, Roland   020495
CEA, Le Bourget-du-Lac, France

Rivas Rodríguez, José Manuel   020326
Enertis Applus+, Madrid, Spain

Robledo, Jesús   020262
LuciSun, Villers-la-Ville, Belgium

Rodríguez Lucas, Delia   020407
EkiLabs, Boston, United States of America

Rodríguez Plaza, José Luis   020508
Autonomous University of Madrid, Madrid, Spain

Rodríguez Rodríguez, Araceli   020501
UCM, Madrid, Spain

Rodríguez Salazar, David Leonardo   020441
District University of Bogotá, Bogotá, Colombia

Rodríguez, Araceli   020508
UCM, Madrid, Spain

Rodríguez, Diego Julián   020526
Francisco José de Caldas District University, Bogota,
Colombia

Rodríguez, Isabel   020257
IMDEA Nanoscience, Madrid, Spain

Rodriguez, Sonia Maria   020289
UPV/EHU, Leioa, Spain

Rodríguez, Velia   020097
UPV/EHU, Bilbao, Spain

Rodríguez-Conde, Sofía   020326
Enertis Applus+, Madrid, Spain

Rodríguez-Gallegos, Carlos D.   020149, 020150
SERIS, Singapore, Singapore

Rodríguez-Romero, Sebastián   020342, 020417, 020422
University of Antofagasta, Antofagasta, Chile

Rodziewicz, Hanna   020498
Gdansk University of Technology, Gdansk, Poland

Römer, Udo   020006, 020063
ISFH, Emmerthal, Germany

Röver, Ingo   020225
LuxChemTech, Freiberg, Germany

Rojas, Christian A.   020422
Federico Santa María Technical University, Valparaíso, Chile

Rojas-Henríquez, Katalina   020129
University of Antofagasta, Antofagasta, Chile

Román, Eduardo   020139
Tecnalia, Donostia - San Sebastián, Spain

Romeo, Alessandro   020057, 020089, 020093
University of Verona, Verona, Italy

Romer, Pascal   020231
Fraunhofer ISE, Freiburg, Germany

Roodt, Roelof   020185
Nelson Mandela University, Port Elizabeth, South Africa

Roosloot, Nathan   020169
Institute for Energy Technology, Kjeller, Norway

Rosca, Victor   020030
TNO, Petten, The Netherlands

Rosen, Isaac   020225
Copprint, Jerusalem, Israel

Rosenfeld, Lavi   020379
Agricultural Research Organization, Rishon LeZion, Israel

Rosina, Konstantin   020241
Solargis, Bratislava, Slovakia

Rossa, Carlos   020432, 020434
Sunveon, Madrid, Spain

Rouffie, Brice   020068
SEGTON Advanced Technology, Versailles, France

Roulleau, Lea   020303
CSTB, Marne-la-Vallée, France

Rousset, Jean   020116
EDF, Palaiseau, France

Roy, Shantanu   020519
CSTEP, Bengaluru, India

Rudolph, Dominik   020003, 020068
ISC Konstanz, Konstanz, Germany

Rudzikas, Matas 020380
The Applied Research Institute for Prospective
Technologies, Vilnius, Lithuania

Rüther, Ricardo 020377
Solar Energy Research Laboratory Fotovoltaica/ UFSC,
Florianópolis, Brazil

Rüther, Ricardo 020548
UFSC, Florianopolis, Brazil

Ruf, Manuel 020455
Robert Bosch, Stuttgart, Germany

Ruiz Donoso, Elena 020331
DLR, Almería, Spain

S. Sousa, Graciana 020090
Federal University of Rio de Janeiro, Rio de Janeiro, Brazil

Safarian, Jafar 020011
NTNU, Trondheim, Norway

Sah, Dheeraj 020039
Aarhus University, Aarhus, Denmark

Sahin, Hasret 020479
LUT University, Lappeenranta, Finland

Saito, Kimihiko 020106
Tokyo City University, Setagaya, Japan

Salem, Mohammad 020428
Australian University, Kuwait City, Kuwait

Salerno, Giorgia 020077
University of Milano-Bicocca, Milan, Italy

Salis, Fabio 020541
Iberdrola, Rome, Italy

Salvador, Antonio 020358
MAGTEL, Córdoba, Spain

Sample, Tony 020213
European Commission JRC, Ispra, Italy

Samuolienė, Giedrė 020380
The Lithuanian Research Centre for Agriculture and
Forestry, Kaunas, Lithuania

San José, Luis Javier 020209, 020453
UPM, Madrid, Spain

Sánchez de León Peque, Miguel 020243
ieco.io, Vigo, Spain

Sanchez Garcia, Alfredo 020270
SINTEF, Trondheim, Norway

Sanchez, Hugo 020056, 020158, 020284
Anhalt University of Applied Sciences, Köthen, Germany

Sanchez, Jesus 020437
UPV/EHU, Vitoria-Gasteiz, Spain

Sanchez, Laura UPV/EHU, Leioa, Spain	020437
Sánchez, Yudania IREC, Barcelona, Spain	020085
Sanchez-Friera, Paula Solkeys, Gijón, Spain	020412, 020513, 020521
Sanchez-Ruiz, Alain UPV/EHU, Vitoria-Gasteiz, Spain	020437
Sansavini, Giovanni ETH, Zurich, Switzerland	020296
Sansoni, Paola CNR-INO, Florence, Italy	020066
Santamaría Fernández, Susanna TECNALIA, Derio, Spain	020249
Santamaría-Sancho, Juan UPM, Madrid, Spain	020363
Santos, Jose Domingo TECNALIA, Derio, Spain	020197, 020198, 020358
Santos, Rodrigo Casa dos Ventos, Fortaleza, Brazil	020530
Sanz Martinez, Asier Tecnalia, Bilbao, Spain	020546
Sanz, Asier Tecnalia, BRTA, Derio, Spain	020514
Sanz, Asier TECNALIA, Derio, Spain	020197
Sanz-Cuadrado, Cristina UPM, Madrid, Spain	020575
Sanz-Saiz, Carlos CIEMAT, Madrid, Spain	020297
Sarafijanovic-Djukic, Natasa FFHS, Regensdorf, Switzerland	020204
Saretti, Angelica Polytechnic University of Bari, Bari, Italy	020301
Sarkadi, Monika ISC Konstanz, Konstanz, Germany	020569
Sauer, Thomas EXXERGY, Gräfelfing, Germany	020140
Saura, Juan Antonio University of Murcia, Murcia, Spain	020506
Savisalo, Tuukka Valoe, Mikkeli, Finland	020225
Saw, Min Hsian Technology Innovation Institute, Abu Dhabi, United Arab Emirates	020402
Saxena, Anmol Ratan NIT, Delhi, India	020429

Sayed, Abdullah Abu	020180, 020230
Kiwa PI Berlin, Berlin, Germany

Scaltrito, Luciano	020079
Polytechnic University of Turin, Turin, Italy

Scerri, Kenneth	020334
University of Malta, Msida, Malta

Schading, Steve	020443
University of Agder, Grimstad, Norway

Schäfer, Aysim	020388
Next2Sun Technology, Dillingen, Germany

Schäfer, Sebastian	020539
Frankfurt University of Applied Sciences, Frankfurt am
Main, Germany

Schenk, Paul	020192
Fraunhofer CSP, Halle, Germany

Schermer, John	020067
Radboud University, Nijmegen, The Netherlands

Scherret, Jacqueline	020255
A-Null Development, Vienna, Austria

Schifferegger, Raffael	020162
OFI, Vienna, Austria

Schimanke, Sabrina	020006
ISFH, Emmerthal, Germany

Schirmer, Yoko	020101
HTW, Berlin, Germany

Schläger, Christian	020240
Leibniz University Hannover, Hannover, Germany

Schlatmann, Rutger	020101
HTW, Berlin, Germany

Schmidt Davidsen, Rasmus	020037, 020104
Aarhus University, Aarhus, Denmark

Schnaus, Dominik	020237
TUM, Garching, Germany

Schneider, Andreas	020129, 020183
University of Applied Sciences Gelsenkirchen,
Gelsenkirchen, Germany

Schneider, Astrid	020255
TU Wien, Vienna, Austria

Schneider, Friedrich	020482
LPKF SolarQuipment, Suhl, Germany

Schneider, Marc Gabriel	020522
University of Applied Science Cologne, Cologne, Germany

Schneiderlöchner, Eric	020033
VON ARDENNE, Dresden, Germany

Schnierer, Branislav	020262
Solargis, Bratislava, Slovakia

Schönau, Maximilian Coburg University of Applied Sciences, Coburg, Germany	020361
Schönau, Maximilian smartblue, Munich, Germany	020544
Schönheits, Markus bifa Umweltinstitut, Augsburg, Germany	020468, 020470
Schranz, Christian TU Wien, Vienna, Austria	020255
Schrempf, Michael PTB, Braunschweig, Germany	020199
Schrijvers, Patrick MARIN, Wageningen, The Netherlands	020390
Schröter, Nick Fraunhofer CSP, Halle, Germany	020142
Schubert, Martin C. Fraunhofer ISE, Freiburg, Germany	020475
Schubnel, Baptiste CSEM, Neuchâtel, Switzerland	020238
Schüler, Marc Andre Next2Sun Technology, Dillingen, Germany	020388
Schüler, Marc Andre Next2Sun, Dillingen, Germany	020411
Schueler, Nadine Freiberger Instruments, Freiberg, Germany	020015
Schulte-Huxel, Henning ISFH, Emmerthal, Germany	020008, 020260
Schultz, Christof HTW, Berlin, Germany	020101
Schulz, Philip IPVF, Palaiseau, France	020060
Schulze, Achim Rosenheim Technical University of Applied Sciences, Rosenheim, Germany	020361
Schulze, Patricia S.C. Fraunhofer ISE, Freiburg, Germany	020475
Schwenke, Almut SGL Battery Solutions, Meitingen, Germany	020495
Sciuto, Marcello Enel Green Power, Catania, Italy	020010
Scognamiglio, Alessandra ENEA, Naples, Italy	020541
Scognamiglio, Alessandra ENEA, Portici, Italy	020378
Sedaghat, Ahmad Australian University, Kuwait City, Kuwait	020428
Seiffert, Christoph Institute for Energy Technology, Kjeller, Norway	020169

Seiffert, Daniela   020008
centrotherm international, Blaubeuren, Germany

Seitz, Matthias   020468
bifa Umweltinstitut, Augsburg, Germany

Selj, Josefine H.   020169
Institute for Energy Technology, Kjeller, Norway

Senno, Maximiliano Alejandro   020226
University of Valencia, Paterna, Spain

Senturk, Bilge   020556
ODTU GUNAM, Ankara, Türkiye

Setien, Eneko   020198
TECNALIA, Derio, Spain

Šetkus, Arūnas   020157
Center for Physical Sciences and Technology (FTMC),
Vilnius, Lithuania

Shaaban, Ahmed   020402
Technology Innovation Institute, Abu Dhabi, United Arab
Emirates

Shah, Syed Fawad Ali   020112
KENTECH, Naju-Si, South Korea

Shanmugam, Raphael   020218, 020220
ISC Konstanz, Konstanz, Germany

Sharma, Rajesh Kumar   020071, 020081
SVNIT, Surat, India

Sharma, Sushma   020563
SRM University, Sonipat, India

Shen, Xinyi   020226
University of Oxford, Oxford, United Kingdom

Shen, Zhenjue   020001
YIST, Jiangyin, China

Shin, Donghyeop   020112
KIER, Daejeon, South Korea

Shin, Woo Gyun   020324, 020357
KIER, Daejeon, South Korea

Shin, Woo-gyun   020561
KIER, Daejeon, South Korea

Shirai, Yasuhiro   020115
NIMS, Tsukuba, Japan

Shirazi, Elham   020544
University of Twente, Enschede, The Netherlands

Shishavan, Amir Asgharzadeh   020367
Nextracker, Fremont, United States of America

Shishido, Hirotaka   020106
Tokyo City University, Setagaya, Japan

Shochet, Ofer   020225
Copprint, Jerusalem, Israel

Solórzano, Jorge   020328
Qualifying Photovoltaics, Madrid, Spain

Sondoqah, Mousa   020316
Becquerel Institute, Bolzano, Italy

Sondoqah, Mousa   020261
Eurac Research, Bolzano, Italy

Song, Hee-eun   020045
KIER, Daejeon, South Korea

Spagnolo, Sofia   020462, 020466
RSE, Milan, Italy

Spataru, Sergiu V.   020265, 020267, 020283, 020376, 020451
DTU, Roskilde, Denmark

Spataru, Sergiu Viorel   020346
DTU, Roskilde, Denmark

Spera, Fabian   020411
Next2Sun, Dillingen, Germany

Spihola, Jan   020355
DiSUN Deutsche Solarservice, Werder, Germany

Sraisth,   020005, 020222
RCT Solutions, Konstanz, Germany

Sraisth, Sraisth   020463
RCT Solutions, Konstanz, Germany

Staňková, Tereza   020107
Czech Technical University, Prague, Czech Republic

Steckenreiter, Verena   020063
ISFH, Emmerthal, Germany

Stegemann, Bert   020309
Berlin University of Applied Sciences, Berlin, Germany

Stegemann, Bert   020101
HTW, Berlin, Germany

Stellbogen, Dirk   020312
ZSW, Stuttgart, Germany

Stensborg, Jan F.   020250
Stensborg, Roskilde, Denmark

Stensborg, Jan   020306
Stensborg, Roskilde, Denmark

Stieldorf, Karin   020255
TU Wien, Vienna, Austria

Stierstorfer, Johannes   020225
WIP - Renewable Energies, Munich, Germany

Stierstorfer, Johannes   020551
WIP Renewable Energies, Munich, Germany

Stivanello, Juan José   020226
Eurac Research, Bolzano, Italy

Stoicescu, Liviu   020198
Solarzentrum Stuttgart, Stuttgart, Germany

Tang, Torben   020028
IPU P/S, Virum, Denmark

Tang, Torben   020037
IPU, Virum, Denmark

Tayebjee, Murad J. Y.   020065
UNSW, Sydney, Australia

Taylor, Nigel   020210
European Commission JRC, Ispra, Italy

Tellez Rodriguez, Eduardo   020230
Kiwa PI Berlin, Berlin, Germany

Teppe, Andreas   020005
RCT Solutions, Konstanz, Germany

Terheiden, Barbara   020031
University of Konstanz, Constance, Germany

Terrados, Cristian   020205
University of Valladolid, Valladolid, Spain

Thakur, Dhruv Singh   020071, 020081
SVNIT, Surat, India

Theocharides, Spyros   020371
Univers, Courbevoie, France

Thomas, Jean   020169
Ciel et Terre, Lille, France

Thorning, Jacob K.   020267, 020283
DTU, Roskilde, Denmark

Thorsteinsson, Sune   020039
DTU, Copenhagen, Denmark

Thorsteinsson, Sune   020037
DTU, Lyngby, Denmark

Thorsteinsson, Sune   020028, 020249, 020250, 020265, 020306,
DTU, Roskilde, Denmark   020477

Timofte, Tudor   020218, 020221
ISC Konstanz, Konstanz, Germany

Ting, San-Yu   020161, 020163
ITRI, Hsinchu, Taiwan

Tissier, Corentin   020238
CSEM, Neuchâtel, Switzerland

Tönies, Alexandra   020523
University of Applied Sciences Cologne, Cologne, Germany

Tomšič, Špela   020047
University of Ljubljana, Ljubljana, Slovenia

Tong, Yongfeng   020108, 020109
QEERI, Doha, Qatar

Topič, Marko   020047, 020269, 020319
University of Ljubljana, Ljubljana, Slovenia

Torabi, Narges   020089
University of Verona, Verona, Italy

Torelly, Guilherme   020092
PUC-Rio, Rio de Janeiro, Brazil

Torre, Gorka   020437
UPV/EHU, Leioa, Spain

Torres Aguilar, Moira Itzel   020214
CentraleSupélec, Gif-sur-Yvette, France

Torres Aguilar, Moira Itzel   020406
CNRS, Gif-sur-Yvette, France

Torres Silva, Nicole   020546
ATAMOSTEC, Santiago, Chile

Torres, Oscar   020110
National University of Colombia, Bogotá, Colombia

Tosi, Irene   020037
IPU, Virum, Denmark

Tran Caliste, Thu Nhi   020546
European Synchrotron Radiation Facility (ESRF), Grenoble,
France

Treberspurg, Christoph   020255
Treberspurg und Partner Ziviltechniker, Vienna, Austria

Treberspurg, Martin   020255
Treberspurg und Partner Ziviltechniker, Vienna, Austria

Trefzer, Aaron   020135
Fraunhofer ISE, Freiburg, Germany

Trifiletti, Vanira   020087
University of Milano-Bicocca, Milan, Italy

Trigo-Gonzalez, Mauricio   020342, 020422
University of Antofagasta, Antofagasta, Chile

Tsai, Min-An   020053, 020083, 020161, 020163
ITRI, Hsinchu, Taiwan

Tsanakas, Ioannis (John) A.   020262
CEA / INES, Le Bourget-du-Lac, France

Tsanakas, Ioannis (John) A.   020544
CEA, Le Bourget-du-Lac, France

Tsanakas, Ioannis (John)   020546
CEA / INES, Le Bourget-du-Lac, France

Tsanakas, Ioannis (John)   020317
CEA INES, Le Bourget-du-Lac, France

Tsanakas, Ioannis (John)   020513, 020521
CEA, Le Bourget-du-Lac, France

Tsanakas, Ioannis   020217, 020338
CEA / INES, Le Bourget-du-Lac, France

Tsanakas, Ioannis   020500
CEA, Le Bourget-du-Lac, France

Tsanakas, John A.   020311
CEA / INES, Le Bourget-du-Lac, France

Tseberlidis, Giorgio   020093
University of Milano Bicocca, Milan, Italy

Tseberlidis, Giorgio   020087
University of Milano-Bicocca, Milan, Italy

Tsoi, Konstantin   020113
ODTÜ-GÜNAM, Ankara, Türkiye

Tsombou, Francois M.   020402
Fujairah Research Centre, Fujairah, United Arab Emirates

Tsuno, Yuki   020436
AIST, Koriyama, Japan

Tsunoda, Jun   020484
Hitachi, Kokubunji, Japan

Tsunoda, Jun   020186
Hitachi, Tokyo, Japan

Tulinski, Lona   020385
ZHAW, Winterthur, Switzerland

Tune, Daniel   020220, 020221, 020225
ISC Konstanz, Konstanz, Germany

Turcu, Mircea   020063
ISFH, Emmerthal, Germany

Turek, Marko   020004, 020052
Fraunhofer CSP, Halle (Saale), Germany

Ueda, Yuzuru   020320, 020525
Tokyo University of Science, Tokyo, Japan

Ujvari, Gusztav   020318, 020430
AIT, Vienna, Austria

Ulbikaitė, Vaidvilė   020157
Applied Research Institute for Prospective Technologies,
Vilnius, Lithuania

Ulbikas, Juras   020225
Protechnology, Vilnius, Lithuania

Ulyashin, Alexander G.   020011
SINTEF, Oslo, Norway

Unsur, Veysel   020020
ODTÜ-GÜNAM, Ankara, Türkiye

Urban, Harald   020255
TU Wien, Vienna, Austria

Useni, Yannick   020393
University of Lubumbashi, Lubumbashi, Congo (DRC)

Uzuner, Bahri Eren   020113
ODTÜ-GÜNAM, Ankara, Türkiye

Väisänen, Kaisa-Leena   020423
VTT Technical Research Centre of Finland, Oulu, Finland

Vaicikauskas, Viktoras   020157
Center for Physical Sciences and Technology (FTMC),
Vilnius, Lithuania

Valaski, Rogério 020090
National Institute of Metrology Quality and Technology, Rio de Janeiro, Brazil

Valencia, Felipe 020342, 020546
AtamosTec, Santiago, Chile

Vallerotto, Guido 020209, 020246, 020257
UPM, Madrid, Spain

van Aken, Bas B. 020405
TNO, Petten, The Netherlands

van der Heide, Arvid 020472
imec, Genk, Belgium

van der Zee, Friso F. 020405
Wageningen University and Research, Wageningen, The Netherlands

Van Dyck, Rik 020225
IMEC, Genk, Belgium

van Dyk, E. Ernest 020193, 020416
Nelson Mandela University, Port Elizabeth, South Africa

van Dyk, Ernest E. 020344
Nelson Mandela University, Port Elizabeth, South Africa

Van Overstraeten, Julien 020543
Becquerel Institute France, Lyon, France

Van Overstraeten, Julien 020252
Becquerel Institute, Brussels, Belgium

vanBaal, Rene 020492
Belectric, Kolitzheim, Germany

Vanhanen, Tuomas 020225
Valoe, Mikkeli, Finland

Vargas, Renzo 020348
University of São Paulo, São Paulo, Brazil

Varney, Valérie 020522
University of Applied Science Cologne, Cologne, Germany

Varney, Valérie 020523
University of Applied Sciences Cologne, Cologne, Germany

vas Dyk, Ernest 020185
Nelson Mandela University, Port Elizabeth, South Africa

Vasconcelos, Letícia 020530
Casa dos Ventos, Fortaleza, Brazil

Vavilkin, Tatjana 020302
Soltech, Genk, Belgium

Vázquez Adán, Alejandra 020501
UCM, Madrid, Spain

Vázquez, A. 020508
UCM, Madrid, Spain

Veas, Christian 020136, 020234
PCCL, Leoben, Austria

Vecino, Fernando Román   020346
DTU, Roskilde, Denmark

Veerman, Sebastian   020035
ISC Konstanz, Konstanz, Germany

Vega de Seoane, José Maria   020252
Becquerel Institute Spain, San Sebastian, Spain

Vega de Seoane, Jose   020546
Becquerel Institute, Brussels, Belgium

Vega-Herrera, Jorge   020342
University of Antofagasta, Antofagasta, Chile

Vehus, Tore Sandnes   020443
University of Agder, Grimstad, Norway

Veirman, Jordi   020203, 020226, 020254
Eurac Research, Bolzano, Italy

Velasco, Angel   020367
Nextracker, Fremont, United States of America

Veludo, Jorge   020317
Galp Energia, Lisbon, Portugal

Veneri, Alessandro   020093
University of Verona, Verona, Italy

Vergura, Silvano   020301
Polytechnic University of Bari, Bari, Italy

Verlinden, Pierre   020001
YIST, Jiangyin, China

Vermang, Bart   020064
Hasselt Unversity, Genk, Belgium

Vernay, Christophe   020244
SOLAÏS, Valbonne, France

Vero, Giuseppe   020301
Polytechnic University of Bari, Bari, Italy

Veronese, Elisa   020513
Eurac Research, Bolzano, Italy

Veurman, Welmoed   020063
ISFH, Emmerthal, Germany

Viani, Lucas   020326
Enertis Applus+, Madrid, Spain

Vicente-Laiglesia, Pablo   020181
European Climate, Infrastructure and Environment
Executive Agency, Brussels, Belgium

Vidal de Oliveira, Aline   020377
Solar Energy Research Laboratory Fotovoltaica/ UFSC,
Florianópolis, Brazil

Vidal, Beatriz Muñoz   020414
IaSol, Zaragoza, Spain

Vidal-Fuentes, Pedro   020094
IREC, Barcelona, Spain

Videla-Magnata, Natalia 020129
Universidad de Antofagasta, Antofagasta, Chile

Videla-Magnata, Natalia 020417
University of Antofagasta, Antofagasta, Chile

Vilches, Anna Morales 020388
Next2Sun Technology, Dillingen, Germany

Villalonga Palou, Joan Tomás 020432, 020434
Sunveon, Madrid, Spain

Villén, Raúl 020127, 020414, 020517
ENDEF, Zaragoza, Spain

Villodas, Aritz 020198
TECNALIA, Derio, Spain

Vincent, Laetitia 020058
CNRS, Palaiseau, France

Vincent, Robin 020196
PVsyst, Geneva, Switzerland

Viorel Spataru, Sergiu 020191
DTU, Roskilde, Denmark

Viriyaroj, Bergpob 020298
Aalto University, Espoo, Finland

Viti, Valeria 020541
Legance, Milan, Italy

Vitoshkin, Helena 020379
Agricultural Research Organization, Rishon LeZion, Israel

Vögeli, Pascal 020385
ZHAW, Winterthur, Switzerland

Vogt, Malte R. 020515
TU Delft, Delft, The Netherlands

Vogt, Thomas 020482
DLR, Oldenburg, Germany

Vollbrecht, Joachim 020063, 020114
ISFH, Emmerthal, Germany

Voltan, Alessandro 020010
Applied Materials, Treviso, Italy

von Friedeburg, Christoph 020557
CF Energy Research-Consulting-Operation, Berlin,
Germany

Voronko, Yuliya 020162, 020249
OFI, Vienna, Austria

Vorster, Frederik J. 020193, 020344, 020416
Nelson Mandela University, Port Elizabeth, South Africa

Vorster, Frederik 020185
Nelson Mandela University, Port Elizabeth, South Africa

Vuillon, Laurent 020338
CNRS, Chambery, France

Vulic, Natasa   020296
Univesity of Applied Arts and Sciences Northwestern
Switzerland, Muttenz, Switzerland

Vumbugwa, Monphias   020185, 020193, 020344
Nelson Mandela University, Port Elizabeth, South Africa

Waibel, Christoph   020511
Flemish Institute for Technological Research (VITO), Genk,
Belgium

Wakabayashi, Ryo   020484
Hitachi, Kokubunji, Japan

Wakazono, Kouzen   020131
Gifu University, Gifu, Japan

Wallner, Gernot M.   020227
University of Linz, Linz, Austria

Walpita, Harsha   020169
University of Oslo, Kjeller, Norway

Walsh, Yoselyn   020520
Costa Rica Institute of Technology, Cartago, Costa Rica

Wambach, Karsten   020468, 020470
bifa Umweltinstitut, Augsburg, Germany

Wang, Chia-Chen   020549
ITRI, Hsinchu, Taiwan

Wang, Shuo   020286, 020400
TUAS, Turku, Finland

Wang, Tzuya   020549
ITRI, Hsinchu, Taiwan

Wang, Xiaolin   020381
Mälardalen University, Västerås, Sweden

Wannenwetsch, Jann   020312
EnBW, Karlsruhe, Germany

Wargocki, Pawel   020551
DTU, Roskilde, Denmark

Waschl, Alfred   020255
buildingSMART, Vienna, Austria

Weber, Thomas   020180, 020230
Kiwa PI Berlin, Berlin, Germany

Weeber, Arthur W.   020515
TU Delft, Delft, The Netherlands

Wei, Wenpeng   020484
Hitachi, Kokubunji, Japan

Weihs, Philipp   020281
BOKU, Vienna, Austria

Weinrich, Frank   020177
PTB, Braunschweig, Germany

Weiß, Marius   020361
Coburg University of Applied Sciences, Coburg, Germany

Wellens, Christine   020135
Fraunhofer ISE, Freiburg, Germany

Whyatt, Duncan   020394
Lancaster University, Lancaster, United Kingdom

Wienands, Karl   020218, 020220, 020221
ISC Konstanz, Konstanz, Germany

Wiesenfarth, Maike   020246
Fraunhofer ISE, Freiburg, Germany

Wietler, Tobias   020063
ISFH, Emmerthal, Germany

Wilbert, Stefan   020235, 020237, 020239, 020331
DLR, Almería, Spain

Willers, Guido   020201
Fraunhofer CSP, Halle, Germany

Wilson, Helen R.   020249
Fraunhofer ISE, Freiburg, Germany

Winter, Renate   020063
ISFH, Emmerthal, Germany

Winter, Stefan   020177, 020181
PTB, Braunschweig, Germany

Wirtz, Wiebke   020260
ISFH, Emmerthal, Germany

Witkowska, Agnieszka   020498
Gdansk University of Technology, Gdansk, Poland

Wittmer, Bruno   020196
PVsyst, Geneva, Switzerland

Wolf, Andreas   020031
Fraunhofer ISE, Freiburg, Germany

Wong, Craig   020230
Kiwa PI Berlin, Berlin, Germany

Wu, Li-Guo   020021
TSEC, Hsinchu, Taiwan

Wu, Yu   020030
TNO, Petten, The Netherlands

Wyss, Philippe   020068
CSEM, Neuchâtel, Switzerland

Xiong, Weizhen   020320
Tokyo University of Science, Tokyo, Japan

Xu, Jiahui   020001
YIST, Jiangyin, China

Xu, Wenhao   020144, 020208
TÜV Rheinland, Shanghai, China

Xu, Xiaoqi   020263
SERIS, Singapore, Singapore

Xu, Yu   020263
SERIS, Singapore, Singapore

Xuereb, Steven   020180, 020230
Kiwa PI Berlin, Berlin, Germany

Yadav, Shivendra   020071, 020081
SVNIT, Surat, India

Yamaguchi, Yosuke   020484
Hitachi, Kokubunji, Japan

Yanagida, Masatoshi   020115
NIMS, Tsukuba, Japan

Yanar, T. Meriç   020027
Kalyon PV, Ankara, Türkiye

Yang, Donggeon   020323
K-water, Daejeon, South Korea

Yang, Hyoung-Kyu   020449
KETI, Wonmi-gu, South Korea

Yde, Leif   020250, 020306
Stensborg, Roskilde, Denmark

Ye, JiaYi   020102
SERIS, Singapore, Singapore

Yerci, Selcuk   020113
ODTÜ-GÜNAM, Ankara, Türkiye

Ylikunnari, Mari   020423
VTT Technical Research Centre of Finland, Oulu, Finland

Ylinen, Marko   020444
Satakunta University of Applied Sciences, Pori, Finland

Ylipaino, Juho   020444, 020445, 020554
TUAS, Tampere, Finland

Yılmaz, Büşra   020521
Kameleon Solar, Roosendaal, The Netherlands

Yordadov, Georgi   020389
imec, Diepenbeek, Belgium

Younes, Kareem   020487
Khalifa University, Abu Dhabi, United Arab Emirates

Yu, Cheng-Yeh   020021, 020053
TSEC, Hsinchu, Taiwan

Yu, Shusen   020406
Ecole Polytechnique, Palaiseau, France

Yuan, Xiao   020001
YIST, Jiangyin, China

Yun, Jae Ho   020112
KENTECH, Naju-si, South Korea

Zaimi, Mhammed   020171
University of Chouaib Doukkali, El Jadida, Morocco

KEYWORDS OF EU PVSEC 2025 PROCEEDINGS PAPERS

3D GIS	020457
3D Microstructure	020119
3D Shading Model	020432
Accelerated Aging	020254
Accuracy	020276
Adhesion	020384
Adhesive	020384
Adhesives	020127
Adoption vs. Implementation	020563
Aesthetic	020306
Africa	020272
AgBiS2	020071
Agri-photovoltaics	020396
Agriculture	020409
AgriPV	020464
Agrivoltaic	020398, 020407, 020541
Agrivoltaics	020378, 020379, 020388, 020394, 020400, 020402, 020403, 020409, 020412, 020543, 020565
Albedo	020443
Albedo Measurement	020287
Alkaline Leaching	020011
All-Sky Imagers	020267
AlN	020131
Alternative Materials	020020
Aluminium Frame Removal	020497
Aluminium-backed Modules	020192
Aluminum Oxide	020008
Amorphous Silicon	020043
Amorphous Silicon Carbide Crystallization	020079
Ancillary Services	020571
Anion Exchange	020117
Anomaly Detection	020358
Antimony	020140
Antimony Selenide	020087
Antimony-Doping	020015

Characteristics Addition	020081
Characterization	020050, 020119, 020121, 020151, 020166, 020459
CIGS	020097
CIGS/Perovskite Solar Cell	020104
Circular Economy	020141, 020504, 020510, 020517
Circularity	020470, 020472, 020507, 020517
Citizen Participation	020491, 020575
Clay	020300
Clean Firm Power	020487
Clean Transportation	020428
Cleaning	020332
Cleaning Frequency	020348
Cleaning Optimization Asset Management	020339
Clear-sky	020278
Clear-Sky Detection	020340
Climate Change	020402
Climate-dependent Degradation	020150
Climate-responsive Design	020259
Climate-Specific PV O&M	020546
Cloud Detection	020267
Clustering	020243
Co-Extruded EPE	020135
Co-Visibility	020244
Collective Self-consumption	020490
Color Stability	020254
Colored Photovoltaics	020556
ColorFoil	020306
Comfort	020302
Compact Furnace	020025
Comparative Life Cycle Assessment (LCA)	020303
Competitiveness	020573
Compliance	020444
Composite Encapsulant	020139
Composites	020498
Computational Efficiency	020432
Computer Vision	020336, 020511
COMSOL	020104

ECA	020119
Ecodesign	020470
Ecology Index	020468
Economic Feasibility	020394
Economic Valuation	020492
Economic Value Assessment	020486
Education	020548
Education for Sustainable Development (ESD)	020569
Educational Resources	020100
Effects of Temperature and Irradiance	020171
Efficiency Forecast	020279
EL Images Outdoors	020186
EL Imaging	020185, 020510
EL Signal-to-Noise Ratio	020191
Electric Buses	020422, 020457
Electric Mobility	020420
Electric Vehicle Charging	020441
Electric Vehicle Charging Infrastructure	020526
Electrical Mismatch	020265
Electrically Conductive Adhesive	020218
Electricity Demand Coverage	020562
Electricity Market	020332
Electricity Price	020298
Electroluminescence	020188, 020201, 020205, 020206
Electroluminescence (EL) Images	020164
Electrolyzer	020426
Electron Multiplication	020068
Emitter Sheet Resistance	020025
Encapsulant Defects	020157
Encapsulants	020150
Encapsulation	020227
End-of-life PV	020510
Energy Balance	020439
Energy Communities	020445, 020535, 020575
Energy Community	020567
Energy Curtailment	020492
Energy Loss	020223

Energy Management System	020534
Energy Management System (EMS)	020536
Energy Performance Directive	020477
Energy Performance of Buildings Directive (EPBD)	020551
Energy Poverty	020564
Energy Rating	020173, 020177, 020211
Energy Sharing	020564
Energy Storage	020428, 020487, 020534
Energy Testing	020171
Energy Transition	020479, 020537, 020541
Energy Yield	020175, 020181, 020210, 020286, 020318, 020443, 020453
Energy Yield Estimation	020294
Energy Yield Overestimation	020363
Energy Yield Simulations	020262
Environmental Impact	020418
Environmental Psychology	020523
Epitaxial Lateral Overgrowth	020058
Epoxy Bonding	020092
Epoxy–Fiberglass	020417
EROI	020479
ET	020522
Etching	020007, 020031
EU-LAC Collaboration	020546
Eurocode	020167
EV Charging	020428
Evaporation	020015
Experimental Testing	020127
Exports	020563
Facade-Integrated Photovoltaics (FIPV)	020192
Facade-mounted PV	020359
Failures	020328
Fault Analysis	020217
Fault Clustering	020351
Fault Detection	020337, 020346, 020353, 020375, 020511
Fault Signatures	020351
Field Measurements	020377

Field Performance	020183
Finite Element Analysis	020048
Finite Element Method	020123
Fire Safety	020359
First-principles	020060
Flexibility	020390
Flexible Modules	020304
Flexible PV	020423
Flexible Solar Cells	020090
Flexible Substrate	020090
Floating photovoltaics	020169, 020348
Floating PV	020390, 020418
Fluorescence	020149
Fluoropolymer Materials	020151
Food-Energy Yield	020394
Football Stadiums	020309
Force-Field Analysis	020556
Forecasting	020336
Four-terminal	020066
Frequency Containment Reserve	020571
Fresnel Lens Concentrator	020246
GaAs/Si	020092
Gapless Layup	020221
Gapless Stringing	020221
Gel Content	020135
Generative AI	020164
Geospatial PV Analytics	020340
GHI	020291
Glare	020244
Glass Beads	020227
Glass Breakage	020230, 020231
Glass Cracking	020154
Glass Stress	020167
Glass-Free Laminate	020417
Glass-Glass Modules	020132
Glass-like Alumina	020001
Global Warming Assessments	020477
Graph Neural Network	020338

Lightweight	020384
Long-Term Degradation Rate	020181
Low Intensity Low Temperature (LILT)	020246
Low-Cost Sky Imager	020272
Low-energy Secondary Generation and Multiplication	020013
Luminescence	020206
Machine Learning	020337, 020342, 020355, 020434, 020510, 020522
Machine Learning (ML)	020317
Machine Learning Model	020279
Manufacturing	020007, 020558
Market	020570
Market Potential	020252
Market Uptake	020556
Market Value	020539
Mask	020031
Mass Production	020021
Material Classification	020504
Material Qualification	020574
Maximum Power Line	020449
Maximum Power Point Tracking	020437, 020449
McClear	020278
Mechanical Load Test	020167
Mechanical Loads	020231
Mediterranean Climate PV Performance	020334
Metal Recovery	020501, 020508
Metallization	020020, 020028
Metastability	020215
MgO	020131
Micro-Concentrator Optics	020257
Microalgae	020378
Microclimate	020403, 020565
Microinverter	020386
Minimum Sustainable Price	020482
Mismatch	020056, 020396
Mismatch Losses	020432
Mitigation strategies	020573

Pinholes	020028
Plane-of-Array Irradiation	020348
pLCA	020515
Plug and Play Photovoltaics	020386
Plug-In Photovoltaics	020386
Policy Impacts	020309
Pollution Variables	020279
POLO BJ	020482
Poly Si	020021
Poly-Si	020008, 020035
Polyaniline	020498
Polymer Degradation	020149, 020150
Polymer Properties	020157
Polynomial Surface	020525
Polysilicon	020006, 020031
PolyZEBRA	020035
Positional Effects	020416
Potential-Induced Degradation	020265
Power Fluctuations	020528
Power Loss	020201
Power Optimizers	020359
Power Output Prediction	020338
Power Reserve	020571
Power System Balancing	020554
Predictive Modelling	020317
Production	020050
Profitability	020388
PSC	020083
Public Buildings	020562
Pump Controllers	020429
PV	020252
PV and Buildings	020301
PV Architecture	020453
PV Array Simulator Assessment	020369
PV Degradation	020217, 020329
PV Digital Twin	020319
PV Fault Diagnosis	020351
PV Fire Performance	020359
PV Integration	020139

Salt Spray Corrosion	020161
SAS Quality	020369
Satellite-Derived	020286
Sb-Perovskite	020081
Sb2Se3	020085
SCAPS	020069
SCAPS-1D	020081
School	020548
Screen-Printed Silver	020048
Sealant	020384
Seasonal and Location Coefficient (Temperature and Irradiation)	020180
Second Life	020472
Second-life	020517
Secondary Materials	020468
Segmentation	020188
Selective Emitter	020023
Self-consumption	020298, 020421, 020445
Self-Consumption Systems	020439
Self-sufficiency	020421
Semi-Quantitative UVF	020158
Sensor-free Framework	020320
Sensorisation	020418
Sensors	020403, 020565
Sentiment Analysis	020522
Shading Analysis	020262, 020412
Shading Losses	020434
Shading Removal	020319
Shading-induced Losses	020432
Shared Transportation	020441
Shingled HJT	020254
Shingling	020220
Short-Term Variability	020241
Shunt Resistance	020201
Si heterojunction	020106
Si Modules	020188
Si Solar Cells	020020
Signal Modulation	020205
Silica	020495

Silicon	020007, 020058, 020097, 020468, 020495, 020501, 020507, 020508, 020515
Silicon Heterojunction	020040
Silicon Heterojunction Cell	020046
Silicon Kerf	020495
Silicon Photovoltaics	020144
Silicon Solar Cell	020001, 020013, 020023
Silicon Solar Cells	020006, 020068
Silicone	020384
Silver Recovery	020498
Simulation	020255, 020301
Simulation Acceleration	020243
Single-Axis Tracker Reliability	020314
Sizing Optimization	020530
Smart City	020420
Smart Energy System	020544
Smart Inverter IV Tracing	020361
SMARTS2	020278
Social Cognitive Career Theory (SCCT)	020569
Social Housing	020564
Social Innovation	020575
Social Risks	020505
Socio-Economics	020476
Software Tool	020183
Soil	020403, 020565
Soiling	020311, 020332, 020339, 020361
Soiling Loss Modeling	020317
Soiling Losses	020311, 020348
Soiling Mitigation	020311
Solar	020188, 020276
Solar Array Simulator Evaluation	020369
Solar Cell	020007, 020053, 020083
Solar Cells	020090, 020501, 020508
Solar Energy	020526
Solar Glass	020140
Solar Irradiance	020286
Solar Irradiance Forecasting	020267
Solar Irradiation	020412

Solar Mandate	020551
Solar Modules	020157
Solar Panel Reliability	020154
Solar Photovoltaic Technology	020569
Solar Photovoltaics	020479, 020564
Solar Power	020571
Solar Power Plant	020539
Solar PV	020476, 020549, 020552, 020559, 020573
Solar PV Systems in Buildings	020562
Solar Radiation	020275, 020283
Solar Railways	020421
Solar Resource Variability	020241
Solar Silicon	020011
Solar Water Pumping System	020429
Solder Paste	020220
Solid-State Reaction	020117
Solvent Additives	020096
Soxhlet Extraction	020135
Space	020053
Spatial Planning Integration	020552
Spatio-Temporal Analysis	020338
Spectral Composition	020416
Spectral Irradiance	020283
Spectral Mapping	020149
Spectroscopy	020227
Spectrum Splitting	020379
Stability	020096
Stakeholder Analysis	020556
Stall Detection	020314
Stance Detection	020522
Standardisation	020472
Standards	020211, 020444
STC Parameters	020183
Storage	020429, 020535
Storage Effect	020215
Storage System	020539
Stress Profile	020355
Structural Electronics	020423
Structuring	020031

Thermal Effects	020416
Thermal Image	020193
Thermal Stress	020153, 020260
Thermally Conductive Filler	020131
Thermomechanical Test	020497
Thermophotonics	020067
Thin Film	020071, 020180
Thin Films	020069, 020087
Thin-film	020094
Thin-Film Devices	020067
Thin-Film Solar Cells	020085
Tilt	020532
TOPCon	020010, 020021, 020028, 020031, 020037
TOPCON PV Modules	020229
Tracking Irradiation Gain	020363
Tracking Systems	020402
Transparency	020574
Transparent Conducting Oxide	020046
Tree Shading	020294
UAV-Based Monitoring	020335, 020374
Ultrasonic Characterization	020132
Ultraviolet Fluorescence	020158
Ultraviolet-Fluorescence Imaging	020185
Urban Planning	020420, 020526
Urban Shadowing	020457
Utility-Scale Photovoltaics	020348
Utility-Scale Solar PV	020382
UV Exposure	020229
UV Fluorescence	020166
UV Instability	020229
UV Laser Annealing	020079
UV Laser Scribing	020043
UV-Vis Spectroscopy	020081
Vacuum Refining	020011
Vacuum Thermal Evaporation	020558
Vacuum-Assisted Processing	020079
Validation	020390

Value Chain	020505
Vehicle Integrated Photovoltaics (VIPV)	020459
Vehicle-Integrated Photovoltaics	020453, 020457
Vehicle-Integrated Photovoltaics (VIPV)	020422
Vertical Bifacial PV	020262
Vertical PV	020388, 020400
Very Short-term Solar Forecasting	020272
Vibration Durability	020417
VIPV	020417, 020455
Virtual Power Plant	020554
Virtual Power Plants	020535
Visual inspection	020169, 020185
Water Quality	020418
Weather Station	020371
Weather Variables	020279
Wet Etching	020028
Yield	020180, 020307, 020396
YOLO Classifiers	020335, 020374
ZnSnO	020085